Test Bank

for

Plotnik's

# Introduction to Psychology

Seventh Edition

**Gregory H. Cutler**

*Bay de Noc Community College*

THOMSON

WADSWORTH

Australia • Canada • Mexico • Singapore • Spain • United Kingdom • United States

Printed in the United States of America
1  2  3  4  5  6  7  08  07  06  05  04

Printer: Globus Printing

0-534-63412-5

Cover art: Roger Knox

For more information about our products,
contact us at:
**Thomson Learning Academic Resource Center**
**1-800-423-0563**

For permission to use material from this text or product, submit a request online at
**http://www.thomsonrights.com.**
Any additional questions about permissions can be submitted by email to **thomsonrights@thomson.com.**

**Thomson Wadsworth**
**10 Davis Drive**
**Belmont, CA 94002-3098**
**USA**

**Asia**
Thomson Learning
5 Shenton Way #01-01
UIC Building
Singapore 068808

**Australia/New Zealand**
Thomson Learning
102 Dodds Street
Southbank, Victoria 3006
Australia

**Canada**
Nelson
1120 Birchmount Road
Toronto, Ontario M1K 5G4
Canada

**Europe/Middle East/South Africa**
Thomson Learning
High Holborn House
50/51 Bedford Row
London WC1R 4LR
United Kingdom

**Latin America**
Thomson Learning
Seneca, 53
Colonia Polanco
11560 Mexico D.F.
Mexico

**Spain/Portugal**
Paraninfo
Calle/Magallanes, 25
28015 Madrid, Spain

# Contents

# Preface

Over 5,000 multiple choice, 625 true/false, and 250 short-answer essay questions have been written to accompany the seventh edition of Rod Plotnik's *Introduction to Psychology*. These questions allow the instructor to assess a student's understanding of the theories, concepts, research, and applications presented in the textbook. Questions are ordered in the same fashion as the topics appear in the text and cover all of the important material in the text.

Each multiple choice item contains the following information to assist in the selection of test items:

- Page number - A page number to the text is included to provide reference to where the answer can be found. It is helpful to refer students to these pages when they have questions regarding the answer.

- Objective - Each question contains the heading from the page it was taken.

- Level of difficulty - Each question is rated easy, moderate or difficult. Most questions are at the easy and moderate level.

- Type of question - Questions are factual, applied, and conceptual. These questions test the ability of the student to recall basic knowledge, terms, theories, definitions, names, the ability to apply the information to new situations, and the ability to understand the conceptual basis of text material.

In each module, a number of multiple choice questions from the Power Study program and student Study Guide are included and marked (PS/SG). In addition, several multiple choice, true/false, and short-answer essay questions that appear on the website for Plotnik's *Introduction to Psychology* are clearly marked (www).

# Acknowledgements

The contributions of Jeffrey T. Parson, Rod Plotnik, Paul Rosenfeld, and Harie D. Thomas to prior test banks, which provided the foundation to this test bank, deserve special acknowledgment.

Once again, I want to extend many thanks to Jennifer Wilkinson of Wadsworth Publishing for her encouragement, patience, guidance and helpfulness. I also like to thank Matthew Enos for providing questions from his student study guide. Of course, special thanks are given to Rod Plotnik for writing such an engaging and readable textbook as well as for his words of encouragement and support.

And of course, I could not have completed this type of project without the love and support of my family--thanks to Denise, Alyssa, Miranda, Katelyn, Noelle, and Bethany for putting up with it all.

Finally, I would welcome any suggestions, feedback, or item analysis for improving the test bank.

Gregory Cutler
Bay de Noc Community College
2001 North Lincoln Road
Escanaba, MI 49829
cutlerg@baycollege.edu

# Module 1 - Discovering Psychology

p. 3
Introduction
Level: Moderate
Type: Conceptual
Ans: A

1. Module One is introduced with a discussion of autism and test anxiety. In doing so, the author of your textbook is suggesting:
   A. that psychology attempts to answer questions about real-life problems
   B. the importance of accurate diagnoses
   C. that careful definition of maladaptive behaviors is important
   D. that psychology's main focus is on abnormal behaviors

p. 3
Introduction
Level: Easy
Type: Factual
Ans: A
*PS/SG 1-2*

2. One thing that was different about Donna in school was that
   A. when she made a friend, she tried to avoid getting a friendly hug
   B. when the teacher asked a question, she always had her hand up first
   C. when a student seemed sad, she was sympathetic and understanding
   D. when the school day ended, she always found a friend to walk home with

p. 3
Introduction
Level: Moderate
Type: Applied
Ans: B

3. Which of the following people is most likely to be diagnosed with autism?
   A. Ryan - a five-year-old who is retarded but has a special ability to relate well with others
   B. Paul - a two-year-old who avoids people and spends long periods of time flipping his fingers
   C. Ben - a six-year-old who has a history of depression
   D. Anne - a ten-year-old who just recently has begun to withdraw from others

p. 3
Introduction
Level: Easy
Type: Factual
Ans: C

4. The disorder characterized by impaired development in social behavior, communication, and motor behavior is:
   A. childhood depression
   B. attention deficit disorder
   C. autism
   D. Down syndrome

p. 3
Introduction
Level: Moderate
Type: Applied
Ans: D

5. The local theater group is putting on a play depicting the struggles of a 16-year-old autistic male. Since the director wants the acting to be as realistic as possible, he should tell the actor portraying the autistic child to:
   A. "show normal social behavior on stage"
   B. "display moody behavior"
   C. "demonstrate purposeful behavior"
   D. "act aloof and not really there"

p. 3
Introduction
Level: Moderate
Type: Applied
Ans: A

6. You've just read a case history of an individual. This person has a difficult time relating to other people, has very serious problems in communication, and spends his time engaging in rocking back and forth. Which of the following is the most appropriate title for this case history?
   A. "Autism: A Serious Developmental Disorder"
   B. "Mental Retardation: Lower Than Average Intelligence "
   C. "A Case History of Munchausen Syndrome"
   D. "The Effects of Avoidance Disorder"

p. 3
Introduction
Level: Easy
Type: Applied
Ans: B

7. While doing an internship at a group home for those with mental and physical disabilities, you meet a resident who can tell you what day any date fell on for the past 100 years. This person is probably:
A. a shaman
B. a savant
C. schizophrenic
D. very good at critical thinking

p. 3
Introduction
Level: Easy
Type: Factual
Ans: A

8. You are on a game show that awards one million dollars to successful contestants. One of the questions asks you for the term given to an autistic individual who possesses a special memory or artistic skill. You answer:
A. a savant
B. a Type II schizophrenic
C. a humanist
D. fragile X syndrome

p. 3
Introduction
Level: Easy
Type: Factual
Ans: B

9. With only a couple of moments left in class, your professor says, "Next class meeting we will discuss a condition found in very few autistic people where they possess some unusual ability." Since you keep up on the textbook reading, you know that the professor is referring to:
A. metacognition
B. savants
C. ritual behavior
D. ADHD

p. 3
Introduction
Level: Easy
Type: Factual
Ans: D

10. What are the odds of meeting a person with autism in a group of 100 individuals?
A. about 50 in 100
B. about 25 in 100
C. about 10 in 100
D. about 1 in 100

p. 3
Introduction
Level: Easy
Type: Conceptual
Ans: C

11. You are trying to convince your friend, who is the mother of an autistic child, that psychology is a worthwhile field of study. Which statement would be most effective?
A. Introduction to Psychology is a required course.
B. Most employers expect a class in psychology.
C. Psychology can provide insights into the causes of behavior.
D. The unconscious mind is the focus of study in psychology.

p. 3
Introduction
Level: Easy
Type: Factual
Ans: D

12. The increase in autism is most probably due to:
A. the breakdown of the family
B. increased air and water pollution
C. childhood vaccinations
D. better diagnosis

p. 4
Definition & Goals
Level: Easy
Type: Factual
Ans: A
*www*

13.    The definition of psychology presented in your textbook is:
A.    Psychology is the systematic, scientific study of behaviors and mental processes.
B.    Psychology is the study of abnormal behaviors and ways to psychoanalyze individuals.
C.    Psychology is the systematic application of science to helping people who are mentally disturbed.
D.    Psychology is the systematic, scientific study of human behavior.

p. 4
Definition & Goals
Level: Easy
Type: Factual
Ans: B

14.    Who is least likely to have taken a psychology course?
A.    Kevin believes that behavior refers to observable actions.
B.    Kyle argues that thinking and dreaming are examples of behaviors.
C.    Karen who says, "Psychology is the systematic, scientific study of behaviors and mental processes."
D.    Kesha believes that "Psychology is the study of how to analyze people."

p. 4
Definition & Goals
Level: Easy
Type: Factual
Ans: D

15.    Inez was attempting to recite the definition of psychology she read in her psychology textbook. She said that psychology is the systematic study of behavior and mental processes. What important word did she omit?
A.    rigorous
B.    controlled
C.    psychoanalytical
D.    scientific

p. 4
Definition & Goals
Level: Easy
Type: Factual
Ans: A

16.    Based upon Module One, for a phenomenon to be studied in psychology, it must be:
A.    a behavior or a mental process
B.    an abnormal behavior or abnormal mental process
C.    an unconscious mental process
D.    approved by the American Psychological Association

p. 4
Definition & Goals
Level: Easy
Type: Factual
Ans: B

17.    In the definition of psychology presented in your text, the term behavior refers to:
A.    mental processes
B.    observable actions or responses
C.    thinking
D.    behaviors performed only by human beings

p. 4
Definition & Goals
Level: Moderate
Type: Applied
Ans: B

18.    Professor Yates is lecturing on the definition of psychology. Which example of "behavior" should he use to most effectively communicate the definition?
A.    "Behavior consists of activities such as thinking, forgetting, and problem-solving."
B.    "Acts like eating, walking, and running are examples of behavior."
C.    "Behavior is synonymous with internal processes like memory and learning."
D.    "We make no distinction between the observable and the unobservable - anything that a person does is behavior."

p. 4
Definition & Goals
Level: Easy
Type: Factual
Ans: C

19. Mental processes are described in your textbook as:
A. directly observable
B. observable actions
C. not directly observable
D. only behaviors performed by human beings

p. 4
Definition & Goals
Level: Moderate
Type: Applied
Ans: D

20. As Professor Gilpin is lecturing on the definition of psychology, he asks a student, Rita, to think about an example of a mental process. After thinking about it, Rita is still confused by the term mental processes. To clarify the term, Professor Gilpin should:
A. ask a brighter student to define mental processes
B. point out to Rita that mental processes are emphasized by the cognitive approach
C. suggest that Rita use the SQ3R approach described in her text
D. suggest that Rita, in her attempt to think about mental processes, was in fact giving an example of a mental process

p. 4
Definition & Goals
Level: Difficult
Type: Conceptual
Ans: B

21. The definition of psychology has evolved over time:
A. without much dissent or discussion
B. from specific to more general
C. from general to more specific
D. from a focus on humans to a focus on animals

p. 4
Definition & Goals
Level: Moderate
Type: Conceptual
Ans: C
www

22. Behavior is to mental processes as _____ is/are to _____.
A. thinking; dreaming
B. thoughts; actions
C. observable; not directly observable
D. not directly observable; observable

p. 4
Definition & Goals
Level: Easy
Type: Factual
Ans: C
PS/SG 1-4

23. Which one of the following is not one of the four goals of psychology?
A. to explain the causes of behavior
B. to predict behavior
C. to judge behavior
D. to control behavior

p. 4
Definition & Goals
Level: Easy
Type: Factual
Ans: D
www

24. The four goals of psychology are to describe, explain, predict, and:
A. test
B. interact
C. observe
D. control

p. 4
Definition & Goals
Level: Easy
Type: Factual
Ans: A

25. What are the goals of psychology?
A. describe, explain, predict, and control
B. classify, analyze, test, and treat
C. research, apply, and treat
D. summarize, infer, and assist

p. 4
Definition & Goals
Level: Easy
Type: Applied
Ans: A

26. People smile. This statement <u>best</u> illustrates the _____ goal of psychology.
A. describe
B. analyze
C. explain
D. summarize

p. 4
Definition & Goals
Level: Easy
Type: Applied
Ans: C

27. People smile because they are happy. This statement <u>best</u> illustrates the _____ goal of psychology.
A. describe
B. analyze
C. explain
D. summarize

p. 4
Definition & Goals
Level: Easy
Type: Applied
Ans: A

28. "I bet you will smile when you hear good news." This statement <u>best</u> illustrates the _____ goal of psychology.
A. predict
B. analyze
C. explain
D. summarize

p. 4
Definition & Goals
Level: Easy
Type: Applied
Ans: B

29. An outdated idea of autism was that it was caused by cold and rejecting parents. This idea is <u>most</u> closely related to which goal of psychology?
A. describe
B. explain
C. predict
D. control

p. 4
Definition & Goals
Level: Moderate
Type: Applied
Ans: A

30. Joseph said that several years ago in a long food line in the Soviet Union, an elderly woman fell to the ground and died of a heart attack. No one helped her. He added that this lack of helping is probably due to diffusion of responsibility. Joseph is fulfilling which goal of psychology?
A. to explain behavior
B. to predict behavior
C. to control behavior
D. to influence behavior

p. 4
Definition & Goals
Level: Moderate
Type: Applied
Ans: C

31. In a documentary on TV, you hear of juvenile delinquents who have a hard time managing their anger. A psychologist has taught these troubled youths to think of how other people feel when they lose their temper. This application of psychology illustrates which goal?
A. to explain behavior
B. to predict behavior
C. to control behavior
D. to influence behavior

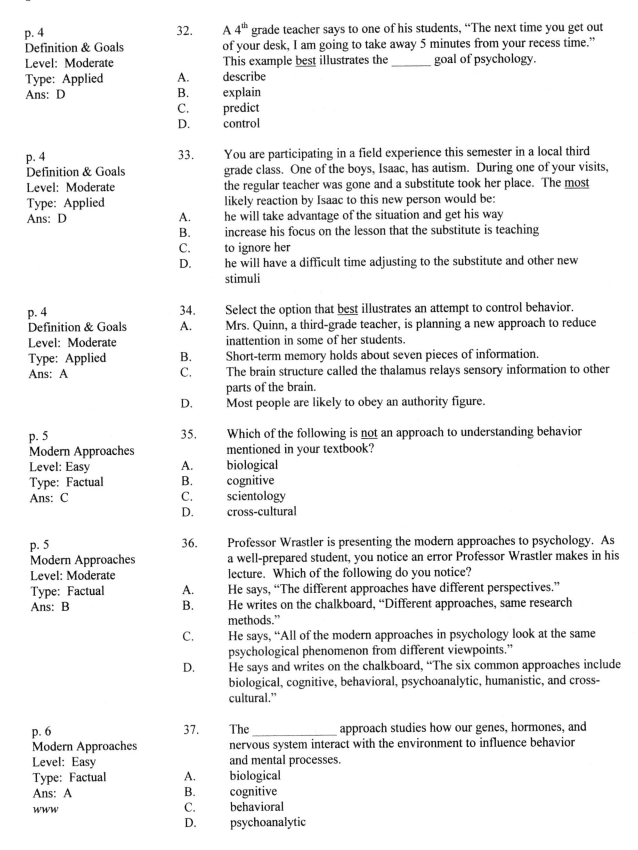

p. 4
Definition & Goals
Level: Moderate
Type: Applied
Ans: D

32. A 4<sup>th</sup> grade teacher says to one of his students, "The next time you get out of your desk, I am going to take away 5 minutes from your recess time." This example best illustrates the _____ goal of psychology.
A. describe
B. explain
C. predict
D. control

p. 4
Definition & Goals
Level: Moderate
Type: Applied
Ans: D

33. You are participating in a field experience this semester in a local third grade class. One of the boys, Isaac, has autism. During one of your visits, the regular teacher was gone and a substitute took her place. The most likely reaction by Isaac to this new person would be:
A. he will take advantage of the situation and get his way
B. increase his focus on the lesson that the substitute is teaching
C. to ignore her
D. he will have a difficult time adjusting to the substitute and other new stimuli

p. 4
Definition & Goals
Level: Moderate
Type: Applied
Ans: A

34. Select the option that best illustrates an attempt to control behavior.
A. Mrs. Quinn, a third-grade teacher, is planning a new approach to reduce inattention in some of her students.
B. Short-term memory holds about seven pieces of information.
C. The brain structure called the thalamus relays sensory information to other parts of the brain.
D. Most people are likely to obey an authority figure.

p. 5
Modern Approaches
Level: Easy
Type: Factual
Ans: C

35. Which of the following is not an approach to understanding behavior mentioned in your textbook?
A. biological
B. cognitive
C. scientology
D. cross-cultural

p. 5
Modern Approaches
Level: Moderate
Type: Factual
Ans: B

36. Professor Wrastler is presenting the modern approaches to psychology. As a well-prepared student, you notice an error Professor Wrastler makes in his lecture. Which of the following do you notice?
A. He says, "The different approaches have different perspectives."
B. He writes on the chalkboard, "Different approaches, same research methods."
C. He says, "All of the modern approaches in psychology look at the same psychological phenomenon from different viewpoints."
D. He says and writes on the chalkboard, "The six common approaches include biological, cognitive, behavioral, psychoanalytic, humanistic, and cross-cultural."

p. 6
Modern Approaches
Level: Easy
Type: Factual
Ans: A
*www*

37. The _____ approach studies how our genes, hormones, and nervous system interact with the environment to influence behavior and mental processes.
A. biological
B. cognitive
C. behavioral
D. psychoanalytic

p. 6
Modern Approaches
Level: Easy
Type: Applied
Ans: C

38. In her research, Dr. Zhing has found that the brain of many autistic children is abnormal. Dr. Zhing <u>most</u> likely uses the _____ approach.
A. behavioral
B. cross-cultural
C. biological
D. psychoanalytic

p. 6
Modern Approaches
Level: Easy
Type: Factual
Ans: D

39. Which of the following brain areas seem to process both objects and human faces in the brains of autistic individuals?
A. basal ganglia
B. cerebellum
C. fusiform gyrus
D. inferior temporal gyrus

p. 6
Modern Approaches
Level: Moderate
Type: Factual
Ans: B

40. Based on the research presented in the textbook, why would autistic individuals have difficulty distinguishing objects from human faces?
A. The autistic brain uses the inferior temporal gyrus to process objects and the fusiform gyrus to process faces.
B. The autistic brain uses the same brain area to process objects and faces.
C. Autistic children have shortages of certain proteins in their brains.
D. The basal ganglia appears to be larger than normal in the autistic brain. children.

p. 6
Modern Approaches
Level: Easy
Type: Factual
Ans: A
*PS/SG 1-5*

41. The biological approach to psychology focuses on:
A. the workings of our genes, hormones, and nervous system
B. conscious processes like perception and memory
C. the effects of reward and punishment on behavior
D. unconscious processes

p. 6
Modern Approaches
Level: Easy
Type: Factual
Ans: D

42. Computerized pictures of the brain are <u>most</u> likely to be used by:
A. psychometric psychologists
B. psychoanalysts
C. clinical psychologists
D.  psychobiologists

p. 6
Modern Approaches
Level: Easy
Type: Factual
Ans: C
*PS/SG 1-6*

43. One of the most powerful new techniques in the biological approach is:
A. testing how people process, store, and use information
B. discovering how individuals learn new behaviors or modify existing ones
C. taking computerized photos of the activity of living brains
D. studying how the first five years affect later personality development

p. 6
Modern Approaches
Level: Easy
Type: Conceptual
Ans: A

44. The research finding that autism is linked to defects in genes provides support for which modern approach?
A. biological
B. cognitive
C. behavioral
D. psychoanalytic

p. 6
Modern Approaches
Level: Easy
Type: Applied
Ans: C

45. Mick and Mike are both 2-year old identical twins. Mick has autism. What are the odds that Mike will develop autism?
A. 100%
B. 90-95%
C. 60-75%
D. 1-10%

p. 6
Modern Approaches
Level: Moderate
Type: Conceptual
Ans: C

46. A biological perspective of a mental disorder may suggest that:
A. mental disorder is the result of traumatic experiences
B. distorted perception is the main cause of mental disorder
C. mental disorders can often be traced to brain dysfunction
D. poor stress management techniques are the main cause of most mental disorders

p. 6
Modern Approaches
Level: Easy
Type: Applied
Ans: A

47. Dr. Walsh is a psychobiologist and has published her work in several scientific journals. Of the following, which is the most likely journal to accept her papers?
A. *Journal of Behavior and Brain*
B. *Journal of Clinical and Consulting Psychology*
C. *Journal of Cognitive Psychology*
D. *Psychometrics in Education*

p. 6
Modern Approaches
Level: Moderate
Type: Applied
Ans: D

48. Stacey believes that, ultimately, the causes of all types of mental disorders will be traced to imbalances in brain chemicals. This statement best represents which psychological perspective?
A. humanistic
B. cognitive
C. behavioral
D. biological

p. 6
Modern Approaches
Level: Easy
Type: Applied
Ans: A

49. Of the following activities, which is most likely to increase palmar sweating?
A. public speaking
B. crossing out all the "t's" in a newspaper article
C. watching a boring movie
D. sitting in a warm sauna

p. 6
Modern Approaches
Level: Easy
Type: Factual
Ans: D

50. One of the best measures of the emotional component of test anxiety is:
A. excessive worrying
B. procrastination
C. attributing success to external causes
D. palmar sweating

p. 7
Modern Approaches
Level: Difficult
Type: Conceptual
Ans: A

51. A cognitive psychologist may study the way we memorize a telephone number by:
A. investigating how we process and store the number in memory
B. analyzing the rewards available for successful memorization
C. researching the extent to which good memory skills are common in a family
D. interviewing to determine what unconscious motives may be associated with certain telephone numbers that a person has memorized

p. 7
Modern Approaches
Level: Easy
Type: Factual
Ans: C

52. Jerry is interested in discovering how people process, store, and use information. His interests reflect which psychological perspective?
A. biological
B. humanistic
C. cognitive
D. behavioral

p. 7
Modern Approaches
Level: Easy
Type: Conceptual
Ans: C

53. Which set of words best fits with the cognitive perspective?
A. cerebellum, brain, biology
B. reinforcement, punishment, learning
C. process, memory, think
D. unconscious, fears, guilty

p. 7
Modern Approaches
Level: Easy
Type: Conceptual
Ans: B

54. Dr. Sanchez reported in class that it is believed that autistic people do not process information properly. This research finding supports the importance of the _____ approach.
A. biological
B. cognitive
C. behavioral
D. psychoanalytic

p. 7
Modern Approaches
Level: Easy
Type: Applied
Ans: B
www

55. As the professor hands him the exam, Andre thinks to himself, "Oh, if I don't do well on this exam, I'll lose my scholarship. And if I lose my scholarship…." Andre is clearly worrying about his performance. This is an example of the _____ component of test anxiety.
A. biological
B. cognitive
C. behavioral
D. psychoanalytic

p. 7
Modern Approaches
Level: Easy
Type: Applied
Ans: A

56. In your psych class tomorrow, a guest lecturer will be presenting her research on identifying the areas of the brain that regulate planning leisure activities. She must be a:
A. cognitive neuroscientist
B. clinical psychologist
C. functionalist
D. structuralist

p. 7
Modern Approaches
Level: Easy
Type: Factual
Ans: C

57. _____ studies cognitive skills by identifying the corresponding areas in the brain.
A. Gestalt psychology
B. Humanistic psychology
C. Cognitive neuroscience
D. Psychoanalysis

| | | |
|---|---|---|
| p. 7<br>Modern Approaches<br>Level: Easy<br>Type: Factual<br>Ans: B | 58.<br><br>A.<br>B.<br>C.<br>D. | While a person with autism is listening to a conversation, what area of the brain is primarily used?<br>cortex<br>right side of the brain<br>medulla<br>temporal lobe |
| p. 7<br>Modern Approaches<br>Level: Easy<br>Type: Applied<br>Ans: D | 59.<br><br>A.<br>B.<br><br>C.<br>D. | These four students experience excessive worrying. Based on the textbook, which student is <u>most</u> likely to increase her achievement?<br>Julie - she channels her worrying into exercise<br>Tiffany - worries so much that she has accused the professor of poor teaching<br>Sara - she complains about how hard the tests are<br>Amber - she channels her worrying into studying |
| p. 7<br>Modern Approaches<br>Level: Moderate<br>Type: Applied<br>Ans: C | 60.<br><br><br>A.<br>B.<br>C.<br>D. | Sam and Ellie are both worried about their upcoming psychology exam. Based upon the research on test anxiety, what would you recommend Sam and Ellie do?<br>Sam and Ellie should provide support for each other<br>The research suggests that Sam and Ellie voice their concerns and complain<br>Both students should redirect their worry into studying<br>Talk to other students about their anxiety |
| p. 8<br>Modern Approaches<br>Level: Moderate<br>Type: Conceptual<br>Ans: D | 61.<br><br>A.<br>B.<br>C.<br>D. | If you had to write a book that describes the basic principle of behaviorism, which title would be <u>best</u> to select?<br>*Your Genes Are Your Friends*<br>*The Inner World*<br>*Studying the Unconscious*<br>*Rewards and Punishments* |
| p. 8<br>Modern Approaches<br>Level: Easy<br>Type: Factual<br>Ans: A | 62.<br><br><br>A.<br>B.<br>C.<br>D. | The rules that Donna, the autistic individual described in Module One, devised to control her unwanted behavior, <u>best</u> illustrate the _____ approach.<br>behavioral<br>psychoanalytic<br>cross-cultural<br>humanistic |
| p. 8<br>Modern Approaches<br>Level: Easy<br>Type: Applied<br>Ans: B | 63.<br><br><br>A.<br>B.<br>C.<br>D. | You hear a motivational speaker who suggests that people need to modify their environment to change behavior. You detect a hint of the _____ perspective in the speech.<br>cognitive<br>behavioral<br>psychoanalytic<br>cross-cultural |
| p. 8<br>Modern Approaches<br>Level: Difficult<br>Type: Applied<br>Ans: B | 64.<br><br>A.<br>B.<br>C.<br>D. | Psychologists adopting a behavioral perspective to the study of psychology look for explanations in:<br>the hereditary background of a person<br>the person's environment<br>idiosyncrasies of the brain<br>unique physical characteristics that may influence thinking |

p. 8
Modern Approaches
Level: Easy
Type: Applied
Ans: B
*www*

65. Rob has taught his dog to roll over on command by rewarding the dog with food whenever she exhibits the appropriate action. Rob's approach to teaching his dog tricks is similar to which psychological perspective?
A. biological
B. behavioral
C. cognitive
D. psychoanalytic

p. 8
Modern Approaches
Level: Moderate
Type: Factual
Ans: C

66. Many principles that utilize rewards to teach animals to press levers are based upon which perspective?
A. structuralism
B. functionalism
C. behaviorism
D. psychoanalysis

p. 8
Modern Approaches
Level: Easy
Type: Factual
Ans: D

67. The behavioral approach was influenced greatly by the work of _____ who stressed the study of observable behavior and reinforcement and punishment.
A. Sigmund Freud
B. Abraham Maslow
C. Erik Erikson
D. B. F. Skinner

p. 8
Modern Approaches
Level: Easy
Type: Applied
Ans: C

68. Who might have said, "All that really matters in our study is how environmental reinforcers influence observable behavior. Forget about mental processes!"?
A. Sigmund Freud - the social cognitive theorist
B. Abraham Maslow - the strict behaviorist
C. B. F. Skinner - the strict behaviorist
D. B. F. Skinner - the social cognitive theorist

p. 8
Modern Approaches
Level: Easy
Type: Factual
Ans: C

69. A revised approach to behaviorism, which examines mental or cognitive processes as well as observable behaviors, is called the _____ approach.
A. psychoanalytic
B. cognitive
C. social cognitive
D. structuralism

p. 8
Modern Approaches
Level: Easy
Type: Applied
Ans: A

70. "Our understanding of behavior must include an understanding of observable behavior as well as cognitive processes." Which theorist might have said that?
A. Albert Bandura
B. Sigmund Freud
C. Abraham Maslow
D. Carl Rogers

p. 8
Modern Approaches
Level: Easy
Type: Factual
Ans: C
*PS/SG 1-9*

71. Some behaviorists, such as Albert Bandura, disagree with strict behaviorism because:
A. there are mysteries in psychology we will never understand
B. animals pressing levers are not the same as real people dealing with life
C. our behaviors are also influenced by observation, imitation, and thought processes
D. most psychologists like to take a position different from everyone else

p. 8
Modern Approaches
Level: Easy
Type: Factual
Ans: A

72. Albert Bandura believed that our behaviors could be influenced by:
A. observations, imitation, and thought processes in addition to the environment
B. understanding our reflexive actions
C. introspection
D. dream analysis

p. 8
Modern Approaches
Level: Easy
Type: Factual
Ans: B

73. Self-management is based on _____ principles.
A. humanistic
B. behavioral
C. structural
D. biological

p. 8
Modern Approaches
Level: Easy
Type: Factual
Ans: C

74. Using the principles of behaviorism, study time can be increased using:
A. dream interpretation
B. relaxation exercises
C. self-management practices
D. social support techniques

p. 8
Modern Approaches
Level: Moderate
Type: Factual
Ans: B

75. Self-management has been used to increase study time. Which of the following is <u>not</u> one of the practices found to be effective?
A. reward yourself for studying
B. punish yourself for failing to reach goal
C. establish priorities
D. keep a record of your study time

p. 9
Modern Approaches
Level: Easy
Type: Factual
Ans: C

76. Select the set of words that are <u>most</u> closely related to the psychoanalytic approach perspectives?
A. cerebellum, palmar sweating, serotonin
B. personal growth, freedom, potential
C. unconscious, dream interpretation, anxiety
D. reinforcement, punishment, behavior

p. 9
Modern Approaches
Level: Easy
Type: Factual
Ans: A
*PS/SG 1-10*

77. The great importance of the unconscious is stressed in the _____ approach.
A. psychoanalytic
B. cognitive
C. behavioral
D. biological

p. 9
Modern Approaches
Level: Easy
Type: Factual
Ans: D

78. Sigmund Freud developed which of the following modern approaches?
A. behavioral
B. cognitive
C. humanistic
D. psychoanalytic

p. 9
Modern Approaches
Level: Easy
Type: Applied
Ans: D
*www*

79.    Seth claims that Juan's anxiety originates from unresolved sexual conflicts residing in his unconscious.  Seth's observation about Juan is <u>most</u> consistent with the _____ perspective.
A.    behavioral
B.    cognitive
C.    humanistic
D.    psychoanalytic

p. 9
Modern Approaches
Level: Moderate
Type: Applied
Ans: C

80.    If Mark has thoughts which make him feel fearful and guilty, Freud would say these thoughts would be:
A.    classically conditioned
B.    totally normal and have no effect on Mark's actual behavior
C.    pushed into Mark's unconscious
D.    reinforced by negative thoughts

p. 9
Modern Approaches
Level: Easy
Type: Factual
Ans: A

81.    According to the psychoanalytic perspective, when is the <u>most</u> critical time of life in the development of personality traits?
A.    childhood
B.    early adolescence
C.    late adolescence
D.    young adulthood

p. 9
Modern Approaches
Level: Easy
Type: Factual
Ans: D

82.    Which of the following schools of thought believes that our dreams could be
A.    structuralism
B.    functionalism
C.    behaviorism
D.    psychoanalytic

p. 9
Modern Approaches
Level: Easy
Type: Factual
Ans: C

83.    Consider this:  It is the early 20th century and you are the personal assistant what he is about to say.  One time, Freud was saying, "Anxiety, fear, and psychological problems are caused by…" and he paused  as he thought. You suddenly said to him what would ultimately become a key concept in psychoanalytic thought.  What did you say?
A.    "…unfulfilled human potential!"
B.    "…imbalance in brain chemicals like serotonin!"
C.    "…Herr Freud, it is unconscious thoughts and feelings!"
D.    "…excessive rewards and punishments!"

p. 9
Modern Approaches
Level: Moderate
Type: Factual
Ans: B

84.    Freud believed that an examination of one's _____ would give insight into the adult personality and adult problems.
A.    culture
B.    childhood relationships with parents
C.    cognitive beliefs
D.    genetic makeup

p. 9
Modern Approaches
Level: Moderate
Type: Applied
Ans: B

85. Karen believes that her boyfriend is afraid of making commitments because of an unconscious hatred for his mother. Her belief is closest to which psychological perspective?
A. humanistic
B. psychoanalytic
C. cross-cultural
D. cognitive

p. 9
Modern Approaches
Level: Easy
Type: Factual
Ans: B

86. In Freud's theory, unconscious, threatening thoughts and feelings lead to:
A. unresolved sexual conflicts
B. anxiety
C. changes in the cerebellum
D. an inability to self-actualize

p. 9
Modern Approaches
Level: Moderate
Type: Factual
Ans: A

87. Research on test anxiety from the _____ perspective focuses on the unconscious reason for _____.
A. psychoanalytic; procrastination
B. cognitive; gender differences
C. humanistic; cultural differences
D. psychoanalytic; differing explanations

p. 9
Modern Approaches
Level: Easy
Type: Applied
Ans: C

88. "I am a procrastinator. According to the psychoanalytic approach, my parents must have:
A. set goals that were too easy when I was a child."
B. ignored my successes."
C. loved me only when I did well in school."
D. gave me their procrastinating genes."

p. 9
Modern Approaches
Level: Easy
Type: Factual
Ans: B

89. Working from the psychoanalytic perspective, a psychologist examining a student's procrastination would focus on:
A. brain chemical imbalance
B. unconscious personality problems
C. poor planning skills
D. how procrastination is reinforced

p. 9
Modern Approaches
Level: Easy
Type: Factual
Ans: D
*PS/SG 1-11*

90. The psychoanalytic approach to understanding procrastination as a component of test anxiety would:
A. emphasize the role of habitual modes of thinking and problem solving
B. study brain scans of procrastinators while they think about schoolwork
C. compare school strategies used by students in different cultures
D. look beneath the obvious reasons and try to identify unconscious personality problems

p. 9
Modern Approaches
Level: Easy
Type: Factual
Ans: D

91. Of the following, which has not been found to be a common reason for procrastination according to your textbook?
A. being lazy
B. lacking motivation
C. inadequate time management
D. poor metacognitive skills

p. 10
Modern Approaches
Level: Moderate
Type: Conceptual
Ans: D

92. Which school of thought discusses behavior in terms of a person's potential for growth and self-fulfillment?
A. psychoanalytical
B. behavioral
C. cognitive
D. humanistic

p. 10
Modern Approaches
Level: Difficult
Type: Applied
Ans: A

93. Professor Kaufman is showing a film describing the modern approaches to psychology. The video is operating, but the sound is not. On the screen you see an individual named Abraham Maslow. If the sound was turned on, which of the following words would you probably hear from Maslow as he describes his views?
A. "...potential for self-fulfillment is important..."
B. "...their environment determines their behaviors...."
C. "...the biology of the brain is critical for understanding..."
D. "...importance of personal freedom and unconscious motives..."

p. 10
Modern Approaches
Level: Easy
Type: Applied
Ans: C

94. This year's graduation speaker spoke of the graduates' ability to control their future by becoming anything that they wished. The speaker has most probably been influenced by which psychological perspective?
A. behavioral
B. cognitive
C. humanistic
D. psychoanalytic

p. 10
Modern Approaches
Level: Moderate
Type: Applied
Ans: C

95. You are listening to the radio when you hear a commercial that is trying to recruit students for the military. It starts off with, "Be all you can be." What approach is best illustrated by the commercial?
A. cross-cultural
B. behavioral
C. humanistic
D. psychoanalytic

p. 10
Modern Approaches
Level: Moderate
Type: Applied
Ans: A

96. Eric is trying to encourage himself to develop his full potential as a human being by learning that he is in control of his fate. What psychological perspective has Eric adopted?
A. humanistic
B. psychoanalytic
C. behavioral
D. cross-cultural

p. 10
Modern Approaches
Level: Moderate
Type: Applied
Ans: B

97. The speaker for commencement announced her topic for the ceremony. Knowing that she adheres to the humanistic approach, which of the following is the most likely title of her message?
A. *Introspection: The Way of Wundt*
B. *Choosing to Become*
C. *Becoming a Better Person Through Rewards*
D. *Who We Are: Answers From the Unconscious*

p. 10
Modern Approaches
Level: Moderate
Type: Factual
Ans: A

98. There are many behaviorists who argue that the humanistic approach is more of a philosophy of life rather than a science of human behavior because humanists:
A. fail to use rigorous experimental methods
B. emphasize environmental effects on behavior
C. focus on genetic predisposition to temperament
D. do not believe that people have intrinsic worth

p. 10
Modern Approaches
Level: Moderate
Type: Applied
Ans: C

99. Miranda received an "A" on an exceptionally hard math exam. Her friend Thomas asked, "Why did you get such a good grade?" According to the research cited in the textbook, Miranda is most likely to reply:
A. "The instructor likes me."
B. "I guess it's just luck."
C. "I worked hard and studied for many hours."
D. "The test was too easy."

p. 10
Modern Approaches
Level: Easy
Type: Factual
Ans: D

100. With your knowledge of how students explain their exam performance, what piece of advice would you give to new teachers that is consistent with the research?
A. Set strict rules for classroom behavior
B. Try to ignore failure and recognize achievement
C. Be blunt and to the point about the future of students who do not do well in school
D. Be supportive and encourage those who perform poorly on tests to reach their highest potential.

p. 11
Modern Approaches
Level: Easy
Type: Factual
Ans: A

101. About sixty years ago, a prevailing explanation of autism was:
A. cold parents
B. threatening unconscious feelings
C. biological causes
D. a lack of reinforcement in the child's school setting

p. 11
Modern Approaches
Level: Easy
Type: Factual
Ans: D

102. Hans, a two-year-old German boy, shows symptoms of autism. At what age is he most likely to be diagnosed with autism in Germany?
A. 6 months old
B. one-years old
C. three-years old
D. six-years old

p. 11
Modern Approaches
Level: Moderate
Type: Factual
Ans: D

103. There are several reasons why the Chinese lagged behind in recognizing autistic symptoms. Of the following, which is not among those reasons?
A. Many Chinese did not believe that disorders could occur in infancy.
B. Many Chinese parents were not aware of an infant's development.
C. It was generally believed that infants would outgrow any early problems.
D. The Chinese Communist Party did not officially recognize the existence of autism.

p. 11
Modern Approaches
Level: Easy
Type: Conceptual
Ans: C

104. The cross-cultural approach adds a valuable dimension to psychology in suggesting that:
A. in order to be a fully developed person, you have to spend some time living with other groups
B. anthropology explains behavior better than psychology does
C. the culture in which you grow up affects your thoughts, feelings, and behaviors
D. what psychology learns about one race is probably not true about other races

p. 11
Modern Approaches
Level: Easy
Type: Conceptual
Ans: C
*PS/SG 1-14*

105. The cross-cultural approach to psychology studies the influence of _____ on psychological functioning.
A. brain chemistry
B. information processing
C. cultural and ethnic similarities and differences
D. automatic behaviors and deeply ingrained habits

p. 11
Modern Approaches
Level: Moderate
Type: Applied
Ans: A

106. A young inexperienced teacher from the rural Midwest is hired to teach in an inner-city public school. In her class, there are a number of cultures and races represented. She is confused by the differences between students in regard to achievement and behavior. Which of the following approaches would most likely provide insights into differences among her students?
A. cross-cultural
B. behavioral
C. ethological
D. psychoanalytic

p. 11
Modern Approaches
Level: Easy
Type: Factual
Ans: B

107. Cross-cultural studies have indicated that test anxiety may be related to:
A. intelligence
B. fewer educational opportunities
C. brain function
D. genetics

p. 11
Modern Approaches
Level: Easy
Type: Factual
Ans: B

108. Which group of students score the lowest on measures of test anxiety?
A. American students
B. Italian students
C. Egyptian students
D. Jordanian students

p. 11
Modern Approaches
Level: Easy
Type: Factual
Ans: C

109. Students in Chile admire successful students:
A. if success was due to great effort
B. less frequently than students in America
C. if success was due to either great effort or natural ability
D. more frequently than students in America

p. 11
Modern Approaches
Level: Easy
Type: Factual
Ans: A

110. Students in America admire successful students:
A. if success was due to great effort
B. less frequently than students in other cultures
C. if success was due to either great effort or natural ability
D. more frequently than students in other cultures

p. 11
Modern Approaches
Level: Easy
Type: Factual
Ans: B

111. The _____ approach is the most recent of those presented in the textbook.
A. behavioral
B. cross-cultural
C. structuralism
D. cognitive

p. 11
Modern Approaches
Level: Moderate
Type: Conceptual
Ans: C

112. With regard to the six modern approaches to psychology discussed in your text, psychologists are most concerned with:
A. which approach gives the best answer
B. which approach is more accepted by the psychological community
C. the likelihood of successfully reaching the goals of description, explanation, prediction, and control
D. the methodology by which the approach is tested

p. 11
Modern Approaches
Level: Moderate
Type: Conceptual
Ans: B

113. There may be a number of plausible psychological explanations for one behavior because:
A. many of the perspectives within psychology are really the same
B. each approach provides additional information regarding the same behavior
C. no one perspective has been sufficiently developed
D. the advancement of any academic discipline depends on controversy

p. 11
Modern Approaches
Level: Easy
Type: Conceptual
Ans: B
PS/SG 1-15

114. Once we understand the six approaches to psychology, Rod Plotnik advises us to:
A. make a personal decision about which approach is best
B. combine and use information from all six approaches
C. place our trust in the approaches that have stood the test of time
D. judge each approach by the famous people who have supported it

p. 11
Modern Approaches
Level: Moderate
Type: Conceptual
Ans: C

115. Given the historical changes in the definition of psychology, which of the following definitions would have been more likely to be used in the early years of psychology?
A. Psychology is the study of observable behavior.
B. Psychology is the study of behaviors and mental processes.
C. Psychology is the study of the basic elements of sensation and perception.
D. Psychology is the study of observable actions and cognitive functions.

p. 12
Historical Approaches
Level: Moderate
Type: Factual
Ans: A

116. Structuralists focused on _____, whereas functionalists focused on _____.
A. elements of the mind; adaptability of the mind
B. objective measurements; subjects' self-reports
C. adaptability of the mind; introspection
D. the continuous flow of mental activity; breaking down mental structures into smaller units

p. 12
Historical Approaches
Level: Easy
Type: Factual
Ans: D
*PS/SG 1-16*

117.  The difference between "structualism" and "functionalism" in the early years of psychology concerned a choice between:
A.  British or American psychology
B.  Abraham Maslow or John B. Watson
C.  studying the brain or the cultural setting of behavior
D.  studying narrow sensations or general adaptations to our changing environment

p. 12
Historical Approaches
Level: Moderate
Type: Factual
Ans: A

118.  Structuralism required subjects to introspect in order to:
A.  report on the basic elements of their mental processes
B.  complete objective measures of mental functioning
C.  assemble sensations into meaningful perceptions
D.  be psychoanalyzed

p. 12
Modern Approaches
Level: Moderate
Type: Conceptual
Ans: C

119.  Which of the following relationships best illustrates introspection?
A.  females to males
B.  trees to leaves
C.  letters to words
D.  cars to airplanes

p. 12
Historical Approaches
Level: Moderate
Type: Conceptual
Ans: B

120.  If Wilhelm Wundt asked you to report your sensations and perceptions by looking inward, you would be engaging in:
A.  functionalism
B.  introspection
C.  psychoanalysis
D.  psychometrics

p. 12
Historical Approaches
Level: Moderate
Type: Factual
Ans: D

121.  Introspection was later criticized as a research method because it:
A.  required too many behavioral observations
B.  focused solely on objective measurements and not on self-reports
C.  was only useful with psychologically disturbed patients
D.  was unscientific since it did not use objective measurement, but rather used only self-reports

p. 12
Historical Approaches
Level: Easy
Type: Factual
Ans: C

122.  Functionalism focused on:
A.  having subjects look inward and report on the workings of their minds
B.  the fact that perception was more than the sum of its parts
C.  how the mind helped the organism to adapt to its surroundings
D.  the objective, scientific analysis of observable behaviors

p. 12
Historical Approaches
Level: Moderate
Type: Conceptual
Ans: D

123.  Wundt is to structuralism as:
A.  Freud is to experimentation
B.  James is to psychoanalysis
C.  Skinner is to ethology
D.  James is to functionalism

p. 12
Historical Approaches
Level: Moderate
Type: Applied
Ans: B

124. An article entitled, "The Mind: Goals and Purposes" would be most likely written by someone who identifies with:
A. Wundt and structuralism
B. James and functionalism
C. Freud and Wertheimer
D. Watson and structuralism

p. 12
Historical Approaches
Level: Easy
Type: Factual
Ans: A

125. What important book did William James publish in 1890?
A. *Principles of Psychology*
B. *Introduction to Psychology*
C. *Psychology as a Behaviorist Views It*
D. *The Structure of Psychological Thought*

p. 12
Historical Approaches
Level: Easy
Type: Factual
Ans: C

126. The father of modern psychology is considered to be:
A. Sigmund Freud
B. George Sanchez
C. William James
D. B.F. Skinner

p. 13
Historical Approaches
Level: Easy
Type: Factual
Ans: D

127. The term "Gestalt" refers to:
A. structuralism
B. observable behaviors
C. introspection
D. whole pattern

p. 13
Historical Approaches
Level: Easy
Type: Factual
Ans: C
*www*

128. The _____ approach emphasizes looking at the whole, rather than the sum of its parts.
A. behavioral
B. functionalism
C. Gestalt
D. psychoanalytic

p. 13
Historical Approaches
Level: Moderate
Type: Factual
Ans: D

129. The phi phenomenon was explained by the Gestalt approach as the result of
A. analyzing its basic structures
B. adding the two lights together
C. unresolved childhood conflicts
D. analyzing the whole pattern

p. 13
Historical Approaches
Level: Easy
Type: Factual
Ans: A
*PS/SG 1-18*

130. By explaining perceptual phenomena like the phi phenomenon (apparent motion), Gestalt researchers gave psychology the idea that:
A. the whole is more than the sum of its parts
B. research results could be profitable when applied to advertising
C. Wundt and the structuralists had been right about the importance of the individual parts
D. individual parts are more significant than resulting wholes

p. 13
Historical Approaches
Level: Moderate
Type: Factual
Ans: B

131. Gestalt psychologists study how sensations are:
A. experienced by the sensory organs
B. assembled into meaningful perceptual experiences
C. observed and recorded
D. composed of smaller elements

p. 13
Historical Approaches
Level: Easy
Type: Conceptual
Ans: C

132. Of the following phenomena, which would be of the greatest interest to Max Wertheimer?
A. cultural differences in body language
B. how diseases of the brain affect behavior
C. seeing a light as moving when in fact individual lights are going on and off
D. a child being toilet trained

p. 13
Historical Approaches
Level: Moderate
Type: Applied
Ans: C

133. If Max Wertheimer's gravestone had an epitaph written on it, which of the following would be most appropriate given his contributions to psychology?
A. "The function of life is to adapt to the environment."
B. "He took a dozen healthy infants and made them great. What a guy!"
C. "His life was more than the sum of its parts."
D. "Even he had unresolved childhood conflicts!"

p. 13
Historical Approaches
Level: Easy
Type: Factual
Ans: A

134. John Watson rejected structuralism and stated that psychology should study:
A. observable behaviors
B. unconscious fears and behaviors
C. sensations and perceptions
D. introspection

p. 13
Historical Approaches
Level: Easy
Type: Applied
Ans: C

135. Simon, who is a TV producer, has an idea for a new TV show. It will ask contestants about John Watson and award money for correct answers. What is the most likely title of this show?
A. Leipzig 90214
B. I Love Cognition
C. Who Wants to Be a Behaviorist?
D. Who Wants to Be a Gestalt?

p. 13
Historical Approaches
Level: Easy
Type: Factual
Ans: B
PS/SG 1-19

136. The pioneering psychologist who offered the famous guarantee about being able to shape a baby into any type of specialist you might want was:
A. William James
B. John B. Watson
C. Max Wertheimer
D. Wilhelm Wundt

p. 13
Historical Approaches
Level: Easy
Type: Applied
Ans: D

137. Noelle refuses to study mental processes, and focuses her research solely on the objective, scientific analysis of observable behaviors. Noelle is a:
A. structuralist
B. functionalist
C. Gestalt psychologist
D. behavioral psychologist

p. 13
Historical Approaches
Level: Difficult
Type: Conceptual
Ans: B

138. What did John B. Watson's famous quote regarding taking a dozen healthy infants really mean?
A. development of personality starts at an early age
B. manipulation of the environment causes changes in behavior
C. only well-trained professionals like psychologists should raise children
D. early training can unleash unconscious predispositions

p. 13
Historical Approaches
Level: Moderate
Type: Applied
Ans: C
*www*

139. If John B. Watson was alive today and had a website, which of the following would he select as his website address?
A. www.gestalt.edu
B. www.biology.edu
C. www.behavior.edu
D. www.superego.edu

p. 13
Historical Approaches
Level: Easy
Type: Factual
Ans: D

140. What approach may be surpassing the popularity of behaviorism in the 1990's?
A. functionalism
B. gestalt approach
C. psychoanalytic approach
D. cognitive approach

p. 14
Cultural Diversity:
  Early Discrimination
Level: Easy
Type: Factual
Ans: B

141. Mary Calkins was denied a Ph.D. in psychology because:
A. she failed to complete her requirements
B. the administration declined to grant a Ph.D. to a woman
C. her professors did not like her work
D. she was a structuralist

p. 14
Cultural Diversity:
  Early Discrimination
Level: Easy
Type: Factual
Ans: A
*PS/SG 1-22*

142. As measured by membership in the American Psychological Association, minorities in psychology:
A. lag far behind other Americans
B. are about the same as their proportion of the general population
C. will soon exceed White Americans
D. may have lagged earlier, but are now rapidly catching up

p. 14
Cultural Diversity:
  Early Discrimination
Level: Easy
Type: Applied
Ans: D

143. If you were a woman with a Ph.D. living around the turn of the century, where would you most likely work?
A. any college or university
B. most small, private liberal arts colleges in the east
C. women were not granted the Ph.D. until the 1940's
D. a women's college

p. 14
Cultural Diversity:
  Early Discrimination
Level: Easy
Type: Factual
Ans: A

144. _____ was the first African American woman to earn a Ph.D. in the United States.
A. Ruth Howard
B. Mary Calkins
C. Margaret Washburn
D. Beatrice Collins

p. 14
Cultural Diversity:
  Early Discrimination
Level: Easy
Type: Factual
Ans: D

145. Who conducted pioneering work on the cultural bias of intelligence tests?
A. William James
B. Mary Calkins
C. Margaret Washburn
D. George Sanchez

p. 14
Cultural Diversity:
 Early Discrimination
Level: Moderate
Type: Factual
Ans: B

146. To remedy past discrimination in psychology and in higher education:
A. standards for program completion are lowered for minority students
B. the American Psychological Association actively recruits minority members
C. the American Psychological Association has formed special interest groups for white males
D. membership fees for minorities in all professional associations have been lowered

p. 14
Cultural Diversity:
 Early Discrimination
Level: Easy
Type: Factual
Ans: D

147. What important contribution to intelligence testing did George Sanchez make?
A. He served as research director of a large corporation that publishes intelligence tests.
B. Sanchez created the concept of IQ.
C. Sanchez developed the first valid and reliable test.
D. He showed that questions on the tests may be biased against minorities.

p. 14
Cultural Diversity:
 Early Discrimination
Level: Easy
Type: Factual
Ans: A
PS/SG 1-23

148. The efforts of American psychology to overcome discrimination may be threatened by:
A. state laws banning affirmative action programs
B. a steady decline in the numbers of men going into psychology
C. wide-spread African-American and Latino disinterest in the subject of psychology
D. a new policy of the American Psychological Association against affirmative action

p. 14
Cultural Diversity:
 Early Discrimination
Level: Easy
Type: Factual
Ans: C

149. What happened after several states banned affirmative action programs?
A. Fewer Anglo-American students enrolled in universities.
B. More minority students enrolled in universities.
C. Fewer minority students enrolled in universities.
D. No change in the number of minority student enrollment.

p. 16
Research Focus:
 Taking Class Notes
Level: Easy
Type: Factual
Ans: A

150. Of the following subject groups, which did not appear in the study on taking lecture notes described in your textbook?
A. note-taking plus preview
B. note-taking plus review
C. note-taking plus answering questions about notes
D. note-taking plus writing summary of notes

p. 16
Research Focus:
 Taking Class Notes
Level: Easy
Type: Factual
Ans: C

151. The group that used _____ scored significantly higher than any other group in a study of note taking methods.
A. note-taking plus preview
B. note-taking plus review
C. note-taking plus answering questions about notes
D. note-taking plus concept maps

p. 17
Careers in Psychology
Level: Easy
Type: Factual
Ans: D

152. In general, a psychologist is someone who:
A. specializes in assessing the physical causes of mental problems
B. often prescribes drugs
C. works in secondary school settings
D. holds a Ph.D. in psychology

p. 17
Careers in Psychology
Level: Easy
Type: Applied
Ans: A

153. Barb, a college sophomore, is having relationship problems with her boyfriend. The <u>best</u> person for Barb to consult would be a(n):
A. clinical psychologist
B. experimental psychologist
C. cognitive psychologist
D. psychiatrist

p. 17
Careers in Psychology
Level: Easy
Type: Applied
Ans: D
*www*

154. Franklin suffers from schizophrenia and requires medication. The <u>best</u> person for Franklin to consult would be a(n):
A. clinical psychologist
B. experimental psychologist
C. cognitive psychologist
D. psychiatrist

p. 17
Careers in Psychology
Level: Moderate
Type: Factual
Ans: C
*www*

155. Which of the following pairs of profession and degree is *correct*?
A. clinical psychologist - M.D.
B. psychiatrist - Ph.D.
C. clinical  psychologist - Ph.D.
D. psychiatrist - master's

p. 17
Careers in Psychology
Level: Easy
Type: Applied
Ans: A

156. Dr. Beenken spends most of his workday at a local clinic. He does individual therapy and tests patients for psychological problems. Which of the following titles is Dr. Beenken <u>most</u> likely to have?
A. clinical psychologist
B. experimental psychologist
C. cognitive psychologist
D. social psychologist

p. 17
Careers in Psychology
Level: Moderate
Type: Applied
Ans: B
*www*

157. Given the percentages presented in your textbook, which of the following settings would be <u>most</u> likely to employ psychologists?
A. a school district
B. a mental health clinic
C. a public university
D. a large automobile manufacturer

p. 17
Careers in Psychology
Level: Easy
Type: Factual
Ans: C

158. The largest percentage of psychologists works in:
A. academic settings of universities and colleges
B. industrial settings
C. private practice or therapy settings
D. secondary schools

p. 17
Careers in Psychology
Level: Easy
Type: Applied
Ans: C

159. Dr. Ivers works in a school district as a psychologist. What is she most likely to do in her work?
A. increase production
B. improve job satisfaction among the staff
C. conduct academic and career testing
D. conduct therapy for those suffering from major psychological problems

p. 17
Careers in Psychology
Level: Moderate
Type: Factual
Ans: B

160. A seventh grader wants to be a psychologist. She tells her mother about the career choice. The girl says that "it'll take a long time to become one." She needs to realize that "a long time" may mean:
A. two to three years after high school
B. about five years after earning an undergraduate degree
C. five years in medical school
D. four years of college

p. 17
Careers in Psychology
Level: Easy
Type: Factual
Ans: C

161. In the last few decades, what trend has been seen in the settings in which psychologist work?
A. elementary and secondary schools are more likely to hire psychologists to design curriculum
B. businesses and industry are more likely to hire psychologists to increase worker productivity
C. increase in psychologists who provide therapy/health services
D increase in psychologists who work in academic settings

p. 17
Careers in Psychology
Level: Moderate
Type: Factual
Ans: C
*PS/SG 1-24*

162. After reading the material on careers and research areas, it would be reasonable to conclude that psychology:
A. requires so much education that few students should consider it
B. will have fewer job opportunities in coming years
C. offers a great variety of intellectual challenges and kinds of work
D. is one of the best paid professions today

p. 17
Careers in Psychology
Level: Moderate
Type: Factual
Ans: A

163. You are reviewing a paper written by a friend on careers in psychology. One of the statements you read does not appear correct. Which of the following statements in the paper would you identify as being *wrong*?
A. In the last 50 years, there has been a decrease in psychologists who provide therapy.
B. A psychiatrist is a medical doctor.
C. Employment opportunities for psychologists will grow much faster than average.
D. A psychologist usually has obtained a Ph.D. in psychology.

p. 18
Research Areas
Level: Easy
Type: Factual
Ans: A

164. The research area of psychology most likely to study stereotypes, group behavior, and aggression is:
A. social psychology
B. psychometrics
C. clinical psychology
D. developmental psychology

p. 18
Research Areas
Level: Easy
Type: Conceptual
Ans: B

165. Dr. Klees has her graduate students pretend to faint while in a subway car to see how many people come to their aid. What type of psychologist is Dr. Klees?
A. clinical
B. social
C. developmental
D. industrial

p. 18
Research Areas
Level: Easy
Type: Conceptual
Ans: A

166. Larry is interested in studying the causes of shyness and would like to know if shy people can change. What type of psychology should Larry explore?
A. personality
B. experimental
C. industrial
D. developmental

p. 18
Research Areas
Level: Easy
Type: Conceptual
Ans: C
*www*

167. Changes in self-esteem through puberty and adolescence would be studied by what type of psychologist?
A. clinical
B. experimental
C. developmental
D. social

p. 18
Research Areas
Level: Easy
Type: Applied
Ans: C

168. If you wanted to learn more about the social, emotional, and cognitive changes over the entire lifespan, in which class should you enroll?
A. PY 300 Biological Psychology
B. PY 250 Personality Psychology
C. PY 220 Developmental Psychology
D. PY 210 Social Psychology

p. 18
Research Areas
Level: Easy
Type: Conceptual
Ans: C

169. Dr. Gilpin and his research assistants are requesting subjects between the ages of four and nine years to participate in a study at the local college. What area of psychology is <u>most</u> likely being investigated?
A. industrial
B. experimental
C. developmental
D. physiological

p. 18
Research Areas
Level: Easy
Type: Conceptual
Ans: B

170. Dr. Yates studies motivation and perception. He is <u>most</u> likely which type of psychologist?
A. industrial
B. experimental
C. social
D. psychobiology

p. 18
Research Areas
Level: Easy
Type: Factual
Ans: A

171. _____ psychology studies such areas as sensation, perception, and emotion.
A. Experimental
B. Social
C. Cognitive
D. Personality

p. 19
Research Areas
Level: Easy
Type: Conceptual
Ans: C
*www*

172.   Psychobiological psychologists investigate:
A.   how we process, store, and retrieve information
B.   development across the lifespan
C.   how our genetic makeup interacts with our environment
D.   which measures best assess behavior and abilities

p. 19
Research Areas
Level: Easy
Type: Conceptual
Ans: A

173.   Dr. Odland conducts studies on what brain pathways are <u>most</u> affected by alcohol consumption. What type of psychologist is Dr. Odland?
A.   psychobiological
B.   social
C.   clinical
D.   developmental

p. 19
Research Areas
Level: Easy
Type: Factual
Ans: D

174.   If you are interested in the effects of stress on the body, what area of psychology is <u>best</u> to study?
A.   psychometrics
B.   social psychology
C.   personality psychology
D.   biological psychology

p. 19
Research Areas
Level: Easy
Type: Conceptual
Ans: A

175.   Which of the following research areas of psychology combines knowledge of the brain's functions with computer programming to attempt to duplicate "human" thinking and intelligence?
A.   cognitive psychology
B.   psychiatry
C.   experimental psychology
D.   psychometrics

p. 19
Research Areas
Level: Easy
Type: Conceptual
Ans: A

176.   Your friend attends a speech at the local university. She hears about the research of a psychologist. The research centers on special techniques that are designed to increase creativity and problem solving. More than likely, your friend was listening to a(n):
A.   cognitive psychologist
B.   psychiatrist
C.   experimental psychologist
D.   psychobiologist

p. 19
Research Areas
Level: Easy
Type: Applied
Ans: C

177.   Your research paper is on the thinking styles of college students. Which professor is probably the <u>most</u> useful resource?
A.   Dr. Campbell - a psychometrican
B.   Dr. Buckbee - a clinical psychologist
C.   Dr. Karweick - a cognitive psychologist
D.   Dr. Cole - a psychiatrist

p. 19
Research Areas
Level: Easy
Type: Conceptual
Ans: D

178. While working on his Ph.D., James developed a test to evaluate intelligence in children. James is probably studying:
A. clinical psychology
B. psychobiology
C. humanistic psychology
D. psychometrics

p. 19
Research Areas
Level: Easy
Type: Applied
Ans: D
www

179. Dr. Howarth is studying a personality test and has concluded that the test is invalid. He is most likely a specialist in:
A. psychoanalysis
B. functionalism
C. biological psychology
D. psychometrics

p. 20
Application: Study Skills
Level: Moderate
Type: Conceptual
Ans: A

180. As you read your textbook, you notice that throughout each module there are a number of review questions. These questions are actually very specific. Why did the author include these specific questions in each module?
A. To allow you to estimate how ready you are for the exam.
B. The questions provide for previewing for the next section of the module.
C. These questions allow you to gain closure to the material.
D. The specific questions make you focus on the general themes of the module.

p. 20
Application: Study Skills
Level: Moderate
Type: Factual
Ans: C

181. Abdul is a poor judge of what he thinks he knows. According to the textbook, Abdul is most likely to:
A. set too specific performance goals that are inflexible
B. be a victim of poor time management
C. base judgments on general knowledge rather than on specific knowledge
D. base judgments on specific knowledge rather than on general knowledge

p. 20
Application: Study Skills
Level: Moderate
Type: Conceptual
Ans: A

182. In order to judge how prepared you are for an exam, you should:
A. ask yourself specific questions
B. re-read the book two or three times
C. ask yourself how well you think you know the material
D. spend time reviewing your notes

p. 20
Application: Study Skills
Level: Moderate
Type: Factual
Ans: C

183. The three goals discussed in the textbook with regard to studying are:
A. time goal, specific goal, general performance goal
B. cognitive goal, specific goal, specific time goal
C. time goal, general goal, specific performance goal
D. rewarded goal, concrete goal, time goal

p. 20
Application: Study Skills
Level: Easy
Type: Conceptual
Ans: C

184. Tanner did very well on his final exam in his psychology course. Tanner probably:
A. set a time goal
B. set a general goal
C. set a specific performance goal
D. cheated

p. 20
Application: Study Skills
Level: Moderate
Type: Factual
Ans: A

185. According to research cited in Module One, what is the relationship between how well students think they know the class material and their exam performance?
A. almost none
B. weak
C. moderate
D. very strong

p. 21
Application: Study Skills
Level: Moderate
Type: Factual
Ans: A

186. What is not good advice to tell a college freshman to improve note taking?
A. write down everything the instructor says
B. write down lecture material in your own words
C. use headings or an outline
D. ask yourself specific questions about the material

p. 21
Application: Study Skills
Level: Easy
Type: Conceptual
Ans: C

187. The best lecture notes:
A. include everything the professor has said
B. include terms or concepts that you don't understand
C. are in your own words and associated with information you already know
D. list terms that should be learned through sheer memorization

p. 21
Application: Study Skills
Level: Easy
Type: Factual
Ans: D

188. Of the following, which is not a good thing to do to stop procrastination?
A. get organized
B. set specific goals
C. reward yourself
D. think of the final goal

p. 21
Application: Study Skills
Level: Easy
Type: Applied
Ans: C

189. You've been assigned a major research paper in one of your classes. You feel overwhelmed. But then you recall what you learned in psychology, and the task seems less overwhelming. What did you remember?
A. thinking about the final goal of handing the paper in to your professor
B. reminding yourself about other papers and assignments
C. breaking down the assignment into smaller goals
D. visualizing getting an "A" on the paper

True/False

| T | | 1. | The symptoms of autism are usually seen when a child is 2 or 3 years old. |
|---|-----|-----|---|
| F | www | 2. | Psychology is defined as the study of mental disorders. |
| F | | 3. | Palmar sweating occurs when the individual is experiencing excessive bodily warmth. |
| T | www | 4. | The cognitive approach focuses on how information is stored, learned, and remembered. |
| T | | 5. | Women are more sensitive to negative feedback. |
| F | www | 6. | Rewards and punishment play an important role in the psychoanalytic approach. |
| T | | 7. | Self-management is based on behavioral principles. |
| F | www | 8. | Freud argued that people have great freedom in determining the future and have much potential for personal growth. |
| F | | 9. | Procrastinators tend to have parents who place few demands on them. |
| T | www | 10. | Test anxiety from the humanistic perspective is seen as being related to problems in developing potential. |

| T | | 11. | A researcher in the United States believed that autism was caused by "cold" parents. |
|---|-----|-----|---|
| | | 12. | The psychoanalytical approach is the most recent of the approaches presented in Module One. |
| T | www | 13. | Structuralism studied the basic elements of conscious mental experiences. |
| F | | 14. | Introspective was criticized for being too scientific. |
| T | www | 15. | James saw mental activities as serving some adaptive function. |
| F | | 16. | Wilhelm Wundt is considered to be the father of modern psychology. |
| F | | 17. | The Gestalt psychologists were interested in how biology and behavior interact. |
| F | www | 18. | The behavioral approach focused on mental processes. |
| F | | 19. | George Sanchez played an important role in the development of psychoanalysis. |
| T | | 20. | Most psychologists work in private practice or therapy settings. |
| F | www | 21. | A psychologist and a psychiatrist have the same training. |
| F | | 22. | Experimental psychology examines development throughout the lifetime. |
| F | www | 23. | Students have a good sense of how well they know class material. |
| T | | 24. | Setting specific performance goals is better than setting time goals. |
| F | | 25. | An effective way to stop procrastination is to focus on the final goal. |

Short-Answer Essay Questions

1. Describe behavior and mental processes. How has the definition changed over the years? *(www)*
2. What are the four goals of psychology? Give a real-life example for each goal. *(www)*
3. Select two of the modern approaches to psychology (e.g., biological, cognitive) and explain what their focus would be in studying depression or helping behavior. *(www)*
4. Why might there be differences in test anxiety among student from various cultures?
5. Compare and contrast structural, functional, gestalt, and behavioral approaches.
6. Why are Mary Calkins, Ruth Howard, and George Sanchez important in the history of psychology?
7. Describe how note taking could be improved based on the research cited in Module One. *(www)*
8. What are the typically settings in which psychologists are employed?
9. Discuss the research areas of social psychology, cognitive psychology, and psychometrics.
10. Describe time goal, general goal, and specific performance goal. Which one appears to be better with regard to grades? *(www)*

## Module 2 - Psychology and Science

p. 27
Introduction
Level: Moderate
Type: Conceptual
Ans: B

1. Why does Module Two include information on ADHD?
   A. because ADHD is a biological disorder
   B. to understand how psychology must use research methods to answer questions
   C. to understand how ADHD affects the family unit
   D. to understand the degree to which ADHD is caused by unresolved conflicts

p. 27
Introduction
Level: Easy
Type: Factual
Ans: B
*PS/SG 2-2*

2. Rod Plotnik begins this module with the example of Dusty, a hyperactive seven-year old, to show that:
   A.. often psychology must yield to medical science
   B. psychology needs accurate answers to highly complex problems
   C. science must recognize the problems for which it cannot find answers
   D. hyperactivity can be controlled by high doses of vitamin C

p. 27
Introduction
Level: Easy
Type: Factual
Ans: C

3. What disorder is characterized by the behavioral problems of inattention and excessive activity and can be treated with Ritalin?
   A. Conduct Disorder
   B. Learning Disability Disorder
   C. Attention-Deficit Hyperactivity Disorder
   D. Autism

p. 27
Introduction
Level: Easy
Type: Factual
Ans: A
*www*

4. Of the following symptoms, which is not present in Attention-Deficit Hyperactivity Disorder?
   A. hallucinations
   B. frequently leaving the desk or chair in the classroom
   C. making careless mistakes
   D. talking excessively

p. 27
Introduction
Level: Moderate
Type: Applied
Ans: B

5. Your next door neighbor has a son named James. James, who is seven, has problems with attention and excessively fidgets. Based upon your interactions with James, you notice that he talks much of the time and has difficulty following instructions. What is James' most likely diagnosis?
   A. Childhood Schizophrenia
   B. Attention-Deficit Hyperactivity Disorder
   C. Mental Retardation
   D. Autism

p. 27
Introduction
Level: Moderate
Type: Factual
Ans: D

6. Your friend has two children. The youngest of them, a three-year-old boy, was recently diagnosed with ADHD. You find that odd because:
   A. ADHD rarely shows up in males.
   B. The symptoms of ADHD typically are first observed around the age of ten.
   C. In general, the youngest child in a family does not show ADHD.
   D. A diagnosis of ADHD before the age of 6 does not follow the guidelines of the American Academy of Pediatrics.

p. 27
Introduction
Level: Moderate
Type: Factual
Ans: C

7. With regard to Attention-Deficit Hyperactivity Disorder, which of the following is <u>not</u> a controversy in light of the material presented in your textbook?
A. diagnosis of ADHD
B. the use of Ritalin as a treatment for ADHD
C. too much reliance on medical tests
D. making judgments of ADHD in children who are naturally active

p. 27
Introduction
Level: Moderate
Type: Conceptual
Ans: B

8. Ritalin is to _____ as aspirin is to _____.
A. stimulant; depressant
B. attention-deficit hyperactivity disorder; headache
C. depression; headache
D. analgesic; amphetamine

p. 27
Introduction
Level: Moderate
Type: Factual
Ans: C

9. Stimulants, like Ritalin, affect children by:
A. increasing activity but only in nonhyperactive children
B. increasing activity
C. decreasing activity
D. decreasing activity but only in hyperactive children

p. 27
Introduction
Level: Moderate
Type: Applied
Ans: A

10. You're listening to a talk show on the radio. The guest happens to be an expert on attention-deficit hyperactivity disorder. One question asked of the guest is treatment. The expert says, " Ritalin is used to control this disorder. It is a depressant and has side effects." What was wrong the expert's comments?
A. Ritalin is a stimulant, not a depressant
B. Ritalin doesn't control the disorder; it cures it
C. Ritalin is never prescribed for ADHD
D. Ritalin has been shown to cause no side effects

p. 27
Introduction
Level: Moderate
Type: Applied
Ans: B

11. Your ten-year-old cousin is currently taking Ritalin. Based on your knowledge of Ritalin's side effects, you were <u>not</u> surprised to hear that he is having problems in:
A. gaining too much weight
B. sleeping
C. depression
D. maintaining attention

p. 27
Introduction
Level: Moderate
Type: Applied
Ans: D

12. A newspaper reporter wants to do a story on the controversy surrounding attention-deficit hyperactivity disorder. She wants to focus on the biggest controversy. Based upon your reading of this Module, what should be the focus in her story?
A. the side effects of treating it with changes in diet
B. the diagnosis of the disorder
C. the unwillingness of insurance companies to pay for treatment
D. the use of Ritalin

p. 28
Introduction
Level: Moderate
Type: Conceptual
Ans: D

13. According to the textbook, the fact that Attention-Deficit Hyperactivity Disorder was a small problem in the United States 25 years ago and now is commonly diagnosed suggests the need to:

A. improve the training of psychologists and psychiatrists
B. adequately define the disorder in terms of behavior rather than medical tests
C. inform the public on alternative medicines
D. carefully conduct research to clear up the controversies that surround the disorder

p. 28
Answering Questions
Level: Easy
Type: Factual
Ans: B

14. Of the following, which has not been a name for what we now call ADHD?

A. Hyperactivity
B. Childhood Attention Disability
C. Minimal Brain Damage
D. Attention Deficit Disorder

p. 28
Answering Questions
Level: Moderate
Type: Factual
Ans: A

15. The diagnosis of ADHD is difficult because:

A. it is based on behavioral symptoms and not medical tests
B. it is based on medical tests and not behavioral symptoms
C. the law states that two mental health professions must agree on the diagnosis
D. ADHD is so poorly defined

p. 28
Answering Questions
Level: Moderate
Type: Factual
Ans: C

16. Johnny, who has ADHD, attends Mrs. Whitney's fourth grade class. Recently, Johnny was prescribed Ritalin. Which of the following statements by Mrs. Whitney illustrates that she is knowledgeable about ADHD and Ritalin?

A. "Poor Johnny. The medical tests must have been positive."
B. "Ritalin won't have any effect on his activity level."
C. "We will still need to give Johnny support since Ritalin may not improve his academic performance."
D. "I will have to be careful not to give any Nutrasweet to him, since he is allergic to it."

p. 28
Answering Questions
Level: Easy
Type: Factual
Ans: C
*www*

17. Which of the following is not a commonly used method for answering questions?

A. survey
B. case study
C. introspection
D. experiment

p. 29
Surveys
Level: Moderate
Type: Factual
Ans: D

18. The discussion of hand washing in the textbook illustrates what important point about surveys?

A. The results may be accurate if you carefully define the words used in the survey.
B. Self-fulfilling prophecy introduces errors into survey results.
C. Surveys show cause and effect.
D. Sometimes people do not answer truthfully.

| | | |
|---|---|---|
| p. 29<br>Surveys<br>Level: Easy<br>Type: Factual<br>Ans: C | 19. | About _____ of school-age children are diagnosed with ADHD.<br>A. .5%<br>B. 1-3%<br>C. 4-12%<br>D. 20-25% |
| p. 29<br>Surveys<br>Level: Easy<br>Type: Factual<br>Ans: B | 20. | What percentage of children with ADHD continue to have the symptoms as adults?<br>A. 2-6%<br>B. 30-50%<br>C. 60-65%<br>D. 80-90% |
| p. 29<br>Surveys<br>Level: Easy<br>Type: Factual<br>Ans: A | 21. | According to the textbook, which group has the lowest incidence of ADHD?<br>A. Asian Americans<br>B. Hispanic Americans<br>C. Anglo Americans<br>D. African Americans |
| p. 29<br>Surveys<br>Level: Easy<br>Type: Factual<br>Ans: C<br>*www* | 22. | Which research method involves questioning a group of people?<br>A. experimental method<br>B. naturalistic observation<br>C. survey method<br>D. laboratory observation |
| p. 29<br>Surveys<br>Level: Easy<br>Type: Conceptual<br>Ans: D | 23. | As part of a group project, you are required to write a survey. Which of the following research questions would be best answered using the survey method?<br>A. How do chimps establish dominance hierarchies in the wild?<br>B. Among the elderly, does caffeine help problem solving ability?<br>C. How many past Presidents were Democrats?<br>D. Is the President doing an overall good job? |
| p. 29<br>Surveys<br>Level: Moderate<br>Type: Applied<br>Ans: A | 24. | Marcus wants to accurately assess students' attitudes toward the cafeteria food on his college campus for his psychology research project. What research method should he use to collect this information?<br>A. survey method<br>B. laboratory observation<br>C. case study<br>D. experimental method |
| p. 29<br>Surveys<br>Level: Easy<br>Type: Factual<br>Ans: B | 25. | One disadvantage of survey research is that:<br>A. they take too much time<br>B. the sample may be biased due to over- or under- representation<br>C. you cannot compare answers across different ethnic groups<br>D. they can only reach a small number of people |

p. 29
Surveys
Level: Easy
Type: Factual
Ans: B
*PS/SG 2-4*

26. Among the disadvantages of the survey method is that:
A. many people won't go to the trouble of filling out the survey
B. responses can be affected by how the questions are worded and who asks them
C. it is difficult to survey enough subjects to make the results valid
D. it takes so long to conduct a survey that the method is impractical for most purposes

p. 29
Surveys
Level: Easy
Type: Factual
Ans: D

27. Which of the following is a disadvantage of surveys as presented in your textbook?
A. Surveys collect much information.
B. Answers from different groups cannot be compared.
C. Surveys cannot identify problems of treatment programs for ADHD.
D. The ethnicity of the questioner can affect subjects' responses.

p. 29
Surveys
Level: Moderate
Type: Applied
Ans: A

28. You are conducting a survey on racism. You have a group of well-trained assistants, about half white, half African American. Should you keep track of which subjects are questioned by white assistants and which by African Americans assistants?
A. Yes - ethnicity of assistant may affect subjects' answers
B. Yes - ethnicity of assistant may affect their ability to accurately record subjects' answers
C. No - you might offend your assistants
D. No - ethnicity has no effect one way or the other

p. 29
Surveys
Level: Difficult
Type: Conceptual
Ans: B

29. Which of the following surveys demonstrates the most biased sample?
A. a random cross-section of American males asked for their attitudes toward male contraception
B. the subscribers to the Wall Street Journal polled to determine Americans' views on welfare programs
C. all of the homeowners in a given neighborhood asked their opinions of a community center that is planned for the area
D. teachers and students of a given high school asked to give their impressions of the impact that integration has had on the school

p. 29
Surveys
Level: Easy
Type: Factual
Ans: A

30. During a recent trip to the shopping mall, someone working for the mall asked you to fill out a survey on shopping habits. As a student of psychology, what concerns might you have about this survey?
A. wording of the questions
B. confounded causes
C. placebo effect
D. correlation versus cause and effect relationships

p. 30
Case Study
Level: Easy
Type: Factual
Ans: A

31. What research method can be described as an in-depth analysis of a single person?
A. case study
B. correlation
C. survey method
D. experimental method

p. 30
Case Study
Level: Easy
Type: Applied
Ans: D

32. You recently read a book about a celebrity who battled alcoholism throughout her adult life. This book best illustrates the:
A. experimental method
B. naturalistic observation
C. survey method
D. case study

p. 30
Case Study
Level: Easy
Type: Applied
Ans: C

33. Of the following, which best relates to a case study?
A. the telephone book
B. a shopping list
C. your medical records
D. a psychology textbook

p. 30
Case Study
Level: Easy
Type: Factual
Ans: A

34. When you give your _____, you are presenting a statement that supports a viewpoint based upon _____.
A. testimonial; personal experience
B. testimonial; confounded causes
C. correlation; placebos
D. testimonial; introspection

p. 30
Case Study
Level: Easy
Type: Applied
Ans: C

35. "When I start feeling a little tired and run-down, I just take a couple of Vitamin C tablets and I feel better." This is an example of a(n):
A. experiment
B. survey
C. testimonial
D. correlation coefficient

p. 30
Case Study
Level: Easy
Type: Factual
Ans: B

36. A testimonial is defined as:
A. a type of objective evidence gathered in experiments
B. a statement in support of a particular viewpoint based on personal experience
C. a correlation that takes place in more than one context
D. a correlation between two variables that exist independently of each other

p. 30
Case Study
Level: Easy
Type: Applied
Ans: C

37. Charles and Sara, parents of a child with ADHD, claim that when Peter has _____ his hyperactivity worsens. This is an example of a(n) _____.
A. peanuts; experiment
B. organically grown apples; self-fulfilling prophecy
C. artificial additives; testimony
D. a cold; survey

p. 30
Case Study
Level: Moderate
Type: Applied
Ans: B

38. JoHannah is studying ADHD and has asked the mothers of ADHD children how diet has affected their children's symptoms. According to the textbook, what response is JoHannah most likely to get from the mothers?
A. when children were given diets with high levels of sodium their hyperactivity worsened
B. the children's symptoms increase when they consumed an artificial sweetener
C. the symptoms decreased when the diet is low in protein
D. low calorie diets decrease the symptoms of the disorder

<table>
<tr><td>

p. 30<br>
Case Study<br>
Level: Difficult<br>
Type: Conceptual<br>
Ans: A

</td><td>

39.

A.<br>
B.<br>
C.<br>
D.

</td><td>

The observation that testimonials of parents concerning ADHD children contradict studies done by researchers suggests that:<br>
errors and bias make testimonials questionable<br>
researchers used confounded research designs<br>
parents know more than researchers about their children<br>
research studies conducted with children are often poorly designed

</td></tr>

<tr><td>

p. 30<br>
Case Study<br>
Level: Moderate<br>
Type: Conceptual<br>
Ans: A

</td><td>

40.

A.<br>
B.<br>
C.<br>
D.

</td><td>

Which of the following would be <u>most</u> likely presented in the form of a testimonial?<br>
a UFO sighting<br>
medical evidence of the effectiveness of a new cold medication<br>
the results of an intelligence test<br>
the results of a television-viewing survey

</td></tr>

<tr><td>

p. 30<br>
Case Study<br>
Level: Moderate<br>
Type: Applied<br>
Ans: B

</td><td>

41.

A.<br>
B.<br>
C.<br>
D.

</td><td>

A man claims he was cured of a serious disease through meditation and jogging. His claim is an example of:<br>
a survey<br>
a testimonial<br>
naturalistic observation<br>
laboratory observation

</td></tr>

<tr><td>

p. 30<br>
Case Study<br>
Level: Moderate<br>
Type: Factual<br>
Ans: A

</td><td>

42.

A.<br>
B.<br>
C.<br>
D.

</td><td>

A person claims in a newspaper article that he has improved his memory by taking megavitamins. Psychologists would be skeptical of this finding because:<br>
the data were presented in the form of a testimonial<br>
megavitamins have been proven to have no effect on memory<br>
a great deal of what is printed in the newspaper is not true<br>
memory cannot be improved

</td></tr>

<tr><td>

p. 30<br>
Case Study<br>
Level: Moderate<br>
Type: Applied<br>
Ans: C

</td><td>

43.

A.<br>
B.<br>
C.<br>
D.

</td><td>

Recently Willie broke up with his girlfriend and attributes the breakup to her. Jared, his best friend, thinks differently. Jared says of Willie, "I wish he would just consider that he is the real problem! But he has made up his mind." This situation is <u>most</u> closely related to:<br>
a self-fulfilling prophecy<br>
a confounded experience<br>
personal beliefs biasing perceptions<br>
correlation

</td></tr>

<tr><td>

p. 30<br>
Case Study<br>
Level: Easy<br>
Type: Factual<br>
Ans: A<br>
www

</td><td>

44.

A.<br>
B.<br>
C.<br>
D.

</td><td>

A(n) _____ is a strong belief about future behavior that can affect the behavior so that the belief appears to have predicted it.<br>
self-fulfilling prophecy<br>
confounded experience<br>
introspection<br>
testimonial

</td></tr>
</table>

p. 30
Case Study
Level: Easy
Type: Applied
Ans: A

45. Molly strongly believes that she will hurt herself while playing basketball. A few weeks later, she actually does hurt herself during a basketball game. Her injury may have been the result of:
A. a self-fulfilling prophecy
B. a confounded experience
C. a subliminal message
D. ESP

p. 30
Case Study
Level: Moderate
Type: Applied
Ans: D
*PS/SG 2-6*

46. According to the _____, if we strongly believe that something is going to happen, we may unknowingly behave in such a way as to make it happen.
A. wish fulfillment theory
B. testimonial effect
C. personal-belief problem
D. self-fulfilling prophecy

p. 30
Case Study
Level: Moderate
Type: Applied
Ans: A
*PS/SG 2-7*

47. A good example of a self-fulfilling prophecy is the belief that:
A. there's no use studying for multiple-choice exams because the questions are tricky
B. psychology requires more study than literature
C. if you do all your studying the night before the exam you'll do better
D. you don't have to take notes in class if you listen carefully

p. 30
Case Study
Level: Difficult
Type: Factual
Ans: C

48. According to the textbook, what can reinforce testimonials?
A. recognizing the bias inherent in testimonials
B. correlation
C. self-fulfilling prophecy
D. the scientific method

p. 30
Case Study
Level: Difficult
Type: Applied
Ans: B

49. A person suffering from anxiety predicts that he will make a fool of himself at a social gathering and, in fact, he does. A psychologist predicts that students in his morning class invariably outperform those in his afternoon class and, in fact, they do. What do the anxious person and the psychologist share in common?
A. they are both anxious
B. they both produce a self-fulfilling prophecy
C. they both create bias in those who observe them
D. both are very good at predicting behavior

p. 30
Case Study
Level: Moderate
Type: Applied
Ans: B

50. A psychologist is concerned that a colleague's research is yielding a certain type of finding because the colleague expects that finding. The psychologist suspects the effect of:
A. need bias
B. self-fulfilling prophecy
C. predictive invalidity
D. achievement bias

p. 30
Case Study
Level: Moderate
Type: Applied
Ans: A

51. Ollie is having a bad day. He's not feeling very good about himself. He also notices that people are treating him differently. Friends who are usually very considerate are acting rude and impatient toward Ollie. Is his low self-esteem affecting how he interacts with people? Or are his friends influencing how Ollie feels about himself? These questions are a classic example of:
A. a self-fulfilling prophecy
B. a confound
C. a fundamental attribution error
D. cognitive dissonance

p. 30
Case Study
Level: Easy
Type: Factual
Ans: A

52. When the focus of research is on a particular person, the most appropriate method is a(n):
A. case study
B. experiment
C. survey
D. correlation

p. 31
Cultural Diversity:
  Use of Placebos
Level: Easy
Type: Factual
Ans: D

53. A treatment that resembles medical treatment, but has no real effect is termed a:
A. pseudo
B. debrief
C. confound
D. placebo

p. 31
Cultural Diversity:
  Use of Placebos
Level: Easy
Type: Applied
Ans: C

54. Which subject group is most likely receiving a placebo?
A. Group 1 - receive an antibiotic
B. Group 2 - receive a drug that will relieve migraine headaches
C. Group 3 - receive salt water
D. Group 4 - receive Ritalin

p. 31
Cultural Diversity:
 Use of Placebos
Level: Easy
Type: Applied
Ans: C
*www*

55. Your grandmother's cure for your upset stomach is to rub vinegar on your ear lobes. And it works much of the time, but has no real medical effect. Psychologists would probably say that this is an example of a:
A. double blind effect
B. biased effect
C. placebo effect
D. confounding effect

p. 31
Cultural Diversity:
 Use of Placebos
Level: Moderate
Type: Applied
Ans: C

56. Calvin goes to Dr. Payne because of back pain. Dr. Payne is a grumpy, cold, and compassionless physician. He gives Calvin a placebo for the pain. Joyanne calls on Dr. Povich for the same problem. Joyanne's physician is warm and friendly. He, too, prescribes a placebo for Joyanne's pain. Which patient is most likely to report a decrease in pain and why?
A. Both Calvin and Joyanne - the placebo effect works independent of the physician's bedside manner
B. Calvin - the placebo effect is most effective for male patients
C. Joyanne - her doctor is warm and friendly
D. Neither patient - placebos rarely work for pain

p. 31
Cultural Diversity:
  Use of Placebos
Level: Easy
Type: Applied
Ans: A

57. Juan has been smoking for years and really wants to quit. He decided to buy a specially formulated vitamin that he saw advertised on TV. Since he has taken the vitamin, his urge to smoke has disappeared. Juan is most likely to have experienced a(n):

A. placebo effect
B. double blind effect
C. experimenter effect
D. dependent effect

p. 31
Cultural Diversity:
  Use of Placebos
Level: Easy
Type: Factual
Ans: D

58. Placebo effects occur because of:

A. distrust of science
B. distrust of medicine
C. powerful correlations
D. self-fulfilling prophecy

p. 31
Cultural Diversity:
  Use of Placebos
Level: Easy
Type: Factual
Ans: A

59. Which of the following are presented in your textbooks as examples of placebos?

A. bear gallbladders and magnets
B. rhino horns and elephant tusks
C. tiger bones and bear livers
D. tiger bones and garlic

p. 31
Cultural Diversity:
  Use of Placebos
Level: Moderate
Type: Applied
Ans: B

60. Your grandmother's cure for an upset stomach is to rub vinegar on your ear lobes. According to your relatives, the treatment works much of the time, but has no real medical effect. Placebos are often widely accepted because _____ is (are) very influential.

A. double blind effect
B. testimonials
C. placebo effect
D. confounding effect

p. 31
Cultural Diversity:
  Use of Placebos
Level: Moderate
Type: Applied
Ans: C
*www*

61. Late one night you are watching TV as an ad promoting magnetic pads to relieve pain comes on. You count more than 15 past customers appearing in the commercial claiming the product's effectiveness in relieving pain from injuries and arthritis. One customer is a former professional football star. You realize that the commercial is cleverly using:

A. debriefing
B. a placebo
C. testimonials
D. experimentation

p. 31
Cultural Diversity:
  Use of Placebos
Level: Easy
Type: Factual
Ans: C

62. You are writing a paper on the effects of magnets of pain reduction. Based

A. Using magnets is an effective method to relieve pain.
B. Magnets can reduce pain, but only in localized areas of the body.
C. Magnets have no effect on pain reduction.
D. Certain types of pain are most likely to be reduced with magnets

p. 31
Cultural Diversity:
 Use of Placebos
Level: Easy
Type: Factual
Ans: A

63. Which of the following world-wide placebos is *incorrectly* paired with its alleged effect?
A. Tiger bones - treating headaches
B. magnets - reducing pain
C. Tiger bones - treating ulcers
D. rhino horn - aphrodisiac

p. 32
Correlation
Level: Easy
Type: Factual
Ans: C

64. A correlation is used to:
A. explain how one variable causes another variable
B. show the effect that one variable has on another variable
C. describe a relationship between two or more variables
D. prove theories

p. 32
Correlation
Level: Easy
Type: Factual
Ans: A

65. What technique is a measure of the relationship between two variables?
A. correlation
B. survey
C. testimonial
D. observation

p. 32
Correlation
Level: Easy
Type: Factual
Ans: A
*PS/SG 2-8*

66. A "correlation" is defined as:
A. an association or relationship between the occurrence of two or more events
B. the connection between a cause and an effect
C. the association of family members into the extended family
D. an occurrence that can only be explained as random

p. 32
Correlation
Level: Easy
Type: Factual
Ans: D

67. If Christa wants to study the relationship between income and years of education, she ought to use the _____ method.
A. observation
B. experimentation
C. naturalistic
D. correlation

p. 32
Correlation
Level: Easy
Type: Factual
Ans: D

68. A number that describes the strength of a relationship between events is called a(n) _____; it can range between _____.
A. mean coefficient; 0.00 and +1.00
B. average correlation; 0.00 and +10.00
C. average; .00 and +1.00
D. correlation coefficient; -1.00 and +1.00

p. 32
Correlation
Level: Easy
Type: Conceptual
Ans: D

69. A newspaper article reports that crime increases each month when the moon is full. This relationship is a(n):
A. testimonial
B. experiment
C. survey
D. correlation

p. 32
Correlation
Level: Moderate
Type: Applied
Ans: B

70. A study reports a positive correlation between acts of aggression and the amount of TV a child watches. The <u>best</u> interpretation of this statement would be:
A. TV viewing causes children to act aggressively
B. children who watch a great deal of TV tend to be more aggressive than children who watch less TV
C. there is no relationship between the amount of TV watched and aggressive behavior
D. children should not be allowed to view violent TV programs.

p. 32
Correlation
Level: Easy
Type: Conceptual
Ans: B

71. "The more you study, the fewer errors you will make on the next exam" is an example of a _____ correlation.
A. positive
B. negative
C. perfect
D. zero

p. 32
Correlation
Level: Easy
Type: Applied
Ans: A

72. Tennis players who have a high percentage of successful first serves have a greater chance of winning tennis matches than players who are not as successful on their first serve. This is an example of a _____ correlation.
A. positive
B. negative
C. perfect
D. zero

p. 32
Correlation
Level: Easy
Type: Applied
Ans: C

73. Karen and Kassie are twins participating in a research project on intelligence. Karen is very intelligent. Which of the following would tell us the likelihood that Kassie is very intelligent as well?
A. experiment
B. testimonial
C. correlation
D. naturalistic observation

p. 32
Correlation
Level: Easy
Type: Factual
Ans: D
*www*

74. What does correlation tell us?
A. the order in which variables occur
B. which variables influence other variables
C. what causes change in a variable
D. the relationship and strength of relationship between two or more variables

p. 32
Correlation
Level: Easy
Type: Applied
Ans: A

75. If we find that intelligent parents tend to have intelligent children, then we would be correct in describing the relationship as a _____ correlation.
A. positive
B. negative
C. perfect
D. zero

p. 32
Correlation
Level: Easy
Type: Applied
Ans: B
*www*

76.    As the price of gas increases, we tend to drive less.  This is an example of a
        _____ correlation.
A.    positive
B.    negative
C.    perfect
D.    zero

p. 32
Correlation
Level: Easy
Type: Factual
Ans: D

77.    Which of the following correlation coefficients represents the <u>highest</u>
        degree of association between two variables?
A.    +.70
B.    +.30
C.    -.20
D.    -.90

p. 32
Correlation
Level: Easy
Type: Factual
Ans: B

78.    Which of the following correlation coefficients represents the <u>lowest</u>
        degree of association between two variables?
A.    +.40
B.    +.15
C.    -.50
D.    -.75

p. 32
Correlation
Level: Easy
Type: Factual
Ans: D

79.    Which of the following correlation coefficients represents a situation in which
        an increase in one variable is associated with a <u>decrease</u> in the other variable?
A.    +.90
B.    +.30
C.     .00
D.    -.70

p. 32
Correlation
Level: Easy
Type: Factual
Ans: D

80.    Which of the following correlation coefficients represents a situation in which
        an increase in one variable is associated with an <u>increase</u> in the other variable?
A.    -.45
B.    -.61
C.     .00
D.    +.45

p. 32
Correlation
Level: Easy
Type: Factual
Ans: D

81.    Which of the following correlation coefficients represents a situation in which
        there is no relationship between variables?
A.    -1.00
B.    .99
C.    10.00
D.    .00

p. 32
Correlation
Level: Moderate
Type: Applied
Ans: C

82.    Andy measured the size of each of his friends' heads and also asked them for
        their SAT scores, in order to determine whether a relationship existed
        between head size and intelligence.  His computed correlation coefficient
        was .00.  What should Andy conclude?
A.    As head size increases, intelligence increases.
B.    As head size increases, intelligence decreases.
C.    There is no relationship between head size and intelligence.
D.    A small head causes a lowered level of intelligence.

p. 33
Correlation
Level: Difficult
Type: Conceptual
Ans: D

83. Select one of the following statements about methods that is <u>incorrect</u>.
A. A survey gives us information about a large number of people.
B. A case study provides information about one person.
C. The experiment suggests cause and effect relationships.
D. A correlation shows us cause and effect relationships.

p. 33
Correlation
Level: Moderate
Type: Conceptual
Ans: D

84. Correlations are <u>not</u> appropriate to _____ but are useful to _____.
A. predict behavior; make cause and effect statements
B. make cause and effect statements; pinpoint confounding effects
C. evaluate testimonials; evaluate surveys
D. make cause and effect statements; make predictions about behavior

p. 33
Correlation
Level: Moderate
Type: Applied
Ans: A

85. Abdul was listening to a radio talk show and heard the announcer talk about "a high correlation between crime and poverty." The announcer then proceeded to say since there was a high correlation, poverty causes crime. Abdul is taking psychology, and is skeptical of what he just heard. He knows that:
A. correlation does not indicate cause and effect relationships
B. to properly evaluate the statement, he needs to know the magnitude of the correlation
C. poverty is difficult to measure
D. the research indicates that crime causes poverty not vice versa

p. 33
Correlation
Level: Moderate
Type: Conceptual
Ans: D

86. If the professional football team the Minnesota Vikings (National Football Conference) wins the Super Bowl next year, then the stock market will:
A. rise
B. fall
C. no correlation exists between the Super Bowl and the stock market
D. correlations do not indicate cause and effect

p. 33
Correlation
Level: Moderate
Type: Factual
Ans: A

87. The correlation between smoking and lung cancer shows that:
A. correlations may, in fact, give clues to real causes
B. there is no way of determining whether smoking causes lung cancer
C. smoking does not cause lung cancer
D. even strong correlations can be misleading

p. 33
Correlation
Level: Moderate
Type: Factual
Ans: C

88. Recent research shows that the relationship between smoking and lung cancer may be caused by:
A. the paper in which cigarettes are wrapped
B. smokers not getting enough exercise
C. a chemical in cigarette smoke that turns off a gene that normally suppresses tumors
D. excessive drinking that occurs while the smoker smokes cigarettes

p. 33
Correlation
Level: Moderate
Type: Conceptual
Ans: C

89. If the correlation between number of siblings and college GPA is .86, then we could:
A. explain why students who are the only child do so poorly in college
B. explain why students who are the only child do so well in college
C. predict that students who have several siblings will have higher GPA's
D. predict that students who have no siblings will have higher GPA's

p. 33
Correlation
Level: Moderate
Type: Conceptual
Ans: B

90. Assume there is a correlation of .00 between shoe size and number of siblings. If you know someone's shoe size:
A. your prediction of number of siblings will be very accurate
B. it would be very difficult to accurately predict the person's number of siblings
C. your prediction of number of siblings will depend upon the strength of the relationship
D. then you could explain why the person has the number of siblings she does

p. 33
Correlation
Level: Moderate
Type: Conceptual
Ans: B

91. Grade school students are often given IQ tests because IQ tests:
A. predict mental health
B. are highly correlated with academic performance
C. cause students to improve their study skills
D. are negatively correlated with cognitive abilities

p. 34
Decisions about Doing
 Research
Level: Easy
Type: Conceptual
Ans: A

92. Manuel is watching a game show on TV that provides the answer and the contestants give the question. He hears, "The answer is 'Questionnaires, interviews, standardized tests, and animal models.'" Manuel knows the question and it is:
A. "What are some examples of research techniques?"
B. "What are some examples of research settings?"
C. "What are some methods to control self-fulfilling prophecy?"
D. "How are independent variables identified?"

p. 34
Decisions about Doing
 Research
Level: Moderate
Type: Factual
Ans: B

93. As you start your research project on depression, you're faced with two important questions. Based upon your textbook, what are the two questions?
A. Which research technique should I use?; Who are my subjects?
B. What research technique should I use?; Which research setting should I use?
C. How do I define depression?; Who are my subjects?
D. What type of experiment do I conduct?; How do I measure depression?

p. 34
Decisions about Doing
 Research
Level: Easy
Type: Factual
Ans: D

94. Which of the following is not an example of a research technique presented in your textbook?
A. laboratory experiment
B. questionnaire
C. standardized test
D. naturalistic study

p. 34
Decisions about Doing
 Research
Level: Easy
Type: Factual
Ans: B

95. A research subject is reading a list of questions. The type of research method being used is a(n):
A. interview
B. questionnaire
C. test
D. experiment

p. 34
Decisions about Doing
 Research
Level: Easy
Type: Factual
Ans: C

96. A standardized test is a type of research technique that:
A. assesses physiological responses
B. asks open-ended questions
C. reliably measures specific traits, cognitive processes, or behaviors
D. is used in animal models

p. 34
Decisions about Doing
  Research
Level: Easy
Type: Factual
Ans: D

97. One disadvantage in using standardized tests is that:
A. subjects often lie about their thought patterns, personality, and emotions
B. they are given in controlled settings
C. the law prohibits the use of the results in occupational or educational settings
D. they may be biased toward certain groups.

p. 34
Decisions about Doing
  Research
Level: Easy
Type: Factual
Ans: B
*www*

98. A test that is given to hundreds of people and is used to make comparisons among people is called a _____ test.
A. projective
B. standardized
C. controlled
D. double blind

p. 34
Decisions about Doing
  Research
Level: Moderate
Type: Factual
Ans: A

99. If a researcher wants to study a behavior in a controlled environment, the researcher should utilize a(n):
A. laboratory experiment
B. testimonial
C. naturalistic study
D. case study

p. 34
Decisions about Doing
  Research
Level: Moderate
Type: Factual
Ans: C

100. A new laboratory experiment to diagnose ADHD involves:
A. a test that measures the amount of protein in the blood
B. taking a standardized test
C. a subject pressing a button when seeing an object while her brain is scanned
D. asking the person questions about her behaviors and attitudes

p. 34
Decisions about Doing
  Research
Level: Moderate
Type: Applied
Ans: B
*www*

101. Phuong is interested in investigating the effects of radiation on learning. Phuong should use:
A. questionnaires
B. animal models
C. standardized tests
D. interviews

p. 34
Decisions about Doing
  Research
Level: Moderate
Type: Applied
Ans: D

102. Dr. Lee wants to conduct research examining the effects of social deprivation on brain development in children. Which research technique is most appropriate and why?
A. standardized test - the results would be more accurate
B. interview - she can ask both children and their parents relevant questions
C. animal model - it is easier to care for animals than children
D. animal model - it is unethical to expose children to social deprivation

p. 34
Decisions about Doing
  Research
Level: Easy
Type: Factual
Ans: D

103. Scientists have found a gene in mice that may provide clues as to the genetics of obesity. The research technique used by these scientists is the:
A. case study
B. testimonial
C. naturalistic study
D. animal model

p. 35
Decisions about Doing
  Research
Level: Moderate
Type: Applied
Ans: B

104.    Kristy is interested in conducting research on the table manners of children while eating. She concludes that a laboratory setting would be most appropriate for the research. Kristy's research supervisor at college disagrees and suggests she rethink her research setting. What piece of advice would you give to Kristy?

A.    get another research supervisor
B.    conduct the research in a naturalistic setting
C.    use case study technique
D.    consider using the animal model focusing on baby chimps

p. 35
Decisions about Doing
  Research
Level: Moderate
Type: Factual
Ans: C

105.    If you are conducting an experiment in a naturalistic setting, which of the following will you avoid?

A.    trying to observe the organisms' behavior
B.    watching the organisms in their own environment
C.    attempting to change or control the situation
D.    using a large city as the experimental setting

p. 35
Decisions about Doing
  Research
Level: Moderate
Type: Factual
Ans: D

106.    A disadvantage of naturalistic observation is that:

A.    the behavior is controlled
B.    the situation is too artificial
C.    the manipulation of the independent variable may be insufficient
D.    the psychologists' own beliefs and values might affect their observation

p. 35
Decisions about Doing
  Research
Level: Moderate
Type: Factual
Ans: C
*PS/SG 2-13*

107.    Whether to do research in a naturalistic or laboratory setting involves the issue of:

A.    comprehensiveness versus cost
B.    testimonial versus science
C.    realism versus control
D.    objectivity versus subjectivity

p. 35
Decisions about Doing
  Research
Level: Easy
Type: Applied
Ans: A

108.    Jocelyn wants to study in great depth the personality development, behaviors, and feelings of a young child. Jocelyn should utilize:

A.    a case study
B.    an animal model
C.    a laboratory setting
D.    standardized testing

p. 35
Decisions about Doing
  Research
Level: Easy
Type: Factual
Ans: B

109.    If you collect a great deal of information regarding the thoughts, feelings, and behaviors of an individual person, you are conducting a(n):

A.    survey questionnaire
B.    case study
C.    experiment
D.    standardized test

p. 35
Decisions about Doing
 Research
Level: Easy
Type: Factual
Ans: C

110. Information obtained in _____ is unique to an individual and may not apply to or help understand the behaviors of others.
A. a laboratory setting
B. an animal model
C. a case study
D. standardized testing

p. 35
Decisions about Doing
 Research
Level: Easy
Type: Factual
Ans: D

111. Dr. Allkins is conducting a case study of an individual with ADHD. Dr. Allkins should keep in mind that:
A. correlation will help to reveal cause and effect relationships
B. the independent variable must be carefully controlled
C. random assignment will prevent error from being introduced into the study
D. what is true of this one individual may not be true of other individuals

p. 35
Decisions about Doing
 Research
Level: Easy
Type: Conceptual
Ans: A

112. In your study, you must control temperature, lighting, and sound levels. Of the following, which is most appropriate for your research given these requirements?
A. a laboratory setting
B. a natural setting
C. a case study
D. standardized testing

p. 35
Decisions about Doing
 Research
Level: Easy
Type: Factual
Ans: C
PS/SG 2-14

113. Which one of the following has the *lowest* potential for error or bias?
A. case study
B. survey
C. experiment
D. testimonial

p. 35
Decisions about Doing
 Research
Level: Difficult
Type: Conceptual
Ans: C

114. Art has conducted a study in a laboratory setting and is currently preparing a presentation describing his research. Which of the following is the most likely criticism he will receive about his research setting.
A. The dependent variable was measured instead of manipulated.
B. He did random selection of his subjects.
C. The setting is too controlled and the results may not apply to real-life situations.
D. Bias was introduced because he used a setting where he had little control over extraneous variables.

p. 35
Decisions about Doing
 Research
Level: Easy
Type: Factual
Ans: A

115. Research has found that Ritalin causes an increase in activity in the _____
A. basal ganglia
B. hippocampus
C. cerebellum
D. cortex

p. 35
Decisions about Doing
 Research
Level: Easy
Type: Conceptual
Ans: D

116. The best research setting is:
A. a laboratory setting because we can control interference from the environment
B. naturalistic setting since much of real life cannot be duplicated in the laboratory
C. case study in a natural environment - much information about an individual is obtained
D. impossible to say since each has advantages and disadvantages

p. 35
Decisions about Doing
 Research
Level: Easy
Type: Conceptual
Ans: B

117. Naturalistic setting is to laboratory setting as _____ is to _____.
A. independent variable; dependent variable
B. real-life setting; controlled setting
C. dependent variable; independent variable
D. controlled setting; real-life setting

p. 36
Scientific Method:
 Experiment
Level: Easy
Type: Factual
Ans: C

118. What is the approach that attempts to gather information and to answer questions in a way that errors and bias are minimized?
A. debriefing
B. random selection
C. scientific method
D. manipulation of variables

p. 36
Scientific Method:
 Experiment
Level: Moderate
Type: Conceptual
Ans: A

119. The "scientific" part of psychology refers to its use of:
A. the scientific method
B. introspection
C. theories
D. statistics

p. 36
Scientific Method:
 Experiment
Level: Moderate
Type: Conceptual
Ans: B

120. The scientific method attempts to:
A. propose theoretical ideas to answer questions
B. minimize errors and bias in gathering information and answering questions
C. promote common sense understanding
D. dispute common sense by forcing scientists to do experiments

p. 36
Scientific Method:
 Experiment
Level: Easy
Type: Factual
Ans: A
PS/SG 2-15

121. The scientific method is defined as:
A. an approach to answering questions that minimizes errors and bias
B. a faith that precise equipment will produce accurate information
C. all of the findings of science in the modern era
D. a set of guidelines published by the American Academy of Science

p. 36
Scientific Method:
  Experiment
Level: Easy
Type: Factual
Ans: D

122. Of the following, which is <u>not</u> among the seven (7) rules of conducting an experiment according to your textbook?
A. identify
B. choose
C. manipulate
D. observe

p. 36
Scientific Method:
  Experiment
Level: Easy
Type: Factual
Ans: B

123. To determine cause and effect relationships, you are <u>best</u> advised to conduct a(n):
A. correlation
B. experiment
C. case study
D. interview

p. 36
Scientific Method:
  Experiment
Level: Moderate
Type: Conceptual
Ans: C

124. If an experiment could "talk" what would it say about itself?
A. "If you want to know how variables correlate with each other, I'm your research method."
B. "Don't worry about random selection or independent variables with me…they're a waste of time."
C. "Suggesting cause and effect is my specialty."
D. "I specialize in revealing in-depth information about a person."

p. 36
Scientific Method:
  Experiment
Level: Moderate
Type: Conceptual
Ans: A

125. What words are <u>most</u> illustrative of experiments?
A. cause, effect
B. individual, unique
C. relationship, test
D. predicting, correlation

p. 36
Scientific Method:
  Experiment
Level: Easy
Type: Applied
Ans: D

126. "I'm interested in whether playing classical music while studying has a positive effect on test scores." The <u>most</u> appropriate way to find out is to:
A. do introspection
B. ask a person who gets good grades how they study
C. do a survey
D. conduct an experiment

p. 36
Scientific Method:
  Experiment
Level: Moderate
Type: Applied
Ans: A

127. In her research, Professor Marrs is following a set of rules and guidelines:
A. she's conducting an experiment
B. Professor Marrs is calculating a correlation coefficient
C. she's using a standardized test
D. conducting research in a naturalistic setting

p. 36
Scientific Method:
  Experiment
Level: Easy
Type: Factual
Ans: B

128. If Wanda makes an educated, precisely worded guess about the behavior of her friends in a specific situation, she is making a(n):
A. theory
B. hypothesis
C. principle
D. manipulation of variables

p. 36
Scientific Method:
  Experiment
Level: Easy
Type: Conceptual
Ans: C
*www*

129. When we make a hypothesis, we are:
A. identifying
B. choosing
C. guessing
D. assigning

p. 36
Scientific Method:
  Experiment
Level: Easy
Type: Factual
Ans: A

130. In conducting an experiment, a precisely worded, educated guess is:
A. a hypothesis
B. a hunch
C. a variable
D. random selection

p. 36
Scientific Method:
  Experiment
Level: Moderate
Type: Conceptual
Ans: C

131. Among the following, which is the best hypothesis?
A. Often times, people will go out of their way to help others
B. Children who watch a lot of television will be more aggressive
C. Students who review their notes each night for one hour will score significantly higher on the next day's quiz than students who do not review their notes
D. Taking an aspirin a day helps keep the doctor away

p. 36
Scientific Method:
  Experiment
Level: Easy
Type: Applied
Ans: D

132. If you are conducting an experiment on the usefulness of Ritalin on ADHD,
A. Children, with ADHD, who are given Ritalin will become better students.
B. Ritalin will make students with ADHD more manageable.
C. Ritalin will help students with ADHD.
D. Ritalin will decrease negative classroom behaviors of children with ADHD.

p. 36
Scientific Method:
  Experiment
Level: Easy
Type: Factual
Ans: A

133. If you are studying the effects of various drugs on ADHD, the independent variable is:
A. the drugs
B. ADHD
C. the subjects getting the drugs
D. the subjects getting the placebo

p. 36
Scientific Method:
  Experiment
Level: Easy
Type: Factual
Ans: C

134. The treatment which is controlled by the researcher is called the:
A. dependent variable
B. confounding variable
C. independent variable
D. control variable

p. 36
Scientific Method:
  Experiment
Level: Moderate
Type: Applied
Ans: C

135. A psychologist wants to know if eating a large breakfast improves IQ test scores in a sample of thirty 10-year-olds. The psychologist divides the subjects into three groups of ten and has one group eat a small breakfast, one group eat a medium-sized breakfast, and one group eat a large breakfast. In this study, the independent variable is:
A. the IQ test
B. the scores on the IQ test
C. the size of the breakfast
D. the number of subjects in each group

p. 36
Scientific Method:
  Experiment
Level: Moderate
Type: Applied
Ans: B

136. Denise conducts a study to find out which of three subway routes gets her to work in the shortest amount of time. In Denise's experiment, the independent variable is the _____, and the dependent variable is the _____.
A. speed of the subway car; route she took
B. route she took; amount of time to get to work
C. amount of time to get to work; number of routes she tried
D. fastest route; shortest route

p. 36
Scientific Method:
  Experiment
Level: Moderate
Type: Applied
Ans: C
*www*

137. Alfredo is conducting an experiment on the effects of exercise on concentration. The independent variable is _____ and the dependent variable is _____.
A. subjects; control group
B. experimental group; concentration
C. exercise; concentration
D. concentration; exercise

p. 36
Scientific Method:
  Experiment
Level: Easy
Type: Factual
Ans: D

138. Behavior that is measured in an experiment is called the:
A. independent variable
B. experimental variable
C. random variable
D. dependent variable

p. 36
Scientific Method:
  Experiment
Level: Moderate
Type: Conceptual
Ans: D

139. Independent variable is to _____ as dependent variable is to _____.
A. cause; confound
B. effect; treatment
C. measure; outcome
D. cause; effect

p. 36
Scientific Method:
  Experiment
Level: Easy
Type: Applied
Ans: A

140. The dependent variable depends upon:
A. the independent variable
B. subjects
C. selective assignment
D. the control group

p. 36
Scientific Method:
  Experiment
Level: Easy
Type: Factual
Ans: B
*PS/SG 2-16*

141.   The special treatment given to the subjects in the experimental group is called the:
  A.   hypothesis
  B.   independent variable
  C.   dependent variable
  D.   control variable

p. 36
Scientific Method:
  Experiment
Level: Moderate
Type: Conceptual
Ans: B

142.   Manipulated is to measured as _____ is to _____.
  A.   dependent variable; independent variable
  B.   independent variable; dependent variable
  C.   effect; cause
  D.   case study; placebo

p. 36
Scientific Method:
  Experiment
Level: Easy
Type: Factual
Ans: B

143.   If each subject in a sample population has an equal chance of being selected, it is called:
  A.   a control group
  B.   random selection
  C.   an experimental group
  D.   measurement error

p. 36
Scientific Method:
  Experiment
Level: Easy
Type: Applied
Ans: D
*PS/SG 2-17*

144.   The reason why researchers choose their subjects by random selection is that:
  A.   in random selection, there is a positive correlation between subjects
  B.   it is a tradition that goes back to the days of Wilhelm Wundt's psychology lab
  C.   this method guarantees that the more motivated subjects will be selected
  D.   only this method guarantees an equal chance of being selected for the experiment

p. 36
Scientific Method:
  Experiment
Level: Easy
Type: Applied
Ans: A
*PS/SG 2-18*

145.   Which of the following is an example of random selection?
  A.   winning numbers in the lottery
  B.   annual National Football League player draft
  C.   numbers people play in the lottery
  D.   Miss America contest

p. 36
Scientific Method:
  Experiment
Level: Moderate
Type: Applied
Ans: C

146.   Shyla conducted an experiment. She went to the student union and asked people if they would like to be subjects in her study. She decided to ask only those people who smiled at her. Is this an appropriate way to select subjects?
  A.   Yes - since these individuals smiled and are likely to be cooperative and friendly subjects
  B.   Yes - the student union has a diverse group of people
  C.   No - it is not random selection
  D.   No - Shyla failed to assign her subjects to groups first

p. 36
Scientific Method:
 Experiment
Level: Easy
Type: Factual
Ans: A

147. To get subjects who are representative of the population, experimenters use:
A. random selection
B. random assignment
C. naturalistic selection
D. double-blind procedure

p. 37
Scientific Method:
 Experiment
Level: Easy
Type: Factual
Ans: C

148. What does randomly assigning subjects to different groups ultimately do?
A. random assignment makes the selection of subjects less time consuming
B. it prevents subjects from knowing what group they are in
C. random assignment controls any factors that might influence the results of the study
D. it ensures that there is an equal number of males and females in each group

p. 37
Scientific Method:
 Experiment
Level: Moderate
Type: Factual
Ans: B

149. An advantage of randomly assigning subjects to groups is:
A. to make the groups equal in number
B. that it reduces the chance that other variables will bias the results
C. to ensure that the sample is representative of the population
D. to make the groups as different as possible from each other

p. 37
Scientific Method:
 Experiment
Level: Easy
Type: Factual
Ans: C
*PS/SG 2-19*

150. The purpose of having a control group in an experiment is to:
A. show what results the opposite treatment would produce
B. show how a different group would react to the treatment
C. identify and rule out the behavior that results from simply participating in the experiment
D. provide backup subjects in case any members of the experimental group drop out

p. 37
Scientific Method:
 Experiment
Level: Moderate
Type: Applied
Ans: D

151. Fawzi wants to see if nicotine causes cancer in rats. Half of his rats are given nicotine, and the other half are not. In this experiment, the rats that receive nicotine are the _____, and the rats that do not are the _____.
A. independent variable; dependent variable
B. dependent variable; independent variable
C. control group; experimental group
D. experimental group; control group

p. 37
Scientific Method:
 Experiment
Level: Moderate
Type: Factual
Ans: A
*www*

152. An experiment is designed to test how the _____ affects the behavior selected as the _____.
A. independent variable; dependent variable
B. dependent variable; independent variable
C. double-blind procedure; dependent variable
D. self-fulfilling prophecy; dependent variable

p. 37
Scientific Method:
 Experiment
Level: Moderate
Type: Conceptual
Ans: D

153. Experimental group is to treatment as control group is to:
A. subject
B. random selection
C. manipulate
D. placebo

p. 37
Scientific Method:
 Experiment
Level: Moderate
Type: Applied
Ans: D

154. Tina is assigned to a group where she receives some special treatment. Beth is in the group that does not receive the treatment. Identify the correct groups these two subjects are in.
A. Tina is in the independent group; Beth is in the dependent group
B. Tina is in the dependent group; Beth is in the independent group
C. Tina is in the control group; Beth is in the experimental group
D. Tina is in the experimental group; Beth is in the control group

p. 37
Scientific Method:
 Experiments
Level: Easy
Type: Factual
Ans: C
PS/SG 2-20

155. A double-blind procedure means that:
A. the subjects are not informed that they are participating in an experiment
B. the subjects are not allowed to interact with each other
C. neither participants nor researchers know which group is receiving which treatment
D. neither drug companies nor doctors know that research is going on

p. 37
Scientific Method:
 Experiments
Level: Easy
Type: Factual
Ans: A

156. What is the procedure where neither the subject nor the experimenter know which group is receiving which treatment?
A. double-blind procedure
B. single-blind procedure
C. random selection
D. random assignment

p. 37
Scientific Method:
 Experiments
Level: Easy
Type: Conceptual
Ans: C

157. What is the most likely thing that a subject in a double-blind procedure would say?
A. "It is a great honor to have been selected for the experimental group."
B. "Being in the control group is boring."
C. "I have no idea if I am in the experimental or control group and the researcher doesn't know either!"
D. "I wonder what group I am in? I suppose I could ask the researcher and she would know."

p. 37
Scientific Method:
 Experiments
Level: Easy
Type: Factual
Ans: B

158. Which of the following does the double-blind procedure control for?
A. wording effects
B. self-fulfilling prophecy
C. counterbalancing
D. random selection

p. 37
Scientific Method:
  Experiments
Level: Moderate
Type: Factual
Ans: B

159. In order to determine if differences between experimental and control groups are due to the treatment or to error or chance occurrence, a researcher employs:
A. introspection
B. statistical procedures
C. commonsense judgment
D. an animal model

p. 37
Scientific Method:
  Experiments
Level: Moderate
Type: Conceptual
Ans: D

160. The difference between the behaviors of the subjects in the experimental group and the subjects in the control group is not likely due to:
A. the independent variable
B. error
C. chance occurrence
D. the dependent variable

p. 37
Scientific Method:
  Experiments
Level: Moderate
Type: Applied
Ans: D

161. In Professor's Walsh's experiment, she finds a significant difference at the .05 level between two strains of rats in eating behavior. What this really means is that Professor Walsh is:
A. 100% sure that the difference is due to some unknown error
B. 5% sure that the independent variable had some effect on eating
C. 100% sure that the difference is due to the independent variable
D. 95% sure that the difference observed is due to the independent variable

p. 37
Scientific Method:
  Experiments
Level: Moderate
Type: Factual
Ans: C

162. According to your textbook, statistical procedures are used to:
A. determine if the control group was randomly assigned to the dependent variable
B. determine if the experimental group was randomly assigned to the dependent variable
C. determine if the observed differences in the dependent variables are due to the independent variable or to something else
D. determine if the observed differences in the independent variables are due to the dependent variable or to something else

p. 39
Research Focus:
  ADHD Controversies
Level: Easy
Type: Factual
Ans: C

163. An accurate diagnosis of ADHD is
A. based on blood tests
B. based on CAT scans
C. difficult
D. most likely when the child is from an upper-class family

p. 39
Research Focus:
  ADHD Controversies
Level: Easy
Type: Factual
Ans: C

164. Based upon the textbook, what is an advantage of using a stimulant such as Ritalin to treat ADHD?
A. social skills improve dramatically
B. improves sleeping habits
C. decreases hyperactivity and improves attention
D. athletic ability improves

p. 39
Research Focus:
  ADHD Controversies
Level: Moderate
Type: Applied
Ans: A

165. Forrest has been treated with Ritalin for ADHD for nine years. He is now 16 years old. Using the available research, what can we say about Forrest's future?
A. he is less likely to graduate from high school
B. grades are likely to improve since his activity level has decreased
C. his treatment with Ritalin does not increase his risk for any type of problem
D. Forrest is likely to do well in high school if he continues with Ritalin

p. 39
Research Focus:
  ADHD Controversies
Level: Moderate
Type: Factual
Ans: D

166. To improve the outcome of treating ADHD:
A. Ritalin should be given before the age of 5
B. the child's diet should be modified to avoid Nutrasweet
C. Ritalin should be given only after the age of 2
D. both Ritalin and behavior treatment should be used

p. 39
Research Focus:
  ADHD Controversies
Level: Moderate
Type: Factual
Ans: B

167. Since Ritalin does not cure ADHD, what should parents be most concerned about in managing their child's disorder?
A. consistency in taking Ritalin even when the child seems to be doing better
B. developing behavioral programs such as setting rules and establishing rules
C. giving the same opportunities for intellectual growth as they would to a child who does not have ADHD
D. provide psychoanalysis to the child on weekly basis

p. 39
Research Focus:
  ADHD Controversies
Level: Easy
Type: Applied
Ans: A

168. Who is the best case for benefiting from a behavioral treatment program for ADHD?
A. Joe who is the 9th grade
B. Leo who is in preschool
C. Kevin who possesses average social skills
D. Kenny who has severe ADHD

p. 40
Application:
  Research Concerns
Level: Easy
Type: Factual
Ans: B
PS/SG 2-22

169. Should you volunteer to be a subject in a psychological experiment?
A. no, because you are completely at the mercy of the researcher
B. yes, because ethical guidelines protect subjects from danger or undue deception
C. no, because they'll never tell you what the experiment was really about
D. yes, because looking dumb or foolish occasionally makes us more humble

p. 40
Application:
  Research Concerns
Level: Easy
Type: Factual
Ans: A

170. What organization has published a code of ethics of conduct for psychologists to follow when conducting research?
A. American Psychological Association
B. American Psychiatric Institute
C. Big Ten Conference
D. National Education Association

p. 40
Application:
  Research Concerns
Level: Moderate
Type: Conceptual
Ans: D

171. Gail conducts an experiment that may produce harmful effects. To protect her subjects, she thoroughly explains the purpose of the experiment, and helps subjects deal with possible doubts or guilt arising from their behaviors in the experiment. Gail is going through the process of:
A. random selection
B. statistical procedures
C. introspection
D. debriefing

p. 40
Application:
  Research Concerns
Level: Moderate
Type: Applied
Ans: C

172. Dr. Rose conducts a study to determine if caffeine can aid memory. Her three groups of subjects receive either a high dose, a low dose, or no caffeine. They all receive identical-looking pills so that they are unaware of how much caffeine they take. In addition, when the researcher tests the memory of each subject, she is not aware of what group each subject is in. This research design utilizes which of the following?
A. random assignment
B. single-blind technique
C. double-blind technique
D. self-selection bias

p. 40
Application:
  Research Concerns
Level: Moderate
Type: Factual
Ans: A
www

173. A psychologist uses the double-blind technique in her research design. She is trying to avoid:
A. experimenters and subjects' expectations from affecting the study
B. self-reinforcement
C. a biased sample
D. self-selection bias

p. 40
Application:
  Research Concerns
Level: Moderate
Type: Factual
Ans: D

174. With regard to a subject's answers or behavior in an experiment, psychologists take seriously the subject's right to:
A. free speech
B. question the validity of the experiment
C. explain their answers and behavior
D. privacy and confidentiality

p. 40
Application:
  Research Concerns
Level: Moderate
Type: Applied
Ans: B

175. Professor Aguayo is recruiting subjects for a study. She is advised not to give potential subjects the exact title of the study, which is "The negative effects of mild anxiety on eye-hand coordination." Why not share the title with potential subjects?
A. Professor Aguayo may change the hypothesis after the data are collected and analyzed.
B. The title may create specific expectations that could bias the subjects.
C. It's really none of the subjects' business, since Professor Aguayo is the researcher.
D. She's not really sure if mild anxiety will affect eye-hand coordination.

p. 41
Application:
    Research Concerns
Level: Moderate
Type: Conceptual
Ans: B

176. An animal rights group claims that there are no regulations or agencies that monitor the care and treatment of animals in research. As an educated psychology student, what is your response?
A. "True, but there is no need for regulatory agencies."
B. "Regulations are established by the federal government and academic institutions."
C. "Only the government sets standard for the care and treatment of animals."
D. "Animal rights groups have a point and something needs to be done."

p. 41
Application:
    Research Concerns
Level: Easy
Type: Factual
Ans: D
*PS/SG 2-24*

177. The basic justification for using animals in biomedical research is that:
A. it has not been proven that animals are harmed in research
B. animals do not feel pain and suffering like humans do
C. most religions place humans above animals in importance
D. the potential human benefits outweigh the harm done to the animal subjects

p. 41
Application:
    Research Concerns
Level: Easy
Type: Factual
Ans: C

178. Which of the following is true about research involving animals?
A. most animals are mistreated by researchers
B. nobody watches over the care and treatment of animals
C. animal research has led to important medical advances such as medical treatments
D. the rights of animals are not considered important

p. 41
Application:
    Research Concerns
Level: Moderate
Type: Factual
Ans: B

179. If animals had not been used in research, what would we probably lack today?
A. special interest groups for animal rights
B. treatment for many human diseases
C. cure for AIDS
D. ethical guidelines for psychologists

p. 41
Application:
    Research Concerns
Level: Difficult
Type: Conceptual
Ans: D
*www*

180. A basic issue in the use of animals in research is:
A. which special interest groups have the greatest lobbying clout
B. documenting the major medical advances from their use
C. developing computer models to take the place of animals
D. striking a balance between the rights of animals and our need to find answers to important research questions

True/False

| | | | |
|---|---|---|---|
| F | | 1. | Ritalin, which is commonly used for ADHD, is a depressant. |
| T | | 2. | The sex of the person asking survey questions may affect the answer received. |
| F | *www* | 3. | Testimonials are based on careful objective observations. |
| T | | 4. | Self-fulfilling prophecy may occur in parents as they attempt to determine the cause of ADHD in their children. |
| F | *www* | 5. | A case study is a close-up view of a group of people. |
| T | | 6. | The effects of rhino horn, bear gallbladder, tiger bones, and magnets illustrate the placebo effect. |

| T |  | 7. | The placebo effect works because of a person's beliefs and thoughts. |
| F |  | 8. | Correlation indicates cause and effect. |
| F |  | 9. | A negative correlation indicates a harmful relationship between two variables. |
| T | www | 10. | One concern of standardized tests is that they may be biased to certain groups. |
| F | www | 11. | A laboratory setting would be most appropriate if a researcher is observing individuals without attempting to control the situation. |
| T |  | 12. | If a researcher wanted to identify cause-and-effect relationships, an experiment would be the most appropriate method. |
| F | www | 13. | The dependent variable is the treatment that the researcher is manipulating. |
| F | www | 14. | Random selection refers to how subjects are assigned to experimental or control groups. |
| T |  | 15. | An educated guess about a phenomenon is called a hypothesis. |
| F | www | 16. | The dependent variable is dependent upon the control group. |
| T |  | 17. | The experimental group consists of those individuals who receive the treatment. |
| T |  | 18. | When the researcher nor the participant knows what treatment the participant is receiving, a double-blind procedure is being used. |
| T | www | 19. | The independent variable is being manipulated in an experiment. |
| T |  | 20. | The diagnosis of ADHD in the United States is based on behavioral symptoms. |
| F |  | 21. | Ritalin is an effective cure for ADHD. |
| F | www | 22. | Researchers decide for themselves what ethical guidelines to follow. |
| T |  | 23. | In debriefing, a researcher asks a participant her feelings about being in the experiment. |
| F | www | 24. | Researchers must always tell the participants in an experiment the real purpose of the study. |
| T |  | 25. | The double-blind procedure can avoid bias in research participants. |

Short Answer Essay Questions

1. What advantage is there for a researcher to use a combination of research methods to answer questions about ADHD?

2. If you were developing a survey, what concerns would you have about it based upon what you've read in Module Two? *(www)*

3. Describe the relationship between testimonials and the self-fulfilling prophecy.

4. Draw a graph that illustrates a positive correlation, negative correlation, and no correlation. Provide an example of each correlation. *(www)*

5. Discuss an advantage and a disadvantage of conducting research in naturalistic settings.

6. In conducting an experiment, why would the researcher use random selection and random assignment? Include a definition for each. *(www)*

7. What role does debriefing play in an experiment? *(www)*

8. Create an experiment to test a new computer program to teach middle school students algebra. Make sure you include and identify control group, experimental group, independent variable, and dependent variable. How will you decide what subjects are assigned to groups? *(www)*

9. Why do psychologists sometimes use deception in research? Under what circumstances is deception appropriate?

10. Discuss the ethics of animal research. What safeguards are in place to prevent mistreatment of animals?

# Module 3 - Brain's Building Blocks

p. 47
Introduction
Level: Easy
Type: Factual
Ans: D
*www*

1.  What progressive neurological disorder is characterized by memory loss, personality deterioration and emotional outbursts?
    A.  Parkinson's disease
    B.  Multiple Sclerosis
    C.  Autism
    D.  Alzheimer's disease

p. 47
Introduction
Level: Easy
Type: Applied
Ans: A

2.  Ina is introduced in Module Three as having Alzheimer's disease. What can Ina and her family expect in the coming years?
    A.  Her condition will worsen.
    B.  Ina's cognitive function will deteriorate, but her personality should not dramatically change.
    C.  Ina will have good days and she will have bad days.
    D.  The course of Alzheimer's is difficult to describe.

p. 47
Introduction
Level: Easy
Type: Factual
Ans: D
*PS/SG 3-1*

3.  Rod Plotnik begins with the example of Alzheimer's disease to illustrate the:
    A.  sad fact that the brain inevitably wears out
    B.  hope offered by a new operation for those afflicted with the disease
    C.  type of disease that could be prevented if people would take care of themselves
    D.  key importance of the building blocks that make up the brain's informational network

p. 47
Introduction
Level: Easy
Type: Applied
Ans: A

4.  Grandpa Frank is often confused and doesn't know where he is much of the time. You visit him, but he doesn't seem to recognize you. He has gotten much worse over the past few years. The doctor says that there is no cure and that a protein which is destroying brain cells is the suspected cause. Grandpa Frank has been diagnosed with:
    A.  Alzheimer's disease
    B.  Parkinson's disease
    C.  stroke
    D.  Fragile X syndrome

p. 47
Introduction
Level: Easy
Type: Factual
Ans: C

5.  If you drew a graph to accurately represent the number of Alzheimer's patients projected in the future, the graph would:
    A.  have a level line
    B.  be difficult to draw since researchers are unsure of its future
    C.  have a rising slope
    D.  have a decreasing slope

<table>
<tr><td>

p. 47
Introduction
Level: Easy
Type: Conceptual
Ans: A

</td><td>

6. Alex, a 69-year-old man, can't seem to remember things anymore. Researchers discover that there is a progressive decline in communication between his neurons. In addition, he is forgetful and sometimes cannot recognize his own children. Alex is probably suffering from:
A. Alzheimer's disease
B. Broca's aphasia
C. Parkinson's disease
D. old age

</td></tr>
</table>

p. 47
Introduction
Level: Easy
Type: Factual
Ans: D

7. One factor causing Alzheimer's disease results from:
A. normal aging
B. damaged neurons
C. drug abuse
D. naturally occurring proteins and peptides

p. 47
Introduction
Level: Easy
Type: Factual
Ans: B

8. According to your text, the behavioral, cognitive, and personality problems of a person with Alzheimer's disease are caused by:
A. anger over having a terminal illness
B. widespread damage in the brain
C. the need to reside in a nursing home
D. abandonment by family and friends

p. 47
Introduction
Level: Easy
Type: Factual
Ans: B

9. Which of the following is currently not suspected to be a cause of Alzheimer's disease?
A. genetic factors
B. brain injury from accidents
C. neurological abnormalities
D. environmental factors

p. 47
Introduction
Level: Moderate
Type: Factual
Ans: D

10. Which of the following is correct regarding the role of genetic factors in Alzheimer's disease?
A. Genetics is believed not to play a role in Alzheimer's.
B. Alzheimer's is 100 times greater among people when both parents have it.
C. Alzheimer's is 10 times greater among people when both parents have it.
D. Alzheimer's is 5 times greater among people when both parents have it.

p. 47
Introduction
Level: Easy
Type: Factual
Ans: D

11. There is a reliable test to diagnose Alzheimer's disease. What is it?
A. PET scan
B. behavioral observation by trained specialist
C. clinical interview
D. administering a questionnaire to the patient

p. 47
Introduction
Level: Moderate
Type: Conceptual
Ans: B
*www*

12. Which of the following statements best explains why psychologists should study the nervous system?
A. the brain and mind are separate entities
B. behavior, both normal and abnormal, has its roots in the nervous system
C. the biological bases of behavior is important to understand
D. most psychology textbooks include a chapter on the nervous system

p. 48
Overview: Human Brain
Level: Easy
Type: Factual
Ans: A

13. _____ are chains of chemicals arranged like rungs on a twisting ladder.
A. Genes
B. Neurons
C. Opsins
D. Neurotransmitters

p. 48
Overview: Human Brain
Level: Easy
Type: Factual
Ans: C

14. What is the suspected cause of the excess formation of a glue-like substance in the brains of Alzheimer's patients?
A. allergies
B. death of brain cells
C. faulty genetic instructions
D. uncontrolled growth of glial cells

p. 48
Overview: Human Brain
Level: Easy
Type: Factual
Ans: C

15. To help the general public better understand the human brain, a famous neurologist is fond of correctly saying that there are _____ of glial cells in the human brain.
A. "hundreds and hundreds"
B. "millions and millions"
C. "billions and billions"
D. "trillions and trillions"

p. 48
Overview: Human Brain
Level: Moderate
Type: Applied
Ans: B

16. Consider this: A tired, listless brain walks into a restaurant and looks on the menu for something that could provide fuel for it. What "entree" does the brain order?
A. Hormone deluxe
B. Glucose platter
C. Calorie soup
D. Neurotransmitter buffet

p. 48
Overview: Human Brain
Level: Easy
Type: Factual
Ans: D

17. The two groups of cells in your brain are:
A. glial cells and astrocytes
B. neurons and axons
C. genes and peripheral cells
D. neurons and glial cells

p. 48
Overview: Human Brain
Level: Moderate
Type: Applied
Ans: A

18. You're directing actors in a movie on the human brain. The actor portraying the role of glial cell is giving you a hard time. What can you say to the actor to improve his performance?
A. "You are a glial cell. You need to be more supportive of the actors playing neurons, so think support!"
B. "Do you remember your lines? Do you remember how glial cells help to connect the two hemispheres together to allow information back and forth? You better read the script better!"
C. "Acting? You call that acting? A glial cell transmits electrical messages!"
D. "Look, there are many other actors who could do your job. Keep in mind that you, as a glial cell, cross the synapse. Listen for your cue!"

p. 48
Overview: Human Brain
Level: Easy
Type: Factual
Ans: C

19. Which of the following functions is <u>not</u> the responsibility of glial cells?
A. insulating neurons
B. providing support to neurons to guide their growth
C. transmitting electrical messages
D. releasing a chemical to influence the growth of neurons

p. 48
Overview: Human Brain
Level: Easy
Type: Factual
Ans: D

20. Which brain cells are responsible for providing insulation around the neuron?
A. GABA cells
B. curare cells
C. axon cells
D. glial cells

p. 48
Overview: Human Brain
Level: Easy
Type: Factual
Ans: D
*PS/SG 3-4*

21. The functions of the glial cells include:
A. sending messages within the brain
B. providing chemical instructions for the development of the body and brain
C. providing sugar to fuel the brain
D. guiding the growth and functioning of neurons

p. 48
Overview: Human Brain
Level: Easy
Type: Conceptual
Ans: A

22. Glial cells are to _____ as neurons are to _____.
A. support; transmit
B. transmit; insulate
C. support; insulate
D. Alzheimer's disease; ADHD

p. 48
Overview: Human Brain
Level: Easy
Type: Factual
Ans: A

23. The functions of neurons include:
A. transmitting and receiving electrical messages
B. providing support for glial cells
C. insulating axons
D. opening sodium gates in glial cells

p. 48
Overview: Human Brain
Level: Easy
Type: Factual
Ans: B
*www*

24. Which cells specialize in receiving electrical signals and transmitting electrical signals?
A. glial cells
B. neurons
C. dendrites
D. astrocytes

p. 48
Overview: Human Brain
Level: Easy
Type: Factual
Ans: B
*PS/SG 3-5*

25. A neuron is a brain cell that:
A. determines the sex of the individual
B. receives and transmits electrical signals
C. looks likes a small wrinkled melon
D. coats and protects the brain

p. 48
Overview: Human Brain
Level: Moderate
Type: Conceptual
Ans: C

26. A mad scientist is designing "a new and improved" nervous system. Which of the following structures should he design first - that is, which should be the building block of the new nervous system?
A. motor cortex
B. hindbrain
C. neuron
D. central nervous system

p. 48
Overview: Human Brain
Level: Easy
Type: Factual
Ans: A

27. What do the two main extensions of a neuron do?
A. receive and transmit electrical signals
B. wrap around glial cells
C. support mature glial cells
D. provide the mechanisms by which glial cells repair themselves

p. 48
Overview: Human Brain
Level: Easy
Type: Factual
Ans: A

28. Electrical messages can be transmitted in the neuron up to:
A. 2 miles per hour
B. 200 miles per hour
C. 2000 miles per hour
D. 20,000 miles per hour

p. 49
Overview: Human Brain
Level: Easy
Type: Factual
Ans: A

29. Each autumn, the male canary must relearn the "breeding" song. This process of relearning the song results in:
A. the formation of new neurons in the canary's brain
B. a decrease in the size of the canary's brain
C. the loss of other brain functions
D. the canary being able to learn the "breeding" songs of other birds

p. 49
Overview: Human Brain
Level: Moderate
Type: Factual
Ans: C

30. Research shows that as a mature male canary relearns a breeding song, there is at least a _____ in the areas of the brain that control singing.
A. 5% increase
B. 25% increase
C. 50% increase
D. 50% decrease

p. 49
Overview: Human Brain
Level: Easy
Type: Factual
Ans: A

31. The brains of primates can grow new neurons in:
A. areas of the brain related to learning and memory
B. brain areas devoted to basic reflexes
C. only young members of the species
D. areas of the brain related to perception and reasoning

p. 49
Overview: Human Brain
Level: Easy
Type: Factual
Ans: B

32. Which of the following areas is most likely to be able to grow new neurons in the adult brain?
A. Broca's area
B. hippocampus
C. hypothalamus
D. medulla

p. 49
Overview: Human Brain
Level: Moderate
Type: Conceptual
Ans: C

33. Which of the following is the best explanation for why neurons related to learning and memory can regrow?
A. The regrowth only occurs in early life, when most of our learning occurs.
B. We can't learn without memory.
C. Our need to learn and remember is a lifelong necessity.
D. All brain cells can regrow; learning and memory, while important, are no more important than other functions.

p. 49
Overview: Human Brain
Level: Moderate
Type: Factual
Ans: D

34. According to Module Three, in what way can the human brain repair itself?
A. A damaged neuron can grow several new axons.
B. The action potential can seek out new undamaged neurons.
C. A damaged neuron can grow new dendrites.
D. Undamaged neurons can make new connections with damaged neurons.

p. 49
Overview: Human Brain
Level: Difficult
Type: Conceptual
Ans: D

35. Consider this: You are a full-grown neuron in a brain that is damaged. What happens to you?
A. I can repair only if the damage is limited to the brainstem.
B. I can repair because brain cells have a great capacity to recover from damage.
C. I don't repair since healing glial cells release an enzyme that destroys me.
D. I have a limited capacity to repair since my genetic program turns off regrowth.

p. 49
Overview: Human Brain
Level: Easy
Type: Factual
Ans: B

36. The question of the relationship between our mental capacities and the physical aspects of the nervous system is typically termed:
A. nature versus nurture
B. the mind-body question
C. reciprocal determinism
D. idealism versus realism

p. 49
Overview: Human Brain
Level: Easy
Type: Factual
Ans: B
*PS/SG 3-8*

37. Is the mind the same as the brain? Rod Plotnik says that the:
A. the mind must be separate — otherwise there would be no soul
B. brain and mind are closely linked, and researchers are studying these links
C. physical brain is the only thing—there is no actual "mind"
D. questions like this are best left to philsophers

p. 49
Overview: Human Brain
Level: Moderate
Type: Conceptual
Ans: D

38. During a time of deep contemplation of the meaning of life and other related issues, you wonder how your memories are stored and retrieved much of the time without effort. Where are these memories in the brain? You ask, "how does physical matter think?" You are pondering the:
A. nature versus nurture debate
B. epistemology versus theology debate
C. cosmological puzzle
D. mind-body question

p. 49
Overview: Human Brain
Level: Difficult
Type: Conceptual
Ans: A

39. If Thomas argues that there is only the physical brain, he would believe that:
A. mental functions and physical functions are interdependent
B. physical functions affect mental functions
C. mental functions and physical functions are independent
D. mental functions affect physical functions

p. 49
Overview: Human Brain
Level: Moderate
Type: Conceptual
Ans: D

40. Roger Sperry, in the mind-body debate, argues that:
A. electrochemical functioning happens independently of mental functioning
B. electrochemical functioning does not influence mental functioning
C. all of what we do, think, feel, and remember is reducible to the physical activities of the brain
D. the brain is like a two-sided coin; one side is the electrochemical side and the other involves mental functions

p. 49
Overview: Human Brain
Level: Moderate
Type: Conceptual
Ans: D

41. The mind is to brain as:
A. running is to walking
B. glial cells is to neurons
C. right is to left
D. mental activities is to physical structure

p. 49
Overview: Human Brain
Level: Moderate
Type: Conceptual
Ans: B

42. Which of the following best supports Sperry's view that the brain is like a coin with two sides?
A. mental activities cannot be scientifically studied
B. the brain's chemicals influence mental activities
C. the brain cannot repair itself
D. brain cells are destroyed in Alzheimer's disease

p. 50
Neurons: Structure and Function
Level: Easy
Type: Factual
Ans: C

43. The _____ keeps the neuron in working order and has specialized extensions that arise from it.
A. axon
B. myelin sheath
C. cell body
D. synapse

p. 50
Neurons: Structure and Function
Level: Moderate
Type: Conceptual
Ans: D

44. Consider this scenario: The neuron is dying. All of the structures except the cell body are healthy and undamaged. Why might damage to the cell body be the reason for the neuron's impending death?
A. the cell body is responsible for insulating the neuron
B. the nucleus may be damaged
C. the cell body receives nourishment from the glial cells
D. the cell body keeps the neuron in working order

p. 50
Neurons: Structure and Function
Level: Easy
Type: Factual
Ans: B

45. If the axon is the "output" structure of the neuron, the input structure is the:
A. end bulb
B. dendrite
C. myelin
D. lobe

p. 50
Neurons: Structure and Function
Level: Easy
Type: Factual
Ans: A

46. If a neuron lacked dendrites, theoretically it could _____, but not _____.
A. send messages; receive messages
B. process messages; send messages
C. grow new extensions; have myelin sheaths
D. open sodium channels; produce negative charged ions

p. 50
Neurons:  Structure and
  Function
Level:  Easy
Type:  Factual
Ans:  B

47.  As we mature, the structure of the neuron is responsible for much of the gains in brain size.  What structure is it?
A.  cell body
B.  dendrite
C.  axon
D.  synapse

p. 50
Neurons:  Structure and
  Function
Level:  Easy
Type:  Conceptual
Ans:  D
*www*

48.  Dendrite is to _____ as axon is to _____.
A.  PNS; receive
B.  CNS; transmit
C.  fast; slow
D.  receive; transmit

p. 50
Neurons:  Structure and
  Function
Level:  Easy
Type:  Factual
Ans:  A

49.  Which part of a neuron carries signals away from the cell body?
A.  axon
B.  cell body
C.  end bulb
D.  dendrites

p. 50
Neurons:  Structure and
  Function
Level:  Easy
Type:  Factual
Ans:  B
*PS/SG 3-10*

50.  The purpose of the myelin sheath is to:
A.  receive signals from neurons, muscles, or sense organs
B.  wrap around and insulate an axon
C.  protect the nucleus of the cell body
D.  drain dangerous electricity away from the brain

p. 50
Neurons:  Structure and
  Function
Level:  Easy
Type:  Applied
Ans:  C
*www*

51  Alyssa is writing a paper on the function of the myelin sheath.  Which of the following is the best title for her paper?
A.  "Myelin Sheath: Storing Neurotransmitters"
B.  "Myelin Sheath: Receiving Signals"
C.  "Myelin Sheath: Insulating the Axon"
D.  "Myelin Sheath: Releasing Neurotransmitters into the Synapse"

p. 50
Neurons:  Structure and
  Function
Level:  Easy
Type:  Conceptual
Ans:  B

52.  The color of gray is to _____ as the color of white is to _____.
A.  myelin sheath; cell bodies
B.  cell bodies; myelin sheath
C.  synapse; end bulbs
D.  dendrites; cell bodies

p. 50
Neurons:  Structure and
  Function
Level:  Moderate
Type:  Applied
Ans:  A

53.  "This is a bad television set.  We're getting lots of interference from other electrical appliances in our apartment."  You remember the structures of the neuron and say, "I wish we had a television set covered with a ..."
A.  myelin sheath
B.  axon
C.  dendrite
D.  neurotransmitter

p. 50
Neurons: Structure and
  Function
Level: Easy
Type: Factual
Ans: B

54. If the dendrite is the "input" structure of the neuron, the output structure is the:
A. end bulb
B. axon
C. myelin
D. lobe

p. 50
Neurons: Structure and
  Function
Level: Easy
Type: Factual
Ans: A

55. The end of a neuron resembles a bulb-like swelling. This structure is known as the:
A. end bulb
B. dendrite
C. myelin
D. axon

p. 50
Neurons: Structure and
  Function
Level: Easy
Type: Factual
Ans: A

56. Tiny sacs or vesicles that are filled with neurotransmitters are located in the:
A. end bulbs
B. axon
C. dendrites
D. synapse

p. 50
Neurons: Structure and
  Function
Level: Moderate
Type: Conceptual
Ans: C

57. If neurotransmitters could talk, what would they say about where they are stored?
A. "Branch-like extensions from the cell body give us a storage place."
B. "Home sweet home is right next to the nucleus."
C. "We are all stored in tiny containers located in the end bulb."
D. "This synapse is just too small - we're packed in here very tightly."

p. 50
Neurons: Structure and
  Function
Level: Easy
Type: Factual
Ans: B

58. A synapse is the:
A. part of the dendrite that receives incoming signals
B. small space between the end bulb and its neighboring dendrite, muscle fiber or body organ
C. chemical that transmits signals from one neuron to another
D. signal that travels from one neuron to another

p. 50
Neurons: Structure and
  Function
Level: Easy
Type: Factual
Ans: B
*www*

59. End bulbs release neurotransmitters into the:
A. cell body
B. synapse
C. myelin sheath
D. axon

p. 50
Neurons: Structure and
  Function
Level: Easy
Type: Factual
Ans: D

60. Sarah is a medical student. She is examining the brain of a patient who had Alzheimer's. What would she notice about the brain as she examines it?
A. The brain is larger since it grows many tumors.
B. The size of the brain is normal.
C. The "creases" in the brain have gotten more shallow.
D. The brain is smaller because it has shrunk due to cell loss.

| | | |
|---|---|---|
| p. 51<br>Neurons versus Nerves<br>Level: Easy<br>Type: Factual<br>Ans: C<br>*PS/SG 3-11* | 61.<br>A.<br>B.<br>C.<br>D. | John Thomas' arms could be reattached because:<br>neurons have the ability to regrow, regenerate, or reattach<br>neurons are part of the central nervous system<br>nerves have the ability to regrow, regenerate, or reattach<br>nerves are part of the peripheral nervous system |
| p. 51<br>Neurons versus Nerves<br>Level: Difficult<br>Type: Conceptual<br>Ans: B | 62.<br>A.<br>B.<br>C.<br>D. | Nerves are to neurons as _____ are to _____.<br>males; females<br>words; letters<br>trees; leaves<br>numbers; art |
| p. 51<br>Neurons versus Nerves<br>Level: Easy<br>Type: Factual<br>Ans: A | 63.<br><br>A.<br>B.<br>C.<br>D. | The nerves that make up the body, except the brain and spinal cord, make up the:<br>peripheral nervous system<br>central nervous system<br>primary nervous system<br>secondary nervous system |
| p. 51<br>Neurons versus Nerves<br>Level: Easy<br>Type: Factual<br>Ans: C | 64.<br>A.<br>B.<br>C.<br><br>D. | Patients who have their severed limbs reattached are at risk for:<br>uncontrollable movement of the limb<br>reduced cognitive function<br>serious infectious disease since their immune system is suppressed by drugs given to prevent rejection<br>serious infectious disease because their reattached limb produces enzymes that suppress the immune system |
| p. 51<br>Neurons versus Nerves<br>Level: Moderate<br>Type: Conceptual<br>Ans: C | 65.<br><br><br>A.<br>B.<br>C.<br><br>D. | Sylvester severed a toe in an accident with his lawn mower. If the toe is not too damaged, what is the chance that the toe can be reattached to his foot?<br>Poor - nerves in the peripheral nervous system cannot regenerate<br>Poor - nerves in the central nervous system cannot regenerate<br>Good - nerves in the peripheral nervous system have the capacity to regenerate<br>Good - nerves in the autonomic system have the capacity to regenerate |
| p. 51<br>Neurons versus Nerves<br>Level: Moderate<br>Type: Factual<br>Ans: D | 66.<br><br>A.<br>B.<br>C.<br>D. | If the neurons in the central nervous system have a limit capacity for repair or regrowth, what is <u>most</u> likely to happen in the spinal cord?<br>stay the same size and in number of connections<br>stay the same size, but decrease in the number of connections<br>stay the same size, but increase in the number of connections<br>wither and die |
| p. 51<br>Neurons versus Nerves<br>Level: Easy<br>Type: Factual<br>Ans: B<br>*PS/SG 3-6* | 67.<br>A.<br>B.<br>C.<br>D. | Unlike nerves, neurons:<br>are not replaced or regrown<br>have the ability to regrow or reattach<br>are located outside the brain and spinal cord<br>have no dendrites or axons |

p. 51
Neurons versus Nerves
Level: Moderate
Type: Applied
Ans: C

68.   As you're waiting to visit a friend in the hospital, you overhear a physician talking to a patient's parents. You don't hear the entire conversation, but only bits and pieces. There is something about an accident and a question regarding nerves reattaching. The physician replied that the nerves do have the ability to regrow. From your education in psychology, you guess that the nerves were probably part of the:

A.   spinal cord
B.   central nervous system
C.   peripheral nervous system
D.   limbic system

p. 51
Neurons versus Nerves
Level: Moderate
Type: Factual
Ans: D

69.   According to your textbook, new research on the regeneration of neurons includes:
A.   mild electrical currents passed through the damaged neurons
B.   drugs that suppress the immune system
C.   megadoses of Vitamin A
D.   providing a tube for the damaged axons to grow through

p. 51
Neurons versus Nerves
Level: Moderate
Type: Conceptual
Ans: B
PS/SG 3-12

70.   The fact that John Thomas can use arms but Christopher Reeve is unlikely to walk illustrates the difference between:
A.   nerves vs muscles
B.   the peripheral nervous system vs the central nervous system
C.   receiving medical attention immediately vs not for several hours
D.   neurons vs fetal tissue

p. 51
Neurons versus Nerves
Level: Moderate
Type: Factual
Ans: A

71.   There is new research that involves replacing damaged neurons with:
A.   transplanted stem cells
B.   tiny computers that can process information very quickly
C.   computerized sodium pumps
D.   transplanted tubes from monkeys

p. 52
Sending Information
Level: Moderate
Type: Factual
Ans: C

72.   The membrane of the axon has the unique ability to:
A.   ionize itself
B.   change its size
C.   open and close its chemical gates
D.   negatively charge the dendrites

p. 52
Sending Information
Level: Moderate
Type: Factual
Ans: A
PS/SG 3-13

73.   The purpose of the ions in the axon's membrane is to:
A.   generate a miniature electrical current
B.   plug up the tiny holes in the membrane's semipermeable skin
C.   pump excess sodium out of the neuron
D.   dry up the watery fluid that collects in the membrane

p. 52
Sending Information
Level: Moderate
Type: Factual
Ans: A

74.   Opposite-charged ions _____ and like-charged ions _____ .
A.   attract; repel
B.   are permeable; are semipermeable
C.   have sodium; have protein
D.   are positive; are negative

p. 52
Sending Information
Level: Moderate
Type: Factual
Ans: A

75. When a neuron is in a resting state, the majority of the particles in the fluid surrounding the neuron are:
A. positive sodium ions
B. sodium ions that have yet to pick up a charge
C. chloride ions
D. chemically inert

p. 52
Sending Information
Level: Moderate
Type: Conceptual
Ans: B

76. A psychology instructor is lecturing on the processes and mechanisms of messages in the nervous system. She has come to the part on the action potential. Which example should she use to illustrate the idea of a nerve impulse?
A. how a washer cleans clothes
B. "The Wave" at a sports stadium where sections of fans stand up and then sit down
C. a bright flash of light
D. a merry go-round

p. 52
Sending Information
Level: Moderate
Type: Conceptual
Ans: C

77. Of the following, which is the poorest example of the all-or-none law?
A. cruise control on a car maintaining the same speed
B. a marathon runner that has disciplined himself to run at a consistent rate throughout the race
C. a snowball rolling down a hillside gaining size and speed
D. a person walking at a constant speed

p. 52
Sending Information
Level: Easy
Type: Factual
Ans: B
PS/SG 3-15

78. The "all-or-none law" explains what happens when:
A. positively and negatively charged ions meet
B. an impulse starts at the beginning of an axon
C. electrical impulses spread throughout the body
D. your brain gets the idea of a six-pack

p. 52
Sending Information
Level: Easy
Type: Factual
Ans: A

79. What accounts for the action potential moving down the axon at a constant speed?
A. all-or-none law
B. paced resistance principle
C. snowball effect
D. neuronal push rule

p. 53
Sending Information
Level: Easy
Type: Factual
Ans: D

80. During a class meeting, a student asks the psychology professor to define a nerve impulse. Before the professor can open his mouth to answer, you remember the definition, which is:
A. a surge of electrical activity simultaneously occurring down the entire axon
B. the release of neurotransmitters into the synapse
C. a tiny electrical current
D. a series of individual action potentials that occur segment by segment down the axon

p. 53
Sending Information
Level: Easy
Type: Factual
Ans: B

81. If the stimulation is strong enough, the neuron's chemical gates _____ and _____ will come into the neuron.
A. open; negative sodium ions
B. open; positive sodium ions
C. close; positive sodium ions
D. close; vesicles

p. 53
Sending Information
Level: Moderate
Type: Factual
Ans: D

82. If the positive sodium ions rush inside the axon, the axon will:
A. enter the resting state
B. release a neurotransmitter
C. change its threshold
D. experience an action potential

p. 53
Sending Information
Level: Moderate
Type: Factual
Ans: A

83. Which statement is true if there is an action potential at a particular point along the axon? At that point in the axon, the
A. inside of the axon is positively charged; the outside is negatively charged
B. inside of the axon is negatively charged; the outside is positively charged
C. sodium pumps are highly active
D. chemical gates are closed to sodium ions

p. 53
Sending Information
Level: Moderate
Type: Factual
Ans: B

84. During an action potential, the inside of the axon becomes _____ and the outside becomes _____.
A. negative; positive
B. positive; negative
C. positive; positive
D. negative; neutral

p. 53
Sending Information
Level: Easy
Type: Factual
Ans: C

85. A tiny electrical current generated in the axon is called a(n)
A. electropotential
B. ion wave
C. action potential
D. resting potential

p. 53
Sending Information
Level: Easy
Type: Factual
Ans: B

86. According to your textbook, axons that are wrapped in myelin are capable of:
A. surviving traumatic changes in the body
B. sending nerve impulses much more quickly
C. sending nerve impulses to the brain
D. being repaired surgically

p. 53
Sending Information
Level: Easy
Type: Factual
Ans: C

87. What structure in the neuron helps to speed up the transmission of the action potential?
A. axon
B. dendrites
C. myelin sheath
D. end bulb

p. 53
Sending Information
Level: Moderate
Type: Applied
Ans: C

88. The horror movie you are watching has a mad scientist plotting to destroy the world by altering nervous systems of politicians. His desire is to slow down the transmission of nerve impulses. How should he do it?
A. use radiation to destroy ions
B. create a bacteria that destroys dendrites
C. design a drug to destroy the myelin sheath
D. put L-dopa in the water supply

p. 53
Sending Information
Level: Moderate
Type: Conceptual
Ans: A

89. Larry suffers from a degenerative disorder that is causing the myelin in his brain to disintegrate. How is this likely to affect transmission of nerve impulses?
A. The messages are likely to slow down
B. The messages are likely to speed up
C. There should be no effect since myelin can rapidly repair itself
D. The messages will initially slow down, but then later will speed up

p. 53
Sending Information
Level: Easy
Type: Factual
Ans: C

90. While speeding down an axon, the impulse reaches an incredible speed by jumping at the breaks in the:
A. end bulb
B. dendrite
C. myelin sheath
D. synapse

p. 54
Transmitters
Level: Easy
Type: Factual
Ans: A

91. _____ is/are (a) chemical messenger(s) that transmit(s) information between nerves and body organs.
A. Transmitters
B. Ion
C. THC
D. L-dopa

p. 54
Transmitters
Level: Easy
Type: Factual
Ans: A

92. What substance is found in the end bulbs?
A. neurotransmitters
B. sodium ions
C. inhibitory sodium
D. L-dopa

p. 54
Transmitters
Level: Easy
Type: Factual
Ans: D

93. Neurotransmitters are found in the:
A. myelin sheath
B. sodium ions
C. inhibitory sodium
D. end-bulbs

p. 54
Transmitters
Level: Moderate
Type: Applied
Ans: A

94. If the release of neurotransmitters was being broadcast over CNN, the reporter would say:
A. "The action potential is triggering an explosion releasing the neurotransmitters into the synapse."
B. "The neurotransmitters have entered the axon through sodium channels."
C. "The resting potential is causing the cell body to release neurotransmitters."
D. "I have never seen so many neurotransmitters being released into the myelin sheath!"

p. 54
Transmitters
Level: Easy
Type: Factual
Ans: D

95. If receptors in muscle fibers are thought of as locks, the keys are:
A. the action potential of the axon
B. synapses
C. the resting state of the axon
D. neurotransmitters

PS/SG 3-17

p. 54      96.     In the neuron, the electrical charge jumps the synapse. Right?

Transmitters     A.      Yes, it is like how a spark plug works.

Level: Easy      B.      Yes, but only in the central nervous system.

Type: Factual     C.      Yes and no, both an electrical charge *and* neurotransmitters cross the

Ans: D                synapse.

                D.      No, neurotransmitters cross the synapse.

p. 54      97.     After the release of neurotransmitters in the synapse, neurotransmitters

Transmitters             cross the synapse and:

Level: Moderate    A.      fit into specially designed axons

Type: Factual     B.      cause the second neuron to open its chemical locks

Ans: D         C.      cause the process known as reuptake

                D.      fit into specially designed receptors located on the second neuron's

                          dendrites

p. 54      98.     If a neurotransmitter key *opens* the receptor's lock, then the

Transmitters             neurotransmitter is said to be:

Level: Moderate    A.      at the threshold

Type: Factual     B.      excitatory

Ans: B         C.      positively charged

                D.      at an action potential

p. 54      99.     If a neurotransmitter key *closes* the receptor's lock, then the

Transmitters             neurotransmitter is said to be:

Level: Moderate    A.      at the threshold

Type: Factual     B.      excitatory

Ans: B         C.      positively charged

                D.      at an action potential

p. 54      100.    An evil dictator is plotting to overthrow the world's governments by making

Transmitters             the nervous systems of world leaders "slow down" and mellow out.

Level: Easy           Assuming it is possible, what drug should be put into their water supply?

Type: Factual     A.      Drug A - increases the release of excitatory transmitters

Ans: D         B.      Drug B - prevents reuptake

                C.      Drug C - completely inhibits the release of transmitters

                D.      Drug D - increases the release of inhibitory transmitters

p. 54      101.    Excitatory neurotransmitters:

Transmitters     A.      open the receptor's lock

Level: Moderate    B.      slow down the speed of a nerve impulse

Type: Factual     C.      reverse the charge of a sodium ion

Ans: A         D.      are released during the resting state

p. 54      102.    Inhibitory neurotransmitters:

Transmitters     A.      block the receptor's lock

Level: Moderate    B.      slow down the speed of a nerve impulse

Type: Factual     C.      reverse the charge of a sodium ion

Ans: A         D.      are released during the resting state

p. 54
Transmitters
Level: Easy
Type: Factual
Ans: C
*PS/SG 3-16*

103. The effect of a neurotransmitter on an adjacent neuron, muscle, or organ is:
A. excitatory
B. inhibitory
C. either excitatory or inhibitory
D. determined by the all-or-none law

p. 54
Transmitters
Level: Moderate
Type: Applied
Ans: D

104. Jason, a three-year old boy, has just spilled apple juice on his mother's new laptop computer, and she is very upset! If you could go inside his mother's nervous system at this point, you would find an abundance of:
A. anandamide
B. serotonin
C. inhibitory transmitters
D. excitatory transmitters

p. 54
Transmitters
Level: Easy
Type: Factual
Ans: B

105. Excitatory transmitters _____ chemical locks; inhibitory transmitters _____ chemical locks.
A. close; open
B. open; close
C. destroy; open
D. open, destroy

p. 54
Transmitters
Level: Moderate
Type: Factual
Ans: C

106. Could neurotransmitter A fit into the receptors for neuron B?
A. yes - all neurotransmitters fit into all receptors
B. maybe - if both neurotransmitters are excitatory
C. no - each neurotransmitter has it own unique receptor
D. maybe - if both neurotransmitters are inhibitory

p. 55
Transmitters
Level: Easy
Type: Factual
Ans: B
*www*

107. Alcohol is classified as a(n):
A. stimulant
B. depressant
C. serotonin
D. anandamide

p. 55
Transmitters
Level: Easy
Type: Factual
Ans: A

108. Alcohol molecules closely resemble:
A. GABA
B. dopamine
C. THC
D. anandamide

p. 55
Transmitters
Level: Moderate
Type: Applied
Ans: D

109. Jack has had a few beers and he is feeling pretty good and is more sociable. If we could look inside his brain, we would find that alcohol has:
A. increased endorphin production
B. decreased endorphin production
C. inhibited GABA neurons
D. excited GABA neurons

p. 55
Transmitters
Level: Easy
Type: Factual
Ans: A

110. Excited GABA neurons lead to:
A. inhibitory effects
B. excitatory effects
C. increased self-control
D. increased neural activity

| | | |
|---|---|---|
| p. 55 | 111. | Rose drinks too much and claims that alcohol is a stimulant. Is she right? |
| Transmitters | A. | yes - alcohol is a stimulant since it excites GABA neurons |
| Level: Moderate | B. | yes - alcohol is a stimulant since it inhibits GABA neurons |
| Type: Factual | C. | no - alcohol is a depressant since it excites GABA neurons |
| Ans: C | D. | no - alcohol is a depressant since it inhibits GABA neurons |

| | | |
|---|---|---|
| p. 55 | 112. | Endorphins are secreted when we are: |
| Transmitters | A. | falling asleep |
| Level: Easy | B. | under great stress |
| Type: Factual | C. | depressed |
| Ans: B | D. | studying |

| | | |
|---|---|---|
| p. 55 | 113. | As a preview to the next lecture, Dr. Cooper said that your brain has its own |
| Transmitters | | drug factory. What did your professor mean by that remark? |
| Level: Moderate | A. | like a regular factory, a certain percentage of the manufactured product is |
| Type: Applied | | defective |
| Ans: C | B. | dopamine is a powerful pain killer |
| | C. | your brain produces its own pain killer called endorphin |
| | D. | illegal drugs can affect the brain |

| | | |
|---|---|---|
| p. 55 | 114. | The brain produces a neurotransmitter called _____ to decrease the effects |
| Transmitters | | of pain during great bodily stress, such as an accident. |
| Level: Easy | A. | endorphin |
| Type: Factual | B. | anandamide |
| Ans: A | C. | nitric oxide |
| *PS/SG 3-19* | D. | happy dust |

| | | |
|---|---|---|
| p. 55 | 115. | Endorphin, a natural pain killer in the brain, offers an example of: |
| Transmitters | A. | the key role that neurotransmitters play in regulating our lives |
| Level: Moderate | B. | the way neurotransmitters out of control can cause diseases like |
| Type: Applied | | Alzheimer's |
| Ans: A | C. | hope for finding a cure for Parkinson's disease |
| | D. | left-over entities in the brain |

| | | |
|---|---|---|
| p. 55 | 116. | Alcohol is to GABA as marijuana is to: |
| Transmitters | A. | serotonin |
| Level: Moderate | B. | dopamine |
| Type: Conceptual | C. | endorphins |
| Ans: D | D. | anandamide |

| | | |
|---|---|---|
| p. 55 | 117. | A newly discovered neurotransmitter has a chemical structure similar to the |
| Transmitters | | active ingredient in marijuana. This neurotransmitter is: |
| Level: Easy | A. | anandamide |
| Type: Factual | B. | dopamine |
| Ans: A | C. | serotonin |
| | D. | epinephrine |

p. 55
Transmitters
Level: Moderate
Type: Applied
Ans: C

118. In which of the following situations, would you be most likely to feel the effects of anandamide?
A. You are watching a cooking show on television.
B. You are watching a very funny movie and are laughing out loud.
C. You are getting very anxious about a big speech you have to give to several hundred people.
D. You are in REM.

p. 55
Transmitters
Level: Easy
Type: Factual
Ans: B

119. Nitric oxide may be involved in the regulation of:
A. hunger
B. aggression
C. sexual behavior
D. memory

p. 55
Transmitters
Level: Easy
Type: Factual
Ans: A

120. What happens to mice that are genetically altered to lack nitric oxide?
A. They are more likely to pick a fight with other mice.
B. They are more likely to become very submissive.
C. They experience severe memory problems.
D. They gain weight very rapidly.

p. 56
Reflex Responses
Level: Moderate
Type: Factual
Ans: C

121. A child puts her hand on a hot stove. She quickly removes it. This is an example of a(n) _____, and it involves _____.
A. learned response; reflexes
B. activating stimulus; voluntary reaction
C. reflex; involuntary reaction
D. excitatory signal; efferent neurons

p. 56
Reflex Responses
Level: Easy
Type: Factual
Ans: C

122. Neurons that carry information from the senses to the spinal cord are called _____ neurons.
A. spinal
B. motor
C. afferent
D. efferent

p. 56
Reflex Responses
Level: Moderate
Type: Conceptual
Ans: B

123. If all the efferent neurons were removed from your nervous system, you would be unable to:
A. process language
B. move your body
C. solve complex problems
D. control your emotions

p. 56
Reflex Responses
Level: Easy
Type: Factual
Ans: D

124. Efferent neurons carry information away from the:
A. axon
B. muscles
C. synapse
D. spinal cord

p. 56
Reflex Responses
Level: Easy
Type: Factual
Ans: A

125. Afferent is to efferent as _____ is to _____.
A. sensory; motor
B. motor; sensory
C. sensory; spinal
D. spinal; neuron

p. 56
Reflex Responses
Level: Moderate
Type: Conceptual
Ans: C
*www*

126. A patient suffers damage to the nervous system.   He can move his hands, but he does not feel anything with them.  Which explanation is the neurologist <u>most</u> likely to offer?
   A.   efferent neurons are damaged
   B.   the reflex arc is damaged
   C.   afferent neurons have been damaged
   D.   Alzheimer's disease

p. 58
Research Focus:
   Phantom Limb
Level: Easy
Type: Factual
Ans: B
*www*

127. Which of the following is <u>most</u> closely related to phantom limb?
   A.   reattached limb
   B.   amputated limb
   C.   Alzheimer's disease
   D.   mescaline use

p. 58
Research Focus:
   Phantom Limb
Level: Easy
Type: Factual
Ans: C

128. An individual who has had a limb amputated, but continues to experience sensation and feelings that appear to be from that limb, experiences:
   A.   ghost pain
   B.   nonregenerated pain perception
   C.   phantom limb
   D.   limb plasticity

p. 58
Research Focus:
   Phantom Limb
Level: Easy
Type: Factual
Ans: A

129. According to Donald, who is described in Module Three, the toughest part of have an artificial leg is/are:
   A.   phantom limb
   B.   limb plasticity
   C.   loss of smooth movements
   D.   tremors and shakes

p. 58
Research Focus:
   Phantom Limb
Level: Easy
Type: Factual
Ans: C

130. _____ refers to feeling sensation or pain coming from a limb that has been removed.
   A.   Ghost pain
   B.   Nonregenerated pain perception
   C.   Phantom limb
   D.   Limb plasticity

p. 58
Research Focus:
   Phantom Limb
Level: Easy
Type: Factual
Ans: B

131. The <u>most</u> common report after removal of a limb is:
   A.   severe pain
   B.   sensations of pins and needles
   C.   sensations of numbness
   D.   a burning sensation

p. 58
Research Focus:
   Phantom Limb
Level: Easy
Type: Factual
Ans: C

132. Which is <u>not</u> an accepted explanation for phantom limb?
   A.   brain pieces together sensations to form an image
   B.   brain remembers the body part
   C.   sensations from the spinal cord
   D.   sensations from the brain

| | | |
|---|---|---|
| p. 58<br>Research Focus:<br>  Phantom Limb<br>Level: Easy<br>Type: Factual<br>Ans: A | 133.<br>A.<br>B.<br>C.<br>D. | It appears that the source of the pain experienced in phantom limb is the:<br>brain<br>amputated stump<br>spinal cord<br>damaged nerves of the remaining part of the limb |
| p. 58<br>Research Focus:<br>  Phantom Limb<br>Level: Easy<br>Type: Factual<br>Ans: B<br>*PS/SG 3-21* | 134.<br><br>A.<br>B.<br>C.<br>D. | Donald, who had to amputate his own leg to survive an accident, now suffers from phantom limb. Researchers suspect that his pain comes from:<br>cut nerves in the stump<br>a body image stored in the brain<br>the spinal cord<br>terrifying memories of the horrible ordeal |
| p. 58<br>Research Focus:<br>  Phantom Limb<br>Level: Easy<br>Type: Conceptual<br>Ans: D | 135.<br><br>A.<br>B.<br>C.<br>D. | You are reading a newspaper article on phantom limb. Which of the following is the <u>most</u> appropriate title for the article?<br>"Phantom Limb: An Excuse for Sympathy"<br>"Cut Nerves in Limb Cause Pain in Phantom Limb"<br>"Damaged Neurons in Spinal Cord Cause Damage"<br>"Sensations Come from Brain's Image of Limb" |
| p. 59<br>Cultural Diversity:<br>  Plants and Drugs<br>Level: Easy<br>Type: Factual<br>Ans: C<br>*www* | 136.<br>A.<br>B.<br>C.<br><br>D. | Reuptake is a process that:<br>causes the neurotransmitter to continue its effects<br>prevents neurotransmitters from entering the receptor<br>removes the neurotransmitter from the synapse and is returned to the vesicles of the end bulb<br>causes neural plasticity |
| p. 59<br>Cultural Diversity:<br>  Plants and Drugs<br>Level: Easy<br>Type: Factual<br>Ans: A | 137.<br>A.<br>B.<br>C.<br>D. | Reuptake is disrupted by:<br>cocaine<br>curare<br>mescaline<br>ADHD |
| p. 59<br>Cultural Diversity:<br>  Plants and Drugs<br>Level: Moderate<br>Type: Factual<br>Ans: B | 138.<br>A.<br>B.<br>C.<br>D. | If reuptake is prevented,<br>the neurotransmitter will be transported back to the end bulbs<br>the neurotransmitter will remain in the synapse<br>phantom limb occurs<br>the neuron will die |
| p. 59<br>Cultural Diversity:<br>  Plants and Drugs<br>Level: Easy<br>Type: Factual<br>Ans: A<br>*www* | 139.<br><br>A.<br>B.<br><br>C.<br>D. | Cocaine causes its effects of physiological arousal and feelings of euphoria by:<br>preventing reuptake from occurring<br>blocking receptors thereby preventing neurotransmitters from affecting the neuron<br>its similar chemical makeup to norepinephrine<br>increasing the amount of dopamine released into the synapse |

p. 59
Cultural Diversity:
  Plants and Drugs
Level: Moderate
Type: Factual
Ans: C

140. You are reading an anthropologist's experiences with South American Indians. You are struck at the description of Indians chewing coca leaves because it reminds you of something you learned in psychology. What was it?
A. Coca leaves contain THC.
B. Coca leaves contain mescaline.
C. Cocaine comes from coca leaves and blocks reuptake.
D. Curare comes from coca leaves and mimics the effects of acetylcholine.

p. 59
Cultural Diversity:
  Plants and Drugs
Level: Easy
Type: Applied
Ans: B

141. A monkey is shot with a blow dart by a South American Indian. The blow dart is covered with curare. The monkey's muscles are paralyzed. What does curare do to the nervous system of the monkey (and to humans)?
A. prevents reuptake from occurring
B. blocks receptors thereby preventing acetylcholine from affecting the neuron
C. mimics the effects of norepinephrine because of its similar chemical makeup
D. increases the amount of dopamine released into the synapse

p. 59
Cultural Diversity:
  Plants and Drugs
Level: Easy
Type: Factual
Ans: D
*www*

142. Which neurotransmitter does curare block?
A. anandamide
B. norepinephrine
C. dopamine
D. acetylcholine

p. 59
Cultural Diversity:
  Plants and Drugs
Level: Moderate
Type: Applied
Ans: B

143. You and some friends are watching a television show about an emergency room in a hospital. One of the scenes shows a doctor inserting a breathing tube down the throat of a patient. You suddenly remember that in real-life _____ is used to induce muscle paralysis to allow the tube to be inserted.
A. cocaine
B. curare
C. nitric oxide
D. GABA

p. 59
Cultural Diversity:
  Plants and Drugs
Level: Easy
Type: Factual
Ans: C

144. The filtering system that prevents most substances from reaching the brain is called the:
A. glial-brain barrier
B. blood sheathing system
C. blood-brain barrier
D. mescaline-brain filter

p. 59
Cultural Diversity:
  Plants and Drugs
Level: Easy
Type: Factual
Ans: A

145. A purified form of _____ is used to induce muscle paralysis in humans to allow a breathing tube to be inserted down a patient's throat.
A. curare
B. cocaine
C. dopamine
D. mescaline

p. 59
Cultural Diversity:
  Plants and Drugs
Level: Easy
Type: Factual
Ans: C

146. Mescaline is found in peyote and is used in some Native American religious rites. It causes visual hallucinations and physiological arousal. Its effects are due to its ability to:
A. prevent reuptake from occurring
B. block receptors thereby preventing acetylcholine from affecting the neuron
C. mimic the effects of norepinephrine because of its similar chemical makeup
D. increase the amount of dopamine released into the synapse

p. 59
Cultural Diversity:
  Plants and Drugs
Level: Moderate
Type: Conceptual
Ans: A
www

147. Curare is to mescaline as _____ is to _____.
A. block; mimic
B. reuptake; action potential
C. norepinephrine; dopamine
D. CNS; PNS

p. 59
Cultural Diversity:
  Plants and Drugs
Level: Moderate
Type: Conceptual
Ans: B

148. The examples of cocaine, curare, and mescaline presented in your text suggest that:
A. illegal drugs are used legally by other cultures
B. drugs and other substances affect behavior by affecting the processes of the neuron
C. each culture has a drug problem
D. all cultural groups have experienced drugs

p. 60
Application:
  Fetal Tissue Transplant
Level: Easy
Type: Factual
Ans: B

149. A disease that is caused by an insufficient supply of dopamine and characterized by difficulties with movement is called:
A. Alzheimer's disease
B. Parkinson's disease
C. Sensory dementia
D. a stroke

p. 60
Application:
  Fetal Tissue Transplant
Level: Easy
Type: Factual
Ans: C
www

150. To function properly, the basal ganglia need a sufficient supply of:
A. mescaline
B. anandamide
C. dopamine
D. acetylcholine

p. 60
Application:
  Fetal Tissue Transplant
Level: Easy
Type: Applied
Ans: B

151. Your elderly neighbor has rigidity and tremors in his arms. It did not surprise you that he was recently diagnosed with:
A. Alzheimer
B. Parkinson's
C. Presenile dementia
D. food poisoning from eating a Puffer fish

p. 60
Application:
  Fetal Tissue Transplant
Level: Easy
Type: Applied
Ans: B

152. Connie has difficulty with behaviors that require voluntary movement. The cause of her problem involves a deficiency of dopamine in part of her brain. Connie suffers from:
A. schizophrenia
B. Parkinson's disease
C. Huntington's disease
D. Alzheimer's disease

p. 60
Application:
  Fetal Tissue Transplant
Level: Easy
Type: Factual
Ans: A
*www*

153. How does L-dopa control the symptoms of Parkinson's disease?
A. it increases the production of dopamine
B. it cures the symptoms
C. it relaxes the muscles
D. it reduces the number of "on-periods"

p. 60
Application:
  Fetal Tissue Transplant
Level: Easy
Type: Factual
Ans: C

154. In treating Parkinson's disease, fetal brain tissue:
A. can take the place of myelin
B. can produce acetylcholine
C. can make new connections in the patient's brain
D. has little effect

p. 60
Application:
  Fetal Tissue Transplant
Level: Easy
Type: Factual
Ans: A

155. A potential treatment for Alzheimer's patients and persons suffering from neurotransmitter deficits involves:
A. stem cell transplants
B. nerve regeneration
C. drugs that repair damaged neurons
D. preventing electrical signals from reaching the spinal cord

p. 60
Application:
  Fetal Tissue Transplant
Level: Easy
Type: Factual
Ans: D

156. In treating Parkinson's disease, stem cells are believed to:
A. create L-dopa
B. block dopamine receptors
C. develop into dopamine
D. develop into neurons

p. 61
Application:
  Fetal Tissue Transplant
Level: Easy
Type: Factual
Ans: A

157. In treating Parkinson's disease, the area of the brain that fetal brain tissue or stem cells is transplanted into is the:
A. basal ganglia
B. hippocampus
C. cerebellum
D. occipital lobe

p. 61
Application:
  Fetal Tissue Transplant
Level: Easy
Type: Factual
Ans: C

158. The procedure that is used to transplant fetal or stem cells into a precise location in either animal or human brains is called the _____ procedure.
A. ganglia
B. Parkinson's
C. stereotaxic
D. Lindvall

p. 61
Application:
  Fetal Tissue Transplant
Level: Easy
Type: Factual
Ans: D
*PS/SG 3-25*

159. The stereotaxic procedure for treating Parkinson's disease involves:
A. deceiving the patient and relying on the placebo effect
B. playing loud music into the patient's ear to block out symptoms
C. removing the patient's adult brain and replacing it with a fetal brain
D. fixing a patient's head in a holder and drilling a small hole through the skull

p. 61
Application:
  Fetal Tissue Transplant
Level: Easy
Type: Factual
Ans: B

160. Stereotaxic procedures:
A. cause a great deal of brain damage
B. are used for brain tissue transplants
C. have been shown to be ineffective in treating Parkinson's disease
D. have only been performed on animals

p. 61
Application:
  Fetal Tissue Transplant
Level: Easy
Type: Factual
Ans: C

161. What was the result of the study described in your textbook regarding the transplantation of fetal brain tissue into Parkinson's patients?
A. All patients reported significant improvement.
B. All patients reported serious side effects.
C. There was no significant difference between the experimental and control groups.
D. The experimental group showed that Parkinson's disease was cured.

p. 61
Application:
  Fetal Tissue Transplant
Level: Easy
Type: Factual
Ans: A

162. Who is most likely to show improvement following fetal tissue transplants?
A. those under 60 years of age
B. those over 60 years of age
C. male patients
D. female patients

p. 61
Application:
  Fetal Tissue Transplant
Level: Easy
Type: Factual
Ans: C

163. Promising but preliminary results have been observed in transplanting cells from the _____ of cadavers to treat Parkinson's disease.
A. medulla
B. basal ganglia
C. eyeball
D. hypothalamus

True/False

| | | | |
|---|---|---|---|
| F | | 1. | Genetics do not play a role in Alzheimer's disease. |
| T | | 2. | Glial cells are the most numerous brain cells. |
| T | www | 3. | The hippocampus and olfactory bulb may be able to grow new neurons. |
| T | | 4. | The input portion of the neuron is the dendrites. |
| F | www | 5. | The axon stores chemicals called neurotransmitters. |
| T | | 6. | The space between neurons is called the synapse. |
| F | www | 7. | In Alzheimer's disease, gluelike substances in the brain help to fight the disease. |
| F | | 8. | As the action potential is traveling down the axon, it can increase or decrease in speed. |
| T | www | 9. | The nerve impulse is called an action potential. |
| F | | 10. | The action potential occurs when negative sodium ions rush inside the axon. |
| F | www | 11. | The action potential triggers the release of neurotransmitters from the dendrites. |
| T | | 12. | Inhibitory neurotransmitters block the chemical locks in the heart muscle. |
| T | www | 13. | The relationship between a neurotransmitter and receptor is like a key and lock. |
| F | | 14. | Afferent neurons carry information away from the spinal cord. |
| T | | 15. | Interneurons make connections between other neurons. |
| T | www | 16. | One explanation of phantom limb pain is that the brain can create sensations coming from any body part. |
| F | | 17. | Cocaine blocks the release of neurotransmitters from the end bulbs. |
| T | www | 18. | Reuptake is a process where neurotransmitters are removed from the synapse and transported back to the end bulbs. |
| F | | 19. | Curare mimics the neurotransmitter acetylcholine. |
| T | | 20. | Mescaline causes visual hallucinations. |
| T | www | 21. | Parkinson's disease involves the neurotransmitter dopamine. |
| T | | 22. | Stem cells can change into and become a different type of cell. |
| F | | 23. | The area of the brain affected by Parkinson's disease is the hypothalamus. |
| F | www | 24. | Stem cell transplantation cures Parkinson's disease. |
| T | | 25. | Preliminary research shows that there are cells in the eyeball which can produce dopamine. |

Short-Answer Essay Questions

1.  Why should psychologists study the brain?  (*www*)
2.  Describe what Sperry meant when he said that the brain is like a coin with two sides.  What are the two sides and what is their relationship?
3.  Briefly explain the function of the cell body, dendrites, axon, myelin sheath, and end bulbs. Make sure to specify where the structures are located.  (*www*)
4.  Contrast the peripheral nervous system and central nervous system.  (*www*)
5.  Describe how information travels from one end of the neuron to the other end.  Make sure you include in your answer the terms ions, all-or-none law, resting state, and action potential.
6.  What effect does alcohol have on GABA neurons?
7.  What roles do afferent neurons, interneurons, and efferent neurons play in a reflex?  (*www*)
8.  Describe the mechanism by which cocaine affects neurotransmitters.
9.  What are the important characteristics of Parkinson's disease and what causes it?  (*www*)
10. Discuss why stems cells could be potentially used to treat Parkinson's disease.

# Module 4 - Incredible Nervous System

p. 67
Introduction
Level: Moderate
Type: Conceptual
Ans: B

1. An inexperienced psychology teacher is about to start a lecture on the biological bases of behavior. Which opening line should she use to convince students of the importance of this module?
   A. "This chapter explains how the brain works."
   B. "Our thoughts and our actions may change if the brain's physical functions change."
   C. "The nervous system is made up of two parts - central nervous system and peripheral nervous system."
   D. "Chemicals and electrical activity are found in our brains."

p. 67
Introduction
Level: Moderate
Type: Factual
Ans: A
*www*

2. Based on Module Four, why would a baby born with almost no brain even survive for a couple of days?
   A. The baby would still have a brain area that regulates vital reflexes.
   B. The cortex would probably be intact.
   C. The somatic nervous system still functions.
   D. The baby's forebrain still functions to keep the body alive.

p. 67
Introduction
Level: Moderate
Type: Factual
Ans: B
*PS/SG 4-3*

3. The behavioral problems plaguing Scott, the child who had inherited fragile X syndrome, illustrate the role of _____ in human development.
   A. evolution
   B. genetic instructions
   C. fertilization
   D. skull size

p. 67
Introduction
Level: Easy
Type: Factual
Ans: C
*www*

4. The most common cause of an inherited development disorder is:
   A. autism
   B. Broca's aphasia
   C. fragile X syndrome
   D. Down syndrome

p. 68
Genes and Evolution
Level: Easy
Type: Factual
Ans: A

5. Upon conception, the father and the mother each contribute _____ to their offspring.
   A. 23 chromosomes
   B. 2 chromosomes
   C. hundreds of chromosomes
   D. 23 pairs of chromosomes

p. 68
Genes and Evolution
Level: Moderate
Type: Factual
Ans: D

6. When a sperm from a man fertilizes the egg of a woman, the result is a _____ and it consists of _____ pairs of chromosomes.
   A. zygote; 46
   B. gene; 46
   C. phenotype; 46
   D. zygote; 23

p. 68
Genes and Evolution
Level: Easy
Type: Factual
Ans: C

7. Chromosomes consist of:
A. zygotes
B. sperm
C. DNA
D. phenotypes

p. 68
Genes and Evolution
Level: Easy
Type: Factual
Ans: A

8. A _____ is a specific segment on the long strand of DNA.
A. gene
B. zygote
C. chromosome
D. phenotype

p. 68
Genes and Evolution
Level: Easy
Type: Factual
Ans: C

9. Which of the following statements is *incorrect*?
A. The father's sperm contains 23 chromosomes.
B. A zygote results when an egg is fertilized.
C. DNA is made up of large strands of chromosomes.
D. The zygote is the largest human cell.

p. 68
Genes and Evolution
Level: Moderate
Type: Factual
Ans: D

10. Which statement is <u>most</u> accurate in describing the order from smallest to largest?
A. zygote, genes, DNA, chromosomes
B. genes, DNA, chromosomes, zygote
C. DNA, zygote, genes, chromosomes
D. DNA, genes, chromosomes, zygote

p. 68
Genes and Evolution
Level: Easy
Type: Factual
Ans: C
*www*

11. In what specific structure, is the "chemical alphabet" found - the alphabet that will provide the instructions for growth and development?
A. zygotes
B. genes
C. DNA
D. chromosomes

p. 68
Genes and Evolution
Level: Easy
Type: Factual
Ans: D

12. This structure can <u>best</u> be described as being made up of 4 chemicals which form a chemical alphabet.
A. Fragile X
B. chromosome
C. zygote
D. DNA

p. 68
Genes and Evolution
Level: Easy
Type: Factual
Ans: A

13. "The shape of your eyes is due to genes." Genes provide instructions for making:
A. protein
B. genomes
C. DNA
D. chromosomes

p. 68
Genes and Evolution
Level: Easy
Type: Factual
Ans: B

14. Loi believes that science has <u>not</u> identified the location of any human genes. Is Loi right?
A. Yes - Project Genome is scheduled to begin in 2005
B. No - Project Genome has identified many genes
C. No - since 1980, all human genes have been identified
D. Yes - scientists have expressed disinterest in genetic research

p. 68
Genes and Evolution
Level: Moderate
Type: Conceptual
Ans: A

15. Of the following, which is the <u>best</u> way to think about Project Genome?
A. It is like making a blue print of genes.
B. Project Genome is like mixing chemicals together to form a new chemical.
C. It is like calling all the phone numbers in a telephone directory.
D. Project Genome is much like baking a cake and forgetting to add flour.

p. 68
Genes and Evolution
Level: Easy
Type: Factual
Ans: D

16. There are a total of about _____ human genes located on the 23 pairs of chromosomes.
A. 100
B. 3,000
C. 10,000
D. 30,000

p. 68
Genes and Evolution
Level: Easy
Type: Factual
Ans: C

17. A common characteristic in cases of Fragile X syndrome is:
A. visual disturbances
B. a susceptibility to violent behavior
C. mental retardation
D. cardiovascular abnormalities

p. 68
Genes and Evolution
Level: Easy
Type: Factual
Ans: A

18. The defect on the X chromosome that can cause physical abnormalities and mental retardation is called:
A. Fragile X syndrome
B. anecephaly
C. aphasia
D. Down syndrome

p. 69
Genes and Evolution
Level: Easy
Type: Factual
Ans: B

19. Concepts such as evolution and survival of the fittest are <u>most</u> associated with:
A. Roger Sperry
B. Charles Darwin
C. Sigmund Freud
D. B. F. Skinner

p. 69
Genes and Evolution
Level: Easy
Type: Factual
Ans: D

20. Which statement is <u>not</u> consistent with Darwin's view of evolution?
A. Different species arouse from a common ancestor.
B. Humans and chimps share 98.5% of their DNA.
C. Present day humans descended from a creature related to apes.
D. Humans belong to their own family tree.

p. 69
Genes and Evolution
Level: Easy
Type: Factual
Ans: C

21. According to the theory of evolution:
A. Different species arouse from a different ancestors
B. Humans belong to their own family tree
C. Present day humans descended from a creature related to apes
D. Humans and chimps share only 1% of their DNA

p. 69
Genes and Evolution
Level: Moderate
Type: Conceptual
Ans: C

22. Darwin's view of evolution is:
A. considered out-of-date by most scientists
B. consistent with the beliefs of most religions
C. a theory
D. fact

p. 69
Genes and Evolution
Level: Easy
Type: Factual
Ans: B

23. The brain of *Homo sapiens* is ____ larger than the brain of Lucy (*Australopithecus afarensis*).
A. 2 times
B. 3 times
C. 4 times
D. 10 times

p. 69
Genes and Evolution
Level: Easy
Type: Factual
Ans: B

24. According to the theory of evolution, descendants of homo erectus are called:
A. *Homo afarensis*
B. *Homo sapiens*
C. *Australopithecus africansis*
D. *Australopithecus sapiens*

p. 69
Genes and Evolution
Level: Easy
Type: Factual
Ans: D

25. It is theorized by some that an increase in brain size allowed *Homo sapiens* to:
A. grow crops
B. live in communities
C. develop language
D. all of the above

p. 69
Genes and Evolution
Level: Moderate
Type: Factual
Ans: A

26. Two mechanisms are believed to be responsible for the evolution of brain size. They are:
A. genetic mutation and natural selection
B. genetic mutation and mitosis
C. genetic codominance and incomplete dominance
D. natural selection and recessive genes

p. 69
Genes and Evolution
Level: Moderate
Type: Factual
Ans: B

27. Order the brain size from smallest to largest.
A. Homo sapiens, Australopthecus africanus, Homo erectus
B. Australopthecus africanus, Homo erectus, Homo sapiens
C. Homo erectus, Homo sapiens, Homo sparticus
D. Homo erectus, Homo sapiens, Australopthecus africanus

p. 70
Studying the Living Brain
Level: Easy
Type: Factual
Ans: A

28. The doctor explained to the patient's family that the pictures of their loved one's brain were normal. She passed radio frequencies through the brain. Which method was used by the doctor to study her patient's brain?
A. MRI scan
B. EEG
C. PET scan
D. ADHD scan

| p. 70<br>Studying the Living Brain<br>Level: Moderate<br>Type: Factual<br>Ans: A<br>*www* | 29.<br>A.<br>B.<br>C.<br>D. | Which technique uses radio frequencies to study the structure of the brain?<br>MRI scan<br>SET scan<br>PET scan<br>the stereotaxic procedure |
|---|---|---|
| p. 70<br>Studying the Living Brain<br>Level: Easy<br>Type: Applied<br>Ans: B | 30.<br><br>A.<br>B.<br>C.<br>D. | As a physician, you need to have a very detailed view of the structure of your patient's brain. The method <u>most</u> appropriate given your needs is:<br>SET scan<br>MRI scan<br>PET scan<br>EEG |
| p. 70<br>Studying the Living Brain<br>Level: Easy<br>Type: Factual<br>Ans: A<br>*PS/SG 4-5* | 31.<br>A.<br>B.<br>C.<br>D. | The new techniques of brain scans have a great advantage:<br>they permit a look inside the living, functioning brain<br>the information they yield is more than worth the harm they do<br>it is no longer necessary to perform frontal lobotomies in mental hospitals<br>it's so hard to find volunteers for experimental brain surgery |
| p. 70<br>Studying the Living Brain<br>Level: Easy<br>Type: Applied<br>Ans: B | 32.<br><br><br><br>A.<br>B.<br>C.<br>D. | Your grandmother is having problems with headaches. She goes to have a test and you accompany her. She lies down with her head in the center of a large "donut." You hear a dull drumming sound as the test proceeds. Your grandmother is having a(n):<br>SET scan<br>MRI scan<br>PET scan<br>EEG |
| p. 70<br>Studying the Living Brain<br>Level: Difficult<br>Type: Conceptual<br>Ans: B | 33.<br><br><br><br>A.<br>B.<br>C.<br>D. | The family doctor is concerned about the complaints of eight-year-old Tommy. The doctor would like to run some tests to determine the structure of Tommy's brain. Which of the following tests would be <u>most</u> appropriate?<br>SET scan<br>MRI scan<br>PET scan<br>fMRI scan |
| p. 70<br>Studying the Living Brain<br>Level: Difficult<br>Type: Conceptual<br>Ans: A | 34.<br><br><br>A.<br>B.<br>C.<br>D. | Benito's doctors fear the worst and believe that there is damage to the structure of his brain. The suspected damage is on the left side of the brain. To assess Benito's brain, the doctors order a(n) _____ on his brain.<br>MRI scan<br>SET scan<br>PET scan<br>x-ray scan |
| p. 70<br>Studying the Living Brain<br>Level: Easy<br>Type: Conceptual<br>Ans: B | 35.<br>A.<br>B.<br>C.<br>D. | fMRI is to _____ as MRI is to _____.<br>structure; function<br>function; structure<br>organization; function<br>x-ray; gamma ray |

p. 70
Studying the Living Brain
Level: Easy
Type: Applied
Ans: C

36. Ivan is having his brain scanned. As the machine is working, he is asked to read words on a screen. He is <u>most</u> likely having a(n):
A. MRI scan
B. SET scan
C. fMRI scan
D. x-ray scan

p. 70
Studying the Living Brain
Level: Easy
Type: Applied
Ans: D

37. Dr. Woodward wishes to determine what area of the brain is involved in listening to classical music. What type of brain scan would you recommend that he use that would allow a study of brain function?
A. MRI scan
B. SET scan
C. x-ray scan
D. fMRI scan

p. 70
Studying the Living Brain
Level: Easy
Type: Factual
Ans: D

38. Based on fMRI scans, what part of the brain is especially active while watching a funny TV program?
A. hypothalamus
B. cerebellum
C. right frontal area
D. amygdala

p. 71
Studying the Living Brain
Level: Moderate
Type: Factual
Ans: B

39. Positron Emission Tomography (PET) differs from Magnetic Resonance Imaging (MRI) in that a PET scan:
A. studies the structure of the brain
B. studies the function of the brain
C. uses radio frequencies
D. identifies spinal cord injuries

p. 71
Studying the Living Brain
Level: Easy
Type: Factual
Ans: C

40. Positron emission tomography (PET scan) is a technique used to:
A. transplant fetal brain tissue
B. repair damaged neurons in the spinal cord
C. study the function of brain areas
D. perform a frontal lobotomy

p. 71
Studying the Living Brain
Level: Easy
Type: Factual
Ans: C

41. Which method of studying the living brain involves injecting a slightly radioactive solution into the blood and measuring the amount of radiation absorbed by brain cells?
A. SET scan
B. MRI scan
C. PET scan
D. EEG

p. 71
Studying the Living Brain
Level: Easy
Type: Factual
Ans: A
*PS/SG 4-6*

42. Today, through the use of _____ scans, neuroscientists are able to obtain "pictures" of cognitive activities.
A. PET
B. POS
C. MRI
D. fPET

p. 71
Studying the Living Brain
Level: Moderate
Type: Conceptual
Ans: C

43.  MRI scan is to PET scan as _____ is to _____.
A.  radio frequencies; function
B.  function; structure
C.  structure; function
D.  CNS; PNS

p. 71
Studying the Living Brain
Level: Moderate
Type: Conceptual
Ans: A

44.  MRI scan is to PET scan as _____ is to _____.
A.  radio frequencies; radioactive solution
B.  radioactive solution; radio frequencies
C.  x-ray; radioactive solution
D.  ultrasound; x-ray

p. 71
Studying the Living Brain
Level: Moderate
Type: Factual
Ans: A

45.  One of the reasons that PET scans can indicate brain activity is that very active neurons absorb more:
A.  radioactive solution than less active ones
B.  radio frequencies than less active ones
C.  magnetism than less active ones
D.  ultrasound than less active ones

p. 71
Studying the Living Brain
Level: Moderate
Type: Applied
Ans: D

46.  As a PET scan was assessing Reggie's brain, he was instructed to think about the words being shown on a computer screen in front of him. What will the PET scan most likely reveal?
A.  PET scan is an inappropriate measure of this brain function
B.  no one particular area of the brain was more active than other areas
C.  most of the neural activity occurred near the front of the brain
D.  most of the neural activity occurred near the back of the brain

p. 71
Studying the Living Brain
Level: Easy
Type: Factual
Ans: C

47.  Based on PET scans, if you were to say words the _____ would be very active.
A.  genome
B.  amygdala
C.  front-middle part of the brain
D.  back part of the brain

p. 71
Studying the Living Brain
Level: Moderate
Type: Factual
Ans: A

48.  In silently naming tools such as pliers, the brain area that is most active is:
A.  the front of the brain
B.  the back of the brain
C.  front-middle part of the brain
D.  back-middle part of the brain

p. 71
Studying the Living Brain
Level: Easy
Type: Factual
Ans: C

49.  The new area of study that maps the paths of cognitive processes in the brain is called:
A.  behavioral neuroscience
B.  psychoanalysis
C.  cognitive neuroscience
D.  cognitive psychobiology

p. 71
Studying the Living Brain
Level: Easy
Type: Factual
Ans: C

50.  Dr. Fassid studies the relationship between cognitive abilities and neural activity. Dr. Fassid is an expert in:
A.  cognitive psychobiology
B.  clinical pharmacology
C.  cognitive neuroscience
D.  behavioral neuroscience

p. 72
Organization of the Brain
Level: Easy
Type: Factual
Ans: D
*www*

51. The two divisions of the nervous system are:
A. sympathetic division and parasympathetic division
B. somatic nervous system and central nervous system
C. autonomic nervous system and central nervous system
D. peripheral nervous system and central nervous system

p. 72
Organization of the Brain
Level: Easy
Type: Conceptual
Ans: A

52. What part of your nervous system do you use to correctly answer this question which requires deep thought?
A. central nervous system
B. somatic nervous system
C. autonomic nervous system
D. parasympathetic division

p. 72
Organization of the Brain
Level: Easy
Type: Applied
Ans: D

53. You stub your big toe on the chair leg. The pain message is being carried to the brain on nerves that are part of the:
A. sympathetic division
B. central nervous system
C. autonomic nervous system
D. peripheral nervous system

p. 72
Organization of the Brain
Level: Easy
Type: Applied
Ans: D

54. As you take this test, you feel the texture of the pencil you are using. Nerves that carry that sensory information from your fingers to your spinal cord are part of the:
A. sympathetic division
B. central nervous system
C. autonomic nervous system
D. peripheral nervous system

p. 72
Organization of the Brain
Level: Easy
Type: Factual
Ans: C

55. The brain and spinal cord comprise the _____ nervous system.
A. peripheral
B. sympathetic
C. central
D. primary

p. 72
Organization of the Brain
Level: Easy
Type: Factual
Ans: A

56. The central nervous system is made up of two components:
A. brain and spinal cord
B. sensory organs and afferent nerves
C. brain and efferent nerves
D. brain and somatic nerves

p. 72
Organization of the Brain
Level: Easy
Type: Factual
Ans: C
*PS/SG 4-7*

57. Which one of the following is not included in the peripheral nervous system?
A. somatic nervous system
B. autonomic nervous system
C. central nervous system
D. sympathetic nervous system

| | | |
|---|---|---|
| p. 72 | 58. | The somatic nervous system: |
| Organization of the Brain | A. | consists of nerves connected to either sensory receptors or to muscles |
| Level: Easy | B. | regulates heart rate, breathing, blood pressure, and digestion |
| Type: Factual | C. | controls the fight or flight response |
| Ans: A | D. | is in a constant state of homeostasis |

| | | |
|---|---|---|
| p. 72 | 59. | The somatic nervous system contains: |
| Organization of the Brain | A. | sympathetic division and parasympathetic division |
| Level: Easy | B. | afferent and efferent fibers |
| Type: Factual | C. | sensory and afferent fibers |
| Ans: B | D. | motor fibers and latent fibers |

| | | |
|---|---|---|
| p. 72 | 60. | You're looking at a book entitled *Your Autonomic Nervous System*. One of |
| Qrganization of the Brain | | the chapter titles is really confusing based upon your knowledge of the |
| Level: Moderate | | autonomic nervous system. Which chapter seems to <u>not</u> fit your |
| Type: Conceptual | | knowledge? |
| Ans: C | A. | The Sympathetic Division: Activating in Times of Stress |
| | B. | Relaxing with the Parasympathetic Division |
| | C. | The Autonomic Nervous System: You CAN Control It All! |
| | D. | The Autonomic Nervous System: Part of The Peripheral Nervous System |

| | | |
|---|---|---|
| p. 72 | 61. | Karen was able to live in a coma for several years even when taken off the |
| Organization of the Brain | | respirator. This is because parts of the body not under conscious control |
| Level: Easy | | continue to function. These parts are regulated by the: |
| Type: Factual | A. | central nervous system |
| Ans: B | B. | autonomic nervous system |
| | C. | somatic nervous system |
| | D. | forebrain |

| | | |
|---|---|---|
| p. 72 | 62. | You are videotaping a segment for a TV show that highlights funny |
| Organization of the Brain | | situations and people caught on video. Your friend is hiding in a large box |
| Level: Easy | | ready to jump out and scare unsuspecting people. When the "victims" yell |
| Type: Applied | | and scream indicating arousal, you speculate that their |
| Ans: A | | _____ becomes activated. |
| | A. | sympathetic division |
| | B. | parasympathetic division |
| | C. | parietal lobe |
| | D. | cerebellum |

| | | |
|---|---|---|
| p. 72 | 63. | You are about to give a speech to a group of 100 people. Your _____ |
| Organization of the Brain | | division is especially active as you notice butterflies in your stomach, a dry |
| Level: Easy | | mouth, and sweaty palms. |
| Type: Applied | A. | sympathetic division |
| Ans: A | B. | parasympathetic division |
| *www* | C. | parietal lobe |
| | D. | cerebellum |

| | | |
|---|---|---|
| p. 72 | 64. | "I'm glad that is over!" Your speech was a success. You feel your body |
| Organization of the Brain | | calming down. Your _____ is activated. |
| Level: Easy | A. | sympathetic division |
| Type: Applied | B. | parasympathetic division |
| Ans: B | C. | parietal lobe |
| | D. | cerebellum |

p. 72
Organization of the Brain
Level: Easy
Type: Factual
Ans: A

65. The specific part of the nervous system that is responsible for returning the body to a relaxed state is the:
A. parasympathetic division
B. somatic nervous system
C. autonomic nervous system
D. peripheral nervous system

p. 73
Organization of the Brain
Level: Easy
Type: Conceptual
Ans: C
*www*

66. The three main divisions of the human brain are:
A. forebrain, midbrain, cerebrain
B. topbrain, midbrain, hindbrain
C. forebrain, midbrain, hindbrain
D. neobrain, lateralbrain, medialbrain

p. 73
Organization of the Brain
Level: Easy
Type: Factual
Ans: D
*PS/SG 4-8*

67. Which of the following is <u>not</u> one of the three main parts of the human brain?
A. forebrain
B. midbrain
C. hindbrain
D. topbrain

p. 73
Organization of the Brain
Level: Easy
Type: Conceptual
Ans: C
*www*

68. The part of the brain that directly allows you to contemplate the answer to this question is the:
A. hindbrain
B. midbrain
C. forebrain
D. cerebellum

p. 73
Organization of the Brain
Level: Easy
Type: Factual
Ans: B

69. The ability to perform higher reasoning, speak and use language, and plan is housed in the:
A. brainstem
B. forebrain
C. hypothalamus
D. occipital lobe

p. 73
Organization of the Brain
Level: Moderate
Type: Applied
Ans: D

70. Rex is an evil scientist and wants to take away humans' ability to use language, plan, and make decisions. Want part of the brain should his newly invented "Death Ray Gun" destroy?
A. limbic system
B. reticular formation
C. thalamus
D. forebrain

p. 71
Studying the Living Brain
Level: Moderate
Type: Applied
Ans: D

71. You are listening to a few songs that you really like since they are very relaxing. What part of your brain has a reward or pleasure center that is very active as you listen to the songs?
A. Broca's area
B. medulla
C. cerebellum
D. midbrain

p. 73
Organization of the Brain
Level: Moderate
Type: Applied
Ans: B

72. If you have ever been driving and "nod" for a brief moment or two and then pull your head back up, you can probably thank your _____ for its role in arousal and preparing the forebrain for sensory input.
   A. brainstem
   B. reticular formation
   C. hypothalamus
   D. occipital lobe

p. 73
Organization of the Brain
Level: Easy
Type: Factual
Ans: A

73. In what brain area do you find the reticular formation?
   A. midbrain
   B. medulla
   C. occipital lobe
   D. cerebellum

p. 73
Organization of the Brain
Level: Moderate
Type: Applied
Ans: C

74. One day in class, ten-year old Pasquel and her classmates all turned their heads at the same time toward the windows when a large clap of thunder sounded. What brain area was most responsible for the automatic turning of the heads toward the noise?
   A. pons
   B. Wernicke's area
   C. midbrain
   D. somatosensory cortex

p. 73
Organization of the Brain
Level: Moderate
Type: Conceptual
Ans: D

75. Steve, a ten year old, is doing a "karate chop" to the base of the skull on the back of the neck of his younger brother. Their mother yells, "Stop that Steve!" What would be the best explanation for his mother's protest?
   A. The forebrain is located there and it controls vital reflexes. Damage to this area may be fatal.
   B. The reticular formation is found in that area. Damage to this structure may lead to mental retardation.
   C. The parietal lobe is found in that area. Damage to this lobe leads to paralysis.
   D. The hindbrain is located there and it controls vital reflexes. Damage to this area may be fatal.

p. 73
Organization of the Brain
Level: Easy
Type: Factual
Ans: D

76. The pons:
   A. controls vital reflexes such as respiration, heart rate, and blood pressure
   B. coordinates voluntary movements
   C. contains Purkinje cells
   D. connects the spinal cord to the brain and makes chemicals important in sleep

p. 73
Organization of the Brain
Level: Easy
Type: Factual
Ans: A

77. The medulla:
   A. controls vital reflexes such as respiration, heart rate, and blood pressure
   B. initiates voluntary movements
   C. regulates the production of speech
   D. connects the spinal cord to the brain and makes chemicals important in sleep

p. 73
Organization of the Brain
Level: Moderate
Type: Conceptual
Ans: D

78. In a fit of uncontrollable panic and depression, a person drinks a quart of hard liquor in less than an hour. If this proves fatal, it will be because the alcohol:
A. permanently damaged synapses around muscles
B. anesthetized parts of the neocortex
C. created a neural apathy that prevented the person from defending himself against trauma
D. inhibited neurons in the medulla, causing vital life support reflexes to stop

p. 73
Organization of the Brain
Level: Easy
Type: Factual
Ans: C
*PS/SG 4-9*

79. The cerebellum is an important part of the hindbrain that:
A. initiates voluntary movement
B. influences social-emotional behavior
C. coordinates voluntary movements
D. makes humans distinct from all other animals

p. 73
Organization of the Brain
Level: Moderate
Type: Conceptual
Ans: C
*www*

80. Which of the following activities would most likely involve the cerebellum?
A. experiencing emotion
B. long-term memory
C. dancing
D. listening to a foreign language

p. 73
Organization of the Brain
Level: Moderate
Type: Factual
Ans: A

81. The cerebellum, according to new research, may be involved in:
A. learning to perform to timed motor responses
B. reading
C. initiating voluntary movements
D. writing computer programs

p. 73
Organization of the Brain
Level: Moderate
Type: Factual
Ans: D

82. You are a subject in a study. Your eye to being conditioned to blink to a noise. According to Module Four, which part of your brain is involved in this reflexive learning?
A. pons
B. medulla
C. midbrain
D. cerebellum

p. 73
Organization of the Brain
Level: Moderate
Type: Applied
Ans: C

83. Mike has had too much to drink. He shows decreased coordination and has difficulty rapidly touching a finger to his nose. Of the following brain areas, which is most responsible for these altered behaviors?
A. pons
B. reticular formation
C. cerebellum
D. medulla

| | | |
|---|---|---|
| p. 73<br>Organization of the Brain<br>Level: Easy<br>Type: Conceptual<br>Ans: B | 84.<br>A.<br>B.<br>C.<br>D. | The graceful movements of a ballet dancer are due to the coordination of movement performed by the:<br>medulla<br>cerebellum<br>hypothalamus<br>pons |
| p. 74<br>Control Centers:<br>  Four Lobes<br>Level: Easy<br>Type: Factual<br>Ans: A<br>*www* | 85.<br>A.<br>B.<br>C.<br>D. | The thin layer of cells that cover the surface of the forebrain is called the:<br>cortex<br>myelin sheath<br>cerebellum<br>thalamus |
| p. 74<br>Control Centers:<br>  Four Lobes<br>Level: Moderate<br>Type: Factual<br>Ans: B | 86.<br>A.<br>B.<br>C.<br>D. | The human cortex is wrinkled because:<br>it is very old compared to more primitive brains<br>wrinkling increases the surface area<br>the cell body causes a constriction at the surface<br>the axons pull down on certain parts of the cortex |
| p. 74<br>Control Centers:<br>  Four Lobes<br>Level: Easy<br>Type: Factual<br>Ans: C | 87.<br>A.<br>B.<br>C.<br>D. | The thin layer of cells that "cover" the surface of the forebrain is called the:<br>cerebellum<br>thalamus<br>cortex<br>association area |
| p. 74<br>Control Centers:<br>  Four Lobes<br>Level: Moderate<br>Type: Conceptual<br>Ans: C | 88.<br>A.<br>B.<br>C.<br>D. | How is the cortex like an 18-inch television screen?<br>both a cortex and a TV screen are the result of many networks working together<br>both must be activated by electrical signals<br>when the cortex is unfolded it is about as large as an 18-inch television screen<br>both give off energy that can be detected and measured |
| p. 74<br>Control Centers:<br>  Four Lobes<br>Level: Easy<br>Type: Factual<br>Ans: C | 89.<br>A.<br>B.<br>C.<br>D. | The forebrain can be divided into lobes. Which of the following is not a lobe?<br>frontal<br>parietal<br>lateral<br>occipital |
| p. 74<br>Control Centers:<br>  Four Lobes<br>Level: Easy<br>Type: Factual<br>Ans: B | 90.<br>A.<br>B.<br>C.<br>D. | Which of the following descriptions of the lobes of the cortex is incorrect?<br>frontal – involved with personality and emotion<br>parietal – involved with motor behaviors<br>temporal – involved with processing auditory experience<br>occipital – involved with processing visual information |

p. 74
Control Centers:
  Four Lobes
Level: Moderate
Type: Conceptual
Ans: D

91. The brain area that <u>most</u> distinguishes us from animals is the:
A. thyroid
B. cerebellum
C. pons
D. cortex

p. 74
Control Centers:
  Four Lobes
Level: Easy
Type: Factual
Ans: D

92. Baby Theresa is described in the textbook as having a rare condition where the fetal brain does not develop normally. What is the proper diagnosis of this condition?
A. encephalitis
B. meningitis
C. fragile X syndrome
D. anencephaly

p. 74
Control Centers:
  Four Lobes
Level: Moderate
Type: Conceptual
Ans: C

93. If Baby Theresa's life could have been saved, would she have been able to recognize her parents' faces and voices at 6 months of age? Why?
A. yes - her lobes would have allowed recognition to take place
B. yes - but only visually, since she would be deaf
C. no - she was born without the four lobes
D. maybe - if she was placed in a rigorous physical therapy program

p. 74
Control Centers:
  Four Lobes
Level: Moderate
Type: Factual
Ans: A

94. Babies born with anencephaly may survive for days or weeks. Why?
A. Parts of the hindbrain may be present.
B. The frontal lobe is able to take over damaged brain areas.
C. The cerebellum is usually normal.
D. The thalamus is functioning normally.

p. 75
Control Centers:
  Four Lobes
Level: Easy
Type: Factual
Ans: B

95. Of the following functions, which is <u>not</u> a function of the frontal lobe?
A. performing voluntary movements
B. processing sensory information from parts of the body
C. paying attention
D. executing plans

p. 75
Control Centers:
  Four Lobes
Level: Easy
Type: Factual
Ans: A

96. The frontal lobe is involved in:
A. social-emotional behaviors
B. reflexive actions
C. sensory experiences
D. Wernicke's Aphasia

p. 75
Control Centers:
  Four Lobes
Level: Easy
Type: Applied
Ans: D

97.  Leo's new roommate, Patrick, is a little odd. He seems to act strange in social situations, shows problems with his emotions, and has difficulty making decisions. You later learn that he has a tumor in one of his lobes and are not surprised to learn it is located in the _____ lobe.
A.  sensory
B.  occipital
C.  temporal
D.  frontal

p. 75
Control Centers:
  Four Lobes
Level: Moderate
Type: Applied
Ans: A

98.  Susan has a problem making and carrying out plans. Her doctor has diagnosed her as having a brain tumor. Most likely, Susan's tumor is in her:
A.  frontal lobe
B.  pons
C.  reticular formation
D.  parietal lobe

p. 75
Control Centers:
  Four Lobes
Level: Moderate
Type: Applied
Ans: C

99.  After a serious blow to the head, Hector underwent a dramatic personality change. A well-organized, extroverted person before the accident, he no longer could plan, or adjust to new social situations. Hector would also laugh uncontrollably at inappropriate times. What part of Hector's brain appears to have been damaged?
A.  thalamus
B.  temporal lobe
C.  frontal lobe
D.  hippocampus

p. 75
Control Centers:
  Four Lobes
Level: Moderate
Type: Applied
Ans: B

100.  Suzy is having her brain scanned. She is asked to imagine butterflies. The doctor is puzzled because the area of the brain expected to be very active is not. Instead, her frontal lobe is very active. What was Suzy most likely experiencing to cause this unexpected finding?
A.  Suzy is hearing the soft humming sound of the scanning equipment.
B.  She is planning her big party at her apartment this weekend.
C.  She feels the texture of the sweater she is wearing.
D.  She is trying to understand what the doctor is telling her.

p. 75
Control Centers:
  Four Lobes
Level: Easy
Type: Conceptual
Ans: D

101.  Who probably had the first frontal lobotomy?
A.  Baby Theresa
B.  Samuel Morton
C.  Egas Moniz
D.  Phineas Gage

p. 75
Control Centers:
  Four Lobes
Level: Moderate
Type: Conceptual
Ans: A
*www*

102.  The story of Phineas Gage demonstrates that:
A.  the frontal lobe seems to be involved in emotion and decision making
B.  a person cannot live if the frontal lobe is damaged
C.  a person cannot walk if the frontal lobe is damaged
D.  the frontal lobe seems to be a large mass of tissue that does not have any particular function

p. 75
Control Centers:
 Four Lobes
Level: Moderate
Type: Factual
Ans: A
*PS/SG 4-12*

103. The incredible story of Phineas Gage's accident shows that:
A. the frontal lobe is critical to personality
B. a person lives at best in a vegetative state after a frontal lobotomy
C. the frontal lobe is wired to the opposite side of the body
D. the frontal lobe receives sensory information from the body

p. 75
Control Centers:
 Four Lobes
Level: Moderate
Type: Conceptual
Ans: B

104. Cases like Phineas Gage, Alzheimer's patients, lobotomy patients, and aphasia patients suggest the principle that:
A. the nervous system cannot heal itself
B. changes in the nervous system lead to changes in behavior, cognitive ability, and personality
C. prevention is better than treatment
D. drugs can change the functioning of the nervous system

p. 75
Control Centers:
 Four Lobes
Level: Easy
Type: Factual
Ans: A

105. Who first used the frontal lobotomy on patients with emotional problems?
A. Egas Moniz
B. Phineas Gage
C. Charles Darwin
D. Stephen Jay Gould

p. 75
Control Centers:
 Four Lobes
Level: Easy
Type: Factual
Ans: B

106. Taber is researching his family tree. He is surprised to find out that in the 1940s a distant relative had surgery in which a large portion of the frontal lobe was removed. What treatment did Taber's relative receive?
A. split brain operation
B. frontal lobotomy
C. parietal lobotomy
D. hypothalamic lobotomy

p. 75
Control Centers:
 Four Lobes
Level: Easy
Type: Factual
Ans: C

107. How many frontal lobotomies were performed in the 1940s and 1950s?
A. 2,000
B. 12,000
C. 18,000
D. 100,000

p. 75
Control Centers:
 Four Lobes
Level: Moderate
Type: Factual
Ans: A

108. Well-controlled, long-term studies on frontal lobotomies found:
A. mixed results
B. overwhelming failure
C. overwhelming success
D. people adjust to new social demands

p. 75
Control Centers:
  Four Lobes
Level: Easy
Type: Factual
Ans: C

109. In frontal lobotomy, patients who saw improvements in their social-emotional behavior, often had problems in
A. sleeping
B. managing their anger
C. their ability to make and carry out plans
D. short-term memory

p. 75
Control Centers:
  Four Lobes
Level: Easy
Type: Factual
Ans: C

110. A major reason for the decline in the use of frontal lobotomies was that:
A. the majority of patients were turned into "vegetables"
B. it received negative publicity from movies like *One Flew Over the Cuckoo 's Nest*
C. antipsychotic drugs controlled behavior better
D. the operation caused severe memory loss in patients

p. 75
Control Centers:
  Four Lobes
Level: Easy
Type: Applied
Ans: B

111. Dr. Beenken, a noted neurologist, is studying the brain. She is interested in the cognitive functions found in the frontal lobe. How could she use the PET scan to further her study?
A. The PET scan could be used to analyze the structure of the lobe
B. She could ask subjects to perform mental tasks while being scanned
C. Subjects could make muscle movements while being scanned
D. The PET scan is not appropriate to study the frontal lobe

p. 75
Control Centers:
  Four Lobes
Level: Easy
Type: Factual
Ans: A

112. By using PET scans, scientists are finding that the frontal lobe is involved with:
A. thinking
B. olfaction
C. visual recognition
D. audition

p. 75
Control Centers:
  Four Lobes
Level: Easy
Type: Factual
Ans: D

113. Based upon your textbook, the cognitive functions of the frontal lobe include all but one of the following. Which one is not among the functions found in the frontal lobe?
A. attention
B. decision making
C. organizing
D. processing tactile information

p. 76
Control Centers:
  Four Lobes
Level: Easy
Type: Factual
Ans: A

114. Nerves on the _____ cross over and control the movements on the _____ side of the body.
A. left hemisphere; right
B. left occipital lobe; right
C. right occipital lobe; right
D. left hemisphere; left

p. 76
Control Centers:
  Four Lobes
Level: Easy
Type: Applied
Ans: D

115. If you wanted to reach with your right hand to grab a pen, where would that message originate in your nervous system?
A. in the left somatosensory cortex
B. in the ascending pathway of the spinal cord
C. in the right motor cortex
D. in the left motor cortex

*www*

p. 76
Control Centers:
 Four Lobes
Level: Easy
Type: Factual
Ans: B

116. The motor cortex is located in the _____ lobe.
A. somatosensory
B. frontal
C. temporal
D. occipital

p. 76
Control Centers:
 Four Lobes
Level: Easy
Type: Factual
Ans: D

117. The strip of the cortex in the frontal lobe that is involved in the initiation of all voluntary movements is called:
A. the somatosensory cortex
B. the sensory homunculus
C. Broca's area
D. the motor cortex

p. 76
Control Centers:
 Four Lobes
Level: Moderate
Type: Applied
Ans: C

118. Mr. Aaholm has a tumor in the right motor cortex. What is the most likely symptom he experiences?
A. Disturbances in vision with his right eye.
B. Disturbances in vision with his left eye.
C. Disturbances in movement on the left side of his body.
D. Disturbances in movement on the right side of his body.

p. 76
Control Centers:
 Four Lobes
Level: Easy
Type: Factual
Ans: D

119. The motor cortex that initiates all voluntary movements is found in:
A. the limbic system
B. the parietal lobe
C. Broca's area
D. the frontal lobe

p. 76
Control Centers:
 Four Lobes
Level: Easy
Type: Conceptual
Ans: B

120. Which of the following parts of the body would have the greatest representation of cells in the motor cortex?
A. shoulder
B. finger
C. neck
D. trunk

p. 76
Control Centers:
 Four Lobes
Level: Easy
Type: Factual
Ans: D

121. In addition to starting voluntary movements, the motor cortex also:
A. helps us to understand language
B. plays a role in visual perception
C. processes auditory information
D. remembers the order of events across time

p. 76
Control Centers:
 Four Lobes
Level: Easy
Type: Factual
Ans: A

122. Recent research indicates that the body parts in the motor cortex have :
A. considerable overlap
B. discrete area
C. a one-to-one relationship between size of body part and area in the motor cortex
D. specific locations on the motor homunculus

p. 76
Control Centers:
  Four Lobes
Level: Moderate
Type: Conceptual
Ans: C

123. Considering the functions of the frontal lobe, which person in a large company best illustrates those functions?
A. Kathy - secretary to the chief executive officer
B. Dan - graphic artist
C. Patti - chief executive officer
D. Connie - custodian

p. 76
Control Centers:
  Four Lobes
Level: Easy
Type: Factual
Ans: D

124. Given the functions of the frontal lobe, it acts as a(n):
A. factory
B. robot
C. teacher
D. executive

p. 76
Control Centers:
  Four Lobes
Level: Easy
Type: Factual
Ans: B

125. The unusual drawing of the motor cortex that illustrates how much of the cortex is devoted to various body parts is called the:
A. sensory homunculus
B. motor homunculus
C. cerebral homunculus
D. visual homunculus

p. 77
Control Centers:
  Four Lobes
Level: Easy
Type: Factual
Ans: B

126. The somatosensory cortex that receives sensory input is located in the:
A. frontal lobe
B. parietal lobe
C. motor cortex
D. occipital lobe

p. 77
Control Centers:
  Four Lobes
Level: Moderate
Type: Conceptual
Ans: B

127. A young gymnast practices on the balance beam. What part of her brain will be especially active in locating the positions of her arms and legs?
A. occipital lobe
B. somatosensory cortex
C. amygdala
D. pons

p. 77
Control Centers:
  Four Lobes
Level: Moderate
Type: Applied
Ans: A

128. Dakota's right somatosensory cortex was severely injured in a car accident. As a result, Dakota has great difficulty:
A. processing sensory information from the left side of the body
B. moving the right and left hands
C. understanding written words
D. carrying out plans

p. 77
Control Centers:
  Four Lobes
Level: Moderate
Type: Applied
Ans: C

129. As a result of a workplace accident, a person damages the left somatosensory cortex resulting in:
A. loss of movement on the left side of the body
B. loss of feeling on the left side of the body
C. loss of feeling on the right side of the body
D. loss of movement on the right side of the body

p. 77
Control Centers:
  Four Lobes
Level: Moderate
Type: Conceptual
Ans: B

130. Given the organization of the somatosensory cortex, which of the following parts of the body would an injury like a cut hurt the most?
A. elbow
B. lips
C. heel
D. forearm

p. 77
Control Centers:
  Four Lobes
Level: Easy
Type: Factual
Ans: A
*www*

131. The unusual drawing of the somatosensory cortex that illustrates how much of the cortex is devoted to various body parts is called the:
A. sensory homunculus
B. motor homunculus
C. cerebral homunculus
D. visual homunculus

p. 77
Control Centers:
  Four Lobes
Level: Moderate
Type: Applied
Ans: D

132. Gerald was looking for a phone number in a telephone book. He had to repeat the number over and over since he had nothing to write with. Which area of his brain becomes very active?
A. frontal lobe
B. cerebrum
C. thalamus
D. parietal lobe

p. 77
Control Centers:
  Four Lobes
Level: Moderate
Type: Applied
Ans: D

133. Noelle and Josiah were visiting their new house while it was still under construction. With only the frame of the house up, they tried to visually analyze their living room. Based upon the research cited in your textbook, Noelle and Josiah's _____ were especially active during this moment.
A. frontal lobes
B. cerebrums
C. thalamuses
D. parietal lobes

p. 78
Control Centers:
  Four Lobes
Level: Easy
Type: Factual
Ans: C

134. The temporal lobe contains the:
A. sensory homunculus
B. motor homunculus
C. primary auditory cortex
D. primary visual cortex

p. 78
Control Centers:
  Four Lobes
Level: Easy
Type: Factual
Ans: A

135. The primary auditory cortex turns electrical signals into _____, while the auditory association area turns raw sensory information into _____ .
A. basic sensations; recognizable sounds
B. coherent sounds; electrical messages
C. perceptions; coherent sounds
D. perceptions; sensations

p. 78
Control Centers:
 Four Lobes
Level: Easy
Type: Factual
Ans: D

136. The _____ changes electrical signals into basic sound sensations.
A. somatosensory cortex
B. medulla
C. auditory association area
D. primary auditory cortex

p. 78
Control Centers:
 Four Lobes
Level: Easy
Type: Applied
Ans: C

137. If you are able to recognize the tune "Row, Row, Row Your Boat" then your _____ has worked.
A. primary auditory cortex
B. medulla
C. auditory association area
D. Broca's area

p. 78
Control Centers:
 Four Lobes
Level: Moderate
Type: Conceptual
Ans: A

138. During the game show "Jeopardy," the host says the answer, "the temporal lobe." Which of the following is the best question?
A. "Which lobe is critical to hearing and speech?"
B. "What is the name of the lobe that sends motor messages to the body?"
C. "What is the lobe that does not have an association cortex?"
D. "Which lobe is critical to vision?"

p. 78
Control Centers:
 Four Lobes
Level: Easy
Type: Conceptual
Ans: C
www

139. A stroke patient suffers damage to the left temporal lobe. This damage is likely to be manifested by problems with:
A. motor coordination
B. vision
C. speech
D. emotional expression

p. 78
Control Centers:
 Four Lobes
Level: Moderate
Type: Applied
Ans: A

140. Simon has difficulty in understanding spoken or written words. He also tends to talk gibberish and cannot utter meaningful sentences. Simon has most likely been diagnosed with:
A. Wernicke's aphasia
B. Occipital aphasia
C. Broca's aphasia
D. Alzheimer's disease

p. 78
Control Centers:
 Four Lobes
Level: Easy
Type: Factual
Ans: B

141. Wernicke's area is located in the _____ lobe, whereas Broca's area is located in the _____ lobe.
A. occipital; temporal
B. temporal; frontal
C. parietal; occipital
D. frontal; parietal

p. 78
Control Centers:
 Four Lobes
Level: Moderate
Type: Factual
Ans: D

142. If you are right-handed, chances are your Broca's area is located in the _____ and Wernicke's area is located in the _____.
A. temporal lobe; left hemisphere
B. frontal lobe; right hemisphere
C. temporal lobe; frontal lobe
D. left hemisphere; left hemisphere

p. 78
Control Centers:
  Four Lobes
Level: Easy
Type: Conceptual
Ans: A

143. Wernicke's area is to _____ as Broca's area is to _____.
A. understanding; fluency
B. temporal; frontal
C. fluency; production
D. frontal; parietal

p. 78
Control Centers:
  Four Lobes
Level: Moderate
Type: Applied
Ans: C

144. Mahrok is unable to speak in fluent sentences, but can still understand written and spoken words. Mahrok probably has:
A. Wernicke's aphasia
B. Occipital aphasia
C. Broca's aphasia
D. Alzheimer's disease

p. 78
Control Centers:
  Four Lobes
Level: Easy
Type: Factual
Ans: B
*PS/SG 4-15*

145. Wernicke's aphasia and Broca's aphasia are evidence that:
A. language abilities are more inherited than acquired
B. special areas of the lobes of the cortex control language abilities
C. if one area is damaged, the other takes over for it
D. human language is so complex that a number of things can go wrong with it

p. 79
Control Centers:
  Four Lobes
Level: Easy
Type: Factual
Ans: A
*www*

146. The occipital lobe contains the _____ cortex.
A. primary visual
B. primary auditory
C. sensory
D. motor

p. 79
Control Centers:
  Four Lobes
Level: Easy
Type: Factual
Ans: A

147. A crushing left hook to the head knocks down a boxer. He "sees stars" because:
A. neurons in the occipital lobe were stimulated by the blow
B. his eyes were jarred from their sockets
C. his frontal lobe was disturbed
D. memory cells in the association area were stimulated

p. 79
Control Centers:
  Four Lobes
Level: Moderate
Type: Factual
Ans: A

148. The primary visual cortex turns electrical signals into _____, while the visual association area turns raw sensory information into _____.
A. basic sensations; recognizable visual perceptions
B. coherent sights; electrical messages
C. perceptions; coherent sights
D. perceptions; sensations

p. 79
Control Centers:
  Four Lobes
Level: Easy
Type: Factual
Ans: D

149. The _____ changes electrical signals into basic visual sensations.
A. somatosensory cortex
B. medulla
C. visual association area
D. primary visual cortex

p. 79
Control Centers:
 Four Lobes
Level: Moderate
Type: Applied
Ans: C

150. A stimulus you are looking at appears to be a pattern of light. This is due to the _____, but the _____ sees the pattern of light as a close friend.
A. primary visual cortex; Broca's area
B. Broca's area; Wernicke's area
C. primary visual cortex; visual association area
D. Wernicke's area; primary visual cortex

p. 79
Control Centers:
 Four Lobes
Level: Easy
Type: Applied
Ans: C

151. If you are able to recognize a picture of the White House, then your _____ has worked.
A. primary visual cortex
B. hypothalamus
C. visual association area
D. Wernicke's area

p. 79
Control Centers:
 Four Lobes
Level: Moderate
Type: Applied
Ans: C

152. If your visual association area was damaged, the result would be:
A. total blindness
B. neglect syndrome only if the damage was confined to the left hemisphere
C. visual agnosia
D. insignificant

p. 79
Control Centers:
 Four Lobes
Level: Easy
Type: Factual
Ans: B

153. A patient with visual agnosia would have problems:
A. with transmitting electrical messages from the eyes to the primary visual cortex
B. recognizing some object or person
C. seeing parts of a visual stimulus
D. seeing objects on one side or another

p. 79
Control Centers:
 Four Lobes
Level: Moderate
Type: Applied
Ans: A

154. Mike's visual association area on the right hemisphere is damaged. The doctors have diagnosed him with neglect syndrome. What can his family expect from Mike's neurological problem?
A. Mike's failure to see things on the left side
B. problems with understanding speech spoken from the right side
C. an inability to recognize people
D. blindness

p. 79
Control Centers:
 Four Lobes
Level: Moderate
Type: Applied
Ans: D

155. A patient of Dr. Howarth's has visual agnosia. When the patient was asked to copy a picture of the United States laying in front of him, he:
A. only drew the states on the left side of the picture
B. could not draw the picture because he did not understand the instructions
C. only drew the states on the right side of the picture
D. could not recognize that the picture was of the United States

p. 79
Control Centers:
 Four Lobes
Level: Moderate
Type: Applied
Ans: C

156. One of Dr. Odland's patients has neglect syndrome caused by right-sided brain damage. When the patient was asked to copy a picture of the United States laying in front of him, he:
A. only drew the states on the left side of the picture
B. could not draw the picture because he did not understand the instructions
C. only drew the states on the right side of the picture
D. could not recognize that the picture was of the United States

p. 79
Control Centers:
  Four Lobes
Level: Easy
Type: Factual
Ans: A

157.  Which disorder is characterized by the failure to see objects or parts of the body on the side opposite the brain damage?
A.  neglect syndrome
B.  lateral syndrome
C.  association syndrome
D.  Wernicke's syndrome

p. 79
Control Centers:
  Four Lobes
Level: Moderate
Type: Applied
Ans: D

158.  On your visit to the local nursing home, you meet a man with neglect syndrome caused by brain damage to the right side. You notice his:
A.  inability to speak in a clear voice
B.  speech to be full of gibberish
C.  tremors and difficulty walking
D.  failure to comb the hair on the left side of his head

p. 79
Control Centers:
  Four Lobes
Level: Moderate
Type: Conceptual
Ans: B

159.  Visual agnosia is to neglect syndrome as _____ is to _____.
A.  understanding; production
B.  recognizing; seeing
C.  Broca's area; hypothalamus
D.  frontal lobe; occipital lobe

p. 80
Limbic System:
  Old Brain
Level: Easy
Type: Factual
Ans: C

160.  What part of the brain do we share in common with the alligator?
A.  Broca's area
B.  cortex
C.  limbic system
D.  Wernicke's area

p. 80
Limbic System:
  Old Brain
Level: Easy
Type: Factual
Ans: A

161.  One of the functions of the limbic system is to:
A.  regulate motivational and emotional behaviors
B.  moderate pain signals from the muscles
C.  regulate blood pressure and heart rate
D.  pass information from one hemisphere of the brain to the other

p. 80
Limbic System:
  Old Brain
Level: Moderate
Type: Conceptual
Ans: C
PS/SG 4-17

162.  When you understand the limbic system, you begin to see why:
A.  modern humans are so advanced over their prehistoric ancestors
B.  a human can do so much more than an alligator
C.  modern society is still plagued by so many primitive behaviors
D.  the social life of human beings is so much more complex than that of alligators

p. 80
Limbic System:
  Old Brain
Level: Easy
Type: Factual
Ans: D

163.  The area of the brain responsible for such primary motives as hunger, thirst, and sex is the:
A.  reticular activating system
B.  pons
C.  frontal lobe
D.  hypothalamus

p. 80
Limbic System:
  Old Brain
Level: Easy
Type: Factual
Ans: B

164. What controls the two divisions of the autonomic nervous system?
A. reticular activating system
B. hypothalamus
C. amygdala
D. thalamus

p. 80
Limbic System:
  Old Brain
Level: Easy
Type: Applied
Ans: C

165. Guy has a massive tumor in his hypothalamus. What problems can we expect Guy to display?
A. memory
B. understanding language
C. eating, drinking, and emotional behavior
D. recognizing simple visual stimuli

p. 80
Limbic System:
  Old Brain
Level: Moderate
Type: Conceptual
Ans: B

166. A researcher stimulates, with a small electrical charge, a portion of a cat's limbic system. The cat suddenly jumps up and acts as if it is fighting. What portion of the limbic system was stimulated?
A. hippocampus
B. hypothalamus
C. cortex
D. thalamus

p. 80
Limbic System:
  Old Brain
Level: Easy
Type: Applied
Ans: D

167. You are watching a really scary movie. The main character is about to be attacked by a monster. You look over to the person sitting next to you and see fear in his face. What part of the limbic system allows you to evaluate his expression?
A. hypothalamus
B. hippocampus
C. thalamus
D. amygdala

p. 80
Limbic System:
  Old Brain
Level: Easy
Type: Applied
Ans: C

168. A patient known as H. M., while undergoing brain surgery, suffered accidental brain damage. After the surgery, while he retained all of his old memories, he could no longer make new ones. H. M. could not retain new information for more than about 30 seconds. What part of his limbic system was damaged?
A. hypothalamus
B. thalamus
C. hippocampus
D. cortex

p. 80
Limbic System:
  Old Brain
Level: Easy
Type: Factual
Ans: B

169. The hippocampus is involved with:
A. receiving sensory information
B. putting memories into permanent storage
C. regulating sexual behavior
D. controlling the secretion of hormones

p. 80
Limbic System:
  Old Brain
Level: Moderate
Type: Conceptual
Ans: A

170. What part of the brain could be compared to a switchboard receiving calls from all over the country and then directing the paths of these incoming calls?
A.  thalamus
B.  hypothalamus
C.  occipital lobe
D.  cerebellum

p. 80
Limbic System:
  Old Brain
Level: Easy
Type: Factual
Ans: A

171. Which of the following is involved in the initial processing of sensory information on its way to areas of the cortex?
A.  thalamus
B.  hypothalamus
C.  amygdala
D.  hippocampus

p. 80
Limbic System:
  Old Brain
Level: Moderate
Type: Applied
Ans: B

172. LuAnn has problems with her vision, but her retina, optic nerve, and visual cortex are normal. What part of the brain is <u>most</u> likely causing her visual problems?
A   corpus callosum
B.  thalamus
C.  amygdala
D.  hippocampus

p. 80
Limbic System:
  Old Brain
Level: Easy
Type: Factual
Ans: A

173. What part of the brain regulates the limbic system's powerful urges?
A.  frontal lobe
B.  hippocampus
C.  amygdala
D.  hypothalamus

p. 81
Limbic System:
  Old Brain
Level: Easy
Type: Applied
Ans: D

174. You come to class not having read the assignment. Your professor arrives, orders everyone to put away books and notes, and hands out a pop quiz. Your heart starts pounding and you begin to sweat because of which nervous system division?
A.  central
B.  somatic
C.  parasympathetic
D.  sympathetic

p. 81
Limbic System:
  Old Brain
Level: Easy
Type: Factual
Ans: D

175. The activation of the sympathetic division would prepare people for:
A.  digestion of food
B.  relaxation
C.  energy conservation
D.  fight-flight response

p. 81
Limbic System:
  Old Brain
Level: Easy
Type: Applied
Ans: C

176.   A college freshman is about to give her first speech in class. As she walks to the podium, she feels her heart pounding much faster and harder than normal. After the speech, she notices that her heart begins to return to a normal pace because:
A.     her peers congratulate her on a job well done
B.     walking settles her heart
C.     the parasympathetic division calms her heart
D.     the heart cannot maintain a fast, hard rate for very long

p. 81
Limbic System:
  Old Brain
Level: Easy
Type: Factual
Ans: B

177.   What effect of the parasympathetic nervous systems presented below is *incorrect*?
A.     pupils constriction
B.     dry mouth
C.     decreased heart rate
D.     stimulated digestion

p. 81
Limbic System:
  Old Brain
Level: Easy
Type: Conceptual
Ans: C

178.   Sympathetic is to arouse as parasympathetic is to _____.
A.     fight
B.     flight
C.     calm
D.     homeostasis

p. 81
Limbic System:
  Old Brain
Level: Easy
Type: Factual
Ans: D

179.   The tendency for the autonomic nervous system to maintain the body's internal environment in a balanced state of optimum functioning is called:
A      synaptic regulation
B.     reflexive functioning
C.     stereotaxis
D.     homeostasis

p. 81
Limbic System:
  Old Brain
Level: Easy
Type: Applied
Ans: A

180.   When Mark is cold, he shivers; when Mark is hot, he sweats. By regulating body temperature, these behaviors help Mark to maintain:
A.     homeostasis
B.     reflexive functioning
C.     stereotaxis
D.     myelination

p. 81
Limbic System:
  Old Brain
Level: Easy
Type: Applied
Ans: A
*PS/SG 4-19*

181.   If you saw a snake crawling out from under your car, what would happen next is an example of the:
A      fight-flight response
B.     homeostatic reaction
C.     parasympathetic push
D.     arouse-or-die response

p. 82
Endocrine System
Level: Easy
Type: Factual
Ans: A

182.   Hormones are secreted from glands located throughout the body. The _____ is made up of these glands.
A.     endocrine system
B.     endorphin system
C.     limbic system
D.     pituitary system

p. 82
Endocrine System
Level: Easy
Type: Factual
Ans: A
*PS/SG 4-20*

183. The endocrine system and the nervous system are basically:
A. similar — they both send information throughout the body
B. similar — they are both chemical systems
C. different — the nervous system affects the brain and the endocrine system affects the body
D. different — the nervous system causes positive functioning and the endocrine system causes dysfunctions

p. 82
Endocrine System
Level: Easy
Type: Factual
Ans: B

184. _____ are secreted by the glands that make up the endocrine system.
A. Gonads
B. Hormones
C. Rhodopsins
D. Pancreas

p. 82
Endocrine System
Level: Easy
Type: Factual
Ans: C

185. The structure known as the "control center" of the endocrine system is the:
A. thyroid
B. adrenal
C. hypothalamus
D. parathyroid

p. 82
Endocrine System
Level: Easy
Type: Factual
Ans: D

186. Joan has a medical problem called diabetes that is caused by a lack of insulin. What gland in the endocrine system is responsible for Joan's condition?
A. gonads
B. endorphin
C. thyroid
D. pancreas

p. 82
Endocrine System
Level: Easy
Type: Factual
Ans: D

187. Which of the following regulates growth through secretion of growth hormone?
A. pancreas
B. gonads
C. thyroid
D. anterior pituitary

p. 82
Endocrine System
Level: Moderate
Type: Applied
Ans: A

188. "Wow, look at that guy," David remarks looking at a picture of a man standing over 8 feet tall. "This guy must have had a dysfunctional _____ that caused too much growth hormone to be secreted."
A. anterior pituitary
B. posterior pituitary
C. lateral pituitary
D. thyroid

| p. 82 | 189. | As a physician specializing in the endocrine system, you see many patients with various types of problems. One patient has dysfunctional adrenal glands. You have advised her to take a course on stress management. Why? |
|---|---|---|

p. 82
Endocrine System
Level: Easy
Type: Applied
Ans: A

A. her endocrine system cannot produce cortical hormones which would lead to problems in coping with stress
B. many physical problems can be treated by stress management
C. because the adrenal glands control growth and stress management may help her
D. stress reduces the amount of calcium in the body

p. 82
Endocrine System
Level: Easy
Type: Factual
Ans: B

190. Hormones which regulate sexual development and the growth of the sex organs are produced by the:
A. pancreas
B. gonads
C. adrenal glands
D. posterior pituitary

p. 84
Research Focus:
 Sexual Differences
in the Brain?
Level: Easy
Type: Factual
Ans: A

191. With regard to performance on rotating figure problems:
A. males are faster and more accurate than females
B. males are slower but more accurate than females
C. males are more likely to answer more problems, but also make more errors than females
D. there appears to be no consistent significant difference between males and females

p. 84
Research Focus:
 Sexual Differences
in the Brain?
Level: Easy
Type: Factual
Ans: B

192. Women tend to be better than men at tasks that measure:
A. spatial ability
B. perceptual speed
C. logic
D. rotating mental objects

p. 84
Research Focus:
 Sexual Differences
in the Brain?
Level: Easy
Type: Factual
Ans: B

193. Women tend to be better than men at tasks that require:
A. spatial ability
B. verbal fluency
C. analytic ability
D. rotating mental objects

p. 84
Research Focus:
 Sexual Differences
in the Brain?
Level: Easy
Type: Factual
Ans: C

194. If you ask 10 women and 10 men to list as many words as they can that begin with the letter "T", which sex will generally list the most words?
A. men - but only if given extra incentive
B. women - but only if given practice before hand
C. women
D. men

p. 84
Research Focus:
 Sexual Differences
 in the Brain?
Level: Easy
Type: Factual
Ans: B

195.  Research has found that the brains of men, when solving rotating figure problems, were especially active in the:
A.  right parietal-temporal area
B.  right frontal area
C.  left frontal area
D.  left occipital area

p. 84
Research Focus:
 Sexual Differences
 in the Brain?
Level: Easy
Type: Factual
Ans: A

196.  PET scans reveal that when women are solving rotating figure problems, their _____ shows maximum activity.
A.  right parietal-temporal area
B.  right frontal area
C.  left frontal area
D.  left occipital area

p. 84
Research Focus:
 Sexual Differences
 in the Brain?
Level: Moderate
Type: Factual
Ans: C

197.  As men are doing a virtual reality maze:
A.  only their left hippocampus is active
B.  only their right hippocampus is active
C.  both sides of their hippocampus are active
D.  both sides of their pons is active

p. 84
Research Focus:
 Sexual Differences
 in the Brain?
Level: Moderate
Type: Factual
Ans: B

198.  As Cynthia is participating in a study using a virtual reality maze, the PET scan indicates:
A.  only her left hippocampus is active
B.  only her right hippocampus is active
C.  both sides of her hippocampus are active
D.  both sides of her pons are active

p. 84
Research Focus:
 Sexual Differences
 in the Brain?
Level: Moderate
Type: Factual
Ans: A

199.  Recent research indicates that the brains of women process _____ differently than the brains of men.
A.  intense emotional experiences
B.  pain
C.  language
D.  boredom

p. 84
Research Focus:
 Sexual Differences
 in the Brain?
Level: Easy
Type: Factual
Ans: A
*PS/SG 4-21*

200.  Me Tarzan, you Jane.  Therefore, according to research on sex differences in the brain:
A.  me spatial, you verbal
B.  me verbal, you spatial
C.  me emotional, you logical
D.  me lusty, you cold

p. 85
Cultural Diversity:
  Brain Size and
  Racial Myths
Level: Moderate
Type: Conceptual
Ans: B
*PS/SG 4-22*

201.  The sad history of research on the relationship between intelligence and skull and brain size shows that:
A.  when a Nobel Prize is involved, some scientists will fudge their data
B.  science can be influenced by the prejudices of the times
C.  science is not always the best way to answer a question about human behavior
D.  sloppy measurement can undercut a sound hypothesis

p. 85
Cultural Diversity:
  Brain Size and
  Racial Myths
Level: Moderate
Type: Factual
Ans: C

202.  The flaw in Samuel George Morton's research on skull size was:
A.  failing to adequately identify the independent variable
B.  he used different size pellets to measure skull size
C.  he selected skulls that matched his own bias
D.  only the skulls of Asians and Native Americans were used

p. 85
Cultural Diversity:
  Brain Size and
  Racial Myths
Level: Easy
Type: Factual
Ans: C

203.  The correlation between the amount of neurons in the frontal lobe and intelligence is found to be:
A.  -.99
B.  .10
C.  .45
D.  .76

p. 85
Cultural Diversity:
  Brain Size and
  Racial Myths
Level: Moderate
Type: Factual
Ans: A

204.  Comparing brain size of men and women reveals that:
A.  the brains of women have more densely packed neurons
B.  men are more intelligent than women
C.  the brains of men are actually smaller than the brains of women
D.  the brains of men are larger and have more densely packed neurons

p. 86
Application:
  Split Brain
Level: Moderate
Type: Conceptual
Ans: B

205.  Your psychology instructor enjoys using analogies, similes and metaphors in the class. Today, she is talking about the corpus callosum. As she is lecturing on the corpus callosum, you're thinking of an appropriate metaphor. Which of the following is the most appropriate simile?
A.  "The corpus callosum is like a house in a neighborhood."
B.  "The corpus callosum is like a bridge that connects several islands."
C.  "The corpus callosum is like an interpreter of a foreign language."
D.  "The corpus callosum is like a general ordering his troops."

p. 86
Application:
  Split Brain
Level: Moderate
Type: Factual
Ans: A
*PS/SG 4-23*

206.  Results of the split brain operation demonstrate that:
A.  there is intense communication between the two hemispheres of the brain
B.  we would be better off with only the analytic left brain
C.  we miss a lot by neglecting the holistic right brain
D.  the body piercing movement has gotten *way* out of hand

p. 86
Application:
  Split Brain
Level: Moderate
Type: Conceptual
Ans: C

207.   Your class is watching a video of a split-brain operation. You see the surgeon take a scalpel and sever a structure to disconnect the two hemispheres. Your friend asks you what the structure was that was being cut and you say the:

A.   cerebellum
B.   hypothalamus
C.   corpus callosum
D.   pituitary gland

p. 86
Application:
  Split Brain
Level: Moderate
Type: Conceptual
Ans: A

208.   Why would a split brain patient say that he saw the word "ART" when "HE•ART" is flashed on the screen in front of him?

A.   "ART" goes to the left hemisphere which has the ability to speak.
B.   "ART" goes to the right hemisphere which has the ability to speak.
C.   "ART" goes to the corpus callosum which has the ability to speak.
D.   "ART" goes to the thalamus which has the ability to speak.

p. 87
Application:
  Split Brain
Level: Easy
Type: Factual
Ans: B

209.   The right hemisphere of the brain is better at _____ tasks, whereas the left hemisphere is better at _____ tasks.

A.   mathematical; spatial
B.   nonverbal; verbal
C.   analytic; holistic
D.   visual; auditory

p. 87
Application:
  Split Brain
Level: Easy
Type: Conceptual
Ans: C

210.   A word is flashed before a normal subject so that it is presented to his *left* visual field. Before the subject can say the word, the:

A.   subject must view the word in the right visual field
B.   impulses must be localized in the right hemisphere
C.   impulses must cross hemispheres
D.   impulses must stay in the same hemisphere

p. 87
Application:
  Split Brain
Level: Easy
Type: Factual
Ans: C

211.   Which part of the brain would "see" a face by analyzing piece-by-piece its many separate parts (e.g., nose, eye, lips, cheek, etc.)?

A.   the pons
B.   the corpus callosum
C.   the left hemisphere
D.   the right hemisphere

p. 87
Application:
  Split Brain
Level: Easy
Type: Factual
Ans: A

212.   You are writing a book on understanding oneself. One of the chapters is on the biological basis of understanding self. What hemisphere will you correctly identify as contributing to the conscious understanding of oneself?

A.   left hemisphere
B.   right hemisphere
C.   right hemisphere for right handed individuals
D.   both left and right hemisphere are responsible for understanding

p. 87
Application:
  Split Brain
Level: Easy
Type: Factual
Ans: D

213. When you see a picture of yourself, you recognize your own face. Which part of the brain is responsible for that ability?
A.  hypothalamus
B.  midbrain
C.  the right hemisphere
D.  the left hemisphere

p. 87
Application:
  Split Brain
Level: Moderate
Type: Applied
Ans: B

214. Harry is attending his 10-Year High School Reunion. As he visits with his classmates, he has some trouble putting together faces with names. He sees someone he thinks he knows by the shape of the nose and eyes. Which part of the brain is probably allowing Harry to analyze the features of the many faces he sees?
A.  left hemisphere
B.  right hemisphere
C.  thalamus
D.  somatosensory cortex

p. 87
Application:
  Split Brain
Level: Moderate
Type: Applied
Ans: D

215. When you are reading a novel, what hemisphere are you using?
A.  impossible to know
B.  right hemisphere
C.  left hemisphere
D.  both

p. 87
Application:
  Split Brain
Level: Easy
Type: Factual
Ans: B
*PS/SG 4-25*

216. Are you left-brained or right-brained? The best answer is that you are probably:
A.  left-brained, since you are a college student
B.  constantly using both hemispheres
C.  right-brained if you are female and left-brained if you are male
D.  left-brained, since most people are

p. 87
Application:
  Split Brain
Level: Easy
Type: Factual
Ans: A

217. Gazzaniga believes that when we do some type of activity, the brain uses:
A.  different mental programs simultaneously
B.  a master and several minor mental programs
C.  different mental programs sequentially
D.  one or two mental programs

True/False

| F |  | 1. | DNA is made up of chromosomes. |
| T | www | 2. | There are 23 pairs of chromosomes in humans. |
| F |  | 3. | The species *Australopithecus afarensis* possessed the ability to make tools. |
| F |  | 4. | MRI scans require an injection of a radioactive material into the patient's blood. |
| F |  | 5. | When saying out loud a word we see, most of the neural activity occurs in the back area of the brain. |
| F | www | 6. | The autonomic nervous system is part of the central nervous system. |
| F |  | 7. | Your sympathetic division returns the body to a calmer state. |
| F |  | 8. | The cerebellum controls vital reflexes. |
| T | www | 9. | The forebrain is responsible for planning and making decisions. |
| T |  | 10. | The occipital lobe is involved in processing visual information. |

| F | www | 11. | Your cortex is a thick layer of cells. |
|---|---|---|---|
| F | | 12. | A frontal lobotomy involves cutting the temporal lobe. |
| T | | 13. | The motor cortex is located in the frontal lobe. |
| F | www | 14. | The homunculus is part of the occipital lobe. |
| T | | 15. | The somatosensory cortex processes information about touch. |
| T | | 16. | In Broca's aphasia, the person has difficulty speaking in a fluent way. |
| F | www | 17. | Turning visual sensations into complete meaningful perception is a function of the primary visual cortex. |
| F | | 18. | The hippocampus relays sensory information to areas of the cortex. |
| T | | 19. | An area of the brain that plays a major role in eating, drinking, and sexual responses is the hypothalamus. |
| T | www | 20. | A damaged amygdala would affect a person's ability to recognize facial expressions. |
| T | | 21. | Homeostasis keeps our sympathetic and parasympathetic divisions in balance. |
| F | | 22. | The control center of the endocrine system is the thyroid. |
| F | www | 23. | The brains of women are more effectively wired than the brains of men for solving rotating figures problems. |
| T | www | 24. | Research indicates that the more neurons in the frontal lobe, the higher the IQ score. |
| F | www | 25. | The left hemisphere specializes in processing information by combining parts into a meaningful whole. |

Short-Answer Essay Questions

1. What is the relationship between chromosomes, DNA, and genes?
2. Based upon the theory of evolution, what accounts for the tripling of the human brain?
3. Describe the role that MRI, fMRI, and PET scans have played in helping us to understand the human brain. (*www*)
4. Using the research cited in Module Four, what ability accounts for your ability to identify thousands of objects?
5. Describe the major divisions and their subdivisions of the nervous system. (*www*)
6. What are the four lobes of the brain? Briefly describe the functions they regulate.
7. What does the case of Phineas Gage teach us about the brain? (*www*)
8. Discuss the impact that damage to the frontal lobe might have on an individual.
9. Describe five brain specific brain areas that are especially active as you answer this essay question. (*www*)
10. Describe how split brain patients are tested. What do the results indicate about how the brain is organized? (*www*)

# Module 5 - Sensation

p. 93
Introduction
Level: Moderate
Type: Conceptual
Ans: C

1. The example of Katie, the individual who can experience visual sensations but is blind, serves to point out that:
A. scientific advancements are outpacing our values and ethics
B. no one is ever too young to be tested for glaucoma
C. brain stimulation independent of eye stimulation causes a visual experience
D. life without sight is difficult

p. 93
Introduction
Level: Moderate
Type: Conceptual
Ans: C
*PS/SG 5-1*

2. Rod Plotnik says the experience of Katie, a blind woman who had tiny gold wires implanted into the back of her brain, raises the question:
A. are some cases of blindness actually hysterical?
B. can blind persons regain their sight through intense practice?
C. do you see with your eyes or with your brain?
D. can science go too far in tampering with human capabilities?

p. 93
Introduction
Level: Easy
Type: Factual
Ans: B

3. Which is not a characteristic of all senses?
A. transduction
B. translucence
C. adaptation
D. perception

p. 93
Introduction
Level: Moderate
Type: Factual
Ans: A

4. As a college student, could you be blind and yet have perfectly healthy eyes?
A. yes, because the areas of the brain that interpret visual information may be damaged
B. no, since transduction takes place in higher brain areas
C. yes, if the sensory receptor neurons are damaged
D. no, unless the photoreceptors are damaged

p. 93
Introduction
Level: Easy
Type: Factual
Ans: B

5. When the ear registers sound waves, the sound waves are transformed into electrical signals that become neural impulses. This process is called:
A. perception
B. transduction
C. adaptation
D. a sensory experience

p. 93
Introduction
Level: Easy
Type: Conceptual
Ans: C

6. Which word best describes transduction?
A. stabilizes
B. creates
C. changes
D. reduces

p. 93
Introduction
Level: Easy
Type: Factual
Ans: A

7. The eye changing light waves into impulses and the ear changing sound waves into impulses are examples of:
A. transduction
B. translucence
C. adaptation
D. a sensory experience

p. 93
Introduction
Level: Easy
Type: Factual
Ans: C
*www*

8.  The process of _____ refers to the sense organ changing physical energy into electrical signals that become neural impulses.
    A. adaptation
    B. perception
    C. transduction
    D. accommodation

p. 93
Introduction
Level: Easy
Type: Factual
Ans: D
*www*

9.  If a sense organ is continuously stimulated, the sense organ will decrease responding through the process of:
    A. transduction
    B. perception
    C. agnosia
    D. adaptation

p. 93
Introduction
Level: Moderate
Type: Applied
Ans: C

10. Alyssa can't smell the dirty diapers on the baby, but everyone else can. Why?
    A. Alyssa has experienced transduction.
    B. Alyssa is dichromatic
    C. Alyssa has experienced adaptation.
    D. Alyssa has damaged Pacinian corpuscles

p. 93
Introduction
Level: Easy
Type: Factual
Ans: B
*PS/SG 5-3*

11. A decline in responding with prolonged or continuous stimulation is called:
    A. transduction
    B. adaptation
    C. sensing
    D. experiencing

p. 93
Introduction
Level: Easy
Type: Conceptual
Ans: B

12. If you do <u>not</u> feel the chair you are now sitting in, it is because:
    A. constant rubbing numbs nerve endings
    B. when there is constant stimulation, our senses experience a decrease in responding
    C. sitting tends to constrict blood flow and partially numbs our skin senses
    D. the temperature on the surface of the skin goes up and makes us less sensitive

p. 93
Introduction
Level: Easy
Type: Conceptual
Ans: D

13. Denise is unaware of the feel of the chair she sits in while playing with her computer. Denise's lack of sensitivity is the result of:
    A. hypersensitivity
    B. changing stimuli
    C. lack of stimulation
    D. adaptation

<table>
<tr><td>

p. 93
Introduction
Level: Moderate
Type: Conceptual
Ans: A

</td><td>

14. Miranda and Joy are about to swim in a cool lake. Miranda jumps in and shortly thereafter experiences adaptation to the cool water. What is she most likely to say?
A. "It's nice once you get used to it."
B. "It feels as cold now as when I first jumped in."
C. "Amazing! This doesn't even feel like cool water."
D. "The water seems to have gotten colder."

</td></tr>
<tr><td>

p. 93
Introduction
Level: Moderate
Type: Factual
Ans: D

</td><td>

15. The human senses are most sensitive to which kind of stimuli?
A. constant
B. low intensity
C. mild
D. high intensity

</td></tr>
<tr><td>

p. 93
Introduction
Level: Moderate
Type: Factual
Ans: A

</td><td>

16. Sensations occur:
A. when a stimulus activates a receptor causing an impulse that is processed by the brain
B. right after we experience illusions
C. after the sense organs engage in perception
D. once you react to the sensory input

</td></tr>
<tr><td>

p. 93
Introduction
Level: Moderate
Type: Factual
Ans: C

</td><td>

17. Perception occurs:
A. after the rods and cones become activated
B. when a stimulus activates a receptor causing an impulse that is processed by the brain
C. after meaningful sensory experiences are created
D. before transduction

</td></tr>
<tr><td>

p. 93
Introduction
Level: Moderate
Type: Conceptual
Ans: C

</td><td>

18. Sensations are to perception as _____ is to _____.
A. combining; separating
B. adaptation; transduction
C. meaningless; meaningful
D. illusion; constancy

</td></tr>
<tr><td>

p. 94
Eye: Vision
Level: Easy
Type: Factual
Ans: D

</td><td>

19. Each sense organ is designed to receive a kind of _____.
A. perception
B. chemical
C. visible spectrum
D. physical energy

</td></tr>
<tr><td>

p. 94
Eye: Vision
Level: Easy
Type: Factual
Ans: B

</td><td>

20. What do radio waves, X-rays, TV waves, and light waves all have in common? They are all:
A. located at the shorter end of the electromagnetic energy spectrum
B. forms of electromagnetic energy
C. examples of ultra-violet waves
D. in the invisible spectrum

</td></tr>
<tr><td>

p. 94
Eye: Vision
Level: Easy
Type: Factual
Ans: D

</td><td>

21. The reason that we can "see" a rainbow is because the light waves are:
A. at the shorter end of the electromagnetic energy spectrum
B. at the longer end of the electromagnetic energy spectrum
C. ultra-violet waves
D. in our visible spectrum

</td></tr>
</table>

p. 94
Eye: Vision
Level: Moderate
Type: Factual
Ans: A

22. The portion of the electromagnetic spectrum that receptors in the eye are sensitive to is referred to as the _____ spectrum.
    A. visible
    B. light
    C. upper
    D. lower

p. 94
Eye: Vision
Level: Difficult
Type: Factual
Ans: A

23. The electromagnetic energy in the visible spectrum can stimulate receptors in our eyes because the waves of the visible spectrum are:
    A. near the middle range
    B. in the short range
    C. in the long range
    D. in the very long range

p. 94
Eye: Vision
Level: Easy
Type: Factual
Ans: C
www

24. As an image of an object goes through the front structures of the eye, the object's image:
    A. is perceived by the individual
    B. is converted into a longer electromagnetic wavelength
    C. is turned upside down
    D. undergoes transduction

p. 94
Eye: Vision
Level: Easy
Type: Factual
Ans: B

25. In order for you to see, your eye must change _____ beams of light waves into _____ beams of light waves.
    A. narrow; broad
    B. broad; narrow
    C. invisible; visible
    D. narrow; visible

p. 95
Eye: Vision
Level: Easy
Type: Factual
Ans: C

26. The structure of the eye that first helps focus light waves into a narrower beam is the:
    A. fovea
    B. retina
    C. cornea
    D. lens

p. 95
Eye: Vision
Level: Easy
Type: Factual
Ans: D
PS/SG 5-5

27. The function of the cornea is to:
    A. add color to light waves entering the eye
    B. screen out irrelevant light waves
    C. prevent convergence from occurring too soon
    D. bend and focus light waves into a narrower beam of light

p. 95
Eye: Vision
Level: Moderate
Type: Factual
Ans: B

28. How does the lens of the eye focus light on to the retina?
    A. The lens goes through a process called transduction.
    B. The lens is attached to muscles that change the curve of the lens.
    C. The lens is attached to ganglion cells that send competing nerve impulses to the brain.
    D. The lens goes through a process of adaptation.

p. 95
Eye: Vision
Level: Moderate
Type: Factual
Ans: C

29. The _____ of the eye can adjust its shape and focus light on the back surface of the eye called the _____.
A. cornea; lens
B. iris; fovea
C. lens; retina
E. pupil; ocular membrane

p. 95
Eye: Vision
Level: Easy
Type: Factual
Ans: A
*www*

30. Deb has blue eyes; Erv's eyes are brown. The difference in eye color is the result of different pigments in the:
A. iris
B. pupil
C. cornea
D. lens

p. 95
Eye: Vision
Level: Easy
Type: Factual
Ans: B

31. Vi shines a flashlight into Mike's eye. The bright light will cause Mike's iris to:
A. relax and pupil to enlarge
B. constrict and pupil to become smaller
C. relax and pupil to become smaller
D. constrict and pupil to enlarge

p. 95
Eye: Vision
Level: Easy
Type: Factual
Ans: C

32. With far away objects, the surface of the lens becomes:
A. less transparent
B. more curved
C. less curved
D. more transparent

p. 95
Eye: Vision
Level: Moderate
Type: Factual
Ans: B

33. If the eyeball is too long, light from distant objects focuses at a point slightly in front of the retina, resulting in:
A. farsightedness
B. nearsightedness
C. cataracts
D. night blindness

p. 95
Eye: Vision
Level: Easy
Type: Factual
Ans: A
*PS/SG 5-6*

34. If you see close objects clearly but distant objects appear blurry, you are:
A. nearsighted
B. farsighted
C. normal
D. abnormal

p. 95
Eye: Vision
Level: Easy
Type: Factual
Ans: B

35. If you see distant objects clearly but close objects appear blurry, you are:
A. nearsighted
B. farsighted
C. normal
D. abnormal

p. 95
Eye: Vision
Level: Moderate
Type: Factual
Ans: A

36. If the eyeball is too short, light from distant objects focuses at a point slightly in back of the retina, resulting in:
A. farsightedness
B. nearsightedness
C. cataracts
D. night blindness

p. 95
Eye: Vision
Level: Moderate
Type: Applied
Ans: C

37. Uncle Randy finds that he is having trouble reading the newspaper, even when he holds it at arm's length. In fact, he has trouble focusing on close objects. It is probable that light is being focused:
A. slightly in front of the retina
B. beside the fovea
C. slightly behind the retina
D. slightly in front of the fovea

p. 95
Eye: Vision
Level: Moderate
Type: Factual
Ans: B

38. People wear glasses to correct their vision. Vision is corrected with glasses because glasses:
A. reduce the size of the pupil
B. bend and focus the light directly on the retina
C. open the iris to its maximum size
D. reduce the visual aperture

p. 95
Eye: Vision
Level: Easy
Type: Factual
Ans: A

39. The path that the light takes through your eye is:
A. cornea; pupil; lens; retina
B. pupil; lens; retina
C. lens; cornea; pupil; retina
D. lens, fovea; cornea; retina

p. 95
Eye: Vision
Level: Easy
Type: Factual
Ans: B

40. The surgical technique called LASIK is used to treat:
A. Meniere's disease
B. nearsightedness
C. conduction deafness
D. neural deafness

p. 96
Eye: Vision
Level: Easy
Type: Factual
Ans: D
www

41. A light-sensitive cell in the retina is called:
A. iris
B. cornea
C. lens
D. photoreceptor

p. 96
Eye: Vision
Level: Easy
Type: Factual
Ans: B

42. The kinds of photoreceptors in the retina are:
A. ganglion cells and end bulbs
B. rods and cones
C. cochlea and cones
D. meniere's bodies and glial cells

p. 96
Eye: Vision
Level: Easy
Type: Factual
Ans: C

43. How many layers of cells are found in the retina?
A. one
B. two
C. three
D. four

p. 96
Eye: Vision
Level: Easy
Type: Factual
Ans: C
*www*

44. Transduction in the visual system takes place in the:
A. cornea
B. lens
C. retina
D. iris

p. 96
Eye: Vision
Level: Easy
Type: Factual
Ans: B
*PS/SG 5-7*

45. The work of the retina is to:
A. add sharp focus to what you are seeing
B. transform light waves into electrical signals
C. turn the inverted image we see right side up
D. change impulses into light waves we can see

p. 96
Eye: Vision
Level: Easy
Type: Factual
Ans: C

46. The very back layer of the retina contains cells that can absorb light waves. These cells are called:
A. fovea
B. optic nerves
C. photoreceptors
D. blind spots

p. 96
Eye: Vision
Level: Easy
Type: Factual
Ans: B

47. Rods are primarily located in the:
A. fovea
B. periphery of the retina
C. iris in farsighted individuals
D. optic nerve

p. 96
Eye: Vision
Level: Easy
Type: Factual
Ans: C

48. A heavy concentration of cones can be found in:
A. the periphery of the retina
B. the optic nerve
C. the fovea
D. primary visual cortex

p. 96
Eye: Vision
Level: Easy
Type: Factual
Ans: B

49. The point of exit for impulses on their way from the eye to the brain is called the:
A. fovea
B. blind spot
C. retina
D. optic chiasm

p. 96
Eye: Vision
Level: Easy
Type: Conceptual
Ans: A

50. What is the best description of the eye based upon your reading of Module Five?
A. The eye is a mechanism for transduction.
B. The eye "sees" the world.
C. The eye allows us to see since it operates like a camera.
D. The eye is designed to change impulses into light waves.

p. 96
Eye: Vision
Level: Easy
Type: Factual
Ans: A

51. Most people are not aware of their blind spot because the area that is lost is filled in by the:
A. eyes constantly moving back and forth
B. association areas in the brain which give meaning to sensations
C. optic nerve
D. optic chiasm

p. 96
Eye: Vision
Level: Easy
Type: Factual
Ans: A

52.     The structures responsible for our ability to see color are the:
A.      cones
B.      rods
C.      rhodopsins
D.      foveas

p. 96
Eye: Vision
Level: Easy
Type: Factual
Ans: A

53.     Cones contain:
A.      opsins
B.      chromopsins
C.      transopsins
D.      rhodopsin

p. 96
Eye: Vision
Level: Moderate
Type: Factual
Ans: C

54.     The _____ connect individually to neighboring cells.  This allows us to see _____.
A.      cones; in dim light
B.      rods; fine detail
C.      cones; fine detail
D.      rods; color

p. 96
Eye: Vision
Level: Moderate
Type: Factual
Ans: B

55.     Which of the following structures allows you to read these words and see other stimuli in fine detail?
A.      rods
B.      cones
C.      ganglion cells
D.      cochlea

p. 96
Eye: Vision
Level: Easy
Type: Factual
Ans: D
PS/SG 5-8

56.     Which one of the following accurately describes the work of rods or cones in the retina?
A.      rods – allow us to see bright colors
B.      cones – allow us to see in dim light
C.      rods – allow us to see large objects
D.      cones – allow us to see fine details

p. 96
Eye: Vision
Level: Easy
Type: Factual
Ans: D

57.     Rods contain:
A.      opsins
B.      chromopsins
C.      transopsins
D.      rhodopsin

p. 96
Eye: Vision
Level: Easy
Type: Factual
Ans: A

58.     Rods are used to see:
A.      shades of gray and general outlines
B.      shades of color and fine detail
C.      fine detail and primary colors
D.      colors and general outlines

p. 96
Eye: Vision
Level: Difficult
Type: Applied
Ans: C

59. Your astronomy professor must have taken a psychology class. He says to best look at a dim star, don't look directly at it, but to the side. Why is this good advice?

A. Rods are located in the fovea of the retina and respond best in dim light, whereas cones best respond to bright light and are located in the periphery.

B. Your cornea has special cells that function when looking at dim light from the side.

C. Rods are located in the periphery of the retina and respond best in dim light, whereas cones best respond to bright light and are located in the fovea.

D. Cones are located in the periphery of the retina and respond best in dim light, whereas rods best respond to bright light and are located in the fovea.

p. 96
Eye: Vision
Level: Easy
Type: Applied
Ans: D

60. When you look at objects in dim light, the objects lack color and clarity because:

A. cones are unable to see colors
B. of the process of light adaptation
C. the optic nerve does not register wavelengths of light when it is dark
D. rods do not distinguish colors or fine details

p. 96
Eye: Vision
Level: Moderate
Type: Factual
Ans: B

61. Rods are activated by _____, whereas cones are activated by _____.

A. the fovea; the lens
B. small amounts of light; bright light
C. opsin; rhodopsin
D. light adaptation; dark adaptation

p. 96
Eye: Vision
Level: Easy
Type: Factual
Ans: D
*www*

62. If you look at a dim light, which of the following will show strong activation?

A. the fovea
B. cones
C. opsin
D. rods

p. 97
Eye: Vision
Level: Easy
Type: Factual
Ans: C
*www*

63. Information is transmitted from the eye to the brain through the:

A. fovea
B. cornea
C. optic nerve
D. retina

p. 97
Eye: Vision
Level: Easy
Type: Factual
Ans: A

64. Which brain structure performs the initial processing of visual stimuli?

A. thalamus
B. cornea
C. fovea
D. visual association areas

p. 97
Eye: Vision
Level: Easy
Type: Factual
Ans: B

65. The primary visual cortex:

A. creates perceptions out of visual sensations
B. transforms nerve impulses into simple sensations
C. focuses light waves on the retina
D. transforms sensory information into a nerve impulse

p. 97
Eye: Vision
Level: Moderate
Type: Factual
Ans: B

66. The _____ sends simple visual sensations to the _____ which add(s) meaning to the sensations.
A. retina; lens
B. primary visual cortex; association areas
C. optic nerve; optic chiasm
D. rods; cones

p. 97
Eye: Vision
Level: Moderate
Type: Factual
Ans: C

67. Hubel and Wiesel have shown that cells located in the brain's primary visual cortex respond to _____ stimuli.
A. very general
B. intense
C. very specific
D. weak

p. 97
Eye: Vision
Level: Easy
Type: Applied
Ans: A

68. Todd is responding to dark vertical lines. Al is responding to pictures of people. What is Al using that Todd probably is *not*?
A. visual association areas
B. retina
C. optic chiasm
D. primary visual cortex

p. 97
Eye: Vision
Level: Moderate
Type: Applied
Ans: D

69. Sidney is shown a picture of a dog. He reports being able to see the picture but cannot identify it as a dog. Sidney has likely suffered damage to which part of his brain?
A. hypothalamus
B. thalamus
C. optic lobe
D. visual association areas

p. 97
Eye: Vision
Level: Moderate
Type: Applied
Ans: D

70. Janice comments on the texture of the brush strokes in a painting. She does not notice the complexity of the visual image. Janice is probably relying on information provided by her:
A. thalamus
B. cones
C. visual association areas
D. primary visual cortex

p. 97
Eye: Vision
Level: Moderate
Type: Conceptual
Ans: D

71. After a traffic accident, a patient was diagnosed as having damage to parts of the primary visual cortex of the brain. Such damage will:
A. usually affect one eye
B. always result in total blindness
C. result in an inability to recognize objects
D. result in the loss of sight in patches of the patient's visual field

p. 97
Eye: Vision
Level: Easy
Type: Factual
Ans: C

72. What is the function of association areas?
A. Association areas allow us to see color.
B. Association areas respond to certain kinds of visual stimuli.
C. Association areas add meaning to the sensation.
D. Association areas help to focus light waves on the retina.

p. 97
Eye: Vision
Level: Easy
Type: Applied
Ans: B

73. A car accident completely destroys Ann's primary visual cortex. The most likely effect of the accident is that Ann will:
A. experience double vision
B. be virtually blind
C. lose color but not black-and-white vision
D. be able to see close objects but not distant ones

p. 97
Eye: Vision
Level: Moderate
Type: Applied
Ans: B

74. As you walk on campus, you suddenly recognize an old friend who is heading towards you. What point in the visual pathway is responsible for the creation of this meaningful image of an old friend?
A. rhodopsin
B. visual association areas
C. primary visual cortex
D. cornea

p. 97
Eye: Vision
Level: Easy
Type: Factual
Ans: C

75. A difficulty in assembling simple visual sensations into more complex, meaningful images is called:
A. sensory deficit
B. perceptual aphasia
C. visual agnosia
D. night blindness

p. 98
Eye: Vision
Level: Easy
Type: Factual
Ans: C

76. A fire engine may look red because:
A. it absorbs only those wavelengths corresponding to red
B. it reflects light of red temperature only
C. it absorbs all light waves except those of the wavelength corresponding to red
D. of our past experiences with fire engines

p. 98
Eye: Vision
Level: Easy
Type: Factual
Ans: A

77. White light contains:
A. all the light waves in the visible spectrum
B. long wavelength light
C. all light waves except those of the wavelength corresponding to blue
D. the primary color

p. 98
Eye: Vision
Level: Easy
Type: Factual
Ans: D

78. What effect does a prism have on light?
A. It creates white light.
B. It separates light into white light of three wavelengths.
C. It creates the colors of orange, red, yellow, and blue.
D. It separates light into waves that vary in length.

p. 98
Eye: Vision
Level: Easy
Type: Factual
Ans: C

79. The trichromatic theory explains how:
A. we experience an afterimage
B. the brain changes light waves into color
C. cones in the retina change light waves into colors
D. rods in the retina change light waves into colors

p. 98
Eye: Vision
Level: Easy
Type: Factual
Ans: B

80. A chemist named Thomas Young believed that the cones are most responsive to blue, green, and red light. This theory is called the:
A. opponent-process theory
B. trichromatic theory
C. theory of reasoned colors
D. adaptation theory

p. 98
Eye: Vision
Level: Easy
Type: Factual
Ans: B

81. According to the trichromatic theory, the primary colors are:
A. yellow, blue, white
B. blue, green, red
C. orange, green, gray
D. brown, black, white

p. 98
Eye: Vision
Level: Easy
Type: Factual
Ans: A
*www*

82. The _____ theory identifies three different types of cones in the retina.
A. trichromatic
B. trineural
C. trioptic
D. triconical

p. 98
Eye: Vision
Level: Moderate
Type: Factual
Ans: C

83. Each of the three opsins in the cones is most sensitive to one of the three:
A. types of agnosia
B. different categories of ganglion cells located at the front layer of the retina
C. wavelengths of light that make up the three primary colors
D. association areas

p. 98
Eye: Vision
Level: Moderate
Type: Factual
Ans: A

84. How we individually experience "red" depends on:
A. how many color genes a person has
B. how many rods a person has
C. the gender of the individual
D. the age of the individual

p. 98
Eye: Vision
Level: Easy
Type: Factual
Ans: C

85. A wrestler gets poked in the eye. His color vision will be most affected if the poke damages the:
A. lens
B. rods
C. cones
D. cornea

p. 99
Eye: Vision
Level: Moderate
Type: Factual
Ans: C

86. The trichromatic theory refers to what happens in the _____ whereas the opponent process theory refers to what happens in the _____.
A. hypothalamus; retina
B. occipital lobe; hypothalamus
C. retina; thalamus
D. occipital lobe; thalamus

p. 99
Eye: Vision
Level: Easy
Type: Factual
Ans: C

87. Whereas the trichromatic theory focuses on the functions of the cones, the opponent-process theory explains color vision by studying the:
A. rods
B. opsins
C. ganglion cells and thalamus
D. optic nerve and retina

| | | |
|---|---|---|
| p. 99 | 88. | A ganglion cell responds to the color blue when excited, and to the color yellow when inhibited. This idea is characteristic of the: |
| Eye: Vision | | |
| Level: Easy | A. | opponent-process theory |
| Type: Factual | B. | trichromatic theory |
| Ans: A | C. | theory of reasoned colors |
| | D. | adaptation theory |

| | | |
|---|---|---|
| p. 99 | 89. | Ed has trouble driving because he cannot tell the difference between green and red lights. Ed has: |
| Eye: Vision | | |
| Level: Easy | A. | night blindness |
| Type: Factual | B. | agnosia |
| Ans: C | C. | color blindness |
| | D. | opponent process disorder |

| | | |
|---|---|---|
| p. 99 | 90. | Monochromats are people who: |
| Eye: Vision | A. | have only cones |
| Level: Easy | B. | are totally color blind |
| Type: Factual | C. | see bright colors better than dark colors |
| Ans: B | D. | see only primary colors |
| *www* | | |

| | | |
|---|---|---|
| p. 99 | 91. | A psychology professor is describing the experience of color blindness. She says, "It's like living in a black and white movie." What type of color blindness is she describing? |
| Eye: Vision | | |
| Level: Moderate | | |
| Type: Applied | A. | primary color blindness |
| Ans: D | B. | unichromatic color blindness |
| | C. | trichromatic color blindness |
| | D. | monochromatic color blindness |

| | | |
|---|---|---|
| p. 99 | 92. | An individual who has only one kind of functioning cone will have: |
| Eye: Vision | A. | night blindness |
| Level: Easy | B. | dichromatic color blindness |
| Type: Factual | C. | total color blindness |
| Ans: C | D. | problems with light adaptation |

| | | |
|---|---|---|
| p. 99 | 93. | In first grade, Thomas is found to be a monochromat. Thomas was born without: |
| Eye: Vision | | |
| Level: Easy | A. | attached retinas |
| Type: Applied | B. | functioning cones |
| Ans: B | C. | complete cell development in one of the hemispheres of the occipital lobe |
| | D. | sight in one eye |

| | | |
|---|---|---|
| p. 99 | 94. | The most common problem for a dichromat is: |
| Eye: Vision | A. | an inability to focus both eyes on a near object at the same time |
| Level: Easy | B. | seeing printed stimuli as though they were inside out and backwards |
| Type: Factual | C. | an inability to recognize objects presented visually |
| Ans: D | D. | an inability to distinguish between red and green |

p. 99
Eye: Vision
Level: Easy
Type: Factual
Ans: B

95. People who are color blind:
A. discover their problem as soon as they learn to label colors verbally
B. may not discover their problem until later in life
C. usually have their problem discovered for them by their parents at an early age
D. usually have their problem discovered when they start school

p. 100
Ear: Audition
Level: Easy
Type: Factual
Ans: A

96. Subjective experience on the loudness of sound is determined by the
A. amplitude of the sound wave
B. frequency of the sound wave
C. shape of the sound wave
D. duration of the sound wave

p. 100
Ear: Audition
Level: Easy
Type: Factual
Ans: B

97. Our experience of loudness is determined by the sound's:
A. frequency
B. amplitude
C. pitch
D. speed

p. 100
Ear: Audition
Level: Easy
Type: Factual
Ans: D
*www*

98. As the decibels of a sound increase, the:
A. frequency decreases
B. frequency increases
C. amplitude decreases
D. amplitude increases

p. 100
Ear: Audition
Level: Easy
Type: Factual
Ans: C

99. Which of the following statements regarding sound waves is incorrect?
A. high amplitude is perceived by the brain as loud
B. low amplitude is perceived by the brain as soft
C. the subjective experience of a high note is called frequency
D. fast frequency is perceived as a high note

p. 100
Ear: Audition
Level: Easy
Type: Factual
Ans: B
*PS/SG 5-11*

100. How loud a sound seems is determined by the _____ of the sound waves.
A. frequency
B. amplitude
C. pitch
D. cycle

p. 100
Ear: Audition
Level: Easy
Type: Factual
Ans: B

101. Sound waves that have a slow frequency are perceived to be:
A. a high note
B. a low note
C. loud in volume
D. soft in volume

p. 100
Ear: Audition
Level: Easy
Type: Factual
Ans: D

102. The height of a sound wave is called _____ and the speed of the sound wave is called _____.
A. frequency; decibel
B. volume; frequency
C. altitude; amplitude
D. amplitude; frequency

p. 100
Ear: Audition
Level: Easy
Type: Factual
Ans: C

103. Pitch is determined by:
A. the amplitude of the sound wave
B. the number of molecules of air affected by the sound-producing object
C. the frequency of the sound wave
D. the time it takes for a sound to reach the ear

p. 100
Ear: Audition
Level: Moderate
Type: Applied
Ans: D

104. "That is awful!" says Franco as he listens to a duet singing a song at a concert. "Both singers don't know how to carry a note." Which of the characteristics of sound is most likely the cause of the awful singing?
A. loudness
B. decibel
C. amplitude
D. pitch

p. 100
Ear: Audition
Level: Moderate
Type: Applied
Ans: A

105. At the opera we can distinguish between the low sound of the male bass and the high sound of the female soprano because the voices differ in:
A. pitch
B. loudness
C. amplitude
D. decibels

p. 100
Ear: Audition
Level: Easy
Type: Applied
Ans: A

106. As Diana runs her fingers up the keyboard, the pitch gets higher and higher. As the pitch increases, the:
A. frequency gets faster
B. decibels get smaller
C. amplitude gets slower
D. cycles per second decreases

p. 100
Ear: Audition
Level: Moderate
Type: Conceptual
Ans: B

107. Amplitude is to loudness as _____ is to _____.
A. pitch; frequency
B. frequency; pitch
C. decibel; whisper
D. yell; decibel

p. 101
Ear: Audition
Level: Moderate
Type: Applied
Ans: D

108. Jake is a drummer in a rock-and-roll band and plays 45 rock concerts a year. He is likely to be exposed to sounds reaching as high as:
A. 50 decibels
B. 70 decibels
C. 90 decibels
D. 120 decibels

p. 101
Ear: Audition
Level: Moderate
Type: Factual
Ans: C

109. Too much amplitude in a stimulus can cause:
A. visual agnosia
B. vertigo
C. deafness
D. blindness

p. 102
Ear: Audition
Level: Easy
Type: Factual
Ans: B

110. The artist Vincent Van Gogh cut off his ear toward the end of his life. A psychologist would note more precisely that Van Gogh cut off his:
A. stirrup
B. outer ear
C. cochlea
D. basilar membrane

p. 102
Ear: Audition
Level: Easy
Type: Factual
Ans: C

111. Conrad is always sticking a pencil into his ear to dig out wax. His mother has repeatedly told him, "Get that pencil out of your ear." To be more precise Conrad's mother should say "Get that pencil out of your:
A. middle ear"
B. inner ear"
C. auditory canal"
D. tympanic membrane"

p. 102
Ear: Audition
Level: Easy
Type: Factual
Ans: A

112. The thin membrane that moves in and out in response to sound wave patterns and passes the vibrations to the middle ear is the:
A. tympanic membrane
B. auditory nerve
C. cochlea
D. anvil

p. 102
Ear: Audition
Level: Easy
Type: Factual
Ans: C

113. The vibrations are amplified in the:
A. outer ear
B. inner ear
C. middle ear
D. ear canal

p. 102
Ear: Audition
Level: Easy
Type: Factual
Ans: C
*www*

114. The primary function of the ossicles is to:
A. transform sound waves into impulses
B. gather sound waves and send them into the middle ear
C. pass sound waves from the outer ear to the oval window
D. assemble sensations into perceptions

p. 102
Ear: Audition
Level: Easy
Type: Factual
Ans: B

115. Vibrations of the eardrum set in motion three small bones in the middle ear. These are:
A. cochlea, basilar membrane, oval window
B. hammer, anvil, stirrup
C. stirrup, oval window, canal
D. anvil, cochlea, hammer

p. 102
Ear: Audition
Level: Moderate
Type: Conceptual
Ans: A

116. Which of the following cliches *best* describes the relationship between the hammer, anvil, and stirrup?
A. Passing the buck.
B. A stitch in time saves nine.
C. Out of sight, out of mind.
D. A penny saved is a penny earned.

p. 102
Ear: Audition
Level: Easy
Type: Factual
Ans: B

117. Vibrations in the oval window cause fluid to move back and forth in the:
A. middle ear
B. cochlea
C. auditory nerve
D. auditory receptors

p. 102
Ear: Audition
Level: Easy
Type: Factual
Ans: A
*PS/SG 5-14*

118. The function of the cochlea is to:
A. transform vibrations into nerve impulses
B. move fluid forward toward the oval window
C. house the hammer, anvil, and stirrup
D. house the band of fibers called the auditory nerve

p. 102
Ear: Audition
Level: Moderate
Type: Factual
Ans: C

119. In what order do sound waves pass through the auditory system?
A. external ear, stirrup, auditory canal, tympanic membrane, hammer, anvil, and cochlea
B. external ear, auditory canal, hammer, tympanic membrane, anvil, stirrup, and cochlea
C. external ear, auditory canal, tympanic membrane, hammer, anvil, stirrup, and cochlea
D. external ear, auditory canal, anvil, stirrup, cochlea, tympanic membrane, and hammer

p. 103
Ear: Audition
Level: Easy
Type: Factual
Ans: B

120. Neural impulses in the ear begin with:
A. a liquid chemical stimulating nerve endings
B. the bending of tiny hair cells
C. sound waves stimulating nerve endings
D. the vibration of the basilar membrane stimulating nerve endings

p. 103
Ear: Audition
Level: Easy
Type: Factual
Ans: A

121. A nerve impulse will be generated in the cochlea when:
A. movements of the basilar membrane stimulate the hair cells
B. sound waves vibrate the ossicles
C. the sound is recognized by the primary auditory cortex
D. vibrations travel through the auditory canal

p. 103
Ear: Audition
Level: Easy
Type: Factual
Ans: A

122. The auditory receptors are called:
A. hair cells
B. rods
C. ossicles
D. cones

p. 103
Ear: Audition
Level: Easy
Type: Factual
Ans: D

123. What specific structure in the auditory system triggers a nerve impulse?
A. tympanic membrane
B. ossicles
C. cochlea
D. hair cells

p. 103
Ear: Audition
Level: Moderate
Type: Applied
Ans: A

124. Jeremy is deaf because his hair cells have been damaged. The reason Jeremy cannot hear is because the:
A. sound waves cannot be transformed into nerve impulses
B. sound waves cannot cause the oval window to vibrate
C. tympanic membrane does not receive information from the basilar membrane
D. cochlea has no fluid to generate sound vibrations

p. 103
Ear: Audition
Level: Easy
Type: Factual
Ans: C

125. Nerve impulses are transmitted from the cochlea to the brain via the:
A. oval window
B. basilar membrane
C. auditory nerve
D. stirrup

p. 103
Ear: Audition
Level: Easy
Type: Factual
Ans: B

126. Auditory association areas in the brain:
A. send impulses to the middle ear which vibrate the ossicles
B. transform meaningless sounds into meaningful perceptions
C. trigger nerve impulses which activate the hair cells
D. convert nerve impulses into sensations of sound

p. 103
Ear: Audition
Level: Easy
Type: Factual
Ans: C

127. Nerve impulses from the inner ear are converted into sensations of meaningless sounds in the:
A. association areas
B. cochlea
C. primary auditory cortex
D. tympanic membrane

p. 103
Ear: Audition
Level: Easy
Type: Applied
Ans: B

128. Jackie's primary auditory cortex is damaged, but other structures are healthy. What will be her auditory experience?
A. She can recognize songs, but not spoken words.
B. She can hear basic auditory sounds.
C. Total deafness.
D. She can recognize individual words, but not complete sentences.

p. 103
Ear: Audition
Level: Easy
Type: Factual
Ans: A

129. The _____ transforms auditory sensations into meaningful perception.
A. auditory association area
B. primary auditory cortex
C. vestibular system
D. basilar membrane

p. 104
Ear: Audition
Level: Moderate
Type: Applied
Ans: D

130. A golfer yells "fore" after hitting a golf ball in the direction of Morris. Morris turns in the direction of the yell and is able to avoid the ball. Morris was able to determine the direction of the yell because of:
A. movements of hair cells within the basilar membrane
B. movements of fluid within the cochlea
C. the sound of the yell hitting both ears at the same time
D. the sound of the yell hitting one ear before the other

p. 104
Ear: Audition
Level: Easy
Type: Factual
Ans: B

131. Which of the following best describes how the brain judges the direction of sounds?
A. by calculating the amount of bend in hair cells
B. by calculating the difference in time it takes sound to reach both ears
C. by calculating the speed of fluid movement in the cochlea
D. by calculating the speed that it takes sound to reach the auditory association areas

p. 104
Ear: Audition
Level: Easy
Type: Factual
Ans: D

132. The frequency theory, and place theory are explanations of how the auditory system calculates:
A. amplitude
B. direction
C. loudness
D. pitch

p. 104
Ear: Audition
Level: Easy
Type: Factual
Ans: C

133. According to the frequency theory, the auditory system converts the frequency of sound waves into the subjective experience of:
A. loudness
B. amplitude
C. pitch
D. volley

p. 104
Ear: Audition
Level: Easy
Type: Factual
Ans: C

134. According to the place theory, the auditory system converts the frequency of sound waves into the subjective experience of _____ based upon the place along the basilar membrane where there is maximum vibration.
A. loudness
B. amplitude
C. pitch
D. volley

p. 104
Ear: Audition
Level: Easy
Type: Factual
Ans: B
www

135. The theory which assumes that different frequencies of sound waves stimulate different areas along the basilar membrane is called:
A. volley theory
B. place theory
C. frequency theory
D. opponent-process theory

p. 104
Ear: Audition
Level: Easy
Type: Factual
Ans: A

136. The ear senses loudness by:
A. the rate of nerve impulses that reach the auditory nerve
B. the location of the most intense stimulation in the cochlea fluid
C. the electrical strength of the neural impulse sent to the brain
D. the number of vibrations reaching the cochlea

p. 104
Ear: Audition
Level: Moderate
Type: Factual
Ans: B

137. The brain transforms the rate of impulses into:
A. perceptions of which direction the sound came from
B. sensations of loudness
C. the pitch of the noise that was perceived
D. sound waves of differing pitch

p. 104
Ear: Audition
Level: Moderate
Type: Applied
Ans: C

138. Toan's voice causes a slow rate of nerve impulses in your auditory system, while Hector's voice causes a fast rate. Toan is _____ and Hector is _____.
A. yelling; whispering
B. screaming; yelling
C. whispering; yelling
D. yelling; whispering

p. 105
Vestibular System
Level: Easy
Type: Factual
Ans: A

139. The vestibular organs provide our sense of:
A. position and balance
B. smell
C. taste
D. taste and flavor

p. 105
Vestibular System
Level: Easy
Type: Factual
Ans: B

140. The vestibular organs are located in the:
A. olfactory cells
B. inner ear
C. somatosensory cortex
D. Pacinian corpuscle

p. 105
Vestibular System
Level: Easy
Type: Factual
Ans: B
*PS/SG 5-15*

141. Our sense of movement and position in space is determined by:
A. faint echoes from surrounding objects that the brain can decode
B. movement of fluid in the three semicircular canals of the vestibular system
C. the primary visual cortex and related association areas
D. the movement of fluid in the eardrum

p. 105
Vestibular System
Level: Easy
Type: Factual
Ans: B

142. What structures in the inner ear help us to maintain balance?
A. tympanic membranes
B. semicircular canals
C. ossicles
D. meniere's rings

p. 105
Vestibular System
Level: Easy
Type: Factual
Ans: A

143. The vestibular system helps us to keep balance by providing information:
A. on the position of the head
B. to the cerebellum
C. about the position of the body
D. regarding the outside environment

p. 105
Vestibular System
Level: Easy
Type: Factual
Ans: C

144. Motion sickness results from:
A. the brain's inability to function properly when jostled
B. visual confusion caused by distant objects appearing blurry
C. contradictory information from the vestibular and visual systems
D. the continuous movement of the olfactory cells

| | | |
|---|---|---|
| p. 105<br>Vestibular System<br>Level: Easy<br>Type: Factual<br>Ans: B | 145. | While Sarah and Renee are watching a movie on a large screen of an airplane flying through the Grand Canyon, both of them feel motion sickness. Why? |
| | A. | Expectation of feeling sick from the reports of their friends. |
| | B. | Information from the visual system contradicts information from the vestibular system. |
| | C. | They have flying phobia. |
| | D. | Motion sickness is most common among thrill-seekers like Sarah and Renee. |

| | | |
|---|---|---|
| p. 105<br>Vestibular System<br>Level: Easy<br>Type: Factual<br>Ans: A<br>*PS/SG 5-16* | 146. | Motion sickness is probably caused by: |
| | A. | a sensory mismatch between the information from the vestibular system and the eyes |
| | B. | the violent bouncing around of the head during a rough stretch of road |
| | C. | individual |
| | D. | drug use |

| | | |
|---|---|---|
| p. 105<br>Vestibular System<br>Level: Easy<br>Type: Applied<br>Ans: D | 147. | Your vestibular system says that your head is bouncing around; your eyes say that the physical world is steady and not bouncing around. The result of this inconsistency is: |
| | A. | Meniere's disease |
| | B. | Muller-Lyer illusion |
| | C. | subliminal motion |
| | D. | motion sickness |

| | | |
|---|---|---|
| p. 105<br>Vestibular System<br>Level: Easy<br>Type: Factual<br>Ans: A | 148. | It is believed that the Dutch artist Vincent van Gogh suffered from _____ which affects the _____. |
| | A. | Meniere's disease; vestibular system |
| | B. | Meniere's disease; inner ear |
| | C. | chorionic villus; somatosensory cortex |
| | D. | Ponzo's dementia; Pacinian corpuscle |

| | | |
|---|---|---|
| p. 105<br>Vestibular System<br>Level: Moderate<br>Type: Factual<br>Ans: B | 149. | Rachel suffers from attacks of dizziness. Her doctor says that she has a viral infection of the inner ear. Rachel most likely has: |
| | A. | Parkinson's disease |
| | B. | Meniere's disease |
| | C. | motion sickness |
| | D. | conduction deafness |

| | | |
|---|---|---|
| p. 105<br>Vestibular System<br>Level: Moderate<br>Type: Applied<br>Ans: C | 150. | The doctor told Nanci that she is suffering from Meniere's disease. Nanci now understands why she has: |
| | A. | nearsightedness |
| | B. | chronic back pain |
| | C. | attacks of dizziness, nausea, and spinning |
| | D. | crossed eyes |

| | | |
|---|---|---|
| p. 106<br>Chemical Senses<br>Level: Easy<br>Type: Factual<br>Ans: D | 151. | Taste and smell are classified as chemical senses because they: |
| | A. | respond to chemicals in the sensory neurotransmitters |
| | B. | send chemical impulses to the somatosensory cortex |
| | C. | detect chemical changes in the Pacinian corpuscle |
| | D. | react to chemical stimuli |

p. 106
Chemical Senses
Level: Easy
Type: Factual
Ans: B

152. How many basic tastes can people respond to?
A. three
B. five
C. seven
D. nine

p. 106
Chemical Senses
Level: Moderate
Type: Applied
Ans: C

153. Linda claims to be a very good judge of wine because she has sensitive taste buds. Which of the following does Linda not have receptors for?
A. sweetness
B. sourness
C. acidity
D. bitterness

p. 106
Chemical Senses
Level: Easy
Type: Factual
Ans: A

154. What is the fifth taste that we can detect?
A. umami
B. flowery
C. rancid
D. acidity

p. 106
Chemical Senses
Level: Easy
Type: Applied
Ans: A

155. You have just put a very sour lemon drop in your mouth. Which part of your tongue is detecting the sour taste?
A. the edge
B. underneath
C. middle
D. right side

p. 106
Chemical Senses
Level: Easy
Type: Applied
Ans: C

156. Jimmy's tongue is burned by hot coffee. He then finds it difficult to taste his breakfast. The coffee has damaged Jimmy's:
A. olfactory bulb
B. olfactory cells
C. taste buds
D. saliva glands

p. 106
Chemical Senses
Level: Easy
Type: Factual
Ans: D

157. The receptors for taste are called:
A. Pacinian buds
B. capsaicin buds
C. flavor buds
D. taste buds

p. 106
Chemical Senses
Level: Easy
Type: Applied
Ans: C

158. Louie breaks Jim's nose during a basketball game. In addition to smell, which of Jim's senses will be most affected by the injury?
A. cold
B. pressure
C. taste
D. touch

p. 106
Chemical Senses
Level: Easy
Type: Factual
Ans: D
*www*

159. Humans have an innate preference for _____ taste and avoidance of _____ taste.
A. sweet; salty
B. floral; bitter
C. floral; sour
D. sweet; bitter

p. 106
Chemical Senses
Level: Easy
Type: Factual
Ans: A

160. A supertaster is someone:
A. who has 2-3 times more taste buds than normal
B. who has 10 times more flavor buds than normal
C. whose sense of flavor is exceptionally sensitive
D. whose saliva glands are 2-3 times large than normal

p. 106
Chemical Senses
Level: Easy
Type: Factual
Ans: A

161. Flavors are detected by:
A. combining our senses of taste and smell
B. mixing two or more of the same basic tastes
C. the taste buds translating the taste of the chemicals
D. an innate ability to identify tastes

p. 106
Chemical Senses
Level: Easy
Type: Applied
Ans: B

162. Which of the following would make a cola taste test more difficult?
A. removing the carbonation
B. asking the tester to hold his nose
C. asking the tester to eat a cracker between tastes
D. asking the tester to look at the cola before tasting it

p. 106
Chemical Senses
Level: Easy
Type: Conceptual
Ans: A

163. If we could state flavor in a mathematical formula, what would it look like?
A. taste + smell = flavor
B. taste = flavor
C. taste + spicy = flavor
D. bitter + sour + salty + sweet = flavor

p. 106
Chemical Senses
Level: Easy
Type: Applied
Ans: B

164. Little Austen hates the taste of cough syrup. When he has to take his medicine, he would be happier if he:
A. did not look at the medicine
B. plugged his nose
C. smelled the medicine before drinking it
D. tasted the medicine a little before gulping it down

p. 107
Chemical Senses
Level: Easy
Type: Factual
Ans: B

165. We smell _____ substances.
A. kinetic
B. volatile
C. transductive
D. pacinian

p. 107
Chemical Senses
Level: Easy
Type: Factual
Ans: B

166. Olfactory cells are stimulated by:
A. the taste buds' response to a chemical stimulus
B. molecules dissolving in the mucus covering the cells
C. the sniffing action of the outer nasal passages
D. the primary olfactory cortex

p. 107
Chemical Senses
Level: Easy
Type: Factual
Ans: C

167. If you were to trace the path of neural impulses in olfaction, which of the following paths would be correct?
A. olfactory cells and primary olfactory cortex
B. olfactory cells, thalamus and primary olfactory cortex
C. olfactory cells, olfactory bulb, and primary olfactory cortex
D. hair cells, olfactory bulb, thalamus, and primary olfactory cortex

p. 107
Chemical Senses
Level: Easy
Type: Factual
Ans: A

168. The receptors for smell are called:
A. olfactory cells
B. Pacinian corpuscles
C. ossicles
D. taste buds

p. 107
Chemical Senses
Level: Easy
Type: Factual
Ans: D

169. Which of the following *best* explains why we soon *stop* smelling our deodorant, cologne, or perfume?
A. consolidation
B. olfaction
C. transduction
D. adaptation

p. 107
Chemical Senses
Level: Easy
Type: Factual
Ans: C

170. What is the relationship between age and ability to detect common odors?
A. Beginning in the teenage years, we start losing our ability.
B. The ability to detect common odors deteriorates only occurs in unhealthy older adults.
C. People in the 50s, 60s and 70s increasingly lose their ability.
D. Only after the 80s do people lose their ability.

p. 107
Chemical Senses
Level: Easy
Type: Factual
Ans: C

171. The most recently discovered function of olfaction is that it:
A. provides a system to warn us about spoiled food
B. intensifies the taste of food
C. elicits strong memories
D. helps us to sense danger

p. 108
Touch
Level: Easy
Type: Factual
Ans: D

172. Where are hair receptors in the skin?
A. wrapped around the cones
B. in the somatosensory cortex
C. wrapped around Pacinian corpuscles
D. wrapped around the base of each hair follicle

p. 108
Touch
Level: Easy
Type: Factual
Ans: A

173. Our sense of touch comes from:
A. a half-dozen miniature sensors located in the skin
B. millions of tiny nerves on the surface of the skin
C. special glands for pressure, temperature, and pain
D. stimulation of the tiny hairs that cover the body

p. 108
Touch
Level: Easy
Type: Factual
Ans: C

174. Which of the following allows us to respond to vibrations?
A. the free nerve endings
B. the hair receptors
C. the Pacinian corpuscles
D. the ossicles

p. 108
Touch
Level: Easy
Type: Factual
Ans: A

175. Free nerve endings:
A. can transmit information about temperature and pain
B. respond when hairs on the skin are bent or pulled up
C. are the only receptors to respond to vibration
D. have a protective structure surrounding them

p. 108
Touch
Level: Moderate
Type: Applied
Ans: C

176. Consider this: A free nerve ending, rod, and a Pacinian corpuscle walk into a bar and each orders a cold beer. Which one is most likely to tell the bartender that the beer is warm?
A. rod
B. Pacinian corpuscle
C. free nerve ending
D. rod and Pacinian corpuscle

p. 108
Touch
Level: Easy
Type: Factual
Ans: A

177. The outermost layer of skin:
A. has no sensory receptors
B. contains free nerve endings
C. is composed entirely of hair receptors
D. is called the outerderm

p. 108
Touch
Level: Easy
Type: Conceptual
Ans: B

178. You are capable of shrinking to a small enough size to fit into nerves and be able to follow the transmission of nerve impulses. You would find that nerve impulses from the skin would travel to the:
A. lateral geniculate lobe
B. somatosensory cortex
C. occipital lobe
D. frontal lobe

p. 108
Touch
Level: Easy
Type: Factual
Ans: B

179. Which sense can be suppressed by psychological factors?
A. vibration
B. pain
C. color vision
D. pressure

p. 110
Cultural Diversity:
 Disgust
Level: Moderate
Type: Factual
Ans: A
*PS/SG 5-21*

180. Why do some edible substances produce a feeling of disgust?
A. our culture has taught us that these substances are not food
B. our taste buds warn us that some substances are harmful
C. the taste may be tolerable, but the smell is disgusting
D. some food simply have no flavor

p. 110
Cultural Diversity:
  Disgust
Level: Moderate
Type: Factual
Ans: C

181. According to the theory of evolution, the primary purpose of the expression "disgust" is to:
A. communicate disapproval of the behaviors of others
B. show rejection of young children's behaviors
C. indicate rejection of contaminated or dangerous foods
D. indicate rejection of offensive odors

p. 110
Cultural Diversity:
  Disgust
Level: Easy
Type: Factual
Ans: A

182. Children begin to show the "disgust" expression when they:
A. are learning which foods in their culture are acceptable and which are not
B. are born and have their first drink of breast milk
C. discover the four basic tastes
D. show a preference for sweet and salty tastes

p. 110
Cultural Diversity:
  Disgust
Level: Easy
Type: Factual
Ans: C

183. Children begin to show the expression of disgust:
A. as early as one month of age
B. between 1 and 2 years of age
C. between 2 and 4 years of age
D. after 5 years of age

p. 110
Cultural Diversity:
  Disgust
Level: Moderate
Type: Conceptual
Ans: D

184. The fact that most of us would find fish eyes, blood, and grubs repulsive to eat suggests that:
A. third world cultures have very unhealthy diets
B. our agricultural system is the best in the world
C. our culture is far superior to any other in the world
D. most of our tastes are shaped by our culture

p. 110
Cultural Diversity:
  Disgust
Level: Moderate
Type: Applied
Ans: B

185. You are visiting another culture half way across the world. In a market, someone asks you if you want to buy a dog. You say no thanks and say you already have a cat. The vendor looks at you strangely and says, "Dog...good eating!" You remember what you learned in your psychology class about culture and perception. What was it?
A. Primitive cultures tend to have inaccurate perception.
B. Cultural values can influence perception.
C. Culture has very little effect on perception.
D. A person's diet has a great impact of perception.

p. 111
Research Focus:
  Mind over Body?
Level: Easy
Type: Factual
Ans: A

186. A _____ is an intervention that has no real medical effects; _____ is a change in the person's condition due to the bogus intervention.
A. Placebo; placebo effect
B. Pseudomed; attribution
C. Endorphin; placebo effect
D. Double-blind; placebo

p. 111
Research Focus:
  Mind over Body?
Level: Easy
Type: Factual
Ans: A

187. To test for placebo effects, researchers use a design called:
A.  double-blind procedure
B.  single-blind procedure
C.  random sampling
D.  counterbalancing

p. 111
Research Focus:
  Mind over Body?
Level: Easy
Type: Factual
Ans: D
*PS/SG 5-22*

188. In the double-blind procedure:
A.  there are blinds (screens) separating the researchers from the subjects
B.  both researchers and subjects wear blindfolds in order to guarantee privacy
C.  subjects first receive the treatment, then later receive a placebo
C.  neither the researchers nor the subjects know who is receiving what treatment

p. 111
Research Focus:
  Mind over Body?
Level: Moderate
Type: Applied
Ans: C

189. Dr. Smalley is conducting research on a new high blood pressure drug. He assigns patients to three groups: one group gets the new drug, one receives a placebo; and the third group gets a drug that is the standard drug to treat high blood pressure. But Dr. Smalley and his patients do not know who is receiving what treatment. This is an example of a:
A.  randomized Latin squares design
B.  repeated measures design
C.  double-blind design
D.  stratified sample design

p. 111
Research Focus:
  Mind over Body?
Level: Moderate
Type: Conceptual
Ans: A

190. The fact that fake surgeries and inert medications can cause placebo effects points to the idea that:
A.  mental factors like beliefs and expectations can influence pain perception
B.  the medical community has the ingenuity to save money on health care
C.  pain is just a physical experience
D.  a person's doctor must be watched very closely

p. 111
Research Focus:
  Mind over Body?
Level: Moderate
Type: Factual
Ans: C

191. Research has found that a placebo effect occurred in _____ of people who thought they were taking a pill for headache pain.
A.  0 to 5%
B.  25%
C.  30 to 60%
D.  70 to 99%

p. 111
Research Focus:
  Mind over Body?
Level: Moderate
Type: Factual
Ans: A

192. Psychologists are particularly interested in placebo effect because it suggests a(n):
A.  mind over body interaction
B.  way to reduce medical costs
C.  body over mind interaction
D.  way to take patients from psychiatrists

p. 112
Pain
Level: Easy
Type: Factual
Ans: D

193. The sense of pain differs from the other senses in that:
A.  pain is a mechanical sense, and the other senses are all chemical senses
B.  impulses from the skin receptors do not communicate with the brain
C.  the other senses depend on intensity of the stimulus and psychological factors
D.  many different stimuli can trigger pain

p. 112
Pain
Level: Moderate
Type: Factual
Ans: B

194. Where does the experience of pain take place?
A. free nerve endings
B. somatosensory and limbic areas of the brain
C. neural gates
D. pain receptors

p. 112
Pain
Level: Easy
Type: Applied
Ans: C

195. What effect do social, psychological, and emotional factors have on pain?
A. All three factors can cause pain, but not increase or decrease it.
B. Just social and emotional factors cause pain.
C. All may cause, increase, or decrease pain.
D. Only emotional factors can increase pain.

p. 112
Pain
Level: Easy
Type: Applied
Ans: D

196. You've snubbed your big toe. You start rubbing it to reduce the pain. What would the gate control theory of pain say about your action?
A. It should not be helpful since the gate control theory of pain is not valid.
B. Your action will not help since pain gates are closed through the release of endorphins.
C. Your action should help to reduce pain since it prevents the release of endorphins.
D. It should be helpful since nonpainful nerve messages from rubbing your toe will close the pain gate.

p. 112
Pain
Level: Moderate
Type: Factual
Ans: A

197. According to the gate control theory:
A. rubbing a painful area triggers nonpainful impulses which compete with painful impulses
B. the spinal cord allows only painful impulses to pass through and reach the brain
C. pain is reduced by distracting yourself from thinking about the pain
D. neural gates close when a person's emotional state calms down

p. 112
Pain
Level: Easy
Type: Factual
Ans: C

198. Of the following, which has been shown to reduce the experience of pain?
A. focusing on an unpleasant image
B. decreased attention
C. intense emotion and attention
D. increased motion

p. 112
Pain
Level: Moderate
Type: Applied
Ans: D

199. Four of your friends were hurt in a skiing accident and each is at home recovering from their painful injuries. Based on the gate control theory of pain, which is most likely to have the most pain?
A. Guy reads mystery novels.
B. Travis likes to write in his journal and letters to relatives.
C. Cyndy watches movies on cable.
D. Lacey sits around the house and complains about the pain.

p. 113
Pain
Level: Easy
Type: Applied
Ans: A

200. During Game 6 of the 1988 NBA playoff finals, Isiah Thomas played a great game despite a severely sprained ankle. Thomas's amazing ability to play despite the injury is due to:
A. endorphins being released by the brain
B. small-diameter sensory nerves being activated
C. high pain tolerance in professional athletes
D. superior physical conditioning

| | | |
|---|---|---|
| p. 113<br>Pain<br>Level: Easy<br>Type: Factual<br>Ans: C | 201.<br><br>A.<br>B.<br>C.<br>D. | Chemicals produced in the brain that have many of the same properties as morphine are called:<br>opsins<br>endocrines<br>endorphins<br>estrogens |
| p. 113<br>Pain<br>Level: Easy<br>Type: Factual<br>Ans: B | 202.<br>A.<br>B.<br>C.<br>D. | The brain produces endorphins during:<br>REM sleep<br>periods of severe stress<br>periods of physical pleasure<br>NREM sleep |
| p. 113<br>Pain<br>Level: Easy<br>Type: Factual<br>Ans: D | 203.<br>A.<br>B.<br>C.<br>D. | Endorphins are produced by the body's:<br>gonads<br>posterior pituitary<br>basal ganglia<br>adrenal gland |
| p. 113<br>Pain<br>Level: Easy<br>Type: Conceptual<br>Ans: C | 204.<br><br>A.<br>B.<br>C.<br>D. | Dr. McCurnin says that the brain has its own factory that makes pain killers.  Dr. McCurnin is:<br>describing a theory<br>making a reference to neurotransmitters<br>referring to endorphins<br>wrong |
| p. 113<br>Pain<br>Level: Easy<br>Type: Applied<br>Ans: D | 205.<br><br><br>A.<br>B.<br>C.<br><br>D. | A worker in a lumber mill suffers a serious injury when he gets his arm caught in the machinery.  Though the experience is painful, it is less painful than it might be because:<br>the worker is probably too delirious to experience much pain<br>the pain sensors are probably damaged in such an injury<br>trauma blocks the production of sodium ions and so transmission of pain impulses is blocked<br>the brain produces endorphins, which stop receptors from signaling pain |
| p. 113<br>Pain<br>Level: Easy<br>Type: Applied<br>Ans: B<br>*www* | 206.<br><br><br>A.<br>B.<br>C.<br>D. | Holly hurts her shoulder playing tennis.  A therapist inserts needles in several points on her body and stimulates them.  The therapist is treating Holly's shoulder using:<br>biofeedback<br>acupuncture<br>cognitive programming<br>behavioral programming |
| p. 113<br>Pain<br>Level: Easy<br>Type: Factual<br>Ans: C | 207.<br><br>A.<br>B.<br>C.<br>D. | Scientists have studied how acupuncture is effective in reducing pain.  One idea presented in your textbook suggests that:<br>the needles interfere with the sodium pumps in the neuron<br>it alters the magnetic wave energy surrounding your body<br>endorphins are secreted from stimulating points along the pain pathway<br>the brain is stimulated to produce aspirin |

p. 113
Pain
Level: Easy
Type: Factual
Ans: B
*PS/SG 5-24*

208. Can the ancient Oriental procedure called acupuncture actually relieve pain? Modern science says:

A. yes, because there are some mysteries Western science is not equipped to explain

B. perhaps, because stimulation of certain points may cause the secretion of endorphins

C. no, because there cannot be a relationship between twirling needles in the skin and pain caused by the nervous system

D. no, because there is no research to date that supports acupuncture

p. 114
Application:
  Artificial Senses
Level: Easy
Type: Factual
Ans: D

209. In attempts to develop artificial photoreceptors, researchers hope at least that blind people will:

A. see patches of colors

B. see outlines of objects

C. regain their vision for movement

D. see shades of light

p. 114
Application:
  Artificial Senses
Level: Easy
Type: Factual
Ans: C

210. A microchip implanted into the retina could:

A. restore full vision

B. help farsighted individuals

C. change light waves into electrical signals

D. help dichromats see more colors

p. 114
Application:
  Artificial Senses
Level: Moderate
Type: Applied
Ans: D

211. Stan, who is blind because of damage to the optic nerves, is participating in a research study on artificial senses. He is eligible for an experimental device to help him see, at least partially. Which of the following is best suited for Stan?

A. cochlear implant

B. upon further review Stan cannot be helped

C. artificial eye and retina

D. to implant tiny wires into his visual cortex

p. 115
Application:
  Artificial Senses
Level: Easy
Type: Factual
Ans: C

212. Conduction deafness differs from neural deafness in that:

A. the former cannot be helped

B. the latter cannot be helped

C. the former can be helped with an external hearing aid

D. the latter can be helped with an external hearing aid

p. 115
Application:
  Artificial Senses
Level: Easy
Type: Applied
Ans: C

213. Mary's grandfather suffers from hearing loss. The doctor recommends a hearing aid. Grandfather's condition is most likely:

A. neural deafness

B. auditory fatigue

C. conduction deafness

D. cochlea fatigue

p. 115
Application:
  Artificial Senses
Level: Easy
Type: Factual
Ans: A

214. Conduction deafness involves conditions which:
A. interfere with transmitting vibrations from the tympanic membrane to the cochlea
B. are not improved by the use of a hearing aid
C. involve damage to the auditory receptor cells along the basilar membrane
D. are caused by damage to association areas

p. 115
Application:
  Artificial Senses
Level: Easy
Type: Factual
Ans: D
*www*

215. Neural deafness is caused by:
A. the presence of wax in the auditory canal
B. injury to the tympanic membrane
C. malfunction of the ossicles
D. damage to the hair cells

p. 115
Application:
  Artificial Senses
Level: Moderate
Type: Applied
Ans: B

216. A firecracker explodes near Timmy's ear. Most of his hearing is lost. A doctor's examination shows damage to his auditory nerve. Timmy is suffering from:
A. auditory fatigue
B. neural deafness
C. cochlea implant
D. conduction deafness

p. 115
Application:
  Artificial Senses
Level: Easy
Type: Factual
Ans: D

217. A doctor suggests that a patient may benefit from an electronic ear implant. The person probably has:
A. conductive deafness
B. middle ear damage
C. damage to associative areas of the brain
D. neural deafness

p. 115
Application:
  Artificial Senses
Level: Easy
Type: Factual
Ans: C

218. Cochlear implants involve small electronic devices that take the place of the:
A. ear drum
B. basilar membrane
C. hair cells
D. anvil, hammer, and stirrup

p. 115
Application:
  Artificial Senses
Level: Easy
Type: Factual
Ans: D
*PS/SG 5-25*

219. Cochlear implants are effective:
A. in only a few cases, limiting their use to fewer than 1,000 persons worldwide
B. in conduction deafness, but not in neural deafness
C. because they are surgically planted deep inside the brain
D. because a mechanical device does the work of damaged auditory receptors

p. 115
Application:
  Artificial Senses
Level: Easy
Type: Factual
Ans: D

220. Three-year old John has just received a cochlear implant. Based on material presented in your textbook, he will need:
A. a replacement in two years
B. a replacement in five years
C. intensive motor skill rehabilitation
D. intensive speech rehabilitation

True/False

| F | | 1. | Because of transduction, there is decreased responding in the sense organ when exposed to continuous levels of stimulation. |
|---|-----|-----|---|
| F | *www* | 2. | Sensations refer to meaningful sensory experiences. |
| F | | 3. | The process that refers to changing physical energy into electrical signals is called agnosia. |
| T | | 4. | Objects that you see are turned upside down on the retina. |
| F | *www* | 5. | The pupil of the eye is really a circular muscle. |
| T | | 6. | Farsightedness is due to the eyeball being too short. |
| T | *www* | 7. | The photoreceptors in your eye are called rods and cones. |
| F | | 8. | Cones are extremely light sensitive. |
| F | | 9. | The visual association areas respond to specific kinds of visual stimuli such as lines and shadows. |
| T | *www* | 10. | The trichromatic theory of color vision asserts that there are three kinds of cones in the eye. |
| T | | 11. | The opponent-process theory says that color vision is the result of brain cells responding to two pairs of color. |
| T | | 12. | The cochlea of the ear contains the receptors for hearing. |
| F | *www* | 13. | The rods and cones of the cochlea are stimulated by fluid resulting in nerve messages. |
| F | *www* | 14. | The primary auditory cortex transforms nerve messages into meaningful perceptions. |
| F | | 15. | The semicircular canals provide the brain with information about the pitch of sound. |
| T | | 16. | The symptoms of Meniere's disease include dizziness, nausea, and vomiting. |
| T | | 17. | Umami is the fifth basic taste. |
| T | *www* | 18. | Flavor is the result of taste and smell. |
| F | | 19. | Free nerve endings transmit information about vibration. |
| F | | 20. | The expression of disgust is only found in western cultures. |
| T | *www* | 21. | Endorphins are produced in situations that involve fear, stress, or injury. |
| T | | 22. | Acupuncture can reduce brain activity in areas that are involved in pain. |
| F | *www* | 23. | Conduction deafness is due to damage to the auditory nerve. |
| T | *www* | 24. | Neural deafness can be treated with cochlear implants. |
| F | | 25. | The success of cochlear implants is low. |

Short-Answer Essay Questions

1.  Describe the processes of transduction and adaptation. Include an example of each in your response. (*www*)
2.  Trace the path of a light as it enters the eye. Your answer should include the major structures of the eye. (*www*)
3.  Explain the reason for cones to be able to provide more detail of a visual stimulus.
4.  How do the trichromatic theory and opponent-process theory explain color vision?
5.  Describe the path that sound takes as it enters the ear, is converted to nerve messages, and then is processed by the brain. (*www*)
6.  Describe the frequency theory and place theory of how the brain calculates pitch.

7.      How do we create perceptions of flavor?

8.      What types of information do hair receptors, free nerve endings, and Pacinian corpuscles transmit? (*www*)

9.      How does acupuncture reduce pain? What types of pain or conditions are acupuncture the most effective in treating?

10.     Describe the difference between conduction deafness and neural deafness. In what way do the differences have implications for treatment? (*www*)

# Module 6 - Perception

p. 121
Introduction
Level: Moderate
Type: Conceptual
Ans: C

1. The examples of a subliminal tape, selecting a puppy, and a mammogram underscore the importance of:
A. being a smart consumer of products and services
B. figure-ground in perception
C. perception in everyday life
D. the subliminal threshold

p. 121
Introduction
Level: Moderate
Type: Factual
Ans: A

2. As it relates to the topic of perception, what factor <u>most</u> influences a doctor's ability to detect a cancerous tumor on a mammogram?
A. how large an object must be before we can detect it
B. how we are influenced by our culture
C. what shape an object must be before we can detect it
D. how consistent the object is with the principle of continuity

p. 122
Perceptual Thresholds
Level: Easy
Type: Factual
Ans: B

3. The point above which a stimulus is perceived and below which it is <u>not</u> perceived is called a stimulus _____.
A. perception
B. threshold
C. just noticeable difference
D. sensation

p. 122
Perceptual Thresholds
Level: Easy
Type: Factual
Ans: A
*www*

4. A quality inspector at the local manufacturing plant carefully examines a product for flaws using a special light. The flaws show up as dark green spots of light. For this inspector, the _____ is the point at which a flaw can be detected.
A. threshold
B. JND
C. gestalt
D. subliminal threshold

p. 122
Perceptual Thresholds
Level: Easy
Type: Factual
Ans: A

5. Who initially discovered the idea of the absolute threshold?
A. Fechner
B. Weber
C. Gestalt
D. Pavlov

p. 122
Perceptual Thresholds
Level: Easy
Type: Factual
Ans: D

6. Gustav Fechner defined absolute threshold as:
A. the intensity level that a person detects 50% of the time
B. the amount of stimulus energy needed to develop a perception
C. an increase or decrease in the intensity of stimuli
D. the smallest amount of stimulus energy that can be observed or experienced.

p. 122
Perceptual Thresholds
Level: Moderate
Type: Conceptual
Ans: C

7. You are Gustav Fechner. You have used several methods to measure absolute threshold. What do you conclude?
A. the absolute threshold has finally been measured
B. the absolute threshold is the same as the JND
C. the absolute threshold depends on the subjects' levels of attention
D. the subjects are too slow to perceive absolute thresholds

p. 122
Perceptual Thresholds
Level: Easy
Type: Factual
Ans: A

8. Why did Gustav Fechner's definition of absolute threshold need to be modified?
A. Alertness and the testing situation can influence an individual's thresholds.
B. We now know that absolute threshold is influenced by the JND.
C. Because the concept of absolute threshold was found to be invalid.
D. Fechner's data were made up.

p. 122
Perceptual Thresholds
Level: Easy
Type: Factual
Ans: D
*PS/SG 6-1*

9. An absolute threshold is the intensity level that you:
A. detect every time it is presented
B. guess is there, even if you can't quite detect it
C. just barely detect
D. detect 50 percent of the time

p. 122
Perceptual Thresholds
Level: Easy
Type: Factual
Ans: D

10. A stimulus that is detected less than 50% of the time is called a(n) _____ stimulus.
A. absolute
B. just noticeable
C. detectable
D. subliminal

p. 122
Perceptual Thresholds
Level: Easy
Type: Factual
Ans: A

11. The level at which a stimulus is detected at least 50% of the time is called the:
A. absolute threshold
B. just noticeable threshold
C. perceptional limit
D. subliminal threshold

p. 122
Perceptual Thresholds
Level: Moderate
Type: Conceptual
Ans: C

12. In order to answer the question, "At what point are you aware of a stimulus?" one should measure the:
A. subliminal stimulus
B. proximity
C. absolute threshold
D. just noticeable difference

p. 122
Perceptual Thresholds
Level: Moderate
Type: Applied
Ans: C

13. As part of a psychology experiment, Linda sits in a small, completely darkened room and looks through an apparatus. At the sound of a tone, she is exposed to a brief flash of light. These lights vary in intensity. After each tone, she reports whether she saw the flash. The intensity of light that Linda perceives 50 percent of the time is her:
A. just noticeable difference
B. Weber's constant
C. absolute threshold
D. subliminal limit

p. 122
Perceptual Thresholds
Level: Moderate
Type: Conceptual
Ans: C

14. The implication of the absolute threshold concept is that:
  A. two stimuli must be minimally different in order to be perceived as different stimuli
  B. above a given intensity, a stimulus becomes indistinguishable from other stimuli
  C. a stimulus must be above a minimal intensity in order to be perceived
  D. the intensity required for a stimulus to be perceived is dependent on the context of that stimulus

p. 122
Perceptual Thresholds
Level: Moderate
Type: Applied
Ans: B

15. Lori is participating in a hearing experiment. The researcher presents her with a series of 7 tones, ranging from very quiet to very loud. Over the course of ten trials, Lori can hear Tone #5 every time. However, she only hears Tone #4 during two of the ten trials. For Lori, Tone #4 represents a(n):
  A. absolute threshold
  B. subliminal stimulus
  C. just noticeable difference
  D. principle of continuity

p. 122
Perceptual Thresholds
Level: Easy
Type: Factual
Ans: C

16. A subliminal stimulus is one that has:
  A. a 50-50 chance of being detecting
  B. a variable JND
  C. less than 50% chance of detecting the stimulus
  D. been perceived by association areas of the brain

p. 122
Perceptual Thresholds
Level: Moderate
Type: Applied
Ans: A

17. If the absolute threshold was 50% for detecting breast cancer by mammograms, the death rate from breast cancer would surely:
  A. increase
  B. decrease
  C. stay the same
  D. decrease only slightly

p. 122
Perceptual Thresholds
Level: Easy
Type: Factual
Ans: C

18. Doctors fail to detect about _____ of tumors on mammograms.
  A. 1-5%
  B. 6-8%
  C. 15-30%
  D. 45%

p. 122
Perceptual Thresholds
Level: Easy
Type: Factual
Ans: D

19. Dr. Wilson is reading a mammogram. She knows that one way to increase the accuracy of the mammogram is to:
  A. focus her attention on the black spots since they indicate tumors
  B. use a powerful magnifying glass
  C. reduce the lighting which will lower the absolute threshold
  D. ask another doctor to read the mammogram

p. 123
Perceptual Thresholds
Level: Easy
Type: Factual
Ans: D

20. The JND is defined as the:
  A. amount of a stimulus needed to perceive depth using monocular cues
  B. amount of a stimulus needed to perceive depth using binocular cues
  C. smallest amount of stimulus you can detect
  D. smallest change in intensity of the stimulus that you can detect

p. 123
Perceptual Thresholds
Level: Easy
Type: Factual
Ans: A
*www*

21. The smallest increase or decrease in the intensity of a stimulus that a person is able to detect is called a(n):
   A. just noticeable difference
   B. absolute threshold
   C. perception
   D. retinal disparity

p. 123
Perceptual Thresholds
Level: Easy
Type: Factual
Ans: D

22. The just noticeable difference serves as the foundation for:
   A. transduction
   B. Ponzo illusion
   C. absolute threshold
   D. Weber's Law

p. 123
Perceptual Thresholds
Level: Moderate
Type: Conceptual
Ans: B

23. Fechner is to Weber as _____ is to just noticeable difference.
   A. figure-ground
   B. absolute threshold
   C. interposition
   D. sensation

p. 123
Perceptual Thresholds
Level: Moderate
Type: Applied
Ans: C

24. Danny is taking a shower. After ten minutes in the shower, the hot water runs out. The point at which Danny can tell that the water is getting cold represents his:
   A. absolute threshold
   B. subliminal stimulus
   C. just noticeable difference
   D. principle of closure

p. 123
Perceptual Thresholds
Level: Moderate
Type: Applied
Ans: A

25. Craig is blaring his stereo in his room. His father tells him to turn down the volume. Craig lowers the sound but his father claims the music is as loud as it was before. This is because:
   A. the change in volume did not reach his father's just noticeable difference
   B. Craig's father is unfamiliar with rock music
   C. The music was above his father's absolute threshold
   D. Craig's father subliminally perceived the volume change

p. 123
Perceptual Thresholds
Level: Moderate
Type: Factual
Ans: B

26. The proportioned increase in the intensity of a stimulus needed to produce a just noticeable difference is called:
   A. Fechner's constant
   B. Weber's law
   C. intrastimulus difference
   D. threshold

p. 123
Perceptual Thresholds
Level: Moderate
Type: Factual
Ans: D

27. Weber's law states that:
   A. the accuracy with which we judge the size of a stimulus is directly proportional to the magnitude of that stimulus
   B. the effort required to lift a weight is logarithmically proportional to the magnitude of the weight
   C. a tone must be three times louder in decibels before we perceive it as twice increased
   D. the size of a just noticeable difference is related to the magnitude of the stimulus

p. 123
Perceptual Thresholds
Level: Easy
Type: Factual
Ans: B
*PS/SG 6-3*

28. Weber's law of the just noticeable difference explains why:
A. you study better if you have the radio on
B. your parents don't believe you really turned your stereo down
C. kids like heavy metal and their parents like Montovani
D. the Destiny's Child singers all have different names

p. 123
Perceptual Thresholds
Level: Moderate
Type: Applied
Ans: C

29. Using Weber's law, solve the following: Harry makes $100,000 a year and Bill makes $10,000. Each person gets a raise of $1,000. Who is <u>most</u> likely to detect a just noticeable difference in spending habits based upon salary and why?
A. Harry - he is more likely to have saved some of his earnings
B. Harry - because he makes more money in the first place
C. Bill - because it takes less change for a low salaried person to detect the difference than a high salaried person
D. Bill - he is more used to spending his money wisely than Harry

p. 123
Perceptual Thresholds
Level: Moderate
Type: Factual
Ans: B

30. At low stimulus intensities, it takes _____ changes in order to detect a JND between two stimuli.
A. large
B. small
C. inverse
D. moderate

p. 123
Perceptual Thresholds
Level: Moderate
Type: Factual
Ans: A
*www*

31. At high stimulus intensities, it takes _____ changes in order to detect a JND between two stimuli.
A. large
B. small
C. inverse
D. moderate

p. 123
Perceptual Thresholds
Level: Moderate
Type: Factual
Ans: C

32. How did scientists conclude that fabric softeners worked on towels?
A. Subjects showed a high level of transduction when feeling the towels.
B. The subjects failed to detect a JND in softness.
C. Subjects detected a JND in softness.
D. The absolute threshold was found to be 50%.

p. 124
Sensation vs Perception
Level: Moderate
Type: Factual
Ans: C

33. When sensation occurs, we:
A. become aware of the stimulus's meaning and significance
B. perceive
C. experience an activation of our sensory receptors
D. are acutely aware of inconsistencies in our physical environment

p. 124
Sensation vs Perception
Level: Easy
Type: Factual
Ans: A

34. The first awareness of some outside stimulus is called a(n):
A. sensation
B. perception
C. absolute threshold
D. subliminal experience

p. 124
Sensation vs Perception
Level: Moderate
Type: Applied
Ans: A

35.    A three-month-old child is being prepared to get a shot at a health clinic. She detects the needle just as a long line and does not react to it or interpret it. To her it is just a long line and nothing more. This is an example of:
A.    sensation
B.    perception
C.    size constancy
D.    visual accommodation

p. 124
Sensation vs Perception
Level: Moderate
Type: Conceptual
Ans: C
*www*

36.    Which of the following best represents sensation?
A.    an aircraft pilot making an adjustment in altitude
B.    a college student interpreting an essay by Plato
C.    a fourteen-year-old seeing a bright flash of light
D.    deciding to wear shorts today because the weather is nice

p. 124
Sensation vs Perception
Level: Moderate
Type: Factual
Ans: C

37.    The transformation of sensations into a meaningful perception:
A.    is not influenced by experience
B.    occurs only in the sense organs
C.    is an unconscious, instantaneous process
D.    results in the experience of numerous "raw" sensations

p. 124
Sensation vs Perception
Level: Moderate
Type: Conceptual
Ans: D

38.    An orange blob is to a tiger as _____ is to _____.
A.    Weber's law; sensation
B.    proximity; figure-ground
C.    perception; sensation
D.    sensation; perception

p. 124
Sensation vs Perception
Level: Moderate
Type: Conceptual
Ans: B

39.    Sensation is to _____ as perception is to _____.
A.    monocular; binocular
B.    meaningless; meaningful
C.    similarity; simplicity
D.    JND; Weber's Law

p. 124
Sensation vs Perception
Level: Moderate
Type: Factual
Ans: B

40.    Perception is best defined as the:
A.    process by which sensory receptors detect outside stimuli
B.    combination and interpretation of sensations
C.    process where the brain transmits information to sensory neurons
D.    stimulation of sensory receptors

p. 124
Sensation vs Perception
Level: Moderate
Type: Applied
Ans: A

41.    Craig is taking his family for a car ride. His three-year-old, Katy, and Noelle, who is seven months old, are both looking out the side windows at approaching cars. Noelle sees bright flashes of lights, while Katy understands that the flashes of lights are cars. Which of the girls' experiences in the best example of perception and why?
A.    Katy because she makes sense out of the flashes of lights
B.    Noelle since she is capable of detecting bright flashes of lights
C.    Katy because her sensory receptors are being stimulated by the lights
D.    Noelle because her sensory receptors are transmitting information to her brain

p. 124
Sensation vs Perception
Level: Moderate
Type: Conceptual
Ans: D

42. Based upon your understanding of perception and factors that can influence it, which saying is the <u>most</u> appropriate to describe perception?
A. "Opposites attract"
B. "A stitch in time saves nine"
C. "Easy come, easy go"
D. "Different strokes for different folks"

p. 125
Sensation vs Perception
Level: Moderate
Type: Factual
Ans: B

43. In constructing a perception, sense organs:
A. personalize perceptions
B. transform energy into electrical signals or impulses
C. transform electrical signals into sensations
D. add meanings, feeling, or memories to our perceptions

p. 125
Sensation vs Perception
Level: Moderate
Type: Factual
Ans: D

44. Your roommate thinks that the senses produce sensations. Is she right?
A. Yes - senses produce sensations
B. No - senses produce perceptions
C. No - senses transform electrical signals into nerve impulses
D. No - senses transform energy into electrical signals

p. 125
Sensation vs Perception
Level: Moderate
Type: Conceptual
Ans: D

45. Of the following statements, which one <u>most</u> accurately describes perception?
A. Our perception of the physical world is like a video camera recording it.
B. Our perception of the physical world is an exact copy of reality.
C. Perception requires concentration.
D. Our past experiences and culture can influence what we perceive.

p. 125
Sensation vs Perception
Level: Easy
Type: Factual
Ans: C

46. _____ areas in the brain change sensations to perceptions.
A. Primary
B. Transductive
C. Association
D. Hindbrain

p. 125
Sensation vs Perception
Level: Difficult
Type: Conceptual
Ans: A

47. As the textbook states, perceptions are highly personalized. Select an example that <u>best</u> reflects this unique characteristic of perception.
A. A little girl calling a skunk a cat
B. A middle-aged man taking a sip of coffee in the morning
C. An engineer solving a design problem
D. A tape recorder recording the music of a young musician

p. 125
Sensation vs Perception
Level: Difficult
Type: Conceptual
Ans: C

48. Which of the following <u>best</u> represents perception?
A. a baby blinking her eyes in response to a puff of air
B. a newborn crying
C. ten-year-old Andrew successfully plays a Nintendo game
D. a newborn showing a reflex

p. 125
Sensation vs Perception
Level: Moderate
Type: Conceptual
Ans: D

49. When listening to music, the experience of hearing each individual note would be a _____, while interpreting the meaning of each note is an example of _____.
A. unit; illusion
B. segment; unit
C. perception; sensation
D. sensation; perception

p. 125
Sensation vs Perception
Level: Moderate
Type: Applied
Ans: C

50. Omar and Heidi look at a beautiful flower. Omar sees it as a Grand Lady Hybrid Strain X-6. This illustrates:
A. the perceptual principle of figure-ground
B. the gender difference in perception
C. how perceptions are personalized interpretations
D. how sensations are personalized interpretations

p. 125
Sensation vs Perception
Level: Moderate
Type: Applied
Ans: D

51. The story of Gabrielle and the large brown dog shows:
A. how sensations are personalized interpretations
B. perception is influenced by transduction
C. the perceptual principle of simplicity
D. how perceptions are personalized interpretations

p. 125
Sensation vs Perception
Level: Moderate
Type: Factual
Ans: A

52. The major difference between a sensation and a perception is that a sensation:
A. provides basic information and perceptions add meaning and organization to that information
B. involves the sense of touch and perceptions involve the sense of sight
C. is limited to the peripheral nervous system and perceptions occur in the endocrine system
D. is an active process and perception is a passive process

p. 126
Rules of Organization
Level: Moderate
Type: Factual
Ans: A

53. Structuralists argued that we could understand how perceptions were formed by:
A. breaking them down into smaller units for analysis
B. using one's perceptual experience
C. using principles of organization
D. utilizing the figure-ground principle

p. 126
Rules of Organization
Level: Moderate
Type: Applied
Ans: D

54. As you sit back at the baseball game, you perceive the ball being pitched, the batter hitting it, the ball shooting high into center field, and being caught. The structuralist would argue that this perception is:
A. the result of figure-ground, simplicity, and continuity
B. influenced by your prior experience of the game
C. created because of the brain follows certain rules of perceptual organization
D. formed by many basic units or elements

p. 126
Rules of Organization
Level: Moderate
Type: Applied
Ans: C

55. As you sit back at a baseball game, you perceive the ball being pitched, the batter hitting it, the ball shooting high into center field, and being caught. Gestalt psychologists would argue that this perception is:
A. adding together individual sensations
B. combining larger and larger units of sensations
C. the result of your brain following a set of rules to create a meaningful experience
D. formed by adding many basic elements

p. 126
Rules of Organization
Level: Moderate
Type: Factual
Ans: A

56. Gestalt psychologists explain perceptions based on the principles of organization which are rules that specify how:
A. our brains organize sensations into perceptions
B. we combine sensations together by adding individual units
C. we break down perceptions into smaller units
D. absolute thresholds identify subliminal stimuli

p. 126
Rules of Organization
Level: Easy
Type: Factual
Ans: C
*www*

57. The Gestalt principles of organization:
A. are binocular cues for perceiving three-dimensional objects
B. illustrate how illusions lead to inaccurate perceptions
C. are rules which help us to organize elements into something that is complete
D. were developed by Weber as part of Weber's Law

p. 126
Rules of Organization
Level: Easy
Type: Conceptual
Ans: A

58. If a newspaper had an article about the Gestalt psychologists' position on perception, what would be the headline?
A. "Brain Follows Rules in Perception"
B. "Perception: Adding Together Basic Sensations"
C. "Combining Elements Together"
D. "Breaking Down Perception into its Elements"

p. 126
Rules of Organization
Level: Moderate
Type: Conceptual
Ans: B

59. Structuralism is to Gestalt as _____ is to _____.
A. Weber's Law; JND
B. addition; rules
C. rules; JND
D. rules; addition

p. 126
Rules of Organization
Level: Easy
Type: Factual
Ans: B
*PS/SG 6-6*

60. Gestalt psychologists differed from structuralists in believing that:
A. you add together hundreds of basic elements to form complex perceptions
B. perceptions result from our brain's ability to organize sensations according to a set of rules
C. "the whole is equal to the sum of its parts"
D. "the parts are more real than the whole"

p. 126
Rules of Organization
Level: Easy
Type: Factual
Ans: C
*www*

61. The rules of organization such as figure-ground and closure were developed by the _____ to describe how we perceive.
A. Structuralists
B. Freudians
C. Gestalt psychologists
D. Behavioral psychologists

p. 127
Rules of Organization
Level: Moderate
Type: Applied
Ans: A

62. Looking up at the blue sky, Matt imagined that he saw the clouds as animal shapes. Viewing clouds against the sky is an example of which principle of perceptual organization?
A. figure and ground
B. closure
C. simplicity
D. continuity

p. 127
Rules of Organization
Level: Easy
Type: Factual
Ans: D
*PS/SG 6-7*

63. The perceptual rule that makes important things stand out is called:
A. closure
B. proximity
C. figure dominance
D. figure-ground

p. 127
Rules of Organization
Level: Easy
Type: Factual
Ans: B

64. The ability to separate figure from ground is:
A. learned through experience
B. innate
C. a binocular cue
D. a form of adaptation

p. 127
Rules of Organization
Level: Moderate
Type: Applied
Ans: A

65. Professor Karweick walks into her filled classroom, immediately perceiving students as sitting in rows rather than in a haphazard fashion. This is similar to what principle of perceptual organization?
A. similarity
B. simplicity
C. figure-ground
D. closure

p. 127
Rules of Organization
Level: Easy
Type: Factual
Ans: D

66. The principle of closure states that:
A. we group objects if they are in close physical proximity
B. we group objects together that appear similar
C. memory for organized perceptions is superior to that of unorganized perceptions
D. we tend to fill in missing parts of a figure

p. 127
Rules of Organization
Level: Moderate
Type: Applied
Ans: C

67. A skywriter is writing the words "VOTE FOR JOHNSON" in the blue sky above a football stadium during a game. However, his emission system becomes clogged so that only parts of the letters appear. Johnson tells him not to worry, the crowd will perceive his message by using:
A. continuity
B. proximity
C. closure
D. interposition

p. 127
Rules of Organization
Level: Moderate
Type: Applied
Ans: A

68. A famous artist has made a name for herself by the way she leaves objects in paintings incompletely drawn. Yet when we look at her works, we perceive the complete objects. What organizational rule of perception is occurring?

A. closure
B. simplicity
C. similarity
D. absolute threshold

p. 127
Rules of Organization
Level: Easy
Type: Factual
Ans: D

69. The principle of proximity states that:
A. we think things are close together if they look similar
B. if things are close together when they are in our field of vision, we assume they will stay close together when they leave our sight
C. if we stare at a random collection of objects long enough, they will appear to merge with one another
D. we tend to group together objects that are close to one another physically

p. 127
Rules of Organization
Level: Moderate
Type: Applied
Ans: B

70. At her high school dance, Rhonda perceives her fellow students as small groups of people talking to one another rather than as a large mass of people filling the gym. This situation is similar to what principle of perceptual organization?

A. figure and ground
B. proximity
C. continuity
D. simplicity

p. 127
Rules of Organization
Level: Moderate
Type: Applied
Ans: A

71. If you see two people walking and holding hands, you perceive that they are a couple because of the Gestalt principle of:
A. proximity
B. continuity
C. figure-ground
D. simplicity

p. 127
Rules of Organization
Level: Easy
Type: Factual
Ans: D
*www*

72. The Gestalt rule of _____ states that we tend to organize stimuli in the most basic way possible.

A. continuity
B. closure
C. similarity
D. simplicity

p. 127
Rules of Organization
Level: Easy
Type: Factual
Ans: C

73. We tend to perceive complex figures as divided into several simple figures. Why?
A. continuity rule
B. closure rule
C. simplicity rule
D. proximity rule

| | | |
|---|---|---|
| p. 127<br>Rules of Organization<br>Level: Easy<br>Type: Factual<br>Ans: A | 74. | The principle of continuity states that: |
| | A. | we organize forms along a smooth line or path |
| | B. | we will continue to perceive stimuli in a given manner until we notice a change |
| | C. | we assume objects continue to possess the same form even when removed from our perceptual field |
| | D. | we use similar patterns of organization throughout our lives |

| | | |
|---|---|---|
| p. 127<br>Rules of Organization<br>Level: Easy<br>Type: Factual<br>Ans: B<br>*PS/SG 6-8* | 75. | The perceptual rule that we tend to favor smooth or continuous paths when interpreting a series of points or lines is called: |
| | A. | shortest distance |
| | B. | continuity |
| | C. | closure |
| | D. | simplicity |

| | | |
|---|---|---|
| p. 127<br>Rules of Organization<br>Level: Moderate<br>Type: Applied<br>Ans: C | 76. | Mark is coming in for a night landing in his twin-engine plane. He sees blue lights on the ground before him. Mark perceives this to be the outline of the runway. What principle of perceptual organization is he <u>most</u> likely using? |
| | A. | spread |
| | B. | familiarity |
| | C. | continuity |
| | D. | contour |

| | | |
|---|---|---|
| p. 127<br>Rules of Organization<br>Level: Easy<br>Type: Applied<br>Ans: B | 77. | Of the following people, who is <u>least</u> likely to have learned the Gestalt rules of organizing stimuli into perceptions? |
| | A. | Katelyn – 11 years old |
| | B. | Bethany – 3 months old |
| | C. | Noelle – 8 years old |
| | D. | We actually don't learn the rules. We are born knowing them. |

| | | |
|---|---|---|
| p. 128<br>Perceptual Constancy<br>Level: Easy<br>Type: Factual<br>Ans: C | 78. | A perceptual constancy is defined as the: |
| | A. | tendency for all persons to see the world in the same manner |
| | B. | ability for several different sensory images to form a perception at the same time |
| | C. | tendency to perceive things as unchanging, even though they are changing on the retina |
| | D. | ability to utilize only one sense, even though multiple sensations are being experienced |

| | | |
|---|---|---|
| p. 128<br>Perceptual Constancy<br>Level: Easy<br>Type: Factual<br>Ans: D | 79. | What term describes our tendency to perceive sizes, shapes, and colors as remaining the same even though their physical characteristics keep changing? |
| | A. | convergence |
| | B. | organizational constancy |
| | C. | retinal constancy |
| | D. | perceptual constancy |

p. 128
Perceptual Constancy
Level: Moderate
Type: Applied
Ans: D
*www*

80. You see a friend down the street. The visual image you receive is of a person who is the size of a doll, yet you know your friend hasn't shrunk since you last saw him. This is due to which of the following?
A. motion parallax
B. accommodation
C. relative size
D. size constancy

p. 128
Perceptual Constancy
Level: Moderate
Type: Applied
Ans: D

81. Diane and Debbie are at an outdoor circus. Their father has purchased each a helium balloon. Debbie accidentally lets go of her balloon and it floats farther and farther away. The balloon appears to be becoming smaller and smaller. Both Diane and Debbie believe that the balloon remains the same size. Their perception is best explained by:
A. Gestalt psychology
B. motion parallax
C. interposition
D. size constancy

p. 128
Perceptual Constancy
Level: Easy
Type: Conceptual
Ans: D
*PS/SG 6-10*

82. Thank goodness for size constancy — without it you would:
A. never know for sure how big or small anything really was
B. immediately get bigger after a single large meal
C. see things change in size whenever the light changed in brightness
D. think your Honey is getting smaller and smaller while walking away from you

p. 128
Perceptual Constancy
Level: Moderate
Type: Conceptual
Ans: C

83. If Julie lacks size constancy, what would she probably say about a dog running towards her?
A. "Oh no! That dog shouldn't be allowed to run free like that."
B. "Wow! That dog's color is changing as it runs."
C. "Oh no! That dog is growing with every step he takes."
D. "Look at that dog. He wants to play."

p. 128
Perceptual Constancy
Level: Moderate
Type: Conceptual
Ans: A

84. Given that size constancy appears to be learned, what would a blind person whose sight is suddenly restored say as he looked out the window of an airplane as it flies high above in the sky?
A. "Very small people must live in those very small houses down there."
B. "Why does the color of those houses down there keep changing?"
C. "It seems that the cars down on the ground are moving very slowly."
D. "Amazing I can really see those houses very clearly."

p. 128
Perceptual Constancy
Level: Moderate
Type: Applied
Ans: A

85. Which of the following athletes makes best use of size constancy?
A. a football player catching a pass on the run
B. a gymnast doing a cartwheel
C. a basketball player shooting a foul shot
D. a baseball pitcher throwing a curve ball

p. 128
Perceptual Constancy
Level: Moderate
Type: Factual
Ans: B

86. Brightness constancy results in the tendency to perceive:
A. all stimuli as brighter than they really are
B. brightness as remaining the same in changing illumination
C. colors are grayish in dim light
D. that the sun produces white light

p. 128
Perceptual Constancy
Level: Moderate
Type: Conceptual
Ans: C

87. A green car looks like a green car, regardless of whether it is dawn or dusk, because of:
A. interposition
B. convergence
C. color constancy
D. monocular cues

p. 129
Depth Perception
Level: Easy
Type: Factual
Ans: D

88. What are the three dimensions that our visual system allows us to perceive? Of the three, which one is added by our visual system?
A. depth, convergence, height - depth
B. accommodation, disparity, depth - disparity
C. width, height, diameter - diameter
D. depth, width, height - depth

p. 129
Depth Perception
Level: Moderate
Type: Factual
Ans: C

89. Of the following, what is the most remarkable characteristic about depth perception?
A. We are capable of seeing four dimensions.
B. The retina is capable of detecting three dimensions.
C. Images on the retina are only two dimensional, yet we see three dimensions.
D. Retinal disparity should overload the visual system with information, yet it does not.

p. 129
Depth Perception
Level: Easy
Type: Factual
Ans: A
www

90. We are able see in three dimensions. What are the three dimensions?
A. depth, width, height
B. width, height, diameter
C. height, disparity, depth
D. depth, convergence, height

p. 129
Depth Perception
Level: Easy
Type: Factual
Ans: A

91. The muscles that move the entire eye give cues to depth through:
A. convergence
B. accommodation
C. retinal disparity
D. neural inconsistency

p. 129
Depth Perception
Level: Easy
Type: Factual
Ans: C

92. Of the following depth cues, which is based on the muscles of the eye providing information?
A. accommodation
B. retinal disparity
C. convergence
D. interposition

p. 129
Depth Perception
Level: Moderate
Type: Applied
Ans: B

93.     Because of a problem with her eyes, Julie has trouble with convergence. This would affect her:
A.      ability to focus on the intersections of lines and edges
B.      ability to turn the eyes inward as an object moves closer to her face
C.      ability to block out irrelevant stimuli
D.      ability to perceive figure-ground

p. 129
Depth Perception
Level: Easy
Type: Factual
Ans: D

94.     Because the eyes are separated by several inches, each eye receives a slightly different image. This is called:
A.      interposition
B.      shape inconsistency
C.      convergence
D.      retinal disparity

p. 129
Depth Perception
Level: Moderate
Type: Conceptual
Ans: C

95.     You are writing a paper on the depth cue of retinal disparity. What is the best title for your paper?
A.      "How the Eyes Turn Inward"
B.      "Retinal Disparity: Another Monocular Depth Cue"
C.      "Retinal Disparity: Seeing Depth by Two Images"
D.      "Retinal Disparity: Weber's Discovery"

p. 129
Depth Perception
Level: Moderate
Type: Conceptual
Ans: C
*PS/SG 6-11*

96.     The advantage to the human species of having two eyes is:
A.      figure-ground discrimination
B.      monocular cues
C.      retinal disparity
D.      glasses balance on the nose better

p. 129
Depth Perception
Level: Easy
Type: Applied
Ans: B

97.     As a result of an accident, David has only one eye. Which of the following depth cues would he not be able to use?
A.      accommodation
B.      retinal disparity
C.      linear perspective
D.      interposition

p. 129
Depth Perception
Level: Moderate
Type: Conceptual
Ans: B

98.     Imagine that you are looking at a baseball coming toward you. The farther away you perceive the object to be, the:
A.      greater the convergence
B.      smaller the retinal disparity
C.      greater the relative size
D.      smaller the interposition

p. 129
Depth Perception
Level: Easy
Type: Applied
Ans: A

99.     Because of retinal disparity, we can enjoy:
A.      watching a 3-D movie while wearing special glasses
B.      looking at the Muller-Lyer illusion
C.      being fooled by the Ames room
D.      trying to figure out impossible figures

p. 130
Depth Perception
Level: Easy
Type: Conceptual
Ans: A

100. How could a Cyclops (a mythical figure) land an airplane?
A. by relying on monocular cues
B. by relying on binocular cues
C. by relying on retinal disparity
D. by fitting the plane with special equipment

p. 130
Depth Perception
Level: Moderate
Type: Conceptual
Ans: C
*www*

101. A person who is blind in one eye uses more _____ cues than _____ cues.
A. memory; perceptual
B. binocular; monocular
C. monocular; binocular
D. inferential; stimulus

p. 130
Depth Perception
Level: Easy
Type: Factual
Ans: C

102. If one object partially overlaps another object, the partially overlapping object will appear closer because of the _____ depth cue.
A. motion parallax
B. relative size
C. interposition
D. retinal disparity

p. 130
Depth Perception
Level: Easy
Type: Factual
Ans: A
*PS/SG 6-12*

103. Which one of the following is <u>not</u> a monocular depth cue?
A. retinal disparity
B. linear perspective
C. relative size
D. motion parallax

p. 130
Depth Perception
Level: Easy
Type: Factual
Ans: A

104. As you look down the street, you see an apartment building partially overlapping an office building. Based on the depth cue of _____, you know that the apartment building is closer to you.
A. interposition
B. relative size
C. retinal disparity
D. light and shadow

p. 130
Depth Perception
Level: Easy
Type: Applied
Ans: D

105. In a sketch of the New York downtown area, Vincent creates a feeling of depth by drawing skyscrapers so that they partially overlap. The cue for depth he is using is known as:
A. linear perspective
B. relative size
C. atmospheric perspective
D. interposition

p. 130
Depth Perception
Level: Easy
Type: Factual
Ans: C
*www*

106. The convergence of parallel lines, giving the feeling of distance, is called:
A. relative size
B. convergence
C. linear perspective
D. aerial perspective

p. 130
Depth Perception
Level: Easy
Type: Conceptual
Ans: B

107.     A brochure displays a long stretch of road. The lines that make up the road are drawn so that they converge at the horizon. The result is that the brochure creates a sense of distance. This is based on a monocular cue called:

A.     texture gradient
B.     linear perspective
C.     relative size
D.     convergence

p. 130
Depth Perception
Level: Easy
Type: Conceptual
Ans: A

108.     To show a set of railroad tracks moving off into the distance, an artist paints the tracks so that the rails converge. This depth cue is known as:

A.     linear perspective
B.     atmospheric perspective
C.     relative size
D.     interposition

p. 130
Depth Perception
Level: Easy
Type: Factual
Ans: C

109.     If two objects are the same size, yet one appears to be larger, you make the assumption that that object is closer. Why?

A.     motion parallax
B.     atmospheric perspective
C.     relative size
D.     retinal disparity

p. 131
Depth Perception
Level: Easy
Type: Factual
Ans: B

110.     Which cue for depth relies on the fact that dust, smog, or water vapor give distant objects a hazy look?

A.     linear perspective
B.     atmospheric perspective
C.     closeness to the horizon
D.     interposition

p. 131
Depth Perception
Level: Easy
Type: Factual
Ans: A

111.     The depth cues of light and shadow make brightly-lit objects appear ___ while objects in the shadows are perceived to be _____.

A.     closer; farther away
B.     farther away; closer
C.     larger; smaller
D.     smaller; larger

p. 131
Depth Perception
Level: Easy
Type: Conceptual
Ans: D

112.     If you are looking at a lighthouse in the fog, the lighthouse will appear farther away than it really is because of a monocular depth cue called:

A.     interposition
B.     retinal disparity
C.     linear perspective
D.     atmospheric perspective

p. 131
Depth Perception
Level: Easy
Type: Factual
Ans: A

113.     The light and shadow depth cue:
A.     gives objects a three-dimensional look
B.     makes objects look partially overlapped
C.     creates a sense of texture and distance
D.     gives objects a hazy look, making them appear to be far away

| | | |
|---|---|---|
| p. 131 | 114. | Textures can be used to create a sense of depth because: |
| Depth Perception | A. | each eye sends a different, independent image to the brain |
| Level: Easy | B. | texture results in the figure being more dominant than the background |
| Type: Factual | C. | the loss of sharpness and detail causes a sense of distance |
| Ans: C | D. | the farther away the object is, the more defined the sense of texture |

| | | |
|---|---|---|
| p. 131 | 115. | An artist wishing to use texture as a cue to depth in his painting would: |
| Depth Perception | A. | put finer detail in objects that he wanted to appear farther away |
| Level: Easy | B. | put finer detail into an object that bordered the area to be viewed |
| Type: Conceptual | C. | put finer detail in objects he wanted to appear close |
| Ans: C | D. | space his objects evenly from near to far |

| | | |
|---|---|---|
| p. 131 | 116. | A famous painter used dust and clouds to create a depth cue in her |
| Depth Perception | | paintings. She used _____ as a depth cue. |
| Level: Easy | A. | light and shadow |
| Type: Factual | B. | convergence |
| Ans: D | C. | linear perspective |
| | D. | atmospheric perspective |

| | | |
|---|---|---|
| p. 131 | 117. | The brain transforms the speed of moving objects into indicators of |
| Depth Perception | | distance because of a depth cue called: |
| Level: Easy | A. | interposition |
| Type: Factual | B. | motion parallax |
| Ans: B | C. | linear perspective |
| | D. | retinal disparity |

| | | |
|---|---|---|
| p. 131 | 118. | According to motion parallax, near objects appear _____, whereas |
| Depth Perception | | objects in the distance appear _____. |
| Level: Easy | A. | smaller; larger |
| Type: Conceptual | B. | hazy; clear |
| Ans: D | C. | textured; shadowed |
| | D. | to move quickly; to move slowly |

| | | |
|---|---|---|
| p. 131 | 119. | Which of the following depth cues involves objects in motion? |
| Depth Perception | A. | motion perspective |
| Level: Easy | B. | motion gradient |
| Type: Factual | C. | motion parallax |
| Ans: C | D. | interpositional motion |

| | | |
|---|---|---|
| p. 132 | 120. | An illusion is: |
| Illusions | A. | the perception of an object which is not really there |
| Level: Easy | B. | a reminder that perception is a passive process |
| Type: Factual | C. | a distorted perception of reality |
| Ans: C | D. | the result of a biological deficit in sensory organs |

| | | |
|---|---|---|
| p. 132 | 121. | Illusions demonstrate what happens to our perceptual processes when: |
| Illusions | A. | we use only one eye to view an object |
| Level: Moderate | B. | retinal disparity occurs |
| Type: Conceptual | C. | our eyes fail to converge |
| Ans: D | D. | perceptual cues are distorted |

p. 132
Illusions
Level: Moderate
Type: Conceptual
Ans: D

122.    The study of illusions:
A.      is of interest to magicians, but not to scientists
B.      has failed to explain why the brain is fooled by certain visual images
C.      has been relevant to psychology ever since illusions became popular for the covers of introductory textbooks
D.      helps us to understand that assumptions we make about the world around us are sometimes incorrect

p. 132
Illusions
Level: Difficult
Type: Conceptual
Ans: B

123.    Impossible figures seem impossible because our previous experience with line drawings leads us to interpret figures as:
A.      two dimensional
B.      three dimensional
C.      smaller than they really are
D.      larger than they really are

p. 132
Illusions
Level: Easy
Type: Factual
Ans: B
PS/SG 6-13

124.    The reason you couldn't figure out the two-pronged/three-pronged impossible figure in the textbook is that:
A.      seeing it in the textbook aroused text anxiety and that threw you off
B.      you were attempting to see it as an object in the real world
C.      Westerners aren't as good at this kind of puzzle as Africans are
D.      it was just a joke

p. 132
Illusions
Level: Moderate
Type: Factual
Ans: C

125.    _____ cues make the moon on the horizon look larger because it appears _____.
A.      Distance; closer
B.      Binocular; closer
C.      Distance; farther away
D.      Subliminal; brighter

p. 132
Illusions
Level: Moderate
Type: Factual
Ans: A

126.    With regard to the moon illusion, people tend to perceive an elevated moon to be _____ compared to the horizon moon.
A.      closer
B.      further
C.      larger
D.      darker

p. 132
Illusions
Level: Moderate
Type: Applied
Ans: B

127.    Why might more UFO sightings be reported near the horizon than in other parts of the sky?
A.      Particles in the air make the horizon seem farther away.
B.      Ordinary objects appear larger near the horizon and could be mistaken for aircraft.
C.      Heat waves from the Earth's surface distort images close to the horizon.
D.      Light passing through the atmosphere at an angle produces a distorted image.

| | | |
|---|---|---|
| p. 133<br>Illusions<br>Level: Moderate<br>Type: Factual<br>Ans: D | 128. | In the Ames room: |
| | A. | lighting tricks create a sense of three dimensions when only two exist |
| | B. | the use of mirrors creates the illusion of greater space |
| | C. | cues to depth are distorted by presenting people of different sizes at the same distance |
| | D. | perceived size is distorted by our assumption that the room is rectangular |

| | | |
|---|---|---|
| p. 133<br>Illusions<br>Level: Moderate<br>Type: Factual<br>Ans: B | 129. | The Ames room is an effective illusion because: |
| | A. | linear perspective gives us a sense of depth |
| | B. | depth cues distort our perception of size |
| | C. | we assume outside corners are closer to us than inside corners |
| | D. | motion parallax gives us a sense of depth |

| | | |
|---|---|---|
| p. 133<br>Illusions<br>Level: Easy<br>Type: Factual<br>Ans: A<br>*PS/SG 6-14* | 130. | The reason people seem to change size as they change sides in the Ames room is that: |
| | A. | the room is not actually rectangular |
| | B. | hidden mirrors distort the images you see as you look in |
| | C. | a lens in the peephole forces you to view them upside down |
| | D. | the subtle coloring of the wall creates a hypnotic trance in the viewer |

| | | |
|---|---|---|
| p. 133<br>Illusions<br>Level: Moderate<br>Type: Factual<br>Ans: C | 131. | The Ponzo illusion illustrates that in some illusions: |
| | A. | monocular cues are very misleading |
| | B. | previous experience with corners of rooms leads us to make incorrect judgments |
| | C. | distance cues can distort size cues |
| | D. | eye convergence is susceptible to misapplication |

| | | |
|---|---|---|
| p. 133<br>Illusions<br>Level: Moderate<br>Type: Factual<br>Ans: C<br>*PS/SG 6-15* | 132. | One explanation for why the arrows in the Muller-Lyer illusion don't appear to be the same length is that: |
| | A. | our previous experience with arrows tells us they aren't the same |
| | B. | they really aren't quite the same - there is a tiny difference in length |
| | C. | your experience with the corners of rooms makes you see the arrows differently |
| | D. | this famous illusion remains unexplained - even Professors Muller and Lyer couldn't explain it |

| | | |
|---|---|---|
| p. 133<br>Illusions<br>Level: Moderate<br>Type: Conceptual<br>Ans: A | 133. | In your new job as an editor, you write headlines for newspaper articles. One article describes illusions and various explanations for them. Which of the following headlines best summarizes what we know about them? |
| | A. | "Illusions - Perception Is An Active Process" |
| | B. | "When We See, Perceptual Video Camera Records Reality" |
| | C. | "Illusions Happen Independently of Our Experiences" |
| | D. | "Illusions Caused by Problems in Sense Receptors" |

| | | |
|---|---|---|
| p. 133<br>Illusions<br>Level: Easy<br>Type: Factual<br>Ans: B | 134. | Based on your study of illusions, which of the following best describes perception? |
| | A. | passive |
| | B. | active |
| | C. | impersonal |
| | D. | voluntary |

p. 135
Research Focus:
  Subliminal Perception
Level: Moderate
Type: Factual
Ans: A

135. Research on the effects of subliminal self-help tapes indicates that:
A. changes in behavior are probably due to self-fulfilling prophecy about the tapes' alleged effectiveness
B. subliminal messages can cause improvement in memory, but not improvements in self-esteem
C. subliminal messages do not affect emotional states
D. changes in behavior are due to the subliminal message contained on the tape

p. 135
Research Focus:
  Subliminal Perception
Level: Moderate
Type: Factual
Ans: D
*PS/SG 6-16*

136. Should you scrap the Study Guide and buy a subliminal message tape? Research suggests that any improvement you get with those tapes is probably due to:
A. the effects of extra practice
B. turning the volume up too high
C. the Ponzo illusion
D. a self-fulfilling prophecy

p. 135
Research Focus:
  Subliminal Perception
Level: Moderate
Type: Factual
Ans: B

137. Why didn't Congress make subliminal advertising illegal?
A. Advertisers voluntarily discontinued the use of subliminal messages.
B. There is no reason - subliminal advertising is ineffective.
C. The subliminal advertising lobby put pressure on Congress not to.
D. The president promised to veto any proposal.

p. 135
Research Focus:
  Subliminal Perception
Level: Moderate
Type: Factual
Ans: C

138. The study on subliminal messages cited in your textbook suggests that among the subjects, 50% reported improvements in memory or self-esteem. The type of improvement, memory or self-esteem, was determined by:
A. the actual subliminal messages recorded on the tape
B. subject's own judgment of weakness
C. the title of the tape and not the actual content of messages on the tape
D. the experimenter manipulating title and content

p. 135
Research Focus:
  Subliminal Perception
Level: Easy
Type: Factual
Ans: B

139. When subjects in an experiment on subliminal perception were in happy moods, they:
A. perceived happy words slower than sad subjects
B. perceived happy words faster than sad subjects
C. perceived sad words faster than sad subjects
D. made complex decisions faster than sad subjects

p. 135
Research Focus:
  Subliminal Perception
Level: Easy
Type: Factual
Ans: D

140. Which of the following is correct about subliminal perception?
A. Subliminal messages in self-help tapes help people to improve memory.
B. Subliminal messages in self-help tapes help people to quit smoking.
C. Subliminal messages in self-help tapes help people to lose weight.
D. Subliminal messages in self-help tapes do not affect behavior.

| | | |
|---|---|---|
| p. 135 | 141. | Based on research, subliminal messages can: |
| Research Focus: | A. | prevent self-fulfilling prophecies from occurring |
| Subliminal Perception | B. | persuade us to buy specific items |
| Level: Easy | C. | influence emotional and cognitive processes |
| Type: Factual | D. | help us to modify behavior |
| Ans: C | | |

| | | |
|---|---|---|
| p. 136 | 142. | Dr. Mead visits a remote African tribe and shows them black-and-white and some color photographs of familiar wildlife. The responses of African natives to Dr. Mead's photographs demonstrate that: |
| Cultural Diversity: | | |
| Influence on Perceptions | | |
| Level: Easy | A. | we do not need color to interpret visual input |
| Type: Applied | B. | our cultural experiences affect what we perceive as being real |
| Ans: B | C. | the introduction of color actually confuses perception of photographs for those not familiar with photographs |
| | D. | black-and-white photos are easier to interpret than photos that are colored |

| | | |
|---|---|---|
| p. 136 | 143. | In a story comparing Americans and Japanese subjects on perception of an underwater scene, Americans: |
| Cultural Diversity: | | |
| Influence on Perceptions | A. | tended to focus on the fish |
| Level: Easy | B. | tended to focus on the background |
| Type: Factual | C. | tended to describe the relationship between fish and the background |
| Ans: A | D. | demonstrated holistic thinking |

| | | |
|---|---|---|
| p. 136 | 144. | You want to learn more about holistic thinking. Based on the study described in Module Six, which culture would you want to visit? |
| Cultural Diversity: | | |
| Influence on Perceptions | A. | southern United States |
| Level: Easy | B. | China |
| Type: Factual | C. | Africa |
| Ans: B | D. | northern Europe |

| | | |
|---|---|---|
| p. 137 | 145. | When non-Westerners look at a cartoon drawing of a dog wagging its tail, they will: |
| Cultural Diversity: | | |
| Influence on Perceptions | A. | perceive the dog as only a two-dimensional figure |
| Level: Easy | B. | perceive a perceptual set |
| Type: Factual | C. | not perceive the tail in motion |
| Ans: C | D. | perceive the tail in motion |

| | | |
|---|---|---|
| p. 137 | 146. | Lois tells her friend Karl to always type class assignments on an expensive typewriter because instructors are less likely to spot errors on an official-looking page. Lois's advice relies on: |
| Cultural Diversity: | | |
| Influence on Perceptions | | |
| Level: Easy | A. | instructor bias |
| Type: Applied | B. | perceptual set |
| Ans: B | C. | selective perception |
| | D. | a positive association between reading speed and clarity of the typed page |

| | | |
|---|---|---|
| p. 137 | 147. | The example presented in your textbook about assuming that a body-builder is a large man, but in fact, he is a small man, represents the influence of: |
| Cultural Diversity: | | |
| Influence on Perceptions | | |
| Level: Moderate | A. | continuity |
| Type: Factual | B. | phi phenomenon |
| Ans: C | C. | perceptual set |
| | D. | perception |

p. 137
Cultural Diversity:
  Influence on Perceptions
Level: Moderate
Type: Factual
Ans: A

148. In the past, Burmese women were considered attractive if they had exceptionally:
A. long necks
B. large ears
C. long hair
D. small ears

p. 137
Cultural Diversity:
  Influence on Perceptions
Level: Easy
Type: Conceptual
Ans: D

149. A subject has been exposed to three lights flashing in rapid succession every thirty seconds. After many of these trials, the experimenter has two of them flash. If the subject, in error, reports seeing three lights flash for this trial, it is probably because of:
A. the fact that the stimuli were visual and not auditory
B. long-term memory distortion
C. perceptual acuity
D. perceptual set

p. 137
Cultural Diversity:
  Influence on Perceptions
Level: Easy
Type: Conceptual
Ans: C

150. The key idea in perceptual set is:
A. monocular depth perception
B. figure-ground rule
C. expectation
D. phi movement

p. 138
ESP:
  Extrasensory Perception
Level: Easy
Type: Factual
Ans: C

151. The group of psychic experiences that involve perceiving or sending information outside normal sensory process is called:
A. gestalt perception
B. subliminal perception
C. extrasensory perception
D. telepathy

p. 138
ESP:
  Extrasensory Perception
Level: Easy
Type: Applied
Ans: B
*www*

152. Herb claims that he can read other people's thoughts. This ability is called:
A. psychokinesis
B. telepathy
C. precognition
D. clairvoyance

p. 138
ESP:
  Extrasensory Perception
Level: Easy
Type: Applied
Ans: C

153. Marta sets up a booth at a local fair and claims she can tell the future by looking at a person's palm. She is claiming to have which of the following abilities?
A. psychokinesis
B. telepathy
C. precognition
D. clairvoyance

p. 138
ESP:
  Extrasensory Perception
Level: Easy
Type: Factual
Ans: D

154. If someone reportedly has precognition, then they supposedly have the ability to:
A. read the minds of other people
B. "talk" to people with their minds
C. perceive objects which are invisible
D. foretell events before they happen

p. 138
ESP:
  Extrasensory Perception
Level: Easy
Type: Factual
Ans: D

155. The ability to see things that are not actually present is called:
A. psychokinesis
B. telepathy
C. precognition
D. clairvoyance

p. 138
ESP:
  Extrasensory Perception
Level: Easy
Type: Applied
Ans: B
www

156. Julia says that she can see objects that no one else can see. This is an example of:
A. precognition
B. clairvoyance
C. psychokinesis
D. convergence

p. 138
ESP:
  Extrasensory Perception
Level: Easy
Type: Factual
Ans: B

157. Felipe claims to be able to move objects simply by concentrating on them. This psychic ability is known as:
A. telepathy
B. psychokinesis
C. precognition
D. clairvoyance

p. 138
ESP:
  Extrasensory Perception
Level: Easy
Type: Applied
Ans: A

158. You are at a movie theater and you mentally will your popcorn to rise out of your hands and float through the air, and it does! You have just experienced the phenomenon of :
A. psychokinesis
B. telepathy
C. an out-of-body experience
D. clairvoyance

p. 138
ESP:
  Extrasensory Perception
Level: Easy
Type: Factual
Ans: C

159. James Randi and others have demonstrated that:
A. extrasensory perception does, in fact, exist
B. extrasensory perception is a skill that can be practical
C. most of what passes for ESP is really just trickery
D. people are capable of many unexplainable psychic feats

p. 138
ESP:
  Extrasensory Perception
Level: Easy
Type: Factual
Ans: D
PS/SG 6-20

160. Tops on the list of people not to invite to an ESP demonstration:
A. Gustav Fechner
B. E. H. Weber
C. Max Wertheimer
D. Amazing Randi

p. 138
ESP:
  Extrasensory Perception
Level: Moderate
Type: Factual
Ans: D

161. According to the text, there are people who claim to have psychic powers:
A. but most are never given a chance to prove it
B. but the skepticism of scientists creates negative energy that disrupts these powers when these psychics are being tested
C. and most have been certified as true psychics by James Randi
D. most, however, cannot demonstrate these powers under carefully controlled conditions

p. 138
ESP:
  Extrasensory Perception
Level: Moderate
Type: Applied
Ans: B

162. You're reading about a series of scientific studies that suggests that ESP is a real phenomenon. What aspects of the methodology should you pay close attention to, according to the textbook?
A. random assignment of subjects
B. suggesting that ESP occurs, but it only occurs no more than by chance
C. equal numbers of male subjects and female subjects
D. confounds

p. 138
ESP:
  Extrasensory Perception
Level: Easy
Type: Factual
Ans: C
*PS/SG 6-21*

163. Many people believe in it, but convincing evidence of ESP has been undercut by the:
A. hocus-pocus that surrounds ESP demonstrations
B. refusal of psychologists to investigate it seriously
C. inability to repeat positive results
D. fact that some people have it and others don't

p. 138
ESP:
  Extrasensory Perception
Level: Moderate
Type: Factual
Ans: C

164. How do researchers evaluate testimonials of psi phenomenon?
A. accept - testimonials represent hard, scientific evidence
B. accept - testimonials are factual evidence
C. reject - testimonials are too prone to bias
D. reject - there are not enough testimonials to establish baselines

p. 138
ESP:
  Extrasensory Perception
Level: Moderate
Type: Factual
Ans: A

165. Out of 12 alleged psychics who have accepted James Randi's $100,000 challenge, how many have successfully demonstrated their psychic ability?
A. 0
B. 1
C. 2
D. 3

p. 139
ESP:
  Extrasensory Perception
Level: Easy
Type: Applied
Ans: B

166. Professor Carey wishes to scientifically study ESP. Which is the most preferred method for study?
A. Zener cards
B. Ganzfeld procedure
C. Gestalt procedure
D. testimonials

p. 139
ESP:
  Extrasensory Perception
Level: Easy
Type: Factual
Ans: C

167. The _____ procedure is used to test for telepathic communication and was used by Bem and Honorton in their study.
A. Zener
B. phi
C. Ganzfeld
D. Gestalt

p. 139
ESP:
  Extrasensory Perception
Level: Easy
Type: Conceptual
Ans: B

168. Bem and Honorton report data that support telepathy. The most prudent response to this study is to:
A. conclude that ESP is a reliable phenomenon
B. wait and see if the results can be replicated by someone else
C. judge that Bem and Honorton are frauds
D. question the subjects in the study about their experiences

p. 139
ESP:
  Extrasensory Perception
Level: Moderate
Type: Conceptual
Ans: B

169. As a test of ESP, you ask your friend Jean to predict the numbers on ten cards you pull from the deck. Surprisingly, she gets six correct. Which of the following conclusions is most valid?
A. The cards have been fixed.
B. Repeated tests would reduce Jean's accuracy so she probably doesn't have ESP.
C. Jean would be considered to have ESP since her accuracy rate was greater than 50 percent.
D. Jean was so accurate because friends have a special rapport.

p. 139
ESP:
  Extrasensory Perception
Level: Easy
Type: Factual
Ans: C
*www*

170. One of the biggest problems in conducting psychic research is:
A. getting subjects who are willing to participate
B. getting college students to believe in ESP
C. the inability to repeat positive results
D. that researchers randomize the procedure for choosing images

p. 139
ESP:
  Extrasensory Perception
Level: Easy
Type: Factual
Ans: A

171. Of all the questionable methodology of ESP studies, which one is the most serious?
A. failure to replicate or to repeat the results by another researcher or lab
B. not randomizing presentation of stimuli
C. putting subjects and researchers in close physical proximity during testing
D. unequal numbers of male subjects and female subjects

p. 139
ESP:
  Extrasensory Perception
Level: Easy
Type: Factual
Ans: C

172. Steve wants to call a psychic hotline. He does and is amazed by the psychic's ability to predict Steve's future. What does science say about psychics?
A. No research has been done to examine the accuracy of psychics.
B. Psychics abilities cannot be tested by the scientific method.
C. They are no more accurate than chance at predicting the future.
D. The scientific evidence is mixed.

p. 140
Application:
  Creating Perceptions
Level: Easy
Type: Factual
Ans: D

173. The illusion of lights moving that are actually stationary is called:
A. apparent motion
B. real motion
C. motion parallax
D. phi movement

p. 140
Application:
  Creating Perceptions
Level: Easy
Type: Factual
Ans: C

174.  As you look at a series of still pictures presented at about 24 frames per second, you perceive motion. Which of the following allows you to fill in between the images?
A.  motion parallax
B.  real motion
C.  closure
D.  retinal disparity

p. 140
Application:
  Creating Perceptions
Level: Easy
Type: Factual
Ans: A
*www*

175.  Traffic arrows composed of flashing lights are an example of:
A.  phi movement
B.  virtual reality
C.  the Muller-Lyer illusion
D.  brightness constancy

p. 140
Application:
  Creating Perceptions
Level: Easy
Type: Factual
Ans: A

176.  Phi movement is now known as:
A.  set movement
B.  movement parallax
C.  perceptual movement
D.  apparent movement

p. 140
Application:
  Creating Perceptions
Level: Easy
Type: Factual
Ans: A

177.  In animated cartoons, movement is created by the rapid presentation of still images. This movement is known as:
A.  apparent motion
B.  real motion
C.  motion parallax
D.  the Muller-Lyer illusion

p. 141
Application:
  Creating Perceptions
Level: Easy
Type: Factual
Ans: C

178.  A computer-generated illusionary experience is called:
A.  apparent motion
B.  a phi movement
C.  virtual reality
D.  a motion parallax

p. 141
Application:
  Creating Perceptions
Level: Easy
Type: Factual
Ans: D
*PS/SG 6-24*

179.  When "virtual reality" becomes an accomplished fact, you will be able to:
A.  watch Star Trek reruns in 3-D
B.  dial up famous psychologists on your computer at home
C.  learn all the facts you need in psych while you sleep
D.  trade in your psych textbook for a headset and a DVD

p. 141          180.    According to the textbook, a promising use of virtual reality is to:
Application:       A.     help a blind person see
   Creating Perceptions    B.     treat phobias like a fear of spiders
Level: Easy         C.     experience how other people perceive the world
Type: Factual       D.     train psychologists how to deal with suicidal people
Ans: A

p. 141          181.    Our first impression of other people is influenced by:
Application:       A.     figure-ground
   Creating Perceptions    B.     principles of perceptual organization
Level: Easy         C.     controlled process
Type: Factual       D.     their facial features
Ans: D

p. 141          182.    The fact that our first impressions of people are influenced by their facial features, hairstyles, and skin color suggest that perceptions are:
Application:
   Creating Perceptions    A.     too vague to be trusted
Level: Moderate      B.     interpretations
Type: Conceptual     C.     exact copies of reality
Ans: B            D.     formed by combining sensations

True/False

| | | | |
|---|---|---|---|
| F | www | 1. | The absolute threshold is the intensity level at which a person has a 100% chance of detecting it. |
| T | | 2. | The accuracy of mammogram tests increases by 20% when reviewed by two doctors. |
| T | www | 3. | The smallest change you can detect in a stimulus is called the just noticeable difference. |
| F | | 4. | Weber's law says that low intensity stimuli need greater changes to detect a difference. |
| T | | 5. | In sensation, our sensory receptors are activated by an outside stimulus. |
| F | www | 6. | Our perceptions are typically exact replicas of the original stimuli. |
| F | | 7. | Transduction is the process by which sensations are changed into meaningful perceptions. |
| F | | 8. | Sensation of a stimulus is influenced by our personal experiences and memories. |
| T | www | 9. | The structuralists say that perceptions are really made up of individual basic elements. |
| T | | 10. | According to the gestalt psychologists, perception occurs because of the brain's ability to organize sensations according to rules. |
| F | | 11. | The continuity rule says that stimuli are organized in the simplest way possible. |
| F | www | 12. | The rule of proximity says that we tend to perceive smooth paths when looking at a series of points. |
| F | | 13. | When the image of a stimulus changes shape or size on the retina, we perceive the actual stimulus to be changing. |
| F | www | 14. | Objects projected on the retina are three dimensional. |
| T | www | 15. | Linear perspective is a monocular depth cue. |
| T | | 16. | As objects come close to you, convergence increases. |
| | | 17. | A full moon high in the sky is perceived to be closer to you than a moon on the horizon. |
| T | www | 18. | We perceive the lines in the Muller-Lyer illusion to be corners. |

| F |  | 19. | Any change in memory following listening to tapes with subliminal messages to improve memory is probably due to the effectiveness of subliminal messages. |
|---|---|---|---|
| F |  | 20. | Culture has very little effect on perception. |
| F |  | 21. | Testimonial evidence provides hard scientific evidence that ESP exists. |
| T | *www* | 22. | A tool that ESP researchers have to determine the reliability of psi phenomenon is replication. |
| T |  | 23. | In apparent movement, an object is stationary, but appears to be moving. |
| F | *www* | 24. | Recent research suggests that robotic surgery introduces too much error and is dangerous. |
| T |  | 25. | First impressions of others are influenced by their physical appearances. |

Short-Answer Essay Questions

1.  Describe how the absolute threshold has real-life implications in reading mammogram tests.
2.  Using the research cited in Module Six, how did researchers determine if fabric softeners had an effect on towels?
3.  Contrast sensation and perception. (*www*)
4.  How would the Gestalt psychologist explain the manner in which sensations are organized into perceptions?
5.  Describe each of the following rules of organization: figure-ground, similarity, closure, proximity, simplicity, and continuity. (*www*)
6.  Explain how convergence and retinal disparity can provide information to the brain regarding the distance of an object.
7.  Draw a picture that incorporates the monocular depth cues of linear perspective, interposition, and relative size. Make sure that you label the cues.
8.  Select the Ames room, Ponzo illusion or the Muller-Lyer illusion. Describe the illusion and then describe an explanation for it. (*www*)
9.  What does the research say about subliminal messages changing specific behaviors and changing perceptions? (*www*)
10. Describe the types of extrasensory perception. What is the conclusion your textbook makes regarding ESP? (*www*)

# Module 7 - Consciousness, Sleep, & Dreams

p. 147
Introduction
Level: Easy
Type: Factual
Ans: B

1. The purpose of isolating a person in a cave for many months without clocks, television, or radio was to determine:
   A. if people can live without such modern devices
   B. how much the person sleeps with no time cues
   C. how the devices' electromagnetic waves affect memory
   D. how many books the person could read

p. 147
Introduction
Level: Easy
Type: Factual
Ans: A

2. Stefania, the woman who spent 130 days underground, had a difficult time:
   A. estimating the passage of time
   B. keeping physically fit
   C. being away from her family
   D. with concentration near the end of her ordeal

p. 147
Introduction
Level: Moderate
Type: Conceptual
Ans: D

3. The four months Stefania spent in a Plexiglas module taught researchers:
   A. social deprivation has negative effects on mental health
   B. blood sugar levels are linked to light cues
   C. delusions are commonplace in light deprived settings
   D. without cues of light, it becomes difficult to judge time

p. 147
Introduction
Level: Easy
Type: Factual
Ans: D
*www*

4. Without time cues, the body's preferred length of day was believed to be about:
   A. 22 hours
   B. 23 hours
   C. 24 hours
   D. 25 hours

p. 147
Introduction
Level: Easy
Type: Factual
Ans: A

5. In the 1950s, which of the following gave researchers a method to study dreaming in the laboratory?
   A. discovering rapid eye movement signaled dreaming
   B. development of the PET scan
   C. asking subjects to spend days isolated from all time cues
   D. locating the ventrolateral preoptic nucleus in the human brain

p. 147
Introduction
Level: Easy
Type: Factual
Ans: B

6. What did the discovery of rapid eye movement and its association with dreaming give researchers?
   A. a reliable method to study how the body uses light cues
   B. a reliable method to identify and study dreaming in the laboratory
   C. a reliable method to study the effects of hypnosis on dreams
   D. a reliable method to study the role that vision plays in dreaming

p. 148
Continuum of
  Consciousness
Level: Easy
Type: Factual
Ans: B
*www*

7. Consciousness is defined as:
   A. the process by which a sensation becomes a perception
   B. different levels of awareness of one's thoughts and feelings
   C. cognitive reflection of the physical events one encounters
   D. introspective thinking which results in mental experiences

p. 148
Continuum of
  Consciousness
Level: Easy
Type: Factual
Ans: D

8. Your different levels of awareness of thoughts and feelings is called:
A. apnea
B. perception
C. identity
D. consciousness

p. 148
Continuum of
  Consciousness
Level: Easy
Type: Factual
Ans: C

9. According to your textbook, what is the term that refers to different levels of awareness of one's thoughts and feelings?
A. self-actualization
B. meditation
C. consciousness
D. introspection

p. 148
Continuum of
  Consciousness
Level: Moderate
Type: Conceptual
Ans: A

10. Dr. Barr is an authority on consciousness and wishes to set up a website that summarizes his research in the area. Which of the following website addresses would be most descriptive?
A. www.awareness.edu
B. www.freud.edu
C. www.altered_states.edu
D. www.rem.edu

p. 148
Continuum of
  Consciousness
Level: Moderate
Type: Conceptual
Ans: A

11. The continuum of consciousness ranges from:
A. acute awareness to total unawareness
B. limited awareness to fantasizing
C. automatic process to altered states
D. unconsciousness to dreaming

p. 148
Continuum of
  Consciousness
Level: Easy
Type: Factual
Ans: C
PS/SG 7-2

12. We naturally think in terms of the two states called "conscious" and "unconscious," but actually there:
A. are three states, including the "high" from drugs
B. are four states: conscious, drowsy, dreaming, and unconscious
C. is a continuum of consciousness
D. is no measurable differences between consciousness and unconsciousness

p. 148
Continuum of
  Consciousness
Level: Easy
Type: Factual
Ans: D

13. Activities, such as studying for an exam, which require full awareness and concentration are called:
A. automatic processes
B. conscious processes
C. focused processes
D. controlled processes

p. 148
Continuum of
  Consciousness
Level: Easy
Type: Applied
Ans: A

14. Answering this question correctly is an example of a(n) _____ since it requires concentration and your full attention.
A. controlled process
B. conscious process
C. introspective process
D. automatic process

p. 148
Continuum of
  Consciousness
Level: Easy
Type: Factual
Ans: D
*PS/SG 7-3*

15. Psychologists call activities that require full awareness, alertness, and concentration:
- A. automatic processes
- B. altered states
- C. comas
- D. controlled processes

p. 148
Continuum of
  Consciousness
Level: Easy
Type: Applied
Ans: B
*www*

16. Andy is learning how to juggle three balls. He is not very good at it; he keeps dropping them. But you can see the concentration on his face. Juggling for Andy is a(n):
- A. automatic process
- B. controlled process
- C. attentional process
- D. introspective process

p. 148
Continuum of
  Consciousness
Level: Moderate
Type: Conceptual
Ans: C

17. Why does using a car phone while driving increase the chance of having a car accident, according to your textbook?
- A. Automatic processes like using a car phone disrupts other ongoing activities like driving.
- B. When talking on the phone, we tend to enter an altered state that disrupts consciousness.
- C. Controlled processes like using a car phone disrupts other ongoing activities like driving.
- D. Most of the conversations that take place on car phones tend to be highly emotional and this increases road rage.

p. 148
Continuum of
  Consciousness
Level: Moderate
Type: Applied
Ans: A

18. Although Christine is concentrating on reading her psychology book, she can also eat her breakfast, brush her hair, and put on her nail polish without interfering with her studying. For Christine, these other activities are called:
- A. automatic processes
- B. subliminal processes
- C. uncontrolled processes
- D. unconscious processes

p. 148
Continuum of
  Consciousness
Level: Easy
Type: Factual
Ans: C
*PS/SG 7-4*

19. Activities that require little awareness, take minimal attention, and do not interfere with other ongoing activities are called:
- A. implicit activities
- B. altered states of consciousness
- C. automatic processes
- D. unconsciousness

p. 148
Continuum of
  Consciousness
Level: Moderate
Type: Applied
Ans: C
*www*

20. "I can chew gum and walk at the same time." This best illustrates:
- A. controlled processes
- B. altered states of consciousness
- C. automatic processes
- D. daydreaming

<table>
<tr><td>

p. 148
Continuum of
  Consciousness
Level: Moderate
Type: Conceptual
Ans: D

</td><td>

21. Controlled processes is to automatic processes as _____ is to _____.
A. suprachiasmatic nucleus; basal ganglia
B. absolute threshold; JND
C. daydreaming; night dreaming
D. full awareness; little awareness

</td></tr>

<tr><td>

p. 148
Continuum of
  Consciousness
Level: Easy
Type: Factual
Ans: B

</td><td>

22. People generally daydream during situations which:
A. require a great deal of attention
B. are repetitious or boring
C. are controlled processes
D. immediately precede sleeping

</td></tr>

<tr><td>

p. 148
Continuum of
  Consciousness
Level: Easy
Type: Factual
Ans: C

</td><td>

23. What appears to be a function of daydreaming?
A. to act as a safety valve to release pent-up sexual desires
B. to facilitate the release of growth hormones
C. to remind us of important things in the future
D. to encode memories into the unconscious mind

</td></tr>

<tr><td>

p. 148
Continuum of
  Consciousness
Level: Moderate
Type: Applied
Ans: B

</td><td>

24. Professor Clark is lecturing and notices a student in the back of the room who appears to be daydreaming. Professor Clark startles the student by asking, "Excuse me. Can I be of service to you?" Given what we know about daydreaming, the student is most likely to be daydreaming about:
A. "I was just imagining lying on the beach soaking up the sun."
B. "I was just thinking about a paper I have to write in another course."
C. a sexual fantasy
D. "I was just thinking what I would do if a won the Mega Lotto tonight -- it's up to $10 million dollars."

</td></tr>

<tr><td>

p. 148
Continuum of
  Consciousness
Level: Easy
Type: Factual
Ans: B

</td><td>

25. Meditation, hypnosis, or drug use usually produce which type of consciousness?
A. automatic processes
B. altered states
C. sleep and dreams
D. cognitive unconscious

</td></tr>

<tr><td>

p. 148
Continuum of
  Consciousness
Level: Moderate
Type: Applied
Ans: C

</td><td>

26. Young David is being wheeled into the operating room for surgery and the preoperative drugs are having an effect. His eyes are open, but his perception of the world around him, the voices of the surgical team, and the faces of his relatives are very different than normal. At what point along the continuum of consciousness is David most likely to be?
A. daydreaming
B. unconsciousness
C. altered states
D. cognitive preconscious

</td></tr>
</table>

p. 148
Continuum of
  Consciousness
Level: Easy
Type: Applied
Ans: B

27.    As Jotham is praying, he experiences an awareness that is different from normal consciousness. Jotham is <u>most</u> likely experiencing:
A.    automatic processes
B.    altered states
C.    sleep and dreams
D.    nondeclarative memory

p. 148
Continuum of
  Consciousness
Level: Easy
Type: Factual
Ans: D

28.    _____ refers to awareness that differs from normal consciousness.
A.    Automatic processes
B.    Cognitive unconscious
C.    Controlled processes
D.    Altered states

p. 149
Continuum of
  Consciousness
Level: Easy
Type: Factual
Ans: D

29.    Which type of consciousness involves passing through five different states of differing levels of consciousness?
A.    altered states
B.    automatic processes
C.    coma
D.    sleep

p. 149
Continuum of
  Consciousness
Level: Easy
Type: Factual
Ans: C
*www*

30.    Tim believes that sleep is one continuous state of consciousness. Is Tim right?
A.    Yes - sleep is made up of NREM consciousness
B.    Yes - sleep is made up of REM consciousness
C.    No - sleep is made up of several states of body arousal and consciousness
D.    No - sleep is made up of REM and NREM consciousness

p. 149
Continuum of
  Consciousness
Level: Easy
Type: Factual
Ans: A

31.    As we pass into the deepest stages of sleep, we may:
A.    sleeptalk or sleepwalk
B.    have nightmares
C.    have very vivid and emotional dreams
D.    enter REM

p. 149
Continuum of
  Consciousness
Level: Easy
Type: Factual
Ans: C

32.    The individual <u>most</u> associated with the concept of the unconscious is:
A.    B.F. Skinner
B.    Wilhelm Wundt
C.    Sigmund Freud
D.    Stephen LaBerge

p. 149
Continuum of
  Consciousness
Level: Easy
Type: Factual
Ans: A

33.    According to Freud, where do we place threatening wishes or desires?
A.    unconscious
B.    altered state of consciousness
C.    conscious
D.    unconsciousness

p. 149
Continuum of
  Consciousness
Level: Moderate
Type: Factual
Ans: B
*www*

34. The term _____ refers to mental and emotional processes of which we are unaware but that influence our conscious thoughts and behaviors.
  A. unconsciousness
  B. implicit or nondeclarative memory
  C. coma
  D. altered states

p. 149
Continuum of
  Consciousness
Level: Moderate
Type: Conceptual
Ans: C

35. Can you describe the complex motor movements involved in riding a bicycle according to the cognitive view of the unconscious?
  A. Yes - since motor memories are automatic processes
  B. Yes - motor memories are examples of controlled processes
  C. No - these motor memories are implicit or nondeclarative memories
  D. No - these motor memories are often associated with threatening wishes and desires and therefore are stored in the unconscious

p. 149
Continuum of
  Consciousness
Level: Moderate
Type: Conceptual
Ans: B

36. Implicit memory is to _____ as unconscious is to _____.
  A. subjective; objective
  B. motor and emotional memories; threatening memories
  C. primary; secondary
  D. motor and emotional memories; primary memories

p. 149
Continuum of
  Consciousness
Level: Easy
Type: Factual
Ans: D

37. A hard blow to the head can produce a temporary state of :
  A. cognitive unconscious
  B. brain death
  C. sleep
  D. unconsciousness

p. 149
Continuum of
  Consciousness
Level: Easy
Type: Factual
Ans: A

38. A person who is classified as being in a vegetative state:
  A. has no awareness or responsiveness
  B. is temporarily unconscious
  C. is considered to be in an altered state
  D. is capable of mental processes

p. 149
Continuum of
  Consciousness
Level: Easy
Type: Conceptual
Ans: C

39. Professor Johnson views the unconscious as an active psychological process that protects us from threatening thoughts and desires. Her views are <u>most</u> consistent with:
  A. Czeisler
  B. Kihlstrom
  C. Freud
  D. Mesmer

| | | |
|---|---|---|
| p. 150 | 40. | You have internal timing devices set for hours, a single day, and for |
| Rhythms of Sleeping and | | many days. These are: |
|   Waking | A. | biological clocks |
| Level: Easy | B. | lunar clocks |
| Type: Factual | C. | biorhythms |
| Ans: A | D. | circadian rhythms |

| | | |
|---|---|---|
| p. 150 | 41. | Dr. Buckbee is studying biological clocks. He is <u>most</u> interested in the |
| Rhythms of Sleeping and | | clock that is set for about a single day. Dr. Buckbee studies: |
|   Waking | A. | suprachiasmatic rhythms |
| Level: Moderate | B. | lunar rhythms |
| Type: Applied | C. | daily rhythms |
| Ans: D | D. | circadian rhythms |

| | | |
|---|---|---|
| p. 150 | 42. | What is the literal meaning of circadian? |
| Rhythms of Sleeping and | A. | "the mind's clock" |
|   Waking | B. | "about a day" |
| Level: Moderate | C. | "the mind's day" |
| Type: Factual | D. | "time has no end" |
| Ans: B | | |

| | | |
|---|---|---|
| p. 150 | 43. | Have you noticed that you often wake up just before the alarm clock goes |
| Rhythms of Sleeping and | | off? Credit it to the fact that we humans have a built-in: |
|   Waking | A. | aversion to jangling noise, which we try to avoid |
| Level: Easy | B. | biological clock |
| Type: Conceptual | C. | sense of responsibility |
| Ans: B | D. | brain mechanism that is always monitoring the external environment, even |
| *PS/SG 7-5* | | during sleep |

| | | |
|---|---|---|
| p. 150 | 44. | A researcher wishes to investigate the length of the sleep-wake cycle that |
| Rhythms of Sleeping and | | is regulated by a subject's biological clock. The researcher can do this by: |
|   Waking | A. | letting the subject eat and sleep whenever he or she feels like it |
| Level: Moderate | B. | asking the subject to estimate the time at certain intervals without the use |
| Type: Factual | | of a clock |
| Ans: C | C. | removing all cues to time and measuring when the subject sleeps and |
| | | wakes |
| | D. | analyzing the cycle produced by brain wave patterns |

| | | |
|---|---|---|
| p. 150 | 45. | A circadian rhythm is a(n): |
| Rhythms of Sleeping and | A. | naturally occurring cycle in the body set to about 24 hours |
|   Waking | B. | altered state of consciousness |
| Level: Moderate | C. | type of neurotransmitter involved in sleep |
| Type: Factual | D. | naturally occurring cycle in the body set to about 12 or 13 hours |
| Ans: A | | |

| | | |
|---|---|---|
| p. 150 | 46. | Physiological cycles which are set for a one-day period are called: |
| Rhythms of Sleeping and | A. | REM cycles |
|   Waking | B. | theta movements |
| Level: Easy | C. | circadian rhythms |
| Type: Factual | D. | automatic processes |
| Ans: C | | |
| *www* | | |

p. 150
Rhythms of Sleeping and
  Waking
Level: Easy
Type: Factual
Ans: B

47. If left in a place with no time or light cues, your sleep-wake cycle would:
A. remain at 24 hours
B. change to about a little more than 24 hours
C. keep constant at 12 hours
D. remain unchanged at about 4 hours

p. 150
Rhythms of Sleeping and
  Waking
Level: Easy
Type: Factual
Ans: C
*PS/SG 7-6*

48. If human beings were deprived of all mechanical means of telling time (like clocks), they would:
A. still follow schedules and be punctual, thanks to their biological clocks
B. follow a natural clock with a day about 30 hours long
C. not stick to strict schedules the way we do now
D. lose all sense of when things should be done

p. 150
Rhythms of Sleeping and
  Waking
Level: Moderate
Type: Applied
Ans: D

49. Imagine that NASA conducts a study to find out the length of a person's sleep-wake cycle if all time cues, such as daylight and clocks, are removed. How long would you predict this cycle to be, given these conditions?
A. 16 hours and 32 minutes long
B. 20 hours long
C. 24 hours long
D. 24 hours and 18 minutes long

p. 150
Rhythms of Sleeping and
  Waking
Level: Easy
Type: Factual
Ans: B
*www*

50. Each day _____ resets our circadian clock.
A. alarm clocks
B. morning sunlight
C. the feeling of hunger
D. evening sunlight

p. 150
Rhythms of Sleeping and
  Waking
Level: Easy
Type: Factual
Ans: C

51. The interval timing clock is located in the brain area known as the:
A. circadian
B. frontal lobe
C. basal ganglia
D. suprachiasmatic nucleus

p. 150
Rhythms of Sleeping and
  Waking
Level: Easy
Type: Factual
Ans: B
*PS/SG 7-7*

52. The brain structure that regulates many circadian rhythms is called the:
A. internal timing clock
B. suprachiasmatic nucleus
C. resetting clock center
D. biological stopwatch

p. 150
Rhythms of Sleeping and
  Waking
Level: Easy
Type: Factual
Ans: C

53.   The suprachiasmatic nucleus is found in the:
A.   cerebellum
B.   hippocampus
C.   hypothalamus
D.   basal ganglia

p. 150
Rhythms of Sleeping and
  Waking
Level: Easy
Type: Factual
Ans: B

54.   "I am pretty good at judging the passage of time. I don't need to look at my watch or the clock on the wall to know when I've studied for an hour." This person takes advantage of:
A.   circadian rhythms
B.   her interval timing clock
C.   melatonin
D.   her activation-synthesis clock

p. 150
Rhythms of Sleeping and
  Waking
Level: Easy
Type: Factual
Ans: A

55.   If a rat's interval timing clock is destroyed, it cannot:
A.   time intervals for finding food
B.   reset its suprachiasmatic nucleus
C.   find food
D.   remember where food is located

p. 150
Rhythms of Sleeping and
  Waking
Level: Easy
Type: Factual
Ans: C

56.   Harry can take a one-hour nap and wake up one hour later without an alarm clock. Which of the following is the best explanation?
A.   His optic nerve keeps track of the time.
B.   The clock in his suprachiasmatic nucleus keeps track of the time.
C.   His interval timing clock keeps track of the time.
D.   The light in his dorm room awakens him.

p. 150
Rhythms of Sleeping and
  Waking
Level: Easy
Type: Factual
Ans: C

57.   After telling your friends about the role of light in the sleep-wake cycle, one of them asks about blind people. You mention:
A.   that nearly all blind people have serious problems with their sleep-wake cycle
B.   all blind people must use auditory cues of time passage
C.   that somehow light is transmitted to the brain in some blind people
D.   blindness causes profound disturbances in sleeping which must be treated with hormone injections

p. 151
Rhythms of Sleeping and
  Waking
Level: Moderate
Type: Factual
Ans: B

58.   How does the body reset its genetically preset sleep-wake circadian clock to the 24 hour day?
A.   morning light enters the eye and is sent to the basal ganglia
B.   morning light enters the eye and is sent to the suprachiasmatic nucleus
C.   the sound of the clock alarm resets the circadian clock
D.   eating breakfast in the morning resets hormonal levels

p. 151
Rhythms of Sleeping and
  Waking
Level: Moderate
Type: Conceptual
Ans: A

59.   The fundamental problem underlying jet lag and accidents during graveyard shifts is that:
A.   our circadian clock is preset for a little over 24 hours, but we live in a world set for 24 hours
B.   corporate greed is inconsistent with the biological needs of people
C.   we do not know how to reset circadian rhythms
D.   we do not value good, quality sleep

p. 151
Rhythms of Sleeping and
  Waking
Level: Moderate
Type: Factual
Ans: A

60.    Everyday our circadian clock gets reset by about:
A.    3 minutes
B.    18 minutes
C.    1 hour
D.    3 hours

p. 151
Rhythms of Sleeping and
  Waking
Level: Easy
Type: Applied
Ans: B

61.    Eric usually has problems with attention and alertness at work. Last week he was involved in a minor accident at work. He talks about experiencing a "dead zone." Since Eric does not abuse drugs, the most likely reason for Eric's problems at work is:
A.    that he feels unfulfilled
B.    he works the graveyard shift
C.    family problems at home
D.    his lack of confidence in management

p. 151
Rhythms of Sleeping and
  Waking
Level: Easy
Type: Applied
Ans: C

62.    Tom is working the graveyard shift at the mill. He has just reached the "dead zone" and is experiencing problems with alertness. The clock on the wall reads:
A.    1:00 AM
B.    2:00 AM
C.    5:00 AM
D.    6:00 AM

p. 151
Rhythms of Sleeping and
  Waking
Level: Easy
Type: Factual
Ans: B

63.    Most highway accidents occur:
A.    Monday 6:30-7:30 AM
B.    Saturday 2-3:00 AM
C.    Saturday 7-8:00 AM
D.    Sunday 1-2:00 AM

p. 151
Rhythms of Sleeping and
  Waking
Level: Easy
Type: Factual
Ans: D

64.    If your circadian rhythm becomes out of step with clock time, you experience a phenomenon known as:
A.    sleep spindles
B.    activation-synthesis
C.    paradoxical sleep
D.    jet lag

p. 151
Rhythms of Sleeping and
  Waking
Level: Moderate
Type: Conceptual
Ans: B

65.    A frequent flier has problems with jet lag. He decides that he can control this by changing the seat he normally occupies in the aircraft. This strategy is:
A.    not likely to work because jet lag is caused by protein imbalances that result from having to eat at irregular times
B.    not likely to work because jet lag is caused by a lack of synchrony between biological and chronological clocks
C.    likely to work because jet lag is caused by the nature of movement in an aircraft and this is experienced differently in different parts of the plane
D.    not likely to work because jet lag is caused by the tiring nature of travel

| | | |
|---|---|---|
| p. 151<br>Rhythms of Sleeping and<br> Waking<br>Level: Easy<br>Type: Factual<br>Ans: C | 66.<br><br>A.<br>B.<br>C.<br>D. | The rule of thumb for recovering from jet lag is that it takes about _____ to reset the circadian clock for _____ of time change.<br>one hour; each hour<br>one day; each day<br>one day; each hour<br>two days; each hour |

| | | |
|---|---|---|
| p. 151<br>Rhythms of Sleeping and<br> Waking<br>Level: Easy<br>Type: Factual<br>Ans: A<br>*PS/SG 7-9* | 67.<br>A.<br>B.<br>C.<br>D. | The most promising new treatment for jet lag appears to be:<br>periods of bright light<br>avoidance of food for 24 hours before a long flight<br>surgical resetting of the biological clock<br>drugs that induce sleep in the new time zone |

| | | |
|---|---|---|
| p. 151<br>Rhythms of Sleeping and<br> Waking<br>Level: Easy<br>Type: Factual<br>Ans: A | 68.<br><br>A.<br>B.<br>C.<br>D. | Which of the following did Charles Czeisler find could reset the circadian rhythm of a night worker?<br>exposure to bright light<br>removing all clocks from the workplace<br>injecting high doses of melatonin<br>electroencephalogram tracing |

| | | |
|---|---|---|
| p. 151<br>Rhythms of Sleeping and<br> Waking<br>Level: Easy<br>Type: Factual<br>Ans: C | 69.<br>A.<br>B.<br>C.<br>D. | What does light therapy do in resetting circadian rhythms?<br>light resets the internal timing clock<br>light resets the basal ganglia<br>light resets the suprachiasmatic nucleus<br>light resets the retina |

| | | |
|---|---|---|
| p. 151<br>Rhythms of Sleeping and<br> Waking<br>Level: Easy<br>Type: Factual<br>Ans: B | 70.<br>A.<br>B.<br>C.<br>D. | What hormone is thought to play a role in circadian rhythms?<br>dopamine<br>melatonin<br>estrogen<br>prolixin |

| | | |
|---|---|---|
| p. 151<br>Rhythms of Sleeping and<br> Waking<br>Level: Easy<br>Type: Factual<br>Ans: C | 71.<br><br>A.<br>B.<br>C.<br>D. | The sun is rising. The morning light is becoming brighter. What's happening to your level of melatonin?<br>melatonin is not affected by light levels<br>stabilizing<br>decreases<br>increases |

| | | |
|---|---|---|
| p. 151<br>Rhythms of Sleeping and<br> Waking<br>Level: Moderate<br>Type: Factual<br>Ans: D | 72.<br><br>A.<br>B.<br>C.<br>D. | In people with normal circadian clocks, what effect does melatonin taken in pill form have on jet lag?<br>It helps people to adjust to jet lag.<br>It helps people to adjust to jet lag, but only if traveling east to west.<br>It helps people to adjust to jet lag, but only if traveling west to east.<br>It was no more effective than a placebo in reducing jet lag. |

p. 152
World of Sleep
Level: Easy
Type: Factual
Ans: D

73. Your psychology professor is talking about the changes in the electrical activity of the brain and the accompanying physiological bodily responses you experience as you sleep. What is your professor most likely describing?
A. activation-synthesis stages
B. continuum of sleep
C. states of sleep
D. stages of sleep

p. 152
World of Sleep
Level: Easy
Type: Factual
Ans: D

74. Heidi wants to be an astronaut. As part of her medical exam she is hooked to an electroencephalograph. This device is being used to monitor Heidi's:
A. hypnotic susceptibility
B. blood alcohol level
C. hypothalamic activity in sleep
D. brain waves

p. 152
World of Sleep
Level: Easy
Type: Factual
Ans: D

75. Sleep is divided into stages by examining a person's:
A. activity level during sleep
B. dream activity
C. circadian rhythms
D. EEG pattern

p. 152
World of Sleep
Level: Easy
Type: Factual
Ans: B
*PS/SG 7-10*

76. Sleep can be divided into _____ sleep and _____ sleep.
A. alpha . . . beta
B. REM . . . non-REM
C. REM . . . pre-REM
D. stage 1 . . . stage 2

p. 152
World of Sleep
Level: Easy
Type: Factual
Ans: B

77. Brain waves are described by examining their:
A. frequency and altitude
B. frequency and amplitude
C. pitch and amplitude
D. size and depth

p. 152
World of Sleep
Level: Easy
Type: Factual
Ans: A

78. After time in _____ state, we enter stage 1 of non-REM.
A. alpha
B. beta
C. psi
D. theta

p. 152
World of Sleep
Level: Easy
Type: Applied
Ans: C

79. Whose brain is most likely to have alpha waves?
A. Fran - she is dreaming
B. Gary - he is in stage 1
C. Vi - she is very relaxed and drowsy
D. Erv - he is excited as he watches his favorite football team

| | | |
|---|---|---|
| p. 152<br>World of Sleep<br>Level: Easy<br>Type: Factual<br>Ans: C | 80.<br>A.<br>B.<br>C.<br>D. | In a typical night, we spend about _____ of our sleep time in non-REM.<br>25%<br>50%<br>80%<br>95% |

| | | |
|---|---|---|
| p. 152<br>World of Sleep<br>Level: Easy<br>Type: Factual<br>Ans: B | 81.<br>A.<br>B.<br>C.<br>D. | As we fall deeper into sleep, our brain waves tend to:<br>remain unaltered<br>slow down<br>flatten out<br>speed up |

| | | |
|---|---|---|
| p. 152<br>World of Sleep<br>Level: Easy<br>Type: Applied<br>Ans: B | 82.<br><br><br><br>A.<br>B.<br>C.<br>D. | A commuter who takes the train daily from Connecticut to Manhattan is in his habit of sitting with his eyes closed, but the motion and noise of the train keep him awake. He feels relaxed and is drowsy. The commuter's brain is probably emitting which type of waves?<br>beta<br>alpha<br>delta<br>theta |

| | | |
|---|---|---|
| p. 152<br>World of Sleep<br>Level: Easy<br>Type: Applied<br>Ans: A<br>*www* | 83.<br><br>A.<br>B.<br>C.<br>D. | The phone rings and wakes you just when you first fall asleep. It is <u>most</u> likely you have been woken from:<br>NREM sleep<br>REM sleep<br>SPID sleep<br>paradoxical sleep |

| | | |
|---|---|---|
| p. 152<br>World of Sleep<br>Level: Easy<br>Type: Applied<br>Ans: A | 84.<br><br>A.<br>B.<br>C.<br>D. | Thomas nudges Nancy who is on the couch sleeping. Nancy says, "I feel as if I wasn't even sleeping." Nancy, most likely, woke from _____.<br>Stage 1<br>Stage 2<br>Stage 3<br>paradoxical sleep |

| | | |
|---|---|---|
| p. 152<br>World of Sleep<br>Level: Easy<br>Type: Factual<br>Ans: B | 85.<br>A.<br>B.<br>C.<br>D. | What is the lightest stage of sleep?<br>Stage alpha<br>Stage 1<br>Stage 2<br>Stage 3 |

| | | |
|---|---|---|
| p. 152<br>World of Sleep<br>Level: Easy<br>Type: Factual<br>Ans: B | 86.<br>A.<br>B.<br>C.<br>D. | Sleep spindles and K complexes appear during what stage of NREM?<br>Stage 1<br>Stage 2<br>Stage 3<br>Stage delta |

p. 152
World of Sleep
Level: Easy
Type: Factual
Ans: B

87. As a research assistant, you are monitoring the brain waves of a subject who is asleep. You notice that the subject is entering real sleep. The subject is in what stage of sleep?
A. Stage 1
B. Stage 2
C. Stage 3
D. Stage delta

p. 152
World of Sleep
Level: Easy
Type: Factual
Ans: D
*www*

88. The deepest stage of sleep is characterized by _____ waves.
A. alpha
B. beta
C. theta
D. delta

p. 152
World of Sleep
Level: Easy
Type: Factual
Ans: C

89. Rip's EEG indicates that he has entered delta sleep. We can expect that:
A. his brain will be emitting sleep spindles and K complexes
B. he has just fallen asleep
C. he would be very difficult to awaken
D. he is about to wake up

p. 152
World of Sleep
Level: Easy
Type: Factual
Ans: A

90. A mother tells her son that if he doesn't sleep he won't grow. The mother is:
A. partly correct in that growth hormones are released during NREM sleep
B. relying on an old folk tale that has no support in science
C. partly correct in that a rested body grows faster
D. correct because we do most of our growing when we are asleep

p. 153
World of Sleep
Level: Easy
Type: Factual
Ans: A

91. In a typical night, we spend about _____ of our sleep time in REM.
A. 20%
B. 50%
C. 80%
D. 95%

p. 153
World of Sleep
Level: Easy
Type: Factual
Ans: C

92. REM brain waves have _____ frequency and _____ amplitude.
A. no; slow
B. slow; high
C. high; low
D. low; fast

p. 153
World of Sleep
Level: Easy
Type: Factual
Ans: C

93. Every night, we cycle into REM about:
A. 1-2 times
B. 3-4 times
C. 5-6 times
D. 7-8 times

p. 153
World of Sleep
 Night
Level: Easy
Type: Factual
Ans: C
*www*

94. REM sleep is sometimes referred to as:
A. daydreaming
B. rebound sleep
C. paradoxical sleep
D. delta sleep

p. 153
World of Sleep
Level: Easy
Type: Applied
Ans: B

95. You are looking at two EEG profiles recorded from an individual's full night of sleep. But you have a difficult time telling apart two types of brain waves. What are the two waves that look identical to each other?
A. delta waves and alpha waves
B. beta waves and REM brain waves
C. sleep spindles and theta waves
D. delta and REM brain waves

p. 153
World of Sleep
 Night
Level: Easy
Type: Factual
Ans: B

96. REM sleep is called paradoxical sleep because:
A. the body does not need REM sleep, but does need regular sleep
B. although asleep, the brain waves are identical to those recorded awake
C. dreams often make no sense to the individual once they are awake
D. REM sleep occurs immediately following Stage 1 sleep and immediately before Stage 2 sleep

p. 153
World of Sleep
 Night
Level: Easy
Type: Applied
Ans: A

97. Manuel suffers from REM behavior disorder. Because of the disorder, he:
A. acts out his dreams because his voluntary muscles are not paralyzed
B. experiences an increased percentage of time spent in REM
C. has an excess of Stage 2 sleep
D. has a paralysis of his legs during REM

p. 153
World of Sleep
Level: Easy
Type: Applied
Ans: B

98. Denise is watching Greg sleep. Denise notices that Greg's eyes are rapidly moving back-and-forth behind his closed eyelids. She also notes that his arms lack muscle tension. These suggest that Greg is:
A. experiencing sleep spindles
B. dreaming
C. in gamma sleep
D. emitting theta waves

p. 153
World of Sleep
Level: Easy
Type: Factual
Ans: C

99. According to an EEG, Rachel is in REM sleep. She is probably:
A. sleepwalking
B. in a light state of sleep
C. dreaming
D. just falling asleep

p. 153
World of Sleep
Level: Easy
Type: Applied
Ans: C

100. Emily is watching Mae sleep and concludes Mae is in REM. If Emily awakens Mae, what chance will Mae report having had a vivid, well-organized dream?
A. 20%
B. 50%
C. 80%
D. 100%

p. 153
World of Sleep
Level: Easy
Type: Applied
Ans: B

101. Jayne wants a really creative name for her web site on dreaming. What would be a good choice that is also consistent with the research on dreaming?
A. www.stage1.edu
B. www.rem.edu
C. www.sleep_spindles.edu
D. www.alpha_waves.edu

p. 153
World of Sleep
Level: Easy
Type: Applied
Ans: C

102. A woman has just had a baby and is allowed to have the newborn in the hospital room with her at night. On the third night, however, the nurses decide the woman needs her rest, since the baby has been waking up often in the night. If the baby woke its mother during each of her REM sleep periods, what would we expect on the night when the nurses looked after the baby and the mother was allowed to sleep through?
A. the mother would be very irritable
B. the mother would sleep but wake up depressed
C. the mother would increase her REM sleep that night
D. the mother would experience an increase in Stage 1 sleep

p. 153
World of Sleep
Level: Easy
Type: Applied
Ans: C

103. As a volunteer in a sleep experiment, Isaac was awakened each time he entered REM sleep for two nights. On the third night he was allowed to sleep normally. We would expect that REM deprivation would:
A. have no effect on his normal sleeping pattern
B. cause a temporary depression
C. lead to REM rebound on the third night
D. cause him to be irritable for the next few days

p. 153
World of Sleep
Level: Easy
Type: Factual
Ans: B

104. REM rebound is caused by:
A. delta wave synchrony
B. REM deprivation
C. narcolepsy
D. sleep deprivation

p. 153
World of Sleep
Level: Easy
Type: Factual
Ans: B
*PS/SG 7-13*

105. Evidence that dreaming is a necessary biological process is provided by:
A. REM behavior disorder
B. REM rebound
C. stage 4 sleep
D. alpha stage sleep

p. 153
World of Sleep
Level: Easy
Type: Factual
Ans: A

106. Based upon the research cited in Module Seven, REM may help us to:
A. encode information into memory
B. restore and repair our physical bodies
C. reset our circadian clock
D. increase the accuracy of our perception of images

p. 154
World of Sleep
Level: Moderate
Type: Conceptual
Ans: A

107.  In a lecture on sleep, Professor Kaurala is using a metaphor to explain the cycles between NREM and REM.  Which of the following is <u>most</u> appropriate in describing the journey through the night?
A.  someone hiking in the mountains going up and down hills and valleys
B.  a caterpillar turning into a butterfly and then dying
C.  an acorn growing to be an oak tree
D.  a submarine diving to very deep depths

p. 154
World of Sleep
Level: Easy
Type: Factual
Ans: C

108.  The transition between wakefulness and sleep is:
A.  paradoxical sleep
B.  REM
C.  Non-REM stage 1
D.  Non-REM stage 2

p. 154
World of Sleep
Level: Easy
Type: Factual
Ans: B

109.  When in Stage 2, some people report:
A.  vivid life-like dreams
B.  short, fragmented thoughts
C.  hallucinations
D.  REM rebound

p. 154
World of Sleep
Level: Easy
Type: Factual
Ans: D

110.  We enter REM sleep from:
A.  wakefulness
B.  drowsiness
C.  stage 4 sleep
D.  stage 2 sleep

p. 154
World of Sleep
Level: Easy
Type: Factual
Ans: D

111.  Sleepwalking and night terrors occur during:
A.  Stage 1 sleep
B.  REM sleep
C.  sleep spindles
D.  Stage 4 sleep

p. 154
World of Sleep
Level: Moderate
Type: Factual
Ans: B

112.  Of the following ordered stages, which <u>most</u> resembles the first hour or so of a typical night of sleep?
A.  1, 2, 3, 4, REM
B.  1, 2, 3, 4, 3, 2, REM
C.  1, 2, 3, REM, 4, REM
D.  1, 2, 3, 4, 1, 2, 3, REM

p. 154
World of Sleep
Level: Easy
Type: Factual
Ans: A
*PS/SG 7-14*

113.  Rod Plotnik (author of your textbook) compares sleeping all night to:
A.  riding a roller-coaster
B.  boating on a calm lake
C.  wading in deep water
D.  driving a luxury automobile

p. 154
World of Sleep
Level: Easy
Type: Factual
Ans: B

114.  Elaine is talking in her sleep.  In what stage of sleep is she <u>most</u> likely?
A.  Stage 1
B.  REM sleep
C.  Stage 3
D.  Stage 4

p. 155
Research Focus:
 Circadian Preference
Level: Moderate
Type: Factual
Ans: A

115. Todd scored high on the morning-evening questionnaire. The score indicates Todd to be a _____. Todd's preference is _____.
A. morning person; genetic
B. morning person; learned
C. evening person; abnormal
D. evening person; learned

p. 155
Research Focus:
 Circadian Preference
Level: Moderate
Type: Factual
Ans: C

116. Dr. Ramez studies circadian clocks, specifically, the rhythm of body temperature. In her current study, she needs to disrupt the body temperature rhythm in rats. What part of the rat's brain regulates body temperature?
A. limbic system
B. brainstem
C. suprachiasmatic nucleus
D. hippocampus

p. 155
Research Focus:
 Circadian Preference
Level: Moderate
Type: Applied
Ans: D

117. Consider this case study: Paul eats a light breakfast, is a night worker, but sometimes works in the afternoon. He often complains of being cold in the morning. Paul is most likely a(n):
A. early bird
B. afternoon person
C. morning person
D. evening person

p. 155
Research Focus:
 Circadian Preference
Level: Easy
Type: Factual
Ans: B

118. What happens to body temperature from the time we get up in the morning?
A. declines throughout the day
B. rises throughout the day, peaks, and then declines
C. rises throughout the day but only in a morning person
D. rises throughout the day but only in an evening person

p. 155
Research Focus:
 Circadian Preference
Level: Moderate
Type: Applied
Ans: C

119. You and a group of friends are watching your favorite late-night television show. One of your friends, who is a morning person, says that he is really tired and wants to go to bed, but you think it's still early. Having an understanding of circadian rhythms, you correctly tell your friend that the reason for his wanting to sleep is his:
A. interval timing clock is sounding its alarm
B. melatonin level is decreasing
C. body temperature is peaking before the rest of the group's
D. REM behavior disorder is acting up again

p. 155
Research Focus:
 Circadian Preference
Level: Easy
Type: Factual
Ans: B

120. Lou is a morning person. Adam is an evening person. Why is Lou going to bed earlier than Adam?
A. Lou's body temperature peaks later in the evening.
B. Lou's body temperature peaks earlier in the evening.
C. Adam's body temperature rose more quickly.
D. Lou's body temperature is more variable than Adam's.

p. 155
Research Focus:
 Circadian Preference
Level: Easy
Type: Factual
Ans: D

121. What tends to happen to people as they age with regard to circadian preference?
A. People's tendency for circadian preference remains unchanged until the late 70's.
B. People tend to become more like evening persons after reaching 50.
C. People tend to become more like afternoon persons after reaching 50.
D. People tend to become more like morning persons after reaching 50.

p. 155
Research Focus:
 Circadian Preference
Level: Moderate
Type: Applied
Ans: C

122. Mary Joy is in her sixties and is in good health. In her twenties, she was most like an evening person. What is her most likely status right now?
A. Mary Joy remains an evening person
B. She is a combination - an afternoon person
C. She is a morning person
D. Mary Joy has no strong preference either way

p. 156
Questions About Sleep
Level: Easy
Type: Factual
Ans: C

123. According to survey research, most adults sleep between _____ hours a night.
A. 4-5
B. 5-6
C. 7-8
D. 9-10

p. 156
Questions About Sleep
Level: Easy
Type: Factual
Ans: D

124. As one-year old Gabriella grows up through adolescence, the percentage of time spent in REM will:
A. dramatically fluctuate and stabilize around 25 years of age
B. remain the same
C. gradually increase
D. gradually decline

p. 156
Questions About Sleep
Level: Easy
Type: Applied
Ans: D

125. The local school board wants to change the high school's schedule to be more consistent with the sleep patterns of adolescents. What is their proposal?
A. require practice for sports and music to be held in the early morning
B. start high school classes one hour earlier
C. increase the time allowed between classes without being tardy
D. start high school classes one hour later

p. 156
Questions About Sleep
Level: Easy
Type: Factual
Ans: D

126. Which of the following age groups is most likely to nap during the day and experience difficulties in sleeping through the night?
A. infants
B. children
C. adolescents
D. elderly adults

p. 156
Questions About Sleep
Level: Easy
Type: Factual
Ans: D

127. Who will spend the most time in REM sleep during the course of a 24-hour period?
A. a 60-year-old man
B. a 35-year-old woman
C. a 10-year-old boy
D. a 6-month-old girl

p. 156
Questions About Sleep
Level: Easy
Type: Factual
Ans: A

128. Who will spend about 6.5 hours a day sleeping?
A. a 60-year-old man
B. a 35-year-old woman
C. a 10-year-old boy
D. a 6-month-old girl

p. 156
Questions About Sleep
Level: Easy
Type: Factual
Ans: B

129. The _____ argues that activities during the day deplete key factors in our brain that must be replenished by sleeping.
A. adaptive theory
B. repair theory
C. deprivation theory
D. activation-synthesis theory

p. 156
Questions About Sleep
Level: Easy
Type: Factual
Ans: D

130. Which statement does not support the repair theory's attempt to explain why we sleep?
A. during stage 4 sleep, the secretion of growth hormone increases
B. sleep deprivation leads to a marked desire to sleep
C. sleep deprivation lowers our body's resistance to viruses and infections
D. sleep protects us from dangers that we cannot see at night

p. 156
Questions About Sleep
Level: Easy
Type: Factual
Ans: A

131. The finding that during sleep there is increased production of immune cells supports the _____ theory.
A. repair
B. adaptive
C. activation-synthesis
D. Freudian

p. 156
Questions About Sleep
Level: Easy
Type: Applied
Ans: B

132. Imagine that "sleep" can talk. As the person is falling asleep, "sleep" says, "Finally, I can get some work done. Let's see, I need to release some growth hormone later and look at the immune system. I think there's something wrong with it." Odd as it may be, which theory of sleep is best reflected in these comments?
A. Freudian
B. repair
C. activation-synthesis
D. restorative

p. 156
Questions About Sleep
Level: Easy
Type: Factual
Ans: B

133. The _____ theory suggests that sleep evolved because it prevented energy waste and minimized exposure to dangers.
A. repair
B. adaptive
C. activation-synthesis
D. Freudian

p. 156
Questions About Sleep
Level: Easy
Type: Factual
Ans: B

134. Which theory holds that sleep evolved and endured because it helped our ancestors survive?
A. restorative
B. adaptive
C. Freudian
D. REM

p. 157
Questions About Sleep
Level: Easy
Type: Factual
Ans: C

135. Sleep deprivation appears to negatively affect:
A. blood pressure
B. heart rate
C. immune system functioning
D. hormone secretions

p. 157
Questions About Sleep
Level: Easy
Type: Factual
Ans: C

136. According to a sleep deprivation study described in your textbook, how much sleep did it take for a significant reduction in immune system function to occur?
A. 1 hour
B. 2 hours
C. 3-4 hours
D. 7 hours

p. 157
Questions About Sleep
Level: Easy
Type: Factual
Ans: A

137. Which of the following adverse effects may be caused by sleep deprivation?
A. decrease in performance of tasks that require vigilance and concentration
B. autonomic functions such as heart rate becoming erratic
C. slowed reflexes
D. abnormal reflexes

p. 157
Questions About Sleep
Level: Easy
Type: Factual
Ans: D

138. What role does the ventrolateral preoptic nucleus play in consciousness?
A. focuses our attention during periods of intense awareness
B. influences the quality and quantity of dreams
C. paralyzes voluntary muscles
D. acts like a master switch for sleep

p. 157
Questions About Sleep
Level: Easy
Type: Factual
Ans: A

139. After the ventrolateral preoptic nucleus is turned off, the neurotransmitter _____ is secreted.
A. GABA
B. REM
C. dopamine
D. benzodiazepine

p. 157
Questions About Sleep
Level: Easy
Type: Factual
Ans: C

140. What happens when the VPN is turned on?
A. immune cells are produced
B. it creates hallucinations often seen in sleep deprivation
C. it secretes a neurotransmitter that turns off brain areas
D. it secretes a neurotransmitter that turns on brain areas

p. 157
Questions About Sleep
Level: Easy
Type: Factual
Ans: B
*PS/SG 7-17*

141. The VPN (ventrolateral preoptic nucleus) acts as a:
A. clue that makes it possible to tell if a sleeper is dreaming
B. master on-off switch for sleep
C. censor that disguises sexual and aggressive wishes in dreams
D. light enhancer that combats feelings of depression during the winter months

p. 157
Questions About Sleep
Level: Moderate
Type: Factual
Ans: B

142. If George's hypothalamus is damaged and he shows severe disruption in his circadian rhythms, what specific part of his hypothalamus is malfunctioning?
A. lateral hypothalamus
B. ventrolateral preoptic nucleus
C. pons
D. reticular formation

p. 157
Questions About Sleep
Level: Easy
Type: Factual
Ans: C

143. Which of the following is responsible for keeping our brains awake and alert?
A. the cognitive unconscious
B. the suprachiasmatic nucleus
C. the reticular formation
D. sleep spindles

p. 157
Questions About Sleep
Level: Easy
Type: Factual
Ans: A

144. According to research, _____, which is(are) controlled by the suprachiasmatic nucleus, is(are) important in regulating the sleep-wake cycle.
A. body temperature
B. chemicals in the blood
C. sleep spindles
D. lucid dreams

p. 157
Questions About Sleep
Level: Moderate
Type: Factual
Ans: D

145. You are a psychology professor reviewing the outline of a student's paper on the mechanisms of falling asleep. As you read the outline, you notice that one of the steps is incorrect. Which one is it?
A. the time of falling asleep is regulated by the suprachiasmatic nucleus
B. the VNP turns off the reticular formation
C. melatonin secretions increase
D. go to sleep when body temperature rises

p. 159
Cultural Diversity:
  Incidence of SAD
Level: Easy
Type: Factual
Ans: D

146. Depression typically beginning in fall and ending in the spring characterizes:
A. seasonal depression syndrome
B. bipolar disorder
C. dysthymia disorder
D. seasonal affective disorder

p. 159
Cultural Diversity:
  Incidence of SAD
Level: Easy
Type: Applied
Ans: A

147. "Around November, I started getting feelings of worthlessness and despair. It's really bad in January. I also gain lots of weight and overeat. But around April I start to feel much better, and I have a better outlook on life." This person is most likely suffering from:

A. seasonal affective disorder
B. somatoform disorder
C. dysthymia disorder
D. generalized anxiety disorder

p. 159
Cultural Diversity:
  Incidence of SAD
Level: Easy
Type: Factual
Ans: C

148. What percentage of SAD sufferers reported less depression after exposure to bright light?

A. 10%
B. 25-30%
C. 50-70%
D. 90-95%

p. 159
Cultural Diversity:
  Incidence of SAD
Level: Easy
Type: Factual
Ans: B

149. The role that light plays in SAD is important in triggering the disorder. During the winter months, about _____ of people living in Florida report having SAD compared to _____ of those living in New Hampshire reporting it.

A. 1.5%; 1.9%
B. 1.5%; 7.3%
C. 23%; 12%
D. 12%; 23%

p. 159
Cultural Diversity:
  Incidence of SAD
Level: Easy
Type: Factual
Ans: B

150. If you randomly pick 100 Icelanders, about how many of them would have SAD?

A. 1%
B. 4%
C. 7%
D. 11%

p. 159
Cultural Diversity:
  Incidence of SAD
Level: Moderate
Type: Factual
Ans: C

151. Researchers have found that SAD is _____ prevalent in Iceland than in the United States. The difference is believed to be due to differences in

_____.

A. less; latitude
B. more; culture
C. less; culture
D. more; latitude

p. 159
Cultural Diversity:
  Incidence of SAD
Level: Easy
Type: Factual
Ans: A

152. What has been identified that possibly explains the difference in SAD incidence in Iceland compared to the United States?

A. emotional hardiness
B. population density
C. religious preferences
D. diet

p. 159
Cultural Diversity:
 Incidence of SAD
Level: Easy
Type: Factual
Ans: D

153. Research in both Iceland and Canada showed that seasonal affective disorder (SAD) may be related to:
A. an above average number of days of bright light
B. a combination of diminished light and low temperature
C. personal tragedy and family problems
D. emotional hardiness and genetic factors

p. 159
Cultural Diversity:
 Incidence of SAD
Level: Moderate
Type: Conceptual
Ans: B

154. The research finding that SAD is less frequent in Iceland than in New Hampshire suggests that:
A. researchers need to use consistent, reliable methods of study
B. cultural factors affect behavior
C. weather plays a small role in behavior
D. psychiatrists and psychologists are more competent in New York state

p. 160
World of Dreams
Level: Easy
Type: Applied
Ans: A

155. Dennis reports that he never dreams. Which of the following is the best explanation for why Dennis believes this?
A. Dennis does dream, he just doesn't remember
B. Dennis is experiencing REM rebound
C. Dennis has sleep spindles which prevent him from dreaming
D. Dennis has an abnormality in his reticular formation

p. 160
World of Dreams
Level: Easy
Type: Factual
Ans: D

156. Dreams from nonREM tend to be:
A. very life-like
B. related to waking life
C. sexual in nature
D. dull and contain repetitive thoughts

p. 160
World of Dreams
Level: Easy
Type: Factual
Ans: B
www

157. Which theory of dreams believes that we dream as a result of threatening wishes and desires being changed into harmless symbols?
A. the activation-synthesis theory
B. Freud's theory of dreams
C. the extension of waking life theory
D. spiritual world theory

p. 160
World of Dreams
Level: Moderate
Type: Factual
Ans: C

158. Freud's interpretation of dreams was based on the assumption that:
A. dream content was a continuation of the events in our daily lives
B. dream content reflected what worried us in our waking state
C. the content of dreams had to be considered symbolic
D. dreams were similar to the hallucinations experienced by schizophrenics

p. 160
World of Dreams
Level: Moderate
Type: Factual
Ans: B
PS/SG 7-19

159. According to Freud's famous theory, at the heart of every dream is a:
A. clue to the future
B. disguised wish
C. hate-filled thought
D. shameful sexual memory

p. 160
World of Dreams
Level: Moderate
Type: Applied
Ans: D

160. Dr. Smithson is a therapist and asks his clients to remember their dreams. His task is to:
A. analyze the spiritual dimension of the dreams
B. analyze how the dreams relate to their waking lives since they reflect the same emotions we experience when awake
C. simply carefully record the dreams
D. interpret the symbols in the dreams

p. 160
World of Dreams
Level: Moderate
Type: Applied
Ans: C

161. Consider the following dream description:    I am riding on a train that is going much too fast. We enter a tunnel and suddenly everything goes dark. I wait and wait but we never come out of the tunnel. There is no light at the end of it. At the height of my concern, I wake up. Which of the following may represent a Freudian analysis of the above dream?
A. the person is very anxious about a trip that he must take
B. the person has had a very stressful day at work and wished to escape the pressure quickly
C. the train entering the tunnel represents intercourse and the concern expressed is indicative of sexual problems
D. the person may be a design engineer who has designed something that may not work and he is anxious about it

p. 160
World of Dreams
Level: Easy
Type: Factual
Ans: B

162. Which theory of dream interpretation emphasizes that dreams are related to the same thoughts, problems and emotions that we experience when awake?
A. Freud's theory of dreams
B. extensions of waking life
C. activation-synthesis
D. spiritual world

p. 160
World of Dreams
Level: Moderate
Type: Applied
Ans: C

163. Bob has a dream about running away from a monster. How would the notion of dreams as extensions of waking life interpret Bob's dream?
A. Bob has serious sexual difficulties
B. Bob wants to relive his childhood
C. Bob is running away from some problem
D. Bob needs intensive psychotherapy to deal with his mental disorder

p. 161
World of Dreams
Level: Easy
Type: Factual
Ans: C

164. According to the activation-synthesis theory:
A. dreams reflect unconscious desires and anxieties
B. dreams are a continuation of our waking thoughts
C. there is no reason to interpret dreams
D. it is necessary to dream for our psychological well-being

p. 161
World of Dreams
Level: Easy
Type: Factual
Ans: C
*PS/SG 7-21*

165. The activation-synthesis theory says that dreams result from:
A. a biological need to pull together and make sense of the day's activities
B. "batch processing" of all the information gathered during the day
C. random and meaningless chemical and neural activity in the brain
D. the need to explain hidden sexual and aggressive impulses

p. 161
World of Dreams
Level: Easy
Type: Applied
Ans: C

166. Dr. Van Winkle claims that dreams are nothing more than random activity in the brain. He believes in which theory of dreams?
A. Freudian
B. restorative
C. activation-synthesis
D. behavioral

p. 161
World of Dreams
Level: Easy
Type: Factual
Ans: D

167. Which theory of dreaming suggests that there is no need to interpret dreams?
A. Freudian
B. restorative
C. extension of waking life
D. activation-synthesis

p. 161
World of Dreams
Level: Easy
Type: Factual
Ans: D

168. Which of the following areas of the brain has increased activity during REM?
A. pons
B. auditory cortex
C. prefrontal lobe
D. limbic system

p. 161
World of Dreams
Level: Easy
Type: Conceptual
Ans: A

169. The Inuit people of the arctic in North America believe that dreams:
A. allow one to enter the spiritual world
B. reveal unfulfilled sexual wishes
C. represent what was accomplished in the previous day and plans for the next day
D. are linked to the unconscious mind

p. 161
World of Dreams
Level: Easy
Type: Factual
Ans: C

170. The typical dream is likely to include themes or characteristics of:
A. sexual encounters, black and white, and take place outside
B. recurrent themes of being threatened and our intentions
C. several characters, visual sensations, and motion-like walking
D. one character, pain sensations, and joy

p. 161
World of Dreams
Level: Easy
Type: Factual
Ans: C

171. Research suggests that people seldom dream about:
A. more than one character
B. activities such as running or walking
C. sexual encounters and intercourse
D. being indoors

p. 162
Application: Sleep
 Problems and
 Treatments
Level: Easy
Type: Factual
Ans: A
*www*

172. Insomnia is a sleep problem characterized by:
A. difficulty in going to sleep or staying asleep through the night
B. an excessive amount of lucid dreaming
C. night terrors and sleepwalking
D. irresistible attacks of sleepiness

p. 162
Application: Sleep
  Problems and
  Treatments
Level: Easy
Type: Factual
Ans: C
*PS/SG 7-24*

173. Which one of the following is not a sleep problem?
A. narcolepsy
B. night terrors
C. oversleeping
D. sleepwalking

p. 162
Application: Sleep
  Problems and
  Treatments
Level: Easy
Type: Factual
Ans: A

174. Edward suffers from "Sunday night insomnia." His insomnia is probably caused by:
A. disruption in his normal sleep schedule
B. anxiety about the upcoming week
C. respiratory problems
D. sleep apnea

p. 162
Application: Sleep
  Problems and
  Treatments
Level: Easy
Type: Factual
Ans: B

175. Disrupting circadian rhythms, abusing alcohol or sedatives, and having medical problems or chronic pain are all physiological causes of
A. sleep apnea
B. insomnia
C. night terrors
D. narcolepsy

p. 162
Application: Sleep
  Problems and
  Treatments
Level: Easy
Type: Factual
Ans: C

176. Which of the following is not a step in establishing an optimal sleep pattern?
A. go to bed only when sleepy
B. do not read in bed
C. if you cannot sleep, stay in bed and focus on falling asleep
D. set the alarm for the same time each morning

p. 162
Application: Sleep
  Problems and
  Treatments
Level: Easy
Type: Factual
Ans: A

177. Napping during the day for treating insomnia:
A. is to be avoided
B. will not disrupt your sleep schedule for that night
C. is effective
D. prepares you for a good sleep later than night

p. 162
Application: Sleep
  Problems and
  Treatments
Level: Easy
Type: Factual
Ans: A

178. A person decides to try a non-drug treatment for insomnia. One idea is to:
A. get out of bed and go to another room if she does not sleep within 20 minutes
B. stay awake as long as possible until she inevitably becomes drowsy
C. imagine some exciting scenes at bedtime
D. persevere in bed no matter how awake she feels

p. 162

Application: Sleep
    Problems and
    Treatments

Level: Easy

Type: Factual

Ans: B

*PS/SG 7-23*

179.    The <u>best</u> advice for combating insomnia is to:

A.    get in bed at the same time every night and stay there no matter what happens

B.    get out of bed, go to another room, and do something relaxing if you can't fall asleep

C.    review the problems of the day as you lie in bed trying to go to sleep

D.    try sleeping in another room, or on the couch, if you can't fall asleep in your bed

p. 162

Application: Sleep
    Problems and
    Treatments

Level: Easy

Type: Applied

Ans: C

180.    "I've been having a hard time falling asleep ever since my parents got a divorce, about a month ago." This type of insomnia is called:

A.    rebound insomnia

B.    acute insomnia

C.    chronic insomnia

D.    narcoleptic insomnia

p. 162

Application: Sleep
    Problems and
    Treatments

Level: Easy

Type: Factual

Ans: D

181.    The continued use of benzodiazepines to treat insomnia may cause:

A.    a reduction in anxiety

B.    an increase in REM

C.    REM rebound

D.    dependency on the drug

p. 163

Application: Sleep
    Problems and
    Treatments

Level: Easy

Type: Factual

Ans: D

182.    Sleep apnea refers to

A.    a disorder whereby a person falls asleep uncontrollably for 10 or more seconds

B.    insomnia caused by anxiety

C.    insomnia caused by the excessive use of sedatives during the day

D.    a condition whereby a person stops breathing while asleep for 10 or more seconds

p. 163

Application: Sleep
    Problems and
    Treatments

Level: Easy

Type: Factual

Ans: D

183.    After experiencing months of poor sleep, Ray is evaluated in a sleep laboratory. After his evaluation his doctor tells him that he is suffering from sleep apnea. This means that Ray has:

A.    a disorder in which he falls asleep uncontrollably during the day but not at night

B.    insomnia caused by anxiety

C.    insomnia caused by the excessive use of sedatives during the day

D.    a condition in which he stops breathing while he sleeps

p. 163

Application: Sleep
    Problems and
    Treatments

Level: Easy

Type: Factual

Ans: B

184.    Irresistible attacks of sleepiness and muscle paralysis are symptoms of a sleep disorder called:

A.    insomnia

B.    narcolepsy

C.    sleep apnea

D.    night terrors

p. 163
Application: Sleep
 Problems and
 Treatments
Level: Easy
Type: Factual
Ans: A

185. The sleep attack of narcolepsy is accompanied by:
A. REM sleep
B. auditory hallucinations
C. cessation of breathing
D. outbursts of emotion

p. 163
Application: Sleep
 Problems and
 Treatments
Level: Easy
Type: Factual
Ans: D

186. Narcoleptics describe their sleep attacks as:
A. gradual
B. calming
C. restful
D. irresistible

p. 163
Application: Sleep
 Problems and
 Treatments
Level: Easy
Type: Factual
Ans: A

187. Recent research indicates that a type of neuron that does not develop normally may cause narcolepsy. What type of neuron is it?
A. hypocretin
B. myelinated
C. nonmyelinated
D. afferent

p. 163
Application: Sleep
 Problems and
 Treatments
Level: Easy
Type: Factual
Ans: A

188. A _____ is a sleep disturbance characterized by screaming and sudden wakening in a fearful state.
A. Night terror
B. Nightmare
C. Sleep apnea
D. Narcolepsy

p. 163
Application: Sleep
 Problems and
 Treatments
Level: Easy
Type: Factual
Ans: B
*www*

189. A night terror consists of:
A. cessation of breathing while sleeping
B. piercing scream, waking up in a panic state, and not remembering anything the next morning
C. a bad dream
D. difficulties staying asleep

p. 163
Application: Sleep
 Problems and
 Treatments
Level: Easy
Type: Factual
Ans: C

190. Night terrors occur during _____ sleep, and nightmares occur during _____ sleep.
A. REM; theta
B. alpha; non-REM
C. delta; REM
D. theta; delta

p. 163
Application: Sleep
  Problems and
  Treatments
Level: Easy
Type: Factual
Ans: D
*www*

191. Jason, a ten-year-old, is having a nightmare. In which stage of sleep is Jason <u>most</u> likely?

  A.   Stage 1
  B.   Stage 3
  C.   Stage 4
  D.   REM

p. 163
Application: Sleep
  Problems and
  Treatments
Level: Easy
Type: Applied
Ans: D

192. As Tanner and Patti sit in the living room one night, they watch four-year-old daughter Ellie come into the living room, pick up a book, and say "Baggy dog needs some milk." It is clear to her parents that Ellie is sleepwalking. She must be in Stage ___ of sleep.

  A.   REM
  B.   1
  C.   2
  D.   4

p. 163
Application: Sleep
  Problems and
  Treatments
Level: Easy
Type: Factual
Ans: C

193. About _____ Americans have at least one or more sleep disorders presented in Module Seven.

  A.   12 million
  B.   35 million
  C.   70 million
  D.   120 million

True/False

| | | | |
|---|---|---|---|
| F | *www* | 1. | Using a car phone does not significantly increase the risk of having an accident. |
| T | | 2. | If you are engaged in an activity that requires full awareness, you are doing a controlled process. |
| F | *www* | 3. | The function of daydreams is to escape thinking about the ordinary things of the day. |
| T | | 4. | Meditation or sleep deprivation can create an altered state of consciousness. |
| T | | 5. | In sleep we experience five different states of awareness. |
| F | | 6. | According to Freud, we place threatening wishes or desires into the conscious. |
| F | | 7. | We can describe implicit memories. |
| T | *www* | 8. | Unconsciousness means the person has a total lack of sensory awareness and complete loss of responsiveness to the environment. |
| F | | 9. | Cognitive neuroscience has not found any support for Freud's idea about the unconscious. |
| T | *www* | 10. | A circadian rhythm is a biological clock that regulates some response within a 24 hour period of time. |
| F | | 11. | Morning light has no effect on retinal cells in resetting the circadian clock. |
| T | *www* | 12. | The suprachiasmatic nucleus regulates several circadian rhythms. |
| T | | 13. | The pathway that allows light to get to the suprachiasmatic nucleus is not involved with vision. |
| F | | 14. | In general, it takes about three days for the body to adjust to every one hour of time change. |

| F |     | 15. | Because of the beneficial changes in gravity, astronauts do not experience "jet lag." |
|---|-----|-----|------|
| F | *www* | 16. | We sleep in Stage 4 REM. |
| F |     | 17. | Sleep spindles occur in Stage 1 sleep. |
| T | *www* | 18. | REM sleep is often called paradoxical sleep. |
| T |     | 19. | During sleep there is an increase in the production of immune cells. |
| T |     | 20. | The VPN turns off areas that arouse your brain. |
| T | *www* | 21. | Iceland has less cases of SAD than New Hemisphere, which gets more sun than Iceland. |
| F | *www* | 22. | Freud's theory of dreaming argues that dreaming is the result of the brain stimulation by chemical and neural influences. |
| F |     | 23. | If you have insomnia, it is a good idea to nap during the day. |
| T | *www* | 24. | Night terrors occur in stage 3 or 4. |
| T |     | 25. | The hypocretin neurons play a role in narcolepsy. |

Short-Answer Essay Questions

1.  Briefly discuss the seven states of consciousness and include an example of each state. (*www*)
2.  According to the idea of implicit memory, why can't we recall certain motor and emotional memories?
3.  Why must our circadian clock be reset each day?  Describe the mechanisms that are involved in resetting our circadian clock. (*www*)
4.  Describe the effects of shift work and jet lag on the body's circadian clock.  What is a treatment described in the module for these effects?
5.  In what ways do the four stages of NREM differ?  (*www*)
6.  Create two fictitious people, one is a morning person and the other is a night person.  Describe their circadian rhythms, body temperature, and differences in behavior.
7.  Describe a typical night as a person goes in and out of NREM and REM. (*www*)
8.  Why do we sleep?  In your answer, make sure you describe the repair theory and adaptive theory.  What is the evidence that supports the theories?
9.  Differentiate between insomnia, sleep apnea, narcolepsy, night terrors, and nightmares. (*www*)
10. Explain Freud's theory of dreams and the activation-synthesis model of dreams.

# Module 8 - Hypnosis and Drugs

p. 169
Introduction
Level: Easy
Type: Factual
Ans: B
*PS/SG 8-1*

1. Rod Plotnik tells the story about attending a stage hypnotist's act to illustrate the point that:
   A. a trained psychologist cannot be hypnotized
   B. hypnotism produces remarkable effects, but there is debate about what it really is
   C. hypnotism is an art that many have attempted to learn, but only a rare few have mastered
   D. entertainment pays better than psychology

p. 169
Introduction
Level: Easy
Type: Conceptual
Ans: C

2. What do hypnosis and LSD have in common?
   A. They were both discovered by accident by Sigmund Freud.
   B. At one time, they were both illegal - now just LSD is.
   C. Both have the ability to alter one's consciousness.
   D. Both of them can have therapeutic benefits such as losing weight.

p. 169
Introduction
Level: Easy
Type: Factual
Ans: A
*www*

3. What is the popular name of *d*-lysergic acid diethylamide?
   A. LSD
   B. cocaine
   C. caffeine
   D. magic mushrooms

p. 169
Introduction
Level: Easy
Type: Factual
Ans: B

4. Who discovered LSD in his laboratory?
   A. Sigmund Freud
   B. Albert Hofmann
   C. Anton Mesmer
   D. Milton Erickson

p. 169
Introduction
Level: Easy
Type: Factual
Ans: B

5. Albert Hofmann's strange bike ride was the result of:
   A. a post hypnotic state
   B. LSD
   C. sleep deprivation
   D. alcohol intoxication

p. 170
Hypnosis
Level: Easy
Type: Conceptual
Ans: D

6. If you had attended one of Anton Mesmer's healings, what would you have heard him say about how various symptoms were cured?
   A. "I will give my specially formulated medicine to this patient."
   B. "Please tell me all that you remember about your dream."
   C. "Hypnosis will cure this patient's problems; she will focus on my swinging watch."
   D. "I will pass a force called animal magnetism through my patient's body."

p. 170
Hypnosis
Level: Easy
Type: Factual
Ans: A

7. In the late 1700's, a force called "animal magnetism" (later called hypnosis) was introduced by:
A. Anton Mesmer
B. Sigmund Freud
C. Ernest Hilgard
D. Herman Von Hypnos

p. 170
Hypnosis
Level: Easy
Type: Factual
Ans: B

8. Jacques LeBeau lives in Paris in 1795. He has been suffering ulcers. He visits Anton Mesmer to cure his ulcers. Which of the following treatments does Mesmer offer to Jacques?
A. systematic desensitization
B. use of animal magnetism
C. antibiotic
D. cocaine

p. 170
Hypnosis
Level: Easy
Type: Factual
Ans: C

9. _____ is a situation or set of procedures in which one person suggests to another changes in sensation, perception, cognition, and motor behavior.
A. Social influence
B. Hidden observer
C. Hypnosis
D. Conformity

p. 170
Hypnosis
Level: Easy
Type: Factual
Ans: D

10. Can everyone be easily hypnotized?
A. Yes - about 80% have high susceptibility
B. Yes - about 99% have high susceptibility
C. No - there are not enough high quality hypnotists
D. No - only about 30% have high susceptibility

p. 170
Hypnosis
Level: Difficult
Type: Applied
Ans: C

11. Professor Stewart is giving a lecture on hypnosis. Sarah, a shy young freshman, wonders to herself if she could be hypnotized. Based on what you know about Sarah and the susceptibility of college students to hypnosis, what do you think?
A. Yes -females are more susceptible
B. Probably not since only 10% of college students are susceptible to varying degrees
C. It is impossible to say, but gender and introversion are not related to susceptibility
D. Yes - Sarah is shy and shyness increases susceptibility

p. 170
Hypnosis
Level: Easy
Type: Factual
Ans: D
*www*

12. Which of the following variable is related to susceptibility to hypnosis?
A. intelligence
B. gullibility
C. willpower
D. history of responding to imaginative suggestions

p. 170
Hypnosis
Level: Easy
Type: Factual
Ans: A

13. The Stanford Hypnotic Susceptibility Scale consists of:
A. a set of suggestions made to a hypnotized individual
B. several medical tests such as MRI
C. a number of survey items assessing a person's beliefs in hypnosis
D. an intelligence test and a personality test

p. 170
Hypnosis
Level: Easy
Type: Factual
Ans: C

14. What percentage of a randomly selected group of college students is highly susceptible to hypnosis and therefore could be easily hypnotized?
A. 10%
B. 20%
C. 30%
D. 40%

p. 170
Hypnosis
Level: Easy
Type: Factual
Ans: D

15. Based upon your textbook, which of the following variables increases susceptibility to hypnosis?
A. willpower
B. compliance
C. gullibility
D. positive expectations about hypnosis

p. 170
Hypnosis
Level: Easy
Type: Factual
Ans: B

16. The best-known test for susceptibility to hypnosis is called the:
A. Stanford-Binet Scale of Hypnotic Susceptibility
B. Stanford Hypnotic Susceptibility Scale
C. Michigan Test of Hypnotic Persuadability
D. Minnesota Multiphasic Personality Inventory

p. 170
Hypnosis
Level: Moderate
Type: Factual
Ans: C

17. What happens to one's susceptibility to hypnosis?
A. It continues to change until late adulthood.
B. Susceptibility decreases through midlife and then it increases.
C. Remains stable across the lifetime.
D. Susceptibility increases through midlife and then it decreases.

p. 170
Hypnosis
Level: Easy
Type: Applied
Ans: D

18. Karen is being hypnotized. During the induction, the hypnotist probably won't:
A. establish a sense of trust
B. give Karen a stimulus to concentrate on
C. suggest to Karen that she become relaxed
D. swing a pocket watch in front of her eyes

p. 170
Hypnosis
Level: Easy
Type: Factual
Ans: A
PS/SG 8-2

19. Which of the following is not a necessary part of inducing hypnosis?
A. swing a watch slowly back and forth until the subject's eyes glaze over
B. create a sense of trust
C. suggest that the subject concentrate on something
D. suggest what the subject will experience during hypnosis

p. 170
Hypnosis
Level: Easy
Type: Factual
Ans: D

20. One of the first challenges the hypnotist has in hypnotizing someone is to:
A. tell the individual to focus on an object
B. create an expectation that hypnosis is an interesting experience
C. suggest that the individual is feeling sleepy
D. create a sense of trust with the individual

p. 170
Hypnosis
Level: Easy
Type: Factual
Ans: C

21. The responsiveness of the subject undergoing hypnotic induction depends most on:
A. the specific method of induction
B. the hypnotist's ability to put the subject to sleep
C. the subject's susceptibility
D. the hypnotist's interpersonal skill

p. 170
Hypnosis
Level: Easy
Type: Applied
Ans: A

22. You are watching a movie in which the main character agrees to be hypnotized. The hypnotist suggests that the character focus on an object and then suggest that he is getting sleepy. Then the character, while hypnotized, engages in a criminal act. What is your educated response to this depiction of hypnosis?
A. People who are hypnotized keep to their standards of morality.
B. A hypnotist could force a person to become hypnotized.
C. Hypnosis can make people do things they consider wrong.
D. This Hollywood depiction of the induction of hypnosis is inaccurate.

p. 171
Hypnosis
Level: Easy
Type: Factual
Ans: A

23. The theory of hypnosis which states that the hypnotized individual is in an altered state and is disconnected from reality is called:
A. altered state theory
B. sociocognitive theory
C. hypnotic analgesia theory
D. stimulus control theory

p. 171
Hypnosis
Level: Easy
Type: Factual
Ans: D

24. Michael Nash argues that hypnosis puts clients into a(n):
A. altered state
B. hidden observer frame of mind
C. unconscious-like state
D. trance-like state

p. 171
Hypnosis
Level: Moderate
Type: Factual
Ans: D

25. You are writing a paper on the altered state theory of hypothesis. As you are researching the theory, you find a statement that doesn't seem to fit your understanding of the theory. Which of the following statements is inconsistent with the theory?
A. Hypnosis disconnects the person from reality.
B. The hypnotized person does things without conscious intent.
C. The hypnotized person is able to respond to suggestions.
D. The unhypnotized part of the brain does not receive any sensations or perceptions.

p. 171
Hypnosis
Level: Moderate
Type: Factual
Ans: B

26. Imagine that you have observed a person being hypnotized. The hypnotist says that the person can perform behaviors without conscious intent. The hypnotist adheres to the _____ theory of hypnosis.
A. behavioral
B. altered state
C. psychodynamic
D. sociocognitive

p. 171
Hypnosis
Level: Easy
Type: Factual
Ans: C
*www*

27. The altered state theory of hypnosis supports the hypothesis that hypnosis:
   A. is a stage of sleep
   B. is a form of social behavior
   C. results from a person's disconnection from reality
   D. results from a person's imagination

p. 171
Hypnosis
Level: Easy
Type: Factual
Ans: A

28. Those who argue the sociocognitive theory of hypnosis believe that the behavior seen in hypnotic people is due to:
   A. the ability to respond to imaginative suggestion
   B. trance-like state
   C. an altered state of consciousness
   D. an unconscious desire to please

p. 171
Hypnosis
Level: Moderate
Type: Applied
Ans: D

29. Brad attends a hypnosis show. He goes up on stage and performs many interesting behaviors. Later he tells his friends that he was just going along with the hypnotist because he felt social pressure. Brad's experience supports the idea of hypnosis:
   A. as an altered state of consciousness
   B. from a trance state perspective
   C. as just a stage of sleep
   D. from a sociocognitive perspective

p. 171
Hypnosis
Level: Easy
Type: Factual
Ans: C

30. The behaviors that are seen in hypnotized subjects are also seen in subjects not hypnotized. This supports the _____ theory of hypnosis.
   A. altered state
   B. trance state
   C. sociocognitive
   D. Freudian

p. 171
Hypnosis
Level: Easy
Type: Factual
Ans: B

31. The fact that hypnotic behavior can occur without being hypnotized supports the idea that:
   A. the hypnotist has unexplainable power over the subject
   B. hypnosis is due to the subject's imaginative suggestibility
   C. hypnosis occurs because of a hidden observer
   D. hypnosis is a trance-like state where the subject has high suggestibility

p. 171
Hypnosis
Level: Moderate
Type: Applied
Ans: C

32. You are watching a friend acting like a duck on stage at a hypnosis show. You lean over to the person sitting next to you and say, "She feels social pressure from the audience and hypnosis allows her to act like a duck." Your statement best illustrates the _____ theory of hypnosis.
   A. hidden observer
   B. altered state
   C. sociocognitive
   D. humanistic

p. 171
Hypnosis
Level: Easy
Type: Factual
Ans: D
*PS/SG 8-3*

33. The main issue in the psychological debate over hypnosis is:
A. not whether it exists, but how it is induced
B. why subjects tend to play along with the hypnotist
C. whether hidden observers really can spot stage hypnotists' tricks
D. whether it is a special state of consciousness

p. 171
Hypnosis
Level: Easy
Type: Factual
Ans: A
*PS/SG 8-4*

34. The sociocognitive theory of hypnosis says that hypnosis is based on a(n):
A. special ability of responding to imaginative suggestions and social pressures
B. altered state of consciousness
C. good natured desire to go along with what people want
D. extreme tendency to give in to authority

p. 172
Hypnosis
Level: Easy
Type: Factual
Ans: A

35. A client who undergoes hypnosis for pain and reports a reduction in the unpleasant feeling of pain has experienced:
A. hypnotic analgesia
B. imagined perception
C. posthypnotic amnesia
D. posthypnotic suggestion

p. 172
Hypnosis
Level: Easy
Type: Applied
Ans: C

36. Kris rids herself of headaches by hypnotic suggestions. Which of the following is she experiencing?
A. age regression
B. posthypnotic amnesia
C. hypnotic analgesia
D. imagined perceptions

p. 172
Hypnosis
Level: Moderate
Type: Factual
Ans: C

37. While subjects report a reduction in the unpleasant feelings of pain because of hypnosis, they:
A. later report the pain returning
B. still took pain medication
C. still had sensations of pain
D. still believed that hypnosis was not effective in pain management

p. 172
Hypnosis: Theory,
   Behavior and Use
Level: Easy
Type: Applied
Ans: A

38. As part of a hypnosis demonstration, Anthony is told that when he is awakened from the hypnotic trance, he will have forgotten the number 7. When he is awakened and asked to count from 1 to 10, he skips over 7. Anthony is exhibiting which of the following?
A. posthypnotic suggestion
B. age regression
C. analgesia
D. imagined perception

p. 172
Hypnosis
Level: Easy
Type: Applied
Ans: D

39. When given a cue, a subject who was recently hypnotized, performs a particular behavior. The subject was given a(n):
A. hidden suggestion
B. imagined suggestion
C. hypnotic exhortation
D. posthypnotic suggestion

p. 172
Hypnosis
Level: Easy
Type: Applied
Ans: B
*www*

40. "I know I was hypnotized, but that's all I can remember." This could be an example of:
A. posthypnotic suggestion
B. posthypnotic amnesia
C. hypnotic sensation
D. imagined perception

p. 172
Hypnosis
Level: Easy
Type: Applied
Ans: B

41. Carrie is watching a television show that claims people can go back and relive childhood experiences through hypnosis. Carrie has just read Module Eight and correctly remembers that these individuals are:
A. actually experiencing a posthypnotic suggestion
B. acting in ways they expect children to act
C. probably actually experiencing age regression
D. likely not to remember what happened during hypnosis because of posthypnotic amnesia

p. 172
Hypnosis
Level: Easy
Type: Factual
Ans: C

42. After reviewing many studies on age regression in hypnosis, one scientist concluded:
A. age regression is a viable technique for therapy
B. adults could in fact "go back" to their childhood
C. there was no evidence of subjects actually reliving childhood experiences
D. more research needed to be done

p. 172
Hypnosis
Level: Moderate
Type: Factual
Ans: D

43. The effects of hypnosis are seen as demonstrating the subject's:
A. lack of willpower to the commands of the hypnotist
B. gullibility
C. suggestibility to hypnosis
D. obedience to the hypnotist who is an authority figure

p. 173
Hypnosis
Level: Easy
Type: Factual
Ans: C

44. In using hypnosis for pain reduction, patients highly susceptible to hypnosis _____ than low susceptibility patients.
A. were more likely to experience posthypnotic amnesia
B. were less likely to participate in the study
C. reported significantly lower levels of pain
D. responded more slowly to the induction method

p. 173
Hypnosis
Level: Easy
Type: Factual
Ans: D
*PS/SG 8-5*

45. Which one of the following is not an effect claimed for hypnosis?
A. age regression
B. imagined perception
C. hypnotic analgesia
D. superhuman acts of strength

<table>
<tr><td>

p. 173
Hypnosis
Level: Easy
Type: Applied
Ans: B

</td><td>

46.

A.
B.
C.
D.

</td><td>

Lance has recently been hypnotized to manage his chronic back pain. The posthypnotic suggestion to think about his pain as less unpleasant results in:
decreased activity in the frontal lobe
increased activity in the frontal lobe
reduced sensations of pain
increased perceptions of pain elsewhere in his body

</td></tr>
</table>

p. 173
Hypnosis
Level: Easy
Type: Factual
Ans: D

47. Making the suggestion to subjects to think of pain as more or less unpleasant had no effect on what brain area?
A. occipital lobe
B. temporal lobe
C. frontal lobe
D. parietal lobe

p. 173
Hypnosis
Level: Easy
Type: Factual
Ans: A

48. Hypnosis can modify:
A. a person's perception of pain
B. the number of pain messages that reach the brain
C. pain receptors in the skin
D. the type of pain messages that reach the brain

p. 173
Hypnosis
Level: Moderate
Type: Applied
Ans: D

49. On television you see an info-commercial selling a "hypnosis kit." You hear the announcer claim that hypnosis has been successfully used to reduce pain, decrease tension, stop overeating, and quit smoking. It was also said that people who are highly susceptible to hypnosis respond more favorably. What did the announcer say that you know to be false?
A. hypnosis is not at all successful at reducing pain
B. reduction in tension has not generally occurred with hypnosis
C. susceptibility only refers to the induction of hypnosis, not to benefiting from hypnosis
D. hypnosis has not had as much success dealing with smoking and overeating as the other problems

p. 173
Hypnosis
Level: Moderate
Type: Factual
Ans: B

50. Hypnosis tends to be more effective in addressing problems related to _____, but less effective in problems related to _____.
A. self-control; mind-body interactions
B. mind-body interactions; self-control
C. mind-body interactions; psychosomatic symptoms
D. self-control; impulse control

p. 173
Hypnosis
Level: Easy
Type: Factual
Ans: D

51. Research concerning the use of hypnosis in therapeutic and behavioral change has indicated that hypnosis:
A. is more effective than health education
B. is more effective than behavioral modification
C. is only effective in getting people to quit smoking
D. should be used in combination with other programs

p. 174
Drugs: Overview
Level: Easy
Type: Factual
Ans: B
*PS/SG 8-8*

52. Why do people use drugs? The answer involves:
A. personality factors — there are as many reasons as there are drug users
B. pharmacological, psychological, and cultural factors
C. the power of chemistry, which creates a "one try and you're hooked" result
D. the pressures of modern society (ancient peoples didn't have drugs)

p. 174
Drugs: Overview
Level: Easy
Type: Factual
Ans: C

53. According to the textbook, humans have used drugs continually for at least _____ years.
A. 500
B. 1000
C. 6000
D. 8000

p. 174
Drugs: Overview
Level: Easy
Type: Factual
Ans: B

54. As we look at the 200 years of drug use in the United States, we see:
A. growing tolerance towards drug use
B. cycles of tolerant and intolerant attitudes toward drug use
C. fewer physical and psychological problems associated with drug use
D. decreasing rates of drug use

p. 174
Drugs: Overview
Level: Easy
Type: Factual
Ans: B

55. What is the name of the chemicals that alter our consciousness, sensations, perceptions, mood, and cognitive processes?
A. psychosomatic drugs
B. psychoactive drugs
C. psychomedicinal drugs
D. illicit drugs

p. 174
Drugs: Overview
Level: Moderate
Type: Factual
Ans: C

56. Which of the following is the best definition of a psychoactive drug?
A. a drug produced by the brain in order to stimulate sensory experiences in the visual system
B. any substance which has been declared illegal for use or for use without a prescription
C. chemicals which affect the nervous system, resulting in altered consciousness and perceptions
D. neurotransmitters which, when released, change the behavior of an individual

p. 174
Drugs: Overview
Level: Easy
Type: Factual
Ans: C
www

57. Once the individual has developed a behavioral pattern of drug abuse and an overwhelming desire to get and use the drug, then we say that the individual has developed a(n):
A. withdrawal symptom
B. tolerance
C. addiction
D. psychological dependence

p. 174
Drugs: Overview
Level: Easy
Type: Applied
Ans: C

58. "I really want, need it. I am consumed by getting some of it. I quit, but relapsed again." This person is describing:
A. withdrawal symptom
B. tolerance
C. addiction
D. psychological dependence

| | | |
|---|---|---|
| p. 174<br>Drugs: Overview<br>Level: Easy<br>Type: Factual<br>Ans: D | 59. | According to Module Eight, which famous figure in psychology had a<br>serious drug addiction? |
| | A. | Abraham Maslow |
| | B. | Ivan Pavlov |
| | C. | B. F. Skinner |
| | D. | Sigmund Freud |

| | | |
|---|---|---|
| p. 174<br>Drugs: Overview<br>Level: Easy<br>Type: Factual<br>Ans: B<br>*www* | 60. | When a person's body builds up a resistance to a drug so that larger doses<br>are needed to produce the same effects, that person has developed: |
| | A. | an addiction |
| | B. | tolerance |
| | C. | dependency |
| | D. | immunity |

| | | |
|---|---|---|
| p. 174<br>Drugs: Overview<br>Level: Easy<br>Type: Applied<br>Ans: B | 61. | "When I first started drinking, all I needed to get a buzz was two or three<br>beers. Now it takes me about six or seven. I must have developed: |
| | A. | an addiction |
| | B. | tolerance |
| | C. | dependency |
| | D. | immunity |

| | | |
|---|---|---|
| p. 174<br>Drugs: Overview<br>Level: Easy<br>Type: Factual<br>Ans: D<br>*PS/SG 8-10* | 62. | "Tolerance" for a drug means that the brain and the body: |
| | A. | adjust to the drug and use it with no ill effects |
| | B. | no longer get any effect from using the drug |
| | C. | shut out the drug, which passes harmlessly through the system |
| | D. | require increasingly larger doses of the drug to achieve the same effect |

| | | |
|---|---|---|
| p. 174<br>Drugs: Overview<br>Level: Easy<br>Type: Applied<br>Ans: A | 63. | Laura is not worried about her marijuana use. She has been smoking<br>marijuana for 10 years, and she says that one joint doesn't even get her<br>stoned anymore. Laura is experiencing: |
| | A. | an increased tolerance to marijuana |
| | B. | withdrawal symptoms |
| | C. | a decrease in her psychological dependency on marijuana |
| | D. | a physical need to smoke marijuana |

| | | |
|---|---|---|
| p. 174<br>Drugs: Overview<br>Level: Easy<br>Type: Factual<br>Ans: C | 64. | If a person continues to take a drug to prevent withdrawal symptoms, the<br>person is experiencing: |
| | A. | tolerance |
| | B. | addiction |
| | C. | dependence |
| | D. | withdrawal |

| | | |
|---|---|---|
| p. 174<br>Drugs: Overview<br>Level: Easy<br>Type: Factual<br>Ans: C<br>*www* | 65. | Karl continues to use a drug to avoid withdrawal symptoms from occurring.<br>Karl shows: |
| | A. | tolerance |
| | B. | addiction |
| | C. | dependence |
| | D. | withdrawal |

p. 174    66. Dependency refers to the strong need or desire to use a drug in order to:
Drugs: Overview A. cope with some situation or problem
Level: Easy   B. prevent the onset of withdrawal symptoms
Type: Factual  C. overcome tolerance effects
Ans: B    D. make the body function normally

p. 174    67. Withdrawal symptoms occur when an addicted person:
Drugs: Overview A. uses a drug
Level: Easy   B. overuses a drug
Type: Factual  C. stops using a drug
Ans: C    D. recognizes that they are psychologically dependent

p. 174    68. "After being addicted to pop - I drank at least six cans a day - I stopped. I
Drugs: Overview   got bad headaches and felt so tired." This scenario best describes:
Level: Moderate A. tolerance
Type: Conceptual B. addiction
Ans: C    C. withdrawal symptoms
       D. dependency

p. 174    69. Vera is trying to quit using heroin. The first day without the drug, she
Drugs: Overview   experienced incredible pain and felt like she was "going nuts." Vera is
Level: Moderate   experiencing:
Type: Applied  A. an increase in tolerance
Ans: D    B. drug-induced analgesia
       C. an imagined perception
       D. withdrawal symptoms

p. 175    70. Basically, all drugs work by interfering with the normal operation of:
Drugs: Overview A. neurotransmitters in the brain
Level: Easy   B. glucose in the blood
Type: Factual  C. DNA in the genes
Ans: A    D. sensory receptors in the eyes, ears, nose, tongue, and skin
*PS/SG 8-11*

p. 175    71. _____ and _____ are the two most popular psychoactive drugs.
Drugs: Overview A. Alcohol; nicotine
Level: Easy   B. Alcohol; caffeine
Type: Factual  C. Marijuana; caffeine
Ans: B    D. Nicotine; caffeine

p. 175    72. Among people 12 years and older, what is the most widely used drug?
Drugs: Overview A. alcohol
Level: Easy   B. nicotine
Type: Factual  C. marijuana
Ans: B    D. caffeine

p. 175
Drugs: Overview
Level: Easy
Type: Factual
Ans: B

73. What did the researchers conclude about drug treatment?
A. drug treatment is highly cost-effective only for the treatment of stimulant abuse
B. drug treatment is more cost-effective than imprisonment
C. enforcement of drug laws is more effective than drug treatment
D. drug treatment using psychoanalysis is the most cost-effective treatment

p. 175
Drugs: Overview
Level: Easy
Type: Factual
Ans: A

74. According to Module Eight, because of the results of the government's war on drugs, some have suggested:
A. drug legalization or decriminalization
B. increasing the amount of money spent on law enforcement
C. requiring all tax payers to take drug tests
D. mandatory jail time even for minor drug infractions

p. 175
Drugs: Overview
Level: Easy
Type: Factual
Ans: B

75. Americans spent _____ in 2001 on illicit drugs.
A. 19 million dollars
B. 50 million dollars
C. 1 billion dollars
D. 1.4 billion dollars

p. 175
Drugs: Overview
Level: Easy
Type: Factual
Ans: D

76. Which of the following is not a mechanism by which drugs change behavior?
A. activating the brain's reward/pleasure circuit
B. mimicking the action of neurotransmitters
C. blocking reuptake
D. decreasing the production of synaptic vesicles

p. 175
Drugs: Overview
Level: Difficult
Type: Conceptual
Ans: B

77. You are writing a book on morphine. What should the title be of the chapter that describes morphine's effect on the nervous system?
A. "Clogging Receptors"
B. "The Great Imitator"
C. "Preventing Reuptake"
D. "Increasing the Release"

p. 175
Drugs: Overview
Level: Easy
Type: Factual
Ans: A
*www*

78. Morphine has its effects on the nervous system due to:
A. its similar chemical structure to endorphin
B. its effect on preventing reuptake
C. its similar chemical structure to dopamine
D. its effect on increasing reuptake

p. 175
Drugs: Overview
Level: Easy
Type: Factual
Ans: B

79. One way that cocaine produces its effects is to:
A. block the production of neurotransmitters
B. block reuptake of neurotransmitters
C. reduce the neuronal stimulation
D. stimulate pituitary and adrenal glands

p. 175
Drugs: Overview
Level: Easy
Type: Factual
Ans: C

80. If a drug chemically looks like a neurotransmitter, the drug can:
A. prevent the release of the neurotransmitter
B. cause reuptake to occur more readily
C. mimic the actions of the neurotransmitter
D. prevent reuptake

p. 175
Drugs: Overview
Level: Moderate
Type: Factual
Ans: B

81. Select the option that is <u>incorrect</u> in explaining how the following drug affects the nervous system.
A. morphine - mimics the action of neurotransmitter
B. caffeine - prevents reuptake
C. cocaine - block reuptake of dopamine
D. methamphetamine - increase the release of neurotransmitter

p. 176
Stimulants
Level: Easy
Type: Factual
Ans: C

82. Which of the following stimulants is widely available on the black market?
A. mescaline
B. heroin
C. methamphetamine
D. morphine

p. 176
Stimulants
Level: Easy
Type: Factual
Ans: C

83. Which of the following types of psychoactive drugs increase activity of the nervous system, resulting in heightened alertness, arousal, and euphoria?
A. hallucinogens
B. opiates
C. stimulants
D. marijuana

p. 176
Stimulants
Level: Easy
Type: Factual
Ans: C
*PS/SG 8-14*

84. All of the following are stimulants *except*?
A. cocaine
B. caffeine
C. alcohol
D. nicotine

p. 176
Stimulants
Level: Easy
Type: Applied
Ans: D

85. You're writing a paper on stimulants. You plan to write a section on each of the major stimulants. Which of the following drugs is *not* a member of the stimulant class of drugs?
A. cocaine
B. nicotine
C. caffeine
D. alcohol

p. 176
Stimulants
Level: Easy
Type: Factual
Ans: C
*www*

86. Which of the following is a mild stimulant?
A. cocaine
B. amphetamines
C. nicotine
D. alcohol

p. 176
Stimulants
Level: Easy
Type: Factual
Ans: A

87. The federal government has made amphetamines illegal, except when prescribed for:
A. attention-deficit-hyperactivity disorder
B. major depression
C. anxiety
D. nausea in cancer patients undergoing chemotherapy

| p. 176 | 88. | Methamphetamine is _____ and causes _____. |
|---|---|---|
| Stimulants | A. | taken in pill form; a sudden "crash" |
| Level: Easy | B. | smoked; intense visions or hallucinations |
| Type: Factual | C. | taken in pill form; depression |
| Ans: D | D. | smoked; a near instantaneous high |

| p. 176 | 89. | The most popular illegal drug in Japan is: |
|---|---|---|
| Stimulants | A. | methamphetamine |
| Level: Easy | B. | cocaine |
| Type: Factual | C. | LSD |
| Ans: A | D. | peyote |

| p. 176 | 90. | In the nervous system, amphetamines change the way we feel, think, and act by: |
|---|---|---|
| Stimulants | | |
| Level: Easy | A. | increasing the release of the neurotransmitter dopamine |
| Type: Factual | B. | increasing the rate of reuptake |
| Ans: A | C. | mimicking the effects of melatonin |
| | D. | destroying vesicles in the terminal button |

| p. 176 | 91. | Methamphetamine's effects of enhanced mood, alertness, and energy is due to its ability to: |
|---|---|---|
| Stimulants | | |
| Level: Easy | A. | prevent the reuptake of dopamine |
| Type: Factual | B. | mimic dopamine |
| Ans: D | C. | decrease the release of dopamine |
| | D. | increase the release of dopamine. |

| p. 176 | 92. | Bobby is a heavy user of methamphetamine. He is addicted to it and has developed paranoid feelings about others trying to "get" him. What other signs of Bobby's addiction might be present? |
|---|---|---|
| Stimulants | | |
| Level: Moderate | | |
| Type: Applied | A. | heart irregularities |
| Ans: C | B. | he suffers from insomnia |
| | C. | depression, agitation, and insomnia |
| | D. | difficulty in concentrating |

| p. 176 | 93. | The initial euphoria of methamphetamine use is followed by: |
|---|---|---|
| Stimulants | A. | calm and peaceful feelings |
| Level: Easy | B. | paranoid feelings |
| Type: Factual | C. | intense energy |
| Ans: B | D. | high level of alertness |

| p. 176 | 94. | Methamphetamine users have fewer _____ receptors. |
|---|---|---|
| Stimulants | A. | dopamine |
| Level: Easy | B. | acetylcholine |
| Type: Factual | C. | serotonin |
| Ans: A | D. | GABA |

| p. 176 | 95. | What was the negative consequence of the government's crackdown in the 1970s on amphetamines? |
|---|---|---|
| Stimulants | | |
| Level: Easy | A. | less research on developing antidotes for amphetamine overdose |
| Type: Factual | B. | reduced funding of drug treatment programs |
| Ans: D | C. | increased use of methamphetamine |
| | D. | increased use of cocaine |

p. 176
Stimulants
Level: Easy
Type: Factual
Ans: A

*PS/SG 8-15*

96.    One sad lesson from the history of amphetamine, cocaine, and methamphetamine use is that:

A.    cracking down on one illegal drug leads to an increase in use of another illegal drug

B.    the more dangerous the illegal drug, the harder it is to suppress it

C.    the most dangerous drugs are the depressants

D.    there is a certain class of people who must — and will — have drugs

p. 177
Stimulants
Level: Moderate
Type: Factual
Ans: A

97.    What contributed to the increased popularity of cocaine in the 1970s?

A.    the crackdown on amphetamine usage

B.    development of a new safer form of cocaine

C.    the crackdown on marijuana

D.    lower price

p. 177
Stimulants
Level: Moderate
Type: Factual
Ans: C

98.    Typically, those present-day Andean Indians of Peru who use coca leaves, which contain cocaine, show:

A.    severe addiction problems

B.    psychological dependency

C.    few problems with addiction

D.    increase in crime, violence, and mental disorders

p. 177
Stimulants
Level: Moderate
Type: Factual
Ans: D

99.    In the late 1980s, a "cocaine epidemic" was evident in the United States. Since that time, what has happened to cocaine usage?

A.    cocaine usage has remain stable

B.    the use of cocaine in the United States has increased 20-25%

C.    cocaine usage has decreased by 50-60%

D.    it has decreased by 10-35%

p. 177
Stimulants
Level: Easy
Type: Factual
Ans: C

100.    What was the negative consequence of the government's crackdown in the 1990s on cocaine?

A.    less research on developing antidotes for cocaine overdose

B.    reduced funding of drug treatment programs

C.    increased use of methamphetamine

D.    increased use in cocaine

p. 177
Stimulants
Level: Easy
Type: Factual
Ans: C

101.    _____ is produced from the leaves of the coca plant.

A.    Heroin

B.    Caffeine

C.    Cocaine

D.    Opium

p. 177
Stimulants
Level: Moderate
Type: Applied
Ans: B

102.    Jared is a drug user. He can sniff, smoke, or inject it. What is the drug Jared is addicted to?

A.    caffeine

B.    cocaine

C.    endorphin

D.    LSD

| | | |
|---|---|---|
| p. 177 | 103. | Unlimited access to pure _____ will cause a user to starve to death. |
| Stimulants | A. | marijuana |
| Level: Moderate | B. | alcohol |
| Type: Factual | C. | psilocybin |
| Ans: D | D. | cocaine |

| | | |
|---|---|---|
| p. 177 | 104. | Cocaine's effects on the nervous system center around its ability to: |
| Stimulants | A. | decrease the amount of neurotransmitters available in the nervous system |
| Level: Easy | B. | block reuptake |
| Type: Factual | C. | increase reuptake in the synapse |
| Ans: B | D. | decrease the sensitivity of receptors to norepinephrine |

| | | |
|---|---|---|
| p. 177 | 105. | When the effects of cocaine wear off, users often report feelings of: |
| Stimulants | A. | extreme fatigue |
| Level: Easy | B. | general well-being |
| Type: Factual | C. | mellowness |
| Ans: D | D. | depression |

| | | |
|---|---|---|
| p. 177 | 106. | The only legal use of cocaine is: |
| Stimulants | A. | the treatment of leprosy |
| Level: Easy | B. | as a treatment for severe anorexia nervosa |
| Type: Factual | C. | to block muscles from having spasms |
| Ans: D | D. | as a local anesthetic |

| | | |
|---|---|---|
| p. 177 | 107. | A therapist is working with someone who wants to break a psychological dependency on cocaine. What must therapist and client realize about the dependency? |
| Stimulants | | |
| Level: Moderate | | |
| Type: Factual | A. | It is caused by the unique hallucinations brought about by the drug. |
| Ans: D | B. | There are no physical problems associated with its use. |
| | C. | Use depletes the brain of much-needed neurotransmitters and nutrients that cocaine comes to simulate. |
| | D. | It is caused by the depression that sets in after the experience is over. |

| | | |
|---|---|---|
| p. 177 | 108. | Brian is a heavy cocaine user. What is occurring in his brain because of his use of cocaine? |
| Stimulants | | |
| Level: Moderate | A. | There is an increase in the amount of dopamine released in the brain. |
| Type: Factual | B. | Cocaine stimulates the growth of dendrites. |
| Ans: C | C. | There is a reduction in the number of dopamine receptors in the areas of his brain involved in reward and pleasure. |
| | D. | There is a reduction in the number of acetylcholine receptors in the areas of his brain involved in memory. |

| | | |
|---|---|---|
| p. 178 | 109. | Today, the most widely used psychoactive drug in the world is: |
| Stimulants | A. | alcohol |
| Level: Easy | B. | marijuana |
| Type: Factual | C. | nicotine |
| Ans: D | D. | caffeine |

| | | |
|---|---|---|
| p. 178 | 110. | Which of the following contains the highest concentration of caffeine? |
| Stimulants | A. | one cup of regular coffee |
| Level: Easy | B. | one cup of regular tea |
| Type: Factual | C. | one diet cola |
| Ans: A | D. | one chocolate bar |

p. 178
Stimulants
Level: Easy
Type: Factual
Ans: C

111. What effect is seen after a moderate dose of caffeine?
A. a paradoxical sense of relaxation
B. increased reaction time on complex tasks
C. improved performance in sleep deprived drivers
D. reduced motor impairment from alcohol

p. 178
Stimulants
Level: Easy
Type: Factual
Ans: A
*www*

112. Caffeine belongs to the group of chemicals called:
A. xanthines
B. opiates
C. hallucinogens
D. amphetamines

p. 178
Stimulants
Level: Easy
Type: Factual
Ans: A

113. Caffeine's characteristic effects are due to its:
A. blocking adenosine receptors in the brain
B. decreasing the production of norepinephrine in the dendrite
C. interfering with the production of norepinephrine in the terminal button
D. increasing reuptake rates in the neuron

p. 178
Stimulants
Level: Easy
Type: Factual
Ans: A

114. Which of the following statements about caffeine is *incorrect*?
A. once caffeine reaches the brain, it blocks a depressant neurotransmitter
B. caffeine can cause physical addiction
C. caffeine can cause psychological dependency similar to alcohol
D. 5 cups of coffee a day can result in addiction

p. 178
Stimulants
Level: Moderate
Type: Applied
Ans: C

115. Peter realizes that he drinks too much caffeine a day. He decides to abruptly stop consuming any caffeine. What can Peter expect and for how long?
A. For one day after stopping, Peter will have a slight craving for caffeine and it will last for about two days.
B. He can expect withdrawal symptoms such as fatigue and headaches and they will last about two weeks.
C. Peter will go through withdrawal and experience headaches, fatigue, and cravings. The symptoms will last about one week.
D. Withdrawal symptoms will not be likely since Peter is stopping abruptly.

p. 178
Stimulants
Level: Easy
Type: Factual
Ans: B

116. Molly asks Nancy if she knows the percentage of teens who smoke who will ultimately become habitual smokers. Nancy says yes. What does Nancy know?
A. Only about 3% of teen smokers will become habitual smokers.
B. About 50% of teen smokers will become habitual smokers.
C. 75% of teen smokers will become habitual smokers.
D. 98% of teen smokers will eventual become habitual smokers.

p. 178
Stimulants
Level: Easy
Type: Factual
Ans: C
*PS/SG 8-16*

117. The main reason it is so tough to quit smoking is that the:
A. tolerance for nicotine develops so quickly
B. physical addiction can continue for years after quitting
C. withdrawal symptoms are so painful
D. psychological dependency is deepened by the fact that smoking solves problems

p. 178
Stimulants
Level: Easy
Type: Factual
Ans: B

118. Rose claims that cocaine is the most dangerous drug in terms of the number of deaths caused each year. Her belief is:
A. correct
B. incorrect; nicotine causes far more deaths
C. incorrect; alcohol causes far more deaths
D. incorrect; heroin causes far more deaths

p. 178
Stimulants
Level: Easy
Type: Factual
Ans: D

119. Who said cigarette smoking is the single largest avoidable cause of death in the United States?
A. United States Congress
B. Federal Drug Administration
C. Department of Alcohol, Firearms, and Tobacco
D. United States Surgeon General

p. 178
Stimulants
Level: Moderate
Type: Factual
Ans: C

120. LeRoy is excited that finally he has a real chance to quit smoking. He will be using the nicotine patch. What is the likelihood that he will not be smoking one year later?
A. great - about 1% of smokers who quit smoking relapse within one year
B. good - about 5% of smokers who quit smoking relapse within one year
C. not good - about 75% of smokers who quit smoking relapse within one year
D. ok - about 35% of smokers who quit smoking relapse within one year

p. 178
Stimulants
Level: Easy
Type: Factual
Ans: C
*www*

121. Nicotine is classified as a(n):
A. opiate
B. hallucinogen
C. stimulant
D. depressant

p. 178
Stimulants
Level: Easy
Type: Factual
Ans: A

122. In the brain, nicotine:
A. stimulates the production of dopamine
B. interferes with the reuptake of dopamine
C. binds to serotonin receptors
D. stimulates the production of receptors

p. 178
Stimulants
Level: Easy
Type: Factual
Ans: D
*PS/SG 8-20*

123. Despite all the drug abuse horror stories we hear, the truth is that the two most costly and deadly drugs in our society are:
A. heroin and cocaine
B. marijuana and ecstasy
C. psilocybin and mescaline
D. alcohol and tobacco

p. 178
Stimulants
Level: Moderate
Type: Applied
Ans: B

124. When Gloria lights up a cigarette the nicotine functions as a(n)
_____.
A. amphetamine
B. stimulant
C. opiate
D. depressant

p. 178
Stimulants
Level: Easy
Type: Applied
Ans: C

125. Janice is a smoker who wishes to quit. She has done research at the library to find the most effective smoking cessation method. What did she find in her research?
A. Hypnosis is the most effective approach.
B. The nicotine patch is the best approach.
C. Professional stop-smoking programs are equal to the nicotine patch.
D. Professional stop-smoking programs are most effective.

p. 179
Opiates
Level: Easy
Type: Applied
Ans: B

126. A law enforcement officer was giving a presentation on narcotics and its effects. What did she mean by using the term "narcotics"?
A. she is referring to stimulants
B. narcotics are opiates
C. the term narcotics means any illegal drug
D. hallucinogens are sometimes called narcotics

p. 179
Opiates
Level: Easy
Type: Factual
Ans: D

127. The opiates are said to cause three primary effects. Which of the following is not among the effects?
A. analgesia
B. opiate euphoria
C. constipation
D. hallucinations

p. 179
Opiates
Level: Easy
Type: Factual
Ans: A
PS/SG 8-17

128. The three main effects of _____ are pain reduction, euphoria, and constipation.
A. opiates
B. stimulants
C. hallucinogens
D. designer drugs

p. 179
Opiates
Level: Easy
Type: Applied
Ans: A

129. Ruby, an opiate addict, sits in her apartment and takes heroin. She says that within moments she'll feel the rush. What method did Ruby use to put the heroin into her body and feel the rush?
A. she injected heroin
B. the heroin was smoked
C. heroin, no matter how it gets in the body, does not produce a rush
D. either injection or smoking heroin will cause a rush

p. 179
Opiates
Level: Easy
Type: Factual
Ans: A

130. The body is capable of producing its own opiates in the form of:
A. endorphins
B. dopamine
C. thoraxine
D. adrenaline

p. 179
Opiates
Level: Easy
Type: Factual
Ans: B

131. Which of the following statements best describes opiates?
A. opiates will not produce withdrawal
B. opiates are very addictive
C. marijuana is an example of an opiate
D. opiates are only psychologically addictive

p. 179
Opiates
Level: Easy
Type: Factual
Ans: C

132. What happens to the brain of an opiate user following several weeks of regular use?
A. Endorphin receptors become more sensitive.
B. Endorphin receptors become less sensitive.
C. The brain will produce less of its own endorphins.
D. The brain will produce more of its own endorphins.

p. 179
Opiates
Level: Easy
Type: Factual
Ans: A

133. The newest treatment for heroin addiction is:
A. a drug that blocks the craving for heroin
B. acupuncture
C. methadone
D. self-help programs

p. 179
Opiates
Level: Easy
Type: Factual
Ans: B

134. A long-term study of heroin addicts found that if users do not quit by age _____, they are unlikely to ever stop.
A. 25
B. 30
C. 40
D. 45

p. 179
Opiates
Level: Moderate
Type: Factual
Ans: A

135. The most common treatment for heroin addiction is:
A. methadone maintenance
B. detoxification
C. imprisonment
D. antidepressants

p. 180
Hallucinogens
Level: Easy
Type: Applied
Ans: C
www

136. Jack is taking a psychoactive drug. He reports having perceptual, sensory, and cognitive experiences that are out of the ordinary; but he understands that these experiences are not real. The drug he is most likely taking is one of the _____ drugs.
A. anti-psychotic
B. stimulant
C. hallucinogenic
D. amphetamine

p. 180
Hallucinogens
Level: Moderate
Type: Applied
Ans: D

137. At a party, a number of people are claiming to have weird sensory and perceptual experiences because of some psychoactive drug. Which of the following drugs is probably not the drug taken at this party by these people?
A. LSD
B. psilocybin
C. mescaline
D. methamphetamine

p. 180
Hallucinogens
Level: Easy
Type: Factual
Ans: A

138. Billy takes a drug that causes him to see strange things. For example, he reports that the refrigerator has grown arms and is trying to grab him. What type of drug has he most likely taken?
A. hallucinogen
B. stimulant
C. anti-psychotic
D. depressant

p. 180
Hallucinogens
Level: Moderate
Type: Factual
Ans: D

139. LSD's effect is due to its similarity to:
A. heroin
B. dopamine
C. caffeine
D. serotonin

p. 180
Hallucinogens
Level: Moderate
Type: Factual
Ans: B

140. Use of lysergic acid diethylamide is
A. likely to increase the odds of overdosing
B. tied to experiencing frightening flashbacks for no apparent reason
C. linked to the many cases of death from overdose
D. likely to cause physical addiction

p. 180
Hallucinogens
Level: Moderate
Type: Factual
Ans: B

141. A person is depressed and pessimistic about his future. Feeling this way, he decides to take LSD. It is probable that the person will experience:
A. an elevation of mood
B. a drug experience that is consistent with his depression and pessimism
C. no hallucination
D. an emotional uplifting that ends abruptly when the effects of the drug wear off

p. 180
Hallucinogens
Level: Moderate
Type: Factual
Ans: C

142. You've just read a paper on LSD written by a classmate. In the paper, you read that LSD causes physical addiction. What is your learned reaction?
A. It is widely known that LSD causes physical addiction.
B. Physical addiction to LSD depends on several factors such as age of user.
C. There have been no reports of physical addiction to LSD.
D. LSD does not cause physical addiction or tolerance.

p. 180
Hallucinogens
Level: Easy
Type: Factual
Ans: A

143. The reason why LSD causes hallucinations is because it:
A. resembles serotonin
B. prevents the release of serotonin
C. interferes with the reuptake of serotonin
D. destroys molecules of serotonin

p. 180
Hallucinogens
Level: Easy
Type: Factual
Ans: A

144. The active ingredient in "magic mushrooms" is:
A. psilocybin
B. mescaline
C. cocaine
D. THC (tetrahydrocannabinol)

| p. 180 | 145. | Psilocybin's effects on the nervous system are due to its: |
|---|---|---|
| Hallucinogens | A. | excitatory influence on serotonin receptors |
| Level: Easy | B. | inhibitory action on dopamine receptors |
| Type: Factual | C. | similarity to cocaine with regard to chemical makeup |
| Ans: D | D. | chemical structure resembling LSD |

| p. 180 | 146. | The effects of psilocybin's effects are due to its ability to: |
|---|---|---|
| Hallucinogens | A. | increase the release of dopamine |
| Level: Easy | B. | release endorphins in the visual cortex of the brain |
| Type: Factual | C. | inhibit serotonin receptors |
| Ans: C | D. | prevent reuptake from occurring |

| p. 181 | 147. | Peyote cactus contains the psychoactive drug: |
|---|---|---|
| Hallucinogens | A. | MDMA |
| Level: Easy | B. | mescaline |
| Type: Factual | C. | psilocybin |
| Ans: B | D. | opium |

*www*

| p. 181 | 148. | Which of the following statements about mescaline is true? |
|---|---|---|
| Hallucinogens | A. | It only takes very, very small amounts of mescaline to produce hallucinations. |
| Level: Easy | | |
| Type: Factual | B. | It plays an important part in the religious ceremonies of the Navajo Church of the Americas. |
| Ans: D | | |
| | C. | The parasympathetic division is activated by mescaline. |
| | D. | Mescaline does not impair intellectual functioning. |

| p. 181 | 149. | The effects of mescaline are caused by increasing the activity of: |
|---|---|---|
| Hallucinogens | A. | serotonin and endorphin |
| Level: Easy | B. | norepinephrine and dopamine |
| Type: Factual | C. | dopamine and serotonin |
| Ans: B | D. | MDMA and morphine |

| p. 181 | 150. | At high doses, mescaline typically causes: |
|---|---|---|
| Hallucinogens | A. | a temporary reduction of problem solving skills |
| Level: Easy | B. | disorientation |
| Type: Factual | C. | clear and vivid hallucinations |
| Ans: C | D. | confusion |

| p. 181 | 151. | Bud has manufactured a quantity of MDMA in a lab in his garage. Bud has made a(n): |
|---|---|---|
| Hallucinogens | | |
| Level: Easy | A. | depressant |
| Type: Factual | B. | opiate |
| Ans: C | C. | designer drug |
| | D. | stimulant |

| p. 181 | 152. | The street name of MDMA is: |
|---|---|---|
| Hallucinogens | A. | "ecstasy" |
| Level: Easy | B. | "ice" |
| Type: Factual | C. | "slam" |
| Ans: A | D. | "crack" |

p. 181
Hallucinogens
Level: Moderate
Type: Factual
Ans: B

153. Which of the following *best* illustrates the effects of MDMA?
A. depressant + hallucinogenic
B. hallucinogenic + stimulant
C. stimulant + analgesia
D. euphoria + analgesia

p. 181
Hallucinogens
Level: Easy
Type: Applied
Ans: C

154. A group of drug addicts are talking about their various drug experiences. One mentions a particular drug that is described as the "warmth drug." Which drug was being described?
A. mescaline
B. PCP
C. MDMA
D. opiates

p. 181
Hallucinogens
Level: Moderate
Type: Factual
Ans: B

155. One of the more serious dangers of MDMA is that it can:
A. deplete the brain's natural supply of endorphins
B. damage serotonin neurons
C. destroy the kidneys
D. permanently alter homeostasis

p. 182
Alcohol
Level: Easy
Type: Factual
Ans: C

156. According to the textbook, the oldest drug produced by humans is:
A. mescaline
B. psilocybin
C. alcohol
D. nicotine

p. 182
Alcohol
Level: Easy
Type: Factual
Ans: A
*PS/SG 8-19*

157. The clear lesson of the history of prohibition (1920 to 1933) is that:
A. it may be impossible to ban a drug that is so popular and widely used
B. we must abandon our on-again/off-again enforcement strategies and declare an all-out war on drugs
C. eventually people get tired of any drug
D. legalization would reduce the problem to manageable dimensions

p. 182
Alcohol
Level: Easy
Type: Factual
Ans: B

158. What percentage of Americans who drank alcohol in 2001 were underage?
A. 3%
B. 29%
C. 42%
D. 64%

p. 182
Alcohol
Level: Easy
Type: Factual
Ans: D

159. Harvey and Matt are debating whether the alcohol in beer, wine, and liquor is different. Harvey says that all contain ethyl alcohol. Matt says that each contains a different type of alcohol. Who is right?
A. Harvey is partially right since beer does not contain ethyl alcohol, but wine and liquor do.
B. Matt is right. Each drink contains different types of alcohol.
C. Harvey is partially right. Beer and wine, but not liquor contain ethyl alcohol.
D. Harvey is right. Beer, wine, and liquor contain ethyl alcohol.

p. 182
Alcohol
Level: Easy
Type: Factual
Ans: D
*www*

160. Alcohol is classified as a(n):
A. amphetamine
B. stimulant
C. opiate
D. depressant

p. 182
Alcohol
Level: Moderate
Type: Applied
Ans: A

161. Al and Jim are drinking alcohol at a party. Jim feels a loss of inhibition and starts to act uncharacteristically friendly and outgoing. Al comments that alcohol is a stimulant and points to Jim's behavior as evidence. Is Jim's behavior good evidence that alcohol is a stimulant?
A. No - initially alcohol serves to lessen one's inhibitions and self-control
B. No - Jim's behavior is atypical of someone drinking alcohol
C. Yes - Jim is obviously acting in a way that is out of character for him
D. Yes - only in heavy doses is alcohol considered a depressant, but at low to medium doses, alcohol is a stimulant

p. 182
Alcohol
Level: Easy
Type: Factual
Ans: A

162. Alcohol's effects appear to be due to its ability to:
A. stimulate GABA receptors and impairs the anterior cingulate cortex
B. prevent reuptake of GABA
C. increase the production of acetylcholine
D. increase the production of dopamine

p. 182
Alcohol
Level: Moderate
Type: Applied
Ans: C

163. What is the best evidence that alcohol impairs the anterior cingulate cortex?
A. Alcohol acts as a stimulant.
B. When drinking, people feel less anxious.
C. People who drink may not notice that their motor performance is affected.
D. The brain stem functions are depressed.

p. 182
Alcohol
Level: Easy
Type: Applied
Ans: B

164. For the last few days, Patrick has stopped abusing alcohol. He is presently enduring serious withdrawal symptoms. The presence of withdrawal symptoms most strongly suggests that Patrick:
A. is experiencing a hangover
B. has an addiction to alcohol
C. has serious liver damage
D. has a genetic basis to his alcoholism

p. 182
Alcohol
Level: Easy
Type: Applied
Ans: C

165. "If I want the same buzz, I'll have to drink more." This person is describing:
A. addiction
B. dependency
C. tolerance
D. the effects of GABA stimulation

p. 182
Alcohol
Level: Easy
Type: Applied
Ans: D

166. How might you tell if a person is experiencing withdrawal symptoms following heavy drinking?
A. The person is experiencing short-bursts of energy and alertness.
B. You notice the person has reduced inhibitions.
C. The person needs to drink more and more alcohol.
D. The person experiences shakes, nausea, and anxiety.

p. 182
Alcohol
Level: Easy
Type: Applied
Ans: D

167. Juan attended a party last night, but really can't remember what happened. All that he recalls is drinking a lot of beer. His friends claim that he was obnoxious and rude, but Juan can't remember. This is not the first time for this experience. Last night, Juan had a(n):
A. allergic reaction
B. hangover
C. seizure
D. blackout

p. 182
Alcohol
Level: Easy
Type: Factual
Ans: A

168. A memory lapse associated with drinking is called a:
A. blackout
B. mnemonic
C. hangover
D. seizure

p. 182
Alcohol
Level: Easy
Type: Factual
Ans: A

169. The evidence presented in your textbook regarding the dangers of alcohol has led some to argue that:
A. alcohol is the most dangerous of all drugs - legal or illegal
B. college students do not know how to hold their alcohol
C. the drinking age should be raised to 25 years of age
D. alcohol should be outlawed by tough enforcement practices

p. 182
Alcohol
Level: Easy
Type: Factual
Ans: C

170. The best way to think about risk factors for abusing alcohol is that:
A. they do not include genetic factors
B. risk factors have not been identified by scientific research
C. they increase the chances that a person will be an alcoholic
D. they guarantee that a person will be an alcoholic

p. 183
Alcohol
Level: Easy
Type: Factual
Ans: D

171. Examples of psychological risk factors cited in your textbook include:
A. whether the parent was physically abused as a child
B. the quality of attachment between child and parent
C. how parents respond effectively to stressful situations
D. difficulty showing trust

p. 183
Alcohol
Level: Easy
Type: Factual
Ans: B

172. Sue's biological parents did not drink. She was adopted at the age of three, and her adoptive parents were both alcoholics. While in college, Sue developed a drinking problem. Her drinking problem may have been a result of _____ risk factors.
A. blood alcohol level
B. psychological
C. genetic
D. depressant

p. 183
Alcohol
Level: Easy
Type: Factual
Ans: C

173. Psychological risk factors may increase one's risk of alcoholism by:
A. modifying genetic risk
B. changing one's physiological risk
C. teaching the individual how to inappropriately deal with personal, social, or work-related difficulties
D. increasing one's sensitivity to alcohol

p. 183
Alcohol
Level: Moderate
Type: Factual
Ans: A

174. Research has indicated that sensitivity to alcohol is a genetic risk for alcoholism. Specifically, what kind of sensitivity has the research identified as a risk for developing alcoholism?
A. lower
B. higher
C. the research has not identified degree of sensitivity
D. lower or higher - it doesn't matter, as long as it is an abnormal degree of sensitivity

p. 183
Alcohol
Level: Moderate
Type: Applied
Ans: C

175. Bill and Bob are 22-year-old identical twins. Bill is an alcoholic. Using the data cited in your textbook, what are the chances that Bob is an alcoholic as well?
A. 6%
B. 16%
C. 39%
D. 99%

p. 183
Alcohol
Level: Easy
Type: Conceptual
Ans: B
*PS/SG 8-21*

176. Studies of national rates of alcoholism around the world suggest that alcoholism is a(n):
A. individual problem, relatively unaffected by where the individual lives
B. partly genetic and partly cultural problem
C. genetic problem, independent of national origins
D. family problem, passed down through the generations

p. 183
Alcohol
Level: Moderate
Type: Conceptual
Ans: C

177. Among identical twins, if one is an alcoholic, there is a ___ chance the other is too. Since this number is not 100%, it suggests that:
A. 6%; genetics play a role
B. 16%; environment plays a role
C. 39%; environment plays a role
D. 99%; there are errors in measurement

p. 183
Alcohol
Level: Easy
Type: Factual
Ans: C
*www*

178. Research on alcoholism has demonstrated that the development of alcoholism is associated with:
A. psychological factors
B. genetic factors
C. both psychological and genetic factors
D. neither psychological nor genetic factors

p. 183
Alcohol
Level: Moderate
Type: Conceptual
Ans: D

179. Kari is considered "at risk" for alcoholism. This means that:
A. both her parents are alcoholics
B. she will definitely develop alcoholism during adulthood
C. only genetic factors will influence her actual experiences with alcohol
D. her chances of developing alcoholism are increased but the outcome is not definite

p. 183
Alcohol
Level: Moderate
Type: Factual
Ans: C

180. The family that lives down the street from Lance has several members who struggle with alcoholism. Lance thinks that the family must have the "alcoholic gene." Is Lance right?
A. The "alcoholic gene" has been found on the sex chromosome.
B. There are no genetic factors associated with alcoholism.
C. There are probably several "alcoholic genes" that interact with the environment.
D. There are probably several "alcoholic genes" that influence us independent of the environment.

p. 183
Alcohol
Level: Easy
Type: Factual
Ans: B

181. If you add up all the economic costs of alcoholism, you would find that the cost is estimated to be _____ per year.
A. $150 million
B. $150 billion
C. $52 million
D. $52 billion

p. 183
Alcohol
Level: Easy
Type: Factual
Ans: C

182. The leading cause of mental retardation is _____.
A. marijuana
B. heroin
C. alcohol
D. cocaine

p. 185
Cultural Diversity:
 Alcoholism Rates
Level: Easy
Type: Factual
Ans: B

183. Which of the following is *not* a characteristic of alcoholism?
A. addiction to alcohol
B. liver damage
C. dependency on alcohol
D. continued use of alcohol despite problems

p. 185
Cultural Diversity:
 Alcoholism Rates
Level: Easy
Type: Factual
Ans: C

184. Asians, as a whole, may be less likely to become alcoholics because of:
A. cultural taboos
B. stricter alcohol laws in Asian countries
C. lack of a liver enzyme involved in metabolizing alcohol
D. blood alcohol levels

p. 185
Cultural Diversity:
 Alcoholism Rates
Level: Easy
Type: Factual
Ans: D

185. What happens if you lack a particular liver enzyme involved in metabolizing alcohol?
A. develop liver damage
B. display confabulation
C. shakes
D. facial flushing

p. 185
Cultural Diversity:
  Alcoholism Rates
Level: Easy
Type: Factual
Ans: C

186. Compared to Koreans, those Asians who experience significant _____ are likely to drink less and have _____ rates of alcoholism according to your textbook.
A. facial flushing; higher
B. idiosyncratic alcohol intoxication; higher
C. facial flushing; lower
D. metabolic slow-down; higher

p. 185
Cultural Diversity:
  Alcoholism Rates
Level: Easy
Type: Applied
Ans: A

187. Scott abuses alcohol even though he has paid thousands of dollars in fines, been fired three times, has been divorced, and was advised by his doctor to quit drinking because of possible liver damage. Scott has had several drinks a day for the last three years. Scott:
A. is an alcoholic
B. is a problem drinker
C. is likely to be Japanese
D. suffers from alcohol intoxication

p. 185
Cultural Diversity:
  Alcoholism Rates
Level: Easy
Type: Factual
Ans: D

188. Of the following cultures, which has the highest rates of alcoholism?
A. Germans
B. Americans
C. Taiwanese
D. Koreans

p. 185
Cultural Diversity:
  Alcoholism Rates
Level: Easy
Type: Factual
Ans: B

189. The high rate of alcoholism among Korean men is attributable to:
A. genetic factors
B. cultural pressure to drink heavily in some social situations
C. lack of an liver enzyme involved in metabolizing alcohol
D. stress of living in an industrialized country

p. 185
Cultural Diversity:
  Alcoholism Rates
Level: Easy
Type: Factual
Ans: C

190. According to the textbook, the Confucian moral ethic appears to have influenced the _____ where there are cultural taboos against drinking or being intoxicated in public.
A. Indonesians
B. Buddhist monks
C. Taiwanese
D. Koreans

p. 185
Cultural Diversity:
  Alcoholism Rates
Level: Easy
Type: Factual
Ans: D

191. As your textbook shows, cultural factors are an important factor in explaining differences in the rate of alcoholism. However, culture seems to have little influence on:
A. development of alcoholism
B. types of alcoholism
C. drunk driving rates
D. rate of alcoholism

p. 186
Marijuana
Level: Moderate
Type: Factual
Ans: A

192. Where does marijuana stand in popularity of use in the United States with cocaine, heroin, and ecstasy?
A. first
B. second
C. third
D. fourth

p. 186  193. The most widely used illegal drug in the United States is:
Marijuana A. methamphetamine
Level: Moderate B. opium
Type: Factual C. cocaine
Ans: D D. marijuana

p. 186  194. The gateway effect refers to:
Marijuana A. the use of marijuana leading to use of harder drugs
Level: Easy B. the effects of marijuana on critical thinking
Type: Factual C. the medicinal uses of marijuana
Ans: A D. THC's effect on the reticular formation

p. 186  195. The active ingredient in marijuana is called ____ and is found in
Marijuana _____.
Level: Easy A. xanthine; cannabis roots
Type: Factual B. anandamide; cannabis leaves
Ans: C C. THC; cannabis leaves
D. xanthine; cannabis leaves

p. 186  196. Low doses of marijuana cause _____, whereas high doses cause
Marijuana _____.
Level: Easy A. elevated blood pressure; heart failure
Type: Factual B. time distortions; cognitive dementia
Ans: C C. mild euphoria; delusions
D. distortions of body image; increases in reaction time

p. 186  197. The effects of marijuana on a person depends upon:
Marijuana A. the supply of dopamine in the brain
Level: Easy B. the user's state of mind
Type: Factual C. its effect on the reuptake of dopamine
Ans: B D. the amount of dopamine found in the marijuana joint

p. 186  198. A newly discovered substance in the brain has a chemical structure similar
Marijuana to the active ingredient in marijuana. This neurotransmitter is:
Level: Easy A. anandamide
Type: Factual B. dopamine
Ans: A C. serotonin
D. epinephrine

p. 186  199. Mary and Jane are arguing about the relative carcinogenic content of
Marijuana marijuana smoke and tobacco smoke. Mary says that marijuana smoke is
Level: Moderate more dangerous to one's health than tobacco smoke. Based upon the
Type: Factual research, Mary is:
Ans: D A. wrong since the difference between the two is insignificant
B. wrong because marijuana smoke has half the carcinogenic content of
tobacco smoke
C. right because THC increases the body's susceptibility to carcinogens
D. right because marijuana smoke has about 50 percent greater carcinogenic
content than tobacco smoke

p. 186
Marijuana
Level: Easy
Type: Factual
Ans: A

200. Which of the following is not a danger of marijuana according to the textbook?
A. long-term psychosis
B. addiction
C. impaired ability to drive
D. mild withdrawal symptoms

p. 186
Marijuana
Level: Easy
Type: Factual
Ans: D
*PS/SG 8-23*

201. After years of studying the harmfulness of marijuana, scientists have concluded that it:
A. eventually causes brain damage
B. often leads to mental illness
C. typically leads to the use of hard drugs
D. may or may not be dangerous in the long run - the research is not yet definitive

p. 187
Research Focus:
 Drug Prevention
Level: Easy
Type: Factual
Ans: C

202. The drug prevention program DARE uses _____ and is taught by _____.
A. social influence and role playing; public school teachers
B. former addicts; community volunteers like doctors and businesspeople
C. social influence and role playing; uniformed police officers
D. celebrities; uniformed police officers

p. 187
Research Focus:
 Drug Prevention
Level: Easy
Type: Factual
Ans: C

203. Kevin, a fifth grader, has been participating in a program designed to prevent him and his classmates from ever starting to use drugs and to teach them to refuse drugs in their future. Kevin is most likely participating in:
A. KADA - Kids Against Drug Abuse
B. DARE - Drug Assistance and Recovery Enforcement
C. DARE - Drug Abuse Resistance Program
D. Just Say No!

p. 187
Research Focus:
 Drug Prevention
Level: Easy
Type: Factual
Ans: A

204. Thirty-six elementary schools located in different areas of Illinois took part in a study to evaluate DARE's effectiveness. Some schools received DARE training and other schools did not receive DARE training. Before the study, students were asked to indicate their attitudes toward drugs and use of drugs. Students were retested one year and two to three years later on:
A. their attitudes toward drugs, use of drugs, and self-confidence to resist drugs
B. how they liked DARE training
C. use of drugs
D. classmates' use of drugs

p. 187
Research Focus:
 Drug Prevention
Level: Easy
Type: Factual
Ans: C

205. Results indicated that students who participated in project DARE:
A. had lower rates of drug use
B. had better study habits and achieved higher grades
C. had only temporary gain in self-esteem
D. showed success in resisting drugs

p. 187
Research Focus:
  Drug Prevention
Level: Moderate
Type: Factual
Ans: D

206. Of the following statements, which one best describes DARE's effectiveness based upon a study conducted in Illinois?
A. DARE students had lower rates of drug use
B. DARE had substantial influence on drug use or attitudes toward drug use only at the 1 year follow-up
C. DARE proved to be successful in preventing male students from starting drinking to get intoxicated
D. at 1 year and 2-3 year follow-ups, DARE had no substantial influence on drug use or attitudes toward drug use

p. 187
Research Focus:
  Drug Prevention
Level: Moderate
Type: Factual
Ans: A

207. Why is DARE so popular among police and education officials?
A. biased and error prone testimonials
B. the federal government gives billions of dollars each year to schools to fund DARE and other programs including athletics
C. DARE is highly effective at reducing adolescent drug use
D. DARE can be highly effective when the police officers are well-trained

p. 188
Application: Treatment
  For Drug Abuse
Level: Easy
Type: Factual
Ans: D

208. _____ is defined as a maladaptive pattern of using a substance which leads to significant problems because of continued usage.
A. Psychological addiction
B. Substance dependency
C. Substance addiction
D. Substance abuse

p. 188
Application: Treatment
  For Drug Abuse
Level: Easy
Type: Factual
Ans: A

209. The Minnesota model of treatment emphasizes that:
A. the abuser has lost control with the drug
B. the individual can learn how to moderate the intake of the drug
C. individuals working alone are in the best position to solve their drug problem
D. patients can acquire the skills to not abuse alcohol and to become only social drinkers

p. 188
Application: Treatment
  For Drug Abuse
Level: Easy
Type: Factual
Ans: C

210. The most commonly used inpatient drug treatment model is the:
A. motivational model
B. Michigan model
C. Minnesota model
D. Alcoholics Anonymous model

p. 188
Application: Treatment
  For Drug Abuse
Level: Easy
Type: Factual
Ans: C

211. Bart is an abuser of alcohol. Kent suffers from depression. Based upon the textbook, one important difference between these two individuals is:
A. Bart is far more likely to seek treatment on his own than Kent
B. depression is more difficult to treat because with alcohol one can remain totally isolated from it, whereas depression is part of living
C. Bart probably doesn't recognize his need for treatment while Kent likely seeks treatment voluntarily
D. there is a more negative social stigma associated with treatment for depression, so Kent is likely to get treatment

| | | |
|---|---|---|
| p. 188 | 212. | Larry is a heroin addict. The first step to successful treatment of his problem involves: |
| Application: Treatment | | |
|   For Drug Abuse | A. | admitting to himself that he has a problem |
| Level: Easy | B. | detoxification |
| Type: Applied | C. | aversive conditioning |
| Ans: A | D. | family therapy |

| | | |
|---|---|---|
| p. 189 | 213. | What percentage of alcoholics are treated in clinics as outpatients? |
| Application: Treatment | A. | 5% |
|   For Drug Abuse | B. | 7% |
| Level: Easy | C. | 85% |
| Type: Factual | D. | 97% |
| Ans: C | | |

| | | |
|---|---|---|
| p. 189 | 214. | The most important goal of a drug treatment program is for the individual to: |
| Application: Treatment | | |
|   For Drug Abuse | A. | face up to the drug problem |
| Level: Easy | B. | detoxify |
| Type: Applied | C. | to form new nondrinking friends |
| Ans: D | D. | overcome psychological risk factors |

| | | |
|---|---|---|
| p. 189 | 215. | Mike is in treatment for alcohol abuse and is working on eliminating maladaptive negative thought patterns. His program uses the technique of: |
| Application: Treatment | | |
|   For Drug Abuse | A. | mental rebuilding |
| Level: Easy | B. | abstinence |
| Type: Applied | C. | free association |
| Ans: D | D. | cognitive-behavioral therapy |

| | | |
|---|---|---|
| p. 189 | 216. | As part of a drug treatment program, the subject may experience a spiritual awakening. This therapy is known as: |
| Application: Treatment | | |
|   For Drug Abuse | A. | the 12-step approach |
| Level: Easy | B. | relapse prevention |
| Type: Factual | C. | motivational therapy |
| Ans: A | D. | cognitive-behavioral therapy |

| | | |
|---|---|---|
| p. 189 | 217. | As a way of stopping her nicotine habit, Elyce is taught how to use her own personal resources and to take personal responsibility to abstain. This is _____ therapy. |
| Application: Treatment | | |
|   For Drug Abuse | A. | the 12-step approach |
| Level: Moderate | B. | relapse prevention |
| Type: Factual | C. | motivational |
| Ans: C | D. | cognitive-behavioral |

| | | |
|---|---|---|
| p. 189 | 218. | What popular aftercare program for recovering alcoholics emphasizes a 12-step approach as they recover? |
| Application: Treatment | | |
|   For Drug Abuse | A. | Alcoholics United |
| Level: Easy | B. | Alcoholics Anonymous |
| Type: Factual | C. | Working Through groups |
| Ans: B | D. | DARE |

p. 189
Application: Treatment
 For Drug Abuse
Level: Moderate
Type: Applied
Ans: C

219. Lynn is attending Alcoholics Anonymous and has been doing so for two years. What is Lynn *not* likely to hear being taught at a meeting of AA?
A. "Total abstinence is the only hope for alcoholics."
B. "You must put trust in a Power greater than yourself."
C. "You can learn how to control your drinking."
D. "Alcoholics must learn how to rebuild their character."

p. 189
Application: Treatment
 For Drug Abuse
Level: Easy
Type: Factual
Ans: D

220. Of the therapies for drug treatment described in your textbook, which one was found to be most effective in reducing drinking?
A. cognitive-behavioral therapy
B. motivational therapy
C. the 12-step approach
D. they are equally effective

p. 189
Application: Treatment
 For Drug Abuse
Level: Easy
Type: Factual
Ans: C

221. The goal of most drug treatment programs is:
A. controlled drug use
B. continued use, but only if it causes no problems
C. complete abstinence
D. reducing withdrawal symptoms

p. 189
Application: Treatment
 For Drug Abuse
Level: Easy
Type: Factual
Ans: A

222. About _____ of all drug abusers relapse.
A. 55%- 70%
B. 40%
C. 30%
D. 10-15%%

True/False

| F | www | 1. | Most people are highly susceptible to hypnosis. |
|---|---|---|---|
| F | | 2. | When people are hypnotized, they actually are sleeping. |
| T | | 3. | Hypnosis allows a person to perform behaviors without conscious intent according to the altered state theory of hypnosis. |
| T | www | 4. | Behaviors observed in hypnotized subjects have been observed in nonhypnotized subjects. |
| F | | 5. | People who show age regression following hypnotism are often faking. |
| F | www | 6. | In hypnotic analgesia, pain sensations are reduced. |
| F | | 7. | Hypnotic suggestions to think of pain as less pleasant leads to decreased activity in the frontal lobe. |
| T | | 8. | Hypnosis is most effective in helping people to quit smoking when used with other procedures. |
| T | www | 9. | Problems of self-control are more difficult to treat with hypnosis than problems that involve mind-body interactions. |
| F | | 10. | Dependency to a drug occurs when the person takes the drug to avoid tolerance. |
| T | | 11. | Some drugs mimic how neurotransmitters work. |
| T | | 12. | If a drug prevents reuptake, the neurotransmitter remains in the synapse. |
| T | www | 13. | Addiction occurs when the brain's reward/pleasure center becomes dependent on outside drugs. |

| T | *www* | 14. | Nicotine is a stimulant. |
|---|---|---|---|
| F | | 15. | Cocaine has very similar effects as alcohol. |
| T | | 16. | Opiates provide euphoria and analgesia by its effect on receptors. |
| T | *www* | 17. | LSD can produce hallucinations at very low doses. |
| F | | 18. | Psilocybin is a drug used in religious ceremonies by the Native American Church. |
| T | | 19. | MDMA may be useful in some types of therapy. |
| F | | 20. | Tolerance refers to the person's intense craving for a drug. |
| T | *www* | 21. | Alcohol is a depressant. |
| T | | 22. | Koreans have higher rates of alcoholism than Chinese. |
| F | *www* | 23. | DARE is an effective program in preventing drug use in teenagers. |
| T | | 24. | The Minnesota model of treatment for drug abuse strives for total abstinence. |
| T | *www* | 25. | Most drinkers tend to relapse following treatment. |

Short-Answer Essay Questions

1. What is hypnosis? How do the altered state theory and sociocognitive theory explain hypnosis? (*www*)
2. Describe the mechanism behind how hypnosis reduces pain.
3. If a close friend of yours was thinking about getting hypnosis to stop smoking, what advice would you give based on Module Eight?
4. Describe how morphine and cocaine affect the nervous system. (*www*)
5. What are the consequences of the reduction of dopamine receptors in the brain's of cocaine users?
6. Describe the options for treating heroin addiction.
7. Present a brief summary of tolerance, addiction, dependency, and withdrawal symptoms in drinking alcohol. (*www*)
8. Review the psychological and genetic risk factors for developing alcoholism. (*www*)
9. Is DARE an effective program to prevent drug abuse? Make sure you defend your answer by citing the research presented in Module Eight. (*www*)
10. Describe the effectiveness cognitive-behavioral therapy and the 12-step approach to treating alcoholism.

# Module 9 - Classical Conditioning

p. 195
Introduction
Level: Moderate
Type: Conceptual
Ans: B

1. Presenting the examples of an aftershave causing anxiety, fear of needles, and the smell of dish soap causing nausea illustrates:
   A. how irrational our thinking can be at times
   B. many of our behaviors are the result of learning
   C. the diversity of human behavior
   D. the concept of insight

p. 195
Introduction
Level: Easy
Type: Factual
Ans: A

2. Of the following, which is the best explanation for an individual to become fearful from smelling aftershave?
   A. classical conditioning
   B. observational learning
   C. operant conditioning
   D. biological predisposition

p. 195
Introduction
Level: Easy
Type: Factual
Ans: C
*PS/SG 9-1*

3. Rod Plotnik begins this module with the story of Carla and the dentist's aftershave to show how:
   A. learning often occurs when we least expect it
   B. learning is more likely to occur in some environments than in others
   C. we can learn a response simply because it occurs along with some other response
   D. we can like something very much, then turn against it for no clear reason

p. 195
Introduction
Level: Easy
Type: Factual
Ans: B

4. What percentage of the general population experiences fear of needles and injections?
   A. 1%
   B. 10-20%
   C. 30-40%
   D. 60-70%

p. 195
Introduction
Level: Easy
Type: Factual
Ans: A

5. "A relatively enduring change in behavior that results from previous experience with certain stimuli and responses" is the definition of:
   A. learning
   B. imprinting
   C. extinction
   D. generalization

p. 195
Introduction
Level: Moderate
Type: Factual
Ans: C

6. Simone is listening to her professor's lecture. Class is about to end when the professor previews the topic for the next meeting. "Next time," he says, "we will examine learning." Since Simone has done the assigned reading, she correctly thinks to herself:

A. "Let's see -that's when there is a temporary change in behavior that results from previous experience with certain stimuli and responses."

B. "Oh, that's when there is permanent change in behavior that is due to maturation."

C. "Learning - that's when there is a relatively permanent change in behavior that results from previous experience with certain stimuli and responses."

D. "Learning is the change in behavior that results from biological changes, fatigue, or injury."

p. 195
Introduction
Level: Moderate
Type: Applied
Ans: A

7. After learning the definition of learning, Sami tries to think of relevant examples of learning. Sami comes up with a couple of examples. Which of the following is not an example of learning according to the definition?

A. Whenever Sami's friend Carl drinks too much he has a hard time remembering things.

B. When someone is eating potato chips, Sami hears the munching and starts to feel hungry

C. Sami's cat runs to the kitchen when it hears the can opener opening a can of cat food.

D. Sami associated nausea with pizza after developing the flu after eating a couple of pieces.

p. 195
Introduction
Level: Easy
Type: Factual
Ans: B
*www*

8. Learning can be best defined as:
A. a change in behavior related to mental events
B. a relatively permanent change in behavior resulting from experience
C. an improvement in abilities resulting from formal instruction
D. the acquisition of information through research

p. 195
Introduction
Level: Moderate
Type: Applied
Ans: D

9. Of the following, which would a psychologist consider the best example of learning?
A. a young man's beard beginning to grow at age fifteen
B. a woman experiencing labor pains
C. salmon swimming upstream during the mating season
D. a child being able to ride a bicycle

p. 195
Introduction
Level: Moderate
Type: Factual
Ans: A

10. The example of Michelle becoming nauseous when she smelled dish-washing soap can be best explained by a type of learning called:
A. classical conditioning
B. instrumental conditioning
C. cognitive learning
D. imprinting

p. 195
Introduction
Level: Moderate
Type: Factual
Ans: A

11. The sight of a needle can trigger fear in some people. What type of learning can explain this association?
A. classical conditioning
B. instrumental conditioning
C. cognitive learning
D. imprinting

p. 196
Three Kinds of Learning
Level: Easy
Type: Factual
Ans: D
*PS/SG 9-3*

12. All of the following are approaches to understanding how learning occurs <u>except</u>:
A. classical conditioning
B. operant conditioning
C. cognitive learning
D. physical learning

p. 196
Three Kinds of Learning
Level: Easy
Type: Factual
Ans: D

13. What do classical conditioning, operant conditioning, and cognitive learning all have in common?
A. Each is based upon the law of effect.
B. These forms of learning were once thought to be valid explanations of how we learn, but now are considered by psychologists as inadequate.
C. These forms of learning are common in animals, but rare in humans.
D. These are all forms of learning.

p. 196
Three Kinds of Learning
Level: Easy
Type: Factual
Ans: B
*www*

14. Classical conditioning was discovered by:
A. B. F. Skinner
B. Ivan Pavlov
C. Edward Thorndike
D. Albert Bandura

p. 196
Three Kinds of Learning
Level: Easy
Type: Conceptual
Ans: C

15. Does Pavlov ring a bell?
A. Yes - Pavlov used operant conditioning to relieve children of dental fears
B. Yes - he used cognitive learning to get dogs to escape a box
C. Yes - he used classical conditioning to get dogs to salivate to the sound of a bell
D. Yes - Pavlov used operant conditioning to get dogs to salivate to the sound of a bell

p. 196
Three Kinds of Learning
Level: Moderate
Type: Factual
Ans: A

16. In Pavlov's study of digestion, he noticed that the dogs were salivating at the sight of food. What was Pavlov's initial reaction to this?
A. The salivation was considered to be a bothersome problem.
B. He was very excited since he wanted the dogs to salivate at the sight of food.
C. He expected it, so it did not affect his study of digestion.
D. He could not have cared less.

p. 196
Three Kinds of Learning
Level: Moderate
Type: Applied
Ans: A

17. If you wanted to condition your friends to blink their eyes in response to the word "apple" what would you do?
A. Use classical conditioning and pair the word "apple" with a puff of air to the eyes.
B. Use classical conditioning and reinforce eye blinking with a slice of an apple.
C. Use operant conditioning and reinforce eye blinking to the word "apple" with a dollar.
D. Use operant conditioning and pair the eye blinking with a slice of an apple.

p. 196
Three Kinds of Learning
Level: Easy
Type: Factual
Ans: C

18. Ivan Pavlov was studying _____ before he stumbled on to _____.
A. operant conditioning; classical conditioning
B. problem solving in cats; law of effect
C. digestion in dogs; classical conditioning
D. problem solving in dogs; the law of effect

p. 196
Three Kinds of Learning
Level: Easy
Type: Conceptual
Ans: C

19. Classical conditioning would be best suited to answer which of the following questions?
A. Why do we repeat behaviors when they are followed by something good?
B. Why do children know a lot about driving a car before their first time behind the wheel?
C. Why do some people associate certain foods with nausea?
D. Why are some animals difficult to train to perform certain kinds of behavior?

p. 196
Three Kinds of Learning
Level: Moderate
Type: Factual
Ans: D

20. After eating a hot dog at Chez Dave's restaurant, Elmer gets sick and never wants to eat a hot dog again. This experience is a form of what learning process?
A. imprinting
B. operant conditioning
C. spontaneous learning
D. classical conditioning

p. 196
Three Kinds of Learning
Level: Easy
Type: Applied
Ans: A

21. Humans are naturally frightened by loud noises. Suppose Mr. Bates was taking a shower when an explosion occurred in the building next door. The next time he took a shower, Mr. Bates felt scared and his heart pounded. What form of learning has he experienced?
A. classical conditioning
B. operant conditioning
C. cognitive learning
D. latent learning

p. 196
Three Kinds of Learning
Level: Easy
Type: Factual
Ans: A

22. What form of learning involves a neutral stimulus acquiring the ability to produce a response that was originally produced by a different stimulus?
A. classical conditioning
B. operant conditioning
C. cognitive learning
D. latent learning

p. 196
Three Kinds of Learning
Level: Easy
Type: Factual
Ans: D
*PS/SG 9-4*

23. A theory of learning that became part of operant conditioning was:
A. Bandura's cognitive learning
B. Pavlov's classical conditioning
C. Plotnik's fear conditioning
D. Thorndike's law of effect

p. 196
Three Kinds of Learning
Level: Easy
Type: Factual
Ans: B

24. The Law of Effect states that random actions are strengthened and will be more likely to occur in the future if the actions are:
A. reflexive
B. followed by a reward or pleasurable consequence
C. negatively reinforced
D. put into memory

p. 196
Three Kinds of Learning
Level: Easy
Type: Conceptual
Ans: D

25. Uncle Joe is a very wise old man. One day you ask him for advice and he said, "You are likely to do tomorrow what today lead to a pleasurable consequence." You are impressed because he was defining:
A. stimulus substitution
B. the cognitive perspective of classical conditioning
C. a conditioned stimulus
D. the Law of Effect

p. 196
Three Kinds of Learning
Level: Easy
Type: Factual
Ans: B
*www*

26. The Law of Effect is important in:
A. classical conditioning
B. operant conditioning
C. cognitive learning
D. latent learning

p. 196
Three Kinds of Learning
Level: Easy
Type: Factual
Ans: C

27. Operant conditioning focuses on how:
A. people learn from the examples of others
B. repetition results in reflexive habits
C. behavior is influenced by its consequences
D. stimuli are paired to elicit a response

p. 196
Three Kinds of Learning
Level: Moderate
Type: Factual
Ans: C

28. In which type of learning do the consequences of a behavior influence whether an organism will perform the same behavior in the future?
A. classical conditioning
B. target learning
C. operant conditioning
D. latent learning

p. 196
Three Kinds of Learning
Level: Easy
Type: Conceptual
Ans: B

29. Of the following words, which is central to the form of learning called operant conditioning?
A. cognitive
B. consequence
C. conditioned
D. mental

p. 196
Three Kinds of Learning
Level: Easy
Type: Factual
Ans: A
*PS/SG 9-5*

30. Operant conditioning differs from classical conditioning in placing the emphasis on:
A. consequences that follow some behavior
B. pairing a neutral stimulus with an unconditioned response
C. waiting until the subject accidentally performs the right behavior
D. allowing subjects to watch others perform some behavior

p. 196
Three Kinds of Learning
Level: Easy
Type: Applied
Ans: D

31. What is the best example of operant conditioning?
A. Two boys imitate a professional wrestler they saw on television.
B. A young child becomes fearful whenever seeing the babysitter.
C. A group of pigs come running when they hear the farmer opening the feed box.
D. A student is given a sticker for getting 100% on her math test and consequently studies extra hard for the next exam.

p. 196
Three Kinds of Learning
Level: Easy
Type: Factual
Ans: B

32. Learning that involves mental processes, such as attention and memory, is called:
A. classical conditioning
B. cognitive learning
C. operant conditioning
D. law of effect learning

p. 196
Three Kinds of Learning
Level: Moderate
Type: Factual
Ans: A

33. According to cognitive learning, learning can take place in an individual:
A. who has not received any noticeable rewards
B. only if the learning is reflexive in nature
C. who shows a change in behavior
D. only when the behavior is followed by an effect

p. 196
Three Kinds of Learning
Level: Moderate
Type: Conceptual
Ans: C

34. Pavlov is to Bandura as _____ is to _____.
A. cognitive learning; classical conditioning
B. cognitive learning; operant conditioning
C. classical conditioning; cognitive learning
D. cognitive learning; operant conditioning

p. 196
Three Kinds of Learning
Level: Easy
Type: Factual
Ans: B

35. An individual most closely associated with cognitive learning is:
A. B. F. Skinner
B. Albert Bandura
C. Sigmund Freud
D. Ivan Pavlov

p. 196
Three Kinds of Learning
Level: Easy
Type: Applied
Ans: A

36. You are reading a book entitled "Learning Through Imitation." Who is the most likely author of the book?
A. Albert Bandura
B. Ivan Pavlov
C. B. F. Skinner
D. E. L. Thorndike

p. 197
Procedure: Classical
  Conditioning
Level: Easy
Type: Conceptual
Ans: B

37. Unconditioned is to conditioned as _____ is to _____.
A. food; salivation
B. reflex; learned
C. response; stimulus
D. learned; reflex

p. 197
Procedure: Classical
  Conditioning
Level: Easy
Type: Factual
Ans: C

38. Which of the following is not a step in classical conditioning?
A. selecting stimulus and response
B. establishing the conditioned response
C. determining schedule of reinforcement
D. testing for conditioning

p. 197
Procedure: Classical
  Conditioning
Level: Easy
Type: Factual
Ans: C

39. Before learning, a neutral stimulus:
A. is paired with the unconditioned response
B. is a reflexive action
C. does not produce the reflex being tested
D. only works with humans, not with animals

p. 197
Procedure: Classical
  Conditioning
Level: Moderate
Type: Factual
Ans: B

40. In Pavlov's laboratory experiments with dogs, the tone first served as a(n) _____, and later as a(n) _____.
  A. unconditioned stimulus; conditioned stimulus
  B. neutral stimulus; conditioned stimulus
  C. neutral response; unconditioned stimulus
  D. conditioned stimulus; neutral response

p. 197
Procedure: Classical
  Conditioning
Level: Easy
Type: Factual
Ans: D
*PS/SG 9-8*

41. In Pavlov's experiment, the actual learning took place when the:
  A. neutral stimulus was paired with the unconditioned stimulus
  B. conditioned reflex was presented again and again
  C. unconditioned stimulus was paired with the conditioned stimulus
  D. paired unconditioned and neutral stimuli were presented together in several trials

p. 197
Procedure: Classical
  Conditioning
Level: Moderate
Type: Applied
Ans: C
*www*

42. Dr. Bell sounds a chime during a laboratory experiment. A dog named Cleo does not react. Based on this information, you conclude the chime is a(n) ____ stimulus.
  A. unconditioned
  B. conditioned
  C. neutral
  D. generalized

p. 197
Procedure: Classical
  Conditioning
Level: Easy
Type: Factual
Ans: B

43. In Pavlov's study, the neutral stimulus was:
  A. food
  B. a tone (bell)
  C. salivation
  D. fear

p. 197
Procedure: Classical
  Conditioning
Level: Easy
Type: Factual
Ans: A

44. An unconditioned stimulus:
  A. automatically triggers a physiological reflex
  B. requires conscious effort
  C. is paired with a conditioned response
  D. is acquired through practice

p. 197
Procedure: Classical
  Conditioning
Level: Moderate
Type: Applied
Ans: C

45. You missed class the day classical conditioning was discussed. So, you borrow your friend's notes. As you are reading the notes you see that the neutral stimulus was the bell, the UCS was food, and the UCR was salivation. As you look further in the notes, you cannot read what is written about the CS since your friend was running out of ink as she took notes. Given what you can read, you reason that the CS is:
  A. salivation - since that is the normal response to food
  B. salivation - since the UCR becomes the CS
  C. bell - since the neutral stimulus becomes the CS
  D. food - since the UCS becomes the CS

p. 197
Procedure: Classical
  Conditioning
Level: Easy
Type: Factual
Ans: A

46. That which automatically causes a reflex response is called a(n):
A. unconditioned stimulus
B. unconditioned response
C. conditioned stimulus
D. conditioned response

p. 197
Procedure: Classical
  Conditioning
Level: Easy
Type: Factual
Ans: A
*www*

47. In Pavlov's study, the unconditioned stimulus was:
A. food
B. a tone (bell)
C. salivation
D. fear

p. 197
Procedure: Classical
  Conditioning
Level: Easy
Type: Factual
Ans: C

48. A response that is inborn and automatically elicited by an unconditioned stimulus is called a(n) _____ response.
A. learned
B. imprinted
C. unconditioned
D. neutral

p. 197
Procedure: Classical
  Conditioning
Level: Moderate
Type: Applied
Ans: C
*www*

49. The first time Mindy placed a piece of meat in her pet poodle's mouth, the poodle salivated. The poodle's salivation is a(n):
A. conditioned response
B. conditioned stimulus
C. unconditioned response
D. unconditioned stimulus

p. 197
Procedure: Classical
  Conditioning
Level: Easy
Type: Factual
Ans: A

50. The best example of an unconditioned response is:
A. an eyeblink caused by a particle of dust
B. salivating while watching a food advertisement on TV
C. a knee jerk following the sound of a bell
D. feeling nervous while in the presence of an attractive member of the opposite sex

p. 197
Procedure: Classical
  Conditioning
Level: Easy
Type: Factual
Ans: C

51. In Pavlov's study, the unconditioned response was:
A. food
B. a tone (bell)
C. salivation
D. fear

p. 197
Procedure: Classical
  Conditioning
Level: Easy
Type: Applied
Ans: C
*www*

52. Roy's knee jerks the first time a psychologist taps it with a small hammer during an experiment. The knee jerk is a(n):
A. unconditioned stimulus
B. conditioned response
C. unconditioned response
D. habit

| p. 197 | 53. | Paul is trying to remember the procedure used to establish classical |
| Procedure: Classical | | conditioning. He would be <u>best</u> to remember: |
| Conditioning | A. | CS, UCS, UCR |
| Level: Easy | B. | CS, CR |
| Type: Factual | C. | UCR, UCS, neutral stimulus |
| Ans: D | D. | neutral stimulus, UCS, UCR |

| p. 197 | 54. | Since S -> R, then obviously UCS ->UCR, so naturally CS->: |
| Procedure: Classical | A. | UCS |
| Conditioning | B. | UCR |
| Level: Easy | C. | CR |
| Type: Factual | D. | neutral stimulus |
| Ans: C | | |

*PS/SG 9-7*

| p. 197 | 55. | Which of the following is an example of a reflex? |
| Procedure: Classical | A. | neutral stimulus ->CS |
| Conditioning | B. | CS -> CR |
| Level: Easy | C. | UCR -> UCS |
| Type: Factual | D. | UCS -> UCR |
| Ans: D | | |

| p. 197 | 56. | In classical conditioning, the presentation of both neutral stimulus and UCS |
| Procedure: Classical | | is called a: |
| Conditioning | A. | trial |
| Level: Easy | B. | pairing |
| Type: Factual | C. | step |
| Ans: A | D. | link |

| p. 197 | 57. | Which of the following is true of classical conditioning? |
| Procedure: Classical | A. | UCS produces UCR |
| Conditioning | B. | CR produces CS |
| Level: Easy | C. | UCR produces CS |
| Type: Factual | D. | CS produces UCS |
| Ans: A | | |

| p. 197 | 58. | A farmer always uses the same squeaky wheelbarrow to carry feed out to |
| Procedure: Classical | | his sheep. When he does this, the sheep head for the feed trough in |
| Conditioning | | anticipation. In this example, noise of the wheelbarrow would be a(n): |
| Level: Moderate | A. | unconditioned stimulus |
| Type: Applied | B. | unconditioned response |
| Ans: C | C. | conditioned stimulus |
| | D. | conditioned response |

| p. 197 | 59. | Eric takes part in an experiment where the sound of a bell immediately |
| Procedure: Classical | | precedes a puff of air to the eye that causes him to blink. After a few trials, |
| Conditioning | | Eric blinks as soon as he hears the bell. The sound of the bell is a(n): |
| Level: Moderate | A. | conditioned stimulus |
| Type: Applied | B. | unconditioned stimulus |
| Ans: A | C. | conditioned response |
| | D. | unconditioned response |

p. 197
Procedure: Classical
 Conditioning
Level: Easy
Type: Applied
Ans: C

60. Jacob has a drinking problem and is given a drug that makes him feel nauseated when he ingests alcohol. After becoming sick several times when having a beer at a bar after work, Jacob becomes nauseated while driving past a bar. In this example, the bar can be considered the:
A. unconditioned stimulus
B. unconditioned response
C. conditioned stimulus
D. conditioned response

p. 197
Procedure: Classical
 Conditioning
Level: Easy
Type: Applied
Ans: A
*www*

61. Paul's mother buys him a sailor's cap before they go on a family fishing trip. On the boat, Paul gets nauseated and throws up. The next day he gets nauseated when he sees his sailor's cap. The cap has become a(n):
A. conditioned stimulus
B. conditioned response
C. unconditioned stimulus
D. unconditioned response

p. 197
Procedure: Classical
 Conditioning
Level: Easy
Type: Factual
Ans: C

62. If conditioning has taken place, the neutral stimulus becomes the:
A. unconditioned response
B. conditioned response
C. conditioned stimulus
D. operant

p. 197
Procedure: Classical
 Conditioning
Level: Easy
Type: Factual
Ans: B

63. In Pavlov's study, the conditioned stimulus was:
A. food
B. a tone (bell)
C. salivation
D. fear

p. 197
Procedure: Classical
 Conditioning
Level: Easy
Type: Factual
Ans: D

64. Compared to the unconditioned response, the conditioned response is:
A. different in appearance
B. more intense
C. elicited by the unconditioned stimulus
D. smaller in magnitude

p. 197
Procedure: Classical
 Conditioning
Level: Easy
Type: Applied
Ans: A

65. Debbie is in a traffic accident. As a result of the accident she has become fearful of being inside a car. Debbie's fear is a(n):
A. conditioned response
B. conditioned stimulus
C. example of generalization
D. example of spontaneous recovery

p. 197
Procedure: Classical
 Conditioning
Level: Easy
Type: Applied
Ans: C

66. Len is trying to classically condition his laboratory partner to blink in response to a loud beep. The eyeblink in response to the beep can be said to be classically conditioned when it:
A. is elicited by the combined efforts of the unconditioned and conditioned stimuli
B. is elicited by the unconditioned stimulus alone
C. is elicited by the conditioned stimulus alone
D. cannot be extinguished

p. 197
Procedure: Classical
  Conditioning
Level: Easy
Type: Factual
Ans: C
*www*

67. In Pavlov's study, the conditioned response was:
A. food
B. a tone (bell)
C. salivation
D. fear

p. 197
Procedure: Classical
  Conditioning
Level: Easy
Type: Conceptual
Ans: B

68. The conditioned response is smaller in strength than the unconditioned responses. What does that mean in the context of Pavlov's experiment?
A. The CR elicits a smaller amount of food.
B. The CS elicits a smaller amount of saliva.
C. The UCR elicits a smaller amount of saliva.
D. The UCS elicits a smaller amount of saliva.

p. 197
Procedure: Classical
  Conditioning
Level: Easy
Type: Conceptual
Ans: D

69. What does the subject learn in classical conditioning?
A. CR predicts the UCS.
B. The neutral stimulus predicts the CR.
C. The UCS predicts the UCR.
D. The neutral stimulus predicts the UCS.

p. 197
Procedure: Classical
  Conditioning
Level: Moderate
Type: Factual
Ans: C

70. If you've been classically conditioned to salivate to a bell, you've learn that the:
A. food predicts the bell
B. reinforcement predicts salivating
C. bell predicts food
D. food predicts salivating

p. 198
Procedure: Classical
  Conditioning
Level: Easy
Type: Applied
Ans: A

71. In the textbook example of classical conditioning and aftershave, the neutral stimulus was:
A. aftershave
B. dental procedures
C. nausea
D. anxiety

p. 198
Procedure: Classical
  Conditioning
Level: Easy
Type: Applied
Ans: B

72. If the UCS are dental procedures, the most likely UCR is:
A. aftershave
B. anxiety
C. salivation
D. drilling

p. 198
Procedure: Classical
  Conditioning
Level: Easy
Type: Applied
Ans: D

73. In the example involving Carla and aftershave, the UCS is _____ and the UCR is _____.
A. aftershave; anxiety
B. anxiety; dental procedures
C. anxiety; aftershave
D. dental procedures; anxiety

p. 198
Procedure: Classical
  Conditioning
Level: Easy
Type: Factual
Ans: B

74. Describe the procedure in establishing classical conditioning as presented in the example of Carla and aftershave.
A. food; anxiety; food
B. aftershave; dental procedure; anxiety
C. anxiety; dental procedure; aftershave
D. dental procedure; anxiety; dental procedure

p. 198
Procedure: Classical
  Conditioning
Level: Easy
Type: Applied
Ans: A

75. In the example involving Carla and aftershave, the CS is _____ and the CR is _____.
A. aftershave; anxiety
B. anxiety; dental procedures
C. anxiety; aftershave
D. dental procedures; anxiety

p. 198
Procedure: Classical
  Conditioning
Level: Easy
Type: Applied
Ans: D

76. In the example involving Carla and aftershave, the aftershave was originally the _____ , but later became the _____.
A. unconditioned stimulus; conditioned stimulus
B. unconditioned stimulus; neutral stimulus
C. neutral stimulus; unconditioned stimulus
D. neutral stimulus; conditioned stimulus

p. 198
Procedure: Classical
  Conditioning
Level: Moderate
Type: Conceptual
Ans: C

77. Based on the textbook's example of Carla and aftershave, does Carla show a higher intensity of anxiety when she smells her boyfriend's aftershave than her dentist's aftershave?
A. yes - the anxiety associated with her boyfriend's aftershave is a UCR
B. yes - the anxiety associated with her boyfriend's aftershave is a CR
C. no - the anxiety associated with her boyfriend's aftershave is a CR
D. no - the anxiety associated with her dentist's aftershave is a CR

p. 198
Procedure: Classical
  Conditioning
Level: Moderate
Type: Factual
Ans: A

78. Using the example of Carla as described in the module, how would you know if she was successfully conditioned to the aftershave?
A. The aftershave (CS) would elicit feelings of anxiety (CR).
B. The painful dental procedure (UCS) would elicit feelings of anxiety (UCS).
C. The aftershave (UCS) would elicit feelings of anxiety (neutral stimulus).
D. The painful dental procedure (CS) would elicit feelings of anxiety (CS).

p. 199
Other Conditioning
  Concepts
Level: Easy
Type: Factual
Ans: B

79. Stimuli similar to, but not identical with, a conditioned stimulus elicit conditioned responses through a process known as:
A. discrimination
B. generalization
C. recovery
D. extinction

p. 199
Other Conditioning
  Concepts
Level: Easy
Type: Applied
Ans: A
PS/SG 9-9

80. Now even the smell of her own shampoo can make Carla anxious. This is an example of:
A. generalization
B. extinction
C. discrimination
D. spontaneous recovery

p. 199
Other Conditioning
 Concepts
Level: Easy
Type: Applied
Ans: D

81. After being classically conditioned to feel anxiety to aftershave, Carla finds that her deodorant can elicit similar feelings. This best illustrates:
A. extinction
B. discrimination
C. recovery
D. generalization

p. 199
Other Conditioning
 Concepts
Level: Easy
Type: Applied
Ans: D
*PS/SG 9-10*

82. But the smell of her nail polish does *not* make Carla feel anxious; this is an example of:
A. generalization
B. extinction
C. spontaneous recovery
D. discrimination

p. 199
Other Conditioning
 Concepts
Level: Moderate
Type: Applied
Ans: A
*www*

83. Baby Alice is playing with a white bunny rabbit when a loud noise suddenly startles her, and she begins to cry. Alice is later given a white cat to play with and begins crying again. Her reaction to the white cat illustrates:
A. generalization
B. discrimination
C. spontaneous recovery
D. extinction

p. 199
Other Conditioning
 Concepts
Level: Moderate
Type: Applied
Ans: B

84. Your neighbor's beagle chases Manny the mailman. The next day, he becomes scared when he sees your cocker spaniel. Manny's response to your spaniel is an example of:
A. imprinting
B. generalization
C. discrimination
D. unconditioned response

p. 199
Other Conditioning
 Concepts
Level: Moderate
Type: Applied
Ans: B

85. You have been conditioned to become nauseated whenever you see or smell pizza. Now you've noticed that you don't feel very good when you smell pasta. You realize that you have experienced:
A. shaping
B. generalization
C. conditioned response
D. extinction

p. 199
Other Conditioning
 Concepts
Level: Easy
Type: Applied
Ans: A

86. After her bad experience in the dentist's office and smelling his aftershave, Carla also became anxious when smelling hair shampoo; this is an example of:
A. generalization
B. extinction
C. discrimination
D. spontaneous recovery

p. 199
Other Conditioning
  Concepts
Level: Easy
Type: Applied
Ans: C

87. Pavlov's dogs were conditioned to salivate to the sound of a bell. The dogs may have also salivated to the telephone ringing. This is an example of:
A. discrimination
B. extinction
C. generalization
D. operant conditioning

p. 199
Other Conditioning
  Concepts
Level: Easy
Type: Applied
Ans: C

88. Imagine this: Pavlov has just classically conditioned his dogs to salivate to the sound of a bell. Then, the bell on the microwave "dings" and the dogs start salivating. This is an example of:
A. discrimination
B. extinction
C. generalization
D. operant conditioning

p. 199
Other Conditioning
  Concepts
Level: Easy
Type: Factual
Ans: C

89. According to Pavlov, generalization has:
A. little impact on conditioned response
B. little effect on emotional responses
C. adaptive value
D. been discarded as a reliable phenomenon

p. 199
Other Conditioning
  Concepts
Level: Moderate
Type: Factual
Ans: D

90. In classical conditioning, generalization is adaptive because:
A. dangerous UCS not longer trigger the UCR
B. we learn that some behaviors lead to reinforcement
C. the CR is capable of returning following a period of extinction
D. we are able to respond to a stimulus that resembles the original CS

p. 199
Other Conditioning
  Concepts
Level: Easy
Type: Factual
Ans: A

91. In classical conditioning, when an organism responds to some stimuli, but not to others, the organism is demonstrating:
A. discrimination
B. generalization
C. spontaneous recovery
D. cognitive learning

p. 199
Other Conditioning
  Concepts
Level: Moderate
Type: Applied
Ans: A

92. The best example of stimulus discrimination in classical conditioning is:
A. a child learning to avoid rats but not hamsters
B. recognizing that a police siren sounding in San Diego, California, has a similar meaning to one sounding in Erie, Pennsylvania
C. blinking when words similar to "chime" are spoken
D. refusing to eat Chinese food after associating it with feelings of nausea

p. 199
Other Conditioning
  Concepts
Level: Moderate
Type: Applied
Ans: D

93. Marsha feeds her dog Bubbles if Bubbles barks when the light is turned on, but not if the light is turned off. Soon Bubbles barks only when the light is turned on. Bubbles is exhibiting:
A. spontaneous recovery
B. extinction
C. generalization
D. discrimination

p. 199
Other Conditioning
  Concepts
Level: Moderate
Type: Applied
Ans: C

94. For some reason, Carla becomes anxious when she smells the aftershave "Old Spice" but not other brands of aftershave. What is the reason for this difference?
A. generalization
B. spontaneous recovery
C. discrimination
D. extinction

p. 199
Other Conditioning
  Concepts
Level: Easy
Type: Conceptual
Ans: A
*www*

95. If Pavlov's dogs only salivated to a middle pitch bell, but not to a high pitch bell, then this suggests _____ has taken place.
A. discrimination
B. extinction
C. generalization
D. spontaneous recovery

p. 199
Other Conditioning
  Concepts
Level: Easy
Type: Applied
Ans: C

96. If you've been classically conditioned to be afraid of German shepherd dogs, but not afraid of poodles, this illustrates:
A. generalization
B. extinction
C. discrimination
D. spontaneous recovery

p. 199
Other Conditioning
  Concepts
Level: Moderate
Type: Conceptual
Ans: C

97. Discrimination is to narrow as generalization is to _____.
A. learned
B. restrict
C. broad
D. reappear

p. 199
Other Conditioning
  Concepts
Level: Moderate
Type: Factual
Ans: C

98. Extinction, in classical conditioning terminology, refers to:
A. the generalization of CR to many different stimuli, resulting in a constant UCR
B. the unlearning of a CR via counterconditioning
C. the disappearance of a CR when the CS is no longer paired with the UCS
D. the forgetting of a UCR after a long time has elapsed

p. 199
Other Conditioning
  Concepts
Level: Moderate
Type: Applied
Ans: B

99. A child falls off her bike and becomes afraid to ride. What is likely to occur if she tries to take short, safe rides that do not result in her falling?
A. conditioned learning
B. extinction
C. discrimination
D. generalization

p. 199
Other Conditioning
  Concepts
Level: Easy
Type: Factual
Ans: D

100. Our friend Carla no longer becomes nauseated when smelling her boyfriend's aftershave. Carla is very happy and is grateful for:
A. spontaneous recovery
B. discrimination
C. generalization
D. extinction

p. 199
Other Conditioning
  Concepts
Level: Easy
Type: Factual
Ans: C
*PS/SG 9-11*

101. When a conditioned stimulus (e.g., a tone) is repeatedly presented without the unconditioned stimulus (e.g., meat), _____ eventually will occur.
A. generalization
B. discrimination
C. extinction
D. spontaneous recovery

p. 199
Other Conditioning
  Concepts
Level: Moderate
Type: Factual
Ans: B

102. In an experiment in which tones are generally followed by a puff of air directed at the subject's eyes, repeated presentation of a tone without being followed by a puff of air on the eye would probably result in:
A. classical conditioning
B. extinction
C. discrimination
D. generalization

p. 199
Other Conditioning
  Concepts
Level: Moderate
Type: Applied
Ans: D

103. Morty is involved in a car wreck on Interstate 15. The next day, he becomes anxious and fretful when passing the spot of the accident. After several weeks of passing the spot every day on the way to work, Morty's negative reaction subsides. His anxiety has undergone:
A. discrimination
B. generalization
C. spontaneous recovery
D. extinction

p. 199
Other Conditioning
  Concepts
Level: Moderate
Type: Applied
Ans: A

104. You have classically conditioned your 3-year old niece to shut her eyes in anticipation of a puff of air. But she has since learned that the CS no longer predicts the UCS and has experienced extinction. What has happened?
A. She no longer shuts her eyes in response to the CS.
B. She no longer shuts her eyes in response to the UCS.
C. She shuts her eyes more rapidly now in response to the CS.
D. She no longer shuts her eyes in response to the UCR.

p. 199
Other Conditioning
  Concepts
Level: Moderate
Type: Factual
Ans: B
*www*

105. Spontaneous recovery is defined as the:
A. resultant product of cognitive learning
B. reappearance of a conditioned response
C. discrimination of certain stimuli from other similar stimuli
D. generalization of a response to other similar stimuli

p. 199
Other Conditioning
  Concepts
Level: Moderate
Type: Applied
Ans: A

106. At the beginning of his last vacation, Mike fell off a horse.  He got right back in the saddle, though, and overcame his apprehension.  If Mike experiences spontaneous recovery during his next vacation, he will:
A. experience some fear of horses
B. find that his riding skills have not left him
C. like horseback riding more than ever
D. demand that he ride the same horse again

p. 199
Other Conditioning
  Concepts
Level: Moderate
Type: Applied
Ans: C

107. Carla's fear of aftershave is extinguished.  But a few weeks later, she experiences anxiety when smelling a sample of the aftershave.  Carla has experienced:
A. generalization
B. pseudoextinction
C. spontaneous recovery
D. instrumental learning

p. 199
Other Conditioning
  Concepts
Level: Moderate
Type: Applied
Ans: A

108. "I thought I was over that feeling of nausea following my conditioning to pizza a couple of months ago.  But I guess not."  This best illustrates:
A. spontaneous recovery
B. partial extinction
C. extinction
D. cognitive learning

p. 200
Adaptive Value and Uses
Level: Easy
Type: Factual
Ans: B

109. What concept refers to the usefulness of certain abilities that tend to increase an animal's chance of survival?
A. evolved utility
B. adaptive value
C. survival predisposition
D. unconditioned preparedness

p. 200
Adaptive Value and Uses
Level: Easy
Type: Factual
Ans: A

110. The idea of bait shyness best relates to:
A. taste-aversion learning
B. instrumental conditioning
C. systematic desensitization
D. contiguity theory

p. 200
Adaptive Value and Uses
Level: Easy
Type: Factual
Ans: C

111. Taste-aversion learning occurs when particular stimuli like the taste or smell of food are associated with a(n):
A. conditioned stimulus
B. conditioned response
C. unpleasant response
D. relaxation response

p. 200
Adaptive Value and Uses
Level: Easy
Type: Factual
Ans: B

112. "In elementary school, whenever anyone vomited, the janitor would sprinkle this pink powder on it. Now whenever I smell that odor of the powder, I feel nauseated. I don't like smelling that pink powder." This illustrates:
A. continuity theory
B. taste-aversion learning
C. bait-shyness
D. phobic disorder

p. 200
Adaptive Value and Uses
Level: Easy
Type: Factual
Ans: A

113. Last year, Bill came down with the flu the night after eating clam chowder soup. For several weeks, he couldn't think about clam chowder soup without feeling nauseated. Bill experienced:
A. taste-aversion learning
B. trial learning
C. systematic desensitization
D. discrimination

p. 200
Adaptive Value and Uses
Level: Moderate
Type: Applied
Ans: B

114. Marie bakes a special muffin for Jack's birthday. Jack eats it and gets sick. A year later, Jack still will not eat Marie's muffins. Jack's behavior is an example of a(n):
A. unconditioned aversion
B. learned taste aversion
C. unconditioned response
D. imprinted response

p. 200
Adaptive Value
Level: Easy
Type: Factual
Ans: A

115. When rats eat only enough poison to get sick and then learn to avoid that poison, _____ is said to have occurred.
A. taste-aversion learning
B. aversive conditioning
C. poison-generalization effect
D. imprinting

p. 200
Adaptive Value and Uses
Level: Easy
Type: Factual
Ans: C

116. Exterminators must regularly change their bait poison in order to overcome:
A. systematic desensitization
B. stimulus generalization
C. taste-aversion learning
D. spontaneous recovery

p. 200
Adaptive Value and Uses
Level: Easy
Type: Factual
Ans: B

117. On the positive side, taste-aversion learning may help us:
A. develop our taste for exotic foods
B. survive by avoiding plants or poisons that are harmful or lethal
C. discern foods that have poor nutritional value
D. remember what foods we do not prefer

p. 200
Adaptive Value and Uses
Level: Moderate
Type: Factual
Ans: D

118. Taste-aversion learning is not consistent with a long-standing belief regarding classical conditioning. The belief was:
A. UCS's must be followed by UCR's
B. neutral stimulus could not elicit the CR
C. conditioning is only permanent if the CR is stronger than the UCR
D. conditioning could only take place after many trials and when the neutral stimulus was closely followed by the UCR

p. 200
Adaptive Value and Uses
Level: Moderate
Type: Factual
Ans: C

119. Taste-aversion learning may occur:
A. without a NS being present
B. when the NS does not predict the UCS
C. when there is a delay between the NS and the UCR
D. when reinforcement is delayed

p. 200
Adaptive Value and Uses
Level: Moderate
Type: Factual
Ans: B

120. For some animals, certain combinations of conditioned and unconditioned stimuli which are more easily associated are called:
A. species-specificity
B. preparedness
C. discrimination
D. classical conditioning

p. 200
Adaptive Value and Uses
Level: Moderate
Type: Factual
Ans: C

121. Rats are more likely to acquire taste aversion more easily to stimuli that involve:
A. movement
B. a variety of colors
C. smell and taste cues
D. visual cues

p. 200
Adaptive Value and Uses
Level: Easy
Type: Factual
Ans: D
PS/SG 9-12

122. We seem to be biologically ready to associate some combinations of conditioned and unconditioned stimuli in as little as a single trial, a phenomenon called:
A. conditioned nausea
B. phobia
C. taste-aversion learning
D. preparedness

p. 200
Adaptive Value and Uses
Level: Easy
Type: Factual
Ans: A

123. A "jackalope" has a very sophisticated sense of taste. If we wish to condition taste aversion, we would expect greater success by using:
A. taste cues as stimuli
B. visual cues as stimuli
C. the process known as imprinting
D. gustatory behavior as responses

p. 200
Adaptive Value and Uses
Level: Easy
Type: Factual
Ans: C

124. If coyotes acquire a taste aversion to sheep flesh, there will be a _____ reduction in sheep killing according to research cited in the textbook.
A. 1-5%
B. 15-20%
C. 30-60%
D. 80-90%

p. 201
Adaptive Value and Uses
Level: Easy
Type: Factual
Ans: A

125. For the bluejay, what example signals that a particular food is to be avoided:
A. the distinctive color pattern of monarch butterflies
B. the wing shape of monarch butterflies
C. a clicking sound made by a ground beetle
D. the sounds of a monarch butterfly flapping its wings

p. 201
Adaptive Value and Uses
Level: Easy
Type: Factual
Ans: D

126. Bluejays develop _____ that keep them from eating monarch butterflies.
A. species-specificity
B. preparedness
C. discrimination
D. taste-aversion learning

p. 201
Adaptive Value and Uses
Level: Easy
Type: Factual
Ans: A
*PS/SG 9-13*

127. Bluejays love butterflies, but they won't eat monarch butterflies, because:
A. taste aversion learning teaches them to avoid the distinctive coloring pattern
B. an inborn hatred of black and orange makes them avoid monarchs
C. one bite of a monarch brings instant death to a bluejay
D. monarchs have an evasive flight pattern that makes them almost impossible to catch

p. 201
Adaptive Value and Uses
Level: Moderate
Type: Applied
Ans: B

128. School was not a very pleasant experience for Jose. He would often fail his assignments only to be put down by the teacher. Each time he sees a classroom, he feels fearful and anxious. Jose is experiencing a(n):
A. spontaneous recovery
B. conditioned emotional response
C. flashback
D. UCR

p. 201
Adaptive Value and Uses
Level: Easy
Type: Factual
Ans: C

129. Positive or negative feelings can be experienced when a stimulus is encountered that initially accompanied a painful or pleasant event. This feeling is called a:
A. learned affect
B. mood enhanced response
C. conditioned emotional response
D. phobia

p. 201
Adaptive Value and Uses
Level: Easy
Type: Factual
Ans: C

130. "Whenever I smell that perfume I think of my grandmother and all of the wonderful times we had together." This best illustrates:
A. systematic desensitization
B. mood enhanced response
C. conditioned emotional response
D. preparedness

p. 201
Adaptive Value and Uses
Level: Easy
Type: Factual
Ans: B

131. _____ is an anxiety disorder that involves an intense and irrational fear.
A. Conditioned emotional response
B. Phobia
C. Desensitization disorder
D. Conditioned fear

p. 201
Adaptive Value and Uses
Level: Moderate
Type: Applied
Ans: D

132. Lucy has a conditioned emotional response that has led to a phobia of injections and syringes. Of the following elements of Lucy's case, which is incorrect?
A. CS - syringe
B. neutral stimulus - syringe
C. CR - crying and fear
D. UCS - pain

p. 201
Adaptive Value and Uses
Level: Moderate
Type: Applied
Ans: A

133. While on the first date, Shelly tells Garrison that her father is a dentist. Suddenly Garrison starts feeling bad. He looks pale and feels like he is going to pass out. What accounts for Garrison's unusual reaction?
A. conditioned emotional response
B. contiguity theory
C. stimulus replacement
D. spontaneous recovery

p. 201
Adaptive Value and Uses
Level: Easy
Type: Factual
Ans: C

134. According to Module Nine, classical conditioning of the eye blink requires:
A. that the NS is a puff of air
B. a conditioned emotional response
C. the cerebellum
D. the amygdala

p. 201
Adaptive Value and Uses
Level: Easy
Type: Factual
Ans: D

135. For a conditioned emotional response to be acquired, a person would need:
A. a cerebellum
B. to first learn to relax followed by creating an anxiety hierarchy
C. to experience stimulus substitution
D. an amygdala

p. 202
Three Explanations
Level: Easy
Type: Factual
Ans: A

136. Pavlov's explanation of classical conditioning is called:
A. stimulus substitution
B. cognitive perspective
C. prediction theory
D. generalization theory

p. 202
Three Explanations
Level: Easy
Type: Factual
Ans: D

137. We could say that classical conditioning occurs because two stimuli are paired close together in time. This theory is called the:
A. stimulus substitution theory
B. cognitive perspective
C. prediction theory
D. contiguity theory

p. 202
Three Explanations
Level: Easy
Type: Factual
Ans: A

138. Consider this: The CS acts like a surrogate for the UCS. This explanation is known as the _____ and has been _____.
A. stimulus substitution theory; disproved
B. cognitive perspective; proven
C. prediction theory; disproved
D. contiguity theory; disproved

p. 202
Three Explanations
Level: Easy
Type: Factual
Ans: D
*www*

139. Professor Marsh argues that classical conditioning occurs because two stimuli are paired closely together in time. Professor Marsh supports the _____ of classical conditioning.
A. stimulus substitution theory
B. cognitive perspective
C. prediction theory
D. contiguity theory

p. 202
Three Explanations
Level: Moderate
Type: Conceptual
Ans: B

140. Of the following words, which one is <u>most</u> descriptive of the contiguity theory of classical conditioning?
A. substitute
B. pair
C. predict
D. subtract

p. 202
Three Explanations
Level: Moderate
Type: Applied
Ans: B

141. An organism learns a relationship between two stimuli, such that the occurrence of one stimulus predicts the occurrence of another. This explanation is characteristic of:
A. stimulus substitution theory
B. cognitive perspective
C. prediction theory
D. generalization theory

p. 202
Three Explanations
Level: Easy
Type: Applied
Ans: C

142. Contiguity theory is to _____ as cognitive perspective is to _____.
A. prediction; substitution
B. generalization; discrimination
C. contiguous; prediction
D. substitution; prediction

p. 202
Three Explanations
Level: Moderate
Type: Conceptual
Ans: C

143. Of the following words, which one is <u>most</u> descriptive of the cognitive perspective of classical conditioning?
A. substitute
B. pair
C. predict
D. subtract

p. 202
Three Explanations
Level: Easy
Type: Factual
Ans: B

144. Psychologists now believe that classical conditioning is explained by:
A. two events occurring at the same time
B. one event predicts the occurrence of another
C. events are linked via cognitive processes that identify similarities between the events
D. constant repetition of events fuses them together

p. 202
Three Explanations
Level: Moderate
Type: Applied
Ans: D

145. Chipper, the family cocker spaniel, wags his tail when he hears Father's car come up the driveway. Psychologists believe that Chipper does this because:
A. Father must arrive home at the same time every day and Chipper's internal clock triggers his response
B. dogs will be aroused by any sounds originating from outside the house
C. he has a cognitive representation of his master and this thought causes him to wag his tail
D. the sound of the car predicts the entrance of his beloved master

p. 202
Three Explanations
Level: Easy
Type: Factual
Ans: A

146. A researcher presents an unconditioned stimulus first, which is followed by the conditioned stimulus. The researcher is practicing:
A. backward conditioning
B. classical conditioning
C. operant conditioning
D. stimulus generalization

p. 202
Three Explanations
Level: Easy
Type: Factual
Ans: C

147. The fact that backward conditioning does not usually result in classical conditioning supports:
A. emotional conditioned response
B. the contiguity theory
C. the cognitive perspective
D. stimulus generalization

p. 204
Research Focus:
 Little Albert
Level: Easy
Type: Factual
Ans: A

148. Who was responsible for the classical conditioning of Little Albert?
A. John Watson and Rosalie Rayner
B. B. F. Skinner and John Watson
C. Albert Bandura and John Garcia
D. Robert Kramer and Robert Rescorla

p. 204
Research Focus:
 Little Albert
Level: Moderate
Type: Factual
Ans: C

149. The case of Little Albert provides dramatic insight into _____ through _____.
A. intelligence; systematic desensitization
B. memory development; classical conditioning
C. the development of emotional response; classical conditioning
D. the dangers of poor attachment; the law of stimulus-response

p. 204
Research Focus:
 Little Albert
Level: Easy
Type: Factual
Ans: A
PS/SG 9-21

150. The reason for Little Albert's fame in psychology is the fact that:
A. Watson showed that emotional responses could be classically conditioned in humans
B. Pavlov was unable to replicate his salivation procedure with Little Albert
C. Rescorla used the Little Albert experiment to disprove Pavlov
D. Carla learned not to fear the dentist through the example of this brave little boy

p. 204
Research Focus:
 Little Albert
Level: Easy
Type: Factual
Ans: D

151. Using the example of Little Albert, which of the following is incorrect?
A. neutral stimulus - white rat
B. UCS - loud noise
C. UCR - crying
D. CR - white rat

p. 204
Research Focus:
 Little Albert
Level: Easy
Type: Factual
Ans: C

152. In the case of Little Albert, the _____ was the neutral stimulus and noise was the _____.
A. startle/cry; UCR
B. food; CS
C. white rat; UCS
D. salivation; UCS

p. 204
Research Focus:
 Little Albert
Level: Easy
Type: Factual
Ans: B

153. The significance of the Watson and Rayner study with Little Albert is it:
A. led to stringent ethical guidelines regarding the use of children in research
B. demonstrated that emotional responses could be classically conditioned
C. assisted in the decline of behaviorism in American psychology
D. helped identify common problems in language development among infants

<table>
<tr><td>

p. 204
Research Focus:
  Little Albert
Level: Moderate
Type: Factual
Ans: A
*www*

</td><td>

154. Little Albert showed fear of anything resembling a white rat. This is an example of _____ .
A. generalization
B. systematic desensitization
C. extinction
D. stimulus-response

</td></tr>

<tr><td>

p. 205
Cultural Diversity:
  Dental Fears
Level: Easy
Type: Factual
Ans: B

</td><td>

155. Why would the Scandinavian countries have lower rates of dental fears among children?
A. genetic differences
B. Dental care is part of the free, universal health care program and children receive more regular dental care.
C. Children are taught not to reveal their fears.
D. There is a character in Scandinavian mythology of a kind old dentist that is taught to children from an early age.

</td></tr>

<tr><td>

p. 205
Cultural Diversity:
  Dental Fears
Level: Easy
Type: Factual
Ans: C

</td><td>

156. Dental fear is highest among children living in:
A. Japan
B. Singapore
C. United States
D. Norway

</td></tr>

<tr><td>

p. 205
Cultural Diversity:
  Dental Fears
Level: Easy
Type: Factual
Ans: C

</td><td>

157. What is the best way to reduce dental fear?
A. Avoid routine visits to the dentist.
B. Move to Japan since dental care is free and part of the universal health care program.
C. Receive regular, nonpainful dental checkups.
D. Be patient. The fear is likely to be extinguished anyway.

</td></tr>

<tr><td>

p. 205
Cultural Diversity:
  Dental Fears
Level: Easy
Type: Factual
Ans: B

</td><td>

158. What may account for high rates of dental fears in different parts of the world?
A. genetic differences in tolerance for pain
B. whether children received dental care only when there is an emergency or as part of their regular health care
C. cultural differences regarding the role of dentists
D. attention to dental fears on television

</td></tr>

<tr><td>

p. 205
Cultural Diversity:
  Dental Fears
Level: Easy
Type: Factual
Ans: C
*PS/SG 9-23*

</td><td>

159. American children show more dental fear than Scandinavian children because:
A. American dentists are not as well trained
B. American children have seen many scary movies about cruel dentists
C. health care systems in the two societies are different
D. Scandinavian dentists give their patients lots of candy for not crying

</td></tr>

<tr><td>

p. 205
Cultural Diversity:
  Dental Fears
Level: Easy
Type: Factual
Ans: C

</td><td>

160. In the United States, adults were asked when their dental fears first began. About 66% indicated that the fears began:
A. as teenagers
B. when hearing about someone else's experiences with a dentist
C. in childhood
D. in young adulthood

</td></tr>
</table>

p. 205
Cultural Diversity:
 Dental Fears
Level: Moderate
Type: Factual
Ans: A

161. When someone avoids regular dental checkups, they end up only seeking a dentist for emergency problems typically requiring some painful procedures.  This avoidance serves to:
A. only strengthen their already high level of fears about dental care
B. extinguish fear
C. make them more willing to come in before they run into dental problems
D. punish them for their avoidance

p. 206
Application: Conditioned
 Fear and Nausea
Level: Easy
Type: Factual
Ans: D

162. Anticipatory nausea:
A. immediately follows a chemotherapy treatment
B. happens during chemotherapy treatment
C. is easy to treat and control with medication
D. occurs in anticipation of chemotherapy treatment

p. 206
Application: Conditioned
 Fear and Nausea
Level: Easy
Type: Factual
Ans: A
*PS/SG 9-24*

163. A classically conditioned response often observed in patients receiving chemotherapy is:
A. anticipatory nausea
B. pleasure
C. taste-aversion learning
D. preparedness

p. 206
Application: Conditioned
 Fear and Nausea
Level: Easy
Type: Factual
Ans: A

164. A classically conditioned response often seen in patients who are receiving chemotherapy is:
A. anticipatory nausea
B. phobia
C. taste-aversion learning
D. preparedness

p. 206
Application: Conditioned
 Fear and Nausea
Level: Easy
Type: Factual
Ans: B

165. By the fourth injection, _____ of patients who receive chemotherapy experience anticipatory nausea.
A. 25-35%
B. 60-70%
C. 75%
D. 95%

p. 206
Application: Conditioned
 Fear and Nausea
Level: Moderate
Type: Applied
Ans: D

166. In the case of anticipatory nausea, the neutral stimulus is _____ and UCR could be _____.
A. nurse's voice; chemotherapy
B. nausea; chemotherapy
C. chemotherapy; aftershave
D. smell of treatment room; nausea

p. 206
Application: Conditioned
 Fear and Nausea
Level: Moderate
Type: Applied
Ans: C

167. In the case of anticipatory nausea, the UCS is _____ and CS could be _____.
A. nurse's voice; chemotherapy
B. nausea; chemotherapy
C. chemotherapy; smell of treatment room
D. waiting room; nausea

| p. 207 | 168. | The procedure which pairs a relaxation response with stimuli that elicit unpleasant feelings is called: |
|---|---|---|
| Application: Conditioned Fear and Nausea | | |
| Level: Easy | A. | spontaneous recovery |
| Type: Factual | B. | systematic desensitization |
| Ans: B | C. | operant conditioning |
| | D. | stimulus discrimination |

| p. 207 | 169. | Of the following words, which one best describes systematic desensitization? |
|---|---|---|
| Application: Conditioned Fear and Nausea | | |
| Level: Easy | A. | learn |
| Type: Conceptual | B. | stimulus |
| Ans: C | C. | uncondition |
| | D. | acquire |

| p. 207 | 170. | Which is not a step in the systematic desensitization procedure? |
|---|---|---|
| Application: Conditioned Fear and Nausea | A. | being exposed to the feared stimuli |
| | B. | learning to relax |
| Level: Easy | C. | developing an anxiety hierarchy |
| Type: Factual | D. | imaging fearful stimuli and remaining relaxed |
| Ans: A | | |

| p. 207 | 171. | Which one of the following is not necessary to the systematic desensitization procedure? |
|---|---|---|
| Application: Conditioned Fear and Nausea | A. | learning to relax |
| Level: Easy | B. | identifying unconscious conflicts |
| Type: Factual | C. | making an anxiety hierarchy |
| Ans: B | D. | imagining and relaxing while moving up and down the anxiety hierarchy |
| PS/SG 9-25 | | |

| p. 207 | 172. | Systematic desensitization is effective because it: |
|---|---|---|
| Application: Conditioned Fear and Nausea | A. | leads to spontaneous recovery |
| | B. | causes the UCS to be extinguished |
| Level: Moderate | C. | uses operant conditioning to modify behavior |
| Type: Factual | D. | changes the CS's back to neutral stimuli |
| Ans: D | | |

| p. 207 | 173. | Systematic desensitization is based upon the principles of: |
|---|---|---|
| Application: Conditioned Fear and Nausea | A. | classical conditioning |
| | B. | operant conditioning |
| Level: Moderate | C. | stimulus substitution |
| Type: Factual | D. | cognitive learning |
| Ans: A | | |
| www | | |

| p. 207 | 174. | Of the following situations, which one would be best treated with systematic desensitization? |
|---|---|---|
| Application: Conditioned Fear and Nausea | | |
| Level: Easy | A. | Kevin has a habit of biting his fingernails. |
| Type: Applied | B. | Patrick has a fear of speaking in public. |
| Ans: B | C. | Tommy misbehaves in class when the teacher is giving instructions. |
| | D. | Karol has great difficulty managing her time. |

True/False

| | | | |
|---|---|---|---|
| F | *www* | 1. | Learning is defined by a relatively permanent change in behavior that results from maturation. |
| F | | 2. | In classical conditioning, the neutral stimulus triggers the conditioned response. |
| T | *www* | 3. | The UCS triggers the UCR. |
| T | | 4. | The NS is paired with the UCS. |
| T | *www* | 5. | The UCS and CS are similar. |
| F | | 6. | Following classical conditioning, the CS elicits the UCR. |
| F | *www* | 7. | In the example of aftershave triggering anxiety, the anxiety is the NS. |
| T | | 8. | If a dog that was classically conditioned to salivate to a bell, salivates to a buzzer, then generalization is said to have occurred. |
| F | *www* | 9. | When the CS no longer elicits the CR, spontaneous recovery occurs. |
| T | | 10. | Extinction occurs when the CS no longer elicits the CR. |
| T | | 11. | When a CR reappears after extinction, spontaneous recovery occurs. |
| F | | 12. | The CR following spontaneous recovery is the same magnitude as the original CR was before extinction. |
| F | | 13. | Taste-aversion learning occurs over many trials. |
| F | *www* | 14. | Rats acquire taste–aversion easily when visual stimuli are used. |
| T | *www* | 15. | Animals are more likely to associate some stimuli more easily than others; this is called preparedness. |
| F | | 16. | All stimuli have an equal chance of becoming conditioned stimuli. |
| T | *www* | 17. | If you start getting anxious when thinking about a flu shot, you are experiencing a conditioned emotional response. |
| F | | 18. | According to stimulus substitution, the NS predicts the UCS. |
| T | | 19. | The contiguity theory focuses on the close pairing of the NS and UCS. |
| T | | 20. | According to the cognitive perspective, Pavlov's dogs learn that the NS predicts the UCS. |
| F | | 21. | Backward conditioning makes it possible to predict the UCS. |
| T | *www* | 22. | In Little Albert's case, the rat was the NS. |
| T | | 23. | Anticipatory nausea occurs because the individual associates the smells, sounds, and sights related to treatment with nausea induced by the chemotherapy. |
| F | | 24. | In systematic desensitization the individuals fear is conditioned. |
| T | *www* | 25. | The last step in systematic desensitization is to imagine a stressful situation while remaining relaxed. |

Short-Answer Essay Questions

1. What is learning? (*www*)
2. Using classical conditioning, how would you condition a person to eye blink when hearing a song? Make sure you specify the NS, UCS, UCR, CS, and CR. (*www*)
3. Explain why a person might associate the smell of aftershave with feelings of anxiety.
4. Describe what occurs in generalization, discrimination, extinction, and spontaneous recovery in a case where a dog is classically conditioned to a tone. (*www*)
5. Using your knowledge of classical conditioning, explain how a rancher might condition coyotes from attacking and eating sheep.
6. How does the sensitivity of an animal's senses affect the development of taste-aversion?
7. What is preparedness and how does it influence classical conditioning? (*www*)

8.  Identifying the elements of classical conditioning (NS, UCS, UCR, CS, and CR) in the case of Little Albert's fear. Moreover, describe how Little Albert might have shown generalization and discrimination.

9.  Identify the elements of classical conditioning (NS, UCS, UCR, CS, and CR) in how a cancer patient may develop anticipatory nausea with chemotherapy treatment. (*www*)

10. How would systematic desensitization be used to help a person with a fear of dental work?

# Module 10 - Operant and Cognitive Approaches

p. 213
Introduction
Level: Easy
Type: Factual
Ans: C

1.  According to the textbook, Bart the bear was conditioned using:
    A.  imprinting
    B.  biofeedback
    C.  reinforcement
    D.  punishment

p. 213
Introduction
Level: Easy
Type: Factual
Ans: A

2.  Bart, the ten-foot tall Kodiak bear, learned and performed 45 behaviors for a starring role in a movie through:
    A.  operant conditioning
    B.  imprinting
    C.  insight
    D.  classical conditioning

p. 213
Introduction
Level: Easy
Type: Conceptual
Ans: A
*PS/SG 10-2*

3.  Plotnik's example of Jack the child golf prodigy, raises the possibility that:
    A.  learning can also occur just by observation, without external rewards
    B.  human learning differs greatly from animal learning
    C.  rewards actually interfere with learning
    D.  what Bart the bear did was just trickery, but Jack was really learning

p. 213
Introduction
Level: Easy
Type: Factual
Ans: D

4.  Instrumental conditioning is also known as:
    A.  classical conditioning
    B.  imprinting conditioning
    C.  instinctual conditioning
    D.  operant conditioning

p. 213
Introduction
Level: Easy
Type: Factual
Ans: C
*www*

5.  The focus of operant conditioning is on how:
    A.  people learn from the examples of others without themselves being reinforced
    B.  repetition results in reflexive habits without awareness
    C.  behavior is influenced by its consequences and whether it increases or decreases the likelihood of that behavior being repeated
    D.  stimuli are paired to elicit a response

p. 213
Introduction
Level: Easy
Type: Factual
Ans: B

6.  The type of learning that focuses on the consequences of behavior is called:
    A.  classical conditioning
    B.  operant conditioning
    C.  process conditioning
    D.  latent learning

p. 213
Introduction
Level: Easy
Type: Applied
Ans: D

7. The Great Carlo is an internationally known lion trainer. You ask him how he goes about training his lions. He responds by saying something about consequences that increase the chance that the desired behavior will again be performed. You recognize his method as:

A. trial and error conditioning
B. cognitive learning
C. classical conditioning
D. operant conditioning

p. 213
Introduction
Level: Easy
Type: Applied
Ans: A

8. One of the web sites that you've recently visited was a site describing techniques for parents to manage their children's behavior. You notice that many of the techniques are based on operant conditioning. These techniques share what in common?

A. using consequences to influence behavior
B. using observation and imitation
C. pairing unconditioned stimuli with conditioned stimuli
D. associating unconditioned stimuli with unconditioned responses

p. 213
Introduction
Level: Moderate
Type: Factual
Ans: C

9. In _____, the consequences of a behavior influence whether an organism will perform the same behavior in the future.

A. latent learning
B. target learning
C. operant conditioning
D. classical conditioning

p. 213
Introduction
Level: Moderate
Type: Factual
Ans: A

10. Those who study cognitive learning claim that learning can take place in an individual:

A. who has not received any noticeable rewards, but who simply observes and imitates
B. only if the learning is reflexive in nature
C. who shows a change in behavior
D. only when the behavior is followed by an effect

p. 213
Introduction
Level: Easy
Type: Factual
Ans: C

11. You want to change the behavior of your roommate. You decide to reward his behaviors that you like and punish his behaviors that you do not like. You are using:

A. latent learning
B. cognitive learning
C. operant conditioning
D. classical conditioning

p. 213
Introduction
Level: Easy
Type: Conceptual
Ans: D

12. You are babysitting your three-year old niece and notice that she is acting very much like a character from a television show. Being an astute psychology student, you reason that you are most likely witnessing:

A. operant conditioning
B. instrumental conditioning
C. classical conditioning
D. cognitive learning

p. 214
Operant Conditioning
Level: Easy
Type: Factual
Ans: C

13. What names are <u>most</u> associated with operant conditioning?
A. B. F. Skinner and Carl Rogers
B. Ivan Pavlov and George Miller
C. Edward Thorndike and B. F. Skinner
D. Albert Bandura and Ivan Pavlov

p. 214
Operant Conditioning
Level: Easy
Type: Conceptual
Ans: A

14. Whiskers is a cat being used in Thorndike's studies on learning. The amount of time it takes Whiskers to get out of the puzzle box is decreasing. Thorndike would conclude that:
A. Whiskers' behaviors that lead to escaping the box to get the fish are being strengthened.
B. Whiskers' behavior that lead to escaping the box to get the fish are being weakened.
C. Whiskers is imprinting on Thorndike's behavior.
D. Whiskers' behaviors are under a continuous schedule of reinforcement.

p. 214
Operant Conditioning
Level: Easy
Type: Factual
Ans: C
*www*

15. Trial-and-error learning is associated with experiments conducted with hungry cats placed in a puzzle box. This work was conducted by:
A. B. F. Skinner
B. Ivan Pavlov
C. Edward Thorndike
D. Albert Bandura

p. 214
Operant Conditioning
Level: Easy
Type: Applied
Ans: A

16. In your backyard you have a bird feeder that a particular squirrel likes to eat from. You have tried many ways to prevent it from stealing from it. You notice that the squirrel's random behavior gradually turns into goal-directed behavior. This <u>best</u> illustrates what Thorndike called the:
A. law of effect
B. principle of continuity
C. law of consequence
D. principle of consequence

p. 214
Operant Conditioning
Level: Easy
Type: Factual
Ans: B

17. Thorndike developed the law of effect by studying:
A. the saliva of dogs
B. how a cat learns to escape from a puzzle box
C. how a rat learns to press a lever
D. how to train a bear to hold a stuffed animal

p. 214
Operant Conditioning
Level: Easy
Type: Factual
Ans: D

18. What is described as the idea that behaviors followed by positive consequences are strengthened, while behaviors followed by negative consequences are weakened?
A. behavioral facilitation
B. principle of continuity
C. cognitive learning
D. law of effect

| | | |
|---|---|---|
| p. 214<br>Operant Conditioning<br>Level: Moderate<br>Type: Conceptual<br>Ans: D | 19.<br>A.<br>B.<br>C.<br><br>D. | Thorndike found that a cat learned to escape from a puzzle box by the consequences of its behavior. How could he arrive at such a conclusion?<br>The CR was increasing in magnitude over time.<br>The cat learned by watching Thorndike open the puzzle box.<br>The CS (freedom) provide information about the occurrence of the UCS (piece of fish).<br>The time it took cats to escape decreased over time. |
| p. 214<br>Operant Conditioning<br>Level: Easy<br>Type: Conceptual<br>Ans: B | 20.<br>A.<br>B.<br>C.<br>D. | Law of effect is to _____ as operant conditioning is to _____.<br>Tolman; Bandura<br>Thorndike; Skinner<br>Skinner; Thorndike<br>Skinner; Rescorla |
| p. 214<br>Operant Conditioning<br>Level: Easy<br>Type: Factual<br>Ans: B | 21.<br>A.<br>B.<br>C.<br>D. | Who expanded Thorndike's law of effect?<br>Edward Tolman<br>B. F. Skinner<br>Albert Bandura<br>Robert Rescorla |
| p. 214<br>Operant Conditioning<br>Level: Easy<br>Type: Factual<br>Ans: C | 22.<br>A.<br>B.<br>C.<br>D. | The unit of behavior that Skinner could measure is called a(n):<br>reinforcer<br>conditioned response<br>operant response<br>behavioral index |
| p. 214<br>Operant Conditioning<br>Level: Easy<br>Type: Factual<br>Ans: D | 23.<br><br>A.<br>B.<br>C.<br>D. | _____ is a term suggested by Skinner to indicate a response that can be changed by its consequences.<br>Prepared response<br>Conditioned response<br>Effect response<br>Operant response |
| p. 214<br>Operant Conditioning<br>Level: Easy<br>Type: Factual<br>Ans: C | 24.<br><br><br>A.<br>B.<br>C.<br>D. | Bart the bear picks up a teddy bear. In operant conditioning, this behavior is called a(n) _____. He is given an apple, which is the _____ of picking up the teddy bear.<br>reinforcer; consequence<br>conditioned response; reinforcer<br>operant response; consequence<br>consequence; reinforcer |
| p. 215<br>Operant Conditioning<br>Level: Easy<br>Type: Factual<br>Ans: B | 25.<br>A.<br>B.<br>C.<br>D. | Conditioning a rat to press a lever is <u>most</u> associated with the work of:<br>Ivan Pavlov<br>B. F. Skinner<br>Edward Thorndike<br>Albert Bandura |
| p. 215<br>Operant Conditioning<br>Level: Easy<br>Type: Factual<br>Ans: A | 26.<br>A.<br>B.<br>C.<br>D. | The apparatus used by Skinner to study operant conditioning is called a(n):<br>Skinner box<br>operant chamber<br>puzzle box<br>Pavlov box |

p. 215
Operant Conditioning
Level: Easy
Type: Conceptual
Ans: D
*PS/SG 10-3*

27. Skinner gets the credit for operant conditioning instead of Thorndike because:
A. Skinner studied rats, pigeons, and other animals instead of limiting himself to cats
B. Thorndike's Law of Effect was essentially a restatement of Pavlov's conditioned reflex
C. Skinner realized that there were biological limits on learning
D. Thorndike stated a general principle; Skinner's research explained precisely how it works

p. 215
Operant Conditioning
Level: Easy
Type: Factual
Ans: C

28. If B. F. Skinner was alive today, his web site would be most likely named:
A. www.cognitive.com
B. www.insight.com
C. www.operant.com
D. www.classical.com

p. 215
Operant Conditioning
Level: Easy
Type: Factual
Ans: B

29. In classical conditioning, behavior that can be modified by its _____ is called a(n)_____.
A. antecedents; stimulus
B. consequences; operant response
C. consequences; unconditional stimulus
D. consequences; conditional stimulus

p. 215
Operant Conditioning
Level: Easy
Type: Applied
Ans: D

30. Dr. Peck wishes to operantly condition a pigeon to pick a black card out of a set of white cards. To ensure that Peck's pigeon picks the proper card the reinforcer must:
A. precede the desired behavior
B. occur at the same time as the desired behavior
C. become a predictor for the desired behavior
D. follow the desired behavior

p. 215
Operant Conditioning
Level: Easy
Type: Factual
Ans: C

31. Of the following, which is not a correct procedure in the use of operant conditioning?
A. selecting a target behavior
B. shaping by reinforcing small incremental steps
C. reinforcing a target behavior right before it occurs
D. reinforcing only observable behaviors

p. 215
Operant Conditioning
Level: Easy
Type: Factual
Ans: C
*www*

32. Shaping is defined as:
A. promising a reward in return for performing desired behavior
B. pairing two stimuli to elicit the desired behavior
C. reinforcing behaviors that successively lead up to the desired behavior
D. changing behavior through the use of punishment

p. 215
Operant Conditioning
Level: Moderate
Type: Factual
Ans: A

33. In the early stages of shaping a rat to press a lever, the teacher would:
A. deliver a food pellet if the rat simply faced the lever
B. feed the rat many food pellets to familiarize the rat with the reinforcer
C. delay the delivery of food pellets to present a challenge to the rat
D. wait for the rat to press the lever three times in a row before delivering a food pellet

p. 215
Operant Conditioning
Level: Easy
Type: Applied
Ans: B

34. A researcher is trying to get a pigeon to play "Joy to the World" on a toy piano. If the pigeon plays the first note followed by a reinforcer, and then the pigeon plays the first and second note followed by a reinforcer, the researcher is <u>most</u> likely using:
   A. classical conditioning
   B. shaping
   C. cognitive theory
   D. stimulus substitution

p. 215
Operant Conditioning
Level: Easy
Type: Applied
Ans: D

35. A college student taking a composition class hears that the professors wants a topic for the paper in two weeks, followed by a bibliography in four weeks, then an outline in 6 weeks, a first draft in 8 weeks, and the final version in 12 weeks. These deadlines to reinforce behaviors that lead up to the completed paper <u>best</u> illustrates:
   A. variable ratio schedule
   B. stimulus substitution
   C. cognitive theory
   D. shaping

p. 215
Operant Conditioning
Level: Moderate
Type: Applied
Ans: C

36. Karen is "potty training" Andrew. First she gives him a cookie when he spends time near the potty, then he gets a cookie if he sits on the potty, and finally he gets a cookie for making "poo-poo" in the potty. Karen is using a procedure called:
   A. negative reinforcement
   B. generalization
   C. shaping
   D. intermittent reinforcement

p. 215
Operant Conditioning
Level: Easy
Type: Conceptual
Ans: B
PS/SG 10-5

37. The shaping procedure succeeds or fails depending on:
   A. how long you are willing to wait for the target behavior to occur
   B. exactly which behaviors you reinforce
   C. how many times you reinforce the target behavior
   D. selecting the best one of several reinforcers

p. 215
Operant Conditioning
Level: Easy
Type: Applied
Ans: B

38. You are trying to shape a pig to turn circles. When do you provide a piece of food to the pig?
   A. before the pig does the desired behavior
   B. immediately after the desired behavior
   C. as the pig is turning the circle
   D. about five minutes after the pig performs the desired behavior

p. 215
Operant Conditioning
Level: Easy
Type: Applied
Ans: D

39. Right before a game, a baseball player goes through a series of ritualistic behaviors that he says give him good luck, but in fact are not in reality associated with any reinforcer. This ball player illustrates:
   A. discrimination
   B. generalization
   C. observational learning
   D. superstitious behaviors

p. 215
Operant Conditioning
Level: Easy
Type: Factual
Ans: A

40. According to the textbook, what is the best explanation for a professional baseball player eating chicken every day that a game is scheduled?
A. superstitious behaviors
B. generalization
C. observational learning
D. discrimination

p. 215
Operant Conditioning
Level: Easy
Type: Applied
Ans: D
*www*

41. Alfredo brings his lucky pencil with him for his exams. His pencil was accidentally paired with a good grade on his exams. Alfredo's behavior is an example of a(n):
A. variable-ratio schedule
B. reinforcement
C. conditioned response
D. superstitious behavior

p. 215
Operant Conditioning
Level: Easy
Type: Factual
Ans: D

42. Ali is trying to summarize operant conditioning. Which of the following does the best job?
A. critical analyses can obstruct behavior
B. conditioning a consequence organizes behavior
C. constant attention commands operant behaviors
D. consequences are contingent on behavior

p. 215
Operant Conditioning
Level: Moderate
Type: Conceptual
Ans: C

43. What is incorrect about this statement: The consequences are independent on an animal emitting some behavior.
A. "an animal emitting" - it should read "an animal elicits"
B. the words "consequences" and "behavior" should be switched around
C. "consequences are independent" -it should read "consequences are dependent"
D. "some behavior" - it should read "operant behavior"

p. 216
Operant Conditioning
Level: Easy
Type: Applied
Ans: A

44. If parents wanted to increase the study habits of their children, they might consider using operant conditioning. The first step would be to:
A. identify the target behavior or the goal for the child
B. select reinforcers
C. reinforce appropriate behavior
D. present reinforcers through the shaping procedure

p. 216
Operant Conditioning
Level: Easy
Type: Factual
Ans: D

45. What effect would a reinforcer have on a child's behavior?
A. decreases likelihood that behavior will be repeated only if reinforcer is given before child performs behavior
B. depends on what the child's behavior is
C. decreases likelihood that behavior will be repeated
D. increases likelihood that behavior will be repeated

p. 216
Operant Conditioning
Level: Easy
Type: Applied
Ans: C

46. You are visiting some friends who have a three-year-old who is being toilet trained. You hear the mother reinforcing the child after he says that he has to urinate, after he enters the bathroom, and after he uses the toilet. The mother has used the operant technique called:

A. discrimination
B. spontaneous recovery
C. shaping
D. extinction

p. 216
Operant Conditioning
Level: Easy
Type: Factual
Ans: B
*PS/SG 10-7*

47. In shaping, it is very important that the reinforcer come:

A. immediately before the desired behavior
B. immediately after the desired behavior
C. only after the subject has had time to appreciate what is happening
D. at the same time that the target behavior is occurring

p. 216
Operant Conditioning
Level: Easy
Type: Factual
Ans: C

48. Toilet training should start when the child is about:

A. 6 months old
B. 12 months old
C. 24 months old
D. 36 months old

p. 216
Operant Conditioning
Level: Easy
Type: Factual
Ans: A

49. One of the steps in using operant conditioning to overcome a child's refusal to eat certain foods includes reinforcing her when she notices the food, then when it is placed in her mouth, then when she tastes the food, and when she swallows it. This best describes:

A. shaping
B. conditioned responses
C. spontaneous recovery
D. continuous reinforcement

p. 216
Operant Conditioning
Level: Easy
Type: Factual
Ans: D

50. Which of the following is *not* among the four steps in using operant conditioning to teach young children to taste, chew, and eat a food?

A. identify target behavior
B. provide reinforcer after desired behavior is performed
C. shape behavior
D. pair unconditioned stimulus with conditioned stimulus

p. 217
Operant Conditioning
Level: Moderate
Type: Conceptual
Ans: D

51. The goal of operant conditioning is to _____, while the goal in classical conditioning is to _____.

A. create an association between stimuli; create an association between behavior and consequences
B. create an expectation that conditioned stimulus will lead to behavior; increase or decrease the rate of some behavior
C. decrease the rate of some behavior; increase the rate of some behavior
D. increase or decrease the rate of some behavior; create a new response to a neutral response

p. 217
Operant Conditioning
Level: Moderate
Type: Conceptual
Ans: C

52. Classical is to operant as:

A. learned is to memorized
B. undesirable is to desirable
C. involuntary is to voluntary
D. learned is to innate

p. 217
Operant Conditioning
Level: Moderate
Type: Conceptual
Ans: A

53. Classical is to operant as:
A. elicited is to emitted
B. undesirable is to desirable
C. observable is to invisible
D. consequences is to expectancy

p. 217
Operant Conditioning
Level: Moderate
Type: Conceptual
Ans: D
*www*

54. In operant conditioning, the response is _____. In classical conditioning that response is _____.
A. involuntary; voluntary
B. reflexive; involuntary
C. involuntary; reflexive
D. voluntary; involuntary

p. 217
Operant Conditioning
Level: Moderate
Type: Factual
Ans: B

55. In classical conditioning, a stimulus is paired with _____; in operant conditioning, a behavior is paired with _____.
A. a reward; a stimulus
B. another stimulus; a consequence
C. a reflex; a stimulus
D. a consequence; another organism

p. 217
Operant Conditioning
Level: Moderate
Type: Factual
Ans: B

56. Learned behaviors in operant conditioning are _____ and in classical conditioning they are _____:
A. solicited; illicited
B. emitted; elicited
C. elicited; emitted
D. involuntary; voluntary

p. 217
Operant Conditioning
Level: Easy
Type: Conceptual
Ans: C
*PS/SG 10-9*

57. You could argue that Skinner's discoveries are more important than Pavlov's in that:
A. beginning a quarter of a century later, Skinner could build on Pavlov's discoveries
B. American science offers more freedom than Russian science
C. almost all important human behavior is voluntary (not reflex) behavior
D. the conditioned reflex isn't fully explained until you bring in the concepts of both positive and negative reinforcement

p. 217
Operant Conditioning
Level: Easy
Type: Factual
Ans: D

58. As compared to classical conditioning, the behaviors to be learned in operant conditioning are:
A. reflexive
B. elicited
C. automatic
D. voluntary

p. 217
Operant Conditioning
Level: Easy
Type: Factual
Ans: C
*PS/SG 10-4*

59. The basic principle of operant conditioning is that:
A. conditioned stimuli produce conditioned response
B. the performance of undesired behaviors brings swift consequences
C. consequences are contingent on behavior
D. consequences are less important than feelings of guilt

p. 217
Operant Conditioning
Level: Easy
Type: Conceptual
Ans: C

60. Professor Cao is writing words on the overhead that describe operant conditioning. You notice that she makes a mistake. Which word did she accidentally write down that does not refer to operant conditioning?

A. voluntary
B. contingency
C. conditioned response
D. consequences

p. 217
Operant Conditioning
Level: Moderate
Type: Applied
Ans: B

61. If you wish to modify your roommate's behavior to clean up, which type of learning would you use and why?

A. classical conditioning - cleaning is a conditioned response
B. operant conditioning - cleaning is a voluntary response
C. operant conditioning - cleaning is an unconditioned response
D. classical conditioning - cleaning can be conditioned using backward conditioning

p. 217
Operant Conditioning
Level: Easy
Type: Factual
Ans: D

62. In operant conditioning, _____ increases or decreases the chances that the _____ will occur again.

A. behavior; consequences
B. response; stimulus
C. reflex; stimulus
D. consequences; behavior

p. 218
Reinforcers
Level: Easy
Type: Factual
Ans: C

63. What do positive reinforcement, negative reinforcement, positive punishment, and negative punishment all have in common?

A. They are all examples of responses used in classical conditioning.
B. They all increase the chances that behavior will be repeated.
C. All of them are consequences in operant conditioning.
D. They all decrease the chances that behavior will be repeated.

p. 218
Reinforcers
Level: Easy
Type: Factual
Ans: A

64. In operant conditioning, a stimulus that increases the probability of a behavior occurring again is called a:

A. reinforcer
B. punisher
C. generalizer
D. conditioner

p. 218
Reinforcers
Level: Easy
Type: Conceptual
Ans: C
www

65. Reinforcement is to _____, as punishment is to _____.

A. decrease; increase
B. decrease; decrease
C. increase; decrease
D. operant conditioning; classical conditioning

p. 218
Reinforcers
Level: Easy
Type: Factual
Ans: A

66. According to operant conditioning, an organism is more likely to perform a behavior in the future if the behavior is:

A. reinforced
B. reflexive
C. substituted
D. spontaneously recovered

p. 218
Reinforcers
Level: Easy
Type: Factual
Ans: C
*www*

67. _____ is a consequence that has the effect of decreasing the chance that the behavior that came before it will happen again.
A. Negative reinforcement
B. Shaping
C. Punishment
D. Operant response

p. 218
Reinforcers
Level: Easy
Type: Factual
Ans: A
*PS/SG 10-11*

68. The main difference between reinforcement and punishment is that:
A. reinforcement increases rates of behavior, but punishment decreases them
B. reinforcement is very effective, but punishment rarely is
C. reinforcement leads to good behavior, but punishment often creates pica
D. people obviously dislike punishment, but they don't really like reinforcement much more

p. 218
Reinforcers
Level: Easy
Type: Factual
Ans: B

69. "A consequence of a behavior that decreases the likelihood of that behavior occurring again" is the definition of:
A. negative reinforcement
B. punishment
C. partial reinforcement
D. learned helplessness

p. 218
Reinforcers
Level: Moderate
Type: Applied
Ans: B

70. Ben, a mentally retarded child, has been observed eating inedible objects and substances. Ben's parents are concerned and have taken him to a psychologist. The psychologist has diagnosed Ben as having:
A. autism
B. pica
C. rumination
D. Grant's disease

p. 218
Reinforcers
Level: Moderate
Type: Factual
Ans: D

71. Pica has been successfully treated using operant conditioning. Each time an inedible object was selected, the subject received _____. Each time an appropriate, edible object was selected, _____ was presented.
A. praise; criticism
B. a consequence; reinforcement
C. negative reinforcement; reinforcement
D. mild punishment; reinforcement

p. 218
Reinforcers
Level: Easy
Type: Applied
Ans: A

72. A professor says to her student, "Nice job on that test." She has used:
A. positive reinforcement
B. generalization
C. an unconditioned stimulus
D. negative punishment

p. 218
Reinforcers
Level: Easy
Type: Applied
Ans: D

73. When Beaver learns the meaning of ten new vocabulary words, his father Ward says, "That's a good boy, Beaver." Ward's praise is a(n):
A. unconditioned stimulus
B. conditioned stimulus
C. unconditioned response
D. positive reinforcer

p. 218
Reinforcers
Level: Easy
Type: Factual
Ans: D

*www*

74. Negative reinforcement is:
A. a pleasant stimulus that increases the likelihood of the response occurring again
B. an unpleasant stimulus that increases the likelihood of the response occurring again
C. an unpleasant stimulus that decreases the likelihood of the response occurring again
D. the removal of an unpleasant stimulus that increases the likelihood of the response occurring again

p. 218
Reinforcers
Level: Moderate
Type: Factual
Ans: A

75. You have a painful headache and so you take an aspirin to eliminate the pain. The aspirin works and now you are free of your headache. Taking the aspirin is an example of a:
A. negative reinforcer - it increases the chance of taking aspirin again the next time you have a headache
B. negative reinforcer - it decreases the chance of taking aspirin again the next time you have a headache
C. positive reinforcer - it increases the chance of taking aspirin again the next time you have a headache
D. positive reinforcer - it decreases the chance of taking aspirin again the next time you have a headache

p. 218
Reinforcers
Level: Easy
Type: Applied
Ans: B

76. Kristin wants to go out and play, but her mother has said no. Kristin goes to her room and plays her rock music very loud. The noise drives her mother crazy and Kristin is allowed to go out and play if she will turn off her music. In this example, _____ was a form of negative reinforcement.
A. the music
B. turning off the music
C. going crazy
D. going out to play

p. 218
Reinforcers
Level: Easy
Type: Factual
Ans: D

77. Which of the following is the best example of negative reinforcement?
A. being put in jail for driving while drunk
B. not being allowed to go to the movies on Saturday night
C. a spanking for bad behavior
D. elimination of pain after taking an aspirin

p. 218
Reinforcers
Level: Moderate
Type: Factual
Ans: B

78. Reinforcers, whether they be positive or negative, have the same effect on behavior, which is to:
A. decrease the probability that the behavior will be repeated
B. increase the probability that the behavior will be repeated
C. increase the probability that the behavior will be extinguished
D. decrease the probability that the behavior will be spontaneously recovered

p. 218
Reinforcers
Level: Moderate
Type: Factual
Ans: A

79. Positive reinforcement _____ the likelihood that the preceding behavior will be repeated. Negative reinforcement _____ the likelihood that the preceding behavior will be repeated.
A. increases; increases
B. increases; decreases
C. decreases; increases
D. decreases; decreases

p. 218
Reinforcers
Level: Moderate
Type: Applied
Ans: C

80.  Ricardo and Luis are out walking. Luis says, "Hey, I've got a pebble in my shoe," and proceeds to take off his shoe and to remove the pebble. "That feels better," says Luis. Ricardo believes that Luis' behavior of removing the pebble is a _____ because it increases the chance that Luis will repeat the behavior if another pebble gets in his shoe.

A.  positive punisher
B.  positive reinforcer
C.  negative reinforcer
D.  unconditioned stimulus

p. 219
Reinforcers
Level: Easy
Type: Conceptual
Ans: B

81.  Reinforcement is to increase as punishment is to _____.
A.  increase
B.  decrease
C.  condition
D.  negative

p. 219
Reinforcers
Level: Easy
Type: Applied
Ans: D
www

82.  Whenever little Bobby cries, his father spanks him. Bobby's father is trying to decrease Bobby's crying through the use of:

A.  stimulus substitution
B.  negative reinforcement
C.  positive reinforcement
D.  positive punishment

p. 219
Reinforcers
Level: Easy
Type: Applied
Ans: C

83.  The little child who gets a good hard spanking for running out into the street is experiencing an operant conditioning procedure called:

A.  positive reinforcement
B.  negative reinforcement
C.  positive punishment
D.  extinction

p. 219
Reinforcers
Level: Moderate
Type: Applied
Ans: C

84.  During a lecture on learning, a fellow student accidentally stubs his toe on a table leg and lets out a "yelp." Having heard it, the professor says, " Is that behavior [toe stubbing] likely to happen again in the future?" Answer the professor and indicate the reason for your answer.

A.  No - the behavior was followed by negative reinforcement (pain)
B.  No - the behavior was an example of stimulus substitution
C.  No - the behavior was followed by positive punishment (pain)
D.  No - the consequence was followed by the behavior

p. 219
Reinforcers
Level: Easy
Type: Factual
Ans: C

85.  What refers to presenting an aversive stimulus after a response that decreases the odds that the response will recur?

A.  Negative punishment
B.  Punishment
C.  Positive punishment
D.  Latent punishment

p. 219
Reinforcers
Level: Easy
Type: Factual
Ans: A

86.  What refers to removing a reinforcing stimulus after a response that decreases the odds that the response will recur?
A.  Negative punishment
B.  Punishment
C.  Positive punishment
D.  Latent punishment

p. 219
Reinforcers
Level: Easy
Type: Factual
Ans: B
*www*

87.  You remember a friend of yours in elementary school stuck his tongue on a pole on a playground swing set in the middle of winter. He yelled in pain, but finally pulled his tongue off the pole. He said, "I'll never do that again, it hurts!" His behavior of putting his tongue on the pole involved _____ since he never did it again.
A.  negative punishment
B.  positive punishment
C.  salient punishment
D.  primary punishment

p. 219
Reinforcers
Level: Moderate
Type: Applied
Ans: A
*www*

88.  Miranda comes home late one evening past her curfew only to find her parents waiting up for her. Her father says, "Miranda, you're late! You may not use the car for an entire month." Miranda's father is using:
A.  negative punishment
B.  negative reinforcement
C.  positive punishment
D.  schedule of punishment

p. 219
Reinforcers
Level: Easy
Type: Applied
Ans: B

89.  Tommy, who is severely mentally retarded, continually bites himself and gouges his eyes. This inflicting of serious physical damage to one's body is called:
A.  automutilation
B.  self-injurious behavior
C.  self-damaging behavior
D.  self-mutilative acts

p. 219
Reinforcers
Level: Moderate
Type: Factual
Ans: C

90.  The form of punishment used to treat the self-injurious behavior observed in Suzanne was _____ and it consisted of _____.
A.  negative punishment; face washing
B.  negative reinforcement; electrical shock
C.  positive punishment; electrical shock
D.  negative punishment; electrical shock

p. 219
Reinforcers
Level: Easy
Type: Factual
Ans: D

91.  Positive punishment _____ the likelihood that the preceding behavior will be repeated. Negative punishment _____ the likelihood that the preceding behavior will be repeated.
A.  increases; increases
B.  increases; decreases
C.  decreases; increases
D.  decreases; decreases

p. 219
Reinforcers
Level: Easy
Type: Factual
Ans: A

92. A primary reinforcer _____ he likelihood that the preceding behavior will be repeated. A secondary reinforcer _____ the likelihood that the preceding behavior will be repeated.
A. increases; increases
B. increases; decreases
C. decreases; increases
D. decreases; decreases

p. 219
Reinforcers
Level: Easy
Type: Applied
Ans: C

93. Bart the bear is given an apple when he holds a teddy bear. The apple is a:
A. secondary consequence
B. primary stimulus
C. primary reinforcer
D. secondary reinforcer

p. 219
Reinforcers
Level: Easy
Type: Applied
Ans: A

94. Bethany is a newborn. What type of reinforcer has been present from her birth and requires no training?
A. primary reinforcer
B. primary stimulus
C. secondary reinforcer
D. secondary consequence

p. 219
Reinforcers
Level: Easy
Type: Factual
Ans: A

95. A stimulus that is associated with stimuli such as water, food, and shelter will become a:
A. primary reinforcer
B. continuous reinforcer
C. secondary reinforcer
D. partial reinforcer

p. 219
Reinforcers
Level: Easy
Type: Applied
Ans: C

96. Which of the following would not be an example of a primary reinforcer?
A. a drink of water
B. a sexual encounter
C. a hundred-dollar bonus
D. a warm place to sleep

p. 219
Reinforcers
Level: Easy
Type: Applied
Ans: A

97. Betty-Lou gives her son Pierre a piece of pecan pie if he does all his homework. Betty-Lou is providing Pierre with a _____ reinforcer.
A. primary
B. secondary
C. negative
D. partial

p. 219
Reinforcers
Level: Easy
Type: Applied
Ans: B

98. Monica gave William a nice tie for his help in locating a good used car. The tie is an example of _____ reinforcer.
A. primary
B. secondary
C. negative
D. partial

p. 219
Reinforcers
Level: Moderate
Type: Applied
Ans: D
*PS/SG 10-14*

99. When your date shakes your hand and says, "I had a wonderful evening," you reply, "Gee, I was kind of hoping for a:
A. token of your affection"
B. partial reinforcement"
C. secondary reinforcer"
D. primary reinforcer"

p. 219
Reinforcers
Level: Easy
Type: Conceptual
Ans: C

100. The value of a secondary reinforcer is:
A. innate
B. its association with things like tokens and money
C. learned
D. evident to all humans

p. 219
Reinforcers
Level: Easy
Type: Applied
Ans: D

101. When you get this exam back, your grade may be a(n):
A. terrible shock
B. primary reinforcer
C. unconditioned stimulus
D. secondary reinforcer

p. 219
Reinforcers
Level: Easy
Type: Applied
Ans: A

102. Which of the following should not be used as a secondary reinforcer when teaching young children to read?
A. ice cream
B. poker chips
C. praise
D. colored stickers on a chart

p. 219
Reinforcers
Level: Easy
Type: Factual
Ans: C

103. Which of the following is not a secondary reinforcer?
A. high grades
B. money
C. shelter
D. a gold star

p. 220
Schedules of
  Reinforcement
Level: Moderate
Type: Factual
Ans: D

104. The various rules, programs, and ways that reinforcers occur after performing some behavior are called:
A. cumulative records
B. shaping procedures
C. behavior modifications
D. schedules of reinforcement

p. 219
Reinforcers
Level: Easy
Type: Factual
Ans: B

105. Mrs. Paulson, a third-grade teacher, gives her students a sticker when they do a good job on their homework. A sticker is an example of a(n):
A. primary reinforcer
B. secondary reinforcer
C. basic reinforcer
D. advanced reinforcer

p. 220
Schedules of
  Reinforcement
Level: Easy
Type: Factual
Ans: C

106. How and when a reinforcer is presented is found in:
A. cumulative record
B. contingency schedules
C. schedules of reinforcement
D. reinforcement register

| | | |
|---|---|---|
| p. 220<br>Schedules of<br>  Reinforcement<br>Level: Easy<br>Type: Factual<br>Ans: C | 107. | If you wish to determine the behavior of a rat in a Skinner Box, you can review: |
| | A. | schedules of reinforcement |
| | B. | shaping procedures |
| | C. | cumulative records |
| | D. | videotapes |

| | | |
|---|---|---|
| p. 220<br>Schedules of<br>  Reinforcement<br>Level: Easy<br>Type: Factual<br>Ans: A | 108. | _____ give us a picture of an animal's ongoing responses and reinforcements across time. |
| | A. | Cumulative records |
| | B. | Shaping procedures |
| | C. | Schedules of reinforcement |
| | D. | Puzzle box records |

| | | |
|---|---|---|
| p. 220<br>Schedules of<br>  Reinforcement<br>Level: Easy<br>Type: Factual<br>Ans: B | 109. | If a behavior is reinforced each and every time it occurs, its reinforcement schedule is: |
| | A. | interval schedule of reinforcement |
| | B. | continuous reinforcement |
| | C. | complete reinforcement |
| | D. | stable reinforcement |

| | | |
|---|---|---|
| p. 220<br>Schedules of<br>  Reinforcement<br>Level: Easy<br>Type: Applied<br>Ans: D | 110. | As Toan gets on the bus to go to school each morning, the bus driver says, "Good morning Toan.  It's good to see you!"  This is an example of: |
| | A. | interval reinforcement |
| | B. | basic reinforcement |
| | C. | partial reinforcement |
| | D. | continuous reinforcement |

| | | |
|---|---|---|
| p. 220<br>Schedules of<br>  Reinforcement<br>Level: Easy<br>Type: Factual<br>Ans: C | 111. | When is continuous reinforcement <u>most</u> appropriate? |
| | A. | when the behavior is a voluntary response |
| | B. | when the behavior is an involuntary reflex |
| | C. | in the initial stages of operant conditioning |
| | D. | only after the conditioning has taken place |

| | | |
|---|---|---|
| p. 220<br>Schedules of<br>  Reinforcement<br>Level: Moderate<br>Type: Applied<br>Ans: C | 112. | Shirley is about to teach a group of 8-year-olds the backstroke.  She wants to do this using operant conditioning.  At the outset of the swimming course, Shirley should: |
| | A. | appear quite stern so that later praise will seem more meaningful |
| | B. | praise them for no particular reason but to establish rapport |
| | C. | praise every correct thing the young swimmers do |
| | D. | praise them at the end of each lesson only, since that is what she would do if they were in proper training for a meet |

| | | |
|---|---|---|
| p. 220<br>Schedules of<br>  Reinforcement<br>Level: Moderate<br>Type: Factual<br>Ans: A | 113. | Partial reinforcement is defined as reinforcement in which: |
| | A. | behaviors are not reinforced every time they occur |
| | B. | the organism gives up before full reinforcement is obtained |
| | C. | only secondary reinforcers are utilized |
| | D. | punishment is used to shape behaviors |

p. 220
Schedules of
  Reinforcement
Level: Moderate
Type: Factual
Ans: B

114.  Partial reinforcement schedules:
A.  are less expensive, but they tend to discourage the learner
B.  are very effective in maintaining behavior over the long run
C.  often confuse a learner who has grown used to a continuous pattern of reinforcement
D.  do not follow patterns

p. 221
Schedules of
  Reinforcement
Level: Moderate
Type: Applied
Ans: B

115.  Robert is reinforced by his teacher every sixth time he turns in a homework assignment. Robert's teacher is using a _____ schedule of reinforcement.
A.  fixed-interval
B.  fixed-ratio
C.  variable-interval
D.  variable-ratio

p. 221
Schedules of
  Reinforcement
Level: Easy
Type: Factual
Ans: B

116.  A _____ refers to a reinforcer occurring only after an unchanging number of responses take place.
A.  fixed-interval
B.  fixed-ratio
C.  variable-interval
D.  variable-ratio

p. 221
Schedules of
  Reinforcement
Level: Moderate
Type: Applied
Ans: A

117.  Out in the garden Lucille is given a dime for every five weeds she pulls. What reinforcement schedule is she on?
A.  fixed-ratio
B.  fixed-interval
C.  variable-ratio
D.  variable-interval

p. 221
Schedules of
  Reinforcement
Level: Moderate
Type: Applied
Ans: A

118.  "Every other set of encyclopedias you sell, I will give you $100." Says your supervisor. You realize that you are on a _____ schedule of reinforcement.
A.  fixed-ratio
B.  fixed-interval
C.  variable-ratio
D.  variable-interval

p. 221
Schedules of
  Reinforcement
Level: Moderate
Type: Applied
Ans: C

119.  When Bob plays cards with his friends, he finds that his winning hands seem to come in bunches. Then, he may go as many as ten hands without winning anything. Which schedule best describes the reinforcement Bob receives when playing cards?
A.  fixed-ratio
B.  fixed-interval
C.  variable-ratio
D.  variable-interval

p. 221
Schedules of
  Reinforcement
Level: Easy
Type: Applied
Ans: B

120.  "Poor fool," you think to yourself when your friend tells you she lost on the lottery again, "another helpless victim of the _____ schedule of reinforcement."
A.  fixed-ratio
B.  variable-ratio
C.  fixed-interval
D.  variable-interval

p. 221
Schedules of
  Reinforcement
Level: Moderate
Type: Applied
Ans: C

*www*

121. Mom tells Billy that she will pay him to pull weeds from her flower garden. Because Mom is busy, she sometimes gives Billy a dime when he pulls five weeds, sometimes when he pulls ten weeds, and other times when he pulls twenty or more weeds. The reinforcement schedule Mom is using is:
A. continuous
B. fixed-interval
C. variable-ratio
D. fixed-ratio

p. 221
Schedules of
  Reinforcement
Level: Moderate
Type: Applied
Ans: C

122. "Maybe this lottery ticket will be a winner. The last couple ones I've bought were losers. But I do buy a winner every once in awhile." This person's lottery ticket buying behavior is on what schedule of reinforcement?
A. continuous
B. fixed-interval
C. variable-ratio
D. fixed-ratio

p. 221
Schedules of
  Reinforcement
Level: Moderate
Type: Applied
Ans: C

123. A pattern in which students at a reform school clean up their rooms only before the weekly inspections is typical of which kind of reinforcement schedule?
A. variable-interval
B. variable-ratio
C. fixed-interval
D. fixed-ratio

p. 221
Schedules of
  Reinforcement
Level: Moderate
Type: Applied
Ans: B

124. Bruce gives his son Kenny a quarter if he practices his tennis serve for fifteen minutes. Bruce is using which type of reinforcement schedule?
A. variable-interval
B. fixed-interval
C. variable-ratio
D. fixed-ratio

p. 221
Schedules of
  Reinforcement
Level: Moderate
Type: Applied
Ans: B

125. Every 50 minutes, the class takes a break if their behavior is appropriate. They are on a _____ schedule of reinforcement.
A. variable-interval
B. fixed-interval
C. variable-ratio
D. fixed-ratio

p. 221
Schedules of
  Reinforcement
Level: Moderate
Type: Applied
Ans: C

126. Suzanne randomly checks up on her employees several times throughout the day to praise them if they are working hard. None of the employees know when Suzanne will be checking up on them. Suzanne is using a _____ schedule of reinforcement.
A. fixed-interval
B. fixed-ratio
C. variable-interval
D. variable-ratio

p. 221
Schedules of
  Reinforcement
Level: Moderate
Type: Applied
Ans: C

127. You like to fish. Sometimes, it takes you 30 minutes to catch a fish; other times, you catch a fish every 5 minutes. Fishing, in this case, is on a _____ schedule of reinforcement.
A. fixed-interval
B. fixed-ratio
C. variable-interval
D. variable-ratio

p. 221
Schedules of
  Reinforcement
Level: Easy
Type: Factual
Ans: A

128. Teaching a dolphin to locate mines in the water uses the principles of:
A. operant conditioning
B. insight
C. classical conditioning
D. social cognitive learning

p. 221
Schedules of
  Reinforcement
Level: Easy
Type: Factual
Ans: A

129. A _____ refers to a reinforcer occurring only after an unchanging amount of time has lapsed.
A. fixed-interval
B. fixed-ratio
C. variable-interval
D. variable-ratio

p. 222
Other Conditioning
  Concepts
Level: Moderate
Type: Applied
Ans: D

130. Dakota is using operant conditioning to get his dog Rover to bring him his slippers. He sounds a bell, has Rover bring the slippers, and reinforces the behavior with a dog biscuit. One day, a church bell sounds outside and Rover brings Dakota his slippers. Rover's behavior illustrates:
A. discrimination
B. shaping
C. intermittent reinforcement
D. generalization

p. 222
Other Conditioning
  Concepts
Level: Moderate
Type: Factual
Ans: A

131. In operant conditioning, generalization has occurred when:
A. an organism emits the same response to similar stimuli
B. a response is not emitted in the presence of unreinforced stimuli
C. a behavior is no longer reinforced
D. an organism realizes that it has been operantly conditioned

p. 222
Other Conditioning
  Concepts
Level: Easy
Type: Applied
Ans: D

132. After being praised for learning the word "doggie", a young child will point to anything with four legs and a tail and say "doggie" -- even if the "doggie" is really a cat, a horse, or a cow. This child is demonstrating:
A. discrimination
B. spontaneous recovery
C. extinction
D. generalization

p. 222
Other Conditioning
  Concepts
Level: Moderate
Type: Factual
Ans: A

133. If an organism emits a response only in the presence of reinforced stimuli and not in the presence of unreinforced stimuli, then the organism is displaying:
A. discrimination
B. spontaneous performance
C. extinction
D. generalization

p. 222
Other Conditioning
  Concepts
Level: Moderate
Type: Applied
Ans: C

134.   A child learns that a particular large four-legged animal is a horse. When he learns that the striped animal in the zoo is a zebra, he is able to demonstrate:

A.   selective responding
B.   selective attention
C.   discrimination
D.   spontaneous generalization

p. 222
Other Conditioning
  Concepts
Level: Easy
Type: Factual
Ans: A

135.   In classical conditioning, _____ is the tendency for some stimuli but not others to elicit a conditioned response.

A.   discrimination
B.   selective attention
C.   generalization
D.   spontaneous extinction

p. 222
Other Conditioning
  Concepts
Level: Easy
Type: Factual
Ans: B

136.   In operant conditioning, extinction occurs because:

A.   of disinterest
B.   reinforcement no longer follows the behavior
C.   the task is difficult
D.   of delay of reinforcement

p. 222
Other Conditioning
  Concepts
Level: Easy
Type: Factual
Ans: D

137.   According to operant conditioning, if a behavior is no longer followed by a reinforcer, the frequency of the behavior will:

A.   become more intense
B.   remain unchanged
C.   increase
D.   decrease

p. 222
Other Conditioning
  Concepts
Level: Easy
Type: Factual
Ans: D

138.   In classical conditioning, _____ refers to the reduction in a response when the conditioned stimulus is no longer followed by the unconditioned stimulus.

A.   stimulus discrimination
B.   conditioned generalization
C.   spontaneous recovery
D.   extinction

p. 222
Other Conditioning
  Concepts
Level: Easy
Type: Factual
Ans: B

139.   According to principles of operant conditioning, a response will undergo extinction if the response is:

A.   too difficult to maintain
B.   no longer reinforced
C.   reflexive in nature
D.   reinforced too often

p. 222
Other Conditioning
 Concepts
Level: Easy
Type: Factual
Ans: B

140. After operantly conditioning a rat to press a bar, a psychologist stops providing the reinforcing pellets.  The rat eventually stops pressing the bar.  Bar pressing has undergone:
A. spontaneous performance
B. extinction
C. shaping
D. generalization

p. 222
Other Conditioning
 Concepts
Level: Easy
Type: Factual
Ans: A

141. After a period of extinction, a temporary recovery in rate of responding is called:
A. spontaneous performance
B. extinction
C. discrimination
D. generalization

p. 223
Cognitive Learning
Level: Easy
Type: Factual
Ans: D

142. _____ involves mental processes and learning through observation.
A. Operant conditioning
B. Classical conditioning
C. Gestalt learning
D. Cognitive learning

p. 223
Cognitive Learning
Level: Moderate
Type: Factual
Ans: C
*PS/SG 10-17*

143. Skinner opposed cognitive theories of learning to the end of his life because:
A. it is difficult to admit that the work of a lifetime was misguided
B. they are based on philosophical speculation rather than on laboratory research
C. they bring in the "mind," which Skinner said couldn't be observed or measured
D. you can't teach an old dog new tricks

p. 223
Cognitive Learning
Level: Easy
Type: Conceptual
Ans: A

144. Who said "...cognitive science is the [downfall] of psychology"?
A. Skinner
B. Pavlov
C. Maslow
D. Bandura

p. 223
Cognitive Learning
Level: Easy
Type: Applied
Ans: C

145. Little three-year-old Noelle likes to imitate whatever her big sisters are doing, but she does so only later when she is by herself in her room.  This learning is most probably:
A. operant conditioning
B. classical conditioning
C. cognitive learning
D. imprinting

p. 223
Cognitive Learning
Level: Easy
Type: Factual
Ans: D

146. Cognitive learning refers to:
A. memory
B. problem solving
C. the role of stimulus recognition in classical conditioning
D. learning that involves mental processes such as attention

p. 223
Cognitive Learning
Level: Easy
Type: Factual
Ans: D

147. Which of the following theorists would be <u>most</u> likely to criticize cognitive learning?
A. Albert Bandura
B. Edward Tolman
C. Wolfgang Koehler
D. B. F. Skinner

p. 223
Cognitive Learning
Level: Easy
Type: Conceptual
Ans: D

148. "If you can't observe it then you shouldn't study it." Which of the following theorists would be <u>most</u> likely to say that statement?
A. Albert Bandura
B. Edward Tolman
C. Wolfgang Koehler
D. B. F. Skinner

p. 223
Cognitive Learning
Level: Easy
Type: Factual
Ans: B

149. Which of the following theorists argued that learning involves a mental representation of the environment?
A. Albert Bandura
B. Edward Tolman
C. Wolfgang Koehler
D. B. F. Skinner

p. 223
Cognitive Learning
Level: Easy
Type: Applied
Ans: B

150. "I can see in my mind the layout of the town I visited last summer." This person is using her _____ of the town.
A. latent schema
B. cognitive map
C. cognitive network
D. imprinting

p. 223
Cognitive Learning
Level: Easy
Type: Factual
Ans: A

151. If the shortest path to a food box is blocked, a rat will select the next shortest path if the rat has:
A. developed a cognitive map
B. been continuously reinforced
C. been classically conditioned
D. been punished

p. 223
Cognitive Learning
Level: Easy
Type: Factual
Ans: A

152. Which of the following theorists argued that learning can take place when someone is watching another person and performs that behavior even when not reinforced?
A. Albert Bandura
B. Edward Tolman
C. Wolfgang Koehler
D. B. F. Skinner

p. 223
Cognitive Learning
Level: Moderate
Type: Conceptual
Ans: C

153. You want to write a paper on the effects watching, imitating, and modeling has on behavior. Which of the following journals should you look in?
A. *Journal of Behaviorism*
B. *Journal of Classical Conditioning*
C. *Journal of Social Cognitive Learning*
D. *Journal of Operant Conditioning*

p. 223
Cognitive Learning
Level: Easy
Type: Conceptual
Ans: A

154. Who might have said that we don't need to directly be reinforced or punished to learn?
A. Albert Bandura
B. B. F. Skinner
C. Edward Thorndike
D. Ivan Pavlov

p. 224
Cognitive Learning
Level: Easy
Type: Applied
Ans: B

155. Alex watches a violent TV show and then pretends to shoot his brother James with a toy pistol. A psychologist would say that Alex has learned to "shoot" his brother through:
A. classical conditioning
B. observational learning
C. behavior modification
D. operant conditioning

p. 224
Cognitive Learning
Level: Easy
Type: Factual
Ans: A
*PS/SG 10-19*

156. Which one of the following was *not* an important outcome in Albert Bandura's famous Bobo doll experiment?
A. the children did not imitate the adult model until they were given a reward
B. the children learned even though they did not receive tangible rewards
C. the children learned even though they were not engaging in any overt behavior
D. some subjects did not imitate the model (proving learning had occurred) until they were reinforced for doing so

p. 224
Cognitive Learning
Level: Easy
Type: Factual
Ans: B

157. Children learned to hit a Bobo doll through:
A. reinforcement of aggressive behaviors
B. watching an adult model hit a Bobo doll
C. classical conditioning principles
D. reflexive reactions to a stressful situation

p. 224
Cognitive Learning
Level: Easy
Type: Factual
Ans: C

158. Which subject in Bandura's Bobo doll was most likely to show aggressive behavior?
A. Rachel, because she watched other children hit the Bobo doll.
B. Tamara since she was told by an adult to hit the Bobo doll.
C. Paul who saw a model hit the doll.
D. Claudia, because she was reinforced for her aggression.

p. 224
Cognitive Learning
Level: Easy
Type: Conceptual
Ans: D

159. The most important conclusion from the Bobo doll study is that:
A. behavior can be modified throughout negative punishment
B. behavior can be modified by providing secondary reinforcers
C. we create cognitive maps of dolls
D. behavior can be modified by simply watching a live model

p. 224
Cognitive Learning
Level: Difficult
Type: Conceptual
Ans: A

160. "I know and understand this material," says Paul. His instructor would agree with him. But when it comes time to prove his understanding on the exam, he typically doesn't do well. This exemplifies the idea of:
A. the learning-performance distinction
B. insight learning
C. a lack of preparedness
D. shaping

p. 224
Cognitive Learning
Level: Easy
Type: Factual
Ans: D

161. The learning-performance distinction suggests that:
A. children learn better if required to perform some behavior
B. when something is learned, it is immediately performed
C. reinforcement does not play a role in observational learning
D. learning may occur but may not always be immediately evident

p. 224
Cognitive Learning
Level: Moderate
Type: Applied
Ans: C

162. "I didn't know you knew how to do that!" says a bewildered parent to his young daughter. Apparently, the young girl would watch her dad turn on and play games on the computer. This imitation had been going on for several months, but this was the first time she demonstrated her learned behavior. Her father explained the delay by using the notion of:
A. cognitive learning
B. observational learning
C. learning-performance distinction
D. operant conditioning

p. 225
Cognitive Learning
Level: Easy
Type: Factual
Ans: C

163. The four processes necessary for observational learning are attention, memory, imitation, and _____.
A. discrimination
B. generalization
C. motivation
D. reinforcement

p. 225
Cognitive Learning
Level: Easy
Type: Factual
Ans: C
*PS/SG 10-20*

164. Which one of the following is *not* a factor in Bandura's theory of social cognitive learning?
A. attention
B. memory
C. rehearsal
D. motivation

p. 225
Cognitive Learning
Level: Moderate
Type: Applied
Ans: A

165. "If they don't pay attention, they'll never be able to do it, "a frustrated teacher complains as she attempts to model the steps on how to solve a math problem. Her goal is to have the students learn, but even if she gets her students to pay attention, they will have to, according to Bandura:
A. remember the information, imitate the steps, and have a good reason to model the teacher's behavior
B. generalize to other settings and be motivated
C. know what is not the behavior modeled, be able to remember the behavior, and do the behavior
D. be reinforced for doing the behavior that is being modeled

p. 225
Cognitive Learning
Level: Easy
Type: Applied
Ans: A

166. "I watched a show on television last month about a person eating several cups of earthworms. I paid attention to it and I remember it very well. I suppose I could do, but there's no good reason for me." Which process of social cognitive learning is lacking in this person's case?
A. motivation
B. generalization
C. discriminate
D. imitate

p. 225
Cognitive Learning
Level: Easy
Type: Applied
Ans: D

167. "I watched a show on television last month about people who can perform amazing feats of balance. I paid attention to the show, I remember the show, and I wish I could do the same feats, but I cannot." Using the four processes of social cognitive learning, which process is lacking in this person's case?
A. attention
B. memory
C. discriminate
D. imitate

p. 225
Cognitive Learning
Level: Moderate
Type: Factual
Ans: D

168. The textbook describes a study that successfully used observational learning to:
A. teach teenagers how to drive a car
B. teach mentally retarded students social skills
C. treat test anxiety
D. treat snake phobia

p. 226
Cognitive Learning
Level: Easy
Type: Factual
Ans: C

169. _____ is a mental process marked by sudden and unexpected solution of a problem.
A. Categorical learning
B. Operant conditioning
C. Insight learning
D. Cognitive learning

p. 226
Cognitive Learning
Level: Easy
Type: Factual
Ans: A

170. You are a member of a committee that has been trying to solve a community problem for several months. During a recent low point in the meeting, someone stands up and yells, "Ah-ha, I've got the solution." You recognize this to be an example of:
A. insight learning
B. latent conditioning
C. categorical learning
D. cognitive learning

p. 226
Cognitive Learning
Level: Easy
Type: Factual
Ans: D
*www*

171. Koehler believed that chimps learned to solve problems through:
A. trial and error
B. reinforcement
C. memory
D. insight

p. 226
Cognitive Learning
Level: Easy
Type: Factual
Ans: B

172.    What problem was the chimp in Koehler's study attempting to solve?
A.    getting out of a box to get a banana
B.    getting a banana hung high
C.    pushing a box off a banana
D.    peeling a banana

p. 226
Cognitive Learning
Level: Moderate
Type: Factual
Ans: B

173.    One criticism of Kohler's suggestion that chimps demonstrate insight learning is:
A.    that the chimps were not exposed enough to the problem of getting the banana
B.    Kohler did not explain how chimps solved problems, but merely described it
C.    that the schedule of reinforcement was not identified
D.    that chimps are prepared to climb and jump and do so in the wild

p. 226
Cognitive Learning
Level: Easy
Type: Factual
Ans: D
*PS/SG 10-22*

174.    The important thing about the solution Sultan came up with for the out-of-reach banana problem was:
A.    how an old conditioned reflex spontaneously recovered
B.    how he used trial and error
C.    how he built on previously reinforced behavior
D.    what was *missing* in his solution — namely, all the factors above

p. 226
Cognitive Learning
Level: Moderate
Type: Factual
Ans: D

175.    When faced with a puzzle or riddle, nonsolvers tend to:
A.    focus on testing new concepts that might lead to a solution
B.    focus on reorganizing the parts of the puzzle or riddle
C.    bring in new information to help to solve it
D.    focus on the obvious parts of the puzzle or riddle

p. 226
Cognitive Learning
Level: Easy
Type: Conceptual
Ans: A

176.    "Ah ha!" is to _____ as reinforcement is to _____.
A.    insight learning; operant conditioning
B.    imprinting; classical conditioning
C.    preparedness; cognitive theory
D.    spontaneous recovery; insight learning

p. 228
Biological Factors
Level: Easy
Type: Applied
Ans: C

177.    A newspaper article has the headline, "Scientists find innate tendency that helps learning." You realize that the "innate tendency" refers to:
A.    cognitive factors
B.    environmental stimuli
C.    biological factors
D.    behavioral factors

p. 228
Biological Factors
Level: Easy
Type: Applied
Ans: D

178.    Why would animals and humans have biological predispositions to learn certain behaviors? The behaviors have:
A.    value for scientists to study
B.    value for creating strife among groups
C.    value for psychopathology
D.    adaptive functions

p. 228
Biological Factors
Level: Easy
Type: Applied
Ans: A

179. Dr. Barr studies animals in their natural environments and is very curious about their behavior. Most likely Dr. Barr is a(n):
A. ethologist
B. zoologist
C. biologist
D. behaviorist

p. 228
Biological Factors
Level: Easy
Type: Conceptual
Ans: C

180. If you had to write a slogan for the idea of critical or sensitive periods what would it be:
A. "Don't knock it until you've tried it"
B. "There's more than one way to skin a cat"
C. "It's now or never"
D. "Misery loves company"

p. 228
Biological Factors
Level: Easy
Type: Factual
Ans: D

181. The time period in which imprinting occurs is called the:
A. prepared time
B. ethological period
C. imprint schedule
D. critical period

p. 228
Biological Factors
Level: Easy
Type: Factual
Ans: C

182. Which of the following statements regarding imprinting is not true?
A. imprinting is irreversible
B. imprinting takes place during a critical or sensitive period
C. imprinting is evident in mature animals as well as in newborn animals
D. imprinting improves the chance that the animals will survive

p. 228
Biological Factors
Level: Easy
Type: Factual
Ans: B

183. A young chick will establish a social attachment to anything (or anyone) that moves or provides food due to:
A. stimulus substitution
B. imprinting
C. biological restraint
D. observational learning

p. 228
Biological Factors
Level: Easy
Type: Factual
Ans: B
PS/SG 10-23

184. Limitations on the power of operant conditioning to explain behavior were discovered by:
A. ethnologists studying pica in baby ducks during the insensitive period
B. ethologists studying imprinting during the critical period for learning
C. ethicists studying the virtue of punishing self-injurious behaviors of autistic children
D. ethanologists studying the power of biological products to get us around

p. 228
Biological Factors
Level: Easy
Type: Applied
Ans: D
www

185. Kay raises ducks on a farm. Soon after being hatched, one of the ducks begins following Kay around. The duck's behavior is an example of:
A. classical conditioning
B. operant conditioning
C. spontaneous recovery
D. imprinting

p. 228
Biological Factors
Level: Easy
Type: Factual
Ans: B

186. You and a friend are at the hatching of ducklings. The ducklings first notice you and are now trying to follow you. Your friend says, "Don't worry, they'll get over it." Is your friend right or wrong?
   A. right, because imprinting is only temporary
   B. right, because the ducklings will learn that you can't feed them
   C. wrong, because they won't have other ducks to learn from
   D. wrong, because imprinting is irreversible

p. 229
Biological Factors
Level: Easy
Type: Applied
Ans: A

187. A police dog is quickly taught to detect the smell of drugs such as marijuana and cocaine. Which of the following best explains the ease with which the dog acquires this ability?
   A. prepared learning
   B. imprinting
   C. desensitization
   D. spontaneous recovery

p. 229
Biological Factors
Level: Easy
Type: Factual
Ans: C

188. The nutcracker bird has an impressive memory that enables it to find previously hidden food. It remembers where the hidden food is by recalling important landmarks such as trees. The bird's _____ is responsible for its remarkable memory.
   A. prepared learning
   B. imprinting
   C. larger than normal hippocampus
   D. cerebrum

p. 229
Biological Factors
Level: Easy
Type: Factual
Ans: C

189. A biological tendency found in animals to be able to recognize, attend to, and store certain cues more easily than other cues is called:
   A. prepared learning
   B. imprinting
   C. ethology
   D. insight

p. 229
Biological Factors
Level: Easy
Type: Factual
Ans: D

190. Human babies compared to chimps are _____ to produce sounds necessary for human speech.
   A. slower
   B. eager
   C. initially hindered
   D. biologically prepared

p. 229
Biological Factors
Level: Easy
Type: Factual
Ans: C

191. The fact that all human babies between seven and eight months old start to babble supports the idea of infants being:
   A. slower to vocalize than other mammals
   B. socially ready to speak at an early age
   C. biologically prepared to produce sounds
   D. taught how to produce sounds

p. 230
Research Focus:
 Noncompliance
Level: Conceptual
Type: Factual
Ans: A

192. The best way to describe noncompliance in children is:
A. "no"
B. when you break the speed limit
C. when your professor refuses to give you an extension on a ate paper
D. when your friends decide to go to a movie you've already seen

p. 230
Research Focus:
 Noncompliance
Level: Moderate
Type: Factual
Ans: D

193. The most frequent problem of parents who bring their children to clinics for treatment of behavioral problems is:
A. bedwetting
B. animal fears
C. nightmares
D. noncompliance

p. 230
Research Focus:
 Noncompliance
Level: Easy
Type: Factual
Ans: C

194. Time out is a procedure that:
A. uses positive punishment
B. gives an unpleasant consequence to the child for inappropriate behavior
C. removes a child from a situation where they might receive reinforcement for their noncompliance
D. has been shown to be ineffective in reducing temper tantrums

p. 230
Research Focus:
 Noncompliance
Level: Easy
Type: Applied
Ans: D

195. Little Drew doesn't like his spaghetti dinner so he throws a temper tantrum. His dad Robert puts Drew in an empty room for three minutes and closes the door. Robert is using a procedure called:
A. avoidance conditioning
B. negative reinforcement
C. learned helplessness
D. time-out

p. 230
Research Focus:
 Noncompliance
Level: Easy
Type: Applied
Ans: B

196. Time-out is preferable to physical punishment because:
A. time-out is easier to administer
B. physical punishment may cause negative emotional reactions and negative feelings toward the punisher
C. physical punishment is difficult to record on a cumulative record
D. time-out is more likely to involve observational learning

p. 231
Cultural Diversity:
 East meets West
Level: Easy
Type: Factual
Ans: B
PS/SG 10-25

197. The Suzuki method for teaching violin to very young children closely resembles the processes of:
A. Pavlov's classical conditioning
B. Bandura's observational learning
C. Skinner's operant conditioning
D. Kohler's insight learning

p. 231
Cultural Diversity:
 East meets West
Level: Moderate
Type: Factual
Ans: C

198. How did Shinichi Suzuki adapt the Suzuki method to 3- and 4-year-olds who do not have fully developed verbal skills?
A. The Suzuki method is not appropriate for this age group.
B. The principles of classical conditioning are used to give instructions to young children.
C. Information is given to the child through games and exercises.
D. The child is constantly rewarded for imitating the teacher.

p. 231
Cultural Diversity:
  East meets West
Level: Easy
Type: Factual
Ans: A

199. The basic principles of the Suzuki method of instruction closely resemble:
A. the four mental processes of social cognitive learning
B. the principles of operant conditioning
C. the principles of classical conditioning
D. the structure of cognitive maps

p. 231
Cultural Diversity:
  East meets West
Level: Easy
Type: Factual
Ans: D

200. How is information presented in the Suzuki method?
A. through verbal instruction
B. by watching master violinists
C. through sophisticated computer programs
D through games and exercises

p. 231
Cultural Diversity:
  East meets West
Level: Moderate
Type: Factual
Ans: A

201. With regard to motivation, what would Shinichi Suzuki never do in instructing the child in violin?
A. push the child beyond his/her capacity
B. provide a model who was active and interesting for the child
C. use games
D start at the young age of three years old

p. 232
Application:
  Behavior Modification
Level: Easy
Type: Factual
Ans: C
www

202. The treatment or therapy used to modify problem behavior based on the principles of learning is called:
A. observational learning
B. covert rehearsal
C. behavior modification
D. self-reinforcement

p. 232
Application:
  Behavior Modification
Level: Easy
Type: Factual
Ans: B

203. Which disorder is characterized by abnormal or impaired development in social interactions and communication?
A. depression
B. autism
C. Down syndrome
D. ADHD

p. 232
Application:
  Behavior Modification
Level: Easy
Type: Factual
Ans: C

204. The program described in your textbook for autistic children used principles based primarily upon:
A. classical conditioning
B. cognitive learning
C. operant conditioning
D. psychodynamic theory

p. 232
Application:
  Behavior Modification
Level: Easy
Type: Factual
Ans: A

205. Intensive behavior modification is most effective with an autistic child when it begins:
A. when the child is 2-3 years old
B. suddenly so that the child is caught off guard
C. gradually so that the child can slowly grow accustomed to it
D. when the child is 6-7 years old

p. 233
Application:
  Behavior Modification
Level: Easy
Type: Factual
Ans: B

206. Paula is using a training procedure to help reduce back pain. The procedure allows her to become aware of her physiological responses. Paula is using:
A. classical conditioning
B. biofeedback
C. operant conditioning
D. behavior modification

p. 233
Application:
  Behavior Modification
Level: Easy
Type: Factual
Ans: B

207. The process of learning to control some physiological response is called:
A. behavior modification
B. biofeedback
C. operant conditioning
D. imprinting

p. 233
Application:
  Behavior Modification
Level: Moderate
Type: Factual
Ans: A

208. The administration of a spank will be most effective when it is:
A. applied immediately after the unwanted behavior
B. administered mildly and gradually increased
C. included with signs of caring such as attention
D. not used in conjunction with a timeout procedure

p. 233
Application:
  Behavior Modification
Level: Moderate
Type: Factual
Ans: C

209. Spanking is an example of:
A. negative reinforcement
B. negative punishment
C. positive punishment
D. time-out

p. 233
Application:
  Behavior Modification
Level: Moderate
Type: Applied
Ans: D

210. Harlan and Juanita spank their five-year-old daughter when she misbehaves. But after taking a psychology course, Juanita suggests to Harlan that to increase spanking's effectiveness they ought to:
A. use it in conjunction with a timeout procedure
B. wait a couple of hours after the inappropriate behavior and then give the spanking
C. make the spanking very, very mild
D. tell their daughter the reason for the spanking

p. 233
Application:
  Behavior Modification
Level: Easy
Type: Factual
Ans: A

211. A key to the success of the time-out procedure is that it:
A. eliminates reinforcement of undesired behaviors
B. induces fear that suppresses undesired behaviors
C. is more intense than punishment
D. can be administered more immediately than punishment

p. 233
Application:
  Behavior Modification
Level: Moderate
Type: Factual
Ans: B

212. To increase the effectiveness of time-out, parents should consider:
A. negative reinforcement
B. combining it with positive reinforcement of desired behaviors
C. negative punishment
D. administering it for one to two hours

True/False

| T | www | 1. | Thorndike used cats in puzzle boxes to develop the law of effect. |
|---|---|---|---|
| F | | 2. is | According to the law of effect, behavior that is followed by positive consequences is weakened. |
| F | www | 3. | One of the criticisms of Skinner is that he failed to use an objective measure of behavior. |
| T | | 4. | Operant conditioning focuses on consequences affecting behavior. |
| F | | 5. | When successive behaviors are reinforced, the process of generalization is occurring. |
| T | www | 6. | In superstitious behavior, a behavior is accidentally paired with a reinforcer. |
| T | www | 7. | Reinforcers increase the likelihood that behaviors will be repeated. |
| F | | 8. | In operant conditioning, the reinforcer is contingent on the UCR. |
| T | www | 9. | Behavior is emitted and then followed by a consequence in operant conditioning. |
| F | | 10. | The consequences in operant conditioning are unconditioning and conditioning. |
| F | www | 11. | Negative reinforcement is a type of punishment. |
| T | | 12. | Punishment reduces the chance that a behavior will be repeated. |
| F | | 13. | Something unpleasant is presented in negative punishment. |
| T | www | 14. | A primary reinforcer is a stimulus that is innately satisfying. |
| F | | 15. | Money is a primary reinforcer. |
| T | | 16. | Partial schedules of reinforcement maintain behavior over the long term. |
| F | www | 17. | If you reinforce a person every 30 minutes, she is on a fixed ratio schedule. |
| F | | 18. | A variable ratio schedule indicates that behavior is reinforced after a unchanging number of behaviors have occurred. |
| T | | 19. | If a trained dog sits when a stranger says "sit" then generalization has taken place. |
| T | | 20. | A discriminative stimulus indicates that a behavior will be reinforced. |
| F | www | 21. | Later in his life, Skinner recognized the importance of cognitive factors in learning. |
| T | | 22. | According to social cognitive theory, we watch or imitate others' behaviors. |
| T | | 23. | The "ah-ha" experience is often described as being insight. |
| T | www | 24. | When the principles of learning are used to modify undesirable behavior, it is called behavior modification. |
| F | | 25. | Time-out is a form of positive punishment. |

Short-Answer Essay Questions

1.  Explain the law of effect and how Skinner used it to develop operant conditioning.  (*www*)
2.  Describe how Skinner used the Skinner box to study operant conditioning.  (*www*)
3.  How might a professional athlete develop superstitious behavior?
4.  Discuss the main differences between operant conditioning and classical conditioning.  (*www*)
5.  Define positive reinforcement and negative reinforcement as well as providing an example for each.
6.  Contrast and compare positive reinforcement with positive punishment and negative reinforcement with negative punishment.
7.  Describe the four schedules of reinforcement: fixed ratio, fixed interval, variable ratio, and variable interval.  How is behavior affected by each of these schedules?  (*www*)
8.  Describe the Bobo doll study and how is supports social cognitive theory.  (*www*)
9.  What is imprinting and what implication does it have for teaching animals new behaviors?
10.  Summarize the pros and cons of spanking.

# Module 11 - Types of Memory

p. 239
Introduction
Level: Easy
Type: Factual
Ans: A

1. What earned Rajan Mahadevan much attention?
   A. recalling from memory the first 31,811 digits of pi
   B. recalling the names of 567 strangers in order of presentation
   C. was wrongly accused of a bank robbery
   D. developing a theory of memory

p. 239
Introduction
Level: Easy
Type: Factual
Ans: B

2. Despite Rajan Mahadevan's incredible memory for numbers, he is worse than average at:
   A. recalling birthdates
   B. recalling faces
   C. recalling vocabulary words
   D. reading comprehension

p. 239
Introduction
Level: Easy
Type: Factual
Ans: C

3. In the case of Holly described in Module Eleven, she claimed that her bulimia was caused by:
   A. unresolved unconscious conflicts
   B. a brain chemical imbalance
   C. repressed memories of being abused
   D. flash bulb memories of being abused

p. 239
Introduction
Level: Easy
Type: Factual
Ans: A
*PS/SG 11-2*

4. Plotnik also tells the story of Holly, who accused her father of molesting her when she was a child, to illustrate the controversial idea of:
   A. repressed memories
   B. revenge accusations
   C. stored anger
   D. retrieving information

p. 239
Introduction
Level: Easy
Type: Conceptual
Ans: C

5. The significant difference between Rajan Mahadevan's memories and Holly's memories of abuse is:
   A. Holly's memories were not encoded; Rajan's memories were
   B. Holly's memories were located in the unconscious and Rajan's were in the conscious
   C. Rajan's memories can be verified, while Holly's cannot be
   D. Rajan's memories are stored differently than the memories of Holly

p. 239
Introduction
Level: Easy
Type: Factual
Ans: A
*www*

6. According to the textbook, _____ is the ability to retain information over time through the process of encoding, storing, and retrieving.
   A. memory
   B. repression
   C. metamemory
   D. implicit memory

p. 239
Introduction
Level: Moderate
Type: Conceptual
Ans: B

7. Memory is <u>best</u> described as:
   A. a video camera making an exact copy of what it sees
   B. an artist drawing her subjective impressions of a landscape
   C. a tape recorder recording all the stimuli in the environment
   D. a printer printing everything in a computer file

p. 239
Introduction
Level: Easy
Type: Factual
Ans: C
*PS/SG 11-3*

8. Which of the following is <u>not</u> one of the three processes of memory?
A. encoding
B. storing
C. deciphering
D. retrieving

p. 239
Introduction
Level: Easy
Type: Factual
Ans: D
*www*

9. The three processes of memory are:
A. encode, imitate, retrieve
B. attention, encode, feedback
C. encode, retrieve, motivate
D. encode, store, retrieve

p. 239
Introduction
Level: Easy
Type: Factual
Ans: D

10. Place the three memory processes in their correct order with regard to the flow of memory.
A. retrieval, storage, encoding
B. encoding, retrieval, storage
C. storage, encoding, retrieval
D. encoding, storage, retrieval

p. 239
Introduction
Level: Easy
Type: Conceptual
Ans: B

11. The word that <u>best</u> describes encoding is:
A. output
B. input
C. recall
D. reorder

p. 239
Introduction
Level: Easy
Type: Factual
Ans: A

12. Information is first placed into memory in the form of mental representations through the process of:
A. encoding
B. retrieval
C. storage
D. recording

p. 239
Introduction
Level: Easy
Type: Factual
Ans: A

13. _____ refers to making mental representations of information.
A. Encoding
B. Feedback
C. Storage
D. Retrieval

p. 239
Introduction
Level: Easy
Type: Factual
Ans: C

14. Placing information in a relatively permanent "warehouse" is called:
A. encoding
B. retrieval
C. storage
D. recording

p. 239
Introduction
Level: Easy
Type: Factual
Ans: B

15. Remembering is getting information out of storage. The term _____ refers to the same process.
A. encoding
B. retrieval
C. storage
D. recording

p. 239
Introduction
Level: Easy
Type: Factual
Ans: B
*www*

16. "I've encoded the material and I've stored it. I just can't seem to remember it." This case best describes a problem with:
A. encoding
B. retrieval
C. storage
D. recording

p. 239
Introduction
Level: Easy
Type: Factual
Ans: D

17. If you have no difficulty with encoding and storing, but you still think you've got problems with your memory, then the real problem must be in:
A. levels of processing
B. sensory memory
C. declarative memory
D. retrieving

p. 240
Three Types of Memory
Level: Easy
Type: Factual
Ans: D

18. The correct order for the three kinds of memory is:
A. short-term memory, episodic memory, sensory memory
B. long-term memory, iconic memory, echoic memory
C. semantic, echoic memory, episodic memory
D. sensory memory, short-term memory, long-term memory

p. 240
Three Types of Memory
Level: Easy
Type: Factual
Ans: D

19. "The sound of my voice will enter your sensory memory and:
A. cause interference as you recall other information from sensory memory."
B. short-term memory at the same moment."
C. will be automatically transferred to long-term memory."
D. will be held for a second or two."

p. 240
Three Types of Memory
Level: Easy
Type: Factual
Ans: B

20. The initial kind of memory which holds information in a "raw" form for a few seconds is called:
A. short-term memory
B. sensory memory
C. chunking memory
D. maintenance rehearsal memory

p. 240
Three Types of Memory
Level: Easy
Type: Factual
Ans: C

21. If you pay no attention to the information currently in your sensory memory, that information will:
A. be transferred to short-term memory
B. stay in sensory memory until it is needed
C. disappear
D. be transferred to long-term memory

p. 240
Three Kinds of Memory
Level: Easy
Type: Factual
Ans: A

22. Another name for short-term memory is:
A. working memory
B. facilitative memory
C. permanent memory
D. workbench memory

p. 240
Three Kinds of Memory
Level: Easy
Type: Factual
Ans: C

23. Which kind of memory holds seven or eight items of information for several seconds?
A. sensory memory
B. long-term memory
C. short-term memory
D. echoic memory

p. 240
Three Kinds of Memory
Level: Easy
Type: Factual
Ans: D

24. For how long will information stay in short-term memory if you do not focus on it?
A. up to 5 seconds
B. up to 10 seconds
C. up to 20 seconds
D. up to 30 seconds

p. 240
Three Kinds of Memory
Level: Easy
Type: Factual
Ans: B

25. You are writing an article about short-term memory for the local newspaper. Which of the following would be the most appropriate title for the article?
A. *Unlimited Storage in Short-Term Memory*
B. *Short-Term Memory: Holding Seven Items*
C. *Processing Information from the Senses: Short-Term Memory*
D. *Iconic Memory In Short-Term Memory*

p. 240
Three Kinds of Memory
Level: Easy
Type: Factual
Ans: B

26. An almost unlimited amount of information can be stored in:
A. sensory memory
B. long-term memory
C. short-term memory
D. echoic memory

p. 240
Three Kinds of Memory
Level: Easy
Type: Factual
Ans: A

27. Your success in remembering information from long-term memory depends partly on:
A. how the information was encoded
B. the storage capacity of long-term memory
C. the storage capacity of short-term memory
D. how the information was retrieved

p. 241
Sensory Memory:
  Recording
Level: Easy
Type: Factual
Ans: A

28. The momentary lingering of an image or sound after the stimulus has been removed is called:
A. sensory memory
B. long-term memory
C. short-term memory
D. semantic memory

p. 241
Sensory Memory:
  Recording
Level: Easy
Type: Factual
Ans: A

*PS/SG 11-4*

29. The function of sensory memory is to:
A. hold information in its raw form for a brief period of time
B. make quick associations between new data and things you already know
C. weed out what is irrelevant in incoming information
D. burn sensations into long-term memory for later retrieval and inspection

p. 241
Sensory Memory:
  Recording
Level: Easy
Type: Factual
Ans: B
*www*

30. Iconic memory is a form of sensory memory which holds:
A. auditory information
B. visual information
C. general knowledge, facts, and definitions
D. knowledge about performing motor skills

p. 241
Sensory Memory:
  Recording
Level: Easy
Type: Factual
Ans: D

31. What is a good and accurate way to remember what iconic memory refers to?
A. Iconic memory is visual information in short-term memory.
B. Icon means sound and therefore iconic memory refers to auditory information.
C. "Con" in iconic refers to something false or bogus and therefore iconic memory refers to a false memory.
D. Icon means image and therefore iconic memory refers to visual information.

p. 241
Sensory Memory:
  Recording
Level: Easy
Type: Factual
Ans: D
*PS/SG 11-6*

32. _____ memory holds visual information for about a quarter of a second.
A. Chunk
B. Iconic
C. Verbal
D. Echoic

p. 241
Sensory Memory:
  Recording
Level: Easy
Type: Factual
Ans: D

33. The word "icon" means:
A. difficult idea
B. knowledge
C. sound
D. image

p. 241
Sensory Memory:
  Recording
Level: Moderate
Type: Applied
Ans: D

34. What allows you to see a visual world that is smooth and not jerky?
A. semantic memory
B. short-term memory
C. photographic memory
D. iconic memory

p. 241
Sensory Memory:
  Recording
Level: Moderate
Type: Applied
Ans: D

35. An usher points out a seat to Peter in a darkened theater by moving a flashlight in a rectangular motion. Peter sees the form of a rectangle because images from the flashlight are being briefly stored in:
A. semantic memory
B. short-term memory
C. photographic memory
D. iconic memory

p. 241
Sensory Memory:
  Recording
Level: Moderate
Type: Applied
Ans: B

36. Polly gets a piece of dust in her eye but is still able to drive despite having to blink a lot. Her ability to maintain a visual image of the road is due to:
A. short-term memory
B. iconic memory
C. semantic memory
D. eidetic memory

p. 241
Sensory Memory:
  Recording
Level: Easy
Type: Conceptual
Ans: C

37. Motion pictures rely on the fact that we will perceive a series of rapidly presented still pictures as though there was motion. Which of the following is necessary in order for us to be able to do this?
A. long-term memory
B. working memory
C. iconic memory
D. eidetic memory

p. 241
Sensory Memory:
  Recording
Level: Moderate
Type: Applied
Ans: A

38. A mad scientist plots to take over the world. His plan is to make our visual perception of the world appear to be very jerky and full of darting, discontinuous movements. He has perfected a ray gun that can destroy anything in the world. As his trusted advisor, what do you suggest he destroy to achieve his dastardly objective?
A. iconic memory
B. echoic memory
C. semantic memory
D. eidetic memory

p. 241
Sensory Memory:
  Recording
Level: Easy
Type: Factual
Ans: C

39. In the study described in your textbook on iconic memory, how many letters on average could subjects immediately recall?
A. 4
B. 6
C. 9
D. 12

p. 241
Sensory Memory:
  Recording
Level: Easy
Type: Factual
Ans: A

40. What happened in the study described in your textbook on iconic memory when the delay between the presentation of the letters and when subjects are asked to recall the letters is increased to one second?
A. Memory of the letters is reduced to an average of four letters.
B. Memory of the letters is increased to an average of four letters.
C. Memory of the letters is increased to an average of nine letters.
D. Memory is not affected.

p. 241
Sensory Memory:
  Recording
Level: Easy
Type: Factual
Ans: C

41. Echoic memory allows an individual to:
A. see separate images as continuous
B. see the world as stable, despite the movement of the eyes
C. remember speech sounds long enough to understand words
D. maintain knowledge about one's own personal experiences

p. 241
Sensory Memory:
  Recording
Level: Easy
Type: Conceptual
Ans: A

42. You may be able to repeat a series of words that you thought you did not hear because:
A. the words are stored in echoic memory
B. you did not initially pay attention to the words that had been moved to working memory
C. stimuli often enter long-term memory without our conscious effort
D. of cross-modal memory

p. 241
Sensory Memory:
  Recording
Level: Easy
Type: Factual
Ans: A

43.  Echoic memory lasts as long as:
A.  2 seconds
B.  4 seconds
C.  8 seconds
D.  16 seconds

p. 241
Sensory Memory:
  Recording
Level: Easy
Type: Conceptual
Ans: B

44.  Iconic is to echoic as _____ is to _____.
A.  graphical; visual
B.  visual; auditory
C.  general; specific
D.  long duration; short duration

p. 241
Sensory Memory:
  Recording
Level: Easy
Type: Applied
Ans: A

45.  Who is most likely to have the longest echoic memory?
A.  Alyssa who is 17 years old
B.  Miranda who is 15 years old
C.  Katelyn who is 12 years old
D.  Noelle who is 9 years old

p. 241
Sensory Memory:
  Recording
Level: Easy
Type: Factual
Ans: C

46.  Of the following, which is not a function of sensory memory?
A.  prevents being overwhelmed
B.  gives decision time
C.  allows for rehearsal of information
D.  provides stability, playback, and recognition

p. 241
Sensory Memory:
  Recording
Level: Moderate
Type: Applied
Ans: D

47.  Martin sees a fireworks display on the Fourth of July. The display will first encounter _____ memory which will _____ sensory input.
A.  short-term; limit
B.  eidetic; clarify
C.  working; amplify
D.  sensory; limit

p. 241
Sensory Memory:
  Recording
Level: Easy
Type: Factual
Ans: C

48.  If you do not attend to information in sensory memory, what will happen to the information?
A.  The information will be transferred into secondary memory.
B.  The information will be forgotten for one to three seconds, but then later encoded into short-term memory.
C.  The information will be forgotten.
D.  The information will be transferred into short-term memory.

p. 241
Sensory Memory:
  Recording
Level: Difficult
Type: Factual
Ans: D

49.  Of the following, which is not a feature of sensory memory?
A.  maintaining visual images despite interruptions caused by blinking
B.  recognizing words by momentarily holding strings of speech sounds so that related sounds can be grouped as words
C.  limiting sensory input
D.  facilitating permanent storage through the process of chunking

p. 241
Sensory Memory:
  Recording
Level: Difficult
Type: Factual
Ans: D

50.     Which of the following is <u>true</u> of sensory memory?
A.     It is primarily used to retrieve information from long-term memory.
B.     It is also called semantic memory.
C.     Information in it will be forgotten after about 20 seconds.
D.     There is no voluntary control over the kind of information that enters it.

p. 241
Sensory Memory:
  Recording
Level: Easy
Type: Factual
Ans: C

51.     Which is the most accurate statement regarding sensory memory?
A.     Information stored in it may be recalled without conscious control.
B.     It lasts much longer than it was previously thought.
C.     Information stored in it will rapidly fade unless attended to.
D.     It has a very limited capacity.

p. 241
Sensory Memory:
  Recording
Level: Easy
Type: Conceptual
Ans: B

52.     While walking across campus, you see someone standing on his head. The fact that you pay attention to this person, probably means that you will:
A.     never forget him
B.     process the information into working memory
C.     lose the information in sensory memory
D.     put the information into long-term memory without using working memory

p. 242
Short-Term Memory:
  Working
Level: Easy
Type: Factual
Ans: A

53.     Short-term memory is also referred to as:
A.     working memory
B.     sensory memory
C.     semantic memory
D.     long-term memory

p. 242
Short-Term Memory:
  Working
Level: Easy
Type: Factual
Ans: D
*PS/SG 11-10*

54.     A classic study by George Miller showed that short-term memory can hold:
A.     one item or bit of information at a time
B.     an unlimited amount of information
C.     about a dozen items or bits
D.     about seven items or bits

p. 242
Short-Term Memory:
  Working
Level: Moderate
Type: Applied
Ans: A

55.     Jerry sees an attractive waitress at a restaurant and thinks to himself that he should ask her out on a date. Jerry's thoughts about the waitress are <u>most</u> likely contained in:
A.     short-term memory
B.     sensory memory
C.     procedural memory
D.     semantic memory

p. 242
Short-Term Memory:
  Working
Level: Easy
Type: Conceptual
Ans: A

56. Which of the following pairs accurately describes the two central characteristics of short-term memory?
A. limited duration, limited capacity
B. limited duration, unlimited capacity
C. unlimited duration, unlimited capacity
D. unlimited duration, limited capacity

p. 242
Short-Term Memory:
  Working
Level: Easy
Type: Factual
Ans: C
*www*

57. Repeating information over and over so that it does not fade from short-term memory is called _____ rehearsal.
A. intentional
B. elaborative
C. maintenance
D. episodic

p. 242
Short-Term Memory:
  Working
Level: Easy
Type: Factual
Ans: B

58. Maintenance rehearsal involves:
A. measuring the amount of a person's short-term memory
B. intentionally repeating information
C. processing iconic and echoic images simultaneously
D. recalling items at the beginning of a list, but not at the end of a list

p. 242
Short-Term Memory:
  Working
Level: Easy
Type: Applied
Ans: A

59. Tovio is an actor who is practicing his part. He keeps repeating the lines over and over and over again. What is this called?
A. maintenance rehearsal
B. memory span rehearsal
C. priming
D. chunking

p. 242
Short-Term Memory:
  Working
Level: Easy
Type: Applied
Ans: C

60. If you have ever looked up someone's phone number, but were unable to write it down, and you repeated it over and over again, then you have practiced:
A. iconic memory
B. retrieval
C. maintenance rehearsal
D. interference

p. 242
Short-Term Memory:
  Working
Level: Moderate
Type: Applied
Ans: B

61. Heidi sees a hit-and-run accident. She repeats the license plate number to herself in order to remember it for the police. Heidi's way of remembering is an example of:
A. decoding
B. maintenance rehearsal
C. storage
D. mnemonics

p. 242
Short-Term Memory:
  Working
Level: Moderate
Type: Applied
Ans: D
*www*

62. Alice tells Lana that the combination to her mailbox is 38-24-36. Lana repeats the numbers over and over to herself so that she doesn't forget them. Lana's behavior is an example of:
A. automatic encoding
B. elaborative rehearsal
C. episodic memory
D. maintenance rehearsal

p. 242
Short-Term Memory:
  Working
Level: Easy
Type: Applied
Ans: B

*PS/SG 11-9*

63. Out of change at the pay phone, you frantically repeat the 11-digit number you just got from Information over and over again. That's called:
A. chunking
B. maintenance rehearsal
C. memory span stretching
D. duration enhancement

p. 242
Short-Term Memory:
  Working
Level: Easy
Type: Applied
Ans: B

64. Brian is driving to Candy's house for the first time. As he drives, he repeats to himself the directions she has given him. "Highway 8 'til Lincoln, left on Lincoln, go to the second light and make another left." Brian is engaging in:
A. free recall
B. maintenance rehearsal
C. eidetic imagery
D. chunking

p. 242
Short-Term Memory:
  Working
Level: Easy
Type: Factual
Ans: D

65. What typically happens to information in short-term memory if it is <u>not</u> actively processed?
A. It enters long-term memory.
B. It blocks incoming information.
C. It goes back to sensory storage.
D. It disappears within seconds.

p. 242
Short-Term Memory:
  Working
Level: Easy
Type: Factual
Ans: B

66. The capacity for working memory seems to be about:
A. three items
B. seven items
C. ten items
D. fifteen items

p. 242
Short-Term Memory:
  Working
Level: Easy
Type: Applied
Ans: A

67. Why are telephone numbers seven digits?
A. seven digits is the capacity of short-term memory
B. that is the number of bytes a computer can handle in one millisecond
C. a tradition started by the first telephone operator
D. it is the capacity of sensory memory

p. 242
Short-Term Memory:
  Working
Level: Easy
Type: Factual
Ans: B

68. You are taking a test that measures how many numbers you can correctly repeat back. You are taking a:
A. chunking test
B. memory span test
C. memory limit test
D. encoding limit test

p. 242
Short-Term Memory:
  Working
Level: Easy
Type: Applied
Ans: C

69. As a project for a class, you gave subjects a _____ to test a type of memory. In reviewing your data, you note that around seven digits, errors increase because _____.

A. Rorschach test; the questions get very difficult at that point
B. MMPI; seven items appears to be the limit of long-term memory
C. memory span test; seven items is the storage capacity of short-term memory
D. TAT; fatigue typically takes place at that point in the test

p. 242
Short-Term Memory:
  Working
Level: Easy
Type: Factual
Ans: A

70. Information in short-term memory is forgotten because of:
A. interference
B. maintenance
C. chunking
D. encoding

p. 242
Short-Term Memory:
  Working
Level: Easy
Type: Factual
Ans: D
*PS/SG 11-11*

71. Why doesn't information in short-term memory simply become permanent? Probably because of:
A. limited storage space in the brain
B. fascination with the new and different
C. incompatibility with previously processed information
D. interference caused by newly arriving information

p. 242
Short-Term Memory:
  Working
Level: Easy
Type: Applied
Ans: B

72. Cal is watching a cooking show and wants to try one of the dishes. The recipe is being read aloud by the host. Unfortunately, Cal doesn't write anything down thinking he can remember it. "One cup flour, one teaspoon sugar...oh I just can't keep up. I've forgotten the first couple of ingredients." Cal's problem is best explained by:
A. maintenance
B. interference
C. chunking
D. encoding

p. 242
Short-Term Memory:
  Working
Level: Easy
Type: Factual
Ans: D

73. What results when new information enters short-term memory and overwrites or pushes out information that is already there?
A. encoding
B. maintenance
C. chunking
D. interference

p. 242
Short-Term Memory:
  Working
Level: Easy
Type: Factual
Ans: A

74. A main reason information disappears from short-term memory is:
A. interference
B. lack of rehearsal
C. lack of motivation
D. low intelligence

p. 243
Short-Term Memory:
  Working
Level: Easy
Type: Factual
Ans: D
*www*

75. If you combine separate items of information into large units and then remember these larger units rather than individual items, you are using:
A. attention
B. rehearsal
C. procedural memory
D. chunking

p. 243
Short-Term Memory:
  Working
Level: Easy
Type: Factual
Ans: B

76. The amount of information that can be processed in short-term memory is typically increased through:
A. mood convergence
B. chunking
C. elaborative rehearsal
D. free recall

p. 243
Short-Term Memory:
  Working
Level: Easy
Type: Applied
Ans: B

77. Sly is assigned a locker in gym class with the combination 19, 5, 4. In order to remember it, he thinks of it as the year 1954. His method of remembering best illustrates:
A. decoding
B. chunking
C. rehearsal
D. recollection

p. 243
Short-Term Memory:
  Working
Level: Easy
Type: Applied
Ans: B

78. The social security number 999-61-4374 may be best remembered as:
A. a single echoic sensation
B. three chunks of information
C. an episodic experience
D. an iconic image in sensory memory

p. 243
Short-Term Memory:
  Working
Level: Easy
Type: Applied
Ans: A

79. Gaylord likes to do memory tricks. He can memorize a list of 25 digits in just 25 seconds and then correctly recalls them. Based on this module, what is the most probable way he can do this trick?
A. chunking
B. interfering
C. encoding
D. recoding

p. 243
Short-Term Memory:
  Working
Level: Easy
Type: Factual
Ans: A

80. What "trick" enables Rajan to perform extraordinary memory feats?
A. his ability to chunk
B. Rajan's iconic memory can last several minutes instead of seconds
C. maintenance rehearsal
D. the use an iconic image in short-term memory

p. 243
Short-Term Memory:
  Working
Level: Easy
Type: Factual
Ans: C

81. How does Rajan chunk the numbers "1, 1, 1" so that he can easily remember it as 111 :
A. labeled it "fence posts without a fence"
B. called it "apple trees"
C. named it "Nelson - Admiral Nelson had one eye, one arm, and one leg"
D. called it "a corn field in Iowa"

p. 243
Short-Term Memory:
  Working
Level: Easy
Type: Factual
Ans: B

82. What happens to sensory information when you pay attention to it?
A. The information gets analyzed for a second time in iconic memory.
B. The information enters short-term memory.
C. The information is stored as explicit memory.
D. The information is rehearsed in long-term memory.

p. 243
Short-Term Memory:
  Working
Level: Easy
Type: Factual
Ans: C

83. Research has found that short-term memory most involves the _____ of the brain.
A. brainstem area
B. corpus callosum
C. prefrontal area
D. cerebellum

p. 243
Short-Term Memory:
  Working
Level: Easy
Type: Factual
Ans: D

84. Short-term memory performs three functions. Which of the following is not among the three functions?
A. holds information for a short period of time
B. promotes storage in long-term memory
C. selectively attends to information that is relevant
D. provides a location for network nodes

p. 243
Short-Term Memory:
  Working
Level: Easy
Type: Factual
Ans: A

85. What is a type of memory that allows information to be held for a short period of time until you decide what to do with it?
A. short-term memory
B. long-term memory
C. sensory memory
D. iconic memory

p. 243
Short-Term Memory:
  Working
Level: Easy
Type: Factual
Ans: C
PS/SG 11-8

86. Which statement below describes short-term memory or working memory?
A. your perceptual processes react to it
B. you freeze it briefly in order to pay attention to it
C. you work with it to accomplish some immediate task
D. you retrieve it later when you need it again

p. 244
Long-Term Memory:
  Storing
Level: Easy
Type: Conceptual
Ans: D

87. The textbook suggests thinking about sensory memory, short-term memory, and long-term memory as:
A. neurological locations in the brain
B. separate isolated processes
C. places in the larger memory system
D. interactive processes

p. 244
Long-Term Memory:
  Storing
Level: Moderate
Type: Factual
Ans: A
*PS/SG 11-14*

88.   Plotnik advises you to think of long-term memory as a:
A.    process of storing almost unlimited amounts of information
B.    process of storing much information, but only a fraction of what we learn
C.    place where information is deposited for possible future use
D.    place where important information is kept and unimportant information is discarded

p. 244
Long-Term Memory:
  Storing
Level: Moderate
Type: Factual
Ans: D

89.   As you study for a class, you find that the material is very difficult. To encode the material into long-term memory, you should try to _____.
A.    increase the storage capacity of long-term memory
B.    rehearse it many times
C.    memorize the material
D.    make associations between the material and what you already know

p. 244
Long-Term Memory:
  Storing
Level: Easy
Type: Factual
Ans: C

90.   Of the following, which is not how information is transferred from short-term to long-term memory?
A.    paying attention to it
B.    repeating or rehearsing it
C.    ignoring it
D.    forming new associations

p. 244
Long-Term Memory:
  Storing
Level: Moderate
Type: Conceptual
Ans: A

91.   An education major is interviewing a veteran teacher for a class project. The teacher is asked about how to help students learn and says, "Give lots of examples." Based on the textbook, what is the best reason for teachers to give examples?
A.    Examples help students to connect what they are trying to learn with old information.
B.    Examples facilitate iconic memory.
C.    Examples are actually "fillers" that allow students extra time to think about the lesson.
D.    Examples help students to do maintenance rehearsal.

p. 244
Long-Term Memory:
  Storing
Level: Easy
Type: Factual
Ans: B

92.   Unlike that of short-term memory, the capacity of long-term memory:
A.    depends on cell development in the frontal lobe
B.    is almost unlimited
C.    varies tremendously from one person to the next
D.    is sixty to seventy items that can be consciously recalled

p. 244
Long-Term Memory:
  Storing
Level: Easy
Type: Applied
Ans: C

93.    The student tells the teacher, "I don't think I can remember this material. I don't have much room left in my long-term memory." As a teacher, how would you respond in a helpful and constructive way?

A.    "No, you have plenty of room in long-term memory. It's your attitude that is the problem."

B.    "That's a real possibility. Maybe we can work on mnemonics."

C.    "You have unlimited storage capacity in long-term memory. Maybe the problem is getting the information in or getting the information back out."

D.    "Maybe, since you can only store a limited amount in long-term memory. I'll teach you how to do chunking."

p. 244
Long-Term Memory:
  Storing
Level: Easy
Type: Factual
Ans: A

94.    Information stored in long-term memory:
A.    is relatively permanent
B.    decays after several days
C.    is limited to about seven items at any given moment
D.    requires rehearsal to prevent decay

p. 244
Long-Term Memory:
  Storing
Level: Moderate
Type: Factual
Ans: C

95.    A study of college freshmen's recall of grades showed that:
A.    the recent reforms in education have worked
B.    the recent reforms in education have failed
C.    we often inflate negative events and eliminate or change positive ones
D.    we often inflate positive events and eliminate or change negative ones

p. 244
Long-Term Memory:
  Storing
Level: Moderate
Type: Applied
Ans: B

96.    Given the results of the study of college freshmen's recall grades, which is the most likely to occur?
A.    Recalling the "C-" you got as a "C-."
B.    Remembering the "D" you got in a class as a "C-."
C.    Recalling the "A" you earned as a "B+."
D.    Remembering the "A" you got as a "B."

p. 245
Long-Term Memory:
  Storing
Level: Easy
Type: Factual
Ans: A

97.    What are the two memory systems?
A.    short-term memory and long-term memory
B.    momentary memory and long-term memory
C.    short-term memory and primacy memory
D.    recency memory and short-term memory

p. 245
Long-Term Memory:
  Storing
Level: Easy
Type: Applied
Ans: C

98.    The ability to recall items at the beginning of a list more easily than following items is the result of the _____ effect.
A.    attentional
B.    ordering
C.    primacy
D.    recency

p. 245
Long-Term Memory:
  Storing
Level: Easy
Type: Applied
Ans: B

99.    On the way to her wedding, Maria thinks about all the other men she has dated. Her clearest memory is of Lawrence, her first boyfriend. Maria's recall illustrates the _____ effect.
A.    recency
B.    primacy
C.    semantic
D.    encoding

p. 245
Long-Term Memory:
 Storing
Level: Moderate
Type: Applied
Ans: C

100.  Jack enlists the assistance of a travel agent to help him arrange a business trip to seven military bases for a weapons contractor.  The agent lists all the stops on the trip.  Later, when Jack tells his friend Darlene his itinerary he can accurately remember only the date and location of his first stop.  This is an example of the _____ effect.

A.  attentional
B.  ordering
C.  primacy
D.  recency

p. 245
Long-Term Memory:
 Storing
Level: Easy
Type: Applied
Ans: D
*www*

101.  You are being introduced to several people in your first job interview: Ted, Julie, Benito, Dewayne, Frank, and Andy.  Based on the primacy effect, whose name are you <u>most</u> likely to remember?

A.  Benito
B.  Dewayne
C.  Andy
D.  Ted

p. 245
Long-Term Memory:
 Storing
Level: Moderate
Type: Applied
Ans: B

102.  With the help of a travel agent, Ron plans a Caribbean cruise.  The travel agent lists all the ports of call in the cruise.  Later, when Ron is telling a friend his plans, he can only remember the first stop on the tour.  This is an example of:

A.  recency effect
B.  primacy effect
C.  ordering effect
D.  attentional effect

p. 245
Long-Term Memory:
 Storing
Level: Easy
Type: Factual
Ans: C
*PS/SG 11-15*

103.  If you attempt to remember a list of animal names, you will be more likely to remember:
A.  the first few names
B.  the last few names
C.  both the first and last few names
D.  neither the first or last few names, but the ones occurring in the middle of the list

p. 245
Long-Term Memory:
 Storing
Level: Easy
Type: Factual
Ans: D

104.  The primacy effect is evident because we:
A.  are biologically prepared to remember first items
B.  are biologically prepared to remember last items
C.  have more time to rehearse the last items
D.  have more time to rehearse the first items

p. 245
Long-Term Memory:
  Storing
Level: Moderate
Type: Applied
Ans: B

105. Candy is meeting her boyfriend's cousins at a family reunion. She remembers Cindy, Rick, Dirk, Denece, and Garth. But she forgets Tom, Nancy, David, and Imogene. What is the best explanation?
A. She found those cousins whose name she remembered as being more friendly.
B. The cousins she remembered were introduced to her at the beginning and end of the reunion; the others where introduced in the middle of the reunion.
C. She relied on nondeclarative encoding for the names she remembered.
D. The cousins she did not remember were introduced to her at the beginning and end of the reunion; the others where introduced in the middle of the reunion.

p. 245
Long-Term Memory:
  Storing
Level: Easy
Type: Factual
Ans: A

106. Carlos memorizes a list of 10 grocery items that he needs to buy later that day at Super One supermarket. When at the grocery store, he will have the greatest difficulty remembering the:
A. ones in the middle of the list
B. first one on the list
C. last item
D. next to last item

p. 245
Long-Term Memory:
  Storing
Level: Easy
Type: Applied
Ans: D

107. The psychology textbook Rochelle is reading was written by three authors: Bootzin, Bower, and Loftus. When asked by a friend to name the authors of her psychology text, Rochelle can only remember Loftus. Rochelle's recall illustrates the _____ effect.
A. semantic
B. primacy
C. encoding
D. recency

p. 245
Long-Term Memory:
  Storing
Level: Easy
Type: Applied
Ans: C

108. You were introduced to a number of new people at a study session. But you had a hard time remembering their names, except the last person to whom you were introduced. What best accounts for this memory?
A. encoding effect
B. procedural effect
C. recency effect
D. primacy effect

p. 245
Long-Term Memory:
  Storing
Level: Easy
Type: Applied
Ans: D

109. Dr. Sagan asks Carl to list the names of the moons of Jupiter during an astronomy class quiz on the previous day's lecture. If Carl's recall of the moons is influenced by the recency effect he will:
A. remember the first moon Dr. Sagan named
B. be unable to remember the names of the moons because of material presented in previous lectures
C. be unable to remember the names of the moons because of material presented in lectures after Dr. Sagan's one the previous day
D. remember the last moon Dr. Sagan mentioned

p. 245
Long-Term Memory:
  Storing
Level: Easy
Type: Applied
Ans: B

110.   At a recent family reunion you saw cousins that you have not seen for years. You also met for the first time, the spouses of these cousins. Unfortunately, you don't remember most of their names. The name you do recall was your cousin Tom's wife, Nancy; they came at the very end of the reunion. Why did you remember Nancy, but forget all the other names?

A.   primacy effect
B.   recency effect
C.   maintenance effect
D.   semantic principle

p. 245
Long-Term Memory:
  Storing
Level: Easy
Type: Factual
Ans: A

111.   The recency effect works because subjects:
A.   still have the last items available in short-term memory
B.   cannot transfer information into sensory memory
C.   do not have enough long-term memory for all of the items
D.   rehearsed the last items storing them in long-term memory

p. 245
Long-Term Memory:
  Storing
Level: Moderate
Type: Applied
Ans: D

112.   Joe interviews five candidates for a job. When later asked by his boss who made the greatest lasting impression on him, Joe says Erik and Ted, the first and last candidates interviewed. From a psychologist's view, this favoring of Erik and Ted is <u>most</u> likely the result of which pair of memory effects?

A.   initial, residual
B.   antecedent, consequent
C.   template, salience
D.   primacy, recency

p. 246
Long-Term Memory:
  Storing
Level: Easy
Type: Applied
Ans: C

113.   On an exam, a student is asked to describe the three branches of government. The student must retrieve:
A.   procedural knowledge
B.   episodic knowledge
C.   semantic knowledge
D.   hierarchical knowledge

p. 246
Long-Term Memory:
  Storing
Level: Easy
Type: Applied
Ans: C
*www*

114.   On a chemistry final, Dr. Curie asks Marie to describe the properties of nitrous oxide. Marie will likely retrieve the information from _____ memory.
A.   episodic
B.   elaborative
C.   semantic
D.   procedural

p. 246
Long-Term Memory:
  Storing
Level: Easy
Type: Factual
Ans: A

115.   We can retrieve _____ memory, but not _____ memory.
A.   semantic; procedural
B.   semantic; episodic
C.   procedural; semantic
D.   episodic; semantic

| | | |
|---|---|---|
| p. 246<br>Long-Term Memory:<br> Storing<br>Level: Easy<br>Type: Conceptual<br>Ans: D | 116.<br>A.<br>B.<br>C.<br>D. | Which of the following is an example of semantic knowledge?<br>the first time you water-skied<br>the route you take to the nearest fast-food restaurant<br>how to check your baggage at an airport<br>the alphabet |
| p. 246<br>Long-Term Memory:<br> Storing<br>Level: Easy<br>Type: Conceptual<br>Ans: A | 117.<br>A.<br>B.<br>C.<br>D. | What type of memory must you use to answer this question?<br>semantic memory<br>procedural memory<br>episodic memory<br>contemplative memory |
| p. 246<br>Long-Term Memory:<br> Storing<br>Level: Easy<br>Type: Factual<br>Ans: D | 118.<br>A.<br>B.<br>C.<br>D. | Knowledge of facts and events is called _____ memory.<br>nondeclarative<br>procedural<br>declarative<br>episodic |
| p. 246<br>Long-Term Memory:<br> Storing<br>Level: Easy<br>Type: Applied<br>Ans: D | 119.<br><br>A.<br>B.<br>C.<br>D. | After Einstein proposed that $E = mc^2$, in which memory system did Einstein store it?<br>episodic<br>disjunctive<br>procedural<br>semantic |
| p. 246<br>Long-Term Memory:<br> Storing<br>Level: Easy<br>Type: Factual<br>Ans: C | 120.<br><br>A.<br>B.<br>C.<br>D. | The ability to remember events that we personally experience is possible through _____ memory.<br>semantic<br>procedural<br>episodic<br>attentional |
| p. 246<br>Long-Term Memory:<br> Storing<br>Level: Moderate<br>Type: Factual<br>Ans: C | 121.<br><br>A.<br><br>B.<br>C.<br><br>D. | Why did H. M. not remember doing mirror-drawing, but because of practice each day, improved?<br>His was not capable of automatic encoding, but capable of effortful encoding.<br>His short-term was severely impaired, but his long-term memory was intact.<br>His episodic memory was severely impaired, but his procedural memory was intact.<br>H. M.'s semantic memory was severely impaired, but his episodic memory was intact. |
| p. 246<br>Long-Term Memory:<br> Storing<br>Level: Easy<br>Type: Factual<br>Ans: A<br>*PS/SG 11-17* | 122.<br>A.<br>B.<br>C.<br>D. | Remembering how you did on your last psych test involves _____ memory.<br>episodic<br>semantic<br>consequential<br>procedural |

p. 246
Long-Term Memory:
 Storing
Level: Easy
Type: Conceptual
Ans: A

123. Which of the following is an example of episodic knowledge?
A. the highlights of your summer vacation
B. the steps required to clean a fish
C. the capital of Texas
D. how to the change the oil in your car

p. 246
Long-Term Memory:
 Storing
Level: Easy
Type: Applied
Ans: A

124. Remembering your first day as a college student would be considered:
A. episodic information
B. semantic information
C. consequential information
D. procedural information

p. 246
Long-Term Memory:
 Storing
Level: Easy
Type: Conceptual
Ans: B

125. Of the following, which is an example of knowledge that would be stored in episodic memory?
A. the capital of New Hampshire
B. the highlights of your trip to the Great Wall of China
C. the steps required to bake a cake
D. the differences between gorillas and chimps

p. 246
Long-Term Memory:
 Storing
Level: Easy
Type: Applied
Ans: C

126. Grandpa Homer is about to tell a story. "When I was a young boy..." Grandpa Homer's story illustrates:
A. semantic memory
B. primacy memory
C. episodic memory
D. procedural memory

p. 246
Long-Term Memory:
 Storing
Level: Easy
Type: Applied
Ans: B

127. Suzy is riding in a subway car when a young thug rips off her gold necklace and runs away. Suzy's ability to later describe to the police what happened is due to the functioning of her _____ memory.
A. procedural
B. episodic
C. attentional
D. elaborative

p. 246
Long-Term Memory:
 Storing
Level: Easy
Type: Applied
Ans: B
www

128. On their twenty-fifth anniversary, Carol tells her husband, Charles, "You know, dear, I remember our first kiss very well." In remembering their first kiss, Carol is retrieving information from _____ memory.
A. semantic
B. episodic
C. elaborative
D. procedural

p. 246
Long-Term Memory:
 Storing
Level: Easy
Type: Applied
Ans: D

129. Grandpa Gus had not been on a bicycle for years. As he took off on one, he yelled and said, "I guess once you learn, you never forget." To ride the bike, Grandpa is using:
A. semantic memory
B. episodic memory
C. elaborative memory
D. procedural memory

p. 246
Long-Term Memory:
  Storing
Level: Easy
Type: Factual
Ans: B

130. A memory that allows us to perform motor or perceptual tasks is known as
          memory
  A. semantic
  B. procedural
  C. explicit
  D. episodic

p. 246
Long-Term Memory:
  Storing
Level: Easy
Type: Applied
Ans: A

131. Aunt Mary no longer needs to refer to the recipe when she makes
buttermilk pancakes for her nephew Andrew, because she has stored the
information in          memory.
  A. procedural
  B. episodic
  C. maintenance
  D. elaborative

p. 246
Long-Term Memory:
  Storing
Level: Easy
Type: Applied
Ans: A

132. Tony used to ride motorcycles in college.  Now, as an adult, he'd like to
ride again.  Which of the following systems would most help him remember
how to ride a motorcycle?
  A. procedural memory
  B. episodic memory
  C. semantic memory
  D. sensory memory

p. 246
Long-Term Memory:
  Storing
Level: Easy
Type: Factual
Ans: D

133. We cannot retrieve nor are we aware of _____ memories.
  A. declarative
  B. episodic
  C. semantic
  D. procedural

p. 246
Long-Term Memory:
  Storing
Level: Easy
Type: Applied
Ans: D

134. Alan can't tell you the sequence of motor movements involved in hitting a
golf ball because that information is stored in:
  A. hierarchical knowledge
  B. episodic knowledge
  C. semantic knowledge
  D. procedural knowledge

p. 246
Long-Term Memory:
  Storing
Level: Easy
Type: Applied
Ans: A

135. Which type of memory did the patient known as H. M. lose as a result of a
brain operation to reduce seizures?
  A. declarative
  B. procedural
  C. elaborative
  D. implicit

p. 246
Long-Term Memory:
  Storing
Level: Easy
Type: Applied
Ans: B
*www*

136. What type of memory did the patient known as H. M. retain despite losing
the ability to remember events?
  A. declarative
  B. procedural
  C. elaborative
  D. explicit

p. 247
Research Focus:
  Emotion and Memories
Level: Easy
Type: Factual
Ans: B

137. When rats are given an injection of epinephrine, they show a(n):
A. decrease in retention
B. increase in retention
C. decrease in hierarchical organization of long-term memory
D. increase in encoding of semantic memory

p. 247
Research Focus:
  Emotion and Memories
Level: Moderate
Type: Applied
Ans: C

138. Last week you attended a powerful, emotional-provoking speech. Also one day last week, you had macaroni and cheese for lunch. Based upon research cited in the module, why are you more likely to remember the speech than what you had for lunch?
A. attending speeches is more of an out of the ordinary routine
B. the macaroni and cheese was consumed during the time of day when memory is poorest due to circadian rhythms
C. a hormone triggered by an emotional situation appears to heighten memory
D. implicit memories like attending speeches are more reliably remembered

p. 247
Research Focus:
  Emotion and Memories
Level: Easy
Type: Factual
Ans: A

139. What is the best explanation for why we would remember emotionally charged memories better than memories that are emotionally neutral?
A. Hormones that are released during these emotionally charged events help to encode these memories.
B. Emotionally charged events usually occur at the beginning or end of the day.
C. We are more likely to engage in elaborative rehearsal during emotionally charged events.
D. We experience automatic encoding of emotionally charged events.

p. 247
Research Focus:
  Emotion and Memories
Level: Moderate
Type: Factual
Ans: C

140. The textbook describes a study that tested the hypothesis that hormones released in stressful situations improve memory. On a measure of memory, subjects in the placebo group:
A. recalled significantly more emotionally charged events
B. recalled significantly more neutral events
C. recalled significantly fewer emotionally charged events
D. recalled significantly fewer neutral events

p. 248
Encoding: Transferring
Level: Easy
Type: Factual
Ans: B

141. Placing or storing information in memory by creating mental codes is called:
A. processing
B. encoding
C. elaboration
D. rehearsal

p. 248
Encoding: Transferring
Level: Easy
Type: Factual
Ans: A

142. The process of encoding refers to creating information in the form of _____ in memory.
A. mental codes
B. visual and auditory stimuli
C. emotions
D. memory nodes

p. 248
Encoding: Transferring
Level: Easy
Type: Factual
Ans: B

143. Information that is transferred into long-term memory without deliberate effort or awareness is encoded _____.
A. emotionally
B. automatically
C. acoustically
D. elaborately

p. 248
Encoding: Transferring
Level: Easy
Type: Factual
Ans: B
*www*

144. When you are in the library, you can probably remember what your classroom looks like. You encoded the classroom without any awareness; this is called _____ encoding.
A. attentional
B. automatic
C. maintenance
D. elaborative

p. 248
Encoding: Transferring
Level: Easy
Type: Factual
Ans: B

145. Information derived from such things as personal conversations is transferred into long-term memory through the process of _____ encoding.
A. attentive
B. automatic
C. effortful
D. episodic

p. 248
Encoding: Transferring
Level: Moderate
Type: Factual
Ans: D

146. Personal experiences, which are examples of _____ information are encoded _____ into long-term memory.
A. semantic; with effort
B. semantic; automatically
C. episodic; with effort
D. episodic; automatically

p. 248
Encoding: Transferring
Level: Moderate
Type: Factual
Ans: A

147. The things that matter to us, such as names of family members and close friends and hobbies, are easily remembered. What kind of encoding <u>most</u> probably occurs with this type of information?
A. automatic
B. episodic
C. effortful
D. attentive

p. 248
Encoding: Transferring
Level: Moderate
Type: Factual
Ans: B

148. Interesting facts, which are examples of _____ information are encoded _____ into long-term memory.
A. semantic; with effort
B. semantic; automatically
C. episodic; with effort
D. episodic; automatically

p. 248
Encoding: Transferring
Level: Easy
Type: Applied
Ans: D

149. As your young daughter does a somersault on the trampoline, you think about her ability to remember how to do a somersault. She probably encoded this motor skill:
A. through elaborative rehearsal
B. automatically
C. with much effort and awareness
D. without much awareness

p. 248
Encoding: Transferring
Level: Easy
Type: Factual
Ans: C

150. After a jog, you are asked by your friend if you saw any dogs out walking. Your ability to answer "yes, I think there were a couple or so" indicates that the information was <u>most</u> likely encoded:
   A.   attentionally
   B.   elaboratively
   C.   automatically
   D.   semantically

p. 248
Encoding: Transferring
Level: Moderate
Type: Factual
Ans: D

151. Motor skills, which are examples of _____ information are encoded _____ into long-term memory.
   A.   procedural; with effort
   B.   semantic; automatically
   C.   episodic; with effort
   D.   procedural; automatically

p. 248
Encoding: Transferring
Level: Easy
Type: Applied
Ans: A

152. "This quantum physics book is hard to understand and boring. I really have to focus on what I am reading." This information requires _____ encoding.
   A.   effortful
   B.   procedural
   C.   semantic
   D.   automatic

p. 248
Encoding: Transferring
Level: Moderate
Type: Factual
Ans: A

153. Difficult material, which is an example of _____ information, is encoded _____ into long-term memory.
   A.   semantic; with effort
   B.   semantic; automatically
   C.   episodic; with effort
   D.   episodic; automatically

p. 248
Encoding: Transferring
Level: Easy
Type: Factual
Ans: B

154. The transfer of information into long-term memory by repeating or rehearsing the information or by making associations between the new and old information is called _____ encoding.
   A.   automatic
   B.   effortful
   C.   semantic
   D.   procedural

p. 248
Encoding: Transferring
Level: Easy
Type: Factual
Ans: D

155. Making associations between new and old information is an example of a method for _____ encoding.
   A.   automatic
   B.   semantic
   C.   procedural
   D.   effortful

p. 249
Encoding: Transferring
Level: Easy
Type: Factual
Ans: A

156. Effortful encoding takes two forms. Which of the following is not a form of effortful encoding?
A. chunking
B. making meaningful associations between new information and information already stored in long-term memory
C. maintenance rehearsal
D. repeating the information

p. 249
Encoding: Transferring
Level: Easy
Type: Applied
Ans: B

157. Effective studying is an example of:
A. automatic encoding
B. effortful encoding
C. maintenance rehearsal
D. chunking

p. 249
Encoding: Transferring
Level: Moderate
Type: Applied
Ans: C

158. Claude, a foreign exchange student from France, is teaching Kelli how to say a couple of sentences in French. Kelli repeats the words over and over, but has no idea what the individual sounds mean. By saying the words repeatedly, Kelli is practicing:
A. interference
B. deep processing
C. maintenance rehearsal
D. elaborative rehearsal

p. 249
Encoding: Transferring
Level: Moderate
Type: Applied
Ans: B

159. You are studying in the student union. Another student sitting near you is muttering out loud, "primes, natural numbers, integers, rational numbers, real numbers, complex numbers..." over and over again. That math student is obviously using _____.
A. automatic encoding interference
B. maintenance rehearsal
C. deep processing
D. elaborative rehearsal

p. 249
Encoding: Transferring
Level: Moderate
Type: Conceptual
Ans: C

160. Memorization through repeating information over and over may result in poor retrieval because:
A. interference is more likely to occur as the number of repetitions increases
B. repetition results in learned material rapidly decaying
C. no associations are created by repeating the information
D. memorization through repeating is usually associated with boredom and lack of motivation

p. 249
Encoding: Transferring
Level: Moderate
Type: Factual
Ans: A

161. _____ rehearsal is effective for encoding information into short-term memory, whereas _____ rehearsal is effective for encoding information into long-term memory.
A. Maintenance; elaborative
B. Distinctive; eidetic
C. Semantic; procedural
D. Echoic; iconic

p. 249
Encoding: Transferring
Level: Easy
Type: Factual
Ans: D

162. Repeating information in a way that results in new associations is characteristic of:
A. automatic encoding
B. maintenance rehearsal
C. sensory encoding
D. elaborative rehearsal

p. 249
Encoding: Transferring
Level: Easy
Type: Factual
Ans: C

163. Actively making meaningful connections between the information you are learning with information you already know is called:
A. automatic encoding
B. maintenance rehearsal
C. elaborative rehearsal
D. sensory encoding

p. 249
Encoding: Transferring
Level: Easy
Type: Factual
Ans: A

164. Which type of rehearsal will most likely result in information being encoded into long-term memory?
A. elaborative
B. automatic
C. maintenance
D. attentional

p. 249
Encoding: Transferring
Level: Easy
Type: Factual
Ans: C

165. Encoding information from short-term to long-term memory is most efficient when it:
A. is not overly repetitive
B. is accompanied by relaxation
C. involves the forming of associations
D. is performed subconsciously

p. 249
Encoding: Transferring
Level: Moderate
Type: Applied
Ans: C

166. Early in the semester, a student asks his psychology instructor to back up and repeat a phrase she had said because he did not quite get all the words down. If the instructor is interested in helping the student engage in elaborative rehearsal, she should:
A. slow down so that the student can take dictation word for word
B. slow down so that the student can take notes in full sentences
C. tell the student to put the ideas in his own words rather than try to use those of the instructor
D. tell the student to bring a tape recorder to class so that he doesn't miss any of the instructor's words

p. 249
Encoding: Transferring
Level: Moderate
Type: Applied
Ans: A

167. Two friends are taking the same psychology course. One day over coffee they have an argument about the value of operant conditioning in the treatment of mental illness. Each provides valid arguments for his point of view. It is likely that the argument will:

A. cause them to do better on an exam testing the material because they will have formed new associations using the concepts involved
B. cause them to do better on an exam testing the material only if they go back and reread the material
C. cause them to do worse on an exam testing the material because the competition of the argument will distract them from the material
D. cause them to do worse on an exam testing the material because they will remember their friend's counterarguments better than the actual material

p. 249
Encoding: Transferring
Level: Moderate
Type: Conceptual
Ans: D

168. Which of the following note-taking strategies will best enhance future recall?

A. making sure that you write down major points word for word
B. taking notes in full sentences wherever possible
C. elaborating on the lecturer's main points
D. paraphrasing the lecturer's main points in note form

p. 249
Encoding: Transferring
Level: Easy
Type: Conceptual
Ans: A
PS/SG 11-21

169. Rod Plotnik puts psychology to good use in his textbook by providing _____ to help you encode the material you must learn.

A. distinctive visual associations
B. flashbulb memories
C. maintenance rehearsal drills
D. chunking strategies

p. 249
Encoding: Transferring
Level: Moderate
Type: Conceptual
Ans: A

170. Why would elaborative rehearsal help us to remember information?

A. It allows us to keep track of where we've stored the information.
B. It allows us to keep repeating the information over and over.
C. It changes the information so we are more familiar with it.
D. It prevents encoding from interfering with the information.

p. 249
Encoding: Transferring
Level: Easy
Type: Factual
Ans: B

171. Levels of processing theory focuses on:

A. how many times information is repeated or rehearsed
B. how information is encoded
C. where information is stored in long-term memory
D. how repressed memories are formed

p. 249
Encoding: Transferring
Level: Easy
Type: Factual
Ans: A

172. Levels of processing theory argues that the best way to encode information into long-term memory is to encode it:

A. at the deepest level which requires thinking and forming new associations
B. at the most shallow level which means analyzing only the most important information
C. by maintenance rehearsal
D. by the sound of the information

p. 249
Encoding: Transferring
Level: Moderate
Type: Applied
Ans: D

173. Which of the following is a question requiring the deepest processing of the word "lake"?

A. How many letters are found in the word?
B. With what other words does it rhyme?
C. Does it have a "k" in it?
D. What would a person do with it?

p. 249
Encoding: Transferring
Level: Moderate
Type: Conceptual
Ans: B

174. Why should a college student care about the levels of processing theory?
A. the levels of processing can influence one's social skills
B. because it shows that the way we encode material will influence how easily we can retrieve it
C. one day an employer may ask about it
D. it demonstrates how important explicit memory is to studying and test taking

p. 249
Encoding: Transferring
Level: Easy
Type: Applied
Ans: A

175. If you studied for a test, but at a shallow level of processing, what is the most difficult question you could probably answer?
A. Does "psychology" have an "o" in it?
B. What is the history of psychology?
C. Does the word "psychology" sound similar to the word "sociology?"
D. Describe the definition of psychology.

p. 250
Repressed Memories
Level: Easy
Type: Factual
Ans: C

176. The major controversy surrounding repressed memories is their:
A. bizarreness
B. detail
C. accuracy
D. content

p. 250
Repressed Memories
Level: Easy
Type: Factual
Ans: A

177. The idea of repressed memory is based upon the theory of:
A. Sigmund Freud
B. Albert Bandura
C. George Miller
D. B. F. Skinner

p. 250
Repressed Memories
Level: Easy
Type: Factual
Ans: C
www

178. When the mind pushes some traumatic memory into the unconscious only to stay there until it is released, _____ is said to have taken place.
A. regression
B. sublimation
C. repression
D. rationalization

p. 250
Repressed Memories
Level: Easy
Type: Applied
Ans: D

179. While undergoing therapy, Shelly claimed that her uncle had sexually abused her when she was a young child. Before therapy Shelly did not make such a claim. Supposedly, her memory of the abuse was pushed into her unconscious. This is called:
A. transference
B. deep level of processing
C. effortful encoding
D. repression

| | | |
|---|---|---|
| p. 250<br>Repressed Memories<br>Level: Moderate<br>Type: Conceptual<br>Ans: B | 180.<br><br>A.<br><br>B.<br><br>C.<br><br>D. | Why should we be skeptical of repressed memory?<br>Most people who claim repressed memory also have multiple personality disorder.<br>The formulation of questions about repressed memories can lead to misleading or biased results.<br>Hypnosis is used to uncover these repressed memories, and hypnosis is considered a fraud.<br>Most adults who were sexually abused as children, have clear memories of the abuse. |
| p. 250<br>Repressed Memories<br>Level: Easy<br>Type: Factual<br>Ans: B | 181.<br><br>A.<br>B.<br>C.<br>D. | Because a repressed memory may be so blocked, the therapist might have to be _____ to get the memory released.<br>aggressive<br>suggestive<br>secretive<br>passive |
| p. 250<br>Repressed Memories<br>Level: Easy<br>Type: Factual<br>Ans: D | 182.<br><br>A.<br>B.<br>C.<br>D. | Most women who report repressed memories of sexual abuse were in therapy for:<br>multiple personality disorder<br>schizophrenia<br>phobic disorders<br>depression or eating disorders |
| p. 250<br>Repressed Memories<br>Level: Moderate<br>Type: Conceptual<br>Ans: A | 183.<br>A.<br><br>B.<br>C.<br>D. | With regard to repressed memories, therapists must:<br>document real accounts of repressed memories without shaping or reinforcing those memories<br>try any method to uncover the repressed memories<br>be very forceful at bringing out the repressed memories<br>be supportive so the client keeps coming back for more therapy |
| p. 251<br>Repressed Memories<br>Level: Easy<br>Type: Factual<br>Ans: A | 184.<br>A.<br><br>B.<br>C.<br>D. | In analyzing repressed memories, Loftus contends that therapists:<br>may play some role in suggesting or implanting traumatic memories in their clients<br>only facilitate the release of repressed memories<br>are totally responsible for their clients' repressed memories<br>are skeptical about the existence of any repressed memories |
| p. 251<br>Repressed Memories<br>Level: Easy<br>Type: Factual<br>Ans: B | 185.<br><br>A.<br>B.<br>C.<br>D. | You've just been given truth serum. What effect will it have on your susceptibility to hypnotic suggestibility?<br>Your susceptibility will decrease.<br>Your susceptibility will increase.<br>There will be no change in susceptibility.<br>There are too many other variables that need to be taken into account. |
| p. 251<br>Repressed Memories<br>Level: Easy<br>Type: Factual<br>Ans: C<br>*PS/SG 11-22* | 186.<br>A.<br>B.<br>C.<br><br>D. | The main problem with repressed memories of childhood abuse is that:<br>very few people can remember that far back<br>we now know that the "unconscious" does not exist<br>therapists may unwittingly help patients form memories which seem to explain their key problems<br>so far, all the claimed cases of abuse in childhood have been proven to be lies |

p. 251
Repressed Memories
Level: Moderate
Type: Applied
Ans: C

187. An audience member attending a television talk show, which was focusing on repressed memory, asked a noted expert if false memories could be implanted. The expert responding correctly said:
A. yes - only by a trained psychologist or therapist
B. no - the mind is much too clever for that to happen
C. yes - a false suggestion can become a detailed personal memory
D. we don't know

p. 251
Repressed Memories
Level: Easy
Type: Factual
Ans: B

188. The bottom line on the accuracy of repressed memories is:
A. these are self-reports and can never be accepted as fact
B. to be on guard against false repressed memories
C. that clients have no reason to be untruthful
D. to be ready to further investigate the abuse and bring legal charges against those responsible for the abuse

p. 253
Cultural Diversity:
  Oral versus Written
Level: Easy
Type: Factual
Ans: B

189. If you lived in a poor country where many people could not read or write, encoding information by _____ would be widely practiced.
A. words
B. sounds
C. number
D. sentences

p. 253
Cultural Diversity:
  Oral versus Written
Level: Moderate
Type: Factual
Ans: B

190. A culture that has an oral tradition is a culture that:
A. has an organized, but evolving language
B. emphasizes passing on information through speaking and retelling
C. has a mythology
D. emphasizes good dental hygiene

p. 253
Cultural Diversity:
  Oral versus Written
Level: Easy
Type: Factual
Ans: A

191. Which of the following cultures is most likely to have an oral tradition?
A. Ghana
B. Canada
C. Germany
D. England

p. 253
Cultural Diversity:
  Oral versus Written
Level: Easy
Type: Factual
Ans: B
PS/SG 11-23

192. Students from rural Ghana remembered a story better than New York students because of the:
A. lower intelligence of Ghanaian students due to poverty and a poor diet
B. oral tradition of their culture versus the written tradition of New Yorkers
C. fact that the story was from their culture, which was foreign to New Yorkers
D. cultural tradition of cynical New Yorkers not to believe any story

p. 253
Cultural Diversity:
  Oral versus Written
Level: Moderate
Type: Factual
Ans: D

193. Cultures that value oral traditions tend to perform better on memory tasks that require encoding of information:
A. organized in hierarchies
B. presented as part of a play or drama
C. presented rapidly
D. presented orally

p. 253
Cultural Diversity:
  Oral versus Written
Level: Moderate
Type: Factual
Ans: A

194. In the study presented in this module on oral tradition's effects on memory, compared to American students, Ghanaian students remembered:
A. a higher percentage of themes and more words
B. more references to hunting, fishing, and war
C. less ideas related to television, MTV, and rock n' roll
D. a greater percentage of humor and jokes

p. 253
Cultural Diversity:
  Oral versus Written
Level: Moderate
Type: Factual
Ans: C

195. The study comparing Ghanaian and American students on recall suggests that:
A. the English language is easier to learn than Ghanaian
B. female students have better memories than male students in each culture
C. culture can influence how information is encoded and how easily it can be retrieved
D. culture does not significantly influence how information is encoded and how easily it can be retrieved

p. 254
Application:
  Unusual Memories
Level: Moderate
Type: Applied
Ans: A

196. Jane shows her ten-year-old daughter Meryl a picture of midtown Manhattan. After looking at the picture for half a minute, Meryl is able to describe it from a visual image of the picture that she continues to see in her mind. Meryl has a memory capacity called:
A. eidetic imagery
B. flashbulb memory
C. mood convergence
D. procedural memory

p. 254
Application:
  Unusual Memories
Level: Easy
Type: Factual
Ans: A

197. Out of 100 children between the ages of 6 and 12, how many would you expect to have the capacity for eidetic imagery?
A. 5-8
B. 17-20
C. 25
D. 31-33

p. 254
Application:
  Unusual Memories
Level: Moderate
Type: Factual
Ans: D

198. Which of the following statements regarding eidetic imagery is false?
A. Visual images in individuals with eidetic imagery can last several minutes.
B. Fewer than 10% of children between ages 6 and 12 have the capacity for eidetic imagery.
C. Individuals with eidetic imagery "see" the images they are asked to describe.
D. The capacity for eidetic imagery typically increases in adolescence.

p. 254
Application:
  Unusual Memories
Level: Moderate
Type: Factual
Ans: B

199. Why do adults tend not to have eidetic imagery?
A. Society considers eidetic imagery to be childish.
B. Adults use and rely more on words than pictures.
C. Adults have more sophisticated nervous systems.
D. Eidetic imagery is based on vision, and vision tends to worsen in adulthood.

p. 254
Application:
  Unusual Memories
Level: Easy
Type: Applied
Ans: C
*www*

200. Janel, a college student, can look at a stimulus and then be able to recall later a sharp, vivid, and detailed visual image of the stimulus. Janel's extraordinary memory is called:
A. eidetic memory
B. emotion-dependent memory
C. photographic memory
D. flashbulb memory

p. 254
Application:
  Unusual Memories
Level: Easy
Type: Factual
Ans: B

201. A capacity similar to eidetic imagery that is found in some adults is called _____ memory.
A. flashbulb
B. photographic
C. procedural
D. semantic

p. 255
Application:
  Unusual Memories
Level: Easy
Type: Factual
Ans: A

202. A memory of an emotional or dramatic event that was encoded without effort and with great detail is called:
A. flashbulb memory
B. emotion-dependent memory
C. state-dependent memory
D. explicit memory

p. 255
Application:
  Unusual Memories
Level: Easy
Type: Factual
Ans: B

203. Vivid recollections that are formed of dramatic events are called _____ memories.
A. eidetic
B. flashbulb
C. state-dependent
D. photographic

p. 255
Application:
  Unusual Memories
Level: Easy
Type: Applied
Ans: D
*www*

204. Andre remembers clearly that he was playing ping-pong in his basement when he heard that John Kennedy had just been assassinated. This is an example of:
A. eidetic memory
B. emotion-dependent memory
C. state-dependent memory
D. flashbulb memory

p. 255
Application:
  Unusual Memories
Level: Difficult
Type: Factual
Ans: C

205. You are listening to a talk show on the radio. A memory expert is presenting information about memory. She says that flashbulb memories are a special kind of memory immune from forgetting and distortion. Is she right?
A. Yes - flashbulb memories are a special kind of memory and are only immune from forgetting and distortion if the memory is relatively recent.
B. Yes - flashbulb memories are a special kind of memory and are immune from forgetting and distortion.
C. No - flashbulb memories are not a special kind of memory, but are subject to distortions and forgetting.
D. No - flashbulb memories are not a special kind of memory, but are still immune from forgetting and distortion.

p. 255
Application:
  Unusual Memories
Level: Moderate
Type: Applied
Ans: C

206. Tim claims that flashbulb memories are a separate and special kind of memory. Liz says otherwise; flashbulb memories are subject to the same inaccuracies and biases that characterize ordinary memories. Who is right?
A. Tim - flashbulb memories are complete and immune to forgetting.
B. Tim - flashbulb memories represent a fourth type of memory.
C. Liz - flashbulb memories result from automatic encoding.
D. neither one is correct since more research is needed.

p. 255
Application:
  Unusual Memories
Level: Easy
Type: Factual
Ans: A

207. The most commonly reported flashbulb memory among college students is:
A. being in or witnessing a car accident
B. opening your SAT scores
C. first date
D. first college class

p. 255
Application:
  Unusual Memories
Level: Easy
Type: Factual
Ans: A
*PS/SG 11-25*

208. Research shows that flashbulb memories are:
A. impressive and vivid, but not necessarily accurate
B. blinding images that are impossible to forget
C. associated with tragedies, like where you were when President Reagan was shot
D. frightening memories that you can't quite bring into clear detail

True/False

| T | www | 1. | The processes of memory are encoding, storing, and retrieving. |
|---|---|---|---|
| F | | 2. | Attention plays little role in transferring information from short-term to long-term memory. |
| F | www | 3. | Sensory memory holds information for up to 30 seconds. |
| T | www | 4. | Iconic memory holds visual information. |
| F | | 5. | As children grow, the length of their echoic memory decreases. |
| F | | 6. | A function of sensory memory is that it increases the amount of information coming in to our memory. |
| F | www | 7. | Echoic memory refers to memory about motor skills. |
| F | | 8. | Information in short-term memory is normally held a day or two. |
| T | | 9. | Short-term memory can hold about 7 items. |
| F | www | 10. | Chunking occurs when information blocks other information in memory. |
| F | | 11. | Memories stored in long-term memory are highly accurate. |
| F | | 12. | We tend to remember information presented in the middle of a list. |
| T | | 13. | The recency effect occurs because the last items are still in short-term memory. |
| T | www | 14. | Semantic and episodic memories are examples of declarative memory. |
| T | www | 15. | The case of H. M. illustrates the difference between declarative and procedural memories. |
| F | www | 16. | Hormones released during emotional events decrease the accuracy of memories of the events. |
| T | | 17. | If you are encoding information into memory without much effort or awareness, you are experiencing automatic encoding. |
| F | | 18. | The most effective type of effortful encoding is maintenance rehearsal. |
| T | www | 19. | How information is encoded affects how well the information is retrieved. |
| F | | 20. | Research shows the therapists do not influence recovered memories in their patients. |

| T | | 21. | False memories can be implanted by suggestion. |
| T | | 22. | Ghanaian students have better memory of spoken information because of their oral traditions than American students. |
| F | *www* | 23. | Eidetic imagery is common among children. |
| F | | 24. | Flashbulb memories are a special kind of memory. |
| T | | 25. | The amygdala plays a special role in flashbulb memories. |

Short-Answer Essay Questions

1.  Contrast sensory, short-term memory, and long-term memory with regard to function, storage capacity, and retrieval. (*www*)
2.  Describe how information flows from sensory memory to short-term memory to long-term memory.
3.  Explain how attention plays an important role in memory.
4.  What are iconic memory and echoic memory? In what type of memory are these stored? (*www*)
5.  How does chunking provide a way to address the limited storage of short-term memory?
6.  Contrast semantic memory, episodic memory, and procedural memory by presenting a definition and example of each.
7.  Why do we tend to remember the first and last items in a list? (*www*)
8.  Describe why students should engage in elaborative rehearsal when studying for their classes. What type of processing does elaborative rehearsal provide according to the levels-of-processing theory? (*www*)
9.  Why should we be skeptical of recovered memories? Include in your response the research of Elizabeth Loftus.
10. What are flashbulb memories? Discuss the accuracy of flashbulb memories? (*www*)

# Module 12 - Remembering and Forgetting

| | | |
|---|---|---|
| p. 261<br>Introduction<br>Level: Easy<br>Type: Factual<br>Ans: D | 1. | This module opens with a study of eyewitness testimony of a filmed assailant. Out of 2,000 viewers, what percent identified the wrong man in a six-man lineup? |
| | A. | 20% |
| | B. | 40% |
| | C. | 70% |
| | D. | 90% |

| | | |
|---|---|---|
| p. 261<br>Introduction<br>Level: Easy<br>Type: Conceptual<br>Ans: D<br>*PS/SG 12-1* | 2. | Rod Plotnik begins this module with a scene from a campus mugging. His point is to show that: |
| | A. | crime is so scary that we are likely to remember every detail |
| | B. | crime is a special situation, in which the everyday rules of memory do not apply |
| | C. | remembering and forgetting are automatic in dramatic situations like this one |
| | D. | remembering and forgetting are not as simple as most people think |

| | | |
|---|---|---|
| p. 261<br>Introduction<br>Level: Easy<br>Type: Applied<br>Ans: D | 3. | If you were to sit down at a kitchen table and think about what you needed to buy at the grocery store, you would be using: |
| | A. | recognition |
| | B. | implicit memory |
| | C. | eidetic memory |
| | D. | recall |

| | | |
|---|---|---|
| p. 261<br>Introduction<br>Level: Easy<br>Type: Applied<br>Ans: A | 4. | A professor is writing a test for his introductory psychology class. He decides that he is going to assess his students' recall. What kind of test should he write? |
| | A. | essay |
| | B. | multiple choice |
| | C. | true-false |
| | D. | matching |

| | | |
|---|---|---|
| p. 261<br>Introduction<br>Level: Easy<br>Type: Factual<br>Ans: B<br>*www* | 5. | The retrieval of previously learned information without the assistance of external cues is called: |
| | A. | recognition |
| | B. | recall |
| | C. | a flashbulb memory |
| | D. | effortful encoding |

| | | |
|---|---|---|
| p. 261<br>Introduction<br>Level: Easy<br>Type: Applied<br>Ans: A | 6. | You hear a new song on the radio and want to tell a friend about it. When speaking with the friend you talk about the song, but have difficulty actually remembering it. Your friend starts to hum the song and it helps you remember it. This best illustrates: |
| | A. | recognition |
| | B. | recall |
| | C. | automatic encoding |
| | D. | effortful encoding |

p. 261
Introduction
Level: Easy
Type: Factual
Ans: C

7.    Recognition involves:
A.    retrieving previously learned information with no cues present
B.    encoding new information to replace previously learned information
C.    using available cues to identify information that has been previously learned
D.    looking at an image and retaining a detailed visual image for several minutes

p. 261
Introduction
Level: Easy
Type: Applied
Ans: C

8.    What form of memory retrieval are you using when answering this multiple-choice question?
A.    recall
B.    relearning
C.    recognition
D.    directed search

p. 261
Introduction
Level: Moderate
Type: Applied
Ans: D

9.    Cindy does really well when Dr. Barrios gives a multiple-choice exam but has a lot of trouble when his exams consist of essay questions. Cindy finds _____ easier than _____.
A.    recall; recognition
B.    long-term retrieval; short-term retrieval
C.    short-term retrieval; long-term retrieval
D.    recognition; recall

p. 261
Introduction
Level: Easy
Type: Applied
Ans: A

10.    You are watching a spy thriller on television. In the movie a secret agent is trying to identify a spy for the other side by looking at some pictures of possible spies. The spy is using _____ to identify the correct individual.
A.    recognition
B.    recall
C.    proactive interference
D.    long-term potentiation

p. 261
Introduction
Level: Easy
Type: Conceptual
Ans: C

11.    Which of the following best demonstrates the difference between recognition and recall?
A.    speaking lines in a play versus playing the piano without sheet music
B.    multiple-choice exams versus true-false questions
C.    picking the assailant out of a lineup versus describing the face of an assailant
D.    reporting the color of your socks with your eyes closed versus reciting a poem

p. 262
Organization of
  Memories
Level: Easy
Type: Applied
Ans: B

12. You are listening to a radio talk show hosted by a psychologist. One of her callers asks why memories are so hard to retrieve. The psychologist responds, "After memories are encoded, they are connected in nodes in long-term memory. To find a particular memory, you must sift through all the nodes until you find the one you want." This psychologist is describing the _____ of memory.
  A. cognitive theory
  B. network theory
  C. trash can theory
  D. modal model

p. 262
Organization of
  Memories
Level: Easy
Type: Factual
Ans: D

13. If you believe that memories are stored in nodes that are interconnected, you subscribe to:
  A. Miller's File Theory
  B. the psychomnemonic theory of memory
  C. the trash can theory
  D. the network theory

p. 262
Organization of
  Memories
Level: Moderate
Type: Conceptual
Ans: D

14. The best analogy of the network theory of memory organization is:
  A. a fabric (associations) made of thousands of threads (nodes) lined up in the same direction
  B. a circle that has no starting point (nodes) and no ending point (associations)
  C. a refrigerator that has food (nodes) stacked on shelves (associations)
  D. a map with cities (nodes) interconnected by roads (associations)

p. 262
Organization of
  Memories
Level: Easy
Type: Factual
Ans: A
*PS/SG 12-4*

15. According to network theory, memory is organized by:
  A. nodes, associations, and hierarchies of information
  B. most important to least important information
  C. chronological order, according to when information was acquired
  D. "programs" of information, similar to a TV "network"

p. 262
Organization of
  Memories
Level: Easy
Type: Factual
Ans: D

16. According to the network theory of memory, another name for memory files is:
  A. points
  B. schemas
  C. cells
  D. nodes

p. 262
Organization of
  Memories
Level: Easy
Type: Factual
Ans: A

17. According to the network theory, when we make associations in memory, links are established between:
  A. nodes
  B. center points
  C. short-term and long-term memory
  D. the amygdala and hippocampus

p. 262
Organization of
  Memories
Level: Easy
Type: Conceptual
Ans: D

18. In the network theory, nodes are like _____ that are connected.
  A. waves in an ocean
  B. books in a library
  C. cities on a map
  D. cars on a highway

p. 262
Organization of
 Memories
Level: Easy
Type: Factual
Ans: B
*PS/SG 12-5*

19. Memory files containing related information organized around a specific topic are called:
A. network hierarchies
B. nodes
C. network theories
D. modules

p. 262
Organization of
 Memories
Level: Easy
Type: Factual
Ans: C

20. The network theory proposes that we are capable of "traveling" from node to node because:
A. action potentials propel us
B. nodes physically touch other nodes in the hippocampus
C. the nodes have been linked together through associations
D. nodes are connected to each other alphabetically

p. 262
Organization of
 Memories
Level: Moderate
Type: Factual
Ans: B

21. If you let your memory flow freely, you will find that one memory triggers another memory which triggers another. How would the network theory explain this?
A. Different brain chemicals are associated with different memories.
B. Memories are connected in an enormous cognitive network.
C. Some memories cause interference with others, while those that are not tend to be associated with each other.
D. The neurons that make up a particular memory become more sensitive to each other's signals.

p. 263
Organization of
 Memories
Level: Easy
Type: Factual
Ans: A

22. Network theory relies on the concept of nodes. What is a node?
A. a memory file that contains related information organized around a specific topic
B. the part of the hypothalamus which is responsible for our abilities of recall and recognition
C. a special kind of neurotransmitter released during the retrieval process
D. a mental model of a concept, event, or object, which is based on previous experience

p. 263
Organization of
 Memories
Level: Easy
Type: Factual
Ans: C

23. Nodes, according to the network theory of memory, are arranged in a:
A. random fashion
B. modular hierarchy
C. network hierarchy
D. cue-based structure

p. 263
Organization of
 Memories
Level: Easy
Type: Conceptual
Ans: C

24. The node "dog" would likely be included as a subset of the node:
A. "collie"
B. "spaniel"
C. "mammal"
D. "four legs"

p. 263
Organization of
 Memories
Level: Easy
Type: Applied
Ans: A

25. Which piece of information would be at the top of a network hierarchy?
A. A dog is an animal.
B. Dogs have fur.
C. My dog's name is Frosty.
D. A Golden retriever is a breed of dog.

p. 263
Organization of
 Memories
Level: Easy
Type: Factual
Ans: B

26. Factual information appears to be organized in:
A. groups of nodes that are connected by personal associations
B. hierarchies with abstract information at the top and concrete information at the bottom
C. random ways
D. a linear way from most used information to least used information

p. 263
Organization of
 Memories
Level: Easy
Type: Applied
Ans: C

27. Which of the following questions is answered by searching groups of nodes that are linked by personal associations?
A. "What are the names of the Great Lakes?"
B. "What is the capital of North Dakota?"
C. "What was your great-grandfather's name?"
D. "When was the war of 1812?"

p. 263
Organization of
 Memories
Level: Moderate
Type: Conceptual
Ans: A

28. How would the network theory of memory explain the time that you thought of baseball and in a few seconds you ended up thinking about toothpaste?
A. You were following personal associations or mental modes traveling from node to node.
B. There were objects in your present environment related to both baseball and toothpaste.
C. You were randomly sorting through many, many memories.
D. Unfortunately, examples like this are not easily explained by the network theory of memory.

p. 263
Organization of
 Memories
Level: Easy
Type: Factual
Ans: C

29. As you are remembering your first day of college, you are searching:
A. in a random way
B. in a linear way from most recent to most past personal information
C. groups of nodes that are connected by personal associations
D. network hierarchies

p. 263
Organization of
 Memories
Level: Easy
Type: Factual
Ans: B
*www*

30. A network is made up of:
A. iconic and echoic information
B. thousands of interconnected nodes
C. flashbulb memories
D. interactive memory processes such as encoding, storage, and retrieval

p. 263
Organization of
 Memories
Level: Moderate
Type: Applied
Ans: D

31. Which of the following is the best example of a network hierarchy?
A. local, federal, state, international
B. German shepherd, mammal, animal, cat
C. species, kingdom, phylum, class, human
D. Earth, Western Hemisphere, North America, Midwest, Iowa

p. 263
Organization of
 Memories
Level: Easy
Type: Factual
Ans: B

32. According to research cited in Module 12, when you think of an animal, the
 _____ part of your brain is very active.
A. front
B. back
C. amydala
D. temporal lobe

p. 263
Organization of
 Memories
Level: Moderate
Type: Applied
Ans: B

33. Jorge is watching a show on television that describes how to fix car engines.
 He sees the host of the show using a specialized tool. Jorge thinks he
 knows what the tool is called. Based on the research cited in the module,
 what part of the brain is showing maximal neural activity as he thinks of
 the specialized tool?
A. back of the brain
B. front of the brain
C. brainstem
D. occiptial lobe

p. 263
Organization of
 Memories
Level: Easy
Type: Factual
Ans: A
PS/SG 12-6

34. Recent brain scan research shows that the brain has:
A. prewired categories for processing information
B. specific, tiny locations for each individual bit of information you remember
C. hundreds, or even thousands, of different nodes for filing information
D. identifiable networks that are like well traveled highways connecting nodes

p. 263
Organization of
 Memories
Level: Moderate
Type: Factual
Ans: D

35. Does the brain have built-in categories for sorting and filing information?
A. No - the brain does not sort and file information based on categories
B. Yes - but the categories are developed through experience
C. Yes - but the brain doesn't have specific parts for categories
D. Yes - the brain has different areas for different categories

p. 264
Forgetting Curves
Level: Easy
Type: Factual
Ans: C

36. In general, the earliest event that we have a memory for occurred when we
 were:
A. 1 year old
B. 2 1/2 years old
C. 3 1/2 years old
D. 4 years old

p. 264
Forgetting Curves
Level: Moderate
Type: Factual
Ans: B

37. The two primary reasons why our memory is limited in early life is:
A. limited visual system and limited language skills
B. limited language skills and not having a sense of self
C. limited motor skills and language skills
D. limited visual system development and underdeveloped auditory cortex

p. 264
Forgetting Curves
Level: Moderate
Type: Applied
Ans: A

38. High school seniors Meera and Karen are talking about memories. Meera says that she can remember a song she learned when she was one-year-old. Karen disagrees and says that's not likely. Why?
A. We do not verbally encode before the age of 3 1/2.
B. Memory does not start operating until the age of 3 1/2.
C. A one-year-old's attention span is so poor that a child that young cannot encode anything.
D. Long-term memory does not exist in children that young.

p. 264
Forgetting Curves
Level: Easy
Type: Factual
Ans: C

39. A _____ measures the amount of previously learned information that subjects can remember across time.
A. node
B. mnemonic
C. forgetting curve
D. loci

p. 264
Forgetting Curves
Level: Easy
Type: Factual
Ans: A

40. The classic forgetting curve that Ebbinghaus described for nonsense syllables has a:
A. rapid downward slope, then levels out, and declines gradually
B. slight upward slope followed by a rapid downward slope
C. series of alternating upward and downward slopes
D. slight decline

p. 264
Forgetting Curves
Level: Easy
Type: Factual
Ans: C
*PS/SG 12-8*

41. Analysis of the data yielded by such research (above) would yield:
A. rates of retention
B. memory percentages
C. forgetting curves
D. cognitive charts

p. 264
Forgetting Curves
Level: Easy
Type: Factual
Ans: B

42. In order to study memory and forgetting, Hermann Ebbinghaus utilized:
A. mnemonics
B. three-letter nonsense syllables
C. pictures of common objects
D. five-letter words

p. 264
Forgetting Curves
Level: Moderate
Type: Factual
Ans: A

43. Based upon Ebbinghaus' research using nonsense syllables, forgetting curves show that most unfamiliar information is:
A. forgotten within the first hour
B. forgotten within the first eight hours
C. forgotten within the first day
D. forgotten within the first week

p. 264
Forgetting Curves
Level: Moderate
Type: Factual
Ans: C

44. Based upon forgetting curves, our memory for _____ information is much better than our memory for _____ information:
A. new; old
B. old; new
C. interesting; uninteresting
D. boring; exciting

p. 264
Forgetting Curves
Level: Moderate
Type: Factual
Ans: A

45. In one of your classes last week, you were introduced to some material that was very uninteresting but you were determined to learn it and you did. That was last week! How much of the material can you expect to have forgotten according to Ebbinghaus?

A. 80%
B. 65%
C. 40%
D. 15%

p. 264
Forgetting Curves
Level: Moderate
Type: Factual
Ans: C

46. Wow! The lecture in psychology last week was very interesting. But you wonder how much of it you'll remember in 7 years. The research says that we forget only about _____ of interesting information.

A. 80%
B. 75%
C. 60%
D. 15%

p. 264
Forgetting Curves
Level: Easy
Type: Factual
Ans: A

47. Based on the study of memory of high school classmates, what happens to the accuracy rate for recognition over 47 years?

A. it remains relatively stable
B. the accuracy rate declines significantly
C. the accuracy rate improves
D. the accuracy rates fluctuates

p. 264
Forgetting Curves
Level: Easy
Type: Factual
Ans: A

48. Most students show better memory on _____ tests compared to _____ tests.

A. recognition; recall
B. recall; recognition
C. essay; fill-in-the blank
D. fill-in-the blank; multiple choice

p. 264
Forgetting Curves
Level: Easy
Type: Applied
Ans: B
*www*

49. Bryce attended his 25th high school reunion. As he was driving to the reunion, he tried to remember the names of some of his classmates. This is called _____; at the reunion he could remember his classmates when he saw their faces. This is called _____.

A. recognition; recall
B. recall; recognition
C. potentiation; recognition
D. recall; relearning

p. 264
Forgetting Curves
Level: Easy
Type: Applied
Ans: C

50. You are helping to plan your family reunion. Ninety-six-year old Grandma Cassie is helping you to identify long-lost relatives. She remarks that she hasn't seen some of the relatives for decades and can't exactly remember their names. Which of the following strategies would help Grandma Cassie remember the names of these relatives?
A. Teach Grandma Cassie to use the method of loci to help her with the names.
B. Grandma Cassie should write down all the names she can remember.
C. Show Grandma Cassie some pictures of these relatives.
D. Ask Grandma Cassie to think really hard about these relatives.

p. 265
Reasons for Forgetting
Level: Easy
Type: Factual
Ans: B
www

51. The inability to retrieve, recall, or recognize information that was stored or is still stored in long-term memory is called:
A. interference
B. forgetting
C. disuse
D. decoding

p. 265
Reasons for Forgetting
Level: Easy
Type: Factual
Ans: C

52. What name is best associated with repression?
A. Abraham Maslow
B. Edward Tolman
C. Sigmund Freud
D. Carl Rogers

p. 265
Reasons for Forgetting
Level: Easy
Type: Factual
Ans: C

53. Why would a memory be repressed?
A. The memory regularly blocks more important information, so it is put "away" so that it will not interfere anymore.
B. The memory is incomplete and fragmented due to amnesia.
C. The memory is emotionally threatening or it provokes anxiety.
D. The memory is poorly connected or associated with other information.

p. 265
Reasons for Forgetting
Level: Easy
Type: Factual
Ans: C

54. Much of the controversy surrounding repression involves:
A. the accuracy of eyewitness testimony
B. the accuracy of flashbulb memories
C. recovered memories of sexual abuse
D. the validity of Freud's theory of personality

p. 265
Reasons for Forgetting
Level: Easy
Type: Factual
Ans: C

55. When the mind pushes some traumatic memory into the unconscious only to stay there until it is released, _____ is said to have taken place.
A. regression
B. sublimation
C. repression
D. rationalization

p. 265
Reasons for Forgetting
Level: Easy
Type: Factual
Ans: A
PS/SG 12-9

56. A friend says you did something terribly embarrassing at the party, but you can't remember what it was--this is an example of:
A. repression
B. poor retrieval cues
C. amnesia
D. interference

<table>
<tr><td>

p. 265
Reasons for Forgetting
Level: Moderate
Type: Applied
Ans: B

</td><td>

57.

A.
B.
C.
D.

</td><td>

A man was convicted of involuntary murder of an elderly woman. The incident took place while the two were arguing, and the woman suffered a heart attack and died. The man is very remorseful, but cannot remember anything about the argument. This type of forgetting best illustrates:
regression
repression
decay
consolidation

</td></tr>
</table>

<table>
<tr><td>

p. 265
Reasons for Forgetting
Level: Easy
Type: Factual
Ans: B

</td><td>

58.

A.
B.
C.
D.

</td><td>

You hear about a woman who was receiving therapy and found out that she had repressed memories of being sexually abused 20 years ago. Given the information in this module, what would be the most important question about her case?
How completely was the memory repressed?
Did the therapist implant or contribute to the memory?
How old was the woman when she was abused?
At what age did the repressed memory occur?

</td></tr>
</table>

<table>
<tr><td>

p. 265
Reasons for Forgetting
Level: Easy
Type: Factual
Ans: A

</td><td>

59.

A.
B.
C.
D.

</td><td>

Reminders we create in making associations between previously learned information and newly learned information are called:
retrieval cues
nodes
scripts
schemas

</td></tr>
</table>

<table>
<tr><td>

p. 265
Reasons for Forgetting
Level: Easy
Type: Factual
Ans: B
*PS/SG 12-10*

</td><td>

60.

A.
B.
C.
D.

</td><td>

You were introduced to your friend's professor recently, but there was no time to chat and now you can't recall the professor's name--this is an example of:
repression
poor retrieval cues
amnesia
interference

</td></tr>
</table>

<table>
<tr><td>

p. 265
Reasons for Forgetting
Level: Easy
Type: Factual
Ans: C

</td><td>

61.
A.
B.
C.
D.

</td><td>

Studying by cramming or rote memory tends to:
facilitate encoding
create temporary retrieval cues
create poor retrieval cues
create adequate retrieval cues

</td></tr>
</table>

p. 265
Reasons for Forgetting
Level: Difficult
Type: Applied
Ans: B

62. Professor Wallace, who is notorious for her essay exams, was approached by a student who asked to retake the exam, but in a different form such as a multiple choice. The student claimed that he knew and understood the material and he could demonstrate it better on a multiple-choice exam. Why would he make such a claim?

A. Essay tests require the student to study more.
B. Inadequate retrieval cues are a common cause of forgetting and essay tests, since they rely on recall, are more difficult than multiple choice which are based upon recognition.
C. Essay tests are more difficult since there can be more than one right answer.
D. Tests of recognition, like a multiple choice test, are more difficult than essay tests.

p. 265
Reasons for Forgetting
Level: Easy
Type: Applied
Ans: C

63. Harry can't remember anything that happened after he was kidnapped and tortured. Harry is suffering from:
A. Alzheimer's disease
B. Korsakoff's syndrome
C. amnesia
D. interference

p. 265
Reasons for Forgetting
Level: Easy
Type: Factual
Ans: A

64. If memory loss follows a blow or damage to the brain, the person is said to suffer from:
A. amnesia
B. Korsakoff's syndrome
C. Wernicke's aphasia
D. interference

p. 265
Reasons for Forgetting
Level: Easy
Type: Factual
Ans: A
www

65. Damage to the brain caused by blows to the head or a concussion may cause loss of memories and results in:
A. amnesia
B. Korsakoff's syndrome
C. repression
D. regression

p. 265
Reasons for Forgetting
Level: Easy
Type: Factual
Ans: C

66. The reason which suggests that people forget information because other information gets in the way and blocks its retrieval is called:
A. schema confusion
B. network overload
C. interference
D. eidetic imagery

p. 265
Reasons for Forgetting
Level: Easy
Type: Factual
Ans: D

67. You are creating a web site to describe interference. What would be the most appropriate web site name?
A. www.retrieval.com
B. www.amnesia.com
C. www.emotion.edu
D. www.block.edu

p. 265
Reasons for Forgetting
Level: Easy
Type: Applied
Ans: B
*www*

68. "I've moved so many times in the last five years, I get confused trying to remember all my phone numbers. I don't have any problems remembering my current phone number, but all the others are hard to remember." This most clearly illustrates:
A. repression
B. interference
C. regression
D. memory specificity

p. 266
Reasons for Forgetting
Level: Moderate
Type: Conceptual
Ans: A

69. On the second day of class, you can't remember your psychology professor's name. If fact, you have difficulty remembering your other professors' names. If this is an example of interference, where are those memories?
A. The memories are still stored in long-term memory.
B. The memories no longer exist.
C. The memories are located in the nodes between sensory memory and short-term memory.
D. The memories are located in the primary memory cache of working memory.

p. 266
Reasons for Forgetting
Level: Moderate
Type: Factual
Ans: B

70. When old information interferes with information we are trying to learn, _____ is occurring.
A. selective attention
B. proactive interference
C. repression
D. retroactive interference

p. 266
Reasons for Forgetting
Level: Moderate
Type: Applied
Ans: C

71. Lena has started to watch a video at Tina's house. Lena says that she saw the movie last month. She tries to anticipate the next scene or what a character will say, but she is wrong and says, "Maybe I'm getting this movie confused with another movie I saw last year." Lena is most likely experiencing:
A. long-term potentiation
B. repression
C. proactive interference
D. retroactive interference

p. 266
Reasons for Forgetting
Level: Moderate
Type: Factual
Ans: C
*PS/SG 12-13*

72. Proactive interference is when:
A. information learned later now disrupts retrieval of information learned earlier
B. learning positive information interferes with the retrieval of negative information
C. information learned earlier now disrupts retrieval of information learned later
D. retrospective thinking interferes with potential learning

p. 266
Reasons for Forgetting
Level: Moderate
Type: Applied
Ans: B

73. "When my grandmother was alive, she used to call me Gerald, who was her cousin. And my name is not Gerald." Grandmother was experiencing:
A. selective attention
B. proactive interference
C. repression
D. retroactive interference

p. 266
Reasons for Forgetting
Level: Moderate
Type: Applied
Ans: D

74. This semester you are taking psychology; last semester you took sociology and did well. But sociological terms are interfering with your memory of psychological terms. This illustrates:
A. primary interference
B. secondary interference
C. retroactive interference
D. proactive interference

p. 266
Reasons for Forgetting
Level: Moderate
Type: Applied
Ans: B

75. Kyle is having trouble learning the multiplication tables because he finds that the earlier learned associations interfere with the ones currently being memorized. This is called:
A. selective attention
B. proactive interference
C. repression
D. retroactive interference

p. 266
Reasons for Forgetting
Level: Moderate
Type: Applied
Ans: D
www

76. An anthropology professor prides herself in her ability to remember the names of her students, past and present. However, she finds that the longer she is in the profession, the harder it becomes to remember the names of present students, because they become confused with her past students. The professor is having trouble because of:
A. selective forgetting
B. failure to encode
C. retroactive interference
D. proactive interference

p. 266
Reasons for Forgetting
Level: Moderate
Type: Applied
Ans: C

77. Todd runs into Sarah, his former girlfriend. Oh no! He can't remember her name and calls her Robin, the name of his current girlfriend. What type of interference did Todd just experience?
A. primary interference
B. secondary interference
C. retroactive interference
D. proactive interference

p. 266
Reasons for Forgetting
Level: Moderate
Type: Applied
Ans: C

78. This semester you are taking psychology and doing well; last semester you took sociology and did well. But you don't remember much about sociology because of:
A. primary interference
B. secondary interference
C. retroactive interference
D. proactive interference

p. 266
Reasons for Forgetting
Level: Moderate
Type: Applied
Ans: A

79. If you get up in the morning remembering a wonderful dream only to forget it as you go about the day's activities. You've experienced:
A. retroactive interference
B. secondary interference
C. primary interference
D. proactive interference

p. 266
Reasons for Forgetting
Level: Easy
Type: Factual
Ans: A
*PS/SG 12-14*

80. Retroactive interference is when
A. information learned later now disrupts retrieval of information learned earlier
B. learning positive information interferes with the retrieval of negative information
C. information learned earlier now disrupts retrieval of information learned later
D. retrospective thinking interferes with potential learning

p. 266
Reasons for Forgetting
Level: Moderate
Type: Applied
Ans: C
*www*

81. "I know all of my students' names this semester. But I would have a hard time remembering many of the names from past semesters." This illustrates:
A. primary interference
B. secondary interference
C. retroactive interference
D. proactive interference

p. 266
Reasons for Forgetting
Level: Difficult
Type: Conceptual
Ans: C

82. Proactive interference is to _____ as retroactive interference is to _____.
A. primary; secondary
B. encode; retrieval
C. forward; backward
D. backward; forward

p. 267
Reasons for Forgetting
Level: Easy
Type: Factual
Ans: A

83. Mental reminders that are created when you form vivid mental images of information are called:
A. retrieval cue
B. echoic device
C. pegword cue
D. processing distraction

p. 267
Reasons for Forgetting
Level: Moderate
Type: Applied
Ans: A
*www*

84. Mary uses numerous different colors when she takes notes in her psychology class. If she has difficulty with a question on an exam, she finds it helpful to remember the color of the notes relevant to the question. For Mary, the color of the notes acts as a(n):
A. retrieval cue
B. echoic device
C. pegword cue
D. processing distraction

p. 267
Reasons for Forgetting
Level: Moderate
Type: Applied
Ans: C

85. The Mall of America labels their parking lots with the names of states. Why?
A. It facilitates state-dependent learning.
B. It is a marketing gimmick to get people excited about shopping at the Mall of America.
C. The state names are retrieval cues that help people remember where they parked.
D. To honor the different states.

p. 267
Reasons for Forgetting
Level: Moderate
Type: Applied
Ans: A

86. Albert has to remember many scientific formulas in his physics class. To help him remember them, he associates each one with a different former girlfriend. The former girlfriends are serving as:
A. retrieval cues
B. semantic chains
C. eidetic images
D. pegwords

p. 267
Reasons for Forgetting
Level: Moderate
Type: Conceptual
Ans: D

87. Given the research on retrieval cues, which of the following statements are you more likely to remember?
A. "The warm breeze greeted the campers as they set up their tent."
B. "The dog barked loudly, calling for his master."
C. "Flowers this time of year cast a magical glow."
D. "My car laughed as the grape Jell-O bowled a perfect game."

p. 267
Reasons for Forgetting
Level: Moderate
Type: Factual
Ans: A

88. Research on retrieval cues has found that it is the _____ of associations that leads to improved recall of events or information.
A. bizarreness
B. detail
C. number
D. strength

p. 267
Reasons for Forgetting
Level: Easy
Type: Factual
Ans: C

89. "Oh, I know the answer to this question. I can just feel it. Don't say it. Oh, come on. I know it." If you have ever experienced this, then you are familiar with:
A. proactive interference
B. primary interference
C. tip-of-the tongue phenomenon
D. source misattribution

p. 267
Reasons for Forgetting
Level: Moderate
Type: Factual
Ans: B

90. According to the text, the tip-of-the-tongue phenomenon results from:
A. nodes that are misaligned
B. inadequate retrieval cues or interference
C. amnesia
D. misfirings in the nerves that make up the hippocampus

p. 267
Reasons for Forgetting
Level: Easy
Type: Factual
Ans: A

91. We tend to experience the tip-of-the-tongue phenomenon when trying to name:
A. people and objects
B. emotional states
C. verbs
D. locations and directions

<table>
<tr><td>

p. 267
Reasons for Forgetting
Level: Moderate
Type: Applied
Ans: B

</td><td>

92. Dr. Wilson cannot remember the name of her advisor when she was in medical school 30 years ago. She "knows" that she knows his name, and makes a great effort, but just can't remember. Dr. Wilson is experiencing:
A. state-dependent learning
B. the tip-of-the-tongue phenomenon
C. repression
D. proactive interference

</td></tr>
<tr><td>

p. 267
Reasons for Forgetting
Level: Easy
Type: Applied
Ans: A

</td><td>

93. "What's that thing called? Oh, I know it! What is it? Come on, this is ridiculous." This experience is often called the:
A. tip-of-the-tongue phenomenon
B. competing responses style
C. amnesia
D. memory-cognitive hesitation syndrome

</td></tr>
<tr><td>

p. 267
Reasons for Forgetting
Level: Easy
Type: Factual
Ans: C

</td><td>

94. In her geography class, Kelli is asked by the teacher to name the capital of Michigan. Kelli experiences the tip of the tongue phenomenon. What is the best explanation for the tip of the tongue phenomenon?
A. Underlying the tip of the tongue is source misattribution.
B. Kelli failed to encode using state-dependent learning.
C. The information was encoded using poor retrieval cues.
D. The answer was repressed.

</td></tr>
<tr><td>

p. 267
Reasons for Forgetting
Level: Moderate
Type: Applied
Ans: B

</td><td>

95. "If I take my psych exam in this classroom, then I should study in this classroom." This would be consistent with the idea of:
A. source misattribution
B. state-dependent learning.
C. levels of processing
D. nondeclarative memory

</td></tr>
<tr><td>

p. 267
Reasons for Forgetting
Level: Moderate
Type: Factual
Ans: D

</td><td>

96. You should be in the same physiological state during retrieval of information as you were when learning the information. This is called:
A. latent-dependent learning
B. law of cues
C. encoding-retrieval similarity
D. state-dependent learning

</td></tr>
<tr><td>

p. 267
Reasons for Forgetting
Level: Moderate
Type: Applied
Ans: B
*www*

</td><td>

97. Allison is learning Spanish, but she hates it. When she is in her Spanish classes, she is always unhappy. The phenomenon of state-dependent learning would suggest that she would show better recall of Spanish words if she:
A. was in a better mood
B. was in an unhappy mood
C. could block out the proactive interference
D. developed adequate retrieval cues

</td></tr>
</table>

p. 267
Reasons for Forgetting
Level: Moderate
Type: Conceptual
Ans: C

98. According to state-dependent learning, being in the same emotional state during encoding and retrieving helps recall. This suggests:
A. encoding is facilitated by strong emotions
B. retrieval is facilitated by strong emotions
C. retrieval cues include emotional states
D. elaborative rehearsal is tied to emotional states

p. 267
Reasons for Forgetting
Level: Moderate
Type: Applied
Ans: A

99. "I am always so 'hyper' when I study since I drink a lot of pop. During exams, I don't have caffeine and I try to relax so I can concentrate." According to state-dependent learning, this student might consider:
A. being in the same emotional state during studying and test taking
B. cutting down on pop because of dependency
C. rethinking his relaxation during tests because sometimes it is best to be "psyched" for a test
D. studying earlier in the day to take advantage of his natural circadian rhythms

p. 268
Biological Bases
 of Memory
Level: Easy
Type: Factual
Ans: C

100. Our short-term memory abilities are a function of activity in the:
A. hippocampus
B. amygdala
C. cortex
D. occipital lobe

p. 268
Biological Bases
 of Memory
Level: Easy
Type: Applied
Ans: A

101. Peter sustains damage to his cortex due to a car accident. What can we expect will be the changes to his memory?
A. Peter will have great difficulty with both short-term and long-term memory.
B. Peter will be able to remember new memories, but not old memories.
C. Peter will be able to remember nondeclarative memory, but not declarative memory.
D. Peter's memory will be largely unaffected.

p. 268
Biological Bases
 of Memory
Level: Moderate
Type: Factual
Ans: C
PS/SG 12-17

102. Brain scans are advancing our knowledge of remembering and forgetting by identifying the:
A. struggle of the cortex to control the amygdala and hippocampus
B. neural assemblies that form long-term memories
C. brain areas involved in processing and storing different thoughts and memories
D. precise synapses where new memories are formed

p. 268
Biological Bases
 of Memory
Level: Moderate
Type: Factual
Ans: D

103. If your cortex was damaged, you could not:
A. experience echoic memory
B. transfer information from short-term memory to long-term memory
C. control your heart rate
D. hold information in short-term memory

p. 268
Biological Bases
  of Memory
Level: Moderate
Type: Applied
Ans: B

104. Before the accident, Clive enjoyed singing and playing the piano. Because of the brain damage, he cannot learn new songs. Why would he remember old songs, but fail to learn new ones?
A. Since his cortex is damaged, information like songs cannot be transferred into short-term memory.
B. The words of the songs learned before the accident were already safely stored throughout his cortex.
C. Brain damage often reduces one's motivation for new learning.
D. The accident probably damaged his brainstem thus preventing new songs from being stored in his hippocampus.

p. 268
Biological Bases
  of Memory
Level: Easy
Type: Applied
Ans: A

105. Your cousin's amygdala was seriously damaged in a car accident. Which of the following is most likely to happen with her memory?
A. She will still have memories, but they will not have an emotional component.
B. Suprisingly, her ability to use the method of loci will improve.
C. She will be unable to transfer information from short-term to long-term memory.
D. Her photographic memory is likely to disappear.

p. 268
Biological Bases
  of Memory
Level: Easy
Type: Factual
Ans: D

106. Our memories can evoke emotional experiences due, in part, to the activity of the:
A. cortex
B. hippocampus
C. frontal lobe
D. amygdala

p. 268
Biological Bases
  of Memory
Level: Easy
Type: Applied
Ans: A

107. On your way to school every morning, you observe a dog who always walks on the busy street seemingly without fear or concern. Today, after learning about the biological bases of memory, you offer an explanation for the dog's carefree behavior:
A. the dog's amygdala is damaged and is malfunctioning
B. counterconditioning is responsible for the behavior
C. chemical changes have taken place in the dog's nervous system
D. more neurotransmitters are released in the nervous system of the dog when it walks on the street

p. 268
Biological Bases
  of Memory
Level: Easy
Type: Applied
Ans: B

108. Gabe and Anna have been married for 10 years. During a drive in the country, they both hear "their song" on the radio. They then talk about their wonderful lives together. Which part of the brain provides this emotional dimension to their memories?
A. cortex
B. amygdala
C. frontal lobe
D. hippocampus

p. 268
Biological Bases
  of Memory
Level: Moderate
Type: Factual
Ans: D

109. Damage to the _____ area of the brain appears to prevent the transfer of information from short-term into long-term memory.
A. consolidation
B. amygdala
C. cortex
D. hippocampus

p. 268
Biological Bases
  of Memory
Level: Easy
Type: Factual
Ans: C

110. Harold has sustained damage to his hippocampus. As his neurologist, what should you tell his wife about what she can expect from Harold?
A. Harold will be able to get better at tasks that require motor skills
B. Harold will be unable to transfer declarative information from short-term memory to long-term memory
C. He won't be able to remember new words or facts
D. all of the above

p. 268
Biological Bases
  of Memory
Level: Easy
Type: Factual
Ans: A

111. The hippocampus is crucial for memories involving:
A. declarative information
B. short-term memory
C. procedural information
D. motor-skill abilities

p. 268
Biological Bases
  of Memory
Level: Easy
Type: Applied
Ans: C

112. Steven has a damaged hippocampus. What is he most likely to successfully learn and remember?
A. the latest computer operating system
B. his new cellular phone number
C. how to juggle three balls
D. the name of his new son-in-law

p. 268
Biological Bases
  of Memory
Level: Easy
Type: Factual
Ans: C
*www*

113. Which of the following areas of the brain appears to be most related to memory functioning?
A. cerebellum
B. medulla
C. hippocampus
D. hypothalamus

p. 268
Biological Bases
  of Memory
Level: Easy
Type: Factual
Ans: A

114. People with damage to the hippocampus:
A. cannot save any declarative memories
B. can save declarative memories
C. cannot save nondeclarative memories
D. can save memories of performing motor skills

p. 269
Biological Bases
  of Memory
Level: Easy
Type: Factual
Ans: D

115. In examining the mechanisms of memory, researchers have found that during the formation of memories:
A. the chemical gates of a neuron are always closed
B. neurons secrete fewer neurotransmitters
C. neurons remain inactive
D. new chemicals are synthesized

p. 269
Biological Bases
  of Memory
Level: Easy
Type: Factual
Ans: B

116.   As information is stored in short-term memory, our nervous system uses interconnected groups of neurons called:
A.   neuronal nodes
B.   neural assemblies
C.   hierarchical assemblies
D.   dendrite clusters

p. 269
Biological Bases
  of Memory
Level: Easy
Type: Factual
Ans: C

117.   When we repeat a phone number, _____ are activated that recognize and hold the phone number in short-term memory.
A.   neuronal nodes
B.   hierarchical assemblies
C.   neural assemblies
D.   cortex networks

p. 269
Biological Bases
  of Memory
Level: Easy
Type: Factual
Ans: B

118.   Researchers believe that permanently storing information in long-term memory involves chemical, functional, and _____ changes.
A.   biological
B.   structural
C.   social
D.   classical

p. 269
Biological Bases
  of Memory
Level: Easy
Type: Factual
Ans: C

119.   Why do memory researchers use sea slugs for research?
A.   They are in plentiful supply.
B.   Sea slugs have very large cell bodies in their neurons.
C.   They have only 20,000 neurons.
D.   They lack a peripheral nervous system.

p. 269
Biological Bases
  of Memory
Level: Easy
Type: Factual
Ans: D

120.   If a neuron becomes more sensitive to stimulation after it has been repeatedly stimulated, _____ is said to have occurred.
A.   amplified potentiation
B.   linear activation
C.   spread of activation
D.   long-term potentiation

p. 269
Biological Bases
  of Memory
Level: Easy
Type: Factual
Ans: B
PS/SG 12-19

121.   Long-term potentiation (LTP) works by:
A.   stimulating the amygdala
B.   changing the structure and function of neurons
C.   adding short-term memories together
D.   not repeating new information too many times

p. 269
Biological Bases
  of Memory
Level: Moderate
Type: Factual
Ans: D

122.   When happens when you repeat someone's name over and over?
A.   amplified potentiations occurs
B.   LTP in the hypothalamus is reduced
C.   the structure of LTP changes
D.   some neurons grow and create new connections with other neurons

p. 269
Biological Bases
  of Memory
Level: Moderate
Type: Factual
Ans: B

123. What does LTP do?
A. it increases the ability to use visual retrieval cues
B. changes the structure and function of neurons
C. increases the release of endorphins in the nervous system
D. creates false memories

p. 269
Biological Bases
  of Memory
Level: Moderate
Type: Applied
Ans: A

124. Neuron A says to Neuron B, "Boy, I think I've had long-term potentiation happen to me for that historical date, 1776." Neuron B asks, "So. What does that mean?" Neuron A replies:
A. "I've become more sensitive to that piece of information."
B. "I will stop functioning if I hear that date again."
C. "The historical date causes me to shed my myelin sheath."
D. "I've become more likely to send inhibitory messages when I hear a similar piece of information."

p. 269
Biological Bases
  of Memory
Level: Easy
Type: Factual
Ans: A

125. Repeating someone's address stimulates neurons, which in turn, produces:
A. long-term potentiation
B. linear activation
C. spread of activation
D. long-span assemblies

p. 269
Biological Bases
  of Memory
Level: Moderate
Type: Applied
Ans: D

126. A new science fiction book you're reading describes an evil country wanting to take over the rest of the world by preventing their enemies from forming new long-term memories. How would you do it?
A. putting a chemical into the water supply that destroys the amygdala
B. devise a propaganda plan that would introduce source misattribution
C. preventing state-dependent learning from occurring
D. putting a drug into the water supply that prevents long-term potentiation

p. 269
Biological Bases
  of Memory
Level: Moderate
Type: Conceptual
Ans: A

127. We humans are very proud of our ability to "think" but, when we study creatures like the sea slug, "thought" begins to look more like:
A. structural and functional changes in the nervous system
B. the thinking of a severely retarded person
C. habits shaped through reward and punishment
D. inherited tendencies somewhat modified by experience

p. 271
Mnemonics:
  Memorization Methods
Level: Moderate
Type: Factual
Ans: B

128. Violet has to learn the colors of the visual spectrum for science class. Erv tells her that the name "ROY G. BIV" can be used to remember them because each letter stands for a color (e.g., R = Red). Using ROY G. BIV to remember the colors of the spectrum is an example of:
A. a retrieval node
B. a mnemonic
C. a semantic network
D. the method of loci

p. 271
Mnemonics:
  Memorization Methods
Level: Moderate
Type: Factual
Ans: D
*www*

129.  Methods that help encode and recall information through associations and images are called:
A.  storage cues
B.  proactive devices
C.  semantic cues
D.  mnemonics

p. 271
Mnemonics:
  Memorization Methods
Level: Easy
Type: Factual
Ans: B
*www*

130.  A technique for creating visual associations between memorized places and items to be memorized is called:
A.  eidetic imagery
B.  the method of loci
C.  the peg theory
D.  proactive rehearsal

p. 271
Mnemonics:
  Memorization Methods
Level: Easy
Type: Applied
Ans: C

131.  A man memorizes a shopping list by imagining where each item would be found in his local supermarket. He is using:
A.  hierarchy method
B.  elaboration method
C.  method of loci
D.  peg method

p. 271
Mnemonics:
  Memorization Methods
Level: Moderate
Type: Conceptual
Ans: D

132.  Suppose you had to remember the ten most important battles of the Civil War in the order that they occurred. Which of the following ways would likely be most effective?
A.  chunking
B.  repression
C.  selective attention
D.  method of loci

p. 271
Mnemonics:
  Memorization Methods
Level: Easy
Type: Applied
Ans: A

133.  In a famous case, a Russian man with a fantastic memory would remember the order of lists of numbers by mentally placing the numbers in familiar spots on Gorky Street in his hometown and then mentally walking down the street when he had to retrieve them. The Russian man's way of remembering is closest to the:
A.  method of loci
B.  peg method
C.  chunking technique
D.  selective attention method

p. 271
Mnemonics:
  Memorization Methods
Level: Easy
Type: Factual
Ans: C
*www*

134.  What is the mnemonic called that used associations between number-word rhymes and the items to be memorized?
A.  selective encoding
B.  chunking method
C.  peg method
D.  method of loci

p. 271
Mnemonics:
  Memorization Methods
Level: Easy
Type: Factual
Ans: B

135. The peg method is a mnemonic encoding technique that creates:
A. visual associations between memorized places and items to be memorized
B. associations between number-word rhymes and items to be memorized
C. larger groups out of individual items
D. more effective sensory memory

p. 271
Mnemonics:
  Memorization Methods
Level: Easy
Type: Factual
Ans: A

136. A person memorizing a set of number-word rhymes on which other ideas to be memorized can be hung would be using which mnemonic device?
A. peg method
B. method of loci
C. chunking
D. selective attention

p. 271
Mnemonics:
  Memorization Methods
Level: Easy
Type: Applied
Ans: B

137. Rolando wants to memorize a list of items to take on a camping trip. He uses "Four is a door" to remember the fourth item, imagining a sleeping bag up against the door. Rolando is using:
A. rhyme word system
B. peg method
C. elaboration
D. method of loci

p. 271
Mnemonics:
  Memorization Methods
Level: Easy
Type: Factual
Ans: B
PS/SG 12-20

138. Both the method of loci and the peg method work by:
A. causing learning to be strengthened through repeated practice
B. creating strong associations that will serve as effective retrieval cues
C. connecting material to be learned to the purpose it will be used for
D. considering material to be memorized as easy and pleasant to learn

p. 271
Mnemonics:
  Memorization Methods
Level: Easy
Type: Factual
Ans: C

139. According to your textbook, poor _____ results in poor _____ cues which make recall difficult.
A. mnemonics; source
B. visualization; loci
C. encoding; retrieval
D. chunking; visual

p. 271
Mnemonics:
  Memorization Methods
Level: Easy
Type: Factual
Ans: D

140. According to the textbook, memory-enhancing drugs such as ginkgo,
A. can improve verbal, but not visual memory
B. can improve visual, but not verbal memory
C. can improve memory, but only in individuals with serious memory loss as in Alzheimer's disease
D. have not been found to improve memory

p. 272
Cultural Diversity:
  Aborigines
Level: Easy
Type: Factual
Ans: B

141. In industrialized countries, we spend our lives communicating through verbal information by speaking, reading, and writing. According to the textbook, we probably encode and store information mostly using:
A. echoic memory
B. verbal retrieval cues
C. language-dependent networks
D. verbal nodes

p. 272
Cultural Diversity:
  Aborigines
Level: Easy
Type: Factual
Ans: D

142. In nonindustrialized countries where there is no written language, we would suspect that individuals encode information by using:
A.   verbal nodes
B.   verbal retrieval cues
C.   language-independent networks
D.   visual retrieval cues

p. 272
Cultural Diversity:
  Aborigines
Level: Easy
Type: Factual
Ans: A

143. An Australian Aborigine might not score well on Western intelligence tests because Aborigines:
A.   utilize more visual cues than verbal cues
B.   are not as intelligent as Americans
C.   would score better than Americans
D.   people would score the same, regardless of their cultural background

p. 272
Cultural Diversity:
  Aborigines
Level: Easy
Type: Factual
Ans: D
*PS/SG 12-22*

144. Aborigine children performed significantly better than white Australian children on memory tasks when:
A.   only Aborigine objects were used
B.   the task involved auditory cues
C.   testing was done outdoors in a natural setting
D.   the task involved visual cues

p. 272
Cultural Diversity:
  Aborigines
Level: Moderate
Type: Conceptual
Ans: C

145. A test which assesses ability to encode with visual cues would yield which of the following results?
A.   Americans would score better than Europeans.
B.   Europeans would score better than Aborigines.
C.   Aborigines would score better than Americans.
D.   People would score the same, regardless of their cultural background.

p. 273
Research Focus:
  False Memories
Level: Easy
Type: Factual
Ans: B

146. Why was the conviction of Margaret Kelly Michael overturned?
A.   The adult eyewitnesses lied about what they had seen.
B.   The children's testimony may have been unreliable due to improper interviewing by therapists.
C.   The therapists lied about what the children had told them.
D.   She was made to testify against herself.

p. 273
Research Focus:
  False Memories
Level: Easy
Type: Factual
Ans: A

147. Research on false memories in children indicates:
A.   that false memories can be created by suggestion
B.   false memories cannot be created
C.   children do not accurately recall past events
D.   professionals can detect false memories in children

p. 273
Research Focus:
  False Memories
Level: Easy
Type: Factual
Ans: B

148. Six-year-old Mary is giving testimony in a criminal case in court. She is a prosecution witness. To rebut her damaging testimony, the defense should:
A.   point out that she is only six years old
B.   bring an expert in who will testify that false memories can be implanted in children
C.   remind the jury that she was promised toys for her testimony
D.   point out to the jury that only professionals can detect false memories in children

p. 273
Research Focus:
  False Memories
Level: Easy
Type: Factual
Ans: C

149.  Some believe that a child's lies or made up stories can be detected by:
A.   a polygraph test
B.   threatening the child with physical punishment if they do not tell the truth
C.   facial features and speech patterns
D.   careful questioning

p. 273
Research Focus:
  False Memories
Level: Easy
Type: Factual
Ans: A

150.  According to the textbook, what phrase can convince a child that a false event actually happened?
A.   "to think real hard"
B.   "are you sure that did not happen?"
C.   "I think that happened, don't you?"
D.   "let's play a game"

p. 274
Application:
  Eyewitness Testimony
Level: Easy
Type: Factual
Ans: B

151.  Your textbook presents three problems with eyewitness testimony. Which one of the following statements is not one of the problems?
A.   Law enforcement officials may influence testimony through misleading questions.
B.   The confidence of eyewitnesses regarding their testimony typically declines over time.
C.   Testimony is assumed to be accurate and is thought to be reliable evidence.
D.   There is a weak correlation between the confidence of the eyewitness and the testimony given.

p. 274
Application:
  Eyewitness Testimony
Level: Easy
Type: Factual
Ans: D

152.  Out of 110 people who were wrongly convicted of rape or murder, how many of them were due to mistaken eyewitness testimony?
A.   2
B.   32
C.   83
D.   101

p. 274
Application:
  Eyewitness Testimony
Level: Easy
Type: Factual
Ans: C
www

153.  We tend to better recognize faces of our own race rather than faces of other races. This is called:
A.   self-referent bias
B.   racial attribution
C.   own-race bias
D.   racial bias attributional error

p. 274
Application:
  Eyewitness Testimony
Level: Easy
Type: Factual
Ans: B

154.  The textbook describes a real-life case of a priest who was positively identified incorrectly as a robber. What role, if any, did the police have in this misidentification?
A.   The police had evidence that the priest had a history of robbery.
B.   The police misled the witnesses in their questioning of them.
C.   The police played no role; it was a case of mistaken identity.
D.   One specific witness was very confident that the priest was the criminal and the police were misled.

p. 274
Application:
  Eyewitness Testimony
Level: Moderate
Type: Applied
Ans: D

155.  You and a friend are sitting in the dorm watching a televised trial. A witness currently on the stand repeats several times that he saw the defendant leaving the murder scene and that he is sure. Your friend comments, "Well that about does it. If he says the defendant did it and is confident about it, then that's it!" What do you say?

A.  "Eyewitness testimony is very reliable."
B.  "Accuracy of an eyewitness is usually very high."
C.  "Confidence of a eyewitness is strongly related to accuracy of the testimony."
D.  "Don't be so quick. There is a weak relationship between confidence of the eyewitness and the accuracy of the testimony."

p. 274
Application:
  Eyewitness Testimony
Level: Easy
Type: Factual
Ans: D

156.  Studies of eyewitness testimony have shown:
A.  a close relationship exists between confidence and accuracy
B.  eyewitnesses become more accurate if they are expected to be accurate
C.  eyewitnesses stick stubbornly to stories even when it is proven that the stories must be false
D.  little relationship exists between confidence and accuracy

p. 274
Application:
  Eyewitness Testimony
Level: Easy
Type: Applied
Ans: A

157.  A witness of a bank robbery is asked if she remembers the bank manager wearing a tie. If she is influenced by the question, it is likely the witness will:
A.  say yes because male bank managers usually wear ties
B.  say no because there was too much going on to remember such a detail
C.  say yes and add the color of the tie
D.  say she is not sure

p. 275
Application:
  Eyewitness Testimony
Level: Moderate
Type: Applied
Ans: C

158.  You want a witness to testify that he saw a stop sign at the scene of an accident when, in fact, no such sign exists. Which of the following questions would be most effective?
A.  "Did you see a stop sign at the intersection?"
B.  "Are you sure you didn't see a stop sign?"
C.  "How fast was the white car going when it went through the stop sign?"
D.  "Are there many stop signs in that neighborhood?"

p. 275
Application:
  Eyewitness Testimony
Level: Moderate
Type: Applied
Ans: A

159.  A novice lawyer is about to question her first witness. Before the trial begins, an experienced partner in the law firm tells the novice to choose her verbs carefully when asking questions. The partner's advice is:
A.  based on the finding that memory can be influenced by the nature of a question
B.  common sense for impressing the jury, but does not affect the nature of the witness's answers
C.  of little value, since eyewitness reports are firmly set in memory and cannot be manipulated
D.  based on the belief that juries and judges listen more critically to the words of a female lawyer

p. 275
Application:
  Eyewitness Testimony
Level: Easy
Type: Factual
Ans: C

160. The wording of a question:
A. is usually ignored when people are trying to think of the answer to the question
B. is rarely remembered after a question has been answered
C. can influence the reporting of eyewitness testimony
D. can only cause a witness to be more confident in his or her answer

p. 275
Application:
  Eyewitness Testimony
Level: Easy
Type: Factual
Ans: C
*PS/SG 12-24*

161. When evaluating eyewitness testimony, pay close attention to:
A. whether the eyewitness has anything to gain or lose by testifying
B. how confident the eyewitness appears to be
C. how the questions to the eyewitness are worded
D. whether the eyewitness seems biased in favor of or against the defendant

p. 275
Application:
  Eyewitness Testimony
Level: Easy
Type: Factual
Ans: B

162. _____ can occur when a person cannot decide if a memory came from one source or another source.
A. Source conflict
B. Source misattribution
C. Cognitive labeling
D. Memory loci

p. 275
Application:
  Eyewitness Testimony
Level: Moderate
Type: Applied
Ans: D

163. When Tanner looks at a picture taken thirty years ago of his brother and himself sitting on Santa Claus' lap, he claims he remembers the event. But, what if the reason why he remembers it is because of the picture itself? Or does he have a true memory of his visit with Santa Claus? This is called:
A. source conflict
B. memory loci
C. cognitive labeling
D. source misattribution

p. 275
Application:
  Eyewitness Testimony
Level: Moderate
Type: Factual
Ans: A

164. The cognitive interview is a technique used to:
A. reconstruct memories about crimes
B. assess the capacity of short-term memory
C. block out retroactive interference
D. prevent anterograde amnesia

p. 275
Application:
  Eyewitness Testimony
Level: Easy
Type: Applied
Ans: C

165. Mr. Nguyen witnesses a bank robbery. During the investigation, he was asked to report everything he remembered without holding back anything. He also was asked to describe the crime from several viewpoints. The technique used to record Mr. Nguyen's statement is called:
A. free association
B. memory retrieval association
C. cognitive interview
D. source attribution

p. 275
Application:
  Eyewitness Testimony
Level:  Moderate
Type:  Factual
Ans:  B

166.  An outcome of using the cognitive interview technique is that an eyewitness is:

A.  more likely to reconstruct memories about the incident
B.  less likely to be influenced by the questions and therefore not likely to experience source misattribution
C.  likely to block out prior information that may have been influential
D.  more likely to experience state dependent memory

p. 275
Application:
  Eyewitness Testimony
Level:  Easy
Type:  Factual
Ans:  A
*PS/SG 12-25*

167.  Because of research on eyewitness testimony, police now use a technique called the:

A.  cognitive interview
B.  good cop/bad cop strategy
C.  bait-and-switch method
D.  skeptical questioning interview

True/False

| | | | |
|---|---|---|---|
| T | *www* | 1. | Multiple choice tests require recognition. |
| F | | 2. | According to the network theory, memories are stored in long-term potentiations. |
| T | | 3. | A network hierarchy describes how memories are arranged. |
| T | *www* | 4. | Ebbinghaus found that the forgetting curve for nonsense syllables was rapid at first. |
| F | | 5. | After 47 years following high school graduation, subjects' recall rate of classmates was below 20%. |
| F | | 6. | Repression occurs when we act in a way consistent with an earlier developmental stage. |
| F | *www* | 7. | In proactive interference, new memories are interfering with old memories. |
| T | *www* | 8. | Retroactive interference involves interference that goes from new to old. |
| T | | 9. | We can create retrieval cues by making associations with what we are learning and what we already know. |
| F | | 10. | The tip-of-the-tongue phenomenon most often occurs with dates. |
| T | | 11. | The more bizarre the association the better our memory will be. |
| T | *www* | 12. | It is easier to remember information if you are in the same emotional state as when you originally encoded that information. |
| F | | 13. | Damage to the hypothalamus would negatively affect memory for nondeclarative information. |
| T | *www* | 14. | LTP changes the structure and function of neurons. |
| F | | 15. | Mnemonics are a group of neurotransmitters that facilitate memory. |
| F | *www* | 16. | The method of loci creates associations between number-word rhymes. |
| F | | 17. | Ginkgo improves memory in humans. |
| F | *www* | 18. | Culture appears to have no effect on the encoding and recall of information. |
| T | | 19. | False memories can be easily created in children. |
| T | | 20. | According to the study described in the module, children remembered fictitious events in great detail. |

| F | www | 21. | Eyewitness testimony is accurate and reliable. |
| T | | 22. | People can recognize faces of their own race better than faces of other races. |
| F | www | 23. | The more confident an eyewitness is, the more accurate their memory. |
| T | | 24. | Misinformation can be introduced by the wording of questions. |
| F | | 25. | Cognitive interview is not effective in questioning eyewitnesses. |

Short Answer Essay Questions

1. Explain why answering this essay question is an example of recall.
2. Describe the network theory of memory. How is a map a good illustration of the theory?
3. Discuss how memories are arranged in network hierarchies. (*www*)
4. What are the types of interference? Provide an example for each. (*www*)
5. Present a summary of state-dependent learning and how you might apply it to your own life as a college student.
6. What role does the hypothalamus play in transferring memories? (*www*)
7. Explain the effect that long-term potentiations have on the nervous system.
8. How do the method of loci and peg word method work to improve our memory?
9. Why should courts be skeptical of eyewitness testimony? Include the three problems of eyewitness testimony described in Module 12. (*www*)
10. What is source attribution and how is it related to introducing misinformation in an individual's memory? (*www*)

# Module 13 - Intelligence

p. 281
Introduction
Level: Easy
Type: Factual
Ans: B

1. The cases of Gregg Cox, Serena Williams, Bill Gates, Steve Lu, and Midori bring up the question of:
   A. racial prejudice
   B. intelligence
   C. delinquency and getting into trouble
   D. poor academic performance

p. 281
Introduction
Level: Easy
Type: Conceptual
Ans: D
*PS/SG 13-1*

2. Rod Plotnik challenged you to rank five unusual people according to intelligence to show that:
   A. although Bill Gates dropped out of Harvard, he is clearly the smartest of the group
   B. intelligence is related to gender, race, and social class
   C. although they were all high achievers, only Steve Lu had truly high intelligence (IQ 194)
   D. intelligence could be defined in several different ways

p. 281
Introduction
Level: Easy
Type: Conceptual
Ans: B

3. The examples presented in the introduction of the module illustrate the issue of:
   A. genetics in determining psychological abilities
   B. the definition of intelligence
   C. environmental factors in psychological abilities
   D. social support within the family

p. 281
Introduction
Level: Moderate
Type: Conceptual
Ans: A

4. If each person who is described in the introduction to the module is considered to be intelligent, what does that say about the concept of intelligence?
   A. There is more than one way to be intelligent.
   B. Intelligence is most closely related to academic accomplishments.
   C. Intelligence is primarily determined by genetics.
   D. Intelligence is primarily determined by the environment.

p. 281
Introduction
Level: Easy
Type: Conceptual
Ans: B

5. Why might someone consider Steve Lu to be intelligent?
   A. his creative writing
   B. very high scores on an IQ test and the SAT
   C. his athletic accomplishments
   D. his inventions

p. 281
Introduction
Level: Easy
Type: Factual
Ans: D

6. _____ focuses on development of psychological tests.
   A. Forensic psychology
   B. School psychology
   C. Personality psychology
   D. Psychometrics

| p. 281<br>Introduction<br>Level: Easy<br>Type: Factual<br>Ans: A | 7.<br><br>A.<br>B.<br>C.<br>D. | If your cousin told you she was in psychometrics, what would she be <u>most</u> likely doing in her career?<br>developing psychological tests measuring personality traits<br>studying the causes of schizophrenia<br>providing counseling to displaced factory workers<br>designing better instrumentation panels for aircrafts |
|---|---|---|
| p. 281<br>Introduction<br>Level: Easy<br>Type: Applied<br>Ans: B<br>*www* | 8.<br><br><br>A.<br>B.<br>C.<br>D. | At a career fair, you stop by Dr. Ibanez's booth to talk about her career. Her professional interests include how to best assess people's abilities, skills, beliefs, and personality traits. You guess that Dr. Ibanez specializes in:<br>physiological psychology<br>psychometrics<br>counseling psychology<br>developmental psychology |
| p. 281<br>Introduction<br>Level: Easy<br>Type: Conceptual<br>Ans: C | 9.<br><br>A.<br>B.<br>C.<br>D. | A psychologist employed by a company that develops and publishes intelligence and personality tests is most likely to have a degree in:<br>child development<br>basic research<br>psychometrics<br>clinical psychology |
| p. 281<br>Introduction<br>Level: Easy<br>Type: Factual<br>Ans: B | 10.<br><br>A.<br>B.<br>C.<br>D. | Which of the following is <u>not</u> a major question for psychologists as they measure intelligence?<br>how to define intelligence<br>how to explain intelligence test scores to the general public<br>how to construct a test to measure intelligence<br>how to explain intelligence |
| p. 282<br>Defining Intelligence<br>Level: Easy<br>Type: Factual<br>Ans: D | 11.<br>A.<br>B.<br>C.<br>D. | Who consistently overestimates their IQs?<br>professors<br>college students<br>females<br>males |
| p. 282<br>Defining Intelligence<br>Level: Easy<br>Type: Conceptual<br>Ans: D<br>*www* | 12.<br>A.<br>B.<br>C.<br>D. | Of the following people, who is the <u>most</u> intelligent?<br>Michael Jordan<br>Paul McCartney<br>impossible to say since we don't know their IQ scores<br>impossible to say since we don't have a complete definition of intelligence |
| p. 282<br>Defining Intelligence<br>Level: Easy<br>Type: Factual<br>Ans: C | 13.<br><br><br><br>A.<br>B.<br>C.<br>D. | As the class ends, your psych professor says, "Next time, we will discuss an approach to intelligence that measures the cognitive factors that make up intelligence." Since you have already read the assigned reading, you know that she is talking about the _____ approach to intelligence.<br>triarchic theory<br>multiple-intelligence<br>psychometric<br>Terman |

p. 282
Defining Intelligence
Level: Easy
Type: Factual
Ans: A

14.    A focus on measuring the cognitive factors or abilities that make up intellectual performance is characteristic of the _____ approach to intelligence.

A.    psychometric
B.    information processing
C.    triarchic theory
D.    Binet-Simon

p. 282
Defining Intelligence
Level: Easy
Type: Factual
Ans: B

15.    What historical figure is most closely associated to the two-factor theory of intelligence?

A.    Clarence Thomas
B.    Charles Spearman
C.    Alfred Binet
D.    Lewis Terman

p. 282
Defining Intelligence
Level: Easy
Type: Factual
Ans: D

16.    Charles Spearman developed the _____ theory, which termed the general intelligence factor as "g" and specific factors as "s".

A.    multiple-factor
B.    triarchic
C.    information processing
D.    two-factor

p. 282
Defining Intelligence
Level: Moderate
Type: Factual
Ans: C
*www*

17.    The two-factor theory divides intelligence into:

A.    verbal skills and math skills
B.    spatial abilities and movement abilities
C.    general intelligence and specific abilities
D.    insight about the self and insight about others

p. 282
Defining Intelligence
Level: Easy
Type: Applied
Ans: A

18.    Dottie is very good at making art projects and excels at cooking. Spearman would classify these two skills as:

A.    *"s"*
B.    *"g"*
C.    analytical
D.    practical thinking

p. 282
Defining Intelligence
Level: Easy
Type: Applied
Ans: C

19.    Using the two-factor theory, which of the following individuals, whose cases were introduced in the module, would be considered the <u>most</u> intelligent?

A.    Serena Williams
B.    Midori
C.    Steve Lu
D.    Gregg Cox

p. 282
Defining Intelligence
Level: Easy
Type: Factual
Ans: A
*PS/SG 13-3*

20. Charles Spearman's two-factor theory says that intelligence is:
A. general factors (g) plus specific mental abilities (a)
B. a group of separate and equally important mental abilities
C. a set of processes for solving problems
D. a combination of biological functions of the brain and nervous system

p. 282
Defining Intelligence
Level: Moderate
Type: Factual
Ans: D

21. The most generally agreed upon aspects of intelligence are:
A. creativity, verbal ability, memory
B. social competence, memory, mathematical ability
C. problem-solving skills, motivation, memory
D. general intelligence, specific factors

p. 282
Defining Intelligence
Level: Easy
Type: Factual
Ans: A

22. Most psychologists believe that ___ is what current intelligence tests measure.
A. "g"
B. "s"
C. "x"
D. verbal skill

p. 282
Defining Intelligence
Level: Moderate
Type: Factual
Ans: D

23. General intelligence, or g, correlates positively with:
A. math skills
B. athletic success
C. social skills
D. academic performance

p. 282
Defining Intelligence
Level: Moderate
Type: Factual
Ans: A

24. Dr. Peterson is a strong proponent of the two-factor theory of intelligence. As an advantage, she offers that the theory can:
A. produce a single score for intelligence
B. examine many separate and distinct mental abilities
C. focus on the components of cognitive processes
D. divide intelligence into three ways of gathering information

p. 282
Defining Intelligence
Level: Easy
Type: Factual
Ans: C

25. Dr. Clark is a noted authority on the two-factor theory of intelligence. When asked what is the best predictor of performance in school and academic settings, Dr. Clark correctly responds:
A. "x"
B. IQ score
C. "g"
D. "s"

p. 282
Defining Intelligence
Level: Moderate
Type: Factual
Ans: B

26. Which of the following is a disadvantage to the two-factor theory of intelligence?
A. The single intelligence score is not predictive of anything.
B. It does not take into account other kinds of intelligence.
C. People get credit for being intelligent in several different domains.
D. The intelligence quotient (IQ score) is based on a general intelligence factor.

p. 282
Defining Intelligence
Level: Easy
Type: Factual
Ans: A

27. A criticism of "g" is that it:
A. may not apply to many Asian and African cultures
B. is a poor predictor of academic performance
C. cannot be transformed into an objective score
D. does not focus on cognitive abilities

p. 282
Defining Intelligence
Level: Moderate
Type: Conceptual
Ans: D

28. Jake, an extraordinarily gifted athlete, is asked to take an intelligence test that measures "g." Will his athletic ability come through on this intelligence test?
A. yes - intelligence tests do measure "g"
B. yes - intelligence tests do measure "s"
C. no - intelligence tests do not measure "g"
D. no - intelligence tests do not measure "s"

p. 283
Defining Intelligence
Level: Moderate
Type: Conceptual
Ans: D

29. Imagine this: You are a public relations manager and are writing an advertising campaign for Howard Gardner's multiple-intelligence theory. What would be the best "slogan" for the campaign?
A. "Intelligence - don't leave home without it."
B. "Intelligence - the one and the only."
C. "Intelligence - analytical, creative, and practical skills."
D. "There's more than one way to be smart."

p. 283
Defining Intelligence
Level: Moderate
Type: Factual
Ans: C

30. Howard Gardner defines intelligence as composed of:
A. an overall mental ability
B. a few dependent mental abilities
C. many separate mental abilities
D. analytical and logical thinking

p. 283
Defining Intelligence
Level: Easy
Type: Factual
Ans: A

31. Separate types of intelligence such as musical intelligence and spatial intelligence are the focus of Howard Gardner's _____ theory.
A. multiple intelligence
B. information processing
C. triarchic
D. two-factor

p. 283
Defining Intelligence
Level: Easy
Type: Conceptual
Ans: B

32. Spearman is to Gardner as _____ is to _____.
A. multiple; single
B. single; multiple
C. triarchic; multiple
D. multiple; triarchic

p. 283
Defining Intelligence
Level: Easy
Type: Factual
Ans: D

33. Gardner argues that standard IQ tests measure:
A. spatial intelligence and verbal intelligence
B. verbal intelligence and body movement intelligence
C. intelligence to understand oneself and others
D. verbal intelligence and logical-mathematical intelligence

| | | |
|---|---|---|
| p. 283<br>Defining Intelligence<br>Level: Easy<br>Type: Factual<br>Ans: D | 34.<br><br><br><br>A.<br>B.<br>C.<br>D. | Using multiple-intelligence theory, which of the following individuals, whose cases were introduced in the module, would be considered the <u>most</u> intelligent?<br>Bill Gates<br>Midori<br>Steve Lu<br>none of individuals are more intelligent |
| p. 283<br>Defining Intelligence<br>Level: Difficult<br>Type: Conceptual<br>Ans: D | 35.<br><br>A.<br>B.<br>C.<br><br>D. | If you wanted to develop a school based on Gardner's theory of intelligence, you would provide students with training in:<br>physical education, which improves mental functioning<br>verbal and math skills, which promote general intelligence<br>analytical and logical thinking, which promote better practical thinking skills<br>a variety of areas, which are not traditionally associated with IQ tests |
| p. 283<br>Defining Intelligence<br>Level: Moderate<br>Type: Applied<br>Ans: A | 36.<br><br><br>A.<br>B.<br>C.<br><br>D. | A graduate student wanted to test the multiple-intelligence theory developed by Gardner by giving subjects a standard intelligence test. What would Gardner say to this student's proposal?<br>"Multiple intelligences cannot be measured by the standard intelligence test."<br>"There is a strong, positive correlation between $g$ and IQ score."<br>"The multiple-intelligence theory is best tested by analyzing how people solve problems."<br>"Good idea!" |
| p. 283<br>Defining Intelligence<br>Level: Easy<br>Type: Factual<br>Ans: C<br>*PS/SG 13-4* | 37.<br><br>A.<br>B.<br>C.<br>D. | An advantage of both Howard Gardner's multiple intelligence theory and Robert Sternberg's triarchic theory is that they:<br>yield a single score that is useful for predicting academic performance<br>measure each of the five known areas of intelligence<br>take into account abilities not covered by standard IQ tests<br>define intelligence in a way that is completely free of cultural influence |
| p. 283<br>Defining Intelligence<br>Level: Moderate<br>Type: Conceptual<br>Ans: A | 38.<br><br><br>A.<br>B.<br>C.<br><br>D. | Jake, an extraordinarily gifted athlete, is asked to take an intelligence test that is based on Gardner's multiple intelligence theory. Will his athletic ability come through on this intelligence test?<br>yes - this type of intelligence test measures body movement intelligence<br>yes - this type of intelligence test measures "g"<br>no - this type of intelligence test does not measure body movement intelligence<br>no - this type of intelligence test does not measure "g" |
| p. 283<br>Defining Intelligence<br>Level: Moderate<br>Type: Factual<br>Ans: D | 39.<br>A.<br>B.<br><br>C.<br>D. | An advantage of the multiple intelligence approach is that it:<br>can reduce intelligence to a single score<br>uses standard measuring techniques to assess the different types of intelligence<br>identified all possible types of intelligence<br>recognizes people with different types of intelligence |

p. 283
Defining Intelligence
Level: Easy
Type: Factual
Ans: C

40. Which of the following is a problem with the multiple intelligence approach?
A. emphasizing who is more intelligent
B. giving people credit for several areas of intelligence
C. not knowing how many intelligences there are
D. not allowing for independence among the mental abilities

p. 283
Defining Intelligence
Level: Moderate
Type: Factual
Ans: A

41. For Sternberg, intelligence is measured by:
A. analyzing the steps that people take in solving problems
B. asking people to define various types of words
C. how well they do in academic settings
D. the activation of neural assemblies in the cerebral cortex

p. 283
Defining Intelligence
Level: Moderate
Type: Conceptual
Ans: B

42. Robert Sternberg's model of intelligence differs from the traditional psychometric model in that Sternberg believes that:
A. intelligence is inherited
B. intelligence includes how people process information to solve problems in the real world
C. IQ tests are biased toward minorities
D. there is only one kind of intelligence

p. 283
Defining Intelligence
Level: Easy
Type: Factual
Ans: B
*www*

43. Robert Sternberg's triarchic theory focuses on the three:
A. types of IQ testing procedures
B. ways of gathering and processing information
C. forms of emotional expression
D. parts of the brain used for memory

p. 283
Defining Intelligence
Level: Easy
Type: Factual
Ans: C

44. The triarchic theory focuses on the three aspects of intelligence. Which of the following is not among the three as presented in the textbook?
A. analytical
B. problem solving
C. affective
D. practical

p. 283
Defining Intelligence
Level: Easy
Type: Factual
Ans: B

45. The triarchic theory approach to intelligence emphasizes the:
A. machine-like efficiency with which our computer minds crunch numbers and sort data
B. cognitive processes people use to solve problems
C. biological changes in the brain and nervous system that result from information input
D. single core ability on which all related intellectual skills are based

| | | |
|---|---|---|
| p. 283<br>Defining Intelligence<br>Level: Moderate<br>Type: Conceptual<br>Ans: D | 46. | You take part in a study in which you are asked to talk out loud as you solve a series of difficult problems. The researcher takes notes on your strategies in order to study the mental processes you use to solve various problems. This researcher is using the _____ approach to the study of intelligence. |

A. behavioral
B. humanistic
C. psychometric
D. triarchic

| | | |
|---|---|---|
| p. 283<br>Defining Intelligence<br>Level: Easy<br>Type: Factual<br>Ans: A | 47. | Robert Sternberg's triarchic theory has the advantage of: |

A. giving credit to people for abilities that are not normally measured by standard tests of intelligence
B. explaining differences in intelligence between people
C. stressing affective factors
D. identifying parts of the brain that are involved in critical thinking

| | | |
|---|---|---|
| p. 283<br>Defining Intelligence<br>Level: Easy<br>Type: Factual<br>Ans: C | 48. | Which of the following is a disadvantage to the triarchic approach? |

A. it does not give people credit for being intelligent in multiple ways
B. it ignores the influence that problem-solving skills have on overall intelligence
C. only a few tests are available to measure the various ways that people think
D. there is no consideration of analytical thinking

| | | |
|---|---|---|
| p. 283<br>Defining Intelligence<br>Level: Easy<br>Type: Conceptual<br>Ans: D | 49. | Gardner is to multiple intelligence as Sternberg is to _____. |

A. psychometric
B. specific factors
C. general factor
D. information processing

| | | |
|---|---|---|
| p. 283<br>Defining Intelligence<br>Level: Easy<br>Type: Factual<br>Ans: B<br>*PS/SG 13-5* | 50. | _____theory would best take account of Serena William's tennis and Midori's music achievements. |

A. Spearman's two factor theory of intelligence
B. Gardner's multiple-intelligence theory of intelligence
C. Sternberg's triarchic theory of intelligence
D. Gates' "wealth rules" theory of intelligence

| | | |
|---|---|---|
| p. 283<br>Defining Intelligence<br>Level: Easy<br>Type: Factual<br>Ans: C | 51. | Why has the concept of "g" remained so popular among psychologists? |

A. "g" takes into account musical, athletic, and creative forms of intelligence.
B. The research clearly shows the idea of multiple intelligences is not valid.
C. Most of the research on intelligence is based on the psychometric approach.
D. The multiple-intelligence theory is widely accepted.

| | | |
|---|---|---|
| p. 284<br>Defining Intelligence<br>Level: Easy<br>Type: Factual<br>Ans: D<br>*PS/SG 13-6* | 52. | All of the following except _____ size have been proposed as indications of intelligence. |

A. head
B. skull
C. brain
D. neuron

p. 284
Measuring Intelligence
Level: Easy
Type: Factual
Ans: B

53.    Francis Galton believed that intelligence was:
A.    acquired or learned
B.    inherited or biological
C.    correlated with brain size
D.    due to both nature and nurture

p. 284
Measuring Intelligence
Level: Easy
Type: Factual
Ans: A

54.    Based upon observations, Galton concluded that intelligence could be measured by assessing:
A.    head size
B.    reaction to a puzzle box
C.    responses to inkblots
D.    reading comprehension

p. 284
Measuring Intelligence
Level: Easy
Type: Factual
Ans: D

55.    Francis Galton attempted to determine the relationship between _____ and _____.
A.    brain size; IQ
B.    reaction to a puzzle box; IQ
C.    responses to inkblots; head size
D.    head size; students' grade point averages

p. 284
Measuring Intelligence
Level: Easy
Type: Factual
Ans: B

56.    According to recent research, the correlation between head size and intelligence is:
A.    .05
B.    .19
C.    .68
D.    1.91

p. 284
Measuring Intelligence
Level: Moderate
Type: Conceptual
Ans: C

57.    You are reading a paper written in the late 1800s by Paul Broca on intelligence. Of the following, what are you most likely to read?
A.    "Triarchic theory of intelligence is so burdened with shortcomings as to be useless."
B.    "Gardner's work on the two-factor theory is well-supported by the evidence."
C.    "I believe that there is a relationship between the size of one's brain and one's intelligence."
D.    "The evidence suggests a poor relationship between brain size and intelligence."

p. 284
Measuring Intelligence
Level: Moderate
Type: Factual
Ans: B

58.    What would a positive correlation between brain size and intelligence mean as revealed by MRI scans?
A.    size of brain determines intelligence
B.    there is a relationship between brain size and intelligence
C.    greater use of the brain makes it grow in size
D.    mentally retarded individuals have the smallest brains

| | | |
|---|---|---|
| p. 284<br>Measuring Intelligence<br>Level: Easy<br>Type: Factual<br>Ans: C | 59.<br>A.<br>B.<br>C.<br>D. | The correlation between brain size and intelligence is about:<br>-.25<br>+.01<br>+.35<br>+.75 |

| | | |
|---|---|---|
| p. 284<br>Measuring Intelligence<br>Level: Moderate<br>Type: Factual<br>Ans: D | 60.<br><br>A.<br><br>B.<br><br>C.<br><br>D. | Your cousin says that males are more intelligence because their brains are larger. What is your reasoned response?<br>It is just the opposite; females are more intelligent because their brains are larger.<br>Actually, females have large brains, but there is no gender difference in intelligence.<br>The difference in brain size does account for increased intelligence in males.<br>There is no significant gender difference in intelligence. |

| | | |
|---|---|---|
| p. 285<br>Measuring Intelligence<br>Level: Easy<br>Type: Factual<br>Ans: D | 61.<br>A.<br>B.<br>C.<br><br>D. | Alfred Binet differed from many of his predecessors, in that he:<br>believed that intelligence could not be measured by standardized tests<br>saw intelligence in purely physiological terms<br>believed that tests to measure intelligence were not potentially discriminatory<br>did not believe that intelligence could be measured by assessing head or brain size |

| | | |
|---|---|---|
| p. 285<br>Measuring Intelligence<br>Level: Easy<br>Type: Factual<br>Ans: A<br>*PS/SG 13-8* | 62.<br>A.<br><br>B.<br><br>C.<br>D. | The original purpose of Binet's Intelligence Scale was to:<br>differentiate children of normal intelligence from those who needed extra help<br>identify specially gifted children who could benefit from government scholarships<br>isolate those children who were so slow nothing would help them<br>replace the much criticized SAT in college admissions |

| | | |
|---|---|---|
| p. 285<br>Measuring Intelligence<br>Level: Moderate<br>Type: Factual<br>Ans: B | 63.<br><br>A.<br>B.<br><br>C.<br>D. | Binet believed that intelligence was _____ and that it could be measured by _____.<br>a general ability; putting the individual into novel situations<br>a collection of mental abilities; assessing a person's ability to perform cognitive tasks<br>a collection of mental abilities; reaction time<br>genetic; assessing a person's skull size |

| | | |
|---|---|---|
| p. 285<br>Measuring Intelligence<br>Level: Easy<br>Type: Factual<br>Ans: C | 64.<br><br>A.<br>B.<br>C.<br><br>D. | What provided the motivation behind Alfred Binet developing the first standardized intelligence test?<br>With World War I, the army had to determine who was fit for service.<br>His own child was mentally retarded.<br>He was appointed to a commission to develop a method to identify children who needed special help.<br>He conducted research as part of his graduate studies. |

p. 285
Measuring Intelligence
Level: Easy
Type: Factual
Ans: A

65. Who developed the world's first standardized intelligence test?
A. Alfred Binet and Theodore Simon
B. Francis Galton and B. F. Skinner
C. Howard Gardner
D. Clarence Thomas

p. 285
Measuring Intelligence
Level: Easy
Type: Factual
Ans: B

66. The world's first standardized intelligence test was introduced by Binet and Simon in:
A. 1879
B. 1905
C. 1923
D. 1942

p. 285
Measuring Intelligence
Level: Easy
Type: Factual
Ans: C
www

67. _____ gives an indication of a child's intelligence by comparing her score on an intelligence test to the scores of average children her same age.
A. Intellectual age
B. Cognitive age
C. Mental age
D. Formula age

p. 285
Measuring Intelligence
Level: Easy
Type: Applied
Ans: B

68. Bethany has a mental age of 5. This means that she must:
A. be 5 years of age
B. have answered test items that could be answered by an average 5-year-old
C. have answered at least half of the items considered appropriate for the average 6-year-old
D. have an intelligence level that matches her chronological age

p. 285
Measuring Intelligence
Level: Easy
Type: Factual
Ans: D

69. Name the individual who revised Binet's test and developed the formula for intelligence quotient score.
A. Charles Spearman
B. Paul Simon
C. Karl Stanford
D. Lewis Terman

p. 285
Measuring Intelligence
Level: Easy
Type: Factual
Ans: C

70. The intelligence quotient (IQ) score is computed by dividing a child's _____ by the child's _____ and multiplying by 100.
A. number of correct answers; number of incorrect answers
B. number of correct answers; total number of questions asked
C. mental age; chronological age
D. chronological age; mental age

p. 285
Measuring Intelligence
Level: Easy
Type: Factual
Ans: C
www

71. On an intelligence test, a 5-year-old child is able to answer the questions that the *average 6-year-old* can answer, but is *not* able to answer the 7-year-old questions. The child's IQ would be:
A. 100
B. 125
C. 120
D. 95

p. 285
Measuring Intelligence
Level: Easy
Type: Factual
Ans: D

72. On an intelligence test, a 5-year-old child is able to answer the questions that the *average 4-year-old* can answer, but is *not* able to answer the 5-year-old questions.  The child's IQ would be:
   A. 220
   B. 100
   C. 90
   D. 80

p. 285
Measuring Intelligence
Level: Easy
Type: Factual
Ans: B

73. The average fourteen-year-old will have a ratio IQ score of:
   A. 80
   B. 100
   C. 120
   D. impossible to calculate

p. 285
Measuring Intelligence
Level: Easy
Type: Factual
Ans: D

74. If you were to take an intelligence test, your IQ score would actually be called:
   A. interval IQ
   B. nominal IQ
   C. ratio IQ
   D. deviation IQ

p. 286
Measuring Intelligence
Level: Moderate
Type: Conceptual
Ans: B

75. Harrison is going on a blind date with Nancy.  He knows a limited amount about her, including her IQ.  She has an IQ of 100.  What does that tell Harrison about Nancy?
   A. She is a very creative person.
   B. Nancy has average cognitive abilities.
   C. Nancy can be a very compassionate person, sensitive to the needs of others.
   D. She is a strong-willed, but emotional person.

p. 286
Measuring Intelligence
Level: Moderate
Type: Conceptual
Ans: B

76. John is going on a blind date with Michelle.  He knows a limited amount about her, including her IQ.  She has an IQ of 120.  What does that tell  John about Michelle?
   A. She is a very creative person.
   B. Michelle has above average cognitive abilities.
   C. Michelle can be a very compassionate person, sensitive to the needs of others.
   D. She is a strong-willed, but emotional person.

p. 286
Measuring Intelligence
Level: Easy
Type: Factual
Ans: D

77. According to your textbook, who has the highest IQ?
   A. Jonathan Swift
   B. J. D. Salinger
   C. John F. Kennedy
   D. Marilyn vos Savant

p. 286
Measuring Intelligence
Level: Moderate
Type: Conceptual
Ans: D

78. Professor Lundberg starts his lecture with, "Today, we are going to examine psychometrics."  Which of the following props is Professor Lundberg most likely to have brought to class with him today?
   A. William James' early writings
   B. a video on Sigmund Freud
   C. a model of the brain
   D. the Wechsler Adult Intelligence Scale - Revised

p. 286
Measuring Intelligence
Level: Easy
Type: Factual
Ans: C

79. Of the following, which test is the most widely used IQ test today?
A. Multiple Intelligence Test
B. Binet-Simon Intelligence Test
C. Wechsler Adult Intelligence Scale
D. Stanford-Binet test

p. 286
Measuring Intelligence
Level: Easy
Type: Factual
Ans: D

80. Your friend took an intelligence test. Knowing something about intelligence, you ask her to describe the experience. She says, "There were about 15 other people taking the test at the same time. I think it was called the Wechsler Test." What she correct?
A. Yes
B. No - the Weschler tests are only given in small groups of less than five people.
C. No - the Weschler tests are no longer given and have been replaced by the Binet-Simon test.
D. No - the Wechsler tests are given on a one-to-one basis, not in a group.

p. 286
Measuring Intelligence
Level: Easy
Type: Factual
Ans: A
*www*

81. The current version of the Wechsler Adult Intelligence Scale consists of items which assess:
A. verbal and performance skills
B. general intelligence and specific abilities
C. analytical and logical thinking skills
D. practical thinking and problem-solving abilities

p. 286
Measuring Intelligence
Level: Easy
Type: Factual
Ans: C

82. Which of the following is *not* true about the Wechsler intelligence scales?
A. There is a scale for children called the Wechsler Intelligence Scale for Children - Revised
B. People 16 years and older take the Wechsler Adult Intelligence Scale - Revised
C. All the Wechsler scales give a single IQ score
D. A trained examiner administers the scales

p. 286
Measuring Intelligence
Level: Easy
Type: Factual
Ans: C

83. Which of the following IQ tests for children has a similar test for adults?
A. the Binet-Simon test
B. the Stanford-Binet test
C. the Wechsler test
D. the Tolman test

p. 286
Measuring Intelligence
Level: Easy
Type: Factual
Ans: B

84. The Wechsler scales of intelligence are administered:
A. in large groups
B. one-on-one
C. in groups no larger than five
D. in groups no larger than three

p. 286
Measuring Intelligence
Level: Easy
Type: Factual
Ans: A

85. A psychologist administers an intelligence test consisting of subtests such as arranging pictures in a meaningful order, using codes and assembling objects. The psychologist is administering which test?
A. one of the Wechsler scales
B. the Stanford-Binet
C. the Binet
D. MMPI

p. 286
Measuring Intelligence
Level: Moderate
Type: Applied
Ans: A

86. Dr. Howarth, a psychologist, is giving an intelligence test to a subject. The subject takes a number of subtests including information, comprehension, arithmetic, and digit span. These subtests are for:
A. verbal scale of the Wechsler
B. performance scale of the Wechsler
C. cognitive scale of the Wechsler
D. general knowledge scale of the Stanford-Binet

p. 286
Measuring Intelligence
Level: Moderate
Type: Applied
Ans: B

87. As Gwen reviews her performance on the WAIS-III, she asks the psychologist who administered the test what subtests make up the performance scale. What are some examples of subtests on the performance scale?
A. comprehension, vocabulary
B. digit symbol, block design
C. arithmetic, digit span
D. similarities, digit span

p. 286
Measuring Intelligence
Level: Easy
Type: Applied
Ans: A

88. With what part of the Wechsler Adult Intelligence Scale would a person for whom English is a second language have the most difficulty?
A. vocabulary
B. digit symbol
C. picture arrangement
D. object assembly

p. 286
Measuring Intelligence
Level: Easy
Type: Factual
Ans: D

89. Of the following, which was added to the Wechsler tests of intelligence to rule out cultural or education problems that might hinder a person's score?
A. emotional scale
B. digit span scale
C. similarities scale
D. performance scale

p. 286
Measuring Intelligence
Level: Easy
Type: Applied
Ans: C

90. Jerry has problems with concentration and is a poor test taker. With which part of the Wechsler Adult Intelligence Scale will he have the most difficulty?
A. similarities
B. information
C. performance scale
D. verbal scale

p. 287
Measuring Intelligence
Level: Easy
Type: Factual
Ans: B

91. You have recently had your handwriting analyzed to measure your intelligence. Much to your surprise, handwriting analysis is usually:
A. as good as the Wechsler intelligence scales
B. no better than a good guess
C. as good as the Simon-Binet scale
D. a reliable and valid measure of intelligence

p. 287
Measuring Intelligence
Level: Easy
Type: Factual
Ans: C

92. Psychological tests must have two characteristics and they are:
A. standardization and validity
B. correlation and standardization
C. reliability and validity
D. standardization and reliability

p. 287
Measuring Intelligence
Level: Easy
Type: Factual
Ans: C

93. If a test measures what it is supposed to be measuring, then we can say that the test is:
A. reliable
B. consistent
C. valid
D. organic

p. 287
Measuring Intelligence
Level: Easy
Type: Factual
Ans: A

94. This question measures your understanding of an important concept in an intelligence test because it is designed to. This refers to the question's:
A. validity
B. reliability
C. practical nature
D. clarity

p. 287
Measuring Intelligence
Level: Easy
Type: Conceptual
Ans: D

95. The oil dip stick in your car actually measures how much oil there is in the car's engine. Therefore, the dip stick is a _____ measure.
A. psychometric
B. distributed
C. correlational
D. valid

p. 287
Measuring Intelligence
Level: Moderate
Type: Conceptual
Ans: C
www

96. If a calculator actually subtracted numbers when you pushed the addition button, you would question the _____ of the addition button because it doesn't do what it is supposed to do.
A. deviation score
B. correlation
C. validity
D. reliability

p. 287
Measuring Intelligence
Level: Moderate
Type: Applied
Ans: A

97. A math teacher, wishing to include a practical question on a test, asks students to calculate how many games out of first place a baseball team is, given its won/lost record and that of the first-place team. After the test, a student complains that the question tested knowledge of baseball, not math. The student is criticizing the _____ of the question.
A. validity
B. reliability
C. practical nature
D. clarity

p. 287
Measuring Intelligence
Level: Moderate
Type: Factual
Ans: B

98. How could a test's validity be checked?
A. Let subjects take the test several times within one month.
B. Correlate subjects' scores with their scores from a test with proven validity.
C. Some subjects take the first half of the test and others take the second half and then the scores are compared.
D. Develop two versions of the same test and examine the correlation between the two scores.

p. 287
Measuring Intelligence
Level: Easy
Type: Applied
Ans: D

99. A psychologist says that a verbal aptitude test that he developed is quite valid. His statement is true only if his test:
A. generates the same score each time the test is given
B. provides consistent results
C. generates an overall IQ score
D. correlates with another measure of verbal aptitude that is valid

p. 287
Measuring Intelligence
Level: Moderate
Type: Factual
Ans: D

100. According to Ed Zigler, academic performance depends upon three factors. What are they?
A. family background, age, motivation
B. cognitive abilities, family background, IQ
C. reading ability, motivation, health
D. cognitive abilities, achievement, motivation

p. 287
Measuring Intelligence
Level: Easy
Type: Applied
Ans: C
*PS/SG 13-11*

101. Ten times your sister jumps on the scale and ten times it reads 115 pounds. "Wow, " she exclaims, "I'm taller than the average American woman!" Her results are:
A. both reliable and valid
B. neither reliable nor valid
C. reliable, but not valid
D. valid, but not reliable

p. 287
Measuring Intelligence
Level: Easy
Type: Factual
Ans: B

102. A test is said to be reliable if it:
A. measures what it is supposed to measure
B. gives consistent results for any given person
C. tests many different abilities
D. does not show racial and ethnic differences in scores

p. 287
Measuring Intelligence
Level: Easy
Type: Factual
Ans: A

103. Handwriting analysis to measure intelligence may have _____, but definitely lacks _____.
A. reliability; validity
B. correlation; heritability
C. validity; heritability
D. reliability; correlation

p. 287
Measuring Intelligence
Level: Easy
Type: Conceptual
Ans: C

104. Based on the definition presented in your text, reliability means the same thing as:
A. a correlation
B. standardization
C. consistency
D. validity

p. 287
Measuring Intelligence
Level: Moderate
Type: Conceptual
Ans: B

105. Eric is a good friend of yours, but you really don't know why. Sometimes you can count on him for support or to do something, and other times he forgets or comes up with some excuse. If your friend was a psychological test, he would lack:
A. correlation
B. reliability
C. norming
D. ecology

p. 287
Measuring Intelligence
Level: Easy
Type: Applied
Ans: A

106. Allison scores a 29 the first time she takes her driver's test, and she scores a 28 the second time she takes the test. In this case, the driver's test can be said to have:
A. reliability
B. validity
C. a normal distribution
D. an ecological approach

p. 287
Measuring Intelligence
Level: Moderate
Type: Conceptual
Ans: C

107. "Each time I enter this command on my computer, it does different things." This person ought to toss this computer because it has low:
A. heritability
B. validity
C. reliability
D. distribution

p. 287
Measuring Intelligence
Level: Moderate
Type: Conceptual
Ans: C

108. A psychologist tries out a new intelligence test on a child. One month later, she administers the same test to the same child and finds little correlation between the two administrations of the test. In testing terminology, it would be said that the test is:
A. context-dependent
B. sensitive
C. unreliable
D. invalid

p. 287
Measuring Intelligence
Level: Easy
Type: Applied
Ans: D

109. Scores on the verbal scale of the WAIS-III is stable from age 20 to 74. This suggests that the scale has:
A. a normal distribution
B. high validity
C. high distribution
D. high reliability

p. 287
Measuring Intelligence
Level: Moderate
Type: Factual
Ans: A

110. Why is there an overall decrease in performance on IQ scores from age 20 to 74?
A. changes in psychological and physiological functioning
B. poor reliability
C. poor validity
D. changes in the test itself over the years

p. 288
Distribution and Use
 of IQ Scores
Level: Easy
Type: Factual
Ans: B
*PS/SG 13-12*

111. If you measured the intelligence of everyone in the United States, a distribution of all the scores would look like a:
A. curve sloping gently upward to the right
B. bell-shaped curve
C. flat horizon line with a skyscraper in the middle
D. curve that rises and falls at regular intervals

p. 288
Distribution and Use
  of IQ Scores
Level: Easy
Type: Factual
Ans: C

112.  A normal distribution is one in which:
A.  the majority of scores are high
B.  the majority of scores are low
C.  the majority of scores fall in the middle
D.  all scores fall in the middle range

p. 288
Distribution and Use
  of IQ Scores
Level: Easy
Type: Factual
Ans: A

113.  If you were to describe a normal distribution as a shape, you would say that it resembles:
A.  a bell
B.  two evenly elevated hills
C.  a rectangle
D.  a line slowly moving upward

p. 288
Distribution and Use
  of IQ Scores
Level: Easy
Type: Factual
Ans: B
*www*

114.  The average IQ score in a normal distribution is:
A.  85
B.  100
C.  115
D.  120

p. 288
Distribution and Use
  of IQ Scores
Level: Easy
Type: Factual
Ans: C

115.  In a normal distribution of IQ scores, what percentage of people have a score between 70 and 130?
A.  54%
B.  68.26%
C.  95.44%
D.  99.9%

p. 288
Distribution and Use
  of IQ Scores
Level: Easy
Type: Factual
Ans: B

116.  In a normal distribution of IQ scores, what percentage of people have a score between 85 and 115?
A.  54%
B.  68.26%
C.  95.44%
D.  99.9%

p. 288
Distribution and Use
  of IQ Scores
Level: Easy
Type: Factual
Ans: A

117.  An IQ of 145 or higher suggested a person who is gifted. A score of below 70 suggests mild retardation. One use of IQ tests is to provide:
A.  categories of mental abilities
B.  guidelines for psychotherapy
C.  evidence of probable success in life
D.  labels for people

p. 288
Distribution and Use
  of IQ Scores
Level: Easy
Type: Applied
Ans: C
*www*

118.  Judith has an IQ of 65 and has problems and limitations in communication and self-care. Judith might be considered to be:
A.  mentally retarded in communication, gifted otherwise
B.  autistic
C.  mentally retarded
D.  normal

p. 288
Distribution and Use
  of IQ Scores
Level: Easy
Type: Factual
Ans: D

119.   Dewayne has a subaverage IQ.  Given his IQ, is Dewayne mentally
       retarded?
A.     Yes - Dewayne fits the definition of mental retardation
B.     No - IQ tests are no longer used to defined mental retardation
C.     No - the IQ score must be significantly subaverage
D.     No - Dewayne does not have limitations in adaptive skills

p. 288
Distribution and Use
  of IQ Scores
Level: Easy
Type: Applied
Ans: A
*www*

120.   Laura has an IQ of 87 and has problems with self-care, social skills, and
       safety.  Is Laura considered mentally retarded?
A.     no - her IQ is not subaverage
B.     no - she needs limitations in four areas, she has problems in three areas
C.     no - she does not have limitation in language
D.     yes - she fits the definition of mental retardation

p. 288
Distribution and Use
  of IQ Scores
Level: Easy
Type: Factual
Ans: D

121.   In addition to intelligence, the definition of mental retardation now includes
       the notion of:
A.     temperament
B.     creative abilities
C.     literacy
D.     adaptive skills

p. 288
Distribution and Use
  of IQ Scores
Level: Easy
Type: Factual
Ans: C

122.   Ofelia has borderline mental retardation.  She has an IQ of ____.
A.     27
B.     41
C.     65
D.     103

p. 288
Distribution and Use
  of IQ Scores
Level: Moderate
Type: Applied
Ans: A

123.   Alan is mildly mentally retarded.  What can we expect with regard to
       Alan's functioning in the future?
A.     Alan will become partially independent, but must still rely upon others for
       support
B.     Alan will learn to read and write and become self-supporting
C.     Alan will need custodial care in some kind of institution
D.     He will require much supervision

p. 288
Distribution and Use
  of IQ Scores
Level: Easy
Type: Applied
Ans: D

124.   Every day, Bart travels from home to his work.  At work he stuffs envelopes
       and is taught basic living skills.  At the end of the day, he goes back home.
       He has become a self-supporting member of society.  He has mental
       retardation to the _____ level.
A.     severe
B.     profound
C.     moderate
D.     borderline

125. To be classified as severe/profoundly mentally retarded, one of the requirements is an IQ of:
A. 75 to 105
B. 50 to 75
C. 35 to 50
D. 20 to 40

126. A ten-year-old child suffered brain damage when he fell off his skateboard. What type of mental retardation might follow his accident?
A. cultural-familial retardation
B. organic retardation
C. educational retardation
D. undifferentiated retardation

127. Dr. Smith diagnoses a child as having genetic brain damage. This probably means that the child has:
A. cultural-familial retardation
B. organic retardation
C. educational retardation
D. undifferentiated retardation

128. What type of retardation is most likely to occur from greatly impoverished environments?
A. organic retardation
B. undifferentiated retardation
C. cultural-familial retardation
D. chronic retardation

129. Maggie is mildly mentally retarded, but shows no signs of brain damage or genetic abnormality. However, Maggie was born into an impoverished family environment. She would probably be diagnosed with:
A. organic retardation
B. undifferentiated retardation
C. cultural-familial retardation
D. chronic retardation

130. IQ tests are:
A. moderately good predictors of success in school
B. very good predictors of success in life but not in school
C. moderately good predictors of motivation but not success
D. very poorly correlated with any other measure of achievement

131. If you know Ricardo's IQ score, how easily could you predict his specific academic performance?
A. very easily - there is strong correlation between IQ and academic performance
B. very easily - there is moderate correlation between IQ and academic performance
C. it would be tricky - there is no correlation
D. difficult - there is moderate correlation between IQ and academic performance

p. 289
Distribution and Use
 of IQ Scores
Level: Moderate
Type: Applied
Ans: D

132. Terry, after reading about the correlation between job performance and IQ scores, says to Randy, "There is a positive correlation in the .20 to .30 range between job performance and IQ. Since you're intelligent, you'll be successful in your career." What should Randy's educated response be?
A. "There is no research studying those two variables."
B. "The correlation is more like .50 to .60."
C. "There is no positive correlation between job performance and IQ!"
D. "You can't predict my personal job performance from my specific IQ."

p. 289
Distribution and Use
 of IQ Scores
Level: Moderate
Type: Factual
Ans: A

133. IQ scores have the lowest correlation with:
A. job performance
B. grades
C. reading scores
D. total years of education

p. 289
Distribution and Use
 of IQ Scores
Level: Easy
Type: Factual
Ans: C

134. A moderately gifted child has an IQ between:
A. 100-115
B. 120-135
C. 130-150
D. 180-200

p. 289
Distribution and Use
 of IQ Scores
Level: Moderate
Type: Factual
Ans: D
www

135. Which of the following individuals would be classified as "gifted"?
A. Larry, with an IQ score of 100
B. Tanner, with an IQ score of 110
C. Delaney, with an IQ score of 65
D. Katie, with an IQ of 145

p. 289
Distribution and Use
 of IQ Scores
Level: Easy
Type: Factual
Ans: B

136. Terman's longitudinal study followed:
A. children with average IQ scores
B. gifted children with IQ scores from 130 to 200
C. moderately mentally retarded children
D. severely mentally retarded children

p. 289
Distribution and Use
 of IQ Scores
Level: Easy
Type: Factual
Ans: C

137. Terman's longitudinal studies of gifted individuals indicated that, compared to the general population, gifted individuals:
A. suffer more ill health
B. have more emotional problems and hospitalizations
C. tend to be better adjusted
D. show no significant differences

| | | |
|---|---|---|
| p. 290<br>Potential Problems of IQ<br>  Testing<br>Level: Easy<br>Type: Factual<br>Ans: A | 138.<br><br>A.<br><br>B.<br>C.<br><br>D. | What was Binet's original goal in developing an intelligence test?<br>to identify children who were mentally retarded and needed special help<br>and education<br>to identify children who were gifted<br>to identify children who were predisposed to become scientists and<br>engineers<br>to start tracking students with average intelligence over their lifetime |
| p. 290<br>Potential Problems of IQ<br>  Testing<br>Level: Easy<br>Type: Factual<br>Ans: C | 139.<br><br>A.<br>B.<br>C.<br>D. | Which of the following was not among Binet's warnings about intelligence<br>tests?<br>Intelligence tests do not measure innate abilities.<br>Intelligence tests do not measure natural intelligences.<br>Intelligence tests should not be correlated with grades or job performance.<br>Intelligence tests by themselves should not be used to label people. |
| p. 290<br>Potential Problems of IQ<br>  Testing<br>Level: Easy<br>Type: Conceptual<br>Ans: B | 140.<br><br><br>A.<br><br>B.<br>C.<br>D. | Why would a question such as, "Explain what you would do if one speaker<br>of your stereo system stopped working?" not be a good item for an IQ test?<br>There are a number of ways that the problem can be solved, so answers<br>cannot be rated.<br>Not everyone can afford to own a stereo.<br>The question is too easy.<br>The question is too complicated. |
| p. 290<br>Potential Problems of IQ<br>  Testing<br>Level: Moderate<br>Type: Factual<br>Ans: C | 141.<br><br><br>A.<br>B.<br><br>C.<br><br>D. | A lawsuit brought against the San Francisco school system on behalf of all<br>black schoolchildren in the district was based on the finding that a<br>disproportionately:<br>low percentage of black children were receiving educational testing<br>low percentage of black children were being placed in classes for the<br>learning disabled<br>high percentage of black children were enrolled in classes for the mentally<br>retarded<br>high percentage of black children were dropping out of school because  they<br>were not receiving adequate amounts of instruction |
| p. 290<br>Potential Problems of IQ<br>  Testing<br>Level: Moderate<br>Type: Factual<br>Ans: D | 142.<br><br>A.<br><br>B.<br><br>C.<br>D. | What did the judge rule in the class action suit against the San Francisco<br>school system?<br>IQ tests used to determine mental retardation were valid measures of innate<br>intelligence.<br>IQ tests used to determine mental retardation were valid measures of<br>multiple intelligence.<br>IQ tests used to determine mental retardation were culture-free.<br>IQ tests used to determine mental retardation were biased against people of<br>color. |
| p. 290<br>Potential Problems of IQ<br>  Testing<br>Level: Easy<br>Type: Factual<br>Ans: A | 143.<br>A.<br>B.<br>C.<br>D. | What is the status of IQ testing in schools?<br>IQ tests cannot be the only basis for placement in special education classes.<br>Tests based on multiple intelligences must be used.<br>A trained psychologist must administer and interpret the test.<br>The parents of a child whose IQ is measured must assist in the  interpretation<br>of the score. |

p. 290
Potential Problems of IQ
  Testing
Level: Easy
Type: Factual
Ans: C

144.  Why are African American students overrepresented in special classes in many states?
A.  there is a higher number of African American students in schools
B.  because of especially high levels of disability
C.  because of discriminatory placement procedures
D.  IQ tests are more likely to be given to African American students

p. 291
Potential Problems of IQ
  Testing
Level: Easy
Type: Factual
Ans: B

145.  When IQ items test information that is more common in the experience of certain social groups than other groups, the test is said to be:
A.  culture-free
B.  culturally biased
C.  unreliable
D.  valid

p. 291
Potential Problems of IQ
  Testing
Level: Easy
Type: Factual
Ans: D
*PS/SG 13-15*

146.  In intelligence testing, cultural bias refers to:
A.  whether tests are both valid and reliable
B.  intellectual factors like honors classes and high IQ
C.  distrust of non-western cultures
D.  how questions are worded and what experiences they are based on

p. 291
Potential Problems of IQ
  Testing
Level: Easy
Type: Applied
Ans: D

147.  Assume that you are taking an intelligence test developed by psychologists living in the Upper Peninsula of Michigan. One question asks you to define "holy wah" and another asks you how to make the food called "pasties." You could make the argument that this test has:
A.  ecological validity
B.  validity
C.  questions measuring verbal intelligence
D.  cultural bias

p. 291
Potential Problems of IQ
  Testing
Level: Difficult
Type: Factual
Ans: C

148.  According to your textbook, why are some IQ tests culturally biased?
A.  They tend to be developed in colleges and universities in the Midwest.
B.  They measure accumulated knowledge and problem solving strategies that most people have learned.
C.  They measure accumulated knowledge and problem solving strategies that depend on opportunities available to a particular group.
D.  They tend to be developed by psychologists of color.

p. 291
Potential Problems of IQ
  Testing
Level: Easy
Type: Factual
Ans: C
*PS/SG 13-14*

149.  The problem with IQ tests is that they are:
A.  completely culture-free
B.  seldom used to get children into the right classes in school
C.  sometimes used to label people and discriminate against them
D.  unable to predict how well a child will do in school

p. 291
Potential Problems of IQ
  Testing
Level: Easy
Type: Conceptual
Ans: A

150. You hear someone saying that "intelligence is intelligence, no matter where you go in the world." What is the most appropriate reaction based upon Module 13?
A. Different cultures define intelligence differently.
B. If you are smart in one culture, you are going to be smart in all cultures.
C. The concept of "g" is universal and applies to all cultures.
D. Intelligent behavior in one culture is likely to be intelligent behavior in another culture.

p. 291
Potential Problems of IQ
  Testing
Level: Easy
Type: Factual
Ans: D

151. With regard to intelligence, the Taiwanese culture emphasizes _____; in Zambia, there is an emphasis on _____.
A. problem-solving; understanding and relating to others
B. creativity; problem-solving
C. nonintellectual factors; social responsibility
D. understanding and relating to others; social responsibility

p. 291
Potential Problems of IQ
  Testing
Level: Easy
Type: Factual
Ans: D

152. Shyness, fear of strangers, and cultural expectations are called _____ and can influence performance on intelligence tests.
A. triarchic factors
B. "s"
C. "g"
D. nonintellectual factors

p. 291
Potential Problems of IQ
  Testing
Level: Easy
Type: Factual
Ans: A

153. _____ are noncognitive factors that may help or hinder performance on tests.
A. Non-intellectual factors
B. Cultural principles
C. Nurture factors
D. Abecedarian factors

p. 291
Potential Problems of IQ
  Testing
Level: Easy
Type: Applied
Ans: D

154. Juan doesn't do well on tests. His mother believes that nonintellectual factors are the reasons for Juan's poor performance. What is not an example of a nonintellectual factor?
A. attitude
B. experience
C. shyness
D. problem solving skills

p. 292
Nature-Nurture Question
Level: Easy
Type: Factual
Ans: C

155. Which of the following summarizes the debate on the contributions of genetics and environment on intelligence?
A. heredity-neutral
B. neutral-nurture
C. nature-nurture
D. nature-neutral

p. 292
Nature-Nurture Question
Level: Easy
Type: Factual
Ans: D
*PS/SG 13-17*

156. In the matter of intelligence, the answer to the nature-nurture question is that:
A. twin studies prove the predominance of nurture
B. adoption studies prove the predominance of nature
C. intervention programs show that intelligence is fixed at birth
D. both nature and nurture contribute about equally to the formation of intelligence

p. 292
Nature-Nurture Question
Level: Easy
Type: Factual
Ans: B
*www*

157. The nature-nurture question contemplates the contribution of _____ and _____ to the development of intelligence.
A. cultural factors; family environment
B. genetic factors; environmental factors
C. skull size; brain size
D. wealth; education

p. 292
Nature-Nurture Question
Level: Easy
Type: Factual
Ans: A

158. Which family relationship shares the most genes in common?
A. identical twins reared together
B. fraternal twins reared together
C. siblings raised together
D. fraternal twins reared apart

p. 292
Nature-Nurture Question
Level: Moderate
Type: Conceptual
Ans: A

159. If genetic factors contribute to IQ scores, then fraternal twins should have:
A. less similar IQ scores than identical twins
B. more similar IQ scores than identical twins
C. more similar IQ scores than siblings
D. totally different IQ scores

p. 292
Nature-Nurture Question
Level: Moderate
Type: Factual
Ans: C

160. The median correlation in IQ scores for identical twins reared together is ____, while for fraternal twins reared together it is ___.
A. .60; 1.00
B. 1.00; .50
C. .85; .60
D. .50; .50

p. 292
Nature-Nurture Question
Level: Moderate
Type: Factual
Ans: C

161. Based on twin studies, evidence regarding the influence on IQ scores indicates that:
A. 85% is due to genetics, and 15% is due to the environment
B. 85% is due to the environment, and 15% is due to genetics
C. 50% is due to genetics, and 50% is due to the environment
D. neither genetics nor the environment is predictive of intelligence

p. 292
Nature-Nurture Question
Level: Moderate
Type: Factual
Ans: C

162. What happens to the genetic influence on intelligence throughout life?
A. The influence of genetics decreases throughout life.
B. The influence of genetics increases throughout life.
C. It remains relatively constant.
D. Its influence depends on the relative influence of the environment.

p. 293
Nature-Nurture Question
Level: Moderate
Type: Factual
Ans: D

163. The results of adoption studies have suggested that:
A. the environment has no effect on intelligence
B. lower-class children adopted by higher-class families were more likely to drop out of school
C. genetic factors, rather than environmental factors, contribute more to intelligence
D. intelligence can be improved by improving environmental factors

p. 293
Nature-Nurture Question
Level: Moderate
Type: Applied
Ans: D

164. Because she did not want to raise her child in poverty, Alice put her baby up for adoption. If Alice's baby is raised by a middle-income family that provides a good home, what effect could this have on the child's IQ?

A. It will probably be lower than IQs of children who stay with their biological parents.
B. It will not be significantly different from IQs of children who stay in a disadvantaged setting.
C. It will be higher than IQs of children who stay in the disadvantaged setting only if the adoptive parents have above-average IQs.
D. It may be as much as 10-15 points higher than IQs of children who stay in the disadvantaged setting.

p. 293
Nature-Nurture Question
Level: Moderate
Type: Factual
Ans: C

165. A study of French children who had been abandoned as babies by their lower-class parents and adopted by upper-middle-class families found that:

A. being abandoned in early childhood caused the children to have lower IQs
B. the socioeconomic status of one's parents has no effect on one's IQ
C. the adopted children had IQs that were as much as 14 points higher than those of children raised by their own lower-class parents
D. the children's IQs were affected more by the intelligence of their parents than by socioeconomic status

p. 293
Nature-Nurture Question
Level: Easy
Type: Factual
Ans: A

166. _____ is a number than indicates the amount or proportion of some ability that can be attributed to genetic factors.

A. Heritability
B. Genetic range
C. Reaction range
D. Nature index

p. 293
Nature-Nurture Question
Level: Easy
Type: Factual
Ans: C

167. Of the following attributes, which one has the highest heritability score?

A. spatial ability
B. vocabulary
C. memory
D. extraversion

p. 293
Nature-Nurture Question
Level: Moderate
Type: Factual
Ans: B
www

168. The concept of a reaction range indicates that:

A. intelligence is fixed at birth, due to genetic factors
B. intelligence may increase or decrease as a result of the environment
C. there is a "critical period" for the development of intelligence
D. heredity establishes a very narrow range for intellectual development

p. 293
Nature-Nurture Question
Level: Moderate
Type: Factual
Ans: A

169. Two friends are debating about the nature of IQ. Sam claims that it measures innate abilities. Joseph says that it is influenced strongly by environmental factors. Which of the following could Joseph truthfully use to support his arguments?

A. It has been estimated that IQ can vary up to 15 points depending on environment.
B. Identical twins raised together tend to have similar IQs.
C. It is likely that two unrelated people raised in different environments will have different IQs.
D. Adopted children have IQs that are similar to those of children who have stayed with their natural lower-class parents.

p. 293
Nature-Nurture Question
Level: Moderate
Type: Conceptual
Ans: D

170. You have set up a web site describing the contributions of nature and nurture to intelligence. To accurately describe the contributions, you select the most appropriate web site address. What is it?
A. www.biology.edu
B. www.schooling.edu
C. www.genes.edu
D. www.interaction.edu

p. 294
Nature-Nurture Question
Level: Easy
Type: Factual
Ans: A

171. Herrnstein and Murray argued that the ___ point difference in average IQ scores between Caucasian-Americans and African-Americans was due primarily to _____.
A. 15; inherited or genetic factors
B. 5; environmental factors
C. 20; environmental factors
D. 25; inherited or genetic factors

p. 294
Nature-Nurture Question
Level: Moderate
Type: Factual
Ans: C
*PS/SG 13-21*

172. One problem with the racial conclusions drawn by the authors of *The Bell Curve* is that:
A. Blacks and Whites consistently score the same on intelligence tests
B. the APA prohibits collecting data about race in research on intelligence
C. skin color is not reliable in identifying racial makeup
D. Richard Herrnstein and Charles Murray did not say IQ differences were genetic

p. 294
Nature-Nurture Question
Level: Easy
Type: Factual
Ans: C

173. An "environmental factor" explanation for the racial differences in IQ scores would focus on:
A. hormonal differences
B. genetic differences
C. poverty
D. biological factors

p. 294
Nature-Nurture Question
Level: Moderate
Type: Factual
Ans: B

174. A task force of the American Psychological Association said that the development of an <u>individual's</u> intelligence is significantly influenced by:
A. discrimination
B. genetic factors
C. poverty
D. educational opportunities

p. 294
Nature-Nurture Question
Level: Moderate
Type: Factual
Ans: A

175. The American Psychological Association Task Force on the racial differences in intelligence found:
A. no evidence that genetic factors play a primary role in IQ differences among races
B. evidence that genetic factors play a small role in IQ differences among races
C. that intelligence tests do not discriminate against minorities
D. educational opportunities do not influence intelligence

| | | |
|---|---|---|
| p. 294 | 176. | One shortcoming of the book *The Bell Curve* was its assumption that |
| Nature-Nurture Question | A. | skin color is a good way to identify different races |
| Level: Moderate | B. | intelligence is primarily what is called "g" |
| Type: Factual | C. | intelligence cannot be measured |
| Ans: A | D. | intelligence is multifaceted |

| | | |
|---|---|---|
| p. 294 | 177. | The fact that people differ in genetic instructions by only 3-5% suggests |
| Nature-Nurture Question | | that skin color: |
| Level: Easy | A. | is highly correlated with intelligence |
| Type: Factual | B. | accounts for group differences in intelligence |
| Ans: C | C. | is not a reliable variable to identify racial makeup |
| | D. | is a reliable variable to identify racial makeup |

| | | |
|---|---|---|
| p. 296 | 178. | Lewis Terman recommended that IQ scores be used to: |
| Cultural Diversity: | A. | weed out potential teachers with low IQ's |
| Immigration | B. | prevent retarded people from marrying |
| Level: Moderate | C. | place people in various occupational classes |
| Type: Factual | D. | regulate immigration |
| Ans: C | | |

| | | |
|---|---|---|
| p. 296 | 179. | Laws to regulate immigration, such as the Immigration Law of 1924, were |
| Cultural Diversity: | | often based upon: |
| Immigration | A. | culture-free intelligence tests |
| Level: Moderate | B. | Yerkes' intelligence ranking of European races |
| Type: Factual | C. | the finding that immigrants from northern Europe had the lowest IQ's |
| Ans: B | D. | superior IQ of racial groups from eastern Europe |

| | | |
|---|---|---|
| p. 296 | 180. | Yerkes concluded that the average mental age of white American adults |
| Cultural Diversity: | | was: |
| Immigration | A. | 22 years |
| Level: Easy | B. | 19 years |
| Type: Factual | C. | 13 years |
| Ans: C | D. | 10 years |

| | | |
|---|---|---|
| p. 296 | 181. | Robert Yerkes conducted IQ tests with army recruits for World War I. His |
| Cultural Diversity: | | study found that: |
| Immigration | A. | the IQ test was biased towards ethnic minorities |
| Level: Moderate | B. | immigrants could be ranked by IQ scores according to their country of |
| Type: Factual | | origin |
| Ans: B | C. | the average mental age of white American adults was 25 years, indicative |
| | | of superior intelligence |
| | D. | the use of minimal intelligence scores for occupations was inappropriate |

| | | |
|---|---|---|
| p. 297 | 182. | In comparison to a normal brain, Albert's Einstein's brain: |
| Research Focus: | A. | weighs more |
| New Approaches | B. | has a larger inferior parietal lobe |
| Level: Easy | C. | thicker corpus callosum |
| Type: Factual | D. | has a larger occipital lobe |
| Ans: B | | |

p. 297
Research Focus:
  New Approaches
Level: Easy
Type: Conceptual
Ans: C
*PS/SG 13-23*

183. Can genius, such as Einstein possessed, be found in the brain?
A. yes, because studies of Einstein's brain show enlarged areas (compared to the average brain)
B. no, because genius is composed of variables that can't be measured scientifically
C. possibly, but as yet neuroscience cannot answer this question
D. unlikely, because once a person is deceased the brain can no longer be studied

p. 297
Research Focus:
  New Approaches
Level: Easy
Type: Factual
Ans: B

184. If there is a "g" mental factor then we would expect:
A. the corpus callosum to be especially active when solving language problems
B. a single brain area should be activated when solving different kinds of cognitive tasks
C. that many areas of the brain are activated when solving different types of cognitive problems
D. the inferior parietal lobe to be especially active when solving language problems

p. 297
Research Focus:
  New Approaches
Level: Easy
Type: Factual
Ans: A

185. PET scans provide information on the brain's:
A. blood flow
B. capacity to heal
C. consumption of glucose
D. structure

p. 297
Research Focus:
  New Approaches
Level: Easy
Type: Factual
Ans: C

186. When examining the brains of people engaged in solving verbal or spatial problems, researchers found:
A. different parts of the brain were activated
B. no clear brain area becoming more activated
C. the same general areas of the brain were activated
D. an increase in blood flow to the corpus callosum

p. 298
Application:
  Intervention Programs
Level: Moderate
Type: Factual
Ans: D

187. In an attempt to raise the IQs of children in its district, an inner-city school board opens a number of preschools designed to enrich the environments of these children. Psychologists would call this an:
A. environmental improvement program
B. early advancement program
C. educational-environmental experiment
D. intervention program

p. 298
Application:
  Intervention Programs
Level: Easy
Type: Factual
Ans: C

188. The goal of the Abecedarian Project was to provide:
A. counseling services to parents of children identified as high-risk
B. a well-balanced diet to children who lived in poverty
C. cognitive and social skills needed for success in school to high-risk children
D. financial assistance to mothers who wished to stay home with their young children and give them extra stimulation

| | | |
|---|---|---|
| p. 298<br>Application:<br> Intervention Programs<br>Level: Moderate<br>Type: Factual<br>Ans: B | 189.<br><br>A.<br>B.<br>C.<br>D. | When happened to the IQ scores at ages 12, 15, and 21 of children who participated in the Abecedarian Project?<br>The IQ scores stabilized.<br>Their IQ scores increased.<br>IQ scores of these children decreased.<br>At the age of 12, scores increased, but then decreased at age 21. |
| p. 298<br>Application:<br> Intervention Programs<br>Level: Moderate<br>Type: Factual<br>Ans: A | 190.<br><br>A.<br>B.<br>C.<br>D. | According to research, Head Start children, when they became adolescents were more likely to:<br>be in their age-appropriate class<br>take advanced mathematics in high school<br>drop out<br>make the Honor Roll |
| p. 298<br>Application:<br> Intervention Programs<br>Level: Moderate<br>Type: Factual<br>Ans: C | 191.<br>A.<br>B.<br><br>C.<br>D. | Which of the following is an accurate finding of the Head Start program?<br>Children in Head Start did not show any gains in intellectual skills.<br>Children in Head Start did not show any gains in socio-emotional development.<br>Adolescents who had been in Head Start were more likely to hold jobs.<br>Adolescents who had been in Head Start were more likely to repeat a grade later in schooling. |
| p. 298<br>Application:<br> Intervention Programs<br>Level: Moderate<br>Type: Applied<br>Ans: A | 192.<br><br>A.<br><br>B.<br>C.<br>D. | Alan has been enrolled in the Head Start program. If he is like most children in the project, his parents can expect Alan to:<br>show an improvement in IQ score, but that effect will fade in the next two or three years<br>enjoy school more but not do any better than students not in the project<br>respond well to TV instruction, but not as well to teacher instruction<br>progress in terms of IQ at the same rate as children not in the project |
| p. 299<br>Application:<br> Intervention Programs<br>Level: Moderate<br>Type: Factual<br>Ans: B | 193.<br><br>A.<br>B.<br>C.<br>D. | The IQ scores of children who participated in intervention programs typically _____ once they leave the program.<br>increase<br>decline<br>stabilize<br>destablize |
| p. 299<br>Application:<br> Intervention Programs<br>Level: Moderate<br>Type: Factual<br>Ans: C | 194.<br><br>A.<br>B.<br>C.<br>D. | What is one reason for the decline in IQ scores once children leave an intervention program?<br>Children are no longer wanting to learn.<br>Teachers near the end of the intervention program experience burnout.<br>They return to less stimulating environments.<br>The intervention program is of low quality. |
| p. 299<br>Application:<br> Intervention Programs<br>Level: Easy<br>Type: Applied<br>Ans: C | 195.<br><br><br>A.<br>B.<br>C.<br><br>D. | Dr. Jones, a psychologist working for the government, is evaluating the effectiveness of Head Start. Which of these is the best approach to evaluating its effectiveness?<br>use IQ scores of participants compared to a control group<br>assess social competence of participants<br>use IQ scores, but also measures of social, emotional, and psychological benefits<br>measure the change of IQ scores from pre- to post-program participation |

p. 299
Application:
  Intervention Programs
Level: Easy
Type: Factual
Ans: B

*PS/SG 13-24*

196. Studies of the effectiveness of intervention programs like Head Start suggest that:
A. however well-intentioned, intervention programs don't work
B. there are many social needs and benefits that justify continuing these programs
C. the short-term benefits fail to justify the high costs of these programs
D. the main benefits of these programs go to the middle-class professionals they employ

p. 299
Application:
  Intervention Programs
Level: Easy
Type: Factual
Ans: B

197. According to the textbook, are Head Start and other intervention programs a good deal for the American taxpayer?
A. No - the gains observed in IQ disappear after leaving the program
B. Yes - intervention programs can stop the cycle of poverty
C. No - the two-year Head Start program is ineffective
D. Yes - the self-esteem of Head Start teachers increases

p. 299
Application:
  Intervention Programs
Level: Easy
Type: Factual
Ans: D

*PS/SG 13-25*

198. When you look back at how you rated the intelligence of the five unusual people described on the first page of this module, you might well conclude that intelligence is:
A. a topic that can offend, but people should just get over it
B. like politics and religion, a subject that is beyond scientific discussion
C. a topic psychology would be better off to drop
D. one of the most complicated and controversial topics in psychology

True/False

| | | | |
|---|---|---|---|
| T | | 1. | The psychometric approach to intelligence attempts to measure the cognitive abilities of intelligence. |
| F | *www* | 2. | "g" is a poor predictor of academic performance. |
| F | | 3. | "s" can be represented by an IQ score. |
| T | | 4. | "g" neglects motor and creative abilities. |
| T | *www* | 5. | Gardner proposed that there are several kinds of general intelligence. |
| T | | 6. | Standard intelligence tests measure verbal and logical-mathematical intelligence. |
| T | *www* | 7. | According to Sternberg, intelligence is made up of three different types of reasoning ability. |
| F | | 8. | Gardner and Sternberg support the idea of "g." |
| F | | 9. | Brain size and intelligence are highly correlated. |
| T | *www* | 10. | In the Binet-Simon test, intelligence is measured by cognitive abilities. |
| T | | 11. | In the ratio IQ, the score is a ratio between mental age and chronological age. |
| T | | 12. | The WAIS-III yields a verbal and performance score. |
| T | *www* | 13. | Validity refers to a test's ability to measure what it is supposed to measure. |
| F | | 14. | The changes in performance IQ over the lifespan indicate that the test is not reliable. |
| F | *www* | 15. | The average IQ score is 75. |
| F | | 16. | The most common level of mental retardation is moderate mental retardation. |
| T | *www* | 17. | An impoverished environment would be an example of cultural-familial mental retardation. |
| F | *www* | 18. | IQ is strongly correlated with job performance. |
| F | | 19. | Gifted children are often bored in regular classrooms. |
| F | | 20. | To determine if a student is mentally retarded, just IQ scores should be used. |

| F | www | 21. | Intelligence is not influenced by culture. |
| T |  | 22. | Genetic factors account for about 50% of our intelligence. |
| T |  | 23. | According to the idea of reaction range, intelligence can vary about 10 to 15 points depending upon environmental factors. |
| F | www | 24. | Einstein's brain weighs more than the average adult brain. |
| F |  | 25. | When children leave Head Start, their IQ's typically remain the same. |

Short Answer Essay Questions

1. Describe the two-factor theory. Why is the theory deficient in measuring non-cognitive abilities?

2. Explain the multiple-intelligence theory of Gardner by describing how each of the five cases presented in the introduction are intelligent. (*www*)

3. How might the triarchic theory of intelligence influence the method by which intelligence is measured?

4. What is the relationship between brain size and intelligence? (*www*)

5. Describe the Wechsler Adult Intelligence Scale. Why was a performance scale added to the test?

6. Describe validity and reliability. Why do some people with high IQs do poorly in college? How would you know if an intelligence test was reliable? (*www*)

7. What are the two general causes of mental retardation?

8. What is the nature-nurture question of intelligence? What does an interaction between nature and nurture mean in the context of intelligence?

9. What accounts for group differences in IQ scores? (*www*)

10. What is Head Start? What effect does it have on intelligence over the childhood years? (*www*)

## Module 14 - Thought and Language

p. 305
Introduction
Level: Easy
Type: Factual
Ans: D

1. Module Fourteen starts off by describing a 14-month-old boy's use of _____ to illustrate the complexity of language.
   A. surface structure
   B. definitions
   C. exclamations
   D. single word sentences

p. 305
Introduction
Level: Easy
Type: Factual
Ans: B
*PS/SG 14-1*

2. For Rod Plotnik, this module illustrates the importance of the _____ approach to psychology:
   A. behavioral
   B. cognitive
   C. humanistic
   D. psychodynamic

p. 305
Introduction
Level: Easy
Type: Factual
Ans: B

3. The case of Gordon Parks illustrates:
   A. concept learning
   B. creativity
   C. language development
   D. problem solving

p. 305
Introduction
Level: Easy
Type: Factual
Ans: A

4. The areas of thinking and language are important topics to study in the _____ approach.
   A. cognitive
   B. psychoanalytic
   C. humanistic
   D. behavioral

p. 305
Introduction
Level: Easy
Type: Applied
Ans: C

5. Professor Synder studies how beliefs are changed when information that contradicts the belief is presented. Professor Synder uses the:
   A. humanistic approach
   B. behavioral approach
   C. cognitive approach
   D. psychoanalytic approach

p. 305
Introduction
Level: Easy
Type: Factual
Ans: B

6. The term _____ refers to mental processes that we use to be creative, to form concepts, and to problem solve.
   A. information processing
   B. thinking
   C. cognitive
   D. behavioral

p. 305
Introduction
Level: Easy
Type: Applied
Ans: C
*www*

7. You subscribe to a journal called *Journal of Human Information Processing*. The journal is most likely to take the _____ approach.
   A. psychoanalytical
   B. psychometric
   C. cognitive
   D. behavioral

p. 305
Introduction
Level: Easy
Type: Factual
Ans: C
*www*

8. When we use rules to form and manipulate symbols in order to communicate, we are using:
   A. analogies
   B. prototypes
   C. language
   D. concepts

p. 306
Forming Concepts
Level: Easy
Type: Factual
Ans: D

9. A "concept" can best be defined as a(n):
   A. object that fits a series of prescribed rules
   B. idea regarding the solution to a problem
   C. novel use for an object or tool
   D. way to group items such as events based upon common characteristics

p. 306
Forming Concepts
Level: Easy
Type: Factual
Ans: C
*PS/SG 14-2*

10. Concepts are crucial to effective thinking because without concepts we would:
    A. not know the rules for logical thought
    B. forget most of what we learn
    C. be overwhelmed by apparently unrelated pieces of information
    D. lose our motivation to think

p. 306
Forming Concepts
Level: Easy
Type: Factual
Ans: A
*www*

11. A way we group objects and events based on some shared characteristics is called a _____.
    A. concept
    B. cognition
    C. heuristic
    D. algorithm

p. 306
Forming Concepts
Level: Easy
Type: Applied
Ans: A

12. When you are asked to indicate what Sigmund Freud, Albert Bandura, Abraham Maslow, and Lewis Terman all have in common, you're really being asked to form a(n):
    A. concept
    B. object rule
    C. hierarchy
    D. analogy

p. 306
Forming Concepts
Level: Moderate
Type: Conceptual
Ans: B

13. You overhear Brent talking with David. But the only thing you hear is David saying, "they all have wings." You ask Brent for a clarification and he says, "A bird, a plane, and a butterfly." Then you realize that they're:
    A. talking about transformational rules
    B. grouping objects using some common property they all share
    C. referring to telegraphic speech
    D. overgeneralizing

p. 306
Forming Concepts
Level: Moderate
Type: Factual
Ans: A

14. According to the exemplar theory of concept formation, we list all of the essential properties that define an object, event, or characteristic. When we encounter an event and need to conceptualize it, we proceed to:
    A. find the concept that fits all of the essential properties of that event
    B. compare the selected concept to the prototype
    C. use algorithms
    D. use heuristics

p. 306
Forming Concepts
Level: Moderate
Type: Applied
Ans: B

15. You are playing a guessing game with a child and you want the child to guess "cat." You give clues that the animal has four legs, fur, and whiskers, but the child guesses wrong each time. Then you give the hint that the animal purrs and the child correctly guesses "cat." In terms of concept formation, you supplied the child with a(n):
A. leading clue
B. essential property
C. exemplar
D. prototype

p. 306
Forming Concepts
Level: Moderate
Type: Factual
Ans: D

16. Which of the following is a problem of the exemplar theory of forming concepts?
A. allows us to better store information in memory
B. allows us to identify things without relearning
C. exceptions never occur
D. listing all the defining properties of a concept is very difficult

p. 306
Forming Concepts
Level: Easy
Type: Factual
Ans: C

17. A problem of the exemplar theory of concept formation is that:
A. our memory systems do not function in the way that exemplar theory predicts
B. our prototypes are based upon average features
C. we would have to list all the exceptions that do not fit a particular defintion of an object
D. it takes longer to evaluate events that do not match the prototype

p. 306
Forming Concepts
Level: Easy
Type: Factual
Ans: D

18. A mental image that is based on the average characteristics of an object is called a(n):
A. algorithm
B. heuristic
C. exemplar
D. prototype

p. 306
Forming Concepts
Level: Easy
Type: Conceptual
Ans: D

19. An average bird has feathers, bill, and wings. This is consistent with the:
A. set theory
B. heuristic theory
C. exemplar theory
D. prototype theory

p. 306
Forming Concepts
Level: Moderate
Type: Applied
Ans: C

20. Bill likes to invent. Today he is inventing a new car. He says to himself, "I can visualize what this new car should look like. An average car has an engine, wheels, and so on." His approach to inventing uses the _____ theory of forming concepts.
A. surface
B. heuristic
C. prototype
D. set

p. 306
Forming Concepts
Level: Easy
Type: Conceptual
Ans: B
*www*

21. A prototype for a car would include:
A. all the defining properties of a car
B. the average characteristics of all cars
C. a list of essential features
D. algorithms and heuristics

p. 306
Forming Concepts
Level: Easy
Type: Conceptual
Ans: D

22. When someone says "bear," you think of a grizzly rather than a koala or a polar bear. This is probably because the grizzly bear:
A. has the most memorable teeth
B. is often the largest
C. often rears on its hind legs, reminiscent of humans
D. is a prototype for most North American bears

p. 306
Forming Concepts
Level: Easy
Type: Factual
Ans: C

23. Which of the following is characteristic of prototype theory?
A. exceptions are not included in the list of defining properties
B. listing all of the essential features of an object or event
C. constructing an ideal object and seeing if a new object matches the prototype
D. defining the concept through the use of language and heuristics

p. 306
Forming Concepts
Level: Moderate
Type: Factual
Ans: A

24. An advantage of the prototype theory is that it:
A. allows for quick recognition
B. allows for exceptions
C. explains babbling in infants
D. allows deductive reasoning

p. 306
Forming Concepts
Level: Easy
Type: Applied
Ans: B

25. Tim is developing a concept of an "office." According to _____ theory, Tim should list all the essential features of an office. According to _____ theory, however, Tim should construct an ideal office which is an average of all offices.
A. heuristic; semantic
B. exemplar; prototype
C. Chomsky's; transformational
D. deep structure; surface structure

p. 306
Forming Concepts
Level: Easy
Type: Factual
Ans: D
*PS/SG 14-3*

26. Most psychologists favor the _____ explanation of concept formation because it _____.
A. exemplar model / is based on good, sound definitions
B. exemplar model / accounts for the exceptions to the rule
C. prototype theory / is based on complete listings of essential properties
D. prototype theory / accounts for more objects using fewer features

p. 306
Forming Concepts
Level: Moderate
Type: Conceptual
Ans: D

27. Exemplar theory is _____ as prototype theory is to _____.
A. biological; psychological
B. primary; secondary
C. deep characteristics; surface characteristics
D. essential characteristics; average characteristics

p. 307
Forming Concepts
Level: Easy
Type: Applied
Ans: D

28. Little 15-month-old Jeanie has already developed several concepts. Researchers have found that Jeanie has formed concepts as a result of:
A. parental competence
B. genetic makeup
C. personality disposition
D. experience with objects and growing ability to use language

p. 307
Forming Concepts
Level: Moderate
Type: Conceptual
Ans: B

29. Which of the following would be the <u>most</u> likely order of learning about concepts?
A. heavy, cat, cute
B. dog, big, scary
C. red, apple, ball
D. sour, lemon, ball

p. 307
Forming Concepts
Level: Easy
Type: Factual
Ans: B

30. Research has found that the processes of forming prototypes and matching things to prototypes:
A. go on at a conscious level
B. go on at an unconscious level
C. are influenced by grades in school
D. are influenced by the proficiency of one's memory system

p. 307
Forming Concepts
Level: Easy
Type: Factual
Ans: C

31. According to the textbook, concepts are easily developed by children because:
A. the attention span for interesting things is much larger in children than in adults
B. parents provide much stimulation to children
C. the brain is innately wired to process different concepts in different locations
D. parents are so willing to name objects and events

p. 307
Forming Concepts
Level: Easy
Type: Factual
Ans: D

32. One function of concepts is that they allow us to:
A. form heuristics
B. relearn new things
C. more accurately predict how other people will behave
D. group things into categories and then effectively organize them in memory

p. 307
Forming Concepts
Level: Easy
Type: Factual
Ans: A

33. Once we have formed the concept for a car and encounter the car on another occasion, we:
A. do not have to relearn what a car is or what it does
B. can then form new heuristics
C. can refine the defining properties of car
D. do have to relearn what a car is and what it does

p. 307
Forming Concepts
Level: Moderate
Type: Factual
Ans: D

34. Does the brain have built-in categories for sorting and filing information?
A. No - the brain does not sort and file information based on categories
B. Yes - but the categories are developed through experience
C. Yes - but the brain doesn't have specific parts for categories
D. Yes - the brain has different areas for different categories

p. 308
Solving Problems
Level: Easy
Type: Factual
Ans: A

35. Searching for some rule, plan, or strategy that leads to achieving a goal is called:
A. problem solving
B. mental setting
C. an availability heuristic
D. divergent thinking

p. 308
Solving Problems
Level: Easy
Type: Factual
Ans: A
*www*

36. In problem solving, there are three states. Which of the following is <u>not</u> among the three states?
A. preparation state
B. initial state
C. operations state
D. goal state

p. 308
Solving Problems
Level: Easy
Type: Applied
Ans: B

37. "Which job offer should I take? Do I go to New York, Cincinnati, Minneapolis, Chicago, or Dallas? I need to collect some information about each city with regard to health care, recreation, crime, and housing." This person is in what state of problem solving?
A. preparation state
B. initial state
C. operations state
D. goal state

p. 308
Solving Problems
Level: Easy
Type: Applied
Ans: C

38. "Which job offer should I take? I need to select a city that has good health care, inexpensive housing, and a low crime rate. These are my reasons for selecting a city." This person is in what state of problem solving?
A. preparation state
B. initial state
C. operations state
D. goal state

p. 308
Solving Problems
Level: Easy
Type: Factual
Ans: D

39. The three states of initial, operations, and goal are involved in _____.
A. heuristics
B. concept and prototype formation
C. functional fixedness
D. problem solving

p. 308
Solving Problems
Level: Easy
Type: Factual
Ans: C

40. Which definition of a problem solving state is *incorrect*?
A. initial state - contemplating the unsolved problem
B. operations state - trying various operations or strategies to solve the problem
C. initial state - formulating alternative methods to perceive the problem
D. goal state - solving the problem

p. 308
Solving Problems
Level: Easy
Type: Factual
Ans: D

41. According to the textbook, which of the following is the correct order of the states of problem solving?
A. realization state, operations state, culmination state
B. operations state, review state, decision state, goal state
C. goal state, operations state, review state, decision state
D. initial state, operations state, goal state

p. 308
Solving Problems
Level: Easy
Type: Applied
Ans: B

42. You're watching your four-year-old niece trying to solve some problem she has encountered in an art project. Then, she tries a number of different techniques and methods to solve the problem. Your niece is in the:
A. realization state
B. operations state
C. goal state
D. initial state

p. 308
Solving Problems
Level: Moderate
Type: Factual
Ans: D

43. One difference research has revealed between expert and novice computer programmers is that the expert:
A. uses less insight
B. has more functional fixedness
C. starts with the specifics and works up to the big picture; the novice starts with the big picture
D. starts with the big picture and works down to specific solutions; the novice starts with specifics

p. 308
Solving Problems
Level: Moderate
Type: Applied
Ans: A

44. You are an intern at a giant computer software company. Today you are sitting in a meeting with novice and expert computer programmers discussing the latest project. The project is on writing a program to allow easier surfing of the internet. Which of the following are you most likely to hear?
A. Tom (expert) - "Let's start with the overall goal and work backwards."
B. Jan (expert) - "We should discuss how the program will look."
C. Stuart (expert) - "A good starting point is to brainstorm marketing strategies."
D. Modine (novice) - "Let's be clear on the objective of the program first."

p. 308
Solving Problems
Level: Easy
Type: Factual
Ans: A
*www*

45. Rules which will lead to a solution if followed correctly are called:
A. algorithms
B. availability heuristics
C. representative heuristics
D. brainstorming

p. 308
Solving Problems
Level: Easy
Type: Factual
Ans: C

46. You must calculate your income tax. You carefully follow the instructions to ultimately determine the amount. The instructions act as a(n):
A. representative heuristic
B. artificial rule
C. algorithm
D. availability heuristic

p. 308
Solving Problems
Level: Easy
Type: Factual
Ans: A

47. The computer named "Deep Blue" that recently beat chess master Gary Kasparov used:
A. algorithms
B. availability heuristics
C. representative heuristics
D. brainstorming

<table>
<tr><td>

p. 308
Solving Problems
Level: Easy
Type: Conceptual
Ans: B
*www*

</td><td>

48. Rules of thumb or cognitive strategies are known as:
A. framings
B. heuristics
C. brainstorming
D. prototypes

</td></tr>
<tr><td>

p. 308
Solving Problems
Level: Easy
Type: Factual
Ans: B

</td><td>

49. Heuristics are problem-solving techniques that:
A. result in the sudden grasp of a solution after many incorrect attempts
B. provide us with shortcuts to solve a problem
C. utilize rules and equations
D. are based on trial-and-error

</td></tr>
<tr><td>

p. 308
Solving Problems
Level: Moderate
Type: Applied
Ans: C

</td><td>

50. Travis has developed shortcuts to solving algebraic equations. These shortcuts allow Travis to identify a limited number of calculations and examine them in great depth. Travis is utilizing:
A. algorithms
B. semantics
C. heuristics
D. insight

</td></tr>
<tr><td>

p. 308
Solving Problems
Level: Moderate
Type: Applied
Ans: A

</td><td>

51. When asked to think about the movie he saw last night, Mel reports that he remembers the car chases because he liked those the most, yet he has forgotten about the poor dialogue and plot. For Mel, the car chases represent a(n):
A. availability heuristic
B. algorithm
C. representative prototype
D. analogy

</td></tr>
<tr><td>

p. 308
Solving Problems
Level: Moderate
Type: Applied
Ans: B
*PS/SG 14-6*

</td><td>

52. When your friend remarks pessimistically that crime is increasing ("Did you see that gruesome murder on the news last night?"), you recognize the operation of the:
A. accuracy algorithm
B. availability heuristic
C. prototype theory
D. self-fulfilling prophecy

</td></tr>
<tr><td>

p. 308
Solving Problems
Level: Moderate
Type: Applied
Ans: C

</td><td>

53. Every night Donna asks Larry how his day went. She figures he must hate his job because he does nothing but complain about terrible things that happened during the day. When she attends an office party with him, Donna is surprised to find that Larry's coworkers are pleasant and fun and that Larry seems to enjoy what he does. The fact that Larry remembers the negative aspects of his job more than the positive ones is an example of:
A. framing
B. the representativeness heuristic
C. the availability heuristic
D. brainstorming

</td></tr>
</table>

p. 308
Solving Problems
Level: Easy
Type: Applied
Ans: A

54. Kal thinks that if a person colors their hair pink, they must be strange and maladjusted. This illustrates Kal is using a(n):
A. heuristic
B. definition
C. algorithm
D. psychometric

p. 308
Solving Problems
Level: Moderate
Type: Conceptual
Ans: D

55. Based upon the availability heuristic, which of these events are we probably least likely to remember?
A. an earthquake in California killing hundreds of people
B. a terrorist bombing of an office building in a large city that killed nearly 200 people
C. the three cases of the Black Plague in the United States
D. the 1,000s of victims of car accidents

p. 308
Solving Problems
Level: Moderate
Type: Conceptual
Ans: A

56. Why are we more likely to remember the airplane crash that killed 143 people, but tend to forget the 100s of people killed in car accidents last month in the United States?
A. representative heuristic
B. framing
C. algorithm bias
D. availability heuristic

p. 308
Solving Problems
Level: Moderate
Type: Applied
Ans: A

57. Grandma Grace is terrified of flying in an airplane. On her first flight, she kept talking about crashing. Grandma said that the same thing that happened to those 150 victims of that airplane crash was going to happen to her. She demands that next time, she'll drive a car. Grandma Grace's decision making is influenced by:
A. the availability heuristic
B. the algorithms of flying
C. overregularization
D. morphemes

p. 308
Solving Problems
Level: Moderate
Type: Factual
Ans: B

58. Algorithm is to _____ as heuristic is to _____.
A. language; thinking
B. rule; mental shortcut
C. mental shortcut; rule
D. general; specific

p. 308
Solving Problems
Level: Moderate
Type: Applied
Ans: C

59. Professor Hirst is attempting to program a computer to imitate the way humans think and reason. She is an expert in:
A. heuristics
B. problem solving
C. artificial intelligence
D. deductive reasoning

p. 309
Solving Problems
Level: Easy
Type: Factual
Ans: A
*www*

60. The inability to see new uses for old objects is called:
A. functional fixedness
B. interference
C. divergent thinking
D. braindrumming

p. 309
Solving Problems
Level: Easy
Type: Factual
Ans: C

61. Functional fixedness is defined as:
A. the ability to transfer old learning to new situations
B. a rule that can be used to solve new problems
C. the inability to see new uses for old objects
D. the inability to use heuristics or algorithms

p. 309
Solving Problems
Level: Easy
Type: Factual
Ans: A
*PS/SG 14-7*

62. If you were not able to solve the nine-dot problem, it probably was because of:
A. functional fixedness
B. lack of insight
C. using poor analogies
D. failure to establish subgoals

p. 309
Solving Problems
Level: Moderate
Type: Applied
Ans: C

63. Tom and Allison want to build a play fort. Unfortunately, there is no available lumber to build with. The two think about their problem. Suddenly Tom says, "Let's use the large box that the new refrigerator came in." Allison who appears confused argues, "You can't do that! A box isn't a fort." Tom demonstrates _____ while Allison shows _____.
A. convergent thinking; divergent thinking
B. functional fixedness; analogical thinking
C. insight; functional fixedness
D. anterograde problem-solving; divergent thinking

p. 309
Solving Problems
Level: Easy
Type: Applied
Ans: D

64. Stan does not realize that his stapler can be used as a paper weight. This is an example of:
A. interference
B. convergent thinking
C. linguistic relativity
D. functional fixedness

p. 309
Solving Problems
Level: Easy
Type: Applied
Ans: C
*www*

65. "A toothpick is a toothpick. It can't be used for anything except to pick your teeth." This person is experiencing:
A. interference
B. convergent thinking
C. functional fixedness
D. an availability heuristic

p. 309
Solving Problems
Level: Easy
Type: Applied
Ans: C

66. After spending hours trying to fix a bug in his computer program, Chris suddenly realizes the solution by remembering steps his mother took to can beets. This is an example of:
A. functional fixedness
B. convergent thinking
C. using an analogy
D. overgeneralization

p. 309
Solving Problems
Level: Easy
Type: Factual
Ans: B

67. A person who solves problems by finding a similarity between a new situation and an old situation is utilizing:
A. insight
B. an analogy
C. deep structure
D. transformational rules

p. 309
Solving Problems
Level: Easy
Type: Factual
Ans: D

68. One reason why businesses like to hire people with experience is that these individuals are more likely to draw _____ to solve problems.
A. insight
B. transformational rules
C. functional fixedness
D. analogies

p. 309
Solving Problems
Level: Easy
Type: Factual
Ans: D

69. Most people use _____ to solve the candle problem described in the textbook.
A. subgoals
B. transformational rules
C. functional fixedness
D. an analogy

p. 309
Solving Problems
Level: Easy
Type: Applied
Ans: B

70. What's the problem solving strategy that breaks down the overall problem into separate parts?
A. forming ill-defined goals
B. forming subgoals
C. forming secondary problems
D. forming heuristics

p. 309
Solving Problems
Level: Easy
Type: Applied
Ans: D
PS/SG 14-9

71. One of the best ways to finish your assignment on time is to:
A. have the problem in the back of your mind, and wait for a sudden flash of insight
B. use the analogy of other, similar assignments you have done before
C. fix your thoughts on the function that is involved in the assignment
D. break the assignment down into subtasks and subgoals

p. 309
Solving Problems
Level: Easy
Type: Applied
Ans: B

72. You've accepted a new job that will start in two months, but you have to move to a new city. The idea of moving doesn't appeal to you since it is a very big task. A useful strategy is to break up the task into:
A. general problems
B. subgoals
C. secondary problems
D. phonemes

p. 309
Solving Problems
Level: Easy
Type: Applied
Ans: D

73. When doing a research paper, you break up the assignment into the steps of doing library research, taking notes, making a detailed outline, and writing the paper. This strategy uses:
A. functional fixedness
B. transformational rules
C. an analogy
D. subgoals

p. 309
Solving Problems
Level: Easy
Type: Applied
Ans: A

74. The kids have messed up the living room. There are toys and paper all over the floor. The father tells the kids to clean up. When realizing the large mess they made, the kids start to complain. Then the father suggests to break down the task into smaller parts, and the kids agree. The father has used the strategy of forming:
   A.   subgoals
   B.   an analogy
   C.   insight
   D.   functional fixedness

p. 310
Thinking Creativity
Level: Easy
Type: Factual
Ans: A

75. A combination of flexibility in thinking and reorganization in understanding to produce innovative ideas is important in:
   A.   creative thinking
   B.   semantics
   C.   definitional theory
   D.   concept formation

p. 310
Thinking Creativity
Level: Easy
Type: Applied
Ans: C

76. The professor wrote on Quan's paper, "I am impressed with your creative thinking on this issue." Quan was <u>most</u> likely demonstrating:
   A.   functional fixedness
   B.   the creation of average characteristics of an object
   C.   flexibility in thinking and reorganization in understanding
   D.   the use of rules called algorithms

p. 310
Thinking Creativity
Level: Easy
Type: Factual
Ans: C

77. This individual you know solves problems on a regular basis in very innovative ways that influence other people. This person is:
   A.   divergent
   B.   convergent
   C.   creative
   D.   transformational

p. 310
Thinking Creativity
Level: Easy
Type: Factual
Ans: A

78. Which is <u>not</u> an approach to measuring creativity?
   A.   linguistic
   B.   case study
   C.   psychometric
   D.   cognitive

p. 310
Thinking Creativity
Level: Moderate
Type: Factual
Ans: C

79. If you study creativity using the psychometric approach, you focus on:
   A.   relative linguistics
   B.   functional fixedness and insight
   C.   convergent and divergent thinking
   D.   divergent thinking and overgeneralization

p. 310
Thinking Creativity
Level: Easy
Type: Applied
Ans: A

80. Frank claims that when he is confronted with a problem, he likes to come up with one correct solution. Frank practices:
   A.   convergent thinking
   B.   semantic problem solving
   C.   divergent thinking
   D.   creative thinking

p. 310
Thinking Creativity
Level: Easy
Type: Conceptual
Ans: B
*PS/SG 14-10*

81. A serious problem with too many college courses is that they place all the emphasis on _____ thinking.
A. creative
B. convergent
C. divergent
D. brainstorm

p. 310
Thinking Creativity
Level: Easy
Type: Applied
Ans: A
*www*

82. This type of test question requires:
A. convergent thinking
B. semantic problem solving
C. divergent thinking
D. artificial intelligence

p. 310
Thinking Creativity
Level: East
Type: Applied
Ans: B

83. "There is only one right answer to this exercise," the professor says as the class is reviewing a problem. What type of thinking is the professor describing?
A. divergent thinking
B. convergent thinking
C. heuristics
D. brainstorming

p. 310
Thinking Creativity
Level: Easy
Type: Applied
Ans: C

84. On the first day of a business class, the professor talked about how there might be more than one way to create a business organization. This illustrates what kind of thinking?
A. convergent thinking
B. semantic problem solving
C. divergent thinking
D. operations

p. 310
Thinking Creativity
Level: Easy
Type: Applied
Ans: C

85. In your philosophy class one day, the professor asks, "What is the best tasting food?" You think to yourself that the answer depends on the person. You suddenly realize that the question requires:
A. convergent thinking
B. semantic problem solving
C. divergent thinking
D. operations

p. 310
Thinking Creativity
Level: Moderate
Type: Factual
Ans: D

86. The definition of creativity involving divergent thinking differs from other definitions in that it:
A. defines creativity in terms of the extent to which a person's thoughts differ from the norm
B. defines creativity in terms of the extent to which a person's thoughts produce socially valued products
C. measures creativity in terms of the speed at which problems are solved
D. measures creativity by the number of possible answers a person can come up with to a single question

p. 310
Thinking Creativity
Level: Easy
Type: Conceptual
Ans: D

87.    When you begin with a problem and devise many solutions, it is called
       _____, but if you come up with the one correct solution, it is called
       _____.
A.     semantics; insight
B.     phonology; morphology
C.     analogy; brainstorming
D.     divergent thinking; convergent thinking

p. 310
Thinking Creativity
Level: Easy
Type: Applied
Ans: A

88.    If we give a very creative person a test of divergent thinking, what would
       we probably find out?
A.     She does not necessarily score high on the test.
B.     Since she is very creative, she will score very high.
C.     Divergent thinking cannot be tested.
D.     Tests of divergent thinking have not been created.

p. 310
Thinking Creativity
Level: Easy
Type: Factual
Ans: C

89.    A method of study that examines a creative person in great depth is called
       a(n):
A.     insight study
B.     biography
C.     case study
D.     sociopsychological study

p. 310
Thinking Creativity
Level: Easy
Type: Applied
Ans: C

90.    A common finding in case studies of creative people is:
A.     an unwillingness to take risks
B.     a history of abuse in childhood
C.     they tend to be creative in some areas and poor in others
D.     a lack of desire to be creative

p. 310
Thinking Creativity
Level: Easy
Type: Applied
Ans: A

91.    For her research paper on creativity, Shyla has decided to study her cousin,
       the creator of a famous computer program. What approach to the
       measurement of creativity is Shyla pursuing?
A.     case study approach
B.     psychometric approach
C.     longitudinal approach
D.     behavioral approach

p. 310
Thinking Creativity
Level: Easy
Type: Factual
Ans: D

92.    Howard Gardner's case study of Sigmund Freud revealed that Freud was
       very poor in:
A.     language
B.     social competence
C.     linguistics
D.     musical and spatial ability

p. 310
Thinking Creativity
Level: Easy
Type: Applied
Ans: B

93.    You are studying Albert Einstein and learn that he was very good at
       thinking in visual-spatial terms. You reason that his creativity was due to
       this ability. The approach you are taking in studying creativity is the
       _____ approach.
A.     psychometric
B.     cognitive
C.     psychodynamic
D.     nature-nurture

p. 310
Thinking Creativity
Level: Easy
Type: Factual
Ans: D

94. The cognitive approach to creativity focuses on the:
A. convergent thinking of creative people
B. personal histories of creative individuals
C. differences between creative thinkers
D. tools of creative thinking such as mental imagery

p. 311
Thinking Creativity
Level: Moderate
Type: Factual
Ans: B

95. What type of correlation do we find between IQ and creativity?
A. There is actually a fairly strong negative correlation
B. There is little correlation between IQ and creativity
C. People with high IQ's tend to be very creative as well
D. People with IQ's above 120 tend to be writers and scientists

p. 311
Thinking Creativity
Level: Easy
Type: Factual
Ans: D
*www*

96. What term is given to an autistic person who shows some incredible memory, music, or drawing talent?
A. creative
B. gifted
C. genius
D. savant

p. 311
Thinking Creativity
Level: Moderate
Type: Conceptual
Ans: B

97. What is the best example of the poor correlation between IQ and creativity?
A. Albert Einstein
B. savants
C. Mark Twain
D. Edgar Allan Poe

p. 311
Thinking Creativity
Level: Moderate
Type: Conceptual
Ans: C

98. An article recently appeared in a respected magazine on creativity. Which of the following titles best summarizes creativity's relationship to IQ?
A. "Strong Correlation Found Between Creativity and IQ"
B. "Creativity Involves Extraordinary Cognitive Process"
C. "Creativity Involves Ordinary Cognitive Process"
D. "Creativity and Genius: The Same Phenomenon"

p. 311
Thinking Creativity
Level: Easy
Type: Factual
Ans: C

99. Which of the following is true regarding the relationship between creativity and IQ?
A. Creative people have the same IQ scores as the general population.
B. Those with the highest IQ scores are the most creative.
C. There is little correlation between creativity and IQ among creative people.
D. Creative people actually have slightly lower IQ scores than the general population.

p. 311
Thinking Creativity
Level: Easy
Type: Factual
Ans: D
*PS/SG 14-11*

100. The existence of autistic savants shows that the link between creativity and intelligence is:
A. strong, because savants always have high IQ scores
B. moderate, because savants typically have normal IQ scores
C. nonexistant, because savants seldom show creativity
D. weak, because savants usually have low IQ scores

p. 311
Thinking Creativity
Level: Moderate
Type: Conceptual
Ans: C

101.    Which word describes creative people with regard to their abilities?
A.    diverse
B.    generalists
C.    specialists
D.    many

p. 311
Thinking Creativity
Level: Easy
Type: Factual
Ans: A

102.    If you were to examine the personalities of creative people, you would find them to:
A.    be risk takers
B.    have doubts about their work
C.    be modest
D.    be sensitive to the needs of others

p. 311
Thinking Creativity
Level: Easy
Type: Factual
Ans: B

103.    If you were to examine the personalities of creative people, you would find one of the negative characteristics to be:
A.    high levels of frustration
B.    insensitivity to the needs of others
C.    setting unrealistic goals
D.    poor time management

p. 311
Thinking Creativity
Level: Easy
Type: Factual
Ans: C

104.    Creative people are driven by:
A.    extrinsic motivation
B.    fame and fortune
C.    intrinsic motivation
D.    competition with other creative people

p. 311
Thinking Creativity
Level: Easy
Type: Factual
Ans: B

105.    Which of the following descriptions is inaccurate regarding the traits of creative people?
A.    Have ability to change mental directions
B.    Sensitive to the needs of others
C.    Motivated by challenge of solving problems
D.    Not afraid to take risks

p. 311
Thinking Creativity
Level: Easy
Type: Factual
Ans: A

106.    Based upon data presented in your textbook, which type of creative person is most likely to suffer from psychopathology?
A.    writer
B.    artist
C.    composer
D.    scientist

p. 311
Thinking Creativity
Level: Easy
Type: Factual
Ans: C

107.    Writers are most likely to suffer from what types of psychopathology?
A.    anxiety and headaches
B.    impulse control and schizophrenia
C.    alcoholism and depression
D.    schizophrenia and hypochondriasis

p. 311
Thinking Creativity
Level: Easy
Type: Factual
Ans: D

108.    Which of the following disorders is a creative person most likely to experience compared to the general population?
A.    alcohol abuse disorders
B.    dissociative disorders
C.    anxiety disorders
D.    mood disorders

p. 312
Language: Basic Rules
Level: Easy
Type: Factual
Ans: A

109.    A form of communication that has complex rules that are used to make symbols is called:
A.    language
B.    semantics
C.    grammar
D.    morphemes

p. 312
Language: Basic Rules
Level: Moderate
Type: Factual
Ans: C

110.    You are watching a game show that gives the answer and contestants give the question. One of the items was, "An arbitrary pairing between a sound and a meaning." Not one of the contestants knew the answer, but you do! What is the question?
A.    "What is grammar?"
B.    "What is a heuristic?"
C.    "What is a word?"
D.    "What is language?"

p. 312
Language: Basic Rules
Level: Easy
Type: Factual
Ans: C

111.    The set of rules that are used to regulate how we combine words in phrases and sentences is called:
A.    phonemes
B.    morphemes
C.    grammar
D.    semantics

p. 312
Language: Basic Rules
Level: Moderate
Type: Factual
Ans: C
*PS/SG 14-12*

112.    From most particular to most general in the rules of language, the correct order is:
A.    morpheme, phoneme, syntax, semantics
B.    syntax, phoneme, semantics, morpheme
C.    phoneme, morpheme, syntax, semantics
D.    semantics, syntax, morpheme, phoneme

p. 312
Language: Basic Rules
Level: Easy
Type: Factual
Ans: D

113.    Speakers of different languages all learn the same basic rules. Of the following, which is not one of these rules?
A.    phonology
B.    morphology
C.    semantics
D.    heuristics

p. 312
Language: Basic Rules
Level: Easy
Type: Factual
Ans: A

114.    The most basic speech sounds of a given language are called:
A.    phonemes
B.    morphemes
C.    syllables
D.    semantics

p. 312
Language: Basic Rules
Level: Easy
Type: Conceptual
Ans: D

115.    In the word "sock", the sound of the "s" is a(n) _____, whereas the use of the "s" to make the word plural is a(n) _____.
A.    overgeneralization; transformational rule
B.    concept; unit of grammar
C.    syntax; semantic
D.    phoneme; morpheme

p. 312
Language: Basic Rules
Level: Easy
Type: Factual
Ans: D

116. _____ specifies how we make the meaningful sounds that are used by a particular language.
A. Syntax
B. Grammar
C. Morphology
D. Phonology

p. 312
Language: Basic Rules
Level: Easy
Type: Factual
Ans: D

117. When we correctly combine phonemes into meaningful combinations of sounds and words, we are using:
A. semantics
B. grammar
C. phonology
D. morphology

p. 312
Language: Basic Rules
Level: Easy
Type: Factual
Ans: D

118. A "morpheme" is defined as a:
A. pronunciation that is not phonetic
B. new word that is formed by combining two existing words
C. child's common mispronunciation of a word that is not phonetic
D. combination of sounds that have meaning

p. 312
Language: Basic Rules
Level: Moderate
Type: Conceptual
Ans: B

119. Which of the following words consists of a single morpheme?
A. unspeakable
B. computer
C. books
D. uncomfortable

p. 312
Language: Basic Rules
Level: Easy
Type: Factual
Ans: A

120. Of the following, which one is not an example of a morpheme?
A. d in dog
B. s in cars
C. ing in fishing
D. ed in talked

p. 312
Language: Basic Rules
Level: Easy
Type: Factual
Ans: C

121. The rules that allow us to combine words to make meaningful phrases and sentences is termed:
A. morphology
B. phonology
C. syntax
D. semantics

p. 312
Language: Basic Rules
Level: Easy
Type: Conceptual
Ans: A

122. The phrase "the red house" in Spanish would be "la casa roja" which means, literally, "the house red." This example illustrates that Spanish and English differ in rules of:
A. syntax
B. phonology
C. morphology
D. semantics

p. 312
Language: Basic Rules
Level: Moderate
Type: Conceptual
Ans: D
*www*

123. When a person says "boy rides bike," the meaning is different than if the person says "bike rides boy." This is an example of the rules of:
A. phonology
B. morphology
C. deep structure
D. semantics

p. 312
Language: Basic Rules
Level: Moderate
Type: Applied
Ans: C

124. Joyce and Phil are having an argument. The argument is over the semantics of Joyce calling Phil a "clown." Semantics is involved with:
A. phonology of words
B. morphology of words
C. the meaning of words
D. the order of words in a sentence

p. 312
Language: Basic Rules
Level: Moderate
Type: Applied
Ans: A

125. "Once upon a time, a big spider scared a little girl who was eating some cottage cheese. It was very ugly." You know that the "it" refers to the big spider and not to the cottage cheese. Why?
A. semantics
B. grammar
C. syntax
D. phonology

p. 313
Language: Basic Rules
Level: Easy
Type: Factual
Ans: A

126. Which individual is most associated with explaining how we understand language?
A. Noam Chomsky
B. Alan Cromer
C. Benjamin Whorf
D. Carl Rogers

p. 313
Language: Basic Rules
Level: Easy
Type: Factual
Ans: C

127. What two principles helps us to understand language according to Chomsky?
A. prototypes and morphemes
B. transformational rules and concept learning
C. mental grammar and innate program
D. semantics and functional fixedness

p. 313
Language: Basic Rules
Level: Easy
Type: Factual
Ans: B
*PS/SG 14-13*

128. According to Noam Chomsky, language operates at two levels:
A. spoken words and censored words
B. surface structure and deep structure
C. obvious meaning and implied meaning
D. sentences and telegraphic speech

p. 313
Language: Basic Rules
Level: Easy
Type: Applied
Ans: B

129. As you read a novel, it occurs to you that you have never before read these sentences in your entire life. What allowed the author of this novel to create so many different, brand new combinations of words?
A. morphology
B. mental grammar
C. innate program
D. surface structure

p. 313
Language: Basic Rules
Level: Moderate
Type: Factual
Ans: B

130. Chomsky argues that an innate _____ allows us to create an endless number of sentences.
A. transformational rule
B. mental grammar
C. potential
D. predisposition

p. 313
Language: Basic Rules
Level: Easy
Type: Applied
Ans: D

131. As you look at your newborn daughter, you think of the innate abilities that she possesses. You think about how she will learn the general rules of grammar relatively easily. What is the term used to describe the relative ease of learning grammar?
A. mental grammar
B. inductive reasoning
C. linguistic overgeneralization
D. innate program

p. 313
Language: Basic Rules
Level: Moderate
Type: Conceptual
Ans: C

132. How do we acquire the innate program for understanding language?
A. around age 2, it becomes activated by brain growth
B. by brain stimulation that occurs in REM sleep
C. our brains come with that ability built in
D. through formal schooling starting at age 5

p. 313
Language: Basic Rules
Level: Moderate
Type: Factual
Ans: A

133. How does the child learn the *complex* rules of grammar?
A. interaction between the child's experience and the innate program
B. interaction between inductive reasoning and linguistic overgeneralization
C. linguistic overgeneralization
D. interaction between innate program and morphology

p. 313
Language: Basic Rules
Level: Easy
Type: Conceptual
Ans: D

134. The sentences "Ann kissed Jack" and "Jack was kissed by Ann" have different:
A. semantics
B. deep structures
C. denotations
D. surface structures

p. 313
Language: Basic Rules
Level: Easy
Type: Factual
Ans: C

135. Two sentences may have the same meaning, but the actual wording of the sentences may differ. This difference is referred to as:
A. semantics
B. deep structure
C. surface structure
D. comparative linguistics

p. 313
Language: Basic Rules
Level: Easy
Type: Factual
Ans: B

136. The underlying meaning of a sentence is its:
A. surface structure
B. deep structure
C. phonology
D. transformational grammar

p. 313
Language: Basic Rules
Level: Easy
Type: Factual
Ans: D

137. You are talking to a stranger. He says something that is not clear, but you understand him anyway. You are able to determine the underlying meaning of his speech. You have determined the _____ of his comments.
A. surface structure
B. mental grammar
C. morphology
D. deep structure

p. 313
Language: Basic Rules
Level: Moderate
Type: Conceptual
Ans: C

138. According to Chomsky, the difference between surface structure and deep structure has to do with:
A. single words and two-word combinations
B. learning factors and innate factors
C. wording and meaning
D. overgeneralization and telegraphic speech

p. 313
Language: Basic Rules
Level: Easy
Type: Factual
Ans: A

139. We learn to shift back and forth between surface structure and deep structure by using:
A. transformational rules
B. babbling
C. syntax
D. semantics

p. 313
Language: Basic Rules
Level: Easy
Type: Factual
Ans: C

140. According to Chomsky, transformational rules allow us to:
A. translate words from a foreign language into our own
B. translate words from our language into a foreign one
C. convert surface structures into deep structures and back into surface structures
D. learn new grammatical rules of language

p. 313
Language: Basic Rules
Level: Easy
Type: Factual
Ans: B

141. The ideas of surface structure, deep structure, and transformational rules are part of:
A. the social learning approach
B. Chomsky's theory of language
C. behaviorism
D. basic rules of grammar

p. 313
Language: Basic Rules
Level: Easy
Type: Factual
Ans: A

142. What is one criticism of Chomsky's theory of language?
A. It downplays the importance of environmental influences.
B. It ignores the biological components of language.
C. It does not explain how children learn language.
D. It fails to account for how we can create new sentences.

p. 314
Acquiring Language
Level: Moderate
Type: Factual
Ans: B

143. Children, regardless of culture or language, do not differ in regard to _____ of stages in language acquisition.
A. speed
B. order
C. development
D. age

p. 314
Acquiring Language
Level: Easy
Type: Factual
Ans: D
*www*

144. Of the following, which is not part of the language stages described in the textbook?
A. babbling
B. one-word sentences
C. sentences
D. parentese

p. 314
Acquiring Language
Level: Easy
Type: Factual
Ans: D
*PS/SG 14-15*

145. Which is the correct sequence of stages in children's acquisition of language?
A. crying, begging, asking, reasoning
B. senseless noises, listening, imitation, original productions
C. babbling, one-word, two-word, three-word, four-word, etc.
D. babbling, single word, two-word combinations, sentences

p. 314
Acquiring Language
Level: Easy
Type: Factual
Ans: A

146. At about six months of age, babies begin to verbalize one-syllable sounds called:
A. babbling
B. syntax
C. overgeneralization
D. morphology

p. 314
Acquiring Language
Level: Easy
Type: Factual
Ans: B

147. At what age do children become sensitized to sounds that make up their native language?
A. before 1 month
B. by about 6 months
C. by about 10 months
D. by about one year

p. 314
Acquiring Language
Level: Easy
Type: Factual
Ans: C

148. In deaf children who are only exposed to sign language, babbling is:
A. skipped
B. delayed by about six months
C. manual
D. oral

p. 314
Acquiring Language
Level: Easy
Type: Factual
Ans: B

149. The single word stage of language acquisition begins at:
A. six months of age
B. one year of age
C. one and a half years of age
D. two years of age

p. 314
Acquiring Language
Level: Easy
Type: Factual
Ans: C

150. When a child has reached the single word stage, what percent of single words refer to objects and to actions?
A. 20% to objects and 80% to actions
B. 80% to objects and 20% to actions
C. 50% to objects and 50% to actions
D. 70% to objects and 30% to actions

p. 314
Acquiring Language
Level: Moderate
Type: Applied
Ans: D
*www*

151. Forest, who is about one year old, says "Mom." What does he mean?
A. "Where is mom?"
B. "Mom, pay attention to me."
C. "This is my mom."
D. all of the above

p. 314
Acquiring Language
Level: Easy
Type: Factual
Ans: C

152. "Parentese," which includes speaking in a higher voice and stretching out each word, usually emerges from parents in response to their child's use of:
A. babbling
B. overgeneralization
C. words
D. rules of grammar

p. 314
Acquiring Language
Level: Easy
Type: Factual
Ans: C

153. Which statement about parentese is <u>incorrect</u>?
A. Adults speaking parentese speak in a slower than normal voice
B. Parentese is found in all languages
C. Adults speaking parentese speak using complex sentences
D. A function of parentese is to get the infant's attention

p. 315
Acquiring Language
Level: Easy
Type: Factual
Ans: C

154. The age at which children typically begin using two-word combinations is:
A. 1 year
B. 1 1/2 years
C. 2 years
D. 2 1/2 years

p. 315
Acquiring Language
Level: Easy
Type: Factual
Ans: A

155. According to the textbook, from two years through adolescence, a child learns an average of one new word every:
A. 2 hours
B. 8 hours
C. 1 day
D. 3 days

p. 315
Acquiring Language
Level: Moderate
Type: Factual
Ans: B

156. A child's language development is partly dependent on:
A. the child's gender
B. how responsive the parent or caretaker is
C. the native language of the child
D. the child's culture

p. 315
Acquiring Language
Level: Easy
Type: Factual
Ans: A

157. By the age of two, children have vocabularies of more than:
A. 50 words
B. 150 words
C. 200 words
D. 500 words

p. 315
Acquiring Language
Level: Easy
Type: Factual
Ans: D

158. Telegraphic speech is characterized by:
A. two-word combinations
B. parentese
C. one-syllable verbalization
D. omission of articles, prepositions, and parts of verbs

p. 315
Acquiring Language
Level: Moderate
Type: Factual
Ans: B

159. The stage of sentences in language acquisition occurs at about _____ and is characterized by _____.
A. 4 years of age; overregulation
B. 4 years of age; telegraphic speech
C. 3 years of age; grammatical tenses
D. 3 years of age; concrete speech

p. 315
Acquiring Language
Level: Easy
Type: Factual
Ans: B

160. When a child applies a grammatical rule to cases where it should not be used, the child has committed:
A. overregulation
B. overgeneralization
C. telegraphic speech
D. overspecification

p. 315
Acquiring Language
Level: Easy
Type: Conceptual
Ans: C

161. When a child says, "Me go bye-bye" the child is demonstrating:
A. overregulation
B. overgeneralization
C. telegraphic speech
D. concrete speech

p. 315
Acquiring Language
Level: Easy
Type: Conceptual
Ans: A
*www*

162. When a child says, "I bringed my doll," the child is demonstrating:
A. overgeneralization
B. early speech impairment
C. telegraphic speech
D. concrete speech

p. 315
Acquiring Language
Level: Moderate
Type: Conceptual
Ans: D

163. An incident of overgeneralization represents a(n):
A. step backward for children
B. atypical landmark in acquiring language
C. point between babbling and single word stages
D. understanding of the basic rules of grammar

p. 316
Acquiring Language
Level: Easy
Type: Conceptual
Ans: A

164. If you argue that children are genetically "prewired" physiologically and neurologically to make speech sounds and learn language, you argue for _____ factors in language acquisition.
A. innate
B. social learning
C. environmental
D. learning

p. 316
Acquiring Language
Level: Easy
Type: Factual
Ans: C

165. The notion of a critical language period supports the idea that _____ factors are involved in language acquisition.
A. environmental
B. structural
C. innate
D. social

p. 316
Acquiring Language
Level: Easy
Type: Factual
Ans: A
*PS/SG 14-17*

166. The debate over how we acquire language concerns _____ versus _____.
A. innate language abilities / environmental language factors
B. universal abilities / different skills from one cultural group to another
C. superficial / deep-seated
D. individual / common to the group

p. 316
Acquiring Language
Level: Moderate
Type: Conceptual
Ans: B

167. According to Noam Chomsky's view of language acquisition, a child whose parents speak French will:
A. learn French via genetics
B. be genetically programmed the same way a German child is to facilitate the learning of language
C. begin life with no facility for learning language and, therefore, have to learn it all from his parents and other models
D. have more difficulty than children learning an easier language such as Spanish

p. 316
Acquiring Language
Level: Easy
Type: Factual
Ans: B

168. Feedback, reinforcement, observation, and imitation are examples of _____ related to language acquisition.
A. innate factors
B. environmental factors
C. transformational rules
D. semantics

p. 316
Acquiring Language
Level: Easy
Type: Conceptual
Ans: D

169. That parents smile and praise a child's new words is support for the belief that:
A. language skills are primarily inborn
B. parents are the only ones who can encourage language development in their children
C. children learn language through observational learning
D. language skills are learned operantly

p. 316
Acquiring Language
Level: Moderate
Type: Factual
Ans: C

170. _____ argued that children acquire language through the principles of operant conditioning. A problem with that argument is that children:
A. Noam Chomsky; who are firstborn are spoken to more than laterborns
B. Benjamin Whorf; learn language in the same order world wide
C. B. F. Skinner; understand language before they've received reinforcement
D. Ivan Pavlov; use language without being reinforced

p. 316
Acquiring Language
Level: Moderate
Type: Conceptual
Ans: D

171. Which of the following statements supports the role of operant conditioning in language acquisition?
A. We can create sentences that have never been heard before.
B. It is more difficult for adults to learn language than children.
C. Children of all cultures learn language in similar stages.
D. Children receive reinforcement from their parents for their speech.

p. 316
Acquiring Language
Level: Moderate
Type: Applied
Ans: C

172. Often times young children will say "dirty words" and have no idea what the words mean. Which of the following approaches is best illustrated if these children hear these words from siblings, parents, or television?
A. Chomsky's theory of language
B. Skinner's theory of language
C. social cognitive theory
D. metalinguistics

p. 316
Acquiring Language
Level: Moderate
Type: Applied
Ans: C

173. Dr. Gilpin believes that in language acquisition, the child's interactions with others provide opportunities to observe, imitate, and practice language. Dr. Gilpin supports the:
A. Chomsky's theory of language
B. Skinner's theory of language
C. social cognitive theory
D. metalinguistics theory

| | | |
|---|---|---|
| p. 316<br>Acquiring Language<br>Level: Moderate<br>Type: Factual<br>Ans: B | 174.<br><br>A.<br>B.<br>C.<br>D. | Based on the study described in Module 14, what variable was related to large vocabularies in 2- and 3-year old children?<br>the ability to speak two languages<br>parents who interacted with them<br>having several siblings<br>having interactive toys |
| p. 318<br>Reason, Thought and<br>  Language<br>Level: Easy<br>Type: Factual<br>Ans: A | 175.<br>A.<br>B.<br>C.<br>D. | When you use and apply knowledge to achieve goals, you are:<br>reasoning<br>generalizing<br>thinking divergently<br>thinking convergently |
| p. 318<br>Reason, Thought and<br>  Language<br>Level: Easy<br>Type: Factual<br>Ans: D | 176.<br>A.<br>B.<br>C.<br>D. | The two types of reasoning discussed in your textbook are:<br>preductive and postductive reasoning<br>morphology and phonology<br>heuristic and algorithmatic reasoning<br>deductive and inductive reasoning |
| p. 318<br>Reason, Thought and<br>  Language<br>Level: Easy<br>Type: Factual<br>Ans: A | 177.<br>A.<br>B.<br>C.<br>D. | Deductive reasoning consists of reasoning:<br>from the general to the particular<br>from the particular to the general<br>to find one correct solution<br>to find several correct solutions |
| p. 318<br>Reason, Thought and<br>  Language<br>Level: Easy<br>Type: Factual<br>Ans: B | 178.<br>A.<br>B.<br>C.<br>D. | The statement "If p, then q" illustrates:<br>preductive reasoning<br>deductive reasoning<br>postductive reasoning<br>inductive reasoning |
| p. 318<br>Reason, Thought and<br>  Language<br>Level: Moderate<br>Type: Applied<br>Ans: A | 179.<br><br><br><br>A.<br>B.<br>C.<br>D. | You are visiting a town that you have never been in before. You are hungry and want to eat at some restaurant. You have heard that truck stops have good food. So you find a truck stop in this town and reason that it has good food. This illustrates _____ reasoning.<br>deductive reasoning<br>preductive reasoning<br>postductive reasoning<br>inductive reasoning |
| p. 318<br>Reason, Thought and<br>  Language<br>Level: Moderate<br>Type: Applied<br>Ans: D | 180.<br><br><br><br>A.<br>B.<br>C.<br>D. | Your friends used to tease you for wearing thick glasses. They thought that people who wear thick glasses were geeks. They thought, "Hey, he wears thick glasses, so he must be a geek." You have suffered because of your friends':<br>inductive reasoning<br>preductive reasoning<br>postductive reasoning<br>deductive reasoning |

p. 318
Reason, Thought and
  Language
Level: Easy
Type: Factual
Ans: B

*PS/SG 14-19*

181.  When you use past observations in order to draw a broader conclusion, you
      are using:
A.    deductive reasoning
B.    inductive reasoning
C.    convergent thinking
D.    divergent thinking

p. 318
Reason, Thought and
  Language
Level: Easy
Type: Factual
Ans: B

182.  Inductive reasoning consists of reasoning:
A.    from the general to the particular
B.    from the particular to the general
C.    to find one correct solution
D.    to find several correct solutions

p. 318
Reason, Thought and
  Language
Level: Moderate
Type: Factual
Ans: D

183.  In inductive reasoning, we use _____ to decide the likelihood of some
      conclusion being true.
A.    semantics
B.    surface structure
C.    general ideas
D.    our past experiences

p. 318
Reason, Thought and
  Language
Level: Moderate
Type: Factual
Ans: B

184.  Poor Eugene. The girl he was going out with said she hates him, hasn't
      called him in weeks, gave back the gifts, and has been going out with other
      guys. Eugene finally figures it out. She doesn't like him anymore. Eugene
      has finally engaged in _____.
A.    deductive reasoning
B.    inductive reasoning
C.    convergent thinking
D.    divergent thinking

p. 318
Reason, Thought and
  Language
Level: Easy
Type: Conceptual
Ans: A

185.  Why does reasoning fail? It has been suggested that our brains are
      prewired for _____ challenges rather than _____ reasoning.
A.    practical; abstract
B.    surface; deep
C.    general; specific
D.    verbal; nonverbal

p. 319
Reason, Thought and
  Language
Level: Easy
Type: Factual
Ans: D

186.  The notion that language determines the way people think and perceive the
      world is characteristic of:
A.    Chomsky's theory of language acquisition
B.    overgeneralization
C.    the social learning approach
D.    the theory of linguistic relativity

p. 319
Reason, Thought and
 Language
Level: Moderate
Type: Applied
Ans: D

187. Professor Anderson has discovered a primitive tribe in the Amazon rainforest and has studied their language. She has found that this tribe has only seven emotions. She reasons that they should only perceive these seven emotions. She is basing her hypothesis on:
A. the psychometric approach
B. Chomsky's theory of language acquisition
C. the social learning approach
D. the theory of linguistic relativity

p. 319
Reason, Thought and
 Language
Level: Moderate
Type: Applied
Ans: C

188. Do doctors and nurses perceive injuries differently since they use a special kind of medical jargon to describe such injuries? The theory of linguistic relativity would predict:
A. that thinking and perception are only different if one's culture supports the language
B. no, since thinking and perception occur independently of language
C. that their thinking about and perception of injuries is different
D. that doctors and nurses' original native language does not differentiate between different kinds of injuries

p. 319
Reason, Thought and
 Language
Level: Moderate
Type: Applied
Ans: D

189. Josh is a plumber and Phil knows nothing about plumbing. According to the theory of _____ Josh and Phil would think about and perceive plumbing tools differently.
A. deductive reasoning
B. heuristics
C. prototype
D. linguistic relativity

p. 319
Reason, Thought and
 Language
Level: Easy
Type: Factual
Ans: B

190. Whorf's assertion that Inuits have many more words for snow:
A. has been supported by dozens of studies
B. is wrong
C. has not been studied
D. has been revised since the Inuits have hundreds of words for snow

p. 319
Reason, Thought and
 Language
Level: Easy
Type: Factual
Ans: B

191. Research on bilingual people indicates that:
A. language and thinking are independent processes
B. language influences thinking
C. linguistic relativity is incorrect
D. all people regardless of language think the same way

p. 320
Research Focus:
 Dyslexia
Level: Easy
Type: Factual
Ans: C

192. Dyslexia can be defined as:
A. problems with reading comprehension caused by problems in attention
B. mental retardation that is manifested in reading and writing
C. difficulties in reading despite intelligence, motivation, and education
D. a physical disturbance in the visual system which leads to reading problems

p. 320
Research Focus:
 Dyslexia
Level: Easy
Type: Factual
Ans: C

193. Most individuals with dyslexia:
A. are male
B. are female
C. have average or above-average intelligence
D. are color-blind

p. 320
Research Focus:
 Dyslexia
Level: Easy
Type: Factual
Ans: C

194. According to the textbook, learning to read is different than learning to speak because:
A. the brain does not have innate areas devoted specifically to speaking
B. speaking involves motor movements and hearing
C. the brain does not have innate areas devoted specifically to reading
D. reading is more defined by one's culture than speaking

p. 320
Research Focus:
 Dyslexia
Level: Easy
Type: Factual
Ans: D

195. Which of the following is the correct order of steps in reading?
A. morpheme producer, automatic detector, word analyzer
B. phoneme producer, word analyzer, syntax detector
C. morpheme producer, phoneme analyzer, work detector
D. phoneme producer, word analyzer, automatic detector

p. 320
Research Focus:
 Dyslexia
Level: Easy
Type: Factual
Ans: A

196. The phoneme producer is located in the:
A. left inferior frontal gyrus
B. right parieto-temporal lobe
C. left occipital lobe
D. amygdala

p. 320
Research Focus:
 Dyslexia
Level: Easy
Type: Factual
Ans: C

197. After a word's letters are changed into sound, we must:
A. analyze each phoneme
B. vocalize the sound
C. analyze words
D. create a permanent record of the letters and its sound

p. 320
Research Focus:
 Dyslexia
Level: Easy
Type: Applied
Ans: C

198. Paul is dyslexic. If the current research is correct, Paul would have:
A. fewer cells in the left hypothalamus
B. associated physical problems primarily an overactive thymus gland
C. problems distinguishing between sounds like *pa* and *ba*
D. glasses

p. 320
Research Focus:
 Dyslexia
Level: Easy
Type: Applied
Ans: D

199. Bruce has problems hearing the difference between "*ba, da,* and *pa.*" An outcome described in the textbook of Bruce's problems might be:
A. an attached stigma
B. frustration in social situations
C. problems with visual perception of words with those letters
D. difficulties hearing differences between words with those sounds

p. 320
Research Focus:
  Dyslexia
Level: Easy
Type: Applied
Ans: A

200. Bruce has problems hearing the difference between "*ba, da,* and *pa.*" What is a neurological explanation for his dyslexia?

A. His word analyzer is overanalyzing the individual letters of a word
B. He has defective neural wiring between the phoneme producer, word analyzer, and automatic detector.
C. Bruce has damage in the visual cortex.
D. Bruce has brain damage in the thalamus.

p. 320
Research Focus:
  Dyslexia
Level: Easy
Type: Factual
Ans: C

201. Training dyslexic children using computer games appears to:

A. increase language ability equal to 1 to 2 years' worth
B. decrease neural activity from the cortex that interferes with the word analyzer
C. increase neural activity between the phoneme producer and word analyzer
D. create more neural connections in the thalamus

p. 321
Cultural Diversity:
  Influences on Thinking
Level: Easy
Type: Factual
Ans: B

202. According to the study cited in the textbook, when looking at an underwater scene, Japanese subjects gave more statements about:

A. objects that were the largest
B. the background
C. the improbability of the scene
D. the size of the scene

p. 321
Cultural Diversity:
  Influences on Thinking
Level: Easy
Type: Factual
Ans: A

203. When Americans view objects, they tend to:

A. analyze each object separately
B. analyze objects that are close together as being connected
C. perceive the objects as one
D. focus on objects that are familiar

p. 321
Cultural Diversity:
  Influences on Thinking
Level: Easy
Type: Factual
Ans: C

204. Males and females use language differently. Males use language to _____ and females use it to _____.

A. direct others' behavior; criticize
B. share concerns; maintain their position in a group
C. solve problems; share concerns
D. criticize; maintain their independence

p. 321
Cultural Diversity:
  Influences on Thinking
Level: Easy
Type: Factual
Ans: D
*PS/SG 14-23*

205. Male-female differences in using language may be explained by new research showing that:

A. men and women are raised according to different rules and standards
B. men have developed a better style of speaking
C. women prefer to attack problems while men prefer to listen, give support, or be sympathetic
D. male and female brains process language differently

p. 321
Cultural Diversity:
  Influences on Thinking
Level: Easy
Type: Factual
Ans: D

206. Paul uses language to _____, whereas Paula uses it to _____.

A. share concerns; direct others' behavior
B. share concerns; maintain her position in a group
C. solve problems; express ideas
D. maintain his independence; develop feelings of intimacy

p. 321
Cultural Diversity:
  Influences on Thinking
Level: Easy
Type: Factual
Ans: A

207. Using MRI scans, research has revealed that when males are doing certain word processing tasks, their brain activity occurs:
A. only in the left hemisphere
B. only in the right hemisphere
C. equally in both hemispheres
D. only in the left occipital lobe

p. 321
Cultural Diversity:
  Influences on Thinking
Level: Easy
Type: Applied
Ans: C

208. Jenny is participating in a study where her brain is being studied with MRI. She is currently doing a language task. Which area of her brain is especially active?
A. left hemisphere
B. right hemisphere
C. activity is spread out equally in both hemispheres
D. right parietal lobe

p. 322
Application: Do Animals
  Have Language?
Level: Easy
Type: Factual
Ans: A

209. What term refers to the ability to use sounds, smells, or gestures to exchange communication?
A. communication
B. expression
C. language
D. grammar

p. 322
Application: Do Animals
  Have Language?
Level: Easy
Type: Factual
Ans: B

210. Language uses a set of _____ symbols.
A. auditory
B. abstract
C. practical
D. visual

p. 322
Application: Do Animals
  Have Language?
Level: Easy
Type: Factual
Ans: D

211. There are four criteria for having real language. Which of the following is not one of the criteria?
A. set of abstract symbols
B. use of abstract symbols
C. complex rules for expression
D. verbally expressed

p. 322
Application: Do Animals
  Have Language?
Level: Easy
Type: Factual
Ans: C
*PS/SG 14-25*

212. The bottom line in the debate over whether other animals can acquire true language seems to be that:
A. dolphins may possess a system of communication far superior to human language
B. the pygmy chimp is the only animal able to learn true language
C. only humans clearly meet the four criteria for true language
D. several of the higher primates can acquire the language skills of five-year-old children

p. 322
Application: Do Animals
  Have Language?
Level: Easy
Type: Applied
Ans: B

213.  Which of the following would be the <u>most</u> accurate title of a newspaper article describing dolphins' use of language?

A.  "Dolphins communicate to each other using abstract symbols"
B.  "Dolphins possess language comprehension"
C.  "Studies show dolphins' ability to create novel sentences"
D.  "Science shows dolphins apply rules of grammar"

p. 322
Application: Do Animals
  Have Language?
Level: Easy
Type: Factual
Ans: D

214.  There is little evidence that dolphins:

A.  carry out commands
B.  express emotional states
C.  understand hand signals
D.  can apply the rules of grammar to create meaningful sentences

p. 322
Application: Do Animals
  Have Language?
Level: Easy
Type: Factual
Ans: A

215.  According to Herman, dolphins:

A.  understand word order
B.  use basic rules of grammar
C.  cannot understand concepts
D.  use symbols for communication

p. 323
Application: Do Animals
  Have Language?
Level: Easy
Type: Factual
Ans: B

216.  In addition to sign language, chimpanzees have been taught to communicate with humans by using:

A.  Amalsan
B.  geometric shapes
C.  crude handwriting
D.  words in the form of primitive vocalizations

p. 323
Application: Do Animals
  Have Language?
Level: Easy
Type: Factual
Ans: C

217.  Koko the gorilla has a vocabulary of about _____ signs and Washoe has learned about ____ signs.

A.  200; 20
B.  500; 50
C.  800; 160
D.  1200; 200

p. 323
Application: Do Animals
  Have Language?
Level: Easy
Type: Factual
Ans: C

218.  The research involving the chimp named Nim has indicated that Nim:

A.  actually learned to communicate with language
B.  was capable of rules of grammar
C.  was primarily imitating or responding to cues
D.  used sign language to represent abstract words

p. 323
Application: Do Animals
  Have Language?
Level: Moderate
Type: Conceptual
Ans: A

219.  On a field trip to a primate language lab, you get to see Kinko, a chimp who has learned 250 signs. The researcher says that Kinko really does understand language in the same way that humans do. What do you say about that?

A.  You disagree - primates like Kinko have learned to imitate or respond to cues from their human teachers.
B.  You disagree - no primates have ever been taught to use that many signs.
C.  You agree - it is a well established scientific fact
D.  You agree - but would add that no one really knows how humans understand language

p. 323
Application: Do Animals
Have Language?
Level: Easy
Type: Factual
Ans: B

220. Kanzi, a bonobo, has indicated a knowledge of word order. Psychologists estimate that his comprehension and use of abstract symbols is equivalent to that of a:
A. 1-year-old human
B. 2-year-old human
C. 4-year-old human
D. 4 1/2-year-old human

p. 323
Application: Do Animals
Have Language?
Level: Easy
Type: Factual
Ans: B

221. During research for a paper on Kanzi, you found that he was taught using:
A. chips with symbols on them
B. a keyboard with symbols that stand for words
C. American Sign Language
D. parentese

p. 323
Application: Do Animals
Have Language?
Level: Easy
Type: Factual
Ans: C

222. When examining language and animals, researchers believe that _____ is responsible for the development of human language.
A. parentese
B. social learning
C. a gene called FOXP2
D. education

True/False

| | | | |
|---|---|---|---|
| T | www | 1. | Developing a list of essential characteristics is important in the exemplar theory of concepts. |
| F | | 2. | The prototype theory has not been widely accepted. |
| T | | 3. | The prototype theory focuses on an "average" looking object. |
| T | | 4. | Children develop concepts through experience. |
| F | | 5. | The brain stores different concepts in the same area. |
| T | www | 6. | The initial state, operations state, and goal state occur in problem solving. |
| F | | 7. | An algorithm is a rule of thumb. |
| F | www | 8. | Functional fixedness allows us to see similarities between situations. |
| T | | 9. | A sudden grasp of a solution is called insight. |
| T | | 10. | In divergent thinking, we develop many solutions. |
| F | www | 11. | There is a strong correlation between creativity and IQ. |
| F | | 12. | Creative people are driven by external motivation. |
| F | | 13. | Scientists are more likely than writers to suffer from mental disorders. |
| F | www | 14. | A phoneme is the smallest meaningful combination of sounds. |
| T | | 15. | The syntax of a language refers to the rules of combining words to form sentences. |
| F | www | 16. | A child who says, "I goed there" illustrates telegraphic speech. |
| T | www | 17. | Parentese is a way of speaking to infants. |
| T | | 18. | Both innate and environmental factors play a role in language acquisition. |
| F | | 19. | If then statements reflect inductive reasoning. |
| T | | 20. | In deductive reasoning, we go from a general assumption to specific ones. |
| T | www | 21. | The theory of linguistic relativity argues that our language affects our thinking. |

| F |  | 22. | Using computer programs to treat dyslexia has not been effective. |
| T | www | 23. | Men and women process words differently in their brains. |
| T |  | 24. | Dolphins cannot use grammar to create meaningful sentences. |
| F | www | 25. | Chimps can create novel sentences. |

Short-Answer Essay Questions

1. How would the exemplar theory and prototype theory explain how you develop the concept of bird? (*www*)

2. Describe how a child develops a concept and how increasing language skills influence this development. (*www*)

3. Discuss an algorithm you use when answering test questions. What heuristics are helpful when studying or writing term papers?

4. Compare and contrast convergent and divergent thinking. Include appropriate examples to support your answer. (*www*)

5. Describe the focus and personality of creative individuals. Is their creativity correlated with their intelligence?

6. Explain the four rules of language.

7. Compare and contrast deductive and inductive reasoning. Make sure to include examples that point out the difference.

8. What is dyslexia? Explain the idea that the neural wiring in the brains of dyslexics may be defective. (*www*)

9. Describe three ways that men and women use language differently. What role does the brain play in these differences?

10. In what ways is the use of language by dolphins and chimps similar to the way we use language? In what ways does human language use differ? (*www*)

# Module 15 - Motivation

p. 329
Introduction
Level: Easy
Type: Factual
Ans: B

1.    Mark Wellman's climb up Half Dome in Yosemite National Park was unique because Wellman is:
A.    blind
B.    a paraplegic
C.    only eight years old
D.    moderately mentally retarded

p. 329
Introduction
Level: Easy
Type: Factual
Ans: C
*PS/SG 15-1*

2.    Rod Plotnik tells the story of Mark Wellman's incredible climb to illustrate the fact that:
A.    you can do anything you really put your mind to
B.    you should take risks in life, but also have strong ropes!
C.    the causes of human actions are complex, yet important to understand
D.    there must be a single source of motivation, as yet undiscovered

p. 329
Introduction
Level: Easy
Type: Factual
Ans: A

3.    A psychological or physiological factor that causes humans to act in a specific way at a particular time is called:
A.    motivation
B.    energy
C.    instinct
D.    drive

p. 329
Introduction
Level: Moderate
Type: Factual
Ans: D

4.    When we are motivated, we typically show three characteristics. Which of the following is <u>not</u> one of the three characteristics?
A.    energized to do something
B.    directed to reach a specific goal
C.    different intensities of feelings about reaching a specific goal
D.    increased arousal after reaching a specific goal

p. 329
Introduction
Level: Moderate
Type: Applied
Ans: B

5.    Brian is motivated. According to the textbook, what must he show to be motivated?
A.    Brian's behavior must be instinctual.
B.    He must direct his energies toward a specific goal.
C.    As he reaches his goal, his arousal must subside.
D.    The goal that Brian is working towards must be a general, not specific goal.

p. 329
Introduction
Level: Moderate
Type: Applied
Ans: C

6.    "I have lots of motivation to do something. I want to do something with my life, but I'm not sure what." This person shows _____ but lacks _____.
A.    intensity towards a goal; direction
B.    goal-directed behavior; drive reduction
C.    energized behavior; direction
D.    instinct; incentive

p. 329
Introduction
Level: Moderate
Type: Applied
Ans: B

7.  A potential college student named Sylvia is 44 years old, divorced, and has three children. She says that she really wants to attend college and that "I've worked and have saved up lots of money for tuition. I've even taken a couple of refresher classes. I'm ready!" Sylvia is motivated and shows the characteristic of:
    A. being energized to do something
    B. being directed to reach a specific goal
    C. having different intensities of feelings about reaching a specific goal
    D. having increased arousal after reaching a specific goal

p. 329
Introduction
Level: Moderate
Type: Factual
Ans: C

8.  The young man named Victor whose story is described in the introduction of the module is an exception to the rule. He achieved in school despite:
    A. coming from a single-parent family
    B. a poor academic record in elementary school
    C. negative peer pressure not to succeed in school
    D. being a former gang member

p. 329
Introduction
Level: Easy
Type: Factual
Ans: A

9.  You are studying why some minority students stop studying and dropout of school. According to the research, you found out that the high dropout rates are partially due to:
    A. peer pressure not to succeed in school
    B. ineffective teachers
    C. lack of minority role models
    D. lack of ability

p. 329
Introduction
Level: Moderate
Type: Conceptual
Ans: B

10. Which word best summarizes the study of motivation?
    A. when
    B. why
    C. what
    D. where

p. 330
Theories of Motivation
Level: Easy
Type: Factual
Ans: D
*www*

11. An inborn biological force that determines behavior is the definition of:
    A. motivation
    B. emotion
    C. drive
    D. instinct

p. 330
Theories of Motivation
Level: Easy
Type: Factual
Ans: B
*PS/SG 15-2*

12. Early in this century, most psychologists believed that motivation was explained by:
    A. will power
    B. instincts
    C. environmental incentives
    D. beliefs and expectations

p. 330
Theories of Motivation
Level: Easy
Type: Factual
Ans: C

13. McDougall listed sympathy, curiosity, and self-assertion as:
    A. learned goals
    B. biological needs
    C. human instincts
    D. personality traits

p. 330
Theories of Motivation
Level: Easy
Type: Factual
Ans: D

14. The notion of instincts received much criticism because instincts:
A. are not found in humans
B. require both learning and experience
C. were used to account for general behaviors
D. are not useful in explaining behavior

p. 330
Theories of Motivation
Level: Moderate
Type: Applied
Ans: B

15. "Isn't that darling," says Mary as she watches a young child looking under small boxes at the day care center. "He is curious because humans have a curiosity instinct." In her observation of the child, Mary has:
A. explained his behavior
B. described his behavior
C. seen a very good example of human instinct
D. ignored the child's other behavior

p. 330
Theories of Motivation
Level: Easy
Type: Factual
Ans: A

16. The concept of instinct has been replaced with the idea of:
A. fixed action patterns
B. homeostatic mechanisms
C. extrinsic motives
D. intrinsic motives

p. 330
Theories of Motivation
Level: Easy
Type: Factual
Ans: A

17. Animals have been found to have innate biological forces that predispose them to behave in a fixed way in the presence of specific environmental conditions. These forces are called:
A. fixed action patterns
B. incentive mechanisms
C. extrinsic motivators
D. self-actualization needs

p. 330
Theories of Motivation
Level: Easy
Type: Factual
Ans: B

18. The fixed action patterns of animals predispose them to behave in a fixed way:
A. in order to return their body to homeostasis
B. in the presence of a specific environmental condition
C. in order to develop intrinsic motivation
D. in order to develop extrinsic motivation

p. 330
Theories of Motivation
Level: Easy
Type: Factual
Ans: A
*PS/SG 15-3*

19. What were once called instincts are now called:
A. fixed action patterns
B. incentives
C. rewards
D. energizers

p. 330
Theories of Motivation
Level: Easy
Type: Conceptual
Ans: C

20. The fact that a bird builds a nest in the spring is an example of a(n):
A. extrinsic behavior
B. self-actualization need
C. fixed action pattern
D. drive-reduction

<table>
<tr><td>

p. 330
Theories of Motivation
Level: Easy
Type: Applied
Ans: A

</td><td>

21.    John believes that women make better parents than men because women have an inborn tendency to "mother" children. John's statement would reflect which of the following theories of motivation?

A.    instinct
B.    incentive
C.    cognitive
D.    expectation-attribution

</td></tr>
<tr><td>

p. 330
Theories of Motivation
Level: Easy
Type: Factual
Ans: B

</td><td>

22.    In studying how animals adapt to their environment, ethologists focus on how animals use:

A.    homeostasis
B.    fixed action patterns
C.    incentives
D.    social roles

</td></tr>
<tr><td>

p. 330
Theories of Motivation
Level: Easy
Type: Factual
Ans: C

</td><td>

23.    According to ethologists, imprinting in birds illustrate a(n):
A.    homeostasis
B.    instinct
C.    fixed action pattern
D.    social need

</td></tr>
<tr><td>

p. 330
Theories of Motivation
Level: Easy
Type: Factual
Ans: C

</td><td>

24.    You eat because you like to. This best illustrates the idea the motivation is due to:
A.    unconscious desires to reduce anxiety
B.    instinct
C.    reward/pleasure centers in the brain
D.    drive

</td></tr>
<tr><td>

p. 330
Theories of Motivation
Level: Easy
Type: Applied
Ans: B

</td><td>

25.    In what brain areas have researchers found pleasure centers?
A.    thalamus and amygdala
B.    nucleus accumbens and ventral temgental area
C.    hypothalamus and cerebral cortex
D.    thalamus and corpus callosum

</td></tr>
<tr><td>

p. 330
Theories of Motivation
Level: Easy
Type: Factual
Ans: C
PS/SG 15-4

</td><td>

26.    Brain scans have revealed a new source of motivation, the:
A.    instinct
B.    fixed action pattern
C.    reward/pleasure center
D.    incentive

</td></tr>
<tr><td>

p. 330
Theories of Motivation
Level: Easy
Type: Conceptual
Ans: D

</td><td>

27.    The instinct theory and reward/pleasure center notion both emphasize _____ in motivation.
A.    incentive
B.    need
C.    drive
D.    internal factors

</td></tr>
</table>

p. 330
Theories of Motivation
Level: Easy
Type: Factual
Ans: D

28.   People, who are addicted to cocaine, are motivated to seek it because cocaine stimulates:

A.   the neurotransmitter GABA
B.   neural pathways in the amygdala
C.   creativity
D.   nucleus accumbens and ventral temgental areas of the brain

p. 331
Theories of Motivation
Level: Easy
Type: Factual
Ans: C
*www*

29.   External stimuli or rewards which we desire and can motivate behavior are called:

A.   needs
B.   drives
C.   incentives
D.   peripheral cues

p. 331
Theories of Motivation
Level: Easy
Type: Applied
Ans: C

30.   A race car driver wants to win the prize money and feels as if the money is pulling him to win. Which of the following would explain this behavior?

A.   pleasure center theory
B.   fixed action patterns
C.   incentive theory
D.   instinct theory

p. 331
Theories of Motivation
Level: Easy
Type: Factual
Ans: A
*www*

31.   An incentive is _____, whereas needs are _____.

A.   external; internal
B.   a fixed action pattern; instinctual
C.   a biological need; social needs
D.   a safety need; self-actualization needs

p. 331
Theories of Motivation
Level: Easy
Type: Applied
Ans: B

32.   "I want to get good grades so I can get a good job and makes lots of money." This individual <u>best</u> illustrates:

A.   instinct theory
B.   incentive theory
C.   intrinsic motivation
D.   self-actualization needs

p. 331
Theories of Motivation
Level: Easy
Type: Conceptual
Ans: B

33.   Which of the following behaviors could be explained by incentive theory and *not* by pleasure/reward center theory?

A.   drinking when thirsty
B.   eating when full
C.   buying clothes for work in a cold environment
D.   eating when hungry

p. 331
Theories of Motivation
Level: Moderate
Type: Conceptual
Ans: A

34.   Which of the following words best explains incentive theory of motivation?

A.   pulling us
B.   pushing us
C.   helping us
D.   hurting us

p. 331
Theories of Motivation
Level: Easy
Type: Factual
Ans: D

35. Beliefs, expectations, and goals are important concepts in which of the following theories of motivation?
A. instinct theory
B. drive-reduction theory
C. self-actualization
D. cognitive theory

p. 331
Theories of Motivation
Level: Easy
Type: Factual
Ans: D
*PS/SG 15-5*

36. The newest theory of motivation places greatest emphasis on:
A. will power
B. instincts
C. environmental incentives
D. beliefs and expectations

p. 331
Theories of Motivation
Level: Easy
Type: Factual
Ans: D

37. The newest theory of motivation places greatest emphasis on:
A. drives
B. instincts
C. environmental incentives
D. cognitive factors

p. 331
Theories of Motivation
Level: Moderate
Type: Applied
Ans: B

38. A person takes up the game of racquetball because she feels she has the quickness and coordination to do well at the game. Which theory of motivation is best demonstrated by her behavior?
A. pleasure/reward theory
B. cognitive theory
C. instinct theory
D. psychodynamic theory

p. 331
Theories of Motivation
Level: Moderate
Type: Applied
Ans: A
*www*

39. It is believed that some people become anorexic because they feel that they cannot control anything but their weight and eating behavior. Which motivational theory would best explain this behavior?
A. cognitive theory
B. instinct theory
C. drive-reduction
D. social needs

p. 331
Theories of Motivation
Level: Easy
Type: Factual
Ans: B

40. Intrinsic motivation influences us to engage in behaviors that:
A. obtain rewards or incentives important for survival
B. are personally rewarding
C. satisfy biological needs
D. are instinctual fixed action patterns

p. 331
Theories of Motivation
Level: Easy
Type: Conceptual
Ans: D

41. Intrinsic is to _____ as extrinsic is to _____.
A. biological; psychological
B. instinct; social
C. biological; internal
D. internal; external

p. 331
Theories of Motivation
Level: Easy
Type: Applied
Ans: C

42. Carl works hard to get A's on his report card because his mother pays him 25 dollars. Carl's behavior is being influenced by:
A. fixed action patterns
B. a hierarchy of needs
C. extrinsic motivation
D. drive-reduction theory

p. 331
Theories of Motivation
Level: Easy
Type: Applied
Ans: C

43. Carla works hard to get A's on her report card because it makes her feel good to set goals and reach them. Her behavior is being influenced by:
A. fixed action patterns
B. intrinsic motivation
C. extrinsic motivation
D. drive-reduction theory

p. 331
Theories of Motivation
Level: Moderate
Type: Applied
Ans: A

44. Stacey believes that she will be successful on her diet because she is in control of what happens to her. According to a cognitive theory of motivation, her belief shows that she has a strong sense of:
A. personal expectations and beliefs
B. drive
C. attribution
D. need

p. 331
Theories of Motivation
Level: Moderate
Type: Factual
Ans: A

45. Of the following summary statements of the theories of motivation presented in the textbook, which one is incorrect?
A. Instinct theory explains the behavior of humans
B. Pleasure can motivate us.
C. We can use the incentive theory to explain behavior done to obtain some external reward
D. The cognitive theory focuses its explanation on behaving in such a way to satisfy personal beliefs

p. 332
Biological and Social
  Needs
Level: Easy
Type: Factual
Ans: C

46. Food, sleep, and sex are examples of:
A. social needs
B. safety needs
C. biological needs
D. self-actualization needs

p. 332
Biological and Social
  Needs
Level: Easy
Type: Factual
Ans: C

47. Variables that motivate you because of their importance to our survival and well-being are called:
A. social needs
B. safety needs
C. biological needs
D. self-actualization needs

p. 332
Biological and Social
  Needs
Level: Easy
Type: Factual
Ans: B

48.   What is the disorder that affects the hypothalamus which results in abnormal eating behavior?
A.   autism
B.   Prader-Willis syndrome
C.   dissociative disorder
D.   bulimia

p. 332
Biological and Social
  Needs
Level: Moderate
Type: Conceptual
Ans: B

49.   The example of anorexia nervosa illustrates that:
A.   instinct in some people is weaker than in others
B.   psychological factors can override basic biological needs
C.   social needs are less influential than biological needs
D.   drive-reduction theory adequately explains human motivation

p. 332
Biological and Social
  Needs
Level: Easy
Type: Factual
Ans: D

50.   Social needs are acquired through:
A.   heredity
B.   homeostatic mechanisms
C.   peripheral cues
D.   learning and experience

p. 332
Biological and Social
  Needs
Level: Easy
Type: Applied
Ans: A

51.   Becky and Jeff recently got married. One reason they got married was to form a long lasting relationship with each other. Therefore, marriage for them satisfied their:
A.   need for affiliation
B.   self-actualization
C.   need for autonomy
D.   need for order

p. 332
Biological and Social
  Needs
Level: Easy
Type: Factual
Ans: C

52.   Which of the following social needs has been found to be important in determining physical health and psychological well-being?
A.   avoidance of pain
B.   need for food
C.   need for affiliation
D.   need for shelter

p. 332
Biological and Social
  Needs
Level: Easy
Type: Applied
Ans: A

53.   The need for affiliation is satisfied by:
A.   forming lasting and positive interpersonal attachments
B.   getting good grades in college
C.   keeping one's life orderly and predictable
D.   receiving recognition for hard work

p. 332
Biological and Social
  Needs
Level: Easy
Type: Factual
Ans: C

54.   According to Maslow, we satisfy our needs:
A.   in a somewhat random order
B.   with the overall goal of increasing our self-esteem
C.   in a certain order based on a set hierarchy
D.   only when we feel competent in doing so

p. 332
Biological and Social
  Needs
Level: Easy
Type: Factual
Ans: B
*PS/SG 15-6*

55. The key idea of Maslow's hierarchy of needs is that:
A. unless social needs like esteem are satisfied, one cannot deal effectively with biological needs like safety
B. basic biological needs must be satisfied before higher social needs can be dealt with
C. unless you achieve level five, you are a defective person
D. the higher needs are essential; the lower needs are incidental

p. 332
Biological and Social
  Needs
Level: Easy
Type: Factual
Ans: A

56. Understanding how people decide which needs to satisfy first is the goal of:
A. Maslow's hierarchy of needs
B. peripheral cues
C. drive-reduction theory
D. the Thematic Apperception Test (TAT)

p. 333
Biological and Social
  Needs
Level: Easy
Type: Factual
Ans: A
*www*

57. Arrange Maslow's needs in the correct ascending order.
A. physiological, safety, belongingness, esteem, self-actualization
B. self-actualization, physiological, esteem, belongingness, safety
C. safety, esteem, physiological, self-actualization, belongingness
D. belongingness, self-actualization, physiological, safety, esteem

p. 333
Biological and Social
  Needs
Level: Easy
Type: Factual
Ans: C

58. Maslow defined self-actualization as:
A. affiliation with others
B. achievement, competency, gaining approval, and recognition
C. fulfillment of one's unique potential
D. the perception of one's own body

p. 333
Biological and Social
  Needs
Level: Easy
Type: Factual
Ans: D
*PS/SG 15-7*

59. The highest level need (at the top of the pyramid) in Maslow's hierarchy is:
A. safety needs
B. love and belonging needs
C. esteem needs
D. self-actualization

p. 333
Biological and Social
  Needs
Level: Easy
Type: Factual
Ans: D
*www*

60. Ruben has reached his fullest potential as a human being. According to Maslow, Ruben has achieved:
A. physiological fullness
B. self-esteem
C. incentiveness
D. self-actualization

p. 333
Biological and Social
  Needs
Level: Easy
Type: Conceptual
Ans: D

61. Which of the following book titles would best illustrate the topic of self-actualization?
A. "Meeting Your Goals"
B. "Satisfying Your Body"
C. "Following Your Instincts"
D. "Be All That You Can Be"

p. 333
Biological and Social
  Needs
Level: Easy
Type: Factual
Ans: D

62. Steven is satisfying self-actualization needs, but his basic needs are not satisfied. Steven will most likely:
A. continue to advance up the hierarchy
B. remain at the self-actualized level
C. try and satisfy his esteem needs
D. return to a lower level

p. 333
Biological and Social
  Needs
Level: Easy
Type: Factual
Ans: B

63. To be achieving, competent and to gain approval and recognition from others is to reach the _____ level of Maslow's hierarchy.
A. incentive
B. esteem
C. self-actualization
D. intrinsic

p. 333
Biological and Social
  Needs
Level: Easy
Type: Applied
Ans: A

64. Carlo lives in a high crime neighborhood. Of all Maslow's needs, he is most concerned about:
A. safety needs
B. esteem needs
C. belongingness needs
D. extrinsic needs

p. 333
Biological and Social
  Needs
Level: Easy
Type: Applied
Ans: C

65. "I am a member of the college's chess club and we often get together and talk about life and chess. My best friends are also members." This best illustrates what Maslow's called:
A. safety needs
B. esteem needs
C. belongingness needs
D. self-actualization

p. 333
Biological and Social
  Needs
Level: Easy
Type: Factual
Ans: B

66. One advantage of Maslow's hierarchy is that it:
A. has a strong empirical database to support it
B. establishes a priority for taking care of various needs
C. explains differences among people
D. is universally accepted

p. 333
Biological and Social
  Needs
Level: Easy
Type: Factual
Ans: B

67. Researchers have criticized Maslow's hierarchy of needs because:
A. it integrates biological and social needs
B. it is difficult to measure some of his needs
C. people satisfy social needs before physiological needs
D. it ignores the notion of basic needs

p. 333
Biological and Social
  Needs
Level: Easy
Type: Factual
Ans: C

68. According to the textbook, the one level of Maslow's hierarchy most difficult to assess accomplishment of is:
  A. physiological needs
  B. safety needs
  C. self-actualization needs
  D. incentive needs

p. 334
Hunger
Level: Easy
Type: Factual
Ans: B

69. When the organism has reached a perfect balance between the amount of food consumed and amount of energy needed, the organism is said to have:
  A. homeostasis
  B. optimum or ideal weight
  C. desired weight
  D. caloric-energy balance

p. 334
Hunger
Level: Easy
Type: Factual
Ans: A
*www*

70. What term is used to describe how much energy food contains?
  A. calorie
  B. homeostasis
  C. fuel quantity
  D. glucose potential

p. 334
Hunger
Level: Easy
Type: Factual
Ans: C

71. The two primary reasons for being overweight are:
  A. eating more food than needed and social support for being overweight
  B. eating more food than needed and genetic predisposition
  C. eating more food than needed and lack of exercise
  D. eating foods with high fat content and genetic predisposition

p. 334
Hunger
Level: Easy
Type: Factual
Ans: B

72. To be overweight, an individual is _____ over his or her ideal body weight.
  A. 10%
  B. 20%
  C. 30%
  D. 35%

p. 334
Hunger
Level: Easy
Type: Applied
Ans: D

73. A researcher wishes to investigate the eating patterns of people who would be defined medically as obese. If he uses the definition of obesity provided in the text, his subjects will:
  A. be males having a waist size over 46 and females over 38
  B. have a fat cell to muscle tissue ratio that is greater than 2 to 1
  C. be in the top 20 percent for weight in their age, sex, and height category
  D. weigh 30 percent over their ideal body weight

p. 334
Hunger
Level: Easy
Type: Applied
Ans: D

74. In 2003, if you randomly select 10 adults, how many would be overweight?
  A. 1
  B. 2
  C. 5
  D. 7

| | | |
|---|---|---|
| p. 334<br>Hunger<br>Level: Easy<br>Type: Factual<br>Ans: C | 75. | What percentage of deaths in men due to cancer were related to obesity? |
| | A. | 1% |
| | B. | 6% |
| | C. | 14% |
| | D. | 56% |

| | | |
|---|---|---|
| p. 334<br>Hunger<br>Level: Easy<br>Type: Applied<br>Ans: D | 76. | "Obese people are obese because of their biology make-up." Is this person correct? |
| | A. | Maybe – some obesity is due to biology; other cases due to psychology. |
| | B. | Yes – biology is the sole cause of obesity. |
| | C. | No – hunger is entirely due to social and psychological variables. |
| | D. | No – hunger is influenced by psychosocial factors as well. |

| | | |
|---|---|---|
| p. 334<br>Hunger<br>Level: Easy<br>Type: Factual<br>Ans: D | 77. | The "when", "where", and "how much" we eat are influenced by three factors. Which of the following is <u>not</u> among the three factors cited in your textbook? |
| | A. | biological hunger factors |
| | B. | psychosocial hunger factors |
| | C. | genetic hunger factors |
| | D. | cognitive hunger factors |

| | | |
|---|---|---|
| p. 334<br>Hunger<br>Level: Easy<br>Type: Conceptual<br>Ans: A | 78. | If human hunger was entirely regulated by biological factors, what would happen to your weight? |
| | A. | Your weight would remain at the optimum weight. |
| | B. | Your weight would randomly fluctuate. |
| | C. | Your weight would stay about the same. |
| | D. | Your weight would probably increase. |

| | | |
|---|---|---|
| p. 335<br>Hunger<br>Level: Easy<br>Type: Conceptual<br>Ans: D | 79. | You are searching the internet for information related to biological hunger factors. Which set of search words would you use? |
| | A. | genetics, heredity, set point |
| | B. | depression, body image |
| | C. | sociocultural, personality |
| | D. | blood chemistry, digestion, peripheral cues, CCK |

| | | |
|---|---|---|
| p. 335<br>Hunger<br>Level: Easy<br>Type: Factual<br>Ans: C<br>*www* | 80. | Peripheral cues for hunger come from _____, whereas central cues come from _____. |
| | A. | learning; experience |
| | B. | body image; actual weight |
| | C. | digestive organs; the brain |
| | D. | the hypothalamus; hormones |

| | | |
|---|---|---|
| p. 335<br>Hunger<br>Level: Easy<br>Type: Factual<br>Ans: D | 81. | After a large lunch, Carlie sits in her early afternoon class. Her stomach signals the _____ about its fullness. |
| | A. | liver |
| | B. | bile duct |
| | C. | digestive organs |
| | D. | hypothalamus |

p. 335
Hunger
Level: Easy
Type: Factual
Ans: A

82. Which option lists parts of the body that provide peripheral cues?
A. stomach, liver, intestines, and fat cells
B. galanin, intestines, liver, and lateral hypothalamus
C. hypothalamus, fat cells, liver, and stomach
D. hypothalamus, lateral hypothalamus, ventromedial hypothalamus, and fat cells

p. 335
Hunger
Level: Easy
Type: Applied
Ans: C

83. If you could shrink yourself and enter someone's liver, what would you see the liver do when it detects rising glucose levels?
A. produce norepinephrine
B. stimulate the stomach to produce galanin
C. signal fullness
D. signal hunger

p. 335
Hunger
Level: Easy
Type: Applied
Ans: B

84. The intestines secrete hormones called:
A. norepinephrine and leptin
B. ghrelin, PYY, and CCK
C. dopamine and estrogen
D. androgens

p. 335
Hunger
Level: Easy
Type: Factual
Ans: C
*PS/SG 15-8*

85. Which one of the following is <u>not</u> a biological cue for hunger?
A. glucose in the blood
B. the hypothalamus
C. learned associations
D. the walls of the stomach

p. 335
Hunger
Level: Easy
Type: Factual
Ans: D

86. What effect does falling levels of leptin have on hunger?
A. appetite for fats increase
B. appetite for sweets increase
C. appetite is decreased
D. appetite is increased

p. 335
Hunger
Level: Easy
Type: Factual
Ans: C

87. The master control for eating:
A. stomach
B. liver
C. hypothalamus
D. thalamus

p. 335
Hunger
Level: Easy
Type: Factual
Ans: B

88. A part of the brain that seems to be directly involved with hunger and eating is the:
A. cerebellum
B. hypothalamus
C. thalamus
D. occipital lobe

p. 335
Hunger
Level: Easy
Type: Factual
Ans: B

89. If we were to destroy the ventromedial hypothalamus in a group of rats, what would we expect to find when these rats were compared to a group of control rats?
A. The experimental rats would die of starvation.
B. The experimental rats would be much larger than the control rats.
C. The experimental rats would be dehydrated.
D. The experimental rats would sleep much less than the control rats.

p. 335
Hunger
Level: Moderate
Type: Applied
Ans: A

90. A person begins to suffer weight loss for no apparent reason. All organs are intact. Also, the person does not want to lose weight. However, he claims that he is rarely hungry. Which diagnosis would be most likely in this case?
A. damage to the lateral hypothalamus
B. hyperphagia
C. anorexia nervosa
D. bulimia

p. 335
Hunger
Level: Moderate
Type: Applied
Ans: B
*www*

91. The start eating center in the hypothalamus is the _____. The stop eating center is the _____.
A. hyperphagia; hypophagia
B. lateral hypothalamus; ventromedial hypothalamus
C. CCK, stomach
D. lateral hypothalamus; anterior hyperphagia

p. 335
Hunger
Level: Moderate
Type: Factual
Ans: D

92. The ventromedial hypothalamus interprets the hormones PPY and CCK as:
A. start eating signals
B. signals to eat more carbohydrates
C. hunger signals
D. full signals

p. 336
Hunger
Level: Easy
Type: Factual
Ans: D

93. If an adopted adult's weight is more strongly correlated with the weight of their biological parents rather than their adopted parents, then this provides evidence for:
A. environmental factors
B. psychosocial hunger factors
C. peripheral cues
D. genetic hunger factors

p. 336
Hunger
Level: Moderate
Type: Factual
Ans: C

94. Researchers estimate that in maintaining a particular body size and weight, inherited factors contribute about _____ while environmental factors contribute about _____.
A. 40%; 60%
B. 50%; 50%
C. 70%; 30%
D. 30%; 70%

p. 336
Hunger
Level: Easy
Type: Factual
Ans: C

95. Which of the following is a genetic hunger factor that regulates body weight?
A. peripheral cues
B. fixed action patterns
C. number of fat cells
D. pheromones

p. 336
Hunger
Level: Easy
Type: Factual
Ans: A

96. When do fat cells multiply?
A. when the individual is obese
B. hours after an individual eats large quantities of food
C. when the setpoint decreases
D. when the fat gene produces hyperphagia

p. 336
Hunger
Level: Easy
Type: Factual
Ans: B

97. A person's metabolic rate refers to the:
A. amount of oxygen taken in with one deep breath
B. rate at which food is broken down into energy and how fast the energy is used
C. rate at which glucose is stored
D. rate at which fat stores are burned off

p. 336
Hunger
Level: Easy
Type: Factual
Ans: B

98. If a person has a low metabolic rate, they will:
A. burn more energy
B. store excess energy as fat
C. store less fat
D. have few fat cells

p. 336
Hunger
Level: Easy
Type: Factual
Ans: A

99. Why do smokers gain weight when they quit smoking?
A. nicotine raises metabolic rate
B. CCK is released during smoking
C. nicotine increase the number of fat cells
D. nicotine increases the set point

p. 336
Hunger
Level: Easy
Type: Factual
Ans: C

100. The only known ways to raise metabolic rates are:
A. exercise and consuming sugar
B. exercise and dieting
C. exercise and smoking cigarettes
D. exercise and reducing fat intake

p. 336
Hunger
Level: Easy
Type: Factual
Ans: C

101. The higher one's metabolic rate, the:
A. less fuel burned and more likely excess fuel is stored as fat
B. more fuel burned and more likely excess fuel is stored as fat
C. more fuel burned and less likely excess fuel is stored as fat
D. less fuel burned and less likely excess fuel is stored as fat

p. 336
Hunger
Level: Easy
Type: Factual
Ans: B

102. _____ refers to a certain level of body fat that the body strives to maintain constant throughout our lives.
A. Homeostasis
B. Setpoint
C. Metabolic rate
D. Weight point

p. 336
Hunger
Level: Easy
Type: Factual
Ans: C
*PS/SG 15-10*

103. The best explanation of the common tendency of dieters to regain the weight they lose is the:
A. fat cell
B. metabolic rate
C. set point
D. weight-regulating gene

| | | |
|---|---|---|
| p. 336<br>Hunger<br>Level: Easy<br>Type: Factual<br>Ans: B | 104. | It is believed that Troy has a high setpoint. Dieting will be difficult for him because: |
| | A. | hypothalamus dysfunction prevents Troy from feeling full |
| | B. | when Troy diets, the metabolic rate may slow |
| | C. | Troy is particularly susceptible to learned cues to eating |
| | D. | Troy will experience hunger more often than someone with a low setpoint |
| p. 336<br>Hunger<br>Level: Easy<br>Type: Factual<br>Ans: B | 105. | If a person has a high setpoint, the person: |
| | A. | will have little trouble maintaining normal weight |
| | B. | will very possibly be overweight |
| | C. | has a very low rate of metabolism |
| | D. | has trouble resisting learned cues to eating |
| p. 336<br>Hunger<br>Level: Moderate<br>Type: Factual<br>Ans: D | 106. | Why will an overweight person be unsuccessful with long-term dieting without exercise? |
| | A. | Most people stop dieting after one month of weight loss. |
| | B. | The metabolic rate increases after one month of weight loss. |
| | C. | The body's loses it ability to make CCK. |
| | D. | The body's setpoint is rigorously maintained. |
| p. 336<br>Hunger<br>Level: Easy<br>Type: Factual<br>Ans: C | 107. | Which of the following statements about the weight-regulating gene is true? |
| | A. | The gene plays a role in metabolism, but not the secretion of leptin. |
| | B. | As we become overweight and then obese, the normal gene undergoes mutation and becomes an weight-regulating gene. |
| | C. | The gene influences obesity. |
| | D. | The weight-regulating gene has only been found among women. |
| p. 336<br>Hunger<br>Level: Easy<br>Type: Factual<br>Ans: A | 108. | Lara is so thin, yet she eats high caloric foods and fatty foods. Based on information presented in the textbook, why can Lara stay so thin? |
| | A. | Lara has a gene that increases metabolism. |
| | B. | Lara has a gene that decreases metabolism. |
| | C. | Lara's setpoint is very high. |
| | D. | Lara has a gene that causes an overproduction of neuropeptide Y. |
| p. 337<br>Hunger<br>Level: Easy<br>Type: Applied<br>Ans: D | 109. | Wayne eats a seven-course dinner and claims he cannot eat another bite of food. Then the waiter brings the dessert tray to the table, and Wayne finds that he's hungry for the pecan pie with whipped cream. His hunger is most likely due to: |
| | A. | a drop in blood sugar |
| | B. | a surge in blood sugar |
| | C. | the production of galanin |
| | D. | psychosocial hunger factors |
| p. 337<br>Hunger<br>Level: Easy<br>Type: Applied<br>Ans: C | 110. | "It's noon, so it's time to eat." This person illustrates the role of _____ in hunger. |
| | A. | PYY |
| | B. | genetic factors |
| | C. | learned associations |
| | D. | leptin |

p. 337
Hunger
Level: Easy
Type: Applied
Ans: C

111. "Whenever I am depressed or bored, I tend to eat even when I'm not hungry." This statement best illustrates the role of _____ in hunger.
A. CCK
B. genetic factors
C. psychosocial factors
D. self-handicapping

p. 337
Hunger
Level: Easy
Type: Applied
Ans: B

112. According to the textbook, what is the most serious example of learned associations affecting eating?
A. low to moderate metabolic rates
B. marketing and advertising pressures to sell foods by offering huge servings
C. equating pleasure with eating
D. dessert trays in restaurants

p. 337
Hunger
Level: Easy
Type: Factual
Ans: C

113. What effect have cultural pressures regarding hunger had on women?
A. women are less likely to overestimate their weight
B. women are more likely to eat high calorie foods
C. women are more likely to be concerned with their weight
D. women are less likely to be concerned with their weight

p. 337
Hunger
Level: Easy
Type: Applied
Ans: A

114. Barbara wants to lose weight because when she looks at fashion magazines, she sees that all the attractive models are very thin. Which of the following factors is motivating Barbara to diet?
A. social-cultural factors
B. under-responsiveness to food
C. calories and metabolism
D. setpoint

p. 337
Hunger
Level: Easy
Type: Factual
Ans: C

115. Regarding social-cultural factors involved in body weight, which of the following is true?
A. Being 20% over the recommended range of weights is considered normal in the United States.
B. Social-cultural standards have little influence on perceptions of weight.
C. Because of government subsidies of fatty sausage and dairy products, nearly half of all adult Czechs are obese.
D. Personality does not influence overeating.

p. 337
Hunger
Level: Easy
Type: Factual
Ans: B

116. Which emotion is most often related to overeating?
A. joy
B. anxiety
C. happiness
D. disgust

p. 337
Hunger
Level: Moderate
Type: Conceptual
Ans: C

117. The fact that hunger in humans is the result of genetic, biological, and psychological, social, and cultural factors makes:
A. it impossible to study
B. hunger easier to control
C. it more complex
D. hunger more a matter of survival than pleasure

| | | |
|---|---|---|
| p. 338<br>Sexual Behavior<br>Level: Moderate<br>Type: Conceptual<br>Ans: C | 118. | The fact that sexual behavior in humans is the result of genetic, biological, and psychological sexual factors makes: |
| | A. | it impossible to study |
| | B. | similarity in behavior more likely |
| | C. | it more complex |
| | D. | sex more a matter of reproduction than pleasure |

| | | |
|---|---|---|
| p. 338<br>Sexual Behavior<br>Level: Easy<br>Type: Factual<br>Ans: B<br>*PS/SG 15-12* | 119. | Lions never go on talk shows; their sexual behavior is kept in line by the fact that: |
| | A. | females do most of the hunting |
| | B. | hormones and pheromones prevail |
| | C. | social roles and rules predominate |
| | D. | a lioness's bite can be fatal |

| | | |
|---|---|---|
| p. 338<br>Sexual Behavior<br>Level: Easy<br>Type: Factual<br>Ans: B | 120. | The sexual motivation of animals is almost totally regulated by: |
| | A. | social-cultural factors |
| | B. | genetic and biological factors |
| | C. | the four stages of sexual response |
| | D. | the hypothalamus |

| | | |
|---|---|---|
| p. 338<br>Sexual Behavior<br>Level: Easy<br>Type: Factual<br>Ans: B | 121. | Inherited instructions for the development of sexual organs, the secretion of sex hormones, and the wiring of the neural circuits that control sexual reflexes are examples of: |
| | A. | biological sex factors |
| | B. | genetic sex factors |
| | C. | social cultural factors |
| | D. | learned associations |

| | | |
|---|---|---|
| p. 338<br>Sexual Behavior<br>Level: Easy<br>Type: Factual<br>Ans: A | 122. | If you look in the table of contents of John's paper, you will see topics like secondary sexual characteristics, sexual motivation, and development of ova and sperm.  This paper is <u>most</u> likely on: |
| | A. | biological sex factors |
| | B. | genetic sex factors |
| | C. | social cultural factors |
| | D. | learned associations |

| | | |
|---|---|---|
| p. 338<br>Sexual Behavior<br>Level: Easy<br>Type: Conceptual<br>Ans: C | 123. | Dr. Gonzales is studying gender identity and sexual orientation.  Based on her areas of study, where is Dr. Gonzales <u>most</u> likely to work? |
| | A. | Center for Genetic Influences on Sex |
| | B. | National Institute for Biological Sex Factors |
| | C. | Institute for the Study of Psychological Sex Factors |
| | D. | Center for the Study of Neuropeptide Y |

| | | |
|---|---|---|
| p. 338<br>Sexual Behavior<br>Level: Easy<br>Type: Factual<br>Ans: A | 124. | Sperm and egg cells contain _____ chromosomes. |
| | A. | 23 |
| | B. | 46 |
| | C. | 48 |
| | D. | 64 |

p. 338
Sexual Behavior
Level: Moderate
Type: Factual
Ans: D

125. What determines the sex of an individual?
A. the egg
B. the number of zygotes
C. the interaction between the sex chromosome and the prenatal environment
D. the sex chromosome

p. 338
Sexual Behavior
Level: Easy
Type: Factual
Ans: B

126. An individual with XX sex chromosome is:
A. a male
B. a female
C. red-green colorblind
D. impossible to determine without knowing genotype

p. 338
Sexual Behavior
Level: Easy
Type: Factual
Ans: D

127. The result of a sperm fertilizing an egg is called a _____.
A. chromosome
B. fetus
C. zygote
D. DNA

p. 338
Sexual Behavior
Level: Easy
Type: Applied
Ans: C

128. Grant has five young daughters. One time when he went shopping with his four girls, a stranger came up to Grant and said, "Wow, five girls! What's the matter? Didn't your wife want sons?" In regard to the determination of sex, what was incorrect with the assumption of the stranger's question?
A. It assumes that the Y chromosome is the sex chromosome for a male.
B. The question assumed that the Y chromosome is a dominant allele.
C. It assumes that the woman determines the sex of the child, when, in fact, it's the male.
D. It assumes that the Y chromosome is the sex chromosome for a female.

p. 339
Sexual Behavior
Level: Moderate
Type: Factual
Ans: C

129. The presence of testosterone triggers the development of _____; the absence of testosterone triggers the automatic development of _____.
A. female sex organ; male sex organ
B. female hypothalamus; male hypothalamus
C. male sex organ; female sex organ
D. homosexuality; heterosexuality

p. 339
Sexual Behavior
Level: Easy
Type: Factual
Ans: A

130. During the fifth week of prenatal development, if there is testosterone, the developing child will be _____, but if there is a lack of it the child will be _____.
A. male; female
B. female; male
C. red-green colorblind; blue-green colorblind
D. heterosexual; homosexual

| | | |
|---|---|---|
| p. 339<br>Sexual Behavior<br>Level: Easy<br>Type: Factual<br>Ans: A | 131. | Estrogens are secreted by the _____, whereas androgens are secreted by the _____.<br>A. ovaries; testes<br>B. brain; body organs<br>C. lateral hypothalamus; ventromedial hypothalamus<br>D. male; female |
| p. 339<br>Sexual Behavior<br>Level: Easy<br>Type: Factual<br>Ans: C<br>*www* | 132. | The male sex hormones are called _____. The female sex hormones are called _____.<br>A. ovaries; testes<br>B. estrogens; androgens<br>C. androgens; estrogens<br>D. testosterone; androgens |
| p. 339<br>Sexual Behavior<br>Level: Easy<br>Type: Factual<br>Ans: D | 133. | According to the textbook, there is _____ between levels of sex hormones and sexual motivation in humans.<br>A. a moderate positive relationship<br>B. a strong negative correlation<br>C. a strong positive correlation<br>D. little correlation |
| p. 339<br>Sexual Behavior<br>Level: Easy<br>Type: Factual<br>Ans: B | 134. | Klinefelter's syndrome can be successfully treated with:<br>A. testosterone given at birth<br>B. testosterone given at puberty<br>C. estrogen given at puberty<br>D. estrogen given at birth |
| p. 339<br>Sexual Behavior<br>Level: Easy<br>Type: Factual<br>Ans: B | 135. | In general, increases or decreases in sexual motivation are primarily due to:<br>A. changes in testosterone<br>B. psychological factors<br>C. availability of partners<br>D. changes in estrogens |
| p. 340<br>Sexual Behavior<br>Level: Easy<br>Type: Applied<br>Ans: B | 136. | Your subjective experience and feelings of being either a male or a female is called:<br>A. sexual acceptance schema<br>B. gender identity<br>C. gender role<br>D. sex roles |
| p. 340<br>Sexual Behavior<br>Level: Easy<br>Type: Applied<br>Ans: C | 137. | Nathan, a four-year-old boy, exclaims, "I'm a boy!" Nathan has:<br>A. gender expectations<br>B. sex roles<br>C. gender identity<br>D. gender role |
| p. 340<br>Sexual Behavior<br>Level: Easy<br>Type: Factual<br>Ans: A | 138. | If an individual's gender identity does <u>not</u> match his or her external sex organs, the individual might have:<br>A. gender identity disorder<br>B. transvestism<br>C. negative symptoms of gender identity<br>D. asexualism |

p. 340
Sexual Behavior
Level: Easy
Type: Applied
Ans: D

139. Mitch insists that he feels trapped in a female's body and wants to be a complete man. Mitch could be considered exhibiting:
A. insufficient testosterone syndrome
B. body dysphoric disorder
C. homosexuality
D. transsexualism

p. 340
Sexual Behavior
Level: Easy
Type: Factual
Ans: D

*PS/SG 15-13*

140. Gender identity disorder is commonly referred to as:
A. bisexuality
B. homosexuality
C. sexual disorientation
D. transsexualism

p. 340
Sexual Behavior
Level: Easy
Type: Factual
Ans: A

141. The research on gender identity disorder indicates that:
A. transsexuals have normal genetic makeup and hormonal function
B. abnormal levels of estrogen
C. defects in the sex chromosome
D. abnormal levels of testosterone and defects in the sex chromosome

p. 340
Sexual Behavior
Level: Easy
Type: Factual
Ans: B

142. When we learn traditional behaviors, attitudes, and personality traits that our society regards as masculine or feminine, we have acquired:
A. gender identities
B. gender roles
C. gender labels
D. gender markers

p. 340
Sexual Behavior
Level: Easy
Type: Applied
Ans: D

*www*

143. When Alyssa was five, she enjoyed playing house, taking care of her dolls, and cooking food. Alyssa's _____ was that of a stereotypic female.
A. gender orientation
B. gender marker
C. gender label
D. gender role

p. 340
Sexual Behavior
Level: Easy
Type: Applied
Ans: B

144. Andy, a five-year-old, gets a doll from his grandmother for his birthday. He yells, "A doll? Dolls are for girls. I want a baseball!" Andy is exhibiting:
A. gender identities
B. gender roles
C. gender labels
D. gender markers

p. 340
Sexual Behavior
Level: Moderate
Type: Factual
Ans: C

145. A function of gender roles is that they:
A. influence how hormones interact with body tissue
B. cause sexual dysfunction
C. influence how we think and behave
D. determine sexual orientation

| | | |
|---|---|---|
| p. 340<br>Sexual Behavior<br>Level: Moderate<br>Type: Applied<br>Ans: A | 146.<br><br><br>A.<br>B.<br>C.<br>D. | During a visit to a kindergarten, you ask the children about being boys and girls. One of the students says, "Boys and dads are noisy, like to play football, and can do what they want." This student has learned about:<br>gender roles<br>gender labels<br>gender identities<br>gender markers |
| p. 340<br>Sexual Behavior<br>Level: Moderate<br>Type: Applied<br>Ans: C | 147.<br><br>A.<br>B.<br>C.<br>D. | Two-year old Jennifer has not yet shown stereotypically feminine behavior. Should her parents be concerned?<br>Yes – gender roles emerge around six months of age.<br>Yes – gender roles emerge around 2 years of age.<br>No – gender roles emerge around 3 or 4 years of age.<br>No – gender roles emerge around 5 or 6 years of age. |
| p. 341<br>Sexual Behavior<br>Level: Moderate<br>Type: Factual<br>Ans: B | 148.<br>A.<br><br>B.<br>C.<br>D. | Which statement regarding gender roles is correct?<br>By about 5 years old, children learn the traditional expectations regarding occupations for men and women.<br>Women can be independent and men can be nurturing.<br>Gender roles do not continue into adulthood.<br>Gender roles do not influence our thinking. |
| p. 341<br>Sexual Behavior<br>Level: Easy<br>Type: Factual<br>Ans: A | 149.<br>A.<br>B.<br>C.<br>D. | Your _____ refers to which gender you are sexually aroused by.<br>sexual orientation<br>gender identity<br>sex role<br>gender role |
| p. 341<br>Sexual Behavior<br>Level: Easy<br>Type: Factual<br>Ans: B | 150.<br><br><br>A.<br>B.<br>C.<br>D. | Though Susan and Larry regularly have sex, Larry is also involved sexually with another man. Larry's sexual preference is best characterized as:<br>homosexual<br>bisexual<br>heterosexual<br>polysexual |
| p. 341<br>Sexual Behavior<br>Level: Easy<br>Type: Factual<br>Ans: B | 151.<br><br>A.<br>B.<br>C.<br>D. | If you ask 100 randomly selected people about their sexual orientation, about ___ will have a homosexual orientation.<br>1<br>3<br>10<br>20 |
| p. 341<br>Sexual Behavior<br>Level: Easy<br>Type: Factual<br>Ans: C | 152.<br><br>A.<br>B.<br>C.<br>D. | If you argue that genetic/biological factors and psychological factors influence the development of sexual orientation, you adhere to the:<br>Home-hetero likelihood model<br>Kinsey theory of sexual arousal<br>interactive model of sexual orientation<br>Masters and Johnson model of sexual response |

p. 341
Sexual Behavior
Level: Easy
Type: Factual
Ans: B

153. Why is the term sexual preference preferred over sexual orientation?
A. There is strong evidence that sexual orientation is influenced by genetic factors.
B. People think that their sexual orientation is their own choice and not due to genetic or biological factors.
C. Sexual orientation does not reflect the vast diversity of sexual behavior in humans.
D. Political correctness evident in our society.

p. 341
Sexual Behavior
Level: Easy
Type: Factual
Ans: A

154. The term "sexual preference" suggests:
A. freedom in choosing a particular sexual orientation
B. genetic and biological factors play the major role in sexual orientation
C. an interaction among biological and psychological factors in determining sexual orientation
D. freedom in changing biology and genetic factors

p. 341
Sexual Behavior
Level: Moderate
Type: Factual
Ans: C

155. Based on cases where the individual is born with inconclusive sex organs, researchers have found that:
A. after birth gender identity and gender orientation cannot be changed
B. these individuals are much more likely to have sexual dysfunctions
C. gender identity and gender orientation could be changed, but only before the age of 2
D. gender identity and gender orientation could be changed

p. 341
Sexual Behavior
Level: Moderate
Type: Factual
Ans: A

156. The case of John/Joan illustrates:
A. we are biologically and genetically predisposed for having a female or male gender identity
B. gender identity is easily changed
C. transsexualism can be treated
D. that biology and genetics have minor influence over gender identity

p. 342
Sexual Behavior
Level: Moderate
Type: Factual
Ans: A

157. A major difference between college males' and females' reactions to sexual activity is:
A. males reported more sexual partners
B. males reported a greater need for commitment for engaging in sexual intercourse
C. females were more dissatisfied with lack of opportunity for a variety of partners
D. females experienced less guilt and fear over sexual activity

p. 342
Sexual Behavior
Level: Easy
Type: Factual
Ans: C

158. Which theory focuses on social and cultural forces that create sexual differences by different divisions of labor?
A. evolutionary theory
B. sociobiology theory
C. biosocial theory
D. double standard for sexual behavior

p. 342
Sexual Behavior
Level: Easy
Type: Factual
Ans: B

159. More young men than young women report thinking about sex daily. This may be related to:
A. different level of sex hormones
B. the double standard for sexual behavior
C. physiological response
D. AIDS

p. 342
Sexual Behavior
Level: Easy
Type: Factual
Ans: C
*PS/SG 15-14*

160. The term "double standard" means the:
A. added burden modern women face of both working and caring for their families
B. biological fact that women want one man but men want more than one woman
C. social expectation that men will be more sexually active than women
D. new idea that a woman can ask a man out and still expect him to pick up the check

p. 342
Sexual Behavior
Level: Easy
Type: Factual
Ans: A

161. In selecting a mate, males' top preference was for a mate _____, while for females, a mate _____ is preferred.
A. who is physically attractive; with good earning potential
B. with good earning potential; broad shoulders
C. who is honest; who is sensitive and compassionate
D. who is physically attractive; who is honest

p. 342
Sexual Behavior
Level: Easy
Type: Factual
Ans: B

162. According to the biosocial theory, males and females have different roles because:
A. of genetic differences
B. men and women performed different roles
C. evolutionary pressures
D. these roles helped the species survive

p. 343
Sexual Behavior
Level: Moderate
Type: Factual
Ans: D

163. The genetic influence on sexual orientation has been supported in research suggesting that:
A. parents cause their children to be either heterosexual or homosexual
B. homosexual men have larger areas in their hypothalamus than do heterosexual men
C. homosexual men have fewer chromosomes and genes than do heterosexual men
D. among identical twins, if one brother is homosexual, then usually both brothers are homosexual

p. 343
Sexual Behavior
Level: Moderate
Type: Factual
Ans: C

164. Genetic/biological research reveals:
A. the presence of a hormone among gay men that is generally found in straight men
B. similar EEG readings for the majority of homosexual males
C. an area on the X chromosome that is shared by many homosexual brothers
D. differences in MRI scans between gay and straight males

p. 343
Sexual Behavior
Level: Easy
Type: Factual
Ans: B

165. Studies on the childhoods of male homosexuals have shown that they:
A. were no different from heterosexuals
B. were more likely to have engaged in opposite sex behaviors and activities than heterosexuals
C. were often abused
D. come more often from single-parent families than heterosexuals do

p. 343
Sexual Behavior
Level: Easy
Type: Factual
Ans: C

166. With regard to homosexuality, the American Psychiatric Association, American Psychological Association and American Medical Association have indicated that:
A. homosexuals experience higher rates of depression
B. homosexuality is outside the range of normal sexual behavior
C. homosexuality is within the range of normal sexual behavior
D. homosexuality is superior to the heterosexual lifestyle

p. 343
Sexual Behavior
Level: Moderate
Type: Factual
Ans: A

167. If homosexuality was completely caused by genetic factors, we would expect:
A. 100% of pairs of identical twins to have the same sexual orientation
B. 50% of pairs of identical twins to have the same sexual orientation
C. homosexuals to have become aware of their orientation only after puberty
D. 0% of pairs of identical twins to have the same sexual orientation

p. 343
Sexual Behavior
Level: Easy
Type: Factual
Ans: C

168. Which of the following behaviors in a boy's childhood are associated with developing a homosexual orientation?
A. acting overly "masculine"
B. preferring same sex playmates
C. wearing girls' clothing
D. wanting to rough and tumble play with other boys

p. 344
Sexual Behavior
Level: Easy
Type: Factual
Ans: D

169. _____ are characterized by repetitive or preferred sexual fantasies involving nonhuman objects.
A. Psychosomatic disorders
B. Sexual dysfunctions
C. Sexual disorders
D. Paraphilias

p. 344
Sexual Behavior
Level: Easy
Type: Factual
Ans: B

170. _____ refers to problems of sexual arousal or orgasm that interfere with adequate functioning during sexual behavior.
A. Psychosomatic disorders
B. Sexual dysfunctions
C. Sexual disorders
D. Paraphilias

p. 344
Sexual Behavior
Level: Easy
Type: Factual
Ans: A
www

171. What are the two main causes of sexual dysfunction?
A. organic and psychological causes
B. conscious and unconscious causes
C. excitement- and resolution-related causes
D. biological and organic causes

p. 344
Sexual Behavior
Level: Easy
Type: Applied
Ans: C

172. Kirk is sexually attracted to shoes. Based upon this deviation, Kirk could be diagnosed with a:
A. plateau disorder
B. sexual dysfunction disorder
C. paraphilia
D. inhibited sexual disorder

p. 344
Sexual Behavior
Level: Easy
Type: Factual
Ans: A
*PS/SG 15-16*

173.  Which one of the following is the correct order of human sexual response?
A.  excitement – plateau – orgasm – resolution
B.  plateau – excitement – orgasm – resolution
C.  excitement – orgasm – plateau – resolution
D.  orgasm – excitement – resolution – plateau

p. 344
Sexual Behavior
Level: Easy
Type: Applied
Ans: A

174.  Liz and Rich have had sexual relations on a regular basis since they were married. According to Masters and Johnson, they will likely experience all of the following stages of sexual response except:
A.  fatigue
B.  plateau
C.  orgasm
D.  excitement

p. 344
Sexual Behavior
Level: Easy
Type: Applied
Ans: D

175.  During a long airplane flight, Jack thinks of his girlfriend Juanita and soon notices that he has an erection. According to Masters and Johnson, Jack is in which stage of sexual response?
A.  plateau
B.  resolution
C.  activation
D.  excitement

p. 344
Sexual Behavior
Level: Easy
Type: Factual
Ans: A

176.  In females, lubrication of the vagina is characteristic of which of Masters and Johnson's stages of sexual response?
A.  excitement
B.  plateau
C.  resolution
D.  orgasm

p. 344
Sexual Behavior
Level: Easy
Type: Factual
Ans: B

177.  During intercourse with her husband, Rene's heartbeat and blood pressure increase further. She is most likely in which stage of sexual response?
A.  orgasm
B.  plateau
C.  excitement
D.  resolution

p. 344
Sexual Behavior
Level: Easy
Type: Factual
Ans: D
*www*

178.  Ejaculation occurs in males during which of Masters and Johnson's stages of sexual response?
A.  resolution
B.  plateau
C.  excitement
D.  orgasm

p. 344
Sexual Behavior
Level: Easy
Type: Factual
Ans: C

179.  A combination of pleasurable physiological and psychological feelings are involved in the experience of:
A.  a refractory period
B.  pheromones
C.  an orgasm
D.  cross-gender behaviors

p. 344
Sexual Behavior
Level: Easy
Type: Factual
Ans: A

180.    With regard to Masters and Johnson's model of sexual response, sexual problems occur at:
A.    any stage
B.    excitement stage
C.    orgasm
D.    plateau

p. 344
Sexual Behavior
Level: Moderate
Type: Factual
Ans: B

181.    The first step in Masters and Johnson's treatment for sexual problems is:
A.    assigning the couple homework involving touching one's partner
B.    giving the couple information about sexual response
C.    asking the couple to perform sensate focusing
D.    assigning the couple to have a romantic dinner

p. 344
Sexual Behavior
Level: Easy
Type: Factual
Ans: C

182.    The most common sexual dysfunction disorder in males is:
A.    the "squeeze" disorder
B.    paraphilia
C.    premature or rapid ejaculation
D.    inhibited sexual disorder

p. 344
Sexual Behavior
Level: Easy
Type: Factual
Ans: D

183.    A technique developed by Masters and Johnson that involves nongenital pleasuring is called:
A.    rapid touching
B.    paraphilia
C.    the "squeeze"
D.    sensate focus

p. 344
Sexual Behavior
Level: Easy
Type: Factual
Ans: C

184.    Charles has experienced persistent problems with voluntary control over ejaculation upon penetration.  Charles is most likely to have:
A.    a sexual deviation
B.    paraphilia
C.    premature or rapid ejaculation
D.    inhibited sexual disorder

p. 344
Sexual Behavior
Level: Easy
Type: Factual
Ans: D

185.    A disorder among women that is characterized by a persistent delay or absence of experiencing orgasm after arousal is called:
A.    plateau disorder
B.    sexual deviation disorder
C.    paraphilia
D.    inhibited female orgasm

p. 345
Sexual Behavior
Level: Easy
Type: Factual
Ans: C

186.    The new definition of AIDS is:
A.    having HIV antibodies and at least two infectious diseases
B.    having HIV antibodies and engaging in risky behaviors
C.    having HIV antibodies and a level of T-cells below 200
D.    having HIV antibodies

p. 345
Sexual Behavior
Level: Easy
Type: Factual
Ans: B

187.    As of 2000, there are about _____ people infected with HIV/AIDS in the world.
A.    6 million
B.    22 million
C.    42 million
D.    78 million

p. 345
Sexual Behavior
Level: Easy
Type: Factual
Ans: A

188.    The riskiest behavior for contracting AIDS in the United States is:
A.    homosexual contact
B.    heterosexual intravenous drug use
C.    heterosexual contact
D.    homosexual intravenous drug use

p. 345
Sexual Behavior
Level: Easy
Type: Factual
Ans: A

189.    As compared to the transmission of AIDS in the United States, transmission in the rest of the world occurs more often through:
A.    heterosexual intercourse
B.    homosexual intercourse
C.    blood transfusions
D.    intravenous drug uses

p. 345
Sexual Behavior
Level: Easy
Type: Applied
Ans: B

190.    Rich has just been infected with the HIV virus. The infection cannot be confirmed biochemically for at least ____.
A.    30 days
B.    60 days
C.    1 year
D.    2 years

p. 345
Sexual Behavior
Level: Easy
Type: Applied
Ans: C

191.    Harold has HIV. If his case is average, it will take about ____ for him to develop AIDS.
A.    1 year
B.    3 years
C.    7 years
D.    9 years

p. 345
Sexual Behavior
Level: Easy
Type: Factual
Ans: A
www

192.    How does HIV affect the immune system?
A.    destroys T-cells
B.    causes growth of too many T-cells
C.    causes the development of T-cells to stop
D.    it destroys CCK

p. 345
Sexual Behavior
Level: Easy
Type: Factual
Ans: B

193.    The current approach to treating patients with AIDS is to give them:
A.    AZT alone
B.    a combination of drugs
C.    radiation therapy
D.    antibiotics

p. 345
Sexual Behavior
Level: Easy
Type: Factual
Ans: C

194.    The drug cocktail given to AIDS patients is effective in:
A.    killing T-cells
B.    killing AIDS
C.    causing the virus to "hide" in the body
D.    killing HIV

p. 346
Cultural Diversity:
  Female Circumcision
Level: Easy
Type: Factual
Ans: C

195. When a woman's external genitalia are removed and the remaining edges are sewn together, she has had a:
A. hysterectomy
B. technique that will heighten her sexual pleasure
C. female circumcision
D. necessary medical procedure

p. 346
Cultural Diversity:
  Female Circumcision
Level: Easy
Type: Factual
Ans: A

196. The purpose of female circumcision is to make a woman:
A. clean and virginal until marriage
B. marked as ineligible for marriage
C. more likely to bear children
D. more likely to experience sexual pleasure

p. 346
Cultural Diversity:
  Female Circumcision
Level: Easy
Type: Factual
Ans: D

197. Among women who have had female circumcision, many:
A. stop menstruating
B. have left their communities in shame
C. have reported a reduction in pain during childbirth
D. suffer from anxiety and depression

p. 346
Cultural Diversity:
  Female Circumcision
Level: Easy
Type: Factual
Ans: B

198. What has been the effect of the United Nation's endorsement of anticircumcision laws?
A. Many African societies now recognize it as cruel mutilation.
B. Female circumcision is still practiced because of its strong sociocultural tradition.
C. The practice of female circumcision has been greatly reduced.
D. Female circumcision has become even more common in Africa.

p. 348
Achievement
Level: Easy
Type: Factual
Ans: C

199. Educators believe that many minorities who drop out of school, do so because of:
A. poor academic achievement
B. low expectations from teachers and parents
C. peer pressure not to succeed in school
D. economic pressures to find employment

p. 348
Achievement
Level: Easy
Type: Factual
Ans: A

200. The motivation to set challenging goals and persist in meeting those goals, despite obstacles or setbacks is the definition of:
A. need for achievement
B. self-determination
C. attribution
D. self-handicapping

p. 348
Achievement
Level: Moderate
Type: Applied
Ans: B

201. Ellen is shown a somewhat ambiguous picture of a person in a lab coat studying what looks like a medical chart. Ellen is then asked to tell a story about this person. She says that this person is a new resident in a hospital and is working very long hours, but is happy to have finally reached his goal of becoming a doctor. In this story, Ellen is exhibiting:
A. low achievement motivation
B. high achievement motivation
C. high fear of failure
D. a self-handicapping strategy

p. 348
Achievement
Level: Easy
Type: Factual
Ans: A

202. The need for achievement differs from the need for sex because achievement motivation:
A. is a social rather than a biological need
B. is only found among white males
C. ranks low on Maslow's hierarchy of needs
D. cannot be measured

p. 348
Achievement
Level: Easy
Type: Factual
Ans: C

203. The Thematic Apperception Test (TAT) can be used to measure:
A. sexual motivation
B. hunger and thirst motivation
C. the need for achievement
D. the need for self-actualization

p. 348
Achievement
Level: Easy
Type: Factual
Ans: D

204. The test that involves giving subjects ambiguous pictures to measure achievement is called the:
A. MMPI-II
B. Maslow Test of Needs
C. Rorschach Test
D. Thematic Apperception Test

p. 348
Achievement
Level: Easy
Type: Factual
Ans: A

205. Paper-and-pencil tests have replaced the TAT as measures of need for achievement because:
A. the TAT has limited reliability and validity
B. paper-and-pencil tests can be self-administered
C. need for achievement requires a test of performance
D. paper-and-pencil tests are easier to develop

p. 348
Achievement
Level: Easy
Type: Factual
Ans: D

206. Which of the following is a personality characteristic of a person with a high need for achievement?
A. verbally aggressive behavior while completing group tasks
B. an inability to see the easy solutions to tasks
C. setting unrealistic goals
D. attraction to jobs that require initiative

p. 349
Achievement
Level: Moderate
Type: Factual
Ans: B

207. A(n) _____ motivates students to set higher goals and study hard to get good grades. A(n) _____ motivates students to study just enough to avoid failing exams, but not enough to get good grades.
A. self-handicapping strategy; overjustification effect
B. need for achievement; fear of failure
C. extrinsic motivation; intrinsic motivation
D. peripheral cue; cognitive cue

p. 349
Achievement
Level: Easy
Type: Factual
Ans: A
*PS/SG 15-20*

208. The best motivation for superior academic performance is having a:
A. high need for achievement
B. high fear of failure
C. very efficient self-handicapping strategy
D. reasonable excuse for occasional failure

p. 349
Achievement
Level: Easy
Type: Factual
Ans: A

209. Which of the following is an advantage of using self-handicapping strategies?
A. They keep our positive self-image intact.
B. They help us to take responsibility.
C. They force us to correct a situation.
D. They cause too much pressure to excel.

p. 349
Achievement
Level: Easy
Type: Applied
Ans: D

210. "I don't put my best effort forward. If I do and fail, I'll find out that I'm not smart enough to succeed." Sounds like this students engages in:
A. image defense
B. overjustification effect
C. attribution bias
D. self-handicapping

p. 349
Achievement
Level: Easy
Type: Factual
Ans: B
*www*

211. Making up excuses for failure is referred to as:
A. self-attributing
B. self-handicapping
C. delusional attribution
D. image defense

p. 349
Achievement
Level: Easy
Type: Applied
Ans: D
*PS/SG 15-21*

212. Which of the following is the best example of self-handicapping?
A. choosing easy, nonchallenging tasks where failure is unlikely
B. performing more poorly on an exam than IQ scores would predict
C. getting plenty of sleep before the exam, but doing poorly anyway
D. having a hangover during the exam, then blaming drug use for poor results

p. 349
Achievement
Level: Easy
Type: Applied
Ans: C

213. Eric is a smart person and has scored 115 on an IQ test, yet he does poorly in school. Eric could be:
A. experiencing fear of failure
B. lacking in extrinsic motivation
C. an underachiever
D. a slacker

p. 349
Achievement
Level: Easy
Type: Factual
Ans: C

214. Which statement about underachievers is not consistent with the research?
A. They maintain high self-esteem even when they fail.
B. They have the abilities to succeed.
C. Most underachievers are female.
D. About 15% of all children are underachievers.

p. 349
Achievement
Level: Moderate
Type: Factual
Ans: A

215. An underachiever is likely to:
A. have a poor self-concept
B. lack the ability to succeed
C. inflate self-concept
D. be female

p. 350
Achievement
Level: Easy
Type: Applied
Ans: B

216. Chris sings in a volunteer community chorus because he enjoys the feeling he gets when he masters a complicated piece of music. His behavior reflects:
A. self-handicapping strategy
B. intrinsic motivation
C. overjustification
D. external motivation

p. 350
Achievement
Level: Moderate
Type: Factual
Ans: B
*PS/SG 15-22*

217. Is extrinsic motivation or intrinsic motivation more effective in getting people to donate blood?
A. extrinsic, because people need something tangible when pain is involved
B. it depends on how the rewards are offered and how they are perceived
C. intrinsic, because people want to feel good about doing unselfish deeds
D. neither should be involved in behavior that is our civic duty

p. 350
Achievement
Level: Moderate
Type: Applied
Ans: D

218. In a piece called "Work and Play," Mark Twain points out that London cabbies used to take beautiful care of their carriages and horses without receiving so much as a penny. Then, when the city started paying these men for their labor, the carriages started to look shoddy and many of the men quit doing the job. Twain has cited an example of:
A. how expectancy can lead to extrinsic motivation
B. lack of motivation
C. misattribution in achievement
D. how important cognitive factors are in achievement

p. 350
Achievement
Level: Moderate
Type: Applied
Ans: B

219. A talented potter, who has always done the work as a hobby, is asked by a local boutique to produce ten pieces per month. The potter usually produces about fifteen pieces per month. Now, he perceives much external pressure to be creative. We would predict, based on research on the cognitive factors in achievement, that:
A. the potter will produce about twenty-five pieces per month
B. the potter will enjoy the work less
C. the quality of the potter's work will improve
D. the potter will improve both quantity and quality

p. 350
Achievement
Level: Moderate
Type: Applied
Ans: A

220. Anthony enjoyed his photography hobby very much. He became so skilled that people began buying his photographs, which put much pressure on Anthony. Knowing the research in this area, what is likely to happen to Anthony?
A. He found that he enjoyed photography less because he began to think he was only "doing it for the money."
B. The quality of his photography greatly increased.
C. He experienced a fear of failure that made his pictures even better.
D. It led to a loss of self-determination.

p. 350
Achievement
Level: Moderate
Type: Applied
Ans: C

221. Which of the following is probably the best explanation for why people choose to engage in "bungee jumping"?
A. the fear of failure
B. the overjustification effect
C. intrinsic motivation
D. the self-handicapping strategy

p. 350
Achievement
Level: Easy
Type: Factual
Ans: D

222. What happens when a person is given external rewards that previously brought much personal satisfaction?
A. The amount of satisfaction experienced will increase.
B. The amount of satisfaction experienced will decrease.
C. The person will experience the same amount of satisfaction.
D. It depends on how the person perceives the external rewards.

p. 350
Achievement
Level: Easy
Type: Conceptual
Ans: A

223. As a teacher of six-year-olds, you have noticed that verbal praise increases intrinsic motivation. Is this generally what happens when verbal praise is used?
A. yes - verbal praise increases intrinsic motivation
B. no - any external reward decreases intrinsic motivation
C. yes - verbal praise increases intrinsic motivation, but lowers actual performance
D. no - verbal praise, unlike other external rewards, decreases intrinsic motivation

p. 351
Research Focus:
  Immigrant Students
Level: Easy
Type: Factual
Ans: A

224. Among first generation Asian, Latino, and Black students, which group did the best on a standardized math test?
A. Asian
B. Latino
C. Black
D. There was no significant difference among the groups.

p. 351
Research Focus:
  Immigrant Students
Level: Easy
Type: Factual
Ans: D

225. To explain differences in math achievement among first and third generation Latino, Asian, and Black students, researchers have proposed the importance of:
A. parent discipline regarding sexual promiscuity and appearance
B. genetic differences
C. nutritional diet
D. parental values regarding the worth of education

p. 351
Research Focus:
  Immigrant Students
Level: Easy
Type: Factual
Ans: C

226. The most important implication of the research examining differences in math achievement among first and third generation Latino, Asian, and Black students, is:
A. increasing teacher understanding of cultural differences
B. providing role models for all students
C. encouraging parents to become more involved in their children's education
D. increasing funding for public schools

| p. 352 | 227. | Of those who lose weight on diets, approximately what percentage gain it |
|---|---|---|
| Application: Eating | | back within one year? |
|   Problems and Treatment | A. | 20 |
| Level: Easy | B. | 40 |
| Type: Factual | C. | 60 |
| Ans: D | D. | 90 |

| p. 352 | 228. | Talk-show host Oprah Winfrey regained all her lost weight and then some |
|---|---|---|
| Application: Eating | | because: |
|   Problems and Treatment | A. | her setpoint was lowered |
| Level: Easy | B. | she did not stay on a maintenance program |
| Type: Factual | C. | Oprah's metabolism increased |
| Ans: B | D. | she lost all the weight to feel good about herself |

| p. 352 | 229. | Talk-show host Oprah Winfrey's experience with dieting is: |
|---|---|---|
| Application: Eating | A. | unusual since she gained back her lost weight |
|   Problems and Treatment | B. | unusual because she kept the weight off |
| Level: Easy | C. | typical because of the difficulty of keeping lost weight off |
| Type: Factual | D. | an example of how health benefits will only happen if extreme weight loss |
| Ans: C | | occurs |

| p. 352 | 230. | The key to losing weight and keeping it off is: |
|---|---|---|
| Application: Eating | A. | exercising every day |
|   Problems and Treatment | B. | going on a low carbohydrate diet |
| Level: Easy | C. | going on an effective diet |
| Type: Factual | D. | a change in lifestyle |
| Ans: D | | |

| p. 353 | 231. | Shelly has been on a self-inflicted starvation diet for 8 months and, as a |
|---|---|---|
| Application: Eating | | result, weighs only 82 pounds, yet believes that she can stand to lose a |
|   Problems and Treatment | | couple of more pounds. It is likely that Shelly is suffering from: |
| Level: Easy | A. | anorexia nervosa |
| Type: Applied | B. | a hormonal imbalance |
| Ans: A | C. | depression |
| | D. | bulimia |

| p. 353 | 232. | The disorder characterized by an intense fear of fatness and willful |
|---|---|---|
| Application: Eating | | starvation is called: |
|   Problems and Treatment | A. | anorexia nervosa |
| Level: Easy | B. | bulimia |
| Type: Factual | C. | obesity |
| Ans: A | D. | self-handicapping compulsion |

| p. 353 | 233. | There appear to be personality traits that are common in anorexics as |
|---|---|---|
| Application: Eating | | children, and they include: |
|   Problems and Treatment | A. | rebellious and somewhat nonresponsive to the demands of others |
| Level: Easy | B. | obsessed with getting approval from others and depression |
| Type: Factual | C. | relaxed and high standards for personal achievement |
| Ans: D | D. | tense, rigid, and compulsive |

p. 353
Application: Eating
  Problems and Treatment
Level: Easy
Type: Factual
Ans: C

234. The in-hospital treatment for anorexia nervosa focuses on:
A. dream analysis
B. the use of medication
C. family therapy
D. hypnosis

p. 353
Application: Eating
  Problems and Treatment
Level: Easy
Type: Factual
Ans: B
*www*

235. The eating disorder characterized by a minimum of two binge-eating episodes per week for at least three months, and regularly engaging in vomiting is called:
A. anorexia nervosa
B. bulimia nervosa
C. compulsive overeating
D. distorted body image

p. 353
Application: Eating
  Problems and Treatment
Level: Easy
Type: Factual
Ans: C

236. Which of the following is the most preferred treatment for bulimia nervosa?
A. use of antidepressant drugs
B. encouraging weight gain
C. substituting positive thoughts for negative ones
D. chemotherapy

True/False

| F | *www* | 1. | Instinct theory is a useful theory to explain human behavior. |
|---|---|---|---|
| T | | 2. | The value of incentives can change across time. |
| F | *www* | 3. | Incentives push us to act. |
| F | *www* | 4. | Maslow hierarchy of needs begins with safety needs. |
| F | | 5. | Researchers have found much evidence to support Maslow's hierarchy of needs. |
| F | | 6. | Psychosocial factors of hunger cannot override biological factors. |
| T | | 7. | Stimulation of the lateral hypothalamus cause eating. |
| T | *www* | 8. | Stimulation of the ventromedial hypothalamus causes cessation of eating. |
| T | | 9. | Hormones play a role in hunger. |
| T | | 10. | A person with a low set point will have a lower weight than someone with a higher set point. |
| F | *www* | 11. | In most cases of obesity, the number of fat cells increases. |
| T | | 12. | American men tend to underestimate their weights. |
| T | | 13. | Each chromosome is made up of DNA. |
| T | | 14. | The absence of testosterone results in the development of female sexual organs. |
| T | | 15. | The term "sexual preference" indicates freedom in choosing sexual orientation. |
| T | *www* | 16. | The biosocial model of sexual behavior stresses social and cultural forces. |
| T | *www* | 17. | Homosexuality has a genetic component. |
| F | | 18. | Sexual problems only occur in the excitement and orgasm stage. |
| T | | 19. | The risk for AIDS in the United States is among gay men. |
| T | *www* | 20. | People who self-handicap use excuses for failing to achieve a goal. |
| T | | 21. | If you are extrinsically motivated, you are engaging in an activity to achieve some external reward. |
| F | *www* | 22. | External rewards always reduce intrinsic motivation. |

| T |  | 23. | First-generation Asian students score higher on measures on math achievement than first-generation Latino students. |
|---|------|-----|---|
| F | www | 24. | The best way to reduce weight is to go on an exercise schedule. |
| F |  | 25. | Individuals with bulimia nervosa experience dramatic fluctuations in their weight. |

Short-Answer Essay Questions

1. Compare and contrast the instinct, pleasure/reward, incentive, and cognitive theories of motivation. (*www*)
2. Describe the levels of Maslow's hierarchy of needs. For each level, provide an example from your experiences. (*www*)
3. Discuss peripheral and central cues for hunger.
4. What is gender identity and what is its development in the first five years of life?
5. Describe the results of the John/Joan case. In your response, make sure you discuss the role of genetic/biological factors in gender identity. (*www*)
6. Describe the genetic/biological factors involved in homosexuality.
7. What effects do external rewards have on intrinsic motivation? How might verbal praise increase intrinsic motivation? (*www*)
8. Explain why there are differences in math achievement among first-generation Asian, Latino, and Black students.
9. Based on Oprah Winfrey's experiences, what is the best way to lose weight and to keep it off? (*www*)
10. Describe anorexia nervosa and bulimia nervosa, pointing out the differences between the eating disorders. What are the promising treatments for each disorder?

# Module 16 - Emotion

p. 359
Introduction
Level: Easy
Type: Factual
Ans: A

1.  In which component of emotion might we experience fear, happiness, or disgust?
A.  having subjective feelings
B.  experiencing a physiological response
C.  a change in heart rate and breathing
D.  interpreting or appraising some stimulus

p. 359
Introduction
Level: Easy
Type: Conceptual
Ans: B
*PS/SG 16-1*

2.  Rod Plotnik tells us about the surfer who was attacked by a shark to show that:
A.  sometimes you can feel all the emotions at once
B.  emotions play a major role in our lives
C.  sometimes survival depends on having no emotions
D.  emotions (like the joy of surfing) can get in the way of common sense

p. 359
Introduction
Level: Moderate
Type: Applied
Ans: C

3.  What is the best example of stimulus appraisal in the story on the shark attack that opens the chapter?
A.  Rick's parasympathetic division becomes activated.
B.  Rick shows fearful behavior such as frantic swimming.
C.  Rick interprets the stimulus, or shark, as a threat to his well-being.
D.  Rick's heart rate and breathing rapidly increase.

p. 359
Introduction
Level: Easy
Type: Factual
Ans: C
*www*

4.  An emotion is a feeling made up of:
A.  anger, fear, or happiness
B.  having a subjective feeling and objectively learned behavioral responses
C.  appraising a stimulus, having a subjective feeling, physiological responses, and overt behavior
D.  facial expressions which convey social signals and social needs and physiological responses

p. 359
Introduction
Level: Easy
Type: Factual
Ans: D

5.  An emotion has four components. Which of the following is not one of the four?
A.  appraisal of a stimulus
B.  subjective feeling
C.  observable behavior
D.  unconscious motives

p. 359
Introduction
Level: Easy
Type: Factual
Ans: B

6.  Of the following, which question has most intrigued psychologists studying emotion?
A.  Do people attempt to interpret the stimulus?
B.  In what order do the components occur?
C.  What are the physiological responses in emotions?
D.  Do we show observable behaviors in emotions?

p. 359
Introduction
Level: Easy
Type: Factual
Ans: C

7. You are playing a card game with your friends. You don't know if one of them is about to win because of his poker face. Which of the following components of an emotion does poker face best illustrate?
A. appraising a stimulus
B. subjective feeling
C. overt behavior
D. physiological responses

p. 359
Introduction
Level: Easy
Type: Applied
Ans: D

8. During a study of emotion in children, one of the subjects starts singing a song. She sings, "if you're happy and you know it, clap your hands...if you're happy and you know it, clap your hands." You comment in your notes that "subjects were displaying:
A. appraisal of a stimulus."
B. processing of information."
C. physiological response."
D. subjective experience."

p. 359
Introduction
Level: Moderate
Type: Applied
Ans: A

9. As you get ready for the professor to pass back your graded test you experience the emotion of anxiety. Using the definition of emotion presented in your textbook, which one of the following is incorrect?
A. overt behavior - anxiety
B. overt behavior - tapping your pencil
C. physiological - heart rate is rapid
D. appraising the stimulus - if you do poorly on this exam you won't make the Dean's Honor List

p. 359
Introduction
Level: Easy
Type: Factual
Ans: B

10. Marcus is appraising a stimulus, having a subjective feeling, experiencing physiological responses, and showing overt behavior. Marcus is experiencing:
A. guilt
B. an emotion
C. attribution
D. a nervous breakdown

p. 359
Introduction
Level: Easy
Type: Conceptual
Ans: B

11. Which of the following is an example of the overt behavior component of emotion?
A. increased heart rate
B. raising one's fist in victory
C. feeling happy
D. increased body temperature

p. 359
Introduction
Level: Easy
Type: Conceptual
Ans: A

12. Which of the following is an example of the physiological component of emotion?
A. increased heart rate
B. raising one's fist in victory
C. feeling happy
D. punching a pillow out of frustration

p. 360
Peripheral Theories
Level: Easy
Type: Factual
Ans: A

13.    Theories of emotions tend to fit into two categories. What are the names of the categories?
A.    peripheral theories and cognitive appraisal theories
B.    central theories and social learning theories
C.    peripheral theories and central theories
D.    behavioral theories and cognitive appraisal theories

p. 360
Peripheral Theories
Level: Easy
Type: Applied
Ans: D

14.    Dr. Campbell is an affective neuroscientist. Which of the following journal articles is most likely to have been written by her?
A.    *The role of the superego in experiencing emotion*
B.    *Social learning and the expression of emotion*
C.    *The unconscious effect on emotions*
D.    *The role of the brain's circuits on expressing emotion*

p. 360
Peripheral Theories
Level: Easy
Type: Factual
Ans: C

15.    In explaining the steps in emotions, _____ emphasize(s) our body's physiological changes that lead to subjective feelings.
A.    social learning theory of emotions
B.    central theory of emotions
C.    peripheral theories of emotion
D.    cognitive appraisal theories of emotion

p. 360
Peripheral Theories
Level: Easy
Type: Factual
Ans: D

16.    The _____ explain(s) the steps in emotions by focusing on how we interpret situations.
A.    social learning theory of emotions
B.    central theory of emotions
C.    peripheral theories of emotion
D.    cognitive appraisal theories of emotion

p. 360
Peripheral Theories
Level: Moderate
Type: Conceptual
Ans: D

17.    Peripheral is to _____ as cognitive appraisal is to _____.
A.    learning; innate
B.    brain; emotion
C.    side; interpretation
D.    physiological; interpretation

p. 360
Peripheral Theories
Level: Easy
Type: Factual
Ans: C
*www*

18.    Dr. Arkin has developed a theory to explain emotions which focuses on how emotions result from changes in the body. Dr. Arkin's theory would be considered a(n):
A.    cognitive appraisal theory
B.    arousal theory
C.    peripheral theory
D.    feedback theory

p. 360
Peripheral Theories
Level: Easy
Type: Factual
Ans: D

19.    The subjective feelings of an emotion follow our interpretations or appraisals of the stimulus according to the:
A.    social learning theory of emotions
B.    central theory of emotions
C.    peripheral theories of emotion
D.    cognitive appraisal theories of emotion

p. 360
Peripheral Theories
Level: Easy
Type: Factual
Ans: A

20. Dr. Catson has developed a theory to explain emotions which focuses on how emotions result from the interpretations we make of the stimulus. Dr. Catson's theory would be considered a(n):
A. cognitive appraisal theory
B. arousal theory
C. peripheral theory
D. feedback theory

p. 360
Peripheral Theories
Level: Easy
Type: Factual
Ans: B

21. The James-Lange theory emphasizes the _____ component of emotion.
A. behavioral
B. physiological
C. cognitive
D. active

p. 360
Peripheral Theories
Level: Easy
Type: Factual
Ans: B
*PS/SG 16-4*

22. The _____ theory says emotions result from specific physiological changes in the body.
A. shark bite
B. James-Lange
C. facial feedback
D. cognitive appraisal

p. 360
Peripheral Theories
Level: Moderate
Type: Conceptual
Ans: B

23. If William James of the James-Lange theory was here talking to you as you're taking the test, he would say:
A. "You're anxious because you're taking a very important test."
B. "You're anxious because you're sweating and have a rapid heart rate."
C. "You're anxious because this is a hard test."
D. "You're anxious because you interpret this situation as anxiety-provoking."

p. 360
Peripheral Theories
Level: Moderate
Type: Applied
Ans: A

24. According to the _____, the reason why you feel fear when seeing a shark is because you have experienced a specific pattern of physiological responses that your brain recognizes as fear.
A. James-Lange theory
B. cognitive theory
C. behavioral theory
D. facial feedback theory

p. 360
Peripheral Theories
Level: Moderate
Type: Factual
Ans: D
*www*

25. According to the James-Lange theory, experiencing emotion starts with:
A. changes in facial muscles
B. a show of observable behavior
C. the brain interpreting stimulus
D. physiological changes, brain interprets changes, feel specific emotion,

p. 360
Peripheral Theories
Level: Easy
Type: Factual
Ans: A

26. The idea that different patterns of physiological arousal result in feeling different emotions is known as the _____ of emotion.
A. James-Lange theory
B. cognitive theory
C. behavioral theory
D. facial feedback theory

p. 360
Peripheral Theories
Level: Easy
Type: Factual
Ans: C

27. According to the James-Lange theory, each specific pattern of physiological responses is associated with a:
A. situation
B. facial expression
C. specific emotion
D. specific situation

p. 360
Peripheral Theories
Level: Easy
Type: Factual
Ans: A

28. The James-Lange theory would predict that people with a severed spinal cord at the neck would experience:
A. little or no emotion
B. an intensifying of emotion
C. the same type and intensity of emotion as those with intact spinal cords
D. continuing feedback of physiological responses

p. 360
Peripheral Theories
Level: Easy
Type: Factual
Ans: C

29. The James-Lange theory of emotion has been criticized on the grounds that some emotions:
A. have no physiological component
B. are purely physical
C. require much interpretation or appraisal of the situation
D. are not experienced by spinal cord injured individuals

p. 360
Peripheral Theories
Level: Easy
Type: Factual
Ans: D

30. One criticism of the James-Lange theory of emotion is that:
A. sometimes we feel emotions and we are not aroused physiologically at all
B. not everyone is aroused the same way by a given emotional experience
C. even single-cell organisms experience emotion
D. different emotions do not necessarily have distinct physiological patterns

p. 360
Peripheral Theories
Level: Easy
Type: Factual
Ans: A

31. Which of the following is a criticism of the James-Lange theory of emotions?
A. People with severed spinal cords still experience emotions.
B. The theory is too cognitive to be explanatory.
C. Researchers agree that emotions cannot occur without physiological arousal.
D. Physiological arousal does not increase the intensity of emotions.

p. 360
Peripheral Theories
Level: Moderate
Type: Factual
Ans: C

32. The research indicates that while the James-Lange theory seems incorrect, physiological changes may:
A. cause positive emotions
B. cause emotions
C. increase the intensity of emotions
D. decrease the intensity of emotions

p. 360
Peripheral Theories
Level: Easy
Type: Factual
Ans: C

33. The sequence of components for emotion according to the James-Lange theory is:
A. emotional feeling, physiological changes, interpretation of changes, overt behavior
B. facial muscles change, interpretation of changes, overt behavior, emotional feeling
C. physiological changes, interpretation of changes, emotional feeling, overt behavior
D. physiological changes, overt behavior, interpret cues, emotional feeling

p. 360
Peripheral Theories
Level: Easy
Type: Applied
Ans: D
*www*

34. You read in an article that, "if you see a bear you are frightened because your heart is pounding, rather than your heart pounding because you are frightened." You recognize this statement as describing the:
A. Schachter-Singer theory
B. cognitive appraisal theory
C. facial feedback theory
D. James-Lange theory

p. 360
Peripheral Theories
Level: Easy
Type: Factual
Ans: A

35. According to research, physiological changes may _____ the intensity of emotional experiences.
A. increase
B. decrease
C. stabilize
D. mask

p. 360
Peripheral Theories
Level: Easy
Type: Factual
Ans: B

36. The facial feedback theory emphasizes the _____ component of emotion.
A. behavioral
B. physiological
C. cognitive
D. active

p. 360
Peripheral Theories
Level: Moderate
Type: Applied
Ans: C

37. Professor Akbari is presenting a lecture on emotions. He presents the idea that your facial muscles provide input to your brain. Then he assigns a short paper to everyone to read on the theory. What is the *most* likely title of the short paper?
A. *The Role of Appraisal in Emotions*
B. *Affective-Primary Theory: An Examination*
C. *Emotions Explained by the Facial Feedback Theory*
D. *Thinking Before Feeling: Cognitive-Appraisal Theory*

p. 360
Peripheral Theories
Level: Easy
Type: Factual
Ans: C
*PS/SG 16-5*

38. The _____ theory says emotions result from our brain's interpretation of muscle and skin movements that occur when we express an emotion.
A. Schacter-Singer
B. James-Lange
C. facial feedback
D. cognitive appraisal

p. 360
Peripheral Theories
Level: Easy
Type: Factual
Ans: C

39. Charles Darwin was the originator of the explanation of emotion currently known as:
A. James-Lange theory
B. cognitive theory
C. facial feedback theory
D. behavioral theory

p. 360
Peripheral Theories
Level: Moderate
Type: Conceptual
Ans: C

40. If Charles Darwin of the facial feedback theory was here talking to you as you're taking the test, he would say:
A. "You're anxious because you're taking a very important test."
B. "You're anxious because you're sweating and have a rapid heart rate."
C. "You're anxious because you're biting your lower lip."
D. "You're anxious because you interpret this situation as anxiety-provoking."

p. 360
Peripheral Theories
Level: Easy
Type: Applied
Ans: D

41. If the facial feedback theory is correct, what should we expect when people smile for no apparent reason?
A. It depends on what the person's emotional state was before smiling.
B. Nothing, since there is no situation to interpret why the person is smiling.
C. Nothing, since there is no corresponding physiological change.
D. They should report feeling happy.

p. 360
Peripheral Theories
Level: Easy
Type: Factual
Ans: A

42. The facial feedback theory argues that _____ from the muscles of the face and skin are interpreted as _____ by your brain.
A. feedback; emotional feelings
B. biological byproducts; anger
C. feedback; physiological changes
D. emotional feelings; physiological changes

p. 360
Peripheral Theories
Level: Moderate
Type: Conceptual
Ans: B

43. According to the facial feedback theory, if we are good at masking our emotions so that they don't show on our faces, we will probably:
A. suffer physical upset because we did not vent our emotions
B. experience emotions less severely
C. show a more permanent strain on a long-term basis in the form of crease lines in our faces
D. substitute other kinds of body language for the facial expression

p. 360
Peripheral Theories
Level: Easy
Type: Conceptual
Ans: D
www

44. The song "Put on a Happy Face" implies that if we smile we'll begin to feel happy. Which explanation of emotion does this idea support?
A. James-Lange theory
B. cognitive theory
C. behavioral theory
D. facial feedback theory

p. 360
Peripheral Theories
Level: Easy
Type: Applied
Ans: D

45. The term "poker face" describes a person's ability to hold a very good hand in a card game without letting other players know it by his facial expression. According to the facial feedback theory, the "poker faced" player will:
A. probably be tensing muscles other than those on the face
B. be doing a much poorer job at hiding his emotions than he or she thinks
C. find the game more exciting
D. find the game less exciting

p. 360
Peripheral Theories
Level: Easy
Type: Factual
Ans: D

46. The sequence of components for emotion according to the facial feedback theory is:
A. emotional feeling, facial muscles change, interpretation of changes, overt behavior, emotional feeling again
B. facial muscles change, interpretation of changes, overt behavior, emotional feeling
C. physiological changes, interpretation of changes, emotional feeling, overt behavior
D. facial muscles change, interpretation of changes, emotional feeling, overt behavior

p. 360
Peripheral Theories
Level: Moderate
Type: Factual
Ans: A

47. The research has found that facial feedback:
A. contributes to an emotion
B. leads to specific feelings
C. is an adequate theory that explains how facial muscles produce emotions
D. fails to indicate our general emotional state

p. 360
Peripheral Theories
Level: Moderate
Type: Factual
Ans: D

48. Some recent research on the effect of facial expressions on emotional experience has concluded that:
A. we can initiate emotional experience with appropriate facial expression
B. laughter relieves depression because of what our face is doing
C. facial expressions are learned and therefore do not reflect emotional arousal
D. facial expressions contribute to but not initiate emotional experience

p. 360
Peripheral Theories
Level: Moderate
Type: Conceptual
Ans: C

49. People whose facial muscles are paralyzed still feel emotions. What consequences does this finding have for the facial feedback theory?
A. It questions the validity of the theory because paralysis of the facial muscles would more than likely influence the physiology of the entire body.
B. It has no implication for the facial feedback theory.
C. It undermines it since the theory argues that the facial muscles play a role in experiencing emotions.
D. The finding supports the theory since different emotions are associated with different physiological changes.

p. 361
Cognitive Appraisal
 Theory
Level: Easy
Type: Factual
Ans: C

50. Schachter and Singer's theory emphasizes the _____ component of emotion.
A. behavioral
B. physiological
C. cognitive
D. active

p. 361
Cognitive Appraisal
  Theory
Level: Easy
Type: Factual
Ans: B

51. Which names are most associated with the cognitive appraisal theory of emotions?
A. James and Lange
B. Schachter and Singer
C. Darwin and Ekman
D. Yerkes and Dodson

p. 361
Cognitive Appraisal
  Theory
Level: Easy
Type: Factual
Ans: D
*PS/SG 16-6*

52. The _____ theory says that your interpretations of a situation, object, or event can contribute to, or result in, your experiencing different emotional states.
A. Charles Darwin
B. James-Lange
C. facial feedback
D. cognitive appraisal

p. 361
Cognitive Appraisal
  Theory
Level: Easy
Type: Factual
Ans: A

53. Those subjects who were given epinephrine (blindly) and were later put in a happy situation reported feeling happy. Why?
A. Subjects interpreted their arousal by examining their situation and concluded they were happy because of the situation.
B. They were smiling.
C. Their pattern of physiological arousal was interpreted as happiness.
D. Their facial feedback was consistent with the emotional feeling of happiness.

p. 361
Cognitive Appraisal
  Theory
Level: Easy
Type: Factual
Ans: B

54. The cognitive appraisal theory of emotion stresses the importance of:
A. physiological differences among different emotions
B. labeling an emotion to explain an aroused state
C. facial expressions as causes of emotion
D. other people's reactions to a person's aroused state

p. 361
Peripheral Theories
Level: Easy
Type: Factual
Ans: C

55. The sequence of components for emotion according to the Schachter-Singer cognitive theory of emotion is:
A. emotional feeling, facial muscles change, interpret cues, overt behavior, emotional feeling again
B. facial muscles change, interpret cues, overt behavior, emotional feeling
C. stimulus, interpretation of stimulus, emotional feeling, overt behavior
D. physiological arousal, emotional feeling, interpret cues, overt behavior

p. 361
Cognitive Appraisal
  Theory
Level: Easy
Type: Applied
Ans: A

56. According to Schachter and Singer's cognitive theory of emotion, the experience of happiness would depend on the:
A. context in which one was physiologically aroused
B. nature of the physiological arousal
C. strength of the physiological arousal
D. duration of the physiological arousal

| | | |
|---|---|---|
| p. 361 | 57. | Schachter and Singer's cognitive theory states that physiological arousal: |
| Cognitive Appraisal | A. | causes particular emotions to be experienced |
| Theory | B. | results from the movements of facial muscles |
| Level: Moderate | C. | creates the need for an explanation |
| Type: Conceptual | D. | cannot be cognitively appraised |
| Ans: C | | |

| | | |
|---|---|---|
| p. 361 | 58. | Which of the following is a revision in Schachter and Singer's cognitive theory? |
| Cognitive Appraisal | | |
| Theory | A. | a stimulus causes physiological arousal |
| Level: Easy | B. | physiological arousal creates the need for some kind of explanation |
| Type: Factual | C. | an individual's appraisal of the situational cues results in the experience of an emotion |
| Ans: D | | |
| | D. | emotions may occur without any thought or awareness |

| | | |
|---|---|---|
| p. 361 | 59. | The main argument about the role of cognition in emotion seems to be: |
| Cognitive Appraisal | A. | whether cognition occurs in all emotional experiences |
| Theory | B. | if there is a different cognitive experience for each emotion |
| Level: Moderate | C. | how the frontal lobes interact with the limbic system |
| Type: Factual | D. | whether cognition comes before emotion or emotion comes before |
| Ans: D | | cognition |

| | | |
|---|---|---|
| p. 361 | 60. | The physiological arousal that you experience before taking a test can be interpreted as anxiety or excitement. Which theory would emphasize how this arousal impacts the emotion you feel? |
| Cognitive Appraisal | | |
| Theory | | |
| Level: Easy | A. | cognitive appraisal theory |
| Type: Applied | B. | James-Lange theory |
| Ans: A | C. | facial feedback theory |
| | D. | Price-Waterhouse theory |

| | | |
|---|---|---|
| p. 361 | 61. | The importance of the Schachter and Singer study was to show that: |
| Cognitive Appraisal | A. | appraisal of the stimulus occurs after behavior changes |
| Theory | B. | physiology plays an insignificant role in emotion |
| Level: Easy | C. | cognitive factors could trigger and give rise to emotional feelings |
| Type: Factual | D. | facial muscles trigger emotional feelings |
| Ans: C | | |

| | | |
|---|---|---|
| p. 361 | 62. | The sequence of components for emotion according to the cognitive-appraisal theory of emotion is: |
| Cognitive Appraisal | | |
| Theory | A. | stimulus, interpret, bodily response, emotional feeling |
| Level: Easy | B. | stimulus, interpret, emotional feeling, bodily response |
| Type: Factual | C. | stimulus, emotional feeling, interpret, bodily response |
| Ans: B | D. | stimulus, emotional feeling, bodily response, interpret |

| | | |
|---|---|---|
| p. 361 | 63. | The primary cause of emotions according to the cognitive appraisal theory is: |
| Cognitive Appraisal | | |
| Theory | A. | the extent of change in facial muscles and skin |
| Level: Easy | B. | how the brain interprets physiological changes |
| Type: Factual | C. | how we interpret a situation |
| Ans: C | D. | our degree of physiological arousal |
| *www* | | |

p. 362
Affective Neuroscience
Level: Easy
Type: Factual
Ans: A

64. Which specialty examines the relationship of emotion and how the brain produces or contributes to emotion?
A. affective neuroscience
B. affective physiology
C. mood dynamics
D. bioaffective psychology

p. 362
Affective Neuroscience
Level: Easy
Type: Factual
Ans: A

65. According to affective neuroscience, our appraisal of the stimulus is based upon how it:
A. affects our well-being
B. causes physiological arousal
C. causes an emotional feeling
D. changes our facial expression

p. 362
Affective Neuroscience
Level: Easy
Type: Factual
Ans: B

66. Our emotions are different than other psychological states. What is this difference?
A. Our emotions occur independently of cognitive processes.
B. Our emotions are expressed in stereotypic ways.
C. Our emotions are based solely on biological arousal.
D. Our emotions are more controllable.

p. 362
Affective Neuroscience
Level: Easy
Type: Factual
Ans: C

67. The module describes four unique qualities of emotions. Which of the following is not among those four qualities?
A. Some emotions are hard wired in the brain.
B. Emotions may not respond to reasoning.
C. Emotions is not influenced by one's culture.
D. Emotions are expressed in stereotypic ways.

p. 362
Affective Neuroscience
Level: Easy
Type: Factual
Ans: C

68. Based on the content in the module, why do emotions influence our decisions?
A. Emotions often are related to unconscious conflicts and it is these conflicts which influence decisions we make.
B. Emotions create "neurological confusion" in our memory systems which then disrupts decision making.
C. The forebrain, which makes decisions, does not have complete control over the limbic system.
D. Emotions release stress hormones which can influence our reasoning ability.

p. 362
Affective Neuroscience
Level: Easy
Type: Applied
Ans: A

69. Most people would detect a _____ faster than a _____.
A. snake; book
B. dog; cat
C. square; circle
D. baseball; football

p. 362
Affective Neuroscience
Level: Easy
Type: Factual
Ans: D

70. Most people would detect _____ stimuli faster than _____ stimuli according to affective neuroscience.
A. stationary; moving
B. moving; stationary
C. color; uncolored
D. emotional; unemotional

<table>
<tr><td>

p. 362
Affective Neuroscience
Level: Moderate
Type: Applied
Ans: B

</td><td>

71. You're at a baseball stadium watching a game. Suddenly a ball is hit right at you, and you detect the stimulus very fast. What would affective neuroscientists say about that?
A. The baseball is round and we can detect this shape very fast.
B. The baseball coming right at you represents a potential threat.
C. The baseball represents some unconscious stimulus that symbolizes conflicts experienced in childhood.
D. The baseball is detected very fast because it is moving and not stationary.

</td></tr>
<tr><td>

p. 362
Affective Neuroscience
Level: Easy
Type: Factual
Ans: B

</td><td>

72. Which part of the brain is especially active when viewing facial expressions of fear?
A. hippocampus
B. amygdala
C. thalamus
D. visual cortex

</td></tr>
<tr><td>

p. 362
Affective Neuroscience
Level: Easy
Type: Factual
Ans: D
*PS/SG 16-8*

</td><td>

73. Among the main functions of the amygdala are:
A. suppressing feelings of fear and covering over memories of fear
B. maintaining calm and promoting a meditative state
C. sensing feelings of hunger and maintaining a set weight
D. detecting threats and storing memories with emotional content

</td></tr>
<tr><td>

p. 362
Affective Neuroscience
Level: Easy
Type: Factual
Ans: D
*www*

</td><td>

74. Imagine that the parts of the brain can speak. As you look at a black widow spider coming towards you, which part would say, "It's my responsibility to determine if a stimulus has positive or negative emotional significance"?
A. Broca's area
B. hippocampus
C. thalamus
D. amygdala

</td></tr>
<tr><td>

p. 362
Affective Neuroscience
Level: Easy
Type: Factual
Ans: D

</td><td>

75. "I remember when a dog chased me up a tree. I was scared." What brain part was responsible for storing that memory of that fear?
A. amygdala
B. thalamus
C. Wernicke's area
D. hippocampus

</td></tr>
<tr><td>

p. 362
Affective Neuroscience
Level: Easy
Type: Applied
Ans: D

</td><td>

76. You are a writing an article for the local newspaper on the amygdala and its role in emotion. What would be a catchy and accurate title for your article?
A. Your amygdala: The major relay station of the brain
B. The amygdala: Unconscious motives and conflicts
C. Amygdala: Emotion detector and memorizer
D. Amygdala: Friend or foe?

</td></tr>
<tr><td>

p. 363
Affective Neuroscience
Level: Easy
Type: Factual
Ans: D

</td><td>

77. When noticing an unemotional stimulus, what is the pathway of neural activity?
A. eyes, amygdala, visual cortex
B. eyes, thalamus, amygdala
C. eyes, visual cortex, thalamus
D. eyes, thalamus, visual cortex, thalamus

</td></tr>
</table>

p. 363
Affective Neuroscience
Level: Easy
Type: Factual
Ans: A

78.    "Look over there. It's a poisonous snake," your friend yells as the two of you are hiking. What is the pathway of neural activity?
A.    eyes, amygdala, visual cortex
B.    eyes, thalamus, amygdala
C.    eyes, visual cortex, thalamus
D.    eyes, thalamus, visual cortex, thalamus

p. 363
Affective Neuroscience
Level: Easy
Type: Factual
Ans: B

79.    Matt has problems controlling his emotions. From the affective neuroscience perspective, why might that be the case?
A.    His levels of norepinephrine are out of balance.
B.    His prefrontal cortex is not working properly.
C.    The thalamus is not sending information properly to his visual cortex.
D.    Unconscious motives are responsible for his lack of control.

p. 363
Affective Neuroscience
Level: Easy
Type: Factual
Ans: D

80.    Duane suffers from social phobia. What area of his brain is especially active according to research described in the module?
A.    thalamus
B.    prefrontal cortex
C.    visual cortex
D.    amygdala

p. 364
Universal Facial
  Expressions
Level: Easy
Type: Factual
Ans: D

81.    Universal emotions refer to a(n) _____ number of specific _____ that signal feelings or emotional states.
A.    inherited; verbalizations
B.    learned; facial expressions
C.    large; hand gestures
D.    inherited; facial expressions

p. 364
Universal Facial
  Expressions
Level: Easy
Type: Factual
Ans: C
*www*

82.    A _____ is a universal sign of happiness or friendliness.
A.    hand shake
B.    wave
C.    smile
D.    verbal greeting

p. 364
Universal Facial
  Expressions
Level: Easy
Type: Factual
Ans: A
*PS/SG 16-11*

83.    Which one of the following is not a universally recognized emotion?
A.    indecision
B.    happiness
C.    surprise
D.    anger

p. 364
Universal Facial
  Expressions
Level: Easy
Type: Factual
Ans: A

84.    Which of these is not generally considered an emotion expression recognized across cultures?
A.    frustration
B.    happiness
C.    surprise
D.    sadness

p. 364
Universal Facial
 Expressions
Level: Easy
Type: Factual
Ans: D

85. Who formulated the existence of universal emotions?
A. Stanley Schachter
B. Richard Lazarus
C. Robert Zajonc
D. Charles Darwin

p. 364
Universal Facial
 Expressions
Level: Easy
Type: Factual
Ans: C

86. Cross-cultural studies of facial expression have determined that:
A. there are vast differences in the way people express emotions such as anger and surprise
B. people are very inaccurate in determining what emotion is being portrayed in photographs of facial expressions
C. there is remarkable agreement in the facial expressions representing certain emotions
D. people in some cultures never smile

p. 364
Universal Facial
 Expressions
Level: Easy
Type: Factual
Ans: A

87. Of the following expressions, which one tends to have the least agreement across cultures?
A. surprise
B. happiness
C. anger
D. sadness

p. 364
Universal Facial
 Expressions
Level: Easy
Type: Factual
Ans: D

88. According to cross-cultural evidence, which of the following emotions is least likely to have universal expression?
A. fear
B. anger
C. sadness
D. shame

p. 364
Universal Facial
 Expressions
Level: Easy
Type: Applied
Ans: C
*PS/SG 16-12*

89. The fact that blind infants begin to smile around 4–6 weeks shows that:
A. they are socially delayed, because sighted infants smile almost immediately
B. blind children can learn anything sighted children can
C. some facial expressions are biologically programmed
D. at least in the beginning, humans have a cheerful disposition

p. 364
Universal Facial
 Expressions
Level: Easy
Type: Factual
Ans: D

90. At about _____, infants begin to smile, even infants who are _____.
A. 1-3 days; blind
B. 8 to 10 weeks; blind
C. 1-2 weeks; deaf
D. 4 to 6 weeks; blind

p. 364
Universal Facial
 Expressions
Level: Easy
Type: Factual
Ans: B

91. Which of these statements is not correct in regard to universal facial expression?
A. infants around 5 to 7 months show fear
B. infants develop facial expressions in an unpredictable sequence
C. happiness is expressed the same way in Western and primitive cultures
D. anger is a biologically determined universal emotion

p. 364
Universal Facial
  Expressions
Level: Moderate
Type: Factual
Ans: D

92. As you look at your newborn niece Bethany, you wonder what facial expressions will appear first. Of the following, which lists the correct order of an infant's development of facial expressions?
A. fear, happiness, angry, disgust
B. happiness, fear, angry, disgust
C. angry, fear, disgust, happiness
D. disgust, angry, happiness, fear

p. 365
Functions of Emotions
Level: Moderate
Type: Factual
Ans: A

93. When you see a child smiling, her smile communicates her feelings of happiness to you, and then you wave and smile back to her. Emotion in this regard serves as a(n):
A. social signal
B. adaptive method
C. warning of her intentions
D. outlet for stress

p. 365
Functions of Emotions
Level: Moderate
Type: Factual
Ans: C

94. What function do social signals serve?
A. These social signals are patterns that solve problems in our environment.
B. They help us to adapt to the environment.
C. Different social signals elicit responses from those around us.
D. Social signals alleviate stress.

p. 365
Functions of Emotions
Level: Easy
Type: Factual
Ans: B

95. It was Charles Darwin who argued that emotions function to allow us to:
A. choose mates who are similar to us in emotional disposition
B. adapt and solve problems that are important for our survival
C. communicate our feelings or moods
D. indicate how others are to respond to us

p. 365
Functions of Emotions
Level: Easy
Type: Factual
Ans: A

96. The _____ theory of emotion suggests that we have emotions to help us judge objects and situations to determine if they can help us survive.
A. evolutionary
B. James-Lange
C. cognitive appraisal
D. affective-primacy

p. 365
Functions of Emotions
Level: Easy
Type: Factual
Ans: D

97. The notion that emotions can help or hinder performance is key to the:
A. peripheral theories
B. Schachter and Singer theory
C. adaptation level theory
D. Yerkes-Dodson law

p. 365
Functions of Emotions
Level: Easy
Type: Factual
Ans: C

98. To do well on a difficult task, the Yerkes-Dodson law would recommend:
A. high arousal
B. moderate arousal
C. low arousal
D. that arousal does not play a role in performance

| | | |
|---|---|---|
| p. 365<br>Functions of Emotions<br>Level: Easy<br>Type: Factual<br>Ans: A | 99. | An athlete has a simple task in the game she is playing. According to the Yerkes-Dodson law, she ought to have:<br>A. high arousal<br>B. moderate arousal<br>C. low arousal<br>D. that arousal does not play a role in performance |
| p. 365<br>Functions of Emotions<br>Level: Easy<br>Type: Factual<br>Ans: A<br>*PS/SG 16-14* | 100. | The relationship between emotional arousal and performance on a task is explained by the:<br>A. Yerkes-Dodson law<br>B. James-Lange theory<br>C. Schacter-Singer law<br>D. Darwinian law of survival |
| p. 365<br>Functions of Emotions<br>Level: Easy<br>Type: Applied<br>Ans: C | 101. | Bill has a very difficult test coming up tomorrow. But he is confused on his plan of attack - that is, in which emotional state should he be when taking the exam. The Yerkes-Dodson law would advise Bill to be:<br>A. adequately prepared for his exam<br>B. in a high state of arousal<br>C. in a low state of arousal<br>D. "psyched up" |
| p. 365<br>Functions of Emotions<br>Level: Easy<br>Type: Factual<br>Ans: A | 102. | In order to achieve high performance on a simple, familiar task, the Yerkes-Dodson law would recommend:<br>A. high arousal<br>B. moderate arousal<br>C. low arousal<br>D. that arousal does not play a role in performance |
| p. 365<br>Functions of Emotions<br>Level: Easy<br>Type: Applied<br>Ans: A<br>*www* | 103. | Sue works on a factory line. Her tasks are very simple, but since she wants a promotion, she needs to be productive and make few errors. The Yerkes-Dodson law would advise Sue to be:<br>A. "psyched up"<br>B. in a moderate state of arousal<br>C. in a low state of arousal<br>D. adequately trained for her job |
| p. 365<br>Functions of Emotions<br>Level: Easy<br>Type: Factual<br>Ans: B<br>*PS/SG 16-13* | 104. | Which of the following is <u>not</u> something emotions do for us?<br>A. help us to attain well-being and survival<br>B. help us answer questions of fact<br>C. motivate and arouse us<br>D. help us express social signals |
| p. 365<br>Functions of Emotions<br>Level: Easy<br>Type: Factual<br>Ans: B | 105. | The module describes a study in which students were aroused either because of high test anxiety or drinking coffee. When completing a difficult task, the most highly aroused students:<br>A. did better than less aroused students<br>B. did more poorly than less aroused students<br>C. completed the task more quickly than less aroused students<br>D. completed the task less quickly than less aroused students |

p. 366
Happiness
Level: Easy
Type: Factual
Ans: A

106. What part of the brain recognizes happy facial expressions?
A. amygdala
B. hypothalamus
C. corpus callosum
D. hippocampus

p. 366
Happiness
Level: Easy
Type: Factual
Ans: C

107. What emotion is most related to dopamine, nucleus accumbens, and ventral tegemental areas of the brain?
A. surprise
B. anger
C. happiness
D. fear

p. 366
Happiness
Level: Easy
Type: Conceptual
Ans: B

108. What did Pam, the young woman who won 87 million dollars in the Lottery, discover about money and happiness?
A. Being rich leads to long-term happiness.
B. Money helps and makes life easier, but does not buy long-term happiness.
C. Money has no effect in the short-term or long-term on happiness.
D. More money and things brings a sense of emptiness to life.

p. 366
Happiness
Level: Easy
Type: Applied
Ans: D

109. A friend of yours just won a multi-million dollar lottery. She asks you what you thought would happen to her level of happiness. Given that you've just studied happiness, you would correctly tell her that:
A. she will likely deeply regret winning the money and will suffer from mild to moderate depression
B. she will experience great happiness even in the long-term
C. happiness will actually decrease, but she won't become depressed
D. she will experience a short period of great happiness, but in the long-run will be no happier than before

p. 366
Happiness
Level: Easy
Type: Factual
Ans: D

110. The study of lottery winners indicated that one year after winning:
A. there was a great deal of sorrow for most of the people studied
B. most subjects considered winning the lottery to be the best thing that could have happened to them
C. most subjects experienced few changes in their lifestyle
D. overall, winners were no happier than non-winners

p. 366
Happiness
Level: Moderate
Type: Conceptual
Ans: B

111. Which phrase best describes the adaptation level theory?
A. "easy come, easy go"
B. "taking things for granted"
C. "a level playing field"
D. "so much to do in so little time"

p. 366
Happiness
Level: Easy
Type: Applied
Ans: A

112. Rosie married a very wealthy man and, initially, was extremely happy that she could now afford all the things she could never have before. Six months later her happiness had lessened. She had become accustomed to having money and now took it for granted. According to Brickman, Rosie's reduction in happiness is due to:
A. adaptation level theory
B. overjustification
C. contrast principle
D. attribution

p. 366
Happiness
Level: Easy
Type: Factual
Ans: B

113. According to the adaptation level theory, money cannot buy happiness because:
A. we are greedy
B. we adapt to continuous satisfaction
C. most of us cannot afford to buy those things that create true happiness
D. we find it difficult to put a price tag on happiness

p. 366
Happiness
Level: Easy
Type: Factual
Ans: B

114. The adaptation level theory would suggest that long-term happiness is more dependent on:
A. other people's financial success
B. enjoying good news and the little pleasures of life
C. setting and reaching high goals
D. accumulating material things that give us pleasure

p. 366
Happiness
Level: Easy
Type: Applied
Ans: C
*www*

115. A year after winning a $10 million lottery, the winner is no happier than she was before winning the prize. Which theory would best explain her situation?
A. Schachter and Singer's theory
B. James-Lange theory
C. adaptation level theory
D. cognitive appraisal theory

p. 366
Happiness
Level: Easy
Type: Factual
Ans: C
*PS/SG 16-16*

116. Adaptation level theory explains why people who win big in the lottery:
A. don't come forward to claim their prizes right away
B. often spend lavishly until they are right back where they started
C. don't feel much happier than anyone else after a while
D. often report that winning permanently changed them from discontented to happy persons

p. 366
Happiness
Level: Moderate
Type: Factual
Ans: D

117. Of the following, what would researchers say would have the most impact on long-term happiness?
A. winning a multimillion lottery
B. getting married
C. graduating from college
D. getting a phone call each week from a friend who has moved away

p. 366
Happiness
Level: Easy
Type: Factual
Ans: A

118. "Getting use" to money is most related to the _____.
A. adaptation level theory
B. drive-reduction theory
C. cognitive appraisal theory
D. James-Lange theory

p. 366
Happiness
Level: Moderate
Type: Factual
Ans: B

119. According to research, about _____ of our level of happiness comes from _____.
A. 100%; environmental influences
B. 50%; genetic influences
C. 70%; financial security
D. 30%; reaching personal goals

p. 366
Happiness
Level: Easy
Type: Factual
Ans: D

120. What will tend to happen to happiness that results from receiving an award, graduating from college, or getting a new car?
A. Happiness will remain stable.
B. Happiness will peak and then decrease over the long-term.
C. Happiness will decrease unless the person reminds themselves of the source of their happiness whether it's the award, graduating, or the new car.
D. Happiness will peak and then decrease in a short period of time.

p. 367
Cultural Diversity:
  Emotions Across
  Cultures
Level: Easy
Type: Factual
Ans: D
*www*

121. Specific cultural norms that govern the control of emotional expression in specific situations are called:
A. situational cues
B. social signals
C. adaptation levels
D. display rules

p. 367
Cultural Diversity:
  Emotions Across
  Cultures
Level: Easy
Type: Factual
Ans: A

122. According to the module, what is an explanation of the gender difference in smiling?
A. display rules
B. affective-primacy theory
C. cognitive appraisal
D. biologically differences between males and females

p. 367
Cultural Diversity:
  Emotions Across
  Cultures
Level: Easy
Type: Factual
Ans: A
*PS/SG 16-18*

123. Cultural rules that govern emotional expression in specific situations are called:
A. display rules
B. feelings guides
C. primacy rules
D. intensity rules

p. 367
Cultural Diversity:
  Emotions Across
  Cultures
Level: Moderate
Type: Conceptual
Ans: C

124. The fact that there are some gestures and facial expressions that are specific to particular cultures:
A. leads us to reconsider Charles Darwin's reasoning
B. calls into question the idea of universal facial expression
C. suggests that display rules influence expression of emotion and mood
D. implies that expression of emotion and mood is primarily determined by learning

p. 367
Cultural Diversity:
  Emotions Across
  Cultures
Level: Easy
Type: Factual
Ans: B

125. The study reviewed in your textbook on evaluation of emotional intensity among Japanese and Americans reveal that:
A. Japanese encourage the expression of intense emotions
B. Japanese discourage the expression of intense emotions
C. Americans discourage the expression of intense emotions
D. Americans rate sadness as the most intense emotion

p. 367
Cultural Diversity:
  Emotions Across
  Cultures
Level: Moderate
Type: Factual
Ans: A

126. Sigrid is going on a tour of Japan. She asks you for advice regarding anything she should know about showing emotions in that culture. Of course, she has great confidence in you because of your understanding of this topic. You tell her that:
A. The Japanese people tend to discourage the showing of emotional intensity in public.
B. Japanese excel at identifying the emotions of fear and anger.
C. Japanese love to show positive emotions in public.
D. The Japanese people tend to encourage the showing of strong negative emotions in public.

p. 367
Cultural Diversity:
  Emotions Across
  Cultures
Level: Moderate
Type: Factual
Ans: A

127. Japanese and Americans were asked to rate the most intense emotion out of surprise, anger, happiness, disgust, and sadness. The most intense according to Japanese was _____; Americans perceived _____ as the most intense.
A. disgust; happiness
B. anger; anger
C. disgust; sadness
D. sadness; happiness

p. 367
Cultural Diversity:
  Emotions Across
  Cultures
Level: Easy
Type: Applied
Ans: C

128. You attend a sporting event in Japan. The athletes perform very well. But the mainly Japanese crowd shows less appreciation than what you expected. This is due to:
A. psychodynamic factors
B. genetic differences
C. a difference in display rules
D. differences in how Japanese understand sporting events

p. 369
Research Focus:
  Emotional Intelligence
Level: Easy
Type: Factual
Ans: C
*www*

129. The ability to perceive and express emotion, understand and reason with emotion and regulate one's emotion is called:
A. interpersonal intelligence
B. self-actualization
C. emotional intelligence.
D. emotional maturity

p. 369
Research Focus:
  Emotional Intelligence
Level: Easy
Type: Factual
Ans: A
*PS/SG 16-20*

130. The new concept of emotional intelligence includes all of the following *except:*
A. excluding emotions when making crucial decisions
B. perceiving emotions accurately
C. taking feelings into account when reasoning
D. managing emotions in oneself and others

p. 369
Research Focus:
 Emotional Intelligence
Level: Easy
Type: Applied
Ans: D

131. Peter has the ability to make others feel as if he is one of them. He can also put people at ease. People say Peter does a great job not letting the little things in life bother him. Peter would most likely score high on a test of:
A. achievement motivation
B. verbal ability
C. creativity
D. emotional intelligence

p. 369
Research Focus:
 Emotional Intelligence
Level: Easy
Type: Factual
Ans: B

132. Proponents of emotional intelligence argue that IQ scores:
A. are strong predictors of success in life
B. are poor predictors of success in life
C. place too much emphasis on emotional regulation and expression
D. do a good job reflecting emotional factors

p. 369
Research Focus:
 Emotional Intelligence
Level: Easy
Type: Factual
Ans: A

133. Which statement best reflects the current understanding of measuring emotional intelligence?
A. Paper and pencil tests are currently being developed.
B. Psychologists have agreed that emotional intelligence cannot be measured.
C. There are many valid and reliable measures of emotional intelligence.
D. Emotional intelligence has not captured much interest among psychologists and educators.

p. 369
Research Focus:
 Emotional Intelligence
Level: Easy
Type: Factual
Ans: B

134. With regard to emotional intelligence, there is preliminary evidence that:
A. a large thick cortex in the brain is associated with high scores
B. school children with high scores were rated by their teachers as more helpful
C. high scores are related to low life satisfaction
D. high scores are related to aggression in children

p. 369
Research Focus:
 Emotional Intelligence
Level: Easy
Type: Factual
Ans: D
*PS/SG 16-21*

135. Results from programs attempting to teach and improve emotional intelligence suggest that the concept may be:
A. the breakthrough in teaching that education has been waiting for
B. confirmed by the many new tests developed to measure it
C. the answer to the problem of test anxiety
D. more hype than substance

p. 370
Application:
 Lie Detection
Level: Easy
Type: Factual
Ans: D

136. Which component of an emotion is not critical to the rationale behind lie detector tests?
A. interpretation of stimulus
B. subjective feeling
C. physiological responses
D. overt behaviors

p. 370
Application:
  Lie Detection
Level: Easy
Type: Factual
Ans: D
*www*

137. The use of lie detectors assumes that:
A.   emotions involve various physiological responses that can be detected
B.   emotions consist of overt behavior
C.   the subject correctly interprets the question
D.   all of the above

p. 370
Application:
  Lie Detection
Level: Easy
Type: Factual
Ans: B
*PS/SG 16-22*

138. Lie detector tests measure:
A.   whether a statement is true or false
B.   how much physiological arousal the subject feels
C.   whether the subject is basically honest or dishonest
D.   how much character a person has

p. 370
Application:
  Lie Detection
Level: Easy
Type: Factual
Ans: A

139. Feeling guilty is typically accompanied by _____ physiological responses that can be measured by a polygraph.
A.   involuntary
B.   controlled
C.   voluntary
D.   brief

p. 370
Application:
  Lie Detection
Level: Easy
Type: Factual
Ans: B

140. When given a polygraph, a number of measurements are taken of several physiological responses. Which of the following is <u>not</u> typically assessed during a lie detector test?
A.   galvanic skin response
B.   body core temperature
C.   respiration rate
D.   blood pressure

p. 370
Application:
  Lie Detection
Level: Easy
Type: Conceptual
Ans: A

141. Why is the term "lie detector test" inaccurate?
A.   These tests simply measure changes in arousal.
B.   The test is not detecting lying, but the administrator is.
C.   Using the term "lie" does not accurately reflect guilt.
D.   Only very sophisticated computers can detect lying, not polygraphs.

p. 370
Application:
  Lie Detection
Level: Easy
Type: Factual
Ans: D

142. Which of the following refers to changes in sweating of the fingers or palms that accompany emotional experiences?
A.   skin temperature response
B.   sweat response
C.   polygraphic perspiration reaction
D.   galvanic skin response

p. 370
Application:
  Lie Detection
Level: Easy
Type: Factual
Ans: B
*www*

143. Which of the following statements regarding lie detectors is true?
A.   examiners are more likely to identify liars as truthful people
B.   lie detectors measure only physiological changes
C.   evidence from lie detectors is admissible in most courts of law
D.   polygraph examiners make correct decisions 99% of the time

p. 371
Application:
　Lie Detection
Level: Easy
Type: Factual
Ans: C

144. Two types of questions are used in the Control Question Technique. These types are called:
A. neutral question; elicitor question
B. control question; critical question
C. neutral question; critical question
D. control question; stress question

p. 371
Application:
　Lie Detection
Level: Easy
Type: Factual
Ans: D
*PS/SG 16-23*

145. The purpose of the Control Question Technique is to:
A. eventually eliminate the need for trial by jury
B. control for the effect of the polygraph
C. eliminate the contaminating effect of the galvanic skin response
D. compare responses to neutral questions and critical questions

p. 371
Application:
　Lie Detection
Level: Easy
Type: Applied
Ans: A

146. Guy has been arrested for rape and is currently being given a lie detector test. Which of the following is the best example of a neutral question?
A. "What is your full name?"
B. "Where were you on the night on July 15, 1998?"
C. "Do you know the victim?"
D. "Have you ever committed a violent crime against a woman?"

p. 371
Application:
　Lie Detection
Level: Moderate
Type: Factual
Ans: D

147. One problem of lie detector tests described in the textbook is that:
A. lying means different things to different people
B. high error rates have been observed with lie detection in laboratory settings
C. neutral questions in the control question technique actually are biased
D. a pattern of physiological responses that are unique to lying has never been found

p. 371
Application:
　Lie Detection
Level: Easy
Type: Factual
Ans: A

148. The lie detector test has been estimated to be inaccurate from:
A. 25% to 75% of the time
B. 5% to 10% of the time
C. 75% to 85% of the time
D. 90% to 95% of the time

p. 371
Application:
　Lie Detection
Level: Easy
Type: Factual
Ans: C
*www*

149. In most state and federal courts of law, evidence from lie detector tests is:
A. admissible, but only when a qualified professional administers the test
B. admissible only in federal court
C. prohibited
D. typically used in capital cases

p. 371
Application:
   Lie Detection
Level: Easy
Type: Factual
Ans: C
*PS/SG 16-24*

150.  In most courtrooms, lie detector test results are:
A.  admissible, because they give scientifically derived evidence
B.  admissible, because the jury must hear any evidence available
C.  inadmissible, because of their potential for error
D.  inadmissible, because they would put lawyers out of work

p. 371
Application:
   Lie Detection
Level: Easy
Type: Factual
Ans: C

151.  A promising new brain wave could be used to detect deception. In what area of the brain have researchers noticed distinct patterns of activity when subjects lie?
A.  hypothalamus
B.  amygdala
C.  prefrontal cortex
D.  thalamus

## True/False

| | | | |
|---|---|---|---|
| T | | 1. | Emotions include appraisal and observable behaviors. |
| F | *www* | 2. | The peripheral theory of emotions focuses on how we interpret situations. |
| T | | 3. | The James-Lange theory says that the brain interprets physiological arousal which produces emotions. |
| F | | 4. | The James-Lange theory explains why people with spinal cord injuries can still experience emotions. |
| T | *www* | 5. | Physiological changes may increase the intensity of emotional experiences. |
| T | | 6. | The James-Lange theory argues that the act of running from a bear causes fear. |
| F | *www* | 7. | Feedback from facial muscles can cause emotions. |
| T | | 8. | The cognitive interpretation of events can influence emotions. |
| T | *www* | 9. | In the Schachter-Singer experiment, subjects explained their arousal by focusing on the situation. |
| T | | 10. | Emotions are expressed in stereotypic facial expression. |
| F | *www* | 11. | The forebrain is responsible for regulating emotions. |
| T | | 12. | The amygdala evaluates stimuli to determine their emotional significance. |
| F | | 13. | Recognizing a threatening stimulus takes about .50 seconds. |
| F | | 14. | The prefrontal cortex is a relay station for the senses. |
| T | *www* | 15. | Social phobia may be related to the amygdala. |
| T | | 16. | For simple tasks, it is best to have high arousal. |
| T | *www* | 17. | The Yerkes-Dodson law describes the relationship between arousal and performance on tasks. |
| F | | 18. | According to adaptation level theory, emotions come after arousal. |
| T | *www* | 19. | Lottery winners tend to be happier than normal for about 12 months following their win. |
| F | | 20. | Gestures tend to have the same meaning around the world. |
| T | *www* | 21. | Japanese tend to be more emotionally reserved than Americans. |
| T | | 22. | Specific rules that regulate the expression of emotions are called display rules. |
| T | | 23. | Youths scoring high on tests of emotional intelligence tend to be less aggressive. |
| F | *www* | 24. | There are unique patterns of arousal for lying. |
| F | | 25. | Lie detectors have accuracy rates of around 85%. |

Short-Answer Essay Questions

1.    Describe the four components of an emotion.  (*www*)
2.    Compare and contrast peripheral and cognitive appraisal theories of emotion.
3.    According to the James-Lange theory of emotion, why are you afraid when you see a bear? How would the facial feedback theory explain fear in that situation?
4.    Describe the Schachter-Singer experiment and how that supports the cognitive appraisal theory of emotion.
5.    Explain the optimal level of arousal for difficult and easy tasks according to the Yerkes-Dodson law.  (*www*)
6.    What role does the amygdala play in detecting emotions?
7.    What is the genetic evidence for universal emotional expressions?  (*www*)
8.    Using the adaptation level theory, why would a lottery winner a year after winning, not be any happier than before.
9.    What is emotional intelligence?  What do proponents claim about it relative to success in life? (*www*)
10.   Describe how lie detector tests are performed.  If you were charged with a crime and you were innocent, would you take a lie detector test?  Defend your answer.  (*www*)

# Module 17 - Infancy and Childhood

| | | |
|---|---|---|
| p. 377<br>Introduction<br>Level: Moderate<br>Type: Conceptual<br>Ans: A | 1.<br><br>A.<br>B.<br>C.<br>D. | The ruling by an Iowa court in the baby Jessica case implies _____ significance over _____.<br>nature's; nurture<br>adoptive parents'; biological parents<br>psychology's; biology<br>nurture's; nature |
| p. 377<br>Introduction<br>Level: Easy<br>Type: Conceptual<br>Ans: D<br>*PS/SG 17-1* | 2.<br><br><br><br>A.<br><br>B.<br><br>C.<br>D. | Rod Plotnik begins the module with the heart-wrenching story of little Jessica, who was taken from her potential adoptive parents and given to her birth mother, to illustrate:<br>the danger that adoptive parents will not love children as much as birth parents<br>the mischief that arises when developmental psychologists are brought in<br>a tragic failure of the foster parent program<br>a real-life application of the nature-nurture question |
| p. 377<br>Introduction<br>Level: Easy<br>Type: Factual<br>Ans: C | 3.<br><br>A.<br>B.<br>C.<br>D. | As presented in the textbook, the cases of 2 1/2-year-old Jessica and 4-year-old Michael raise the issue of:<br>parental rights<br>legal precedence<br>nature-nurture<br>prenatal influences |
| p. 377<br>Introduction<br>Level: Easy<br>Type: Conceptual<br>Ans: B<br>*www* | 4.<br>A.<br>B.<br>C.<br>D. | Nature is to nurture as _____ is to _____.<br>culture; society<br>genetics; environment<br>environment; genetics<br>biology; physics |
| p. 377<br>Introduction<br>Level: Easy<br>Type: Conceptual<br>Ans: D | 5.<br><br><br>A.<br>B.<br>C.<br>D. | Kyle is looking into buying a dog for his children. He learns that golden retrievers by their nature are very good with children. What does "by their nature" mean?<br>It refers to how the dog is trained by the owner.<br>Nature refers to how his children will interact with the dog.<br>It refers to their genetic makeup.<br>"By their nature" refers to the dogs' genetic predisposition. |
| p. 377<br>Introduction<br>Level: Easy<br>Type: Factual<br>Ans: A | 6.<br><br>A.<br>B.<br>C.<br>D. | The influence of genetic factors versus experience on development is addressed via:<br>the nature-nurture question<br>stages versus continuity<br>the case study method<br>amniocentesis |

p. 377
Introduction
Level: Easy
Type: Factual
Ans: C

7. Individuals interested in biological, emotional, cognitive, and social factors across the life span are called:
A. humanistic psychologists
B. behavioral psychologists
C. developmental psychologists
D. psychoanalytic psychologists

p. 377
Introduction
Level: Easy
Type: Applied
Ans: A

8. Professor Rose's most recent book describes the changes seen in the drawings of children from four to ten years of age. Professor Rose is most likely a:
A. developmental psychologist
B. behavioral psychologist
C. humanistic psychologist
D. biological psychologist

p. 378
Prenatal Influences
Level: Easy
Type: Applied
Ans: C

9. Samantha, a five-year-old, shows extraordinary musical ability. She is of average intelligence, can play the piano very well, and comes from a very musical family. Samantha is a:
A. mnemonist
B. autistic child
C. prodigy
D. savant

p. 378
Prenatal Influences
Level: Easy
Type: Factual
Ans: C

10. The term "savant" refers to people:
A. with eidetic imagery abilities
B. who have photographic memories
C. who are mentally retarded with unusual artistic or mathematical abilities
D. who have eidetic memory

p. 378
Prenatal Influences
Level: Easy
Type: Factual
Ans: D

11. Prodigies demonstrate the interaction between:
A. developmental psychology and music
B. biology and genetics
C. art and social science
D. genetic and learned influences

p. 378
Prenatal Influences
Level: Easy
Type: Factual
Ans: C

12. What percent contribution does the father make to a child's genetic instructions?
A. depends if the instructions are for behavior or biological functioning
B. depends on age of father
C. 50%
D. 75% for male children; 25% for female children

p. 378
Prenatal Influences
Level: Moderate
Type: Conceptual
Ans: D

13. Which statement best summarizes the current thinking on the nature versus nurture issue?
A. Nature is more important than nurture.
B. Nurture is more important than nature.
C. We can never really know which is most important.
D. There is an interaction between nature and nurture.

p. 378
Prenatal Influences
Level: Easy
Type: Factual
Ans: C

14. The case of Yehudi best illustrates that:
A. Nature is more important than nurture.
B. Nurture is more important than nature.
C. Nature and nurture interact.
D. Neither nature nor nurture is critical in developing musical ability.

p. 378
Prenatal Influences
Level: Easy
Type: Factual
Ans: A

15. You are listening to a talk show on television discussing intelligence. Right before a commercial, the host says, "When we return to our discussion of nature and nurture, we will find out which one is more important." What is your learned reaction to his statement?
A. "The question should not be 'which is more important' but how nature and nurture interact."
B. "Everyone knows that nurture is more important than nature."
C. "Everyone knows that nature is more important than nurture."
D. "How can we know which is more important since psychologists do not study these topics?"

p. 379
Prenatal Influences
Level: Easy
Type: Factual
Ans: A
*www*

16. The period that lasts nine months, extending from conception to birth is called the _____ period.
A. prenatal
B. embryonic
C. germinal
D. fetal

p. 379
Prenatal Influences
Level: Easy
Type: Factual
Ans: D

17. The three phases of the prenatal period in the correct order are:
A. germinal, fascia, zygote
B. embryonic, preoperational, operational
C. mitosial, chromosomal, fetal
D. germinal, embryonic, fetal

p. 379
Prenatal Influences
Level: Easy
Type: Factual
Ans: A
*PS/SG 17-3*

18. The briefest period of prenatal development is the:
A. germinal stage
B. embryonic stage
C. fetal stage
D. baby-making stage

p. 379
Prenatal Influences
Level: Easy
Type: Factual
Ans: A

19. Which of the following is not a stage in prenatal development?
A. zygote
B. embryonic
C. germinal
D. fetal

p. 379
Prenatal Influences
Level: Easy
Type: Factual
Ans: D
*www*

20. The germinal period starts at _____ and lasts _____.
A. conception; 4 weeks
B. 4 weeks; 8 weeks
C. 8 weeks; until birth
D. conception; 2 weeks

p. 379
Prenatal Influences
Level: Easy
Type: Factual
Ans: B

21. _____ refers to the release of an ovum from a woman's ovaries.
A. Conception
B. Ovulation
C. Amniocentesis
D. Fertilization

p. 379
Prenatal Influences
Level: Easy
Type: Applied
Ans: C

22. The Curtis family is made up of mom and dad, 8-year-old Susan, 5-year-old Grant, and the identical twins Christopher and Carson. In regard to genetic make-up, Christopher is most similar to his:
A. mother
B. father
C. identical twin
D. brother

p. 379
Prenatal Influences
Level: Moderate
Type: Factual
Ans: B
*www*

23. If two ova are released and fertilized, what will be the result?
A. identical twins
B. fraternal twins
C. a baby with Down syndrome
D. a baby with fetal alcohol syndrome

p. 379
Prenatal Influences
Level: Easy
Type: Factual
Ans: C

24. Identical twins result from:
A. the release and fertilization of two ova
B. the release of more than 23 strands of chromosomes
C. a single ovum that splits into two parts after fertilization
D. an extra 21st chromosome produced by the father's sperm

p. 379
Prenatal Influences
Level: Easy
Type: Factual
Ans: C

25. Conception occurs when:
A. ova are released by the fallopian tubes
B. the baby is born
C. a sperm penetrates the ovum's membrane
D. the embryo develops

p. 379
Prenatal Influences
Level: Easy
Type: Factual
Ans: D
*www*

26. Following fertilization, the single cell is called a(n):
A. embryo
B. germinal
C. ovum
D. zygote

p. 379
Prenatal Influences
Level: Easy
Type: Factual
Ans: B

27. Which of the following marks the end of the germinal period?
A. fertilization of the ovum
B. the zygote attached itself to the wall of the uterus
C. cells divide and differentiate into bone, muscle, and organs
D. the birth of the fetus

p. 379
Prenatal Influences
Level: Easy
Type: Factual
Ans: C

28. During the embryonic period:
A. the ovum is fertilized
B. the zygote attaches itself to the wall of the uterus
C. cells divide and differentiate into bone, muscle, and organs
D. the fetus is born

p. 379
Prenatal Influences
Level: Easy
Type: Factual
Ans: D

29. Why do most major birth defects occur during the embryonic stage?
A. The amniotic fluid can "leak" into the embryo and cause damage.
B. The placenta is still developing and does a poor job protecting the embryo.
C. Most women do not know they are pregnant until the fetal stage.
D. Most of the basic organs are being formed during the embryonic stage.

p. 379
Prenatal Influences
Level: Easy
Type: Factual
Ans: B

30. Linda, who is pregnant, and Fred, her husband visit her doctor. Upon examination, the doctor concludes that the baby's spinal cord and eyes have appeared and the features of the face are evident for the first time. What stage of the prenatal development is the baby most likely in?
A. germinal stage
B. embryonic stage
C. fetal stage
D. proximodistal stage

p. 379
Prenatal Influences
Level: Easy
Type: Factual
Ans: B

31. Most miscarriages occur:
A. when the fetus is born
B. in the embryonic stage
C. in the germinal stage
D. during conception

p. 380
Prenatal Influences
Level: Easy
Type: Factual
Ans: C

32. The fetal period is characterized by:
A. conception and fertilization
B. attachment to the wall of the uterus
C. functioning vital organs and human physical characteristics
D. the beginnings of the spinal cord, heart, and other organs

p. 380
Prenatal Influences
Level: Easy
Type: Applied
Ans: C

33. Denise is pregnant and has an ultrasound to "see" her unborn baby. Denise's doctor can clearly identify the baby as a female. This suggests that the baby is in the _____ period of prenatal development.
A. zygote
B. embryonic
C. fetal
D. germinal

p. 380
Prenatal Influences
Level: Easy
Type: Factual
Ans: A

34. A six-month-old fetus has a good chance of surviving if born prematurely. Why?
A. the lungs function
B. it has enough body fat to maintain body temperature
C. its nervous system is functional
D. the heart begins to beat around this time

p. 380
Prenatal Influences
Level: Easy
Type: Factual
Ans: A

35. Down syndrome and similar genetic abnormalities can be identified during prenatal development through:
A. amniocentesis
B. ovulation
C. the Lamaze method
D. the proximodistal procedure

p. 380
Prenatal Influences
Level: Easy
Type: Applied
Ans: B

36. Gwen is 16 weeks pregnant. She is undergoing a medical test that involves analyzing amniotic fluid to detect any genetic problems. What test is Gwen undergoing?
A. FAS indexing
B. amniocentesis
C. placentaltesis
D. teratogenic analysis

p. 380
Prenatal Influences
Level: Easy
Type: Factual
Ans: D
PS/SG 17-4

37. The medical test called _____ is performed to indicate genetic problems like _____.
A. teratogen identification / lead poisoning
B. placentosis / fetal alcohol syndrome (FAS)
C. fetal stage assessment / brain damage
D. amniocentesis / Down syndrome

p. 380
Prenatal Influences
Level: Easy
Type: Factual
Ans: D

38. The substance that is analyzed in amniocentesis is:
A. the blood plasma of the mother
B. the cerebrospinal fluid of the baby
C. the blood of the baby
D. amniotic fluid

p. 380
Prenatal Influences
Level: Moderate
Type: Applied
Ans: B

39. Bryan is born with Down syndrome. If we could look at his chromosomes, we would find that:
A. some of the chromosomes would be missing
B. there was an extra 21st chromosome instead of the normal two
C. there was some measurable damage or abnormality in each chromosome pair
D. his chromosomes were normal; Down syndrome is caused by an oxygen deficiency at birth

p. 380
Prenatal Influences
Level: Easy
Type: Factual
Ans: A

40. About how many inherited disorders can be tested for and identified prenatally?
A. 450
B. 500
C. 600
D. 650

p. 380
Prenatal Influences
Level: Easy
Type: Factual
Ans: C
*www*

41. The organ that connects the mother's blood supply to that of the fetus is called the:
A. germinal
B. teratogen
C. placenta
D. blood-baby barrier

p. 380
Prenatal Influences
Level: Easy
Type: Factual
Ans: B

42. The blood supply of the fetus is partially protected by the:
A. germinal
B. placenta
C. teratogen
D. amniotic fluid

p. 380
Prenatal Influences
Level: Easy
Type: Factual
Ans: B

43. Chemicals that can cause birth defects are called:
A. biohazards
B. teratogens
C. amniocentesis
D. biochemoses

p. 380
Prenatal Influences
Level: Moderate
Type: Factual
Ans: D

44. Teratogens can interfere with prenatal development and harm the unborn child by:
A. creating toxins in the mother's body and being passed to the child through the amniotic fluid
B. passing from the mother's lymphatic system to the child
C. being directly mixed with the child's blood system
D. passing from the placenta into the fetus's blood vessels

p. 381
Prenatal Influences
Level: Easy
Type: Factual
Ans: B

45. Based upon research, much attention was given to the effects of cocaine on prenatal development. But, according to your textbook, the effects may have been more due to:
A. dosage
B. multiple drug use
C. age of mother
D. genetic abnormalities

p. 381
Prenatal Influences
Level: Easy
Type: Factual
Ans: D

46. Short-term effects of exposure to nicotine during prenatal development is associated with:
A. poor muscle control
B. loss of reflexes
C. temporary liver damage
D. low birth weight

p. 381
Prenatal Influences
Level: Moderate
Type: Factual
Ans: A

47. Compared to a control group, children whose mothers smoked during their prenatal development had:
A. increased risk for SIDs
B. lower IQs
C. poorly developed brains
D. smaller than normal head size

p. 381
Prenatal Influences
Level: Easy
Type: Factual
Ans: B

48. Prenatal exposure to lead is associated with:
A. poor muscular control
B. lower IQ scores
C. liver damage
D. stunted growth

p. 381
Prenatal Influences
Level: Easy
Type: Factual
Ans: C

49. Research has found that older children (e.g., 4 to 7 years-old), exposed to cocaine in prenatal development, have significant problems in:
A. regulating their own behavior
B. social interactions
C. using and understanding language
D. counting

p. 381
Prenatal Influences
Level: Easy
Type: Factual
Ans: C

50. Heavy drinking during pregnancy can result in:
A. chromosomal damage to the fetus
B. high levels of arousal in the newborn
C. fetal alcohol syndrome
D. a newborn with a large appetite

p. 381
Prenatal Influences
Level: Easy
Type: Factual
Ans: C
*PS/SG 17-5*

51. If you believe what the textbook says about teratogens, you would tell all pregnant women to:
A. watch their weight gain very carefully
B. get plenty of rest--even more as they approach delivery
C. avoid alcohol entirely
D. avoid becoming overly stressed

p. 381
Prenatal Influences
Level: Easy
Type: Factual
Ans: B

52. Which of the following is not generally seen in adolescents and adults with fetal alcohol syndrome?
A. short stature
B. dyslexia
C. below average IQs
D. poor socialization

p. 381
Prenatal Influences
Level: Easy
Type: Factual
Ans: A

53. The effects of fetal alcohol syndrome:
A. continue into adolescence and adulthood
B. are less severe than fetal alcohol effect
C. tend to lessen in adulthood
D. are reduced by vitamin therapy

p. 381
Prenatal Influences
Level: Easy
Type: Factual
Ans: A

54. A less severe form of fetal alcohol syndrome is called:
A. Prenatal Exposure to Alcohol
B. Fetal Alcohol Dysfunction
C. Alcohol-related Prenatal Effect
D. Alcohol Toxin Effect

p. 381
Prenatal Influences
Level: Easy
Type: Applied
Ans: B

55. A woman who is in the habit of having two drinks every day after work discovers that she is pregnant. If she follows the advice of medical findings, she will:
A. cut her drinking in half
B. abstain from alcohol for the duration of her pregnancy
C. maintain her drinking behavior since it is good for her heart
D. drink beer after work since it will help her maintain valuable protein levels

p. 381
Prenatal Influences
Level: Easy
Type: Conceptual
Ans: B

56. The best piece of advice given to pregnant women regarding drug use would be:
A. recreational drug use is probably ok
B. use of all drugs should be avoided
C. we do not know enough about the effects of drugs on prenatal development to give solid advice
D. social drinking does not seem to have any effect on the unborn child

p. 382
Newborns' Abilities
Level: Easy
Type: Factual
Ans: C

57. Chromosomes consist of:
A. zygotes
B. sperm
C. DNA
D. phenotypes

p. 382
Newborns' Abilities
Level: Easy
Type: Factual
Ans: B

58. _____ consist of DNA.
A. Ova
B. Chromosomes
C. Zygotes
D. Phenotypes

p. 382
Newborns' Abilities
Level: Moderate
Type: Factual
Ans: D

59. Which statement is most accurate in describing the order from smallest to largest?
A. zygote, genes, DNA, chromosomes
B. genes, DNA, chromosomes, zygote
C. DNA, zygote, genes, chromosomes
D. DNA, genes, chromosomes, zygote

p. 382
Newborns' Abilities
Level: Easy
Type: Factual
Ans: C

60. In what specific structure is the "chemical alphabet" found - the alphabet that will provide the instructions for growth and development?
A. zygotes
B. genes
C. DNA
D. chromosomes

p. 382
Newborns' Abilities
Level: Moderate
Type: Applied
Ans: C

61. One reason offered by your textbook for the increase in the weight of a baby's brain from birth to 2 years of age is:
A. the expanding skull bones
B. new neurons forming
C. many new neural connections
D. increased production of cerebrospinal fluid

p. 382
Newborns' Abilities
Level: Moderate
Type: Factual
Ans: D

62. A baby's brain gains weight from 340 grams at birth to _____ grams at 2 years old.
A. 400
B. 560
C. 720
D. 900

p. 382
Newborns' Abilities
Level: Easy
Type: Factual
Ans: B
*PS/SG 17-6*

63. Infants first use their more developed arms, and then their fingers, whose control develops later — this is the:
A. cephalocaudal principle
B. proximodistal principle
C. principle of maturation
D. principle of normal development

p. 382
Newborns' Abilities
Level: Moderate
Type: Applied
Ans: B

64. As you listen to a talk show on the radio, a developmental psychologist says, "With regard to recognizing faces, the infant can distinguish his or her mother's face from that of a stranger by age......" And then suddenly all you hear is static. Of the following, what is the most likely statement the psychologist would have said?
A. 1 to 2 months
B. 3 to 6 months
C. 7 to 8 months
D. 9 to 10 months

p. 382
Newborns' Abilities
Level: Easy
Type: Factual
Ans: D

65. In regard to visual abilities, the child will see as well as an adult by:
A. 3 months
B. 6 months
C. 12 months
D. 4 years

p. 382
Newborns' Abilities
Level: Easy
Type: Applied
Ans: C

66. One-month-old Bethany can tell the difference between:
A. the odors of her mother and those of a stranger
B. a short distance and long distance
C. the sounds *bah* and *pah*
D. her mother's face and a stranger's face

p. 382
Newborns' Abilities
Level: Easy
Type: Factual
Ans: B

67. At what age could an infant distinguish between "bah" and "pah?"
A. one week
B. one month
C. two months
D. six months

| | | |
|---|---|---|
| p. 382<br>Newborns' Abilities<br>Level: Easy<br>Type: Factual<br>Ans: B | 68. | Tara is babysitting a six-month-old girl. Since Tara has taken a psychology course, she knows about infancy. Tara says that the baby will need another couple of months to make all the sounds that are necessary to learn English. Is Tara right? |
| | A. | No - children are born with the ability to make all the necessary sounds of their language |
| | B. | No - by six months, infants have developed the ability to make all the necessary sounds of their language |
| | C. | Yes - around 10 months of age, the infant will be able to make all the necessary sounds of the language |
| | D. | It is impossible to say since all infants are different. |

| | | |
|---|---|---|
| p. 382<br>Newborns' Abilities<br>Level: Easy<br>Type: Factual<br>Ans: A | 69. | What are the youngest infants researchers have found who can discriminate between a citrus odor and a floral odor? |
| | A. | one-day-old |
| | B. | one-week-old |
| | C. | four-week-old |
| | D. | six-week-old |

| | | |
|---|---|---|
| p. 382<br>Newborns' Abilities<br>Level: Easy<br>Type: Factual<br>Ans: C | 70. | Newborns have a preference for _____ tasting things. |
| | A. | cool/acidic |
| | B. | sour |
| | C. | sweet/salty |
| | D. | bitter/cool |

| | | |
|---|---|---|
| p. 382<br>Newborns' Abilities<br>Level: Easy<br>Type: Factual<br>Ans: D | 71. | The visual cliff allowed Gibson and Walk to study: |
| | A. | the proximodistal principle |
| | B. | preference for complex patterns |
| | C. | visual acuity |
| | D. | depth perception |

| | | |
|---|---|---|
| p. 382<br>Newborns' Abilities<br>Level: Easy<br>Type: Applied<br>Ans: B | 72. | If a child stops on the shallow side of the visual cliff and refuses to cross the deep side, what is your most likely conclusion? |
| | A. | The child is fatigued because crawling uses much energy. |
| | B. | Depth perception prevents the child from crossing the cliff. |
| | C. | The child has been distracted by something else. |
| | D. | There is not enough incentive for the child to move. |

| | | |
|---|---|---|
| p. 382<br>Newborns' Abilities<br>Level: Easy<br>Type: Factual<br>Ans: A | 73. | Regarding the sensory development of the neonate, research has indicated that newborns: |
| | A. | can discriminate between odors |
| | B. | do not distinguish between sounds until they are 6 months old |
| | C. | have no inborn preferences for taste |
| | D. | cannot smell the difference between their mother and a stranger |

| | | |
|---|---|---|
| p. 382<br>Newborns' Abilities<br>Level: Moderate<br>Type: Conceptual<br>Ans: D | 74. | The perceptual abilities of the newborn: |
| | A. | are very poor |
| | B. | are impossible to measure since a newborn cannot communicate |
| | C. | are such that it is very difficult to interact with newborns |
| | D. | allow it to interact with the world in a more sophisticated way than previously thought |

p. 382
Newborns' Abilities
Level: Easy
Type: Factual
Ans: A

75.     By six months of age, the child should be able to do all of the following
        except:
A.      see as well as an adult
B.      hesitate when they reach the clear glass dropoff on the visual cliff
C.      develop depth perception
D.      make all the sounds necessary in their language

p. 383
Newborns' Abilities
Level: Easy
Type: Factual
Ans: C

76.     Motor development involves the acquisition of:
A.      sensory abilities including hearing and taste
B.      reflexive movements and abilities
C.      the muscular control necessary for coordinated movement
D.      language and speech patterns necessary for communication

p. 383
Newborns' Abilities
Level: Easy
Type: Factual
Ans: A
*www*

77.     The proximodistal principle states that parts of the body that are
        _____ develop before parts of the body that are _____.
A.      close to the center of the body; farther away
B.      close to the head; close to the feet
C.      internal; external
D.      used for processing information; used for motor skills

p. 383
Newborns' Abilities
Level: Easy
Type: Factual
Ans: B

78.     Parts of the body which are close to the head develop before the parts
        closer to the feet according to the:
A.      proximodistal principle
B.      cephalocaudal principle
C.      visual cliff
D.      sensorimotor stage of development

p. 383
Newborns' Abilities
Level: Easy
Type: Factual
Ans: C

79.     Development occurs in a sequential and orderly fashion because of a
        genetic plan called:
A.      proximodistal
B.      cephalocaudal
C.      maturation
D.      norms for development

p. 383
Newborns' Abilities
Level: Easy
Type: Applied
Ans: A

80.     Should a parent be concerned if their 10-month-old is not crawling?
A.      No - development norms represent average ages and not absolute ages
B.      No - development norms have been shown to be false
C.      Yes - the norms represent absolute ages
D.      No - maturation typically does not influence motor skills

p. 383
Newborns' Abilities
Level: Easy
Type: Factual
Ans: D

81.     Chadaron, a one-year old boy, is having his motor development checked.
        The doctor says that his motor skills are normal for his age and says that
        motor skills development is biologically programmed.  The doctor is most
        likely referring to:
A.      proximodistal development
B.      cephalocaudal development
C.      temperament
D.      maturation

p. 383
Newborns' Abilities
Level: Moderate
Type: Applied
Ans: D

82. Jon and Linda, who are both psych majors, are looking at photographs of their son Dakota. A number of pictures show Dakota's motor development. Jon comments on the orderly changes in Dakota's development. Linda points out that this orderly sequence of changes in motor development is mostly due to:
A. the cephalocaudal principle
B. the proximodistal principle
C. experience
D. maturation

p. 383
Newborns' Abilities
Level: Easy
Type: Factual
Ans: A

83. In the early stages of motor development, _____ seems to be the major force guiding development.
A. maturation
B. learning
C. experience
D. genetics

p. 383
Newborns' Abilities
Level: Easy
Type: Factual
Ans: D

84. Development norms refer to:
A. parts of the body growing at differing rates
B. the genetic plan by which individuals are created
C. development occurring in a sequential and orderly fashion
D. the average age at which individuals perform skills

p. 383
Newborns' Abilities
Level: Moderate
Type: Conceptual
Ans: B

85. Gail and Janelle are talking about the differences between their children. Janelle's youngest, who is one year old, has not yet crawled. Gail says that Janelle should be worried. Should Janelle be worried about her son's motor development?
A. yes - normal children crawl by 10 months according to norms of development
B. no - norms for development refer to average age and not absolute age
C. no - motor development at this age is controlled by experience and so Janelle should just spend more time playing with her son
D. yes - 10 months is late for crawling

p. 383
Newborns' Abilities
Level: Difficult
Type: Conceptual
Ans: C

86. Nature and nurture interact. Which of the following best illustrates that interaction?
A. Early in life, maturation determines motor development.
B. There is a predictable order to developmental norms for motor development.
C. Infants need environmental stimulation for motor development.
D. Motor development follows cephalocaudal and proximodistal principles.

p. 384
Emotional Development
Level: Easy
Type: Factual
Ans: A
*www*

87. An infant's characteristic mood, activity level, and attention span are referred to as components of the infant's:
A. temperament
B. personality
C. genotype
D. phenotype

p. 384
Emotional Development
Level: Easy
Type: Factual
Ans: C
*PS/SG 17-7*

88. The term temperament refers to:
A. contrary behavior that is typical of the "terrible twos"
B. emotional characteristics that are largely influenced by environmental factors
C. relatively stable individual differences in mood and emotional behavior
D. the formal name in psychology for childhood temper tantrums

p. 384
Emotional Development
Level: Easy
Type: Applied
Ans: D

89. Brenda gave birth to fraternal twins. After a few months, Brenda notices that one twin is always happy and energetic, whereas the other twin is always fussy and fearful. Brenda's twins are showing differences in:
A. vulnerability
B. maturation
C. resiliency
D. temperament

p. 384
Emotional Development
Level: Easy
Type: Factual
Ans: A

90. According to longitudinal data, the majority of babies have _____ temperaments.
A. easy
B. difficult
C. slow-to-warm-up
D. moderate

p. 384
Emotional Development
Level: Easy
Type: Factual
Ans: A

91. Tony and Julie describe their newborn, Carson, as happy and cheerful, with regular sleeping and eating habits, and the ability to adapt quickly. Carson has a(n) _____ temperament.
A. easy
B. positive
C. optimal
D. optimistic

p. 384
Emotional Development
Level: Easy
Type: Factual
Ans: C

92. A baby who is more withdrawn, moody, and tends to take more time to adapt to new situations has a(n) _____ temperament.
A. easy
B. difficult
C. slow-to-warm-up
D. moderate

p. 384
Emotional Development
Level: Easy
Type: Factual
Ans: B
*www*

93. A baby who is fussy and fearful of new situation has a _____ temperament.
A. negative
B. difficult
C. slow-to-warm-up
D. pessimistic

p. 384
Emotional Development
Level: Easy
Type: Factual
Ans: A
*PS/SG 17-8*

94. A longitudinal study of infant temperament found that:
A. infants develop a distinct temperament in the first two to three months
B. infants' temperaments tend to mirror their parents' temperaments
C. temperament is determined by the emotional state of the mother during pregnancy
D. temperament fluctuates widely during infancy

p. 384
Emotional Development
Level: Easy
Type: Factual
Ans: C

95. Research has indicated that the majority of infants develop distinct temperaments by:
A. 2-3 days
B. 2-3 weeks
C. 2-3 months
D. 2-3 years

p. 384
Emotional Development
Level: Easy
Type: Factual
Ans: C

96. Emotional development is an interaction among:
A. temperament and cognitions
B. maturation and norms for development
C. genetic, cognitive and cultural factors
D. cephalocaudal and proximodistal principles

p. 384
Emotional Development
Level: Easy
Type: Factual
Ans: D

97. In the weeks shortly after birth, infants showed signs of all of the following except:
A. sadness
B. interest
C. distress
D. guilt

p. 384
Emotional Development
Level: Easy
Type: Factual
Ans: C

98. Within 1 year after birth, children will show signs of all of the following except:
A. sadness
B. anger
C. guilt
D. shyness

p. 384
Emotional Development
Level: Moderate
Type: Applied
Ans: A

99. One-month-old Zachary cries and fusses a great deal when the pediatrician gives him a shot. It can be predicted that at 4 months of age:
A. Zachary will still show a great deal of anger when given a shot
B. Zachary's anger will lessen as he becomes more emotionally mature
C. the amount of anger Zachary displays will have changed, but no one knows in what direction
D. Zachary will actually enjoy his trips to the pediatrician

p. 384
Emotional Development
Level: Moderate
Type: Applied
Ans: D

100. Garrison is an infant with a fearful temperament. His parents know that his temperament can change if:
A. he can interact with children his own age
B. Garrison is allowed to express his fear
C. they seek professional help
D. they can provide consistent support

p. 385
Emotional Development
Level: Easy
Type: Factual
Ans: D

101. Tina is introducing her topic by saying, "Today I will be talking about the fundamental emotional bond that develops between the infant and the caregiver." What is the topic of her presentation?
A. psychosocial development
B. closeness
C. temperament
D. attachment

p. 385
Emotional Development
Level: Easy
Type: Factual
Ans: C

102. Which of the following individuals has contributed to our understanding of attachment?
A. Eleanor Gibson
B. Jean Piaget
C. Mary Ainsworth
D. Carol Jacklin

p. 385
Emotional Development
Level: Moderate
Type: Factual
Ans: D

103. Which of the following behaviors is most often associated with the emergence of social attachment in infancy?
A. The child becomes able to focus on objects about seven inches away from the face.
B. The child learns to walk.
C. The child learns his or her first words.
D. The child demonstrates social smiling.

p. 385
Emotional Development
Level: Easy
Type: Applied
Ans: C

104. Baby Michael has just started to smile when his father or mother enters the room, but he does this for no one else. It is likely that Michael is:
A. 1 week old
B. between 4 and 6 weeks old
C. 6 months old
D. 9 months old

p. 385
Emotional Development
Level: Easy
Type: Applied
Ans: C

105. Jane and John were always able to leave baby Rebecca with a baby-sitter, but now, at 6 months of age, she begins to cry loudly when they leave. This separation anxiety indicates that Rebecca:
A. is somewhat retarded in her development
B. must have suffered some type of birth defect
C. has formed a social attachment with her parents
D. will be a child who always clings to her parents

p. 385
Emotional Development
Level: Easy
Type: Applied
Ans: A
www

106. When 1-year-old Terrace is in new surroundings, he will explore freely if his mother watches him. If she leaves the room he begins to cry, but when she returns he smiles and stops fussing. Terrace would be considered a(n) _____ infant.
A. securely attached
B. insecurely attached
C. unattached
D. disturbed

p. 385
Emotional Development
Level: Moderate
Type: Factual
Ans: A

107. One difference between a securely attached infant and one who is insecurely attached is that securely attached infants:
A. explore their environments more freely
B. nurse less
C. show more indifference toward their principal caretakers
D. are less active and alert

p. 385
Emotional Development
Level: Moderate
Type: Factual
Ans: C

108. With regard to attachment, which statement is true?
A. Insecurely attached infants explore their environments more freely.
B. Secure attachment is associated with poor relationships.
C. Secure attachment is associated with mother's sensitivity and responsiveness to the infant.
D. Attachment appears to have no significant long-term effects.

p. 386
Research Focus:
  Temperament
Level: Easy
Type: Factual
Ans: A

109. A study in which the same group of individuals is repeatedly studied across many years is known as a _____ study.
A. longitudinal
B. multilevel
C. repetitional
D. cross-sectional

p. 386
Research Focus:
  Temperament
Level: Moderate
Type: Applied
Ans: D

110. A group of children are initially interviewed at age 7 and then reinterviewed every 7 years until age 28. This is the _____ type of study.
A. multilevel
B. cross-sectional
C. repetitional
D. longitudinal

p. 386
Research Focus:
  Temperament
Level: Easy
Type: Factual
Ans: C

111. The fact that researchers must wait many years for their subjects to grow older, and that subjects may drop out of the study for a variety of reasons, are disadvantages of:
A. cross-sectional designs
B. amniocentesis
C. longitudinal methods
D. the nature-nurture question

p. 386
Research Focus:
  Temperament
Level: Easy
Type: Factual
Ans: D

112. Which of the following is a disadvantage in the use of a longitudinal study in developmental research?
A. It only allows for immediate comparisons of developmental differences.
B. It does not allow for assessment of long-term developmental patterns.
C. It does not focus on the same subjects.
D. Over time some of the subjects may drop out.

p. 386
Research Focus:
  Temperament
Level: Easy
Type: Factual
Ans: D

113. A study in which a group of individuals of different ages is studied at the same time is a _____ study.
A. longitudinal
B. multilevel
C. repetitional
D. cross-sectional

p. 386
Research Focus:
  Temperament
Level: Moderate
Type: Applied
Ans: D

114. You are reviewing a study of emotional development. After you have read it, you wonder if the subjects will remain the same or change across time. You are reading a study using the _____ method.
A. longitudinal
B. multilevel
C. repetitional
D. cross-sectional

p. 386
Research Focus:
  Temperament
Level: Easy
Type: Factual
Ans: D

115. A disadvantage of the cross-sectional method is that:
A. subjects tend to drop out of the study
B. it is difficult to track people over several years
C. it prevents the study of people across the life-span
D. it does not examine the development in each person over time

p. 386
Research Focus:
  Temperament
Level: Easy
Type: Factual
Ans: B

116. Kagan, in his study of fear reactions, identified two distinct temperaments which are called:
A. slow-to-warm-up and warm
B. inhibited and fearless
C. easy and difficult
D. mature and immature

p. 386
Research Focus:
  Temperament
Level: Easy
Type: Applied
Ans: B

117. Two-year-old Jeremy is cautious, tentative, and shy in new situations. Jeremy would be considered a(n) _____ child.
A. unemotional
B. inhibited
C. uninhibited
D. problem

p. 387
Research Focus:
  Temperament
Level: Easy
Type: Factual
Ans: C

118. Which statement is <u>incorrect</u> regarding inhibited and uninhibited children?
A. There is no difference between these two groups in IQ scores.
B. About 10-15% of the population have an inhibited temperament.
C. 90% of children do not change their temperament.
D. There is a strong genetic component in the inhibited temperament.

p. 387
Research Focus:
  Temperament
Level: Easy
Type: Factual
Ans: B

119. According to Kagan, what percentage of children retained their temperament from the ages of 21 months to 7 years?
A. 23%
B. 50%
C. 79%
D. 91%

p. 387
Research Focus:
  Temperament
Level: Easy
Type: Factual
Ans: D

120. According to Kagan, what are the two main temperaments?
A. introverted and extroverted
B. internal and external
C. primary and secondary
D. inhibited and uninhibited

p. 387
Research Focus:
  Temperament
Level: Easy
Type: Applied
Ans: A

121. Sophia is a very shy and inhibited six-year-old. What should her parents do?
A. provide her with support and encouragement
B. show their anger at her shyness
C. nothing - she'll outgrow it
D. protect her from any situation that may prove to be anxiety-provoking

p. 387
Research Focus:
  Temperament
Level: Easy
Type: Applied
Ans: C

122. Zach is 20 years old, but when he was two years old, he was classified as being fearful. Based on the study described in the module, what would occur in his brain when viewing a novel face?
A. His prefrontal cortex would be less active than normal.
B. His prefrontal cortex would be more active than normal.
C. His amygdala would be more active than normal.
D. His amygdala would be less active than normal.

p. 388
Cognitive Development
Level: Easy
Type: Conceptual
Ans: A

123. Your five-year-old nephew thinks about and understands the world differently than you do. This difference illustrates:
A. cognitive development
B. nature versus nurture
C. social development
D. accommodation

p. 388
Cognitive Development
Level: Easy
Type: Factual
Ans: D

124. Which of the following theorists studied the cognitive development of children?
A. Sigmund Freud
B. Erik Erikson
C. Carroll Izard
D. Jean Piaget

p. 388
Cognitive Development
Level: Easy
Type: Factual
Ans: B

125. The work of Jean Piaget led to the current view that children:
A. do not hypothesize about the world
B. are actively involved in their cognitive development
C. accommodate as a result of assimilation
D. solve abstract problems in the sensorimotor stage

p. 388
Cognitive Development
Level: Easy
Type: Factual
Ans: C

126. Piaget argued that a child acts like a(n):
A. uncivilized and unregulated individual
B. bucket holding knowledge and wisdom
C. tiny scientist making hypotheses about how the world works
D. computer attempting to solve problems

p. 388
Cognitive Development
Level: Easy
Type: Conceptual
Ans: C
PS/SG 17-12

127. The essence of Piaget's theory of cognitive development is that:
A. through thousands and thousands of mistakes, the child gradually builds a factual picture of the world
B. a child's picture of the world is slowly, gradually shaped by a steady succession of learning experiences
C. each stage is characterized by a distinctly different way of understanding the world
D. the mind of a child is like the mind of an adult - there just isn't as much information in it

p. 388
Cognitive Development
Level: Easy
Type: Factual
Ans: A
*www*

128. Piaget called the incorporation of new objects into existing knowledge:
A. assimilation
B. object permanence
C. conservation
D. formal operations

p. 388
Cognitive Development
Level: Moderate
Type: Applied
Ans: D

129. A parent throws a beach ball to a young child. After a few throws, the parent switches to a smaller plastic ball. If the child assimilates, she will:
A. adjust her hands to the size of the ball but not the new weight
B. adjust her hands to the new weight of the ball but not the new size
C. wait until her parent throws the beach ball again
D. try to catch the plastic ball the same way she tried to catch the beach ball

p. 388
Cognitive Development
Level: Moderate
Type: Applied
Ans: B

130. An infant is being weaned to drink out of a cup. She continues to suck the cup as if sucking on her mother's breast. This best illustrates:
A. accommodation
B. assimilation
C. preoperations
D. conservation

p. 388
Cognitive Development
Level: Easy
Type: Factual
Ans: D
*PS/SG 17-11*

131. For Jean Piaget, children deal with and adjust to the world through twin processes he called:
A. conservation and revisionism
B. motor learning and cognitive learning
C. egocentric thinking and magical thinking
D. assimilation and accommodation

p. 388
Cognitive Development
Level: Moderate
Type: Applied
Ans: D

132. A three-year-old sees a skunk, but calls it a "kitty." This best illustrates:
A. maturation
B. conservation
C. accommodation
D. assimilation

p. 388
Cognitive Development
Level: Easy
Type: Factual
Ans: C

133. When existing knowledge is changed because of new information being assimilated, the process called _____ has taken place.
A. assimilation
B. object permanence
C. accommodation
D. conservation

p. 388
Cognitive Development
Level: Moderate
Type: Applied
Ans: B

134. A child is used to riding her own bicycle. Then she tries her friend's bike, which is slightly larger. Piaget would call the changes she makes in her riding when she tries to ride her friend's bike:
A. assimilation
B. accommodation
C. adjustment
D. insight

p. 388
Cognitive Development
Level: Easy
Type: Factual
Ans: C

135. Which of the following is the correct sequence for Piaget's cognitive stages?
A. preoperational, formal operations, sensorimotor, concrete operations
B. preoperational, permanent operations, egocentrism, formal operations
C. sensorimotor, preoperational, concrete operations, formal operations
D. sensorimotor, egocentrism, concrete operations, permanent operations

p. 389
Cognitive Development
Level: Easy
Type: Factual
Ans: D

136. Piaget called the knowledge that an object continues to exist even after it has been removed from view:
A. existential constancy
B. substance constancy
C. item memory
D. object permanence

p. 389
Cognitive Development
Level: Easy
Type: Factual
Ans: A
*PS/SG 17-13*

137. The concept of object permanence develops during the _____ stage.
A. sensorimotor
B. preoperational
C. concrete operations
D. formal operations

p. 389
Cognitive Development
Level: Moderate
Type: Applied
Ans: C

138. Hannah is playing with her 7-month-old niece, Elie. She rolls a toy truck toward her and she tries to roll it back. One time the truck rolls behind a chair and is out of sight. Elie seems to forget about the truck and about the game they had both enjoyed playing. This is because Elie has not achieved:
A. conservation
B. sensorimotor memory
C. object permanence
D. egocentrism

p. 389
Cognitive Development
Level: Easy
Type: Factual
Ans: C

139. Children begin to use words to think about things that are out of sight during the _____ stage.
A. object permanence
B. conservation
C. preoperational
D. formal operations

p. 389
Cognitive Development
Level: Easy
Type: Factual
Ans: B

140. Use of symbols such as words and mental images, simple problem solving and talking about things not present characterizes the:
A. sensorimotor stage
B. preoperational stage
C. classical stage
D. attachment stage

p. 389
Cognitive Development
Level: Easy
Type: Factual
Ans: A

141. The term conservation refers to the fact that:
A. the amount of a substance remains the same even though its shape changes
B. children see and think about the world from other people's viewpoints
C. infants interact with and learn about their environment through sensory experiences
D. symbols and words can be used to think about things that do not exist

p. 389
Cognitive Development
Level: Moderate
Type: Applied
Ans: B

142. A child is shown two identical balls of clay. Then an adult squashes one ball into a pancake shape. She then asks the child if one of the shapes contains more clay and the child answers, "Yes, the pancake does." In Piagetian terms, the child has not yet reached:

A. sensorimotor stage
B. concrete operations stage
C. object permanence
D. decentricity

p. 389
Cognitive Development
Level: Moderate
Type: Applied
Ans: C

143. Mothers learn quickly that when serving ice cream to siblings, they must put the ice cream in identically sized bowls. Even if the same amount of ice cream is scooped out in front of the children, putting ice cream in a large bowl will make it appear that there is less ice cream than if it is in a smaller bowl, and this will surely generate arguments. This is because young children do not demonstrate which of the following?

A. egocentrism
B. object permanence
C. conservation
D. assimilation

p. 389
Cognitive Development
Level: Easy
Type: Applied
Ans: D
PS/SG 17-14

144. Watching juice poured from a short, wide glass into a tall, narrow glass, the child cries, "I want [the tall] glass!" thus illustrating the problem of:

A. object permanence
B. egocentric thinking
C. classification
D. conservation

p. 389
Cognitive Development
Level: Easy
Type: Factual
Ans: B

145. _____ refers to seeing and thinking of the world from your own viewpoint and having difficulty appreciating another's viewpoint.

A. Egotistical thinking
B. Egocentric thinking
C. Conceited thinking
D. Conservation

p. 389
Cognitive Development
Level: Moderate
Type: Applied
Ans: B

146. Kerry is talking to his grandfather about Kerry's father and says: "He can't be your son because he is my father!" This inability to see a situation from another person's point of view is called:

A. egotistical thinking
B. egocentric thinking
C. conceited thinking
D. conservation

p. 389
Cognitive Development
Level: Moderate
Type: Applied
Ans: C
www

147. Kerry is talking to his grandfather about Kerry's father and says: "He can't be your son because he is my father!" This inability to see a situation from another person's point of view indicates that Kerry is in which stage of cognitive development?

A. formal operations
B. sensorimotor
C. preoperational
D. concrete operations

p. 390
Cognitive Development
Level: Moderate
Type: Factual
Ans: A

148. During the _____ stage of cognitive development, children are capable of logical mental operations but only on physically present objects.
A. concrete operations
B. sensorimotor
C. preoperational
D. formal

p. 390
Cognitive Development
Level: Moderate
Type: Factual
Ans: D

149. During the concrete operations stage, children can figure out relationships between:
A. hypothetical objects and situations
B. imaginary objects
C. abstract concepts
D. objects which are physically present

p. 390
Cognitive Development
Level: Moderate
Type: Factual
Ans: C

150. You need to sort toys based upon their use and age. What stage of cognitive development would a child have to be in before they would be able to do this kind of classification?
A. sensorimotor
B. preoperational
C. concrete operations
D. primary

p. 390
Cognitive Development
Level: Easy
Type: Factual
Ans: C

151. According to Piaget, the ability to solve problems in a logical manner is characteristic of which of the following stages?
A. concrete operations
B. preoperational
C. formal operations
D. sensorimotor

p. 390
Cognitive Development
Level: Moderate
Type: Applied
Ans: D

152. Lisa asks her 9-year-old daughter Erica the following hypothetical question: "How would the world change if people woke up tomorrow and discovered they could fly?" Erica immediately responded: "But people can't fly!". Erica's answer indicates that she has not reached the stage of:
A. conservation
B. preoperations
C. concrete operations
D. formal operations

p. 390
Cognitive Development
Level: Easy
Type: Factual
Ans: D

153. In what stage can an individual consider abstract ideas and hypothetical concepts?
A. conservation
B. preoperations
C. concrete operations
D. formal operations

p. 390
Cognitive Development
Level: Moderate
Type: Applied
Ans: A

154. Joan is older than Helen. Helen is older than Chris. Joan is (older/younger) than Chris. To solve this problem, a child must have reached which of the following stages?
A. formal operations
B. sensorimotor
C. preoperational
D. concrete operations

p. 391
Cognitive Development
Level: Moderate
Type: Applied
Ans: D

155. A friend with a 3-year-old child has decided to try to accelerate the child's cognitive development by teaching him how to conserve and handle hypothetical problems. The friend's attempts are:
A. a waste of time since the child will not develop faster than the Piagetian stages dictate
B. potentially harmful to the child's self-esteem and psychological well-being
C. going to work only if she is a skilled teacher of preschoolers
D. plausible because preoperational children have been able to do such problems after simplification of instructions

p. 391
Cognitive Development
Level: Easy
Type: Factual
Ans: B

156. Evaluations of Piaget's theory have suggested that:
A. children are passive participants in their cognitive development
B. his stages are not as rigid as he proposed
C. cognitive development should not be divided into subareas for research
D. the order in which cognitive skills are acquired is not affected by culture

p. 391
Cognitive Development
Level: Moderate
Type: Factual
Ans: C

157. Research has indicated that children can complete some tasks earlier than Piaget had theorized if the:
A. child has developed egocentric thinking
B. child has attended day care
C. tasks are presented in different ways
D. tasks involve gender schemas

p. 391
Cognitive Development
Level: Moderate
Type: Conceptual
Ans: A

158. If Piaget could revise his theory of cognitive development, what might he have changed?
A. genetics and the environment influence cognitive abilities
B. children have less long-term memory
C. children are only passively involved in their own cognitive development
D. stages of cognitive development are fixed

p. 391
Cognitive Development
Level: Easy
Type: Factual
Ans: A

159. Piaget's theory has been criticized for:
A. not explaining why the thinking of children changes
B. overemphasizing unconscious conflicts
C. ignoring the role of cultural factors in personality development
D. being too narrow in describing cognitive development

p. 391
Cognitive Development
Level: Easy
Type: Factual
Ans: C

160. According to the module, a three-year old child who is rated high in seeking stimulation will:
A. develop a fearful temperament later in life
B. score lower IQ scores than children rated low in stimulation seeking
C. score higher IQ scores than children rated low in stimulation seeking
D. develop a fearless temperament later in life

p. 392
Social Development
Level: Easy
Type: Factual
Ans: B

161. According to the textbook, developing a sense of self is a focus of _____ development.
A. cognitive
B. social
C. emotional
D. temperament

| | | |
|---|---|---|
| p. 392<br>Social Development<br>Level: Easy<br>Type: Factual<br>Ans: A | 162. | A child's primary goal is to satisfy desires associated with innate biological needs. This statement is characteristic of the theory of: |
| | A. | Sigmund Freud |
| | B. | Jean Piaget |
| | C. | Erik Erikson |
| | D. | Albert Bandura |

| | | |
|---|---|---|
| p. 392<br>Social Development<br>Level: Easy<br>Type: Factual<br>Ans: C | 163. | A key component of Freud's psychosexual theory is _____ between child and parent. |
| | A. | mutual respect |
| | B. | communication |
| | C. | conflict |
| | D. | love |

| | | |
|---|---|---|
| p. 392<br>Social Development<br>Level: Easy<br>Type: Factual<br>Ans: B | 164. | If an individual's wishes are overgratified or undergratified at any particular psychosexual stage, Freud would argue that _____ will occur. |
| | A. | projection |
| | B. | fixation |
| | C. | displacement |
| | D. | Freudian slips |

| | | |
|---|---|---|
| p. 392<br>Social Development<br>Level: Easy<br>Type: Factual<br>Ans: D<br>*www* | 165. | Which of the following is the correct order of psychosexual stages according to Freud? |
| | A. | projection, fixation, displacement, genital |
| | B. | anal, oral, latency, phallic, genital |
| | C. | sensorimotor, preoperational, concrete, formal |
| | D. | oral, anal, phallic, latency, genital |

| | | |
|---|---|---|
| p. 392<br>Social Development<br>Level: Easy<br>Type: Factual<br>Ans: A | 166. | The first of Freud's stages of psychosexual development is called the: |
| | A. | oral stage |
| | B. | anal stage |
| | C. | genital stage |
| | D. | undifferentiated stage |

| | | |
|---|---|---|
| p. 392<br>Social Development<br>Level: Moderate<br>Type: Applied<br>Ans: A | 167. | Oscar's mother refused to breast feed him when he was an infant. Today, Oscar talks all the time, chews his pencils, and chain-smokes. Freud would say that Oscar is: |
| | A. | fixated at the oral stage |
| | B. | utilizing the defense mechanism of rationalization |
| | C. | ignoring the needs of his id |
| | D. | overly dependent on the reality principle |

| | | |
|---|---|---|
| p. 392<br>Social Development<br>Level: Easy<br>Type: Factual<br>Ans: A | 168. | The second of Freud's stages of psychosexual development is called the: |
| | A. | anal stage |
| | B. | oral stage |
| | C. | genital stage |
| | D. | undifferentiated stage |

p. 392
Social Development
Level: Moderate
Type: Applied
Ans: C

169. Steven and Joe are very bad roommates. Steven is incredibly disorganized and messy while Joe is compulsive in his work and insists that the room be completely tidy at all times. According to Freud, it is possible that both Steven and Joe are fixated at the _____ stage.
A. oral
B. phallic
C. anal
D. latency

p. 392
Social Development
Level: Easy
Type: Applied
Ans: C

170. Five-year-old Bethany wants very much to please her Daddy while competing with her mother. Bethany, according to Freud's psychosexual stages, is in the _____ stage.
A. oral
B. anal
C. phallic
D. latency

p. 392
Social Development
Level: Easy
Type: Applied
Ans: D

171. Seven-year-old Noelle only plays with girls, thinks that boys are weird, and attends second grade. She is most likely in which of Freud's psychosexual stages?
A. oral
B. anal
C. phallic
D. latency

p. 392
Social Development
Level: Easy
Type: Factual
Ans: C

172. In Freud's psychosexual stages, when do sexual thoughts become repressed?
A. oral
B. anal
C. latency
D. genital

p. 392
Social Development
Level: Easy
Type: Factual
Ans: A

173. The final psychosexual stage, during which the adolescent experiences sexual feelings toward others, is called the _____ stage.
A. genital
B. phallic
C. latency
D. oral

p. 392
Social Development
Level: Easy
Type: Factual
Ans: A
*www*

174. Twelve-year-old Katelyn has started thinking more and more about boys. In which stage is Katelyn most likely?
A. genital
B. phallic
C. latency
D. oral

| | | |
|---|---|---|
| p. 393<br>Social Development<br>Level: Easy<br>Type: Factual<br>Ans: C | 175.<br>A.<br>B.<br>C.<br>D. | In his theory of development, Erik Erikson focused on:<br>observation<br>resiliency<br>psychosocial issues<br>psychosexual issues |
| p. 393<br>Social Development<br>Level: Easy<br>Type: Factual<br>Ans: A | 176.<br>A.<br>B.<br>C.<br>D. | According to Erikson, the first major task of the child is to:<br>develop basic trust<br>form an intimate attachment with another person<br>become independent of the principal caretaker<br>overcome natural feelings of shame |
| p. 393<br>Social Development<br>Level: Moderate<br>Type: Applied<br>Ans: A | 177.<br><br><br>A.<br>B.<br>C.<br>D. | Two-year-old Brian wants to try to eat and dress himself without his mother's help. According to Erikson, these behaviors reflect which psychosocial stage?<br>autonomy vs. shame<br>initiative vs. guilt<br>intimacy vs. isolation<br>trust vs. mistrust |
| p. 393<br>Social Development<br>Level: Easy<br>Type: Factual<br>Ans: B | 178.<br><br>A.<br>B.<br>C.<br>D. | If the parents of the four-year-old boy encourage his ability to plan, he will successfully resolve the _____ stage.<br>autonomy vs. shame<br>initiative vs. guilt<br>intimacy vs. isolation<br>trust vs. mistrust |
| p. 393<br>Social Development<br>Level: Moderate<br>Type: Applied<br>Ans: C | 179.<br><br>A.<br>B.<br>C.<br>D. | Peter is a seven-year-old. According to Erikson's theory, if Peter has problems in school and is unable to direct his energy, he is likely to:<br>feel ashamed of his abilities and give up<br>develop feelings of guilt<br>develop a feeling of inferiority<br>lose trust in his parents and teachers |
| p. 393<br>Social Development<br>Level: Moderate<br>Type: Applied<br>Ans: B | 180.<br><br>A.<br>B.<br>C.<br>D. | "I don't know what I want to be. Whatever it is, I know I'll have to grow up some." According to Erikson, this individual is experiencing:<br>resiliency state<br>identity vs. role confusion<br>anal stage<br>industry vs. inferiority |
| p. 393<br>Social Development<br>Level: Easy<br>Type: Factual<br>Ans: B | 181.<br>A.<br>B.<br><br>C.<br>D. | Which of the following is true of Erikson's theory:<br>resolving the conflict at one stage enables individuals to skip the next stage<br>one can compensate at a later stage for some problem left over from a previous stage<br>the first five years of life are the most critical<br>each stage builds on the others |

p. 393
Social Development
Level: Easy
Type: Factual
Ans: D
*PS/SG 17-18*

182. Perhaps the most attractive aspect of Erikson's theory is that he sees development as:

A. packed into the formative years, so that a happy child almost automatically becomes a happy adult
B. biologically predetermined in a positive direction, so that only extreme trauma results in negative personality traits
C. arising from a foundation of essential human goodness and positiveness
D. continuing throughout life, with many opportunities for reworking and rebuilding personality traits

p. 393
Social Development
Level: Moderate
Type: Factual
Ans: C

183. Psychologists have evaluated Erikson's psychosocial theory. Many psychologists agree with Erikson that:

A. the formation of personality ceases around 35 years
B. sexuality plays a significant role in development
C. personality development continues into middle adulthood
D. a substitute caregiver can increase a child's resiliency

p. 393
Social Development
Level: Moderate
Type: Factual
Ans: D

184. Freud's theory of development has been criticized for:

A. suggesting that development continues into adulthood
B. ignoring the role that pleasure plays in psychosexual development
C. emphasizing social factors
D. emphasizing childhood sexuality

p. 393
Social Development
Level: Moderate
Type: Factual
Ans: A

185. Both Freud's and Erikson's theories have been criticized for being _____ and not _____.

A. descriptive; explanatory
B. explanatory; descriptive
C. specific; general
D. general; specific

p. 394
Social Development
Level: Easy
Type: Factual
Ans: D

186. The influence of learning via imitation and observation on social development is central to:

A. Freud's psychosexual stages
B. Erikson's psychosocial stages
C. Piaget's theory of cognitive development
D. Bandura's social cognitive theory

p. 394
Social Development
Level: Easy
Type: Factual
Ans: D

187. Scotty, a six-year-old, asks his dad if they could buy some power tools. Scotty enjoys watching his dad work with wood. Which theoretical perspective would explain Scotty's behavior by focusing on modeling?

A. Freud's psychosexual stages
B. Erikson's psychosocial stages
C. Piaget's theory of cognitive development
D. Bandura's social cognitive theory

p. 394
Social Development
Level: Moderate
Type: Factual
Ans: B

188. Psychological and environmental problems which place children at risk for later problems have an effect on:
A. norms for development
B. vulnerability
C. maturation
D. teratogens

p. 394
Social Development
Level: Easy
Type: Factual
Ans: D

189. A number of factors have been identified that decrease the impact of life stresses. These factors are referred to as:
A. assimilation
B. conservation
C. androgyny
D. resiliency

p. 394
Social Development
Level: Easy
Type: Factual
Ans: A

190. The current research on resiliency has cast doubt on Freud's belief that:
A. traumatic events always lead to emotional problems
B. the id and superego battle with each other
C. the unconscious mind influences behavior
D. defense mechanisms protect the ego

p. 394
Social Development
Level: Easy
Type: Factual
Ans: A

191. Which of the following is a factor associated with resiliency in children?
A. positive temperaments
B. androgyny
C. aggression
D. conservation

p. 394
Social Development
Level: Easy
Type: Factual
Ans: B
PS/SG 17-20

192. Which of the following is not an essential ingredient of resiliency?
A. a positive temperament
B. parents free from mental and financial problems
C. a substitute caregiver
D. social support from peers

p. 394
Social Development
Level: Easy
Type: Factual
Ans: B

193. Children who have received social support are more likely to experience:
A. vulnerability
B. resiliency
C. androgyny
D. bidirectionality

p. 395
Social Development
Level: Easy
Type: Applied
Ans: C

194. Three-year-old Jenny knows she's a girl. Jenny's feeling and labeling as a female exemplifies:
A. gender role
B. sex typing
C. gender identity
D. gender orientation

p. 395
Social Development
Level: Easy
Type: Factual
Ans: B
PS/SG 17-21

195. When do you know whether you're a boy or a girl? The answer is:
A. early in the first year
B. between the ages of 2 and 3
C. when you first observe other kids (as in bathing) and notice the obvious anatomical differences
D. it's never really "learned" — it's something you always know

p. 395
Social Development
Level: Easy
Type: Factual
Ans: A

196. The combination of attitudes and behaviors considered appropriate and expected for a particular sex in a given culture is known as:
A.  gender role
B.  sex typing
C.  gender identity
D.  gender orientation

p. 395
Social Development
Level: Easy
Type: Applied
Ans: C

197. Denise instructs her six-year-old daughter to act like a young lady and to cross her legs when she sits on a chair. This expectation of behavior is an example of:
A.  androgynous beliefs
B.  dispositional traits
C.  gender roles
D.  gender stereotypes

p. 395
Social Development
Level: Easy
Type: Applied
Ans: C

198. Martha tries to join the school wrestling team. Her behavior is contrary to the typical female:
A.  cross-gender identity
B.  sexual identity
C.  gender role
D.  character role

p. 395
Social Development
Level: Easy
Type: Applied
Ans: A

199. According to Gary, being a man means playing football, going camping, and studying to become an engineer. Gary has developed a traditional:
A.  gender role
B.  gender trait
C.  dispositional trait
D.  androgynous trait

p. 395
Social Development
Level: Easy
Type: Factual
Ans: B

200. By what age do children develop a clear idea of which occupations are stereotypically for men and for women?
A.  3
B.  between ages 4 and 5
C.  6
D.  between ages 6 and 7

p. 395
Social Development
Level: Moderate
Type: Applied
Ans: D

201. When Amanda's parents had a party, Amanda imitated her mother's hostess behavior by carrying around a tray of cheese and crackers. The guest commented on what a good girl she was and that she was just like her mother. The idea that Amanda learns her gender through modeling and reinforcement is central to _____ theory.
A.  Freudian
B.  vicarious learning
C.  parent modeling
D.  social role

p. 395
Social Development
Level: Easy
Type: Factual
Ans: B

202. Social and cognitive influences on how we interpret, organize, and use information characterizes _____.
A. Freudian theory
B. social role theory
C. parent modeling model
D. affective-primary theory

p. 395
Social Development
Level: Easy
Type: Factual
Ans: B

203. "Boys will be boys and girls will be girls. Parents reward their children whenever they behave like they're supposed to." This statement reflects which theory of gender roles?
A. Freudian theory
B. social role theory
C. parent modeling model
D. affective-primary theory

p. 395
Social Development
Level: Moderate
Type: Conceptual
Ans: C

204. You are reading an article in a popular magazine. The article is on gender roles. As you read, you notice a statement that doesn't seem to be correct. Which is the incorrect statement?
A. Gender role is learned according to the social learning theory.
B. There are rules and knowledge about what are inappropriate gender behaviors.
C. Parents seldom reward children for their behaviors when they match traditional gender roles.
D. The cognitive development theory argues that children play an active role in their own gender role development.

p. 395
Social Development
Level: Moderate
Type: Applied
Ans: A

205. Through observation and practice, Brent has developed an image of what a boy should be like. He then sets out according to that image. This kind of analysis of gender-role acquisition is put forward by _____ theory.
A. cognitive developmental
B. Freudian
C. biological-physiological
D. nature-nurture

p. 395
Social Development
Level: Easy
Type: Factual
Ans: A

206. The idea of gender schema is important for the _____ theory.
A. cognitive developmental
B. Freudian
C. biological-physiological
D. nature-nurture

p. 396
Social Development
Level: Easy
Type: Factual
Ans: C

207. Social role theory stresses learning gender roles because of _____, while cognitive developmental theory emphasizes _____.
A. child-parent conflict; outside pressure
B. cognitive rules; social variables
C. outside pressure; cognitive rules
D. biological influences; cognitive rules

p. 396
Social Development
Level: Easy
Type: Factual
Ans: A

208. Which of the following has been found to be a reliable sex difference?
A. Boys tend to show more aggressive behaviors.
B. Boys tend to perform better on tests of verbal skills.
C. Girls tend to perform better on tests of spatial skills.
D. Girls tend to perform better on tasks involving math.

p. 396
Social Development
Level: Easy
Type: Factual
Ans: A

209. Recent research on gender differences has indicated that:
A. women process language in both sides of their brains
B. women process language only on the left side of the brains
C. women process language only on the right side of the brains
D. men process language in both sides of their brains

p. 396
Social Development
Level: Easy
Type: Factual
Ans: C

210. According to the module, the brain of a woman is wired more effectively for:
A. motor skills
B. problem solving
C. emotional experiences
D. mathematical operations

p. 396
Social Development
Level: Easy
Type: Factual
Ans: A

211. When processing words, females use _____; males use _____.
A. both sides of their brains; the left side of their brains
B. the left side of their brains; both sides of their brains
C. the right side of the brains; both sides of their brains
D. both sides of their brains; the right side of their brains

p. 399
Cultural Diversity:
  Gender Roles
Level: Easy
Type: Factual
Ans: A

212. According to research examining differences in gender roles around the world:
A. young children show much similarity in gender roles
B. young children show many differences in gender roles
C. western cultures show more similarity in gender roles than eastern cultures
D. cultures that emphasize strong family ties tend to show similarity in gender roles

p. 399
Cultural Diversity:
  Gender Roles
Level: Easy
Type: Factual
Ans: D

213. Gender differences are based upon traditional divisions of labor according to the:
A. cognitive developmental theory
B. psychosexual theory
C. evolutionary theory
D. social role theory

p. 399
Cultural Diversity:
  Gender Roles
Level: Easy
Type: Factual
Ans: C

214. Gender differences are based upon adaptation and survival according to the:
A. cognitive developmental theory
B. psychosexual theory
C. evolutionary theory
D. social role theory

p. 400
Application: Child Abuse
Level: Easy
Type: Factual
Ans: A
*www*

215. The most common type of child abuse is:
A. neglect
B. physical
C. sexual
D. emotional

| | | |
|---|---|---|
| p. 400<br>Application: Child Abuse<br>Level: Easy<br>Type: Factual<br>Ans: B | 216.<br><br>A.<br>B.<br>C.<br>D. | During a court trial involving child abuse, the evidence shows that the defendant knew the child. Is this common?<br>Yes – but only in about 50% of all cases<br>Yes – in about 99% of all cases<br>Yes – in about 60-70% of cases<br>No – it occurs in only about 10% of cases of child abuse |
| p. 400<br>Application: Child Abuse<br>Level: Easy<br>Type: Factual<br>Ans: B | 217.<br><br>A.<br>B.<br>C.<br>D. | International studies indicate that _____ of women have been sexually abused:<br>5%<br>7-36%<br>41-45%<br>63-72% |
| p. 401<br>Application: Child Abuse<br>Level: Easy<br>Type: Factual<br>Ans: A | 218.<br>A.<br>B.<br>C.<br>D. | Researchers suggest that child abuse may be a result of :<br>the principle of bidirectionality<br>psychosexual needs<br>gender schemas<br>the proximodistal principle |
| p. 401<br>Application: Child Abuse<br>Level: Easy<br>Type: Factual<br>Ans: C | 219.<br>A.<br>B.<br>C.<br>D. | The principle of bidirectionality states that:<br>children's emotions swing rather rapidly between extremes<br>mothers interact with their children in both play and caretaking<br>children's behaviors influence adults' behaviors and vice versa<br>the same caretaker treatment can produce entirely different behavior in different infants |
| p. 401<br>Application: Child<br> Abuse<br>Level: Easy<br>Type: Applied<br>Ans: B | 220.<br><br><br>A.<br>B.<br>C.<br>D. | Wendy has always been a healthy child. In contrast, Tricia battled with some serious infections and allergies in her first year of life. All other things being equal, Wendy is:<br>more at risk for child abuse<br>less at risk for child abuse<br>more likely to be left on her own early<br>less likely to be left on her own early |
| p. 401<br>Application: Child Abuse<br>Level: Easy<br>Type: Factual<br>Ans: D | 221.<br><br>A.<br>B.<br>C.<br>D. | Recent research has shown that child abuse can affect brain development. What is one finding?<br>The myelin surrounding neurons starts to deteriorate.<br>The prefrontal cortex's ability to make rational decisions becomes impaired.<br>The amygdala become more active even in unemotional situations.<br>There is a reduction in brain areas involved in processing emotional cues. |
| p. 401<br>Application: Child Abuse<br>Level: Easy<br>Type: Factual<br>Ans: C | 222.<br><br>A.<br>B.<br>C.<br>D. | What factor seems to help children make the best recovery from sexual abuse?<br>strong siblings who are not sexually abused themselves<br>a significant other like a friend or teacher who provides support and care<br>strong support and care from a caregiver<br>the father or stepfather apologizing for his behavior |

p. 401
Application: Child Abuse
Level: Easy
Type: Factual
Ans: B

223. According to your textbook, one goal of the treatment of parents who abuse their children is:
A. teaching children how to recognize the signs that predict abuse
B. overcoming the parent's personal problems
C. increasing self-concept
D. lowering vulnerability

p. 401
Application: Child Abuse
Level: Easy
Type: Factual
Ans: D
PS/SG 17-25

224. Treatment for child abuse involves at least two goals:
A. arresting the abusing parent and removing the child from the home
B. placing the child in a temporary foster home and enrolling the parent in counseling
C. teaching the parent to substitute verbal for physical punishment and helping the child learn how to read the parent's moods
D. overcoming the parent's personal problems and changing parent–child interactions

p. 401
Application: Child Abuse
Level: Easy
Type: Factual
Ans: C

225. Research on child abuse indicates that abusive behavior is a function of:
A. the parent's emotional immaturity
B. the child's inborn temperament
C. an interaction between the child and the parent
D. media pressure to have the "perfect" family

True/False

| T | | 1. | Nature refers to the role of genetic factors in development. |
|---|---|---|---|
| T | www | 2. | The embryonic stage is the second stage of prenatal development. |
| F | | 3. | A teratogen causes the disorder called amniocentesis. |
| F | | 4. | Only heavy drinking during pregnancy can cause problems. |
| T | www | 5. | The effects of FAS tend to continue into adulthood. |
| T | | 6. | The growth of the brain in the first two years of life is due to new nerve connections. |
| F | www | 7. | Newborns have an innate preference for bitter tasting things. |
| F | | 8. | By the time a child is about 1 year old, their visual abilities equals that of an adult. |
| T | www | 9. | "Head down" development is described in the cephalocaudal principle. |
| F | | 10. | Development of motor skills is determined solely by biology. |
| F | www | 11. | Secure attachment is associated with trust and dealing better with stress. |
| F | | 12. | The cross-sectional method follows the same people over time. |
| F | www | 13. | In the process of assimilation, the child changes old methods to adjust to a new situation. |
| T | | 14. | In formal operations, the person can think and solve abstract problems. |
| F | | 15. | Erikson focused on pleasure and sexual feelings in his stage theory. |
| T | | 16. | Positive temperaments contribute to resiliency in children. |
| F | | 17. | Unconscious motives play a primary role in social development according to social cognitive theory. |
| F | www | 18. | Gender identity refers to the traditional or stereotypical behaviors associated with males and females. |
| T | | 19. | The cognitive developmental theory suggests that gender schemas are used in shaping gender roles. |

| F |  | 20. | Women only use the left side of their brain compared to men in processing language. |
|---|---|---|---|
| T | www | 21. | Genetics accounts for about 50% of aggressive behavior. |
| T | www | 22. | Division of labor influences gender roles according to the social role theory. |
| T |  | 23. | The most common kind of abuse is neglect. |
| T |  | 24. | Most abused children are abused by people who know them. |
| F | www | 25. | The principle of bidirectionality has been suggested to explain attachment. |

Short-Answer Essay Questions

1. Why are developmental psychologists interested in the nature-nurture question? (*www*)
2. Describe the significant changes in germinal, embryonic, and fetal stages of prenatal development.
3. What are teratogens and why is development in the fetal stage most susceptible to them?
4. Describe the effects of smoking and alcohol on prenatal development. (*www*)
5. Present a summary of the sensory abilities of vision, hearing, and smell of a newborn.
6. Describe the proximodistal and cephalocaudal principles of development. (*www*)
7. Briefly summarize the important aspects of the four stages of cognitive development according to Piaget. (*www*)
8. Select three of Erikson's psychosocial stages and describe the social need in each stage.
9. What is resiliency? Describe the factors that contribute to it. (*www*)
10. Explain the principle of bidirectionality in describing the interaction between a parent and an abused child.

# Module 18 - Adolescence and Adulthood

p. 407
Introduction
Level: Easy
Type: Factual
Ans: A

1. The time of life characterized by many biological, personality, cognitive, and social changes between the ages of 12 and 18 is called:
   A. adolescence
   B. senesce
   C. transition
   D. matriculation

p. 407
Introduction
Level: Easy
Type: Conceptual
Ans: C
*PS/SG 18-1*

2. Rod Plotnik introduces us to the ambitious teen Brandi and the divorced former prom queen Susan in order to show that:
   A. teen Brandi lives a more turbulent life than adult Susan
   B. Brandi's personality is all over the place, while Susan's is calmer and more stable
   C. adolescence and adulthood are both periods of great change, as was childhood
   D. most change occurs in childhood, less in adolescence, and even less in adulthood

p. 407
Introduction
Level: Easy
Type: Applied
Ans: D

3. Heather is experiencing a transitional period in her life characterized by many biological, social, and cognitive changes. For example, Heather is experiencing the stage of identity versus role confusion. Heather is <u>most</u> likely in:
   A. an identity crisis
   B. a care orientation
   C. young adulthood
   D. adolescence

p. 407
Introduction
Level: Easy
Type: Factual
Ans: B
*www*

4. Researchers now believe that most adolescents:
   A. experience great psychological turmoil
   B. successfully negotiate their teenage years
   C. have many emotional problems
   D. pass on to postconventional moral development

p. 407
Introduction
Level: Moderate
Type: Applied
Ans: C

5. A new television show depicting an adolescent and his relationships with his family is described as being life-like. The program displays the adolescent as having a poor sense of self, aloof relationships with family members, and emotional problems. Being the well-educated psychology student that you are, your reaction to this program is that:
   A. most adolescents have a good sense of identity, but that their relationships with family tend to be poor
   B. adolescence is the worst time in life and this program describes it well
   C. it does not portray the majority of teenagers
   D. it does portray the majority of teenagers

p. 407
Introduction
Level: Easy
Type: Factual
Ans: C

6. Which statement most accurately describes the relationship between an adolescent and her family?
A. Adolescents do not get along with their families especially their parents.
B. Adolescents do not get along with their families especially younger siblings.
C. Adolescents maintain close relationships with their families.
D. Most adolescents have distant relationships with their parents and siblings.

p. 407
Introduction
Level: Easy
Type: Factual
Ans: A
*PS/SG 18-2*

7. Experts now believe that adolescence is not a period of:
A. great psychological turmoil
B. considerable biological, cognitive, and social changes
C. searching for personal identity
D. dramatic positive or negative changes in self-esteem

p. 407
Introduction
Level: Easy
Type: Factual
Ans: D

8. Adolescents are more concerned with _____ while adults are more concerned with _____.
A. physical appearance, finding their identities
B. finding their identities; physical appearance
C. making lots of money; finding a good job
D. finding their identities; establishing long-term relationships

p. 408
Puberty and Sexual Behavior
Level: Easy
Type: Factual
Ans: D

9. Puberty refers to:
A. the onset of formal operational thinking in adolescence
B. conventional moral development during adolescence
C. chronically low self-esteem which occurs in adolescence
D. the biological changes that happen during adolescence

p. 408
Puberty and Sexual Behavior
Level: Easy
Type: Applied
Ans: A

10. After returning from summer vacation, Phil notices that his teenage neighbor, Alexander, has begun to shave and his voice had deepened. Phil concludes that these changes are most likely due to:
A. puberty
B. Turner's syndrome
C. increased secretion of progesterone
D. increased secretion of estrogen

p. 408
Puberty and Sexual Behavior
Level: Moderate
Type: Factual
Ans: A

11. There is a sex difference between males and females as to when the biological changes of puberty typically occur. Females experience the changes between ages _____ and males between ages _____.
A. 9 and 13; 10 and 14
B. 10 and 14; 9 and 13
C. 7 and 9; 9 and 13
D. 13 and 16; 10 and 13

p. 408
Puberty and Sexual
  Behavior
Level: Easy
Type: Factual
Ans: D

12.	In girls, the growth spurt begins about _____ before the onset of breast development.
A.	1 month
B.	1-2 months
C.	3-6 months
D.	6-12 months

p. 408
Puberty and Sexual
  Behavior
Level: Easy
Type: Applied
Ans: A

13.	Kelley begins menstruating when she is 12. This beginning is called:
A.	menarche
B.	estrogen
C.	menopause
D.	periodicity

p. 408
Puberty and Sexual
  Behavior
Level: Easy
Type: Factual
Ans: C

14.	The first menstrual period is menarche and is triggered by the:
A.	limbic system
B.	thymus
C.	hypothalamus
D.	hippocampus

p. 408
Puberty and Sexual
  Behavior
Level: Easy
Type: Factual
Ans: C

15.	The pituitary is stimulated to produce hormones by the:
A.	brainstem
B.	ovaries or testes
C.	hypothalamus
D.	cerebral cortex

p. 408
Puberty and Sexual
  Behavior
Level: Easy
Type: Factual
Ans: B

16.	Sharon wonders what changes will occur in her daughter Nicole when she reaches puberty. Of the following, Sharon can expect that Nicole will experience:
A.	reduction in the size of the pituitary gland
B.	an increase in the production of estrogen
C.	subconscious homosexual tendencies
D.	increased blood flow to the vagina

p. 408
Puberty and Sexual
  Behavior
Level: Easy
Type: Factual
Ans: A
*www*

17.	The most important hormone in the development of female sexual characteristics is:
A.	estrogen
B.	progesterone
C.	testosterone
D.	lutenizing hormone

p. 408
Puberty and Sexual
  Behavior
Level: Easy
Type: Factual
Ans: B

18.	The onset of secondary sex characteristics in girls begins at about:
A.	10 years
B.	10.5 years
C.	11 years
D.	11.5 years

p. 408
Puberty and Sexual
  Behavior
Level: Easy
Type: Factual
Ans: C

19. Which of the following is not characteristic of early maturing girls?
A. more shyness
B. rate lower on social skills
C. more popular
D. try cigarettes and alcohol earlier

p. 408
Puberty and Sexual
  Behavior
Level: Easy
Type: Factual
Ans: D

20. Meg is an early maturing girl and has encountered some psychological problems. What does the textbook offer as an explanation for Meg's psychological problems?
A. She does not perceive herself to be attractive.
B. Her parents simply have not accepted the fact that she is growing up.
C. Her estrogen levels are too high, but will decrease once she becomes 15 or 16 years old.
D. She has not yet acquired adult personality traits and social skills.

p. 408
Puberty and Sexual
  Behavior
Level: Easy
Type: Conceptual
Ans: A
www

21. Who is most likely to be shy and introverted?
A. an early-maturing girl
B. a late-maturing girl
C. an early-maturing boy
D. a girl who has not experienced menarche

p. 408
Puberty and Sexual
  Behavior
Level: Easy
Type: Applied
Ans: C

22. Jill is a late maturer. Jane is an early maturer. Compared to Jill, we can expect that Jane will:
A. be more outgoing
B. have more poise
C. try cigarettes and alcohol earlier
D. have a major psychological advantage

p. 408
Puberty and Sexual
  Behavior
Level: Easy
Type: Factual
Ans: C

23. In boys, the growth spurt begins at about _____ years old.
A. 10-11
B. 11-12
C. 13-14
D. 15-16

p. 408
Puberty and Sexual
  Behavior
Level: Easy
Type: Factual
Ans: A
www

24. The production of sperm is triggered by the _____ which stimulates the _____.
A. hypothalamus; pituitary gland
B. pituitary gland; hypothalamus
C. testes; hypothalamus
D. testes; pituitary gland

p. 408
Puberty and Sexual
  Behavior
Level: Easy
Type: Applied
Ans: B

25. Cal is anxious to grow in height so that he can be a better basketball player. He is 10 years old. According to the average growth spurt, how much longer will Cal have to wait?
A. 1 year
B. 3 years
C. 6 years
D. 7 years

p. 408
Puberty and Sexual
  Behavior
Level: Easy
Type: Applied
Ans: A

26. Stanley is 14 and has yet to reach puberty. When he does, we can expect he will experience:
A. an increase in the production of testosterone
B. a reduction in the size of the pituitary gland
C. subconscious homosexual tendencies
D. reduced blood flow to the penis

p. 408
Puberty and Sexual
  Behavior
Level: Easy
Type: Factual
Ans: C

27. The most important hormone in the development of male sexual characteristics is:
A. estrogen
B. progesterone
C. testosterone
D. lutenizing hormone

p. 408
Puberty and Sexual
  Behavior
Level: Easy
Type: Factual
Ans: B

28. Which of the following is an example of a male secondary sex characteristic?
A. production of estrogen
B. the voice change
C. production of testosterone
D. production of sperm

p. 408
Puberty and Sexual
  Behavior
Level: Easy
Type: Factual
Ans: A

29. Early-maturing boys have been found to have all of the following characteristics except:
A. greater dependence on parents
B. higher regard by peers
C. greater confidence
D. greater social responsibility

p. 408
Puberty and Sexual
  Behavior
Level: Easy
Type: Factual
Ans: D

30. Which of the following is generally found in late maturing boys?
A. a sense of social responsibility
B. a general feeling of relaxation
C. greater popularity with peers
D. lack of self-confidence

p. 408
Puberty and Sexual
  Behavior
Level: Easy
Type: Applied
Ans: A

31. Larry reached puberty at a relatively early age. Brent, on the other hand, matured late. It is likely that as a result of this difference:
A. Larry would be more self-confident than Brent during adolescence
B. Brent would be more self-confident than Larry during adolescence
C. Larry's advantages would be maintained throughout adulthood
D. Larry would be less socially responsible than Brent

p. 408
Puberty and Sexual
  Behavior
Level: Easy
Type: Applied
Ans: B
*www*

32. Bobby doesn't go through puberty until age 16. We can expect that compared to other boys his age, he will likely:
A. be more confident
B. have less self-esteem
C. feel less anxious
D. be more socially responsible

p. 408
Puberty and Sexual
  Behavior
Level: Moderate
Type: Factual
Ans: B

33. A sixth-grade teacher has some girls and boys who have reached puberty quite early. According to research, the girls and boys would:
A. differ in that the girls would benefit psychologically from their early maturation, whereas the boys would tend to suffer
B. differ in that the boys would benefit psychologically from their early maturation, whereas the girls would tend to suffer
C. both benefit psychologically from their early maturation
D. both suffer psychologically from their early maturation

p. 408
Puberty and Sexual
  Behavior
Level: Moderate
Type: Factual
Ans: C
*PS/SG 18-3*

34. When you compare the development of sexual maturity in girls and boys during puberty, you find that the changes are:
A. radically different in girls than in boys
B. gradual in girls but sudden in boys
C. essentially the same, but occur about two years earlier in girls
D. somewhat similar, except that the difference between a boy and a man is far greater than the difference between a girl and a woman

p. 408
Puberty and Sexual
  Behavior
Level: Moderate
Type: Factual
Ans: D

35. Studies that followed early and late maturers into adulthood have found:
A. the differences between early and late-maturing boys and girls increase with age
B. the differences between early and late-maturing boys increase with age, while the differences between early and late-maturing girls decrease with age
C. the differences between early and late-maturing girls increase with age, while the differences between early and late-maturing boys decrease with age
D. the differences between early and late-maturing boys and early and late-maturing girls both decrease with age

p. 408
Puberty and Sexual
  Behavior
Level: Easy
Type: Factual
Ans: C
*PS/SG 18-4*

36. In terms of enjoying a psychological advantage in adjustment, it is better to be a(n):
A. early maturing girl
B. late maturing girl
C. early maturing boy
D. late maturing boy

p. 408
Puberty and Sexual
  Behavior
Level: Easy
Type: Factual
Ans: B

37. Of the following, which perceive themselves to be more physically attractive?
A. girls
B. boys
C. early-maturing girls
D. late-maturing girls

p. 409
Puberty and Sexual
Behavior
Level: Easy
Type: Factual
Ans: A

38. According to a survey on sexual activity among teenage girls, most teenagers have their first sexual encounter:
A. earlier than what they consider to be the right time
B. later than what they consider to be the right time
C. close to what they consider to the right time
D. using contraceptives

p. 409
Puberty and Sexual
Behavior
Level: Easy
Type: Factual
Ans: B

39. Which of the following is not among the reasons why teenagers have sex according to a survey cited in your textbook?
A. physically attracted to their partner
B. wanted to become pregnant so they would have someone to love
C. curiosity
D. believed friends were having sex

p. 409
Puberty and Sexual
Behavior
Level: Easy
Type: Factual
Ans: C
www

40. Your textbook describes a model which views adolescent development as a process that involves sexual, cognitive, social, and personality changes which all influence each other. This model is called the:
A. Psychosocial model
B. Psychosexual model
C. BioPsychoSocial model
D. Cognitive Learning model

p. 409
Puberty and Sexual
Behavior
Level: Easy
Type: Factual
Ans: A

41. According to the BioPsychoSocial model, sexuality:
A. must be discussed in the context of the cognitive, personality, and emotional changes of the adolescent
B. is purely biological
C. in adolescents is decreasing because of the number of messages stressing abstinence
D. among teenagers is decreasing since more is known about AIDS

p. 409
Puberty and Sexual
Behavior
Level: Easy
Type: Factual
Ans: B
PS/SG 18-6

42. According to the BioPsychoSocial approach, problems of adolescent sexual behavior:
A. dominate adolescents' biology, their psychology, and their social lives
B. cannot be discussed independently of hormonal, cognitive, personality, or emotional factors
C. tend to be overrated, although they do have a minor effect on many parts of adolescents' lives
D. there is no "BioPsychoSocial" approach; this is a nonsense term

p. 409
Puberty and Sexual
Behavior
Level: Easy
Type: Factual
Ans: D

43. A new sex education class discusses sexuality in the context of cognitive, personality and social changes. The class emphasizes the _____ model.
A. Kohlberg's
B. social role
C. psychodynamic
D. BioPsychoSocial

| | | |
|---|---|---|
| p. 409<br>Puberty and Sexual<br>  Behavior<br>Level: Easy<br>Type: Applied<br>Ans: A | 44.<br><br><br>A.<br>B.<br>C.<br>D. | Rachel is always having arguments with her parents over seemingly trivial matters. Her parents view her as moody and quick to lose her composure. According to the textbook, Rachel's moodiness is the result of:<br>sex hormones<br>peer pressure<br>her parents' permissiveness<br>the stresses of school |
| p. 409<br>Puberty and Sexual<br>  Behavior<br>Level: Easy<br>Type: Factual<br>Ans: C | 45.<br><br>A.<br>B.<br>C.<br>D. | The percentage of adolescents becoming sexually active has changed from _____ in the early 1990s to _____ to the early 2000s.<br>12%; 21%<br>45%; 52%<br>53%; 45%<br>72%; 90% |
| p. 409<br>Puberty and Sexual<br>  Behavior<br>Level: Easy<br>Type: Factual<br>Ans: C | 46.<br><br>A.<br>B.<br>C.<br>D. | Of the following ages, which one is the median age for first intercourse among girls?<br>12.5<br>15.8<br>17.4<br>19.0 |
| p. 409<br>Puberty and Sexual<br>  Behavior<br>Level: Moderate<br>Type: Conceptual<br>Ans: D | 47.<br><br>A.<br>B.<br>C.<br>D. | Given the material on sexual behavior, parent-child interactions and onset of puberty, most parents would most probably prefer an adolescent who:<br>has a few close friends<br>matures on time<br>matures early<br>matures later |
| p. 409<br>Puberty and Sexual<br>  Behavior<br>Level: Moderate<br>Type: Conceptual<br>Ans: B | 48.<br><br><br><br>A.<br><br>B.<br>C.<br><br>D. | After reading an article about teenage sexuality in today's paper, Tom comments, "With the increase in sexual activity among teenagers, I'm just glad the vast majority of them use contraceptives." Comment on the validity of his statement.<br>Tom is wrong - there has been a decrease in sexual activity and most teenagers do not use contraceptives<br>Tom is wrong - about half of adolescents do not use contraceptives<br>Tom is wrong - there has been a decrease in sexual activity among teenagers<br>Tom is right |
| p. 409<br>Puberty and Sexual<br>  Behavior<br>Level: Moderate<br>Type: Factual<br>Ans: A | 49.<br><br>A.<br>B.<br>C.<br>D. | Based upon the material presented in the textbook, why is it more difficult now than 20 years ago to decide whether to become sexually active?<br>more exposure to sex in the media<br>less willingness on the part of parents to discuss sex<br>a growing movement to discourage abstinence until marriage<br>most teenagers are maturing faster than ever before |

p. 410
Cognitive and Emotional
 Changes
Level: Easy
Type: Factual
Ans: D

50.     How do most psychologists view adolescence?
A.      as a time of long-lasting stress
B.      adolescence is viewed as the most important time of life
C.      this is a period of life where the individual has the poorest relationships to authority figures
D.      a time for potential growth

p. 410
Cognitive and Emotional
 Changes
Level: Easy
Type: Factual
Ans: A

51.     The changes in your perception, thinking and understanding of the world through learning and genetic factors is called:
A.      cognitive development
B.      formal operations
C.      operational development
D.      postconventional moral reasoning

p. 410
Cognitive and Emotional
 Changes
Level: Easy
Type: Factual
Ans: D
*www*

52.     The stage of Piaget's theory of cognitive development that starts in adolescence and goes through adulthood is:
A.      postconventional
B.      accommodation
C.      preconventional
D.      formal operations

p. 410
Cognitive and Emotional
 Changes
Level: Easy
Type: Factual
Ans: C
*PS/SG 18-7*

53.     The stage during which adolescents develop the ability to think about abstract or hypothetical concepts and solve problems in a logical way is:
A.      Freud's stage three: the phallic stage
B.      Erikson's stage eight: integrity versus despair
C.      Piaget's stage four: formal operations
D.      Kohlberg's stage two: conventional level

p. 410
Cognitive and Emotional
 Changes
Level: Easy
Type: Factual
Ans: A

54.     Formal operational thought is characterized by:
A.      the ability to solve abstract problems
B.      feelings of high self-esteem
C.      conservation abilities
D.      postconventional moral reasoning

p. 410
Cognitive and Emotional
 Changes
Level: Easy
Type: Factual
Ans: B

55.     Adolescent self-descriptions change from things they are doing to their feelings and psychological states. This transition results from the development of _____ thinking.
A.      egocentric
B.      abstract
C.      postconventional
D.      authoritarian

p. 410
Cognitive and Emotional
 Changes
Level: Easy
Type: Factual
Ans: C

56.     Planning for one's future is characteristic of _____ thinking.
A.      concrete
B.      egocentric
C.      formal operational
D.      conventional

p. 410
Cognitive and Emotional
 Changes
Level: Moderate
Type: Factual
Ans: B

57.

A.
B.
C.
D.

Peter is about to enter formal operations, while his younger brother Bobby is in an earlier stage of development. What will Bobby notice about his brother?
a lack of egocentric thinking
more sophisticated conversations of abstract and hypothetical concepts
care orientation
postconventional moral reasoning

p. 410
Cognitive and Emotional
 Changes
Level: Moderate
Type: Factual
Ans: A

58.

A.

B.
C.
D.

Formal operations allow teenagers to:
critically consider their beliefs, attitudes, values, and a wide range of topics
become able to plan for their future
think independently of what others think
think rationally without emotion clouding their reasoning

p. 411
Cognitive and Emotional
 Changes
Level: Easy
Type: Factual
Ans: B

59.

A.
B.
C.
D.

At the mall you overhear several sixteen-year-olds talk about how a friend is having a big party with alcohol when their parents are gone for the weekend. You marvel at their immaturity and wonder how everyone could be that "stupid." What part of the adolescent's brain is still not fully developed and would account for making decisions and planning?
reticular formation
prefrontal cortex
cerebellum
hypothalamus

p. 411
Cognitive and Emotional
 Changes
Level: Easy
Type: Factual
Ans: D
PS/SG 18-8

60.

A.
B.
C.
D.

New research suggests that teenagers engage in irresponsible, risky behaviors because their:
beliefs include an irrational confidence in their invulnerability
limbic systems are still at a primitive level of development
brains are often "rewired" by alcohol and drug use
brains have underdeveloped executive functions but a well-developed emotional center

p. 411
Cognitive and Emotional
 Changes
Level: Easy
Type: Factual
Ans: C

61.

A.
B.
C.
D.

Larry's teenage daughter Kate is very moody and impulsive. As a psychologist, Larry understands that Kate's behavior is due to:
immature corpus callosum
immature hippocampus
growth in her limbic system
her postconventional thinking

p. 411
Cognitive and Emotional
 Changes
Level: Easy
Type: Factual
Ans: A

62.

A.
B.
C.
D.

What part of the brain is in the process of development in the adolescent and is believed to be responsible for risk taking and other poor decisions?
prefrontal cortex
hypothalamus
thalamus
corpus callosum

p. 411
Cognitive and Emotional
Changes
Level: Easy
Type: Factual
Ans: A

63. As the module describes, adolescents take risks. Why?
A. The executive control area is underdeveloped.
B. Conventional thinking limits their judgment.
C. Postconventional thinking limits their judgment.
D. The ability to think in abstractions limits their judgment.

p. 411
Cognitive and Emotional
Changes
Level: Moderate
Type: Factual
Ans: D

64. Gladys is 15 years old. She has just moved to a new high school. Someone dared her to get her nose pierced, and Gladys did. When asked why, she said that she just had to because of the dare. What is the best neurological explanation for her impulsiveness?
A. immature corpus callosum
B. immature reticular formation
C. her postconventional thinking
D. growth in her limbic system

p. 411
Cognitive and Emotional
Changes
Level: Moderate
Type: Applied
Ans: C
www

65. "Mom, you have no idea what it is like to grow up with young sisters who are brats! They get into my things all the time. You and Dad just don't understand!" This teenager is most likely experiencing:
A. preoperational thinking
B. conventional thinking
C. growth in her limbic system
D. authoritarian parenting

p. 411
Cognitive and Emotional
Changes
Level: Easy
Type: Factual
Ans: A

66. The prefrontal cortex acts as a(n):
A. executive manager
B. initiator of emotion
C. estimator of risk
D. relay switch for sensory messages

p. 411
Cognitive and Emotional
Changes
Level: Moderate
Type: Applied
Ans: C

67. Mike, at age 15, rides a dirt bike without a helmet. This thinking illustrates that:
A. he has not yet figured out what a risk is
B. he is in postconventional thinking
C. his prefrontal cortex is underdeveloped
D. he thinks in a self-centered way

p. 412
Cognitive and Emotional
Changes
Level: Easy
Type: Factual
Ans: D

68. The study of moral development is most associated with the work of:
A. Piaget
B. Erikson
C. Freud
D. Kohlberg

p. 412
Cognitive and Emotional
Changes
Level: Easy
Type: Factual
Ans: A

69. Kohlberg studied moral reasoning through the use of:
A. moral dilemmas
B. conservation tasks
C. telephone surveys
D. observations of parent-adolescent interactions

p. 412
Cognitive and Emotional
 Changes
Level: Easy
Type: Factual
Ans: A

70. The correct order of the stages of moral reasoning according to Kohlberg is:
A. preconventional, conventional, postconventional
B. preconservational, conservational, postconversational
C. sensorimotor, concrete, formal
D. primary, secondary, tertiary

p. 412
Cognitive and Emotional
 Changes
Level: Easy
Type: Applied
Ans: A

71. Sharon does not take a cookie out of Mom's cookie jar because she knows Mom will punish her if she does. Sharon is operating at which of Kohlberg's levels of moral development?
A. preconventional
B. conventional
C. postconventional
D. stage 4

p. 412
Cognitive and Emotional
 Changes
Level: Easy
Type: Applied
Ans: B

72. Should you break the speed limit? Someone from level 1 of moral reasoning would say:
A. no because it is against the law
B. no because you might get caught and punished
C. no because your parents and teachers taught you to obey the limit
D. maybe because it depends on the situation

p. 412
Cognitive and Emotional
 Changes
Level: Easy
Type: Factual
Ans: D

73. A major difference between stage 1 and stage 2 of moral development is that stage 2 focuses on:
A. punishment
B. reward
C. avoiding being caught
D. making a good deal

p. 412
Cognitive and Emotional
 Changes
Level: Moderate
Type: Applied
Ans: B

74. Robert is Italian. Although he wants to date Karen he does not because his parents want him to date only Italian girls and Karen is Irish. At which of Kohlberg's stages does Robert appear to be operating?
A. stage 2
B. stage 3
C. stage 4
D. stage 5

p. 412
Cognitive and Emotional
 Changes
Level: Moderate
Type: Applied
Ans: C
*www*

75. Phil is driving his wife, who is in labor, to the hospital. While his wife is about to deliver a baby, she yells to Phil to drive faster. Phil refuses and says, "It is against the law to speed." Phil is probably at what stage of moral reasoning?
A. stage 1
B. stage 2
C. stage 4
D. stage 5

p. 412
Cognitive and Emotional
 Changes
Level: Moderate
Type: Applied
Ans: D

*www*

76. Phil is driving his wife, who is in labor, to the hospital. While his wife is about to deliver a baby, she yells to Phil to drive faster. Phil does and is pulled over by the police. Phil yells to the officer, "It is more important to get my wife to hospital than to obey this law." Phil is probably at what stage of moral reasoning?
A. stage 1
B. stage 3
C. stage 4
D. stage 5

p. 412
Cognitive and Emotional
 Changes
Level: Moderate
Type: Applied
Ans: B

77. Tracy has just received her driver's license. If she is at the postconventional level of moral reasoning, she will obey the speed limit because:
A. she knows she will get caught and fined by the police if she speeds
B. reckless driving could endanger the safety of people and that would be wrong
C. she wants to be seen as responsible by her parents
D. society expects drivers to obey the law

p. 412
Cognitive and Emotional
 Changes
Level: Moderate
Type: Applied
Ans: D

78. Aaron is against abortion because he feels life is sacred in any form, and the taking of life is morally wrong, despite the fact that the law allows abortion. Aaron is operating at which level of moral development?
A. preconventional
B. conventional
C. anticonventional
D. postconventional

p. 412
Cognitive and Emotional
 Changes
Level: Easy
Type: Factual
Ans: A

79. The highest level of moral reasoning according to Kohlberg is:
A. postconventional
B. conventional
C. postformal
D. formal

p. 412
Cognitive and Emotional
 Changes
Level: Easy
Type: Factual
Ans: B

80. Research on Kohlberg's stages of moral development has found:
A. very little support for the accuracy of his claims
B. people in all cultures used moral reasoning typical of stages 1-4
C. men generally prefer a care orientation when making moral decisions
D. women generally prefer a justice orientation when making moral decisions

p. 412
Cognitive and Emotional
 Changes
Level: Moderate
Type: Factual
Ans: D

81. Which of the following is true of Kohlberg's theory of moral reasoning?
A. Four distinct levels of moral reasoning are identified.
B. Different people progress through the levels in different orders.
C. The conventional level is the highest level of moral reasoning.
D. Not all people reach the higher levels of moral development.

| | | |
|---|---|---|
| p. 412<br>Cognitive and Emotional<br> Changes<br>Level: Moderate<br>Type: Factual<br>Ans: B | 82.<br><br>A.<br><br>B.<br>C.<br><br>D. | Based on Kohlberg's research, which of the following is an accurate evaluation of his theory?<br>People from different cultures progress through the stages in different orders.<br>Moral reasoning is not always reflected in actual moral behavior.<br>Surveys indicate that college students rarely engage in blatantly immoral behaviors.<br>His data were based on research with male and female subjects. |
| p. 412<br>Cognitive and Emotional<br> Changes<br>Level: Moderate<br>Type: Factual<br>Ans: D | 83.<br><br>A.<br>B.<br>C.<br><br>D. | Which of the following has been mentioned as a criticism of Kohlberg's research on moral development?<br>The levels seem to occur only in America.<br>Controlled research studies do not support the theory.<br>Most studies do not support Kohlberg's claim that the stages are organized in a hierarchy.<br>His work does not take into account possible gender differences. |
| p. 412<br>Cognitive and Emotional<br> Changes<br>Level: Easy<br>Type: Applied<br>Ans: D | 84.<br><br>A.<br>B.<br>C.<br>D. | Marian says that she thinks about how her moral decisions will affect her relationships. This is characteristic of:<br>the postconventional level<br>a personal orientation<br>the conventional level<br>a care orientation |
| p. 412<br>Cognitive and Emotional<br> Changes<br>Level: Easy<br>Type: Factual<br>Ans: A | 85.<br><br>A.<br>B.<br>C.<br>D. | "We ought to make the right decisions based on how those decisions will impact others." This person has a(n) _____ orientation.<br>care<br>relative<br>justice<br>other |
| p. 412<br>Cognitive and Emotional<br> Changes<br>Level: Easy<br>Type: Factual<br>Ans: A | 86.<br><br>A.<br>B.<br>C.<br>D. | Gilligan pointed out that, in making moral decisions, the male subjects in Kohlberg's studies relied more on a:<br>justice orientation<br>conventional level<br>care orientation<br>postconventional level |
| p. 412<br>Cognitive and Emotional<br> Changes<br>Level: Easy<br>Type: Factual<br>Ans: A | 87.<br><br>A.<br>B.<br>C.<br>D. | Carol Gilligan's research on moral development found that in making moral decisions, women generally adopt a(n):<br>care orientation<br>relative orientation<br>justice orientation<br>other orientation |

p. 412
Cognitive and Emotional
 Changes
Level: Easy
Type: Factual
Ans: C

88. A politician is running for office. He says that he will support the law, equality, and individual rights. Carol Gilligan would say that the politician has a(n) _____ orientation.
A. care
B. relative
C. justice
D. other

p. 412
Cognitive and Emotional
 Changes
Level: Easy
Type: Conceptual
Ans: B

89. Impersonal moral decisions is to memory as personal moral decisions is to:
A. retrieval
B. emotion
C. justice
D. care

p. 412
Cognitive and Emotional
 Changes
Level: Easy
Type: Applied
Ans: D

90. "I found a ten dollar bill on the sidewalk and I kept it." This illustrates a(n):
A. personal moral decision
B. relative orientation
C. justice orientation
D. impersonal moral decision

p. 412
Cognitive and Emotional
 Changes
Level: Easy
Type: Factual
Ans: D

91. Individuals who had damage to their prefrontal cortex in infancy:
A. show language deficits in adulthood
B. tend to have a justice orientation in adulthood
C. tend to have a care orientation in adulthood
D. have difficulty learning social and moral rules in childhood and adolescence

p. 413
Cognitive and Emotional
 Changes
Level: Easy
Type: Factual
Ans: B

92. A longitudinal study of how different styles of parenting affect adolescent development was conducted by:
A. Jean Piaget
B. Diana Baumrind
C. Carol Gilligan
D. Lawrence Kohlberg

p. 413
Cognitive and Emotional
 Changes
Level: Easy
Type: Factual
Ans: D

93. Which of the following is not among the styles of parenting discussed in this module?
A. authoritarian
B. authoritative
C. permissive
D. congenial

p. 413
Cognitive and Emotional
 Changes
Level: Easy
Type: Factual
Ans: A

94. "My dad sets the rules and that's it. There're no ifs, ands, or buts about it!" This parent has a(n) _____ style.
A. authoritarian
B. authoritative
C. disciplinarian
D. congenial

| p. 413 | 95. | Authoritarian parents tend to have adolescent girls who are: |
|---|---|---|
| Cognitive and Emotional | A. | more competent |
| Changes | B. | achievement oriented |
| Level: Easy | C. | less socially assertive |
| Type: Factual | D. | dependent and submissive |
| Ans: D | | |

| p. 413 | 96. | Theresa says that her parents are supportive and loving. In her family, |
|---|---|---|
| Cognitive and Emotional | | rules are openly discussed, and there is frequent give-and-take. It sounds |
| Changes | | as though Theresa's parents are: |
| Level: Easy | A. | permissive |
| Type: Applied | B. | authoritative |
| Ans: B | C. | authoritarian |
| | D. | overprotective |

| p. 413 | 97. | A parent who is supportive, loving, and encourages verbal give and take |
|---|---|---|
| Cognitive and Emotional | | has a(n) _____ style of parenting. |
| Changes | A. | permissive |
| Level: Easy | B. | overprotective |
| Type: Factual | C. | laissez-faire |
| Ans: D | D. | authoritative |

| p. 413 | 98. | Your new friend seems to be competent, independent, and achievement |
|---|---|---|
| Cognitive and Emotional | | oriented; you guess that she had _____ parents. |
| Changes | A. | authoritarian |
| Level: Easy | B. | authoritative |
| Type: Applied | C. | permissive |
| Ans: B | D. | protective |
| *PS/SG 18-11* | | |

| p. 413 | 99. | Authoritative parents: |
|---|---|---|
| Cognitive and Emotional | A. | use harsh punishment to enforce rules |
| Changes | B. | are less controlling and accept their children's actions |
| Level: Easy | C. | value being independent, but also set limits |
| Type: Factual | D. | make few demands and use reason rather than power |
| Ans: C | | |

| p. 413 | 100. | Boys and girls with _____ parents tend to be less achievement |
|---|---|---|
| Cognitive and Emotional | | oriented. |
| Changes | A. | authoritative |
| Level: Easy | B. | authoritarian |
| Type: Factual | C. | overprotective |
| Ans: D | D. | permissive |

| p. 413 | 101. | "Hey dude. How's it going? I can't believe your mom and dad won't let |
|---|---|---|
| Cognitive and Emotional | | you go the party. My folks...they let me do anything I want to. They're |
| Changes | | awesome." This person's parents have a(n) _____ style of parenting. |
| Level: Easy | A. | authoritative |
| Type: Applied | B. | nondirective |
| Ans: D | C. | overprotective |
| *www* | D. | permissive |

p. 413
Cognitive and Emotional
 Changes
Level: Easy
Type: Factual
Ans: C

102. Compared to authoritarian and permissive parents, authoritative parents tend to have adolescents who:
A. have more autonomy and greater self-esteem
B. have fewer behavioral problems
C. are more competent
D. are more conforming

p. 413
Cognitive and Emotional
 Changes
Level: Easy
Type: Factual
Ans: D

103. A mother was speaking to her 15-year-old son: "You can do whatever you want to do. You know that we've talked about giving you more freedom." This mother most likely has a(n) _____ style of parenting.
A. comforting
B. authoritarian
C. overprotective
D. permissive

p. 413
Cognitive and Emotional
 Changes
Level: Easy
Type: Factual
Ans: B

104. According to your textbook, what type of parenting tends to produce children who have lower self-esteem?
A. dominating
B. authoritarian
C. authoritative
D. permissive

p. 414
Cognitive and Emotional
 Changes
Level: Easy
Type: Factual
Ans: C

105. When do cognitive abilities of memory and processing speed peak?
A. childhood
B. teens
C. 20s to 30s
D. 40s

p. 415
Cognitive and Emotional
 Changes
Level: Moderate
Type: Conceptual
Ans: A

106. As the editor of a popular psychology magazine, you must write the titles for its articles. One article is on the cognitive changes associated with aging in adulthood. Which of the following titles would most accurately represent these changes?
A. "Stability from 20 through 40 Years"
B. "Any Change in Cognitive Skills Due to Alzheimer's"
C. "After 30 Years, It's Downhill!"
D. "Declines in Cognitive Abilities Are Irreversible"

p. 415
Cognitive and Emotional
 Changes
Level: Easy
Type: Factual
Ans: C

107. _____ is the rate at which information is encoded and retrieved from memory.
A. Sorting speed
B. Cognitive manipulation
C. Processing speed
D. Reaction speed

p. 415
Cognitive and Emotional
 Changes
Level: Easy
Type: Factual
Ans: C

108. Encoding, storing, and retrieving information takes longer beginning in the:
A. 30s
B. early 40s
C. late 50s
D. 80s

p. 415
Cognitive and Emotional
 Changes
Level: Easy
Type: Factual
Ans: C

109. "What is that thing out there on the street?" The ability to identify the stimulus is called:
A. processing speed
B. cognitive rate
C. perceptual speed
D. estimation rate

p. 415
Cognitive and Emotional
 Changes
Level: Easy
Type: Factual
Ans: A

110. Slower perceptual rate in older adults is most likely due to:
A. slower encoding of information
B. brain disease
C. decline in attention
D. visual problems

p. 415
Cognitive and Emotional
 Changes
Level: Easy
Type: Factual
Ans: D

111. In your volunteer work, you spend time with older adults at the senior citizens center. You notice that these adults show a decline in memory function. Specifically, what type of decline do you notice in these healthy older adults?
A. in memorizing a list of words
B. recalling specific information
C. encoding information
D. all of the above

p. 415
Cognitive and Emotional
 Changes
Level: Easy
Type: Factual
Ans: D
*PS/SG 18-12*

112. Which one of the following cognitive abilities does not decrease with aging?
A. processing speed
B. perceptual speed
C. reaction time
D. interpretation

p. 415
Cognitive and Emotional
 Changes
Level: Easy
Type: Factual
Ans: D

113. Researchers have found that declines in speed of performance are due to:
A. disuse
B. Alzheimer's
C. high blood pressure
D. the slowing down in mental processing

p. 415
Cognitive and Emotional
 Changes
Level: Easy
Type: Factual
Ans: B

114. Compared to older adults, younger adults are better at:
A. interpreting the significance of information
B. recalling many details
C. extracting the meaning of information
D. using prior information to understand new information

p. 415
Cognitive and Emotional
 Changes
Level: Easy
Type: Factual
Ans: A

115. Compared to younger adults, older adults are better at:
A. interpreting information and underlying meaning
B. recalling many details
C. memorizing long lists of words
D. perceptual speed

p. 415
Cognitive and Emotional
 Changes
Level: Easy
Type: Conceptual
Ans: D

116. What piece of advice would you give young adults about what they can expect in the future regarding cognitive skills?
A. "live a full life now, you'll be over the hill soon"
B. "any changes in reaction time are due to decreased motor and sensory abilities"
C. "if you live to be 85 years old, you won't notice any change"
D. "you'll probably forget unimportant information, but you'll get the big picture"

p. 415
Cognitive and Emotional
 Changes
Level: Easy
Type: Factual
Ans: A

117. What was the result of research examining the effects of ginkgo biloba on memory?
A. It did not improve memory.
B. Ginkgo biloba improved memory in subjects.
C. It improved only declarative memory.
D. It was found to be effective in improving memory, but only in young adults.

p. 415
Cognitive and Emotional
 Changes
Level: Easy
Type: Applied
Ans: A
PS/SG 18-13

118. Grandmother forgets a name and worries that she is "losing it" — you should reassure her that:
A. some memory problems often occur in people 60 and over
B. her memory may be slipping, but her reaction time will speed up
C. if she lives long enough, it is likely she will get Alzheimer's disease
D. daily intake of the supplement ginkgo biloba should improve her memory

p. 416
Personality and
 Social Changes
Level: Easy
Type: Factual
Ans: D

119. The way in which adolescents describe their values, goals, interests, and motivations is called:
A. self-esteem
B. menarche
C. a care orientation
D. identity

p. 416
Personality and
 Social Changes
Level: Easy
Type: Factual
Ans: C

120. How much we like ourselves is referred to as:
A. identity
B. egocentric thought
C. self-esteem
D. conventional moral reasoning

p. 416
Personality and
 Social Changes
Level: Easy
Type: Factual
Ans: B

121. What are the two factors that greatly influence self-esteem in adolescents?
A. their athleticism and social competence
B. their physical attractiveness and social competence
C. their clothes and cars
D. their personality and social competence

p. 416
Personality and
 Social Changes
Level: Easy
Type: Factual
Ans: A

122. Zoann doesn't like herself. She doesn't feel competent or attractive. Zoann has low:
A. self-esteem
B. self-efficacy
C. self-concept
D. identity

p. 416
Personality and
 Social Changes
Level: Easy
Type: Factual
Ans: A

123. You attend a workshop on adolescent development. The speaker says that most adolescents have low self-esteem and we need to take drastic steps to boost their self-esteem. Was the speaker correct? Do most adolescents have low self-esteem?
A. No - 60% have high self-esteem
B. No - 90% have high self-esteem
C. Yes - 15% have high self-esteem
D. Yes - 5% have high self-esteem

p. 416
Personality and
 Social Changes
Level: Easy
Type: Factual
Ans: D

124. The majority of adolescents:
A. experience reversals in self-esteem
B. have chronically low self-esteem
C. show dramatic gains in self-esteem
D. maintain a strong sense of self-esteem

p. 416
Personality and
 Social Changes
Level: Easy
Type: Factual
Ans: B

125. Which of the following is hypothesized to be a reason for reversals in self-esteem among adolescents?
A. sexual behavior without contraception
B. changes in peer groups or parental relationships
C. early development of secondary sex characteristics
D. egocentric thinking

p. 416
Personality and
 Social Changes
Level: Easy
Type: Factual
Ans: C

126. About ____ of adolescents have high self-esteem and about ____ have chronically low self-esteem.
A. 50%; 30%
B. 15%; 60%
C. 60%; 15%
D. 30%; 50%

p. 416
Personality and
 Social Changes
Level: Easy
Type: Applied
Ans: B

127. "I've noticed a change in William," says Rolanda. "Yeah, he used to be confident and outgoing. And now he's just the opposite," replies Felicia. William appears to have experienced:
A. a reversal in role generativity
B. a reversal in self-esteem
C. a reversal in self-efficacy
D. role diffusion

p. 416
Personality and
 Social Changes
Level: Easy
Type: Factual
Ans: D

128. Self-esteem is the most stable in:
A. childhood
B. adolescence
C. midlife
D. young adulthood

p. 416
Personality and
  Social Changes
Level: Easy
Type: Factual
Ans: B

129. The self-esteem of boys is typically based upon _____; girls' self-esteem is dependent upon _____.
A. ability to relate to others; managing anxiety in public
B. managing anxiety in public; ability to relate well to others
C. athletic ability; a care orientation
D. physical aspects; ability to relate well to others

p. 417
Personality and
  Social Changes
Level: Easy
Type: Factual
Ans: D

130. What happens in each of Erikson's eight stages?
A. growth in moral reasoning
B. advancement in cognitive reasoning
C. sexual pleasure moves from one body area to another
D. a unique psychosocial conflict

p. 417
Personality and
  Social Changes
Level: Easy
Type: Applied
Ans: D

131. Betsy, age 17, runs away from home and joins the circus. According to Erikson, she is most likely suffering from which conflict?
A. generativity vs. stagnation
B. integrity vs. despair
C. intimacy vs. isolation
D. identity vs. role confusion

p. 417
Personality and
  Social Changes
Level: Moderate
Type: Factual
Ans: A

132. Among adolescents, a failure to develop more purposeful, responsible, adult-like behaviors results in:
A. identity confusion
B. egocentric thinking
C. a justice orientation
D. postconventional moral reasoning

p. 417
Personality and
  Social Changes
Level: Moderate
Type: Factual
Ans: A

133. According to Erikson, an individual who successfully resolves the identity versus role confusion conflict will achieve a sense of:
A. confidence
B. intimacy
C. generativity
D. integrity

p. 417
Personality and
  Social Changes
Level: Easy
Type: Factual
Ans: B

134. Erikson's psychosocial stage which corresponds to young adulthood is called:
A. generativity versus stagnation
B. intimacy versus isolation
C. industry versus inferiority
D. integrity versus despair

p. 417
Personality and
  Social Changes
Level: Easy
Type: Factual
Ans: A
*PS/SG 18-15*

135. In Erikson's psychosocial stage theory, an adolescent who does not develop a positive sense of identity is likely to suffer from:
A. role confusion
B. stagnation
C. a sense of inferiority
D. isolation

<table>
<tr><td>

p. 417<br>
Personality and<br>
  Social Changes<br>
Level: Easy<br>
Type: Applied<br>
Ans: B

</td><td>

136. While most of his friends have steady girlfriends, Gilbert doesn't date anyone during his college days. According to Erikson, Gilbert is having a negative resolution of which conflict?
A. integrity vs. despair
B. intimacy vs. isolation
C. generativity vs. stagnation
D. identity vs. role confusion

</td></tr>
<tr><td>

p. 417<br>
Personality and<br>
  Social Changes<br>
Level: Easy<br>
Type: Applied<br>
Ans: B

</td><td>

137. Which of the following psychologists would analyze development as follows: Brian is 22 years old and has been dating to find someone with whom to have a loving intimate relationship?
A. Freud
B. Erikson
C. Skinner
D. Siegel

</td></tr>
<tr><td>

p. 417<br>
Personality and<br>
  Social Changes<br>
Level: Easy<br>
Type: Factual<br>
Ans: D

</td><td>

138. Erikson believed that people in middle adulthood could achieve generativity through:
A. personal success
B. developing a healthy identity
C. industrious behavior
D. raising their own children

</td></tr>
<tr><td>

p. 417<br>
Personality and<br>
  Social Changes<br>
Level: Easy<br>
Type: Applied<br>
Ans: B<br>
*www*

</td><td>

139. Although Richard maintains a close relationship with his nieces and nephews, he has no children of his own. According to Erikson, Richard will likely develop:
A. stagnation
B. generativity
C. isolation
D. despair

</td></tr>
<tr><td>

p. 417<br>
Personality and<br>
  Social Changes<br>
Level: Easy<br>
Type: Factual<br>
Ans: C

</td><td>

140. In order to achieve integrity during late adulthood, Erikson argues that one must:
A. find intimacy in caring relationships
B. raise children
C. feel content about past accomplishments
D. continue to be industrious and refuse to retire from work

</td></tr>
<tr><td>

p. 417<br>
Personality and<br>
  Social Changes<br>
Level: Easy<br>
Type: Applied<br>
Ans: D

</td><td>

141. Len's grandmother feels she has wasted her life and wishes she had pursued a career as a teacher rather than being a housewife. According to Erikson, Len's grandmother is experiencing:
A. role conflict
B. isolation
C. stagnation
D. despair

</td></tr>
</table>

p. 417
Personality and
  Social Changes
Level: Easy
Type: Factual
Ans: C
*PS/SG 18-16*

142. According to Erik Erikson's Stage 8, what we need in late adulthood is:
A. recognition, respect, and honor from our family and colleagues
B. a sense of pride in our acquisitions and our standing in the community
C. a sense of contentment about how we lived and what we accomplished
D. mainly good health — without it there is despair

p. 417
Personality and
  Social Changes
Level: Easy
Type: Factual
Ans: A

143. The positive resolution of the conflict of old age as described by Erikson is known as:
A. integrity
B. generativity
C. intimacy
D. identity

p. 417
Personality and
  Social Changes
Level: Moderate
Type: Conceptual
Ans: A

144. The main advantage of Erikson's stage theory of development is that it:
A. alerts you to major crises that arise across your entire life span
B. analyzes development by placing major life developments in an indisputable order
C. offers workable advice for dealing with life's development crises
D. identifies transitions in life

p. 417
Personality and
  Social Changes
Level: Easy
Type: Factual
Ans: B

145. Personality changes seen from end of adolescence through middle adulthood involve becoming:
A. less authoritative
B. more trusting and intimate
C. more introverted
D. less tolerant

p. 418
Gender Roles, Love, and
  Relationships
Level: Easy
Type: Factual
Ans: C

146. Gender roles refer to:
A. the belief that one is male or female
B. one's biological sex
C. behaving in expected ways because one is male or female
D. preference for desired traits in opposite-sex partners

p. 418
Gender Roles, Love, and
  Relationships
Level: Easy
Type: Applied
Ans: B

147. Joy is an auto mechanic. People describe her as strong, aggressive, and independent. Joy behaves in ways which are contrary to:
A. androgyny
B. her gender role
C. her biological sex
D. a care orientation

p. 418
Gender Roles, Love, and
  Relationships
Level: Easy
Type: Factual
Ans: A

148. College students were asked to describe the traits of a typical female and typical male. Their descriptions:
A. were very similar to traditional, stereotypic gender roles
B. were very different from traditional, stereotypic gender roles
C. were very similar to traditional gender role for males, but not for females
D. were very similar to traditional gender role for females, but not for males

p. 418
Gender Roles, Love, and
  Relationships
Level: Easy
Type: Factual
Ans: D

149. Which trait does <u>not</u> match the traditional stereotypic gender role of females:
- A. concern
- B. nurturing
- C. sensitive
- D. dominant

p. 418
Gender Roles, Love, and
  Relationships
Level: Easy
Type: Factual
Ans: C

150. If you argue that men need to be dominant and women need to be caring for survival, then you are arguing for the:
- A. cognitive developmental theory
- B. psychosexual theory
- C. evolutionary theory
- D. social role theory

p. 418
Gender Roles, Love, and
  Relationships
Level: Easy
Type: Factual
Ans: D

151. Gender differences are based upon traditional divisions of labor according to the:
- A. cognitive developmental theory
- B. psychosexual theory
- C. evolutionary theory
- D. social role theory

p. 418
Gender Roles, Love, and
  Relationships
Level: Easy
Type: Factual
Ans: C

152. According to social role theory, males typically held _____ roles while females held _____ roles.
- A. dominant; submissive
- B. internal; external
- C. occupational; family
- D. justice; care

p. 419
Gender Roles, Love, and
  Relationships
Level: Easy
Type: Factual
Ans: C

153. Robert Sternberg's triangular theory of love divides love into three components:
- A. masculine, feminine, and androgynous
- B. infatuation, attraction, and arousal
- C. passion, intimacy, and commitment
- D. companionship, romance, and fidelity

p. 419
Gender Roles, Love, and
  Relationships
Level: Easy
Type: Applied
Ans: D

154. Georgia thinks her classmate Tony is a "real hunk" and hopes he asks her out on a date. According to Sternberg's theory of love, she is experiencing:
- A. intimacy
- B. activation
- C. initiation
- D. passion

p. 419
Gender Roles, Love, and
  Relationships
Level: Easy
Type: Factual
Ans: C

155. Feeling close or connected to someone is characteristic of which component of Sternberg's theory of love?
- A. compassion
- B. commitment
- C. intimacy
- D. passion

p. 419
Gender Roles, Love, and
  Relationships
Level: Easy
Type: Applied
Ans: B

156. Paul is surprised when Marie tells him that she and Gerry are getting engaged and will be married in January. Paul is surprised because he hadn't realized that the relationship had reached the _____ component of Sternberg's theory of love.

  A. compassion
  B. commitment
  C. intimacy
  D. passion

p. 419
Gender Roles, Love, and
  Relationships
Level: Easy
Type: Factual
Ans: A

157. All of the following are components of Sternberg's triangular theory of love except:

  A. compassion
  B. commitment
  C. intimacy
  D. passion

p. 419
Gender Roles, Love, and
  Relationships
Level: Easy
Type: Applied
Ans: D
*www*

158. Rhonda goes to the beach, sees Hud the lifeguard for the first time, and says to her friend Catherine, "I think I'm in love with that hunk." Robert Sternberg would characterize Rhonda's feelings about Hud as _____ love.

  A. romantic
  B. Hollywood
  C. companionate
  D. infatuated

p. 419
Gender Roles, Love, and
  Relationships
Level: Easy
Type: Factual
Ans: A

159. According to Robert Sternberg, Hollywood love results from a combination of:

  A. passion and commitment without intimacy
  B. passion and intimacy with affection
  C. intimacy and passion without commitment
  D. intimacy and commitment without passion

p. 419
Gender Roles, Love, and
  Relationships
Level: Easy
Type: Applied
Ans: D

160. Gladys still feels very much in love with Elmer after 30 years of marriage even though they only have sexual intercourse on their anniversary day and Elmer's birthday. Her feelings toward Elmer are best characterized as _____ love.

  A. romantic
  B. Hollywood
  C. intimate
  D. companionate

p. 419
Gender Roles, Love, and
  Relationships
Level: Easy
Type: Factual
Ans: A

161. According to Robert Sternberg, the combination of intimacy and passion without any commitment is characteristic of _____ love.

  A. romantic
  B. Hollywood
  C. companionate
  D. infatuated

| | | |
|---|---|---|
| p. 419<br>Gender Roles, Love, and<br>  Relationships<br>Level: Easy<br>Type: Conceptual<br>Ans: C | 162.<br><br>A.<br>B.<br>C.<br>D. | Which of the following is the <u>best</u> example of Sternberg's "romantic love"?<br>a marriage that last 50 years<br>a "one-night stand" between people who meet in a bar<br>a 10-week affair between students attending a summer seminar<br>an engagement that occurs a month after a couple meets |
| p. 419<br>Gender Roles, Love, and<br>  Relationships<br>Level: Moderate<br>Type: Conceptual<br>Ans: B | 163.<br><br>A.<br><br>B.<br><br>C.<br><br>D. | With regard to the areas of the brain activated, what is the difference between infatuated love and committed love?<br>Infatuated love activates the emotion areas while committed love activates the reward/pleasure center.<br>Infatuated love activates the reward/pleasure center; committed love activates the emotion areas.<br>Infatuated love stimulates the prefrontal cortex, but committed love activates the thalamus.<br>Infatuated love activates the thalamus and committed love stimulates the emotion areas. |
| p. 420<br>Gender Roles, Love, and<br>  Relationships<br>Level: Easy<br>Type: Factual<br>Ans: D | 164.<br><br>A.<br>B.<br>C.<br>D. | We choose a partner for a long-term relationship by finding someone who:<br>has good earning potential<br>is physically attractive<br>has similar values<br>matches our ideal-partner schema |
| p. 420<br>Gender Roles, Love, and<br>  Relationships<br>Level: Moderate<br>Type: Applied<br>Ans: B | 165.<br><br><br><br>A.<br>B.<br>C.<br>D. | Tom and Cathy are college students who have begun thinking about marriage. In selecting his potential wife, Tom is likely to be more concerned about his future mate's _____ than Cathy is concerned about it in her potential future mate.<br>intelligence<br>physical attractiveness<br>earning capacity<br>creativity |
| p. 420<br>Gender Roles, Love, and<br>  Relationships<br>Level: Easy<br>Type: Factual<br>Ans: C | 166.<br><br>A.<br>B.<br>C.<br>D. | The two variables that males and females place different weights on in their perfect-partner schema are:<br>intelligence and height<br>education level and physical attractiveness<br>physical attractiveness and good earning capacity<br>social skill and good earning capacity |
| p. 420<br>Gender Roles, Love, and<br>  Relationships<br>Level: Easy<br>Type: Factual<br>Ans: D | 167.<br><br>A.<br>B.<br>C.<br>D. | Which of the following characteristics do subjects consider the most desirable in a potential mate?<br>intelligence<br>exciting personality<br>creativity<br>kindness and understanding |

| p. 420 | 168. | Research has indicated that in marriages that fail, couples deal with |
| Gender Roles, Love, and | | marital conflict by: |
| Relationships | A. | venting their anger and frustration |
| Level: Easy | B. | confronting disagreements in an open way |
| Type: Factual | C. | being straightforward about their problems |
| Ans: D | D. | criticism, defensiveness, contempt and stonewalling |

| p. 420 | 169. | A researcher has reported success in predicting divorces among 2,000 |
| Gender Roles, Love, and | | couples. What variable was used to make these predictions? |
| Relationships | A. | social economic status of husband |
| Level: Easy | B. | length of marriage |
| Type: Factual | C. | number of positive and negative moments in their marriage |
| Ans: C | D. | personality profiles of both husband and wife |

| p. 420 | 170. | Research suggests that one important key to the success or failure of |
| Gender Roles, Love, and | | marriage is: |
| Relationships | A. | how couples decide on major purchases |
| Level: Easy | B. | how couples handle conflicts |
| Type: Factual | C. | whether both partners maintain good physical appearance |
| Ans: B | D. | whether both partners remain faithful |
| *PS/SG 18-12* | | |

| p. 420 | 171. | A couple's happiness over 30 years of marriage tends to: |
| Gender Roles, Love, and | A. | reach low points with children, but then return once children start leaving |
| Relationships | | home |
| Level: Easy | B. | increase with the birth of children and then decline once children start |
| Type: Factual | | leaving home |
| Ans: A | C. | increase with the birth of children and continue to increase once children |
| | | start leaving home |
| | D. | decrease initially, then improve slightly with birth of children |

| p. 420 | 172. | Of the following events, what tends to be among the high points of a |
| Gender Roles, Love, and | | marriage? |
| Relationships | A. | when the first child is school age |
| Level: Easy | B. | when the children are adolescents |
| Type: Factual | C. | after the birth of the second child |
| Ans: D | D. | after the children leave home |

| p. 422 | 173. | Your grandfather and grandmother who have been married 60 years are |
| Research Focus: | | giving you advice for a happy marriage. Their advice is consistent with |
| Happy Marriages | | the results of a study of happy marriages presented in your textbook. The |
| Level: Easy | | piece of advice is: |
| Type: Conceptual | A. | "Show how angry you are so you are taken seriously." |
| Ans: C | B. | "Try to see the other person's point of view - that way you feel sympathy." |
| | C. | "Stay calm so you're able to sit down and talk things through." |
| | D. | "When fighting, always repeat your position several times in different |
| | | ways." |

p. 422
Research Focus:
  Happy Marriages
Level: Easy
Type: Factual
Ans: B

174. In Gottman's Love Lab, what responses are being measured?
A. pupil size, facial, and perspiration responses
B. facial and physiological responses
C. alpha brain waves and facial responses
D. breathing, heart rate, and perspiration responses

p. 422
Research Focus:
  Happy Marriages
Level: Easy
Type: Factual
Ans: A
PS/SG 18-19

175. John Gottman has identified four major problems between couples that often lead to divorce:
A. criticism, defensiveness, contempt, stonewalling
B. poverty, impulsive spending, lack of savings, unemployment
C. age differences, religious differences, political differences, language differences
D. physical attractiveness, flirting, jealousy, lack of inhibitions

p. 422
Research Focus:
  Happy Marriages
Level: Easy
Type: Applied
Ans: C

176. Which husband is most likely to have a happy marriage?
A. Paul - he expects his wife to understand that he works long hours at the shop
B. Nick - he makes sure that his wife knows his expectations
C. Mark - he always finds something reasonable in the advice given to him by his wife
D. Michael - he tries to repeat what his wife says in his own words to show that he is paying attention

p. 422
Research Focus:
  Happy Marriages
Level: Easy
Type: Applied
Ans: C

177. Which wife is most likely to have a happy marriage?
A. Pauline - she expects her husband to provide for the family
B. Nicole - she lays down her expectations for her husband in a clear way
C. Mary - she puts her complaints and advice in a gentle soothing way
D. Michelle - she tries to repeat what her husband says in her own words to show that she is paying attention

p. 423
Cultural Diversity:
  Preferences for Partners
Level: Easy
Type: Factual
Ans: A

178. Cross-cultural research that examined desirable traits of partners found numerous similarities between male and female lists. This is indicative of:
A. the powerful influence of culture
B. the great effect of gender on mate preference
C. traditional gender roles
D. companionate love

p. 423
Cultural Diversity:
  Preferences for Partners
Level: Easy
Type: Factual
Ans: A

179. In cross-cultural research, the most desirable trait in a partner is:
A. kind and understanding
B. good looks
C. reciprocal love
D. dependable character

p. 423
Cultural Diversity:
  Preferences for Partners
Level: Easy
Type: Factual
Ans: C

180. Cross-cultural research for mate preferences found that:
A. education and intelligence was ranked highest by most cultures
B. good looks were ranked equally by males and females
C. on average, kindness and understanding were rated highest
D. there were few differences among the different cultures

p. 423
Cultural Diversity:
  Preferences for Partners
Level: Easy
Type: Factual
Ans: C

181. Virginity is most highly ranked by:
A. Swedish males
B. Norwegian females
C. males
D. females

p. 423
Cultural Diversity:
  Preferences for Partners
Level: Easy
Type: Factual
Ans: B

182. Of the following countries, where is love most valued as a reason to marry?
A. China
B. United States
C. Iran
D. Nigeria

p. 423
Cultural Diversity:
  Preferences for Partners
Level: Easy
Type: Factual
Ans: D

183. Cross cultural research indicates that the most common reason men use to dissolve marriages is:
A. disrespect
B. personality quirks
C. unfaithfulness
D. infertility

p. 424
Physical Changes: Aging
Level: Easy
Type: Applied
Ans: B

184. Herb continues jogging well into his 60s. His speed has slowed over the years, but he still jogs 5 miles a day. Herb's decline in speed is an example of:
A. sensory decline
B. normal aging
C. senility
D. pathological aging

p. 424
Physical Changes: Aging
Level: Easy
Type: Factual
Ans: A
*PS/SG 18-22*

185. According to the _____, our bodies age because of naturally occurring problems or breakdowns in the body's cells:
A. aging by chance theory
B. aging by design theory
C. triangular theory (middle, late, and very late adulthood)
D. chronological aging theory

p. 424
Physical Changes: Aging
Level: Easy
Type: Applied
Ans: A

186. Stu's grandmother has Alzheimer's disease and has trouble remembering things. A psychologist would describe Stu's grandmother as experiencing:
A. pathological aging
B. geriatric decline
C. genetic senility
D. normal aging

p. 424
Physical Changes: Aging
Level: Easy
Type: Factual
Ans: D

187. The separation of the causes of normal aging versus pathological aging is a goal of:
A. the wear and tear theory
B. the biological limit theory
C. androgyny
D. gerontology

p. 424
Physical Changes: Aging
Level: Easy
Type: Factual
Ans: A

188. What role do free radicals play in aging?
A. They damage body organs and DNA.
B. They can reduce the impact of proteins on body organs and DNA.
C. They cause Alzheimer's disease.
D. They cause anti-oxidants to be produced.

p. 424
Physical Changes: Aging
Level: Easy
Type: Factual
Ans: C

189. The maximum longevity for humans appears to be about:
A. 115
B. 120
C. 130
D. 140

p. 424
Physical Changes: Aging
Level: Easy
Type: Factual
Ans: A

190. In our _____, our immune system, senses, physiological responses, and mental skills are most efficient.
A. 20s
B. 30s
C. 40s
D. 50s

p. 425
Physical Changes: Aging
Level: Easy
Type: Factual
Ans: A

191. Why aren't people in late adulthood often included in surveys of sexual behavior?
A. common stereotype that they no longer have any interest in sexual activity
B. it is commonly known that these people do not have sex
C. most older people prefer not to participate in these types of surveys
D. most older people have such poor memories that they cannot remember

p. 425
Physical Changes: Aging
Level: Easy
Type: Factual
Ans: C

192. When does menopause occur in most women?
A. 40 years of age
B. 45 years of age
C. 50 years of age
D. 55 years of age

p. 425
Physical Changes: Aging
Level: Easy
Type: Factual
Ans: A

193. What percent of women experience serious physical symptoms during and immediately after menopause?
A. 15%
B. 50%
C. 75%
D. 95%

p. 425
Physical Changes: Aging
Level: Easy
Type: Factual
Ans: A
www

194. What relationship have researchers found between the decrease in hormones in women and their sexual activity?
A. no relationship
B. mild relationship
C. moderate relationship
D. strong relationship

p. 425
Physical Changes: Aging
Level: Moderate
Type: Factual
Ans: C

195. Regarding the effect of aging on sexual activity, it is the case that:
A. interest in sexual activity declines because of significant hormonal changes
B. there is no decrease in sexual responsiveness but there is in activity
C. there is a decrease in sexual responsiveness but it need not interfere with sexual activity
D. there is a decrease in sexual activity but not in sexual responsiveness

p. 425
Physical Changes: Aging
Level: Easy
Type: Factual
Ans: A

196. Hot flashes, moodiness, and changes in the genital organs are symptomatic of:
A. menopause
B. androgyny
C. a midlife crisis
D. progeria

p. 425
Physical Changes: Aging
Level: Easy
Type: Applied
Ans: D

197. Carmen is at the age where she is likely to experience menopause. What variable is likely to greatly affect her experiences with menopause?
A. her access to social support from other women going through menopause
B. her level of exercise
C. her health
D. her expectations

p. 425
Physical Changes: Aging
Level: Easy
Type: Factual
Ans: C

198. Men reaching late adulthood generally experience:
A. infertility around age 50
B. a decrease in hormone secretion
C. a decrease in sexual responsivity
D. an inability to maintain an erection and orgasm

p. 425
Physical Changes: Aging
Level: Easy
Type: Factual
Ans: A

199. What drug was introduced in 1998 as a treatment for impotency?
A. Viagra
B. Prolixin
C. Estrahol
D. Orgasine

p. 425
Physical Changes: Aging
Level: Easy
Type: Factual
Ans: B

200. Micah, who is in his 40's, is thinking about how late adulthood will affect his sexuality. Which of the following is *not* likely to happen to him as long as he remains in good health:
A. requiring more time to reach orgasm
B. difficulty in becoming sexually aroused
C. he'll need more time to get an erection
D. Micah will need longer periods of stimulation

p. 425
Physical Changes: Aging
Level: Easy
Type: Factual
Ans: C

201. What can we conclude about sexual behavior in adulthood?
A. Men become infertile around age 50.
B. The vast majority of married couples over 60 years are not satisfied with their sex lives.
C. As we mature we must learn to be more sensitive to our partner's needs.
D. Few women actually experience physical symptoms of menopause.

p. 426
Application: Suicide
Level: Easy
Type: Factual
Ans: A

202. The highest rate of suicide is among:
A. people over 65 years of age
B. females
C. adolescents
D. young adults

p. 426
Application: Suicide
Level: Easy
Type: Factual
Ans: C

203 Research indicates that among 15-19 year olds, suicide is the number _____ leading cause of death.
A. one
B. two
C. three
D. four

p. 426
Application: Suicide
Level: Easy
Type: Factual
Ans: D

204. Which of the following is not accurate regarding adolescents who attempt or commit suicide:
A. They often express the wish to die or threaten suicide.
B. There are often precipitants of suicide.
C. They make a threat to commit suicide.
D. They show no signs of behavioral or psychological problems.

p. 426
Application: Suicide
Level: Easy
Type: Factual
Ans: B

205. As Jerry looks back, he tries to think of what signs his cousin might have shown before he committed suicide. Which of the following is a common behavioral symptom?
A. a sense of resolve
B. social isolation and withdrawal
C. a peace about things coming to an end
D. talking about the future

p. 426
Application: Suicide
Level: Easy
Type: Factual
Ans: C

206. Looking back in retrospect, Sonny's parents remember that right before he committed suicide, there were a number of events and feelings that probably triggered his taking of his own life. These events and feelings are called:
A. suicide factors
B. pre-suicide predictors
C. precipitators
D. psychosocial provokers

p. 427
Application: Suicide
Level: Easy
Type: Applied
Ans: A

207. Fifteen-year-old Jake becomes depressed after his best friend Mike commits suicide. Jake has made plans for his own suicide. Jake would be considered:
A. in imminent danger of committing suicide
B. at low risk for suicide
C. at risk for suicide
D. in intermittent danger of committing suicide

p. 427
Application: Suicide
Level: Easy
Type: Factual
Ans: D

208. A short-term treatment plan following the identification of someone at risk for suicide would include:
A. therapy to deal with the depression
B. psychiatric medication
C. a program to help improve the individual's self-image
D. a contract with the person not to hurt themselves

p. 427
Application: Suicide
Level: Easy
Type: Factual
Ans: A
*www*

209. The one variable that appears to have the <u>most</u> significant effect on committing suicide among the elderly is:
A. depression
B. loss of a loved one
C. psychological problems
D. prescription-drug related

p. 427
Application: Suicide
Level: Easy
Type: Factual
Ans: D

210. A review of Oregon's assisted suicide law found that:
A. suicide rates among the mentally ill have increased
B. suicide rates actually decreased
C. an increase in elder abuse occurred
D. there had been no abuse or problems anticipated by opponents

p. 427
Application: Suicide
Level: Easy
Type: Factual
Ans: D
*PS/SG 18-25*

211. Perhaps the main reason why the debate over assisted suicide is intensifying is that:
A. a doctor has invented a machine that makes it relatively easy
B. psychologists, as scientists, are unwilling to become involved in a moral question
C. morals in our country are breaking down
D. the population of the elderly will almost double in the next 35 years

True/False

| F | | 1. | Boys who mature early tend to be less confident and more shy. |
|---|---|---|---|
| T | *www* | 2. | Abstinence has increased among teenagers. |
| T | | 3. | Cognitive development refers to changes in perception, thinking and understanding of the world. |
| F | | 4. | The ability to think about abstract and hypothetical concepts takes place in concrete operations. |
| F | *www* | 5. | The adolescent's prefrontal cortex is fully developed. |
| T | | 6. | Morality based on conforming to the laws of society describes level 2 of Kohlberg's moral reasoning. |
| F | | 7. | Carol Gilligan argued that moral development occurs in three levels. |
| F | | 8. | A care orientation occurs because of an underdeveloped prefrontal cortex. |
| T | *www* | 9. | As we grow into middle adulthood, we become more trusting. |
| F | | 10. | In late adulthood, individuals try to achieve generativity by helping the younger generation. |
| F | | 11. | Both males and females have eagerly taken on traits that broaden their gender roles. |
| T | *www* | 12. | The social theory argues that social roles developed out of different divisions of labor. |
| T | | 13. | Infatuated love stimulates the brain's reward/pleasure center of the brain. |
| F | *www* | 14. | Passionate love involves having trusting and tender feelings for another. |
| T | | 15. | The lowest point of marital satisfaction is when the children are in adolescence. |
| T | *www* | 16. | In selecting the ideal-partner, males rank physical attractiveness higher than do females. |
| T | *www* | 17. | In successful marriages, husbands learn how be more accepting of their wives' criticisms. |

| F |  | 18. | There is no difference between males and females with regard to desirability of virginity in marriage partners. |
|---|---|---|---|
| T |  | 19. | In the United States, love is ranked as the most important factor in choosing a spouse. |
| T | www | 20. | Life expectancy in the United States is now 78 years. |
| T |  | 21. | The effects of menopause on sexuality is influenced by sexuality prior to menopause. |
| T |  | 22. | In menopause there is gradual decrease in estrogen. |
| F | www | 23. | The rate of suicide among teenagers is the highest among any age group. |
| T |  | 24. | Males are more likely than females to succeed in killing themselves. |
| F | www | 25. | The rate of murder-suicide among the elderly is decreasing. |

Short-Answer Essay Questions

1. Describe the effects of early versus late maturation for girls and boys. (*www*)
2. Using the BioPsychoSocial approach, create a program to teach adolescents to abstain from sexual intercourse.
3. Discuss how brain development may influence moodiness and risk taking in adolescents.
4. Describe the three levels of moral reasoning according to Kohlberg. What criticisms of Kohlberg's theory have been proposed? (*www*)
5. What are the three parenting styles according to Baumrind? Describe an effect of each style.
6. What is self-esteem? Describe the patterns of self-esteem as it develops in adolescents.
7. What variables are important to men and women as they decide to marry? (*www*)
8. Based on the module, what factors can increase longevity?
9. As men and women age, what changes occur in sexuality? (*www*)
10. Compare and contrast the arguments for and against doctor-assisted suicide. (*www*)

# Module 19 - Freudian and Humanistic Theories

p. 433
Introduction
Level: Easy
Type: Factual
Ans: B

1. According to the module's introduction, the case of Kurt Cobain raises some interesting questions about:
A. psychosocial development
B. personality
C. justice orientation
D. gender roles

p. 433
Introduction
Level: Easy
Type: Factual
Ans: D
*PS/SG 19-1*

2. Rod Plotnik tells the stories of musician Kurt Cobain and actor Charles Dutton to illustrate _____ and _____.
A. the self-destructiveness of greed / the power of religious faith
B. drug use / crime
C. wasted lives / lucky breaks
D. the mysteries of personality / the possibility of personality change

p. 433
Introduction
Level: Easy
Type: Factual
Ans: C

3. If you study people's distinctive behaviors, thoughts, motives, and emotions that influence our reactions and adaptation, then you're studying:
A. traits
B. motivation
C. personality
D. factor analysis

p. 433
Introduction
Level: Easy
Type: Factual
Ans: D

4. What is the main focus in the study of personality?
A. traits
B. id, ego, and superego
C. unconscious conflicts and self-actualization
D. behaviors, thoughts, motives, and emotions

p. 433
Introduction
Level: Easy
Type: Factual
Ans: A

5. What is defined as the combination of lasting and distinctive behaviors, thoughts, and emotions that typify how we react and adapt to other people and situations?
A. personality
B. situational specificity
C. cognitive compliance
D. factor analysis

p. 433
Introduction
Level: Easy
Type: Conceptual
Ans: D

6. "That's just the way she is!" This declaration is describing someone's:
A. locus of control
B. cognitive processes
C. self-efficacy
D. personality

| | | |
|---|---|---|
| p. 433<br>Introduction<br>Level: Easy<br>Type: Factual<br>Ans: B<br>*PS/SG 19-2* | 7.<br><br>A.<br><br>B.<br><br><br>C.<br>D. | In psychology, the term personality means:<br>a fixed way of responding to other people that is based on our inherited emotional makeup<br>a combination of long-lasting and distinctive behaviors, thoughts, motives, and emotions that typify how we react to other people and situations<br>favorable and unfavorable personal characteristics<br>how interesting and attractive we are to other people |
| p. 433<br>Introduction<br>Level: Easy<br>Type: Applied<br>Ans: B | 8.<br><br><br>A.<br>B.<br>C.<br>D. | Your cousin Eddie claims he's a so-called expert in describing and explaining people. His description and explanations could be called a(n):<br>hypothetical construct<br>theory of personality<br>fixation<br>example of self-efficacy |
| p. 433<br>Introduction<br>Level: Easy<br>Type: Factual<br>Ans: A | 9.<br><br>A.<br>B.<br>C.<br>D. | The case of Charles Dutton as described in the module introduction <u>best</u> illustrates:<br>development of one's full potential<br>the impact of the id on behavior<br>how racial discrimination affects people's lives<br>development of conditional positive regard |
| p. 433<br>Introduction<br>Level: Easy<br>Type: Conceptual<br>Ans: C | 10.<br>A.<br>B.<br>C.<br><br>D. | What do theories of personality do?<br>They tell us how early childhood experiences affect our personality.<br>Theories of personality just describe why we are the way we are.<br>Theories attempt to describe and explain how personality develops and why personalities differ.<br>They inform us of ways to modify personality. |
| p. 434<br>Freud's Psychodynamic<br>  Theory<br>Level: Easy<br>Type: Conceptual<br>Ans: D | 11.<br><br>A.<br>B.<br><br>C.<br>D. | What type of experience did Freud have that influenced his theory of human behavior?<br>He spent time in World War I where he witnessed great suffering.<br>His study with B. F. Skinner taught him that unconscious conflicts shape personality.<br>His first wife died as she was giving birth to their second child.<br>He found that some of his patients' symptoms had no observable physical or neurological causes. |
| p. 434<br>Freud's Psychodynamic<br>  Theory<br>Level: Moderate<br>Type: Factual<br>Ans: B | 12.<br><br><br><br><br><br>A.<br>B.<br>C.<br>D. | Dr. Khard is reading a paper on psychodynamic theory written by a student. She first looks at the headings of each section. She is most surprised to find a heading that does not fit with psychodynamic theory. Which of the following headings is <u>most</u> likely to have surprised Dr. Khard?<br>"Unconscious Motivation"<br>"The Importance of Self-Actualization"<br>"The Relationship Between Id, Ego, and Superego"<br>"The Role of Conflict in the Anal Stage" |

| | | |
|---|---|---|
| p. 434<br>Freud's Psychodynamic<br> Theory<br>Level: Easy<br>Type: Factual<br>Ans: B<br>*www* | 13.<br><br><br>A.<br>B.<br>C.<br>D. | If you argue that early childhood experiences, repressed thoughts, and conflicts between conscious and unconscious forces influence our thoughts and behaviors, then you subscribe to the _____.<br>trait theory of personality<br>psychodynamic theory of personality<br>Big Five theory of personality<br>humanistic theory of personality |
| p. 434<br>Freud's Psychodynamic<br> Theory<br>Level: Easy<br>Type: Applied<br>Ans: C | 14.<br><br>A.<br>B.<br>C.<br>D. | Which of the following about Kurt Cobain's life would be of <u>most</u> interest to a psychologist from a psychodynamic perspective?<br>He failed to self-actualize in his 20s.<br>He was unable to develop delay of gratification.<br>He didn't get love and support as he was growing up.<br>He never developed a healthy locus of control. |
| p. 434<br>Freud's Psychodynamic<br> Theory<br>Level: Easy<br>Type: Conceptual<br>Ans: A | 15.<br><br>A.<br>B.<br>C.<br>D. | Which group of words is most appropriate for the psychodynamic theory of Freud?<br>unconscious, repressed thoughts, early childhood, conflict<br>potential, growth, freedom, self-actualization<br>cognitive, behavior, environment, locus of control<br>traits, factor analysis, the Big Five, consistency |
| p. 434<br>Freud's Psychodynamic<br> Theory<br>Level: Easy<br>Type: Factual<br>Ans: A | 16.<br><br>A.<br>B.<br>C.<br>D. | Freud's psychodynamic approach to personality emphasizes which of the following?<br>conscious thoughts, unconscious forces, and unconscious motivation<br>cognitive appraisals of one's environment<br>the measurement of traits and their stability<br>self-actualization and personal freedom |
| p. 434<br>Freud's Psychodynamic<br> Theory<br>Level: Easy<br>Type: Factual<br>Ans: C | 17.<br><br>A.<br>B.<br>C.<br>D. | If you have wishes, desires, or thoughts that you are aware of or can recall at any given moment, you have experienced:<br>manifest thoughts<br>dynamic thoughts<br>conscious thoughts<br>fixated thoughts |
| p. 434<br>Freud's Psychodynamic<br> Theory<br>Level: Easy<br>Type: Applied<br>Ans: D | 18.<br><br>A.<br>B.<br>C.<br>D. | "I don't know why I did that!" Of the following concepts, which one <u>best</u> relates to that statement?<br>real self<br>self-efficacy<br>conscious thoughts<br>unconscious motivation |
| p. 434<br>Freud's Psychodynamic<br> Theory<br>Level: Easy<br>Type: Applied<br>Ans: D | 19.<br><br><br>A.<br>B.<br>C.<br>D. | During your job interview, you were asked to describe your accomplishments, education, and how well you work with others. These are examples of:<br>manifest thoughts<br>unconscious thoughts<br>dynamic thoughts<br>conscious thoughts |

p. 434
Freud's Psychodynamic
  Theory
Level: Easy
Type: Applied
Ans: D

20. "What did you have for supper last night?" "What is your name?"
The answers to these questions are examples of:
A. self-efficacy
B. unconscious thoughts
C. self-referenced thoughts
D. conscious thoughts

p. 434
Freud's Psychodynamic
  Theory
Level: Moderate
Type: Factual
Ans: C

21. While trying to understand why his female patients had profound
physical symptoms in the absence of physical causes, Freud
"discovered" the notion of:
A. the latency stage
B. the superego
C. unconscious forces
D. manifest content

p. 434
Freud's Psychodynamic
  Theory
Level: Easy
Type: Applied
Ans: D

22. Jeff and Cindy are talking. Cindy says to Jeff, "I wish you would
just...go away!" Jeff responds quickly, "What did you mean by that?"
Cindy answers, "Well, I really don't know, I just said it. I didn't
mean it." Freud might disagree and suggest that Cindy is not aware
of why she wants Jeff to leave her. Freud is referring to Cindy's:
A. conscious forces
B. reality content
C. manifest content
D. unconscious forces

p. 434
Freud's Psychodynamic
  Theory
Level: Easy
Type: Factual
Ans: A

23. Freud believed that a person's wishes, thoughts, and desires that
one cannot voluntarily access were represented by:
A. unconscious forces
B. conscious forces
C. manifest content
D. reality content

p. 434
Freud's Psychodynamic
  Theory
Level: Easy
Type: Factual
Ans: D
PS/SG 19-3

24. In Sigmund Freud's psychodynamic theory of personality, the
unconscious contains:
A. everything we are aware of at a given moment
B. feelings and thoughts we remember from long ago
C. material that can easily be brought into awareness
D. repressed wishes, desires, or thoughts

p. 434
Freud's Psychodynamic
  Theory
Level: Moderate
Type: Factual
Ans: B

25. What concepts did Freud use to explain things we say or do that we
cannot explain or understand?
A. Freudian slips and fixation
B. unconscious forces and unconscious motivation
C. conscious forces and fixation
D. free association and unconscious motivation

p. 434
Freud's Psychodynamic
  Theory
Level: Moderate
Type: Factual
Ans: C

26. A young student is listening to Freud give a lecture in the 1920's. Freud claims that repressed thoughts can influence behaviors. The student raises his hand and asks Freud, "Through what mechanism is this possible?" Freud replies:
A. "through fixation and conflict"
B. "behavior is influenced though the collective unconscious"
C. "through unconscious motivation"
D. "though conscious motivation"

p. 434
Freud's Psychodynamic
  Theory
Level: Easy
Type: Factual
Ans: B

27. The term _____ is a Freudian concept which explains how repressed, threatening thoughts can impact our conscious behaviors.
A. collective unconscious
B. unconscious motivation
C. manifest unconscious
D. cognitive unconscious

p. 435
Freud's Psychodynamic
  Theory
Level: Easy
Type: Factual
Ans: C
*www*

28. Free association, dream interpretation, and Freudian slips are:
A. examples of how real self and ideal self conflict with each other
B. techniques to discover the extent of self-actualization
C. techniques to discover the unconscious
D. techniques to discover the conscious

p. 435
Freud's Psychodynamic
  Theory
Level: Moderate
Type: Applied
Ans: A

29. During a session of therapy, Kyle's therapist tells him to sit back and talk about whatever thoughts enter his head. Kyle's therapist is utilizing the Freudian technique of:
A. free association
B. dream interpretation
C. analysis of slips of the tongue
D. exploring manifest content

p. 435
Freud's Psychodynamic
  Theory
Level: Moderate
Type: Factual
Ans: A

30. The technique of free association is based on the premise that:
A. uncensored material will provide clues to the unconscious
B. dreams always have hidden, sexual meanings which must be explored
C. moral values and standards can be applied to satisfying wishes
D. it is healthy to make up acceptable excuses for behaviors that make us feel anxious

p. 435
Freud's Psychodynamic
  Theory
Level: Easy
Type: Factual
Ans: C

31. From a Freudian perspective, dreams:
A. have no meaning
B. are actually by-products of random firing in the brainstem
C. contain underlying hidden meaning and symbols that provide clues to unconscious thoughts and desires
D. contain meaning, but cannot be interpreted successfully

p. 435
Freud's Psychodynamic
  Theory
Level: Easy
Type: Factual
Ans: B

32.  The manifest content of a dream is the:
A.  hidden meaning behind the events
B.  dream's plot
C.  source of sexual energy
D.  unacceptable impulse which is repressed

p. 435
Freud's Psychodynamic
  Theory
Level: Moderate
Type: Factual
Ans: D

33.  "I had a dream last night where I was flying through trees that seemed to sway with a voice I heard near the ground." What is the manifest content of this dream?
A.  The trees refer to friends being persuaded by authority figures.
B.  The voice is one's sexual desire and trees are those that are sexually attracted.
C.  Flying through trees suggests that one needs to escape the present and listen more to the inner child.
D.  Flying through trees that moved with a voice near the ground.

p. 435
Freud's Psychodynamic
  Theory
Level: Easy
Type: Factual
Ans: A
*www*

34.  The hidden or disguised meaning of the events which occur in dreams are termed:
A.  latent content
B.  manifest content
C.  the pleasure principle
D.  the reality principle

p. 435
Freud's Psychodynamic
  Theory
Level: Easy
Type: Factual
Ans: D

35.  Freudian slips are mistakes made in everyday speech which reflect:
A.  the manifest content of dreams
B.  cognitive processing errors
C.  conscious desires and needs
D.  unconscious thoughts or wishes

p. 435
Freud's Psychodynamic
  Theory
Level: Moderate
Type: Applied
Ans: C

36.  "Once I said, 'I need to go to the mall to buy sex shirts...I mean six shirts.'" What would Freud say about this?
A.  The manifest content suggests depression.
B.  The slip of the tongue reflects manifest content of dreams.
C.  The slip of the tongue reflects unconscious desires.
D.  Cognitive processing errors suggest that memories are stored in adjacent areas of the brain.

p. 435
Freud's Psychodynamic
  Theory
Level: Moderate
Type: Applied
Ans: C

37.  Consider this: You are an unconscious wish, desire, or thought. According to the psychodynamic theory, how would you slip out?
A.  through a polygraph test
B.  through an eating disorder
C.  through free association
D.  through an internal locus of control

p. 435
Freud's Psychodynamic
  Theory
Level: Easy
Type: Factual
Ans: A

38. Free association, dream interpretation, and slips of the tongue are mental process that are:
A. the least under the control of our conscious, rational and logical minds
B. the most under the control of our conscious, rational and logical minds
C. best examples of techniques to explore the conscious mind
D. techniques used by Carl Rogers to explore self-actualization

p. 436
Divisions of the Mind
Level: Easy
Type: Factual
Ans: D

39. The three divisions of the mind according to Freud's theory are:
A. id, regulator, and conscious
B. inner, peripheral, and outer
C. pleasurer, governor, and regulator
D. id, ego, and superego

p. 436
Divisions of the Mind
Level: Easy
Type: Factual
Ans: B

40. Freud defined the id as:
A. the conscience
B. the source of energy that contains the biological drives for sex and aggression
C. an unconscious desire to be like one's father
D. the instinctual response to implied social demands

p. 436
Divisions of the Mind
Level: Easy
Type: Factual
Ans: C
www

41. The goal of the id is to:
A. satisfy wishes through socially acceptable methods
B. push unacceptable biological drives into the unconscious
C. pursue pleasure and satisfy biological drives
D. apply moral values in satisfying wishes

p. 436
Divisions of the Mind
Level: Easy
Type: Applied
Ans: D

42. Which division of the mind would say, "I can do anything I want to do"?
A. ego
B. real self
C. superego
D. id

p. 436
Divisions of the Mind
Level: Easy
Type: Factual
Ans: D

43. The id contains two biological drives. What are they?
A. hunger and aggression
B. safety and hunger
C. sex and safety
D. sex and aggression

p. 436
Divisions of the Mind
Level: Easy
Type: Factual
Ans: B

44. Which Freudian term attempts to satisfy drives without concern for moral restrictions or societal regulations?
A. the reality principle
B. the pleasure principle
C. the freedom principle
D. the superego principle

p. 436
Divisions of the Mind
Level: Moderate
Type: Applied
Ans: A

45. Gregory's college roommate finds him very difficult to live with because Gregory is extremely selfish and demands immediate gratification of all his needs and desires. From a psychodynamic point of view, Gregory is still being controlled by the:
A. id
B. ego
C. superego
D. conscience

p. 436
Divisions of the Mind
Level: Moderate
Type: Applied
Ans: B

46. Which of the following best illustrates the id?
A. a six-year-old who wants a toy and finds a way to manipulate her grandparents to buy it
B. a two-year-old who is totally selfish and wants to find as much pleasure as he can without regard for reason, logic, or morality
C. a college student who is faced with a moral decision and selects the right choice
D. a ten-year-old who sneaks a cookie from the kitchen by telling his mother that someone is knocking at the door

p. 436
Divisions of the Mind
Level: Moderate
Type: Factual
Ans: B

47. According to the reality principle, the purpose of the ego is to:
A. determine what actually happened in a given situation
B. search for socially acceptable outlets for the id's desire
C. impose order on our perceptions
D. help us form workable judgments about other people

p. 436
Divisions of the Mind
Level: Easy
Type: Factual
Ans: D

48. Infants discover restrictions to the pleasure principle and learn to control their wishes through the development of the:
A. superego
B. Oedipus complex
C. collective unconscious
D. ego

p. 436
Divisions of the Mind
Level: Moderate
Type: Conceptual
Ans: D

49. Id is to ego as:
A. self is to other
B. trend is to desire
C. need is to drive
D. pleasure is to reality

p. 436
Divisions of the Mind
Level: Easy
Type: Factual
Ans: C
*www*

50. The ego operates on the _____ principle.
A. desire
B. pleasure
C. reality
D. repression

p. 436
Divisions of the Mind
Level: Moderate
Type: Applied
Ans: D

51.  Kevin and Michael were in a stereo store. Both saw a compact disk they wanted badly but did not have the money for. Kevin decided to shoplift it, while Michael figured out that if he did some extra chores at home he could save up enough money for it in two weeks. Freud would say that Kevin is being governed by his _____ and Michael by his _____.

A.  superego; id
B.  superego; ego
C.  ego; id
D.  id; ego

p. 436
Divisions of the Mind
Level: Easy
Type: Factual
Ans: C

52.  Freud assumed that the _____ was totally unconscious, and that the largest part of the _____ was conscious.

A.  ego; superego
B.  ego; id
C.  id; ego
D.  superego; id

p. 436
Divisions of the Mind
Level: Easy
Type: Factual
Ans: C

53.  Freud defined the superego as:

A.  the person we would be if we could act out all the id's desires
B.  the self that is formed when we act instinctually
C.  the part of the mind containing moral standards
D.  the part of the mind that allows us to manipulate social situations to our own ends

p. 436
Divisions of the Mind
Level: Easy
Type: Factual
Ans: C

54.  According to Freud, guilt feelings arise from the operation of the:

A.  id
B.  ego
C.  superego
D.  alter ego

p. 436
Divisions of the Mind
Level: Easy
Type: Conceptual
Ans: A
*PS/SG 19-7*

55.  The ability to create feelings of guilt gives the _____ its power.

A.  superego
B.  ego
C.  id
D.  unconscious

p. 436
Divisions of the Mind
Level: Moderate
Type: Factual
Ans: B
*www*

56.  When Rachel left for college she promised her parents that she would not use any drugs. At a party someone passed her some pot, which she decided to try. If her superego is operating, this behavior will cause Rachel to feel:

A.  pleasure
B.  guilt
C.  sadness
D.  anger

| | | |
|---|---|---|
| p. 436<br>Divisions of the Mind<br>Level: Moderate<br>Type: Factual<br>Ans: A | 57.<br>A.<br>B.<br>C.<br>D. | How does the superego develop?<br>through interactions with parents or caregivers<br>it is innate<br>it develops when the ego realizes that it must be regulated<br>it comes forth from the id |
| p. 436<br>Divisions of the Mind<br>Level: Easy<br>Type: Factual<br>Ans: A | 58.<br><br>A.<br>B.<br>C.<br>D. | According to Freud, the human mind develops in which of the<br>following sequences?<br>id, ego, superego<br>superego, ego, id<br>ego, id, superego<br>superego, id, ego |
| p. 436<br>Divisions of the Mind<br>Level: Easy<br>Type: Factual<br>Ans: A | 59.<br><br>A.<br>B.<br>C.<br>D. | According to Freud, could a person function without conflict or<br>anxiety?<br>yes - when id, ego, and superego have the same goals<br>yes - if the superego maintains supreme control over the id and ego<br>yes - if the ego maintains supreme control over the id and superego<br>no - it's impossible |
| p. 437<br>Divisions of the Mind<br>Level: Easy<br>Type: Factual<br>Ans: C | 60.<br>A.<br>B.<br>C.<br>D. | Freud believed that an unconscious conflict is waged between the:<br>self and outside world<br>repressed memories and current values<br>id and superego<br>id and ego |
| p. 437<br>Divisions of the Mind<br>Level: Easy<br>Type: Factual<br>Ans: D | 61.<br>A.<br>B.<br>C.<br>D. | Anxiety is created by the ego in response to:<br>the manifest content of dreams<br>Freudian slips<br>the collective unconscious<br>id-superego conflict |
| p. 437<br>Divisions of the Mind<br>Level: Easy<br>Type: Factual<br>Ans: B | 62.<br><br>A.<br>B.<br>C.<br>D. | What do we call the unpleasant state that involves uneasiness,<br>apprehension, and heightened physiological arousal?<br>depression<br>anxiety<br>displacement<br>conflict |
| p. 437<br>Divisions of the Mind<br>Level: Easy<br>Type: Factual<br>Ans: C | 63.<br>A.<br>B.<br>C.<br>D. | Defense mechanisms are Freudian processes designed to reduce:<br>the latent content of dreams<br>the ego<br>anxiety<br>self-actualization |
| p. 437<br>Divisions of the Mind<br>Level: Easy<br>Type: Factual<br>Ans: D | 64.<br>A.<br>B.<br>C.<br>D. | If a defense mechanism is successful:<br>the id becomes stronger<br>unconscious motivation is increased<br>anxiety is increased<br>anxiety is reduced |

p. 437
Divisions of the Mind
Level: Easy
Type: Factual
Ans: A

65. Unconscious processes which utilize self-deception to reduce anxiety are called:
A. defense mechanisms
B. unconscious motivations
C. reality principles
D. free associations

p. 437
Divisions of the Mind
Level: Easy
Type: Factual
Ans: C

66. Which defense mechanism uses acceptable excuses for behaviors which cause us to feel anxiety?
A. denial
B. reaction formation
C. rationalization
D. repression

p. 437
Divisions of the Mind
Level: Easy
Type: Factual
Ans: D
*www*

67. As Tad works on his income tax form, he makes the decision to not report some income. He says, "Well, everybody cheats on their income tax and I need the money more than the government." Tad has just experienced:
A. denial
B. reaction formation
C. sublimation
D. rationalization

p. 437
Divisions of the Mind
Level: Moderate
Type: Applied
Ans: D
*PS/SG 19-9*

68. A student who blames poor test performance on "tricky questions" -- rather than admit to poor preparation--is using the defense mechanism of:
A. compensation
B. denial
C. projection
D. rationalization

p. 437
Divisions of the Mind
Level: Moderate
Type: Applied
Ans: D

69. Barbara refuses to believe that drinking and driving is dangerous. Barbara seems to be using the Freudian defense mechanism called:
A. reaction formation
B. sublimation
C. displacement
D. denial

p. 437
Divisions of the Mind
Level: Easy
Type: Factual
Ans: A

70. Refusing to recognize some anxiety-provoking event or information is the Freudian defense mechanism called:
A. denial
B. sublimation
C. rationalization
D. displacement

p. 437
Divisions of the Mind
Level: Easy
Type: Factual
Ans: A

71. When a person pushes threatening feelings into the unconscious, they are engaging in:
A. repression
B. projection
C. denial
D. sublimation

p. 437
Divisions of the Mind
Level: Easy
Type: Applied
Ans: C

72. Tara witnessed a terrible car accident, but now cannot remember any of it. Tara's inability to recall the event is most probably due to:
A. denial
B. projection
C. repression
D. sublimation

p. 437
Divisions of the Mind
Level: Easy
Type: Applied
Ans: D

73. In repression, where do unacceptable or threatening feelings or impulses go?
A. into the manifest mind
B. into the ego
C. into the superego
D. into the unconscious

p. 437
Divisions of the Mind
Level: Easy
Type: Factual
Ans: C

74. The defense mechanism of projection involves the unconscious transfer of:
A. threatening feelings into the unconscious
B. unacceptable wishes into acceptable behaviors
C. one's own unacceptable traits onto other people
D. feelings from the true source to a more acceptable source

p. 437
Divisions of the Mind
Level: Easy
Type: Conceptual
Ans: C

75. Which of the following is an example of projection?
A. A man is angry with his wife, so he yells at his employee.
B. A man denies that he is angry with his wife.
C. A man is angry with his wife, but says that she is the one who is angry.
D. A man makes up excuses for why he is angry with his wife.

p. 437
Divisions of the Mind
Level: Moderate
Type: Applied
Ans: A

76. "You are a slob." No, it is you who is the slop. The illustrates
A. projection
B. reaction formation
C. displacement
D. rationalization

p. 437
Divisions of the Mind
Level: Moderate
Type: Applied
Ans: B

77. In order to alleviate anxiety caused by a desire to be sexually promiscuous with women, John decides to become a priest. Freud would say that John has used the defense mechanism of:
A. projection
B. reaction formation
C. displacement
D. rationalization

p. 437
Divisions of the Mind
Level: Easy
Type: Factual
Ans: B
*PS/SG 19-10*

78. The defense mechanism in which unacceptable wishes are turned into their opposites is known as:
A. projection
B. reaction-formation
C. compensation
D. rationalization

p. 437
Divisions of the Mind
Level: Moderate
Type: Factual
Ans: B

79. What defense mechanism involves turning unacceptable wishes into acceptable behaviors?
A. projection
B. sublimation
C. displacement
D. rationalization

p. 437
Divisions of the Mind
Level: Easy
Type: Conceptual
Ans: A

80. Which of the following is an example of displacement?
A. a man is angry with his wife, so he yells at his employee
B. a man denies that he is angry with his wife
C. a man is angry with his wife, but says that she is the one who is angry
D. a man makes up excuses for why he is angry with his wife

p. 437
Divisions of the Mind
Level: Moderate
Type: Applied
Ans: C

81. Bob is sexually attracted to his professor. In order to deal with these feelings, Bob channels his energy into his homework and study habits. This is an example of the Freudian defense mechanism called:
A. reaction formation
B. rationalization
C. sublimation
D. denial

p. 437
Divisions of the Mind
Level: Moderate
Type: Factual
Ans: C

82. The use of defense mechanisms is:
A. always harmful
B. at a conscious level
C. helpful as long as we work on the real causes of the anxiety
D. to reduce depression caused by the id-superego conflict

p. 437
Divisions of the Mind
Level: Easy
Type: Factual
Ans: C

83. Do we know when we are using a defense mechanism?
A. yes - they are totally conscious
B. sometimes when the defense mechanism comes from the ego
C. no - they are totally unconscious
D. no - they occur within the superego

p. 438
Developmental Stages
Level: Easy
Type: Factual
Ans: B
*www*

84. Freud believed that personality development proceeded through a sequence of ___ stages.
A. cognitive
B. psychosexual
C. biological
D. psychosocial

p. 438
Developmental Stages
Level: Easy
Type: Factual
Ans: A

85. Freud described his developmental stages as periods during which the individual:
A. seeks pleasure from different areas of the body
B. resolves psychosocial conflicts
C. deals with real-life problems
D. matures, eventually becoming self-actualized

| | | |
|---|---|---|
| p. 438<br>Developmental Stages<br>Level: Easy<br>Type: Factual<br>Ans: C | 86. | In Freud's psychosexual stages, how does conflict arise between parent and child? |
| | A. | the parent attempts to teach the child language |
| | B. | the child tries to do good, but often fails to reach the parent's standard |
| | C. | the child seeks pleasure from different body areas associated with sexual feelings |
| | D. | the parent imposes their personality on a child as the child creates his own personality |

| | | |
|---|---|---|
| p. 438<br>Developmental Stages<br>Level: Easy<br>Type: Factual<br>Ans: B | 87. | Erogenous zones, according to Freud, describe areas of the: |
| | A. | brain where anxiety becomes repressed |
| | B. | body that are associated with sexual feelings |
| | C. | personality striving for personal growth |
| | D. | soul that are filled with positive regard |

| | | |
|---|---|---|
| p. 438<br>Developmental Stages<br>Level: Easy<br>Type: Conceptual<br>Ans: A | 88. | Freud believed that: |
| | A. | early childhood is very important in shaping personality |
| | B. | personality develops after puberty |
| | C. | the influence of early childhood experiences in the shaping of personality is greatly overrated |
| | D. | one's personality changes too often to be predicted or studied reliably |

| | | |
|---|---|---|
| p. 438<br>Developmental Stages<br>Level: Moderate<br>Type: Factual<br>Ans: D | 89. | According to Freud, _____ represent potential conflict between an individual's id and their parents. |
| | A. | defense mechanisms |
| | B. | erogenous zones |
| | C. | Freudian slips |
| | D. | psychosexual stages |

| | | |
|---|---|---|
| p. 438<br>Developmental Stages<br>Level: Moderate<br>Type: Applied<br>Ans: B | 90. | You overhear a husband telling his wife who is breastfeeding their newborn, "Careful don't give her too much!" Which of the following Freudian terms best illustrates the husband's concern? |
| | A. | projection |
| | B. | fixation |
| | C. | displacement |
| | D. | free association |

| | | |
|---|---|---|
| p. 438<br>Developmental Stages<br>Level: Easy<br>Type: Factual<br>Ans: B | 91. | If an individual's wishes are overgratified or undergratified at any particular psychosexual stage, Freud would argue that _____ will occur. |
| | A. | projection |
| | B. | fixation |
| | C. | displacement |
| | D. | Freudian slips |

| | | |
|---|---|---|
| p. 438<br>Developmental Stages<br>Level: Easy<br>Type: Factual<br>Ans: A | 92. | Fixation occurs: |
| | A. | in oral, anal, or phallic stages |
| | B. | primarily in males growing up in single-parent households |
| | C. | when the ego realizes the defense mechanism is having little effect |
| | D. | primarily in first-born children |

p. 439
Developmental Stages
Level: Easy
Type: Factual
Ans: D

93. Which of the following is the correct order of developmental stages according to the psychodynamic theory?
A. anal, latency, genital, phallic
B. oral, phallic, genital, latency, self-actualization
C. phallic, anal, latency, belongingness, oral
D. oral, anal, phallic, latency, genital

p. 439
Developmental Stages
Level: Easy
Type: Factual
Ans: A

94. The first of Freud's stages of psychosexual development is called the:
A. oral stage
B. anal stage
C. genital stage
D. undifferentiated stage

p. 439
Developmental Stages
Level: Moderate
Type: Applied
Ans: A

95. Oscar's mother refused to breast feed him when he was an infant. Today, Oscar talks all the time, chews his pencils, and chain-smokes. Freud would say that Oscar is:
A. fixated at the oral stage
B. utilizing the defense mechanism of rationalization
C. ignoring the needs of his id
D. overly dependent on the reality principle

p. 439
Developmental Stages
Level: Moderate
Type: Applied
Ans: B

96. Brad is a very sarcastic individual who eats to excess and is always chewing gum or his pencil. Freud would say that Brad is fixated at the _____ stage.
A. anal
B. oral
C. phallic
D. latency

p. 439
Developmental Stages
Level: Easy
Type: Factual
Ans: A

97. The second of Freud's stages of psychosexual development is called the:
A. anal stage
B. oral stage
C. genital stage
D. undifferentiated stage

p. 439
Developmental Stages
Level: Moderate
Type: Applied
Ans: C
*www*

98. Steven and Joe are very bad roommates. Steven is incredibly disorganized and messy while Joe is compulsive in his work and insists that the room be completely tidy at all times. According to Freud, it is possible that both Steven and Joe are fixated at the _____ stage.
A. oral
B. phallic
C. anal
D. latency

p. 439
Developmental Stages
Level: Moderate
Type: Applied
Ans: C

99. Cal is a carefree and generous person. His home is often a mess and his files at his office are very disorganized. From Freud's perspective, it is possible that Cal is fixated at the _____ stage.
A. oral
B. phallic
C. anal
D. latency

p. 439
Developmental Stages
Level: Easy
Type: Factual
Ans: A

100. After the oral and anal stages, the child enters the _____ stage.
A. phallic
B. latency
C. genital
D. conventional

p. 439
Developmental Stages
Level: Easy
Type: Factual
Ans: A

101. Which of the following is a major event that occurs during the phallic stage?
A. development of the Oedipus complex
B. toilet training
C. first crush on the opposite sex
D. teething

p. 439
Developmental Stages
Level: Moderate
Type: Conceptual
Ans: C

102. A little boy says, "When I grow up I want to marry Mommy!" According to Freud, this could be a manifestation of feelings that occur during which psychosexual stage?
A. latency
B. oral
C. phallic
D. anal

p. 439
Developmental Stages
Level: Easy
Type: Factual
Ans: D

103. During the Oedipus complex, the little boy feels hatred and jealously toward:
A. his older brother(s)
B. his sister(s)
C. his mother
D. his father

p. 439
Developmental Stages
Level: Easy
Type: Factual
Ans: B

104. Among little boys, fears of castration result from:
A. reaction formation
B. the Oedipus complex
C. penis envy
D. the latency stage

p. 439
Developmental Stages
Level: Easy
Type: Factual
Ans: C

105. When a little girl experiences the Electra complex, which of the following results in her turning against her mother and developing sexual desires for her father?
A. sublimation
B. rationalization
C. penis envy
D. the collective unconscious

p. 439
Developmental Stages
Level: Easy
Type: Factual
Ans: D

106. When are a child's sexual thoughts repressed? In the _____ stage.
A. oral
B. anal
C. phallic
D. latency

p. 439
Developmental Stages
Level: Easy
Type: Applied
Ans: D

107. Seven-year-old Megan only plays with girls, thinks that boys are weird, and attends second grade. She is most likely in which of Freud's psychosexual stages?
A. oral
B. anal
C. phallic
D. latency

p. 439
Developmental Stages
Level: Easy
Type: Factual
Ans: A

108. The final psychosexual stage, during which the adolescent experiences sexual feelings toward others, is called the _____ stage.
A. genital
B. phallic
C. latency
D. oral

p. 439
Developmental Stages
Level: Easy
Type: Factual
Ans: A

109. In what stage do sexual desires resurface and become renewed?
A. genital
B. phallic
C. latency
D. oral

p. 439
Developmental Stages
Level: Easy
Type: Factual
Ans: C

110. According to the textbook, what affects the success of someone meeting the conflicts of the genital stage?
A. overall maturity level
B. presence of social support
C. how well the previous stages were resolved
D. how fast the individual was toilet trained

p. 440
Freud's Followers
and Critics
Level: Easy
Type: Factual
Ans: A

111. Who is not considered one of Freud's former followers?
A. Carl Rogers
B. Carl Jung
C. Alfred Adler
D. Karen Horney

p. 440
Freud's Followers
and Critics
Level: Easy
Type: Conceptual
Ans: C

112. What would Carl Jung say to Sigmund Freud?
A. "I disagree with you Sigmund, the notion of a collective unconscious is ridiculous!"
B. "Analytical psychology is impractical and hog-wash!"
C. "Your emphasis on the human sex drive in personality is incorrect!"
D. "You should place even more emphasis on the human sex drive in personality!"

p. 440
Freud's Followers
  and Critics
Level:  Moderate
Type:  Factual
Ans:  D

113.    Which of the following is true of Carl Jung?

A.    He remained devoted to Freud until his death.

B.    His theory influenced psychology, art, literature, and philosophy.

C.    He believed that penis envy was passed on at birth to people of all cultural backgrounds.

D.    His theory was based on his conception of the collective unconscious.

p. 440
Freud's Followers
  and Critics
Level:  Moderate
Type:  Factual
Ans:  C

114.    Your professor explains that the reason a fear of snakes and a fear of the dark are found in so many cultures is that these fears are embedded in the _____. He is expressing an idea first put forth by _____.

A.    id; Sigmund Freud

B.    self-efficacy; Karen Horney

C.    collective unconscious: Carl Jung

D.    inferiority complex; Alfred Adler

p. 440
Freud's Followers
  and Critics
Level:  Easy
Type:  Factual
Ans:  A
PS/SG 19-12

115.    The concept of the collective unconscious was proposed by:

A.    Carl Jung

B.    Alfred Adler

C.    Karen Horney

D.    B. F. Skinner

p. 440
Freud's Followers
  and Critics
Level:  Moderate
Type:  Factual
Ans:  D

116.    Carl Jung and Alfred Adler were critical of Freud's:

A.    emphasis on unconscious processes

B.    reluctance to recognize the role of biological drives

C.    use of hypnosis

D.    emphasis on sexuality

p. 440
Freud's Followers
  and Critics
Level:  Easy
Type:  Factual
Ans:  D

117.    Adler disagreed with Freud by proposing that humans are governed by _____ urges.

A.    sexual

B.    aggressive

C.    unconscious

D.    social

p. 440
Freud's Followers
  and Critics
Level:  Easy
Type:  Factual
Ans:  A

118.    Dr. Katmeh agrees with Alfred Adler on the major influences in a child's development.  On what do Dr. Katmeh and Adler agree?

A.    sibling influences and child-rearing practices

B.    unconscious conflicts

C.    collective unconscious

D.    drive for self-actualization

p. 440
Freud's Followers
  and Critics
Level:  Easy
Type:  Factual
Ans:  A

119.    Which of the following personality theorists had views of women that would be most disputed today?

A.    Sigmund Freud

B.    Karen Horney

C.    Carl Jung

D.    Alfred Adler

p. 440
Freud's Followers
and Critics
Level: Easy
Type: Conceptual
Ans: B

120. Your friend argues that negative characteristics associated with women, such as passivity, are due not to biology, but to child-parent social interactions. Which theorist does your friend agree with?
A. Sigmund Freud
B. Karen Horney
C. Erik Erikson
D. Carl Jung

p. 440
Freud's Followers
and Critics
Level: Easy
Type: Applied
Ans: A

121. Which of the following titles would be most likely given to a book written by Karen Horney?
A. *Our Lives In Child-Parent Interactions*
B. *The Collective Unconscious: Message and Symbols*
C. *The Importance of Biology: Why Freud Was Right*
D. *Our Journey Through Psychosocial Stages*

p. 440
Freud's Followers
and Critics
Level: Easy
Type: Applied
Ans: D

122. Which of the following titles would be most likely given to a book written by Erik Erikson?
A. *Our Lives In Child-Parent Interactions*
B. *The Collective Unconscious: Message and Symbols*
C. *The Importance of Biology: Why Freud Was Right*
D. *Our Journey Through Psychosocial Stages*

p. 441
Freud's Followers
and Critics
Level: Easy
Type: Factual
Ans: C

123. The major weakness of Freud's theory of personality is that it:
A. treats males and females equally
B. does not emphasize biological drives
C. can explain almost any behavior
D. lends itself well to scientific experimentation

p. 441
Freud's Followers
and Critics
Level: Easy
Type: Factual
Ans: D

124. Critics charged that Freud's theory of personality is not very useful in:
A. treating males and females equally
B. explaining biological drives
C. explaining behavior
D. making predictions

p. 441
Freud's Followers
and Critics
Level: Easy
Type: Factual
Ans: C

125. Freud's theory of personality has been criticized on a number of grounds, including:
A. it is too limited in scope
B. its emphasis on psychological and social influences
C. difficulty in testing Freudian concepts
D. its ability to interpret behavior

p. 441
Freud's Followers
and Critics
Level: Easy
Type: Factual
Ans: A

126. Freud's ideas such as id, ego, superego, repression, and unconscious forces:
A. are very difficult to demonstrate experimentally or verify
B. have been proved in several studies
C. were actually developed by Carl Jung
D. are assumed to be incorrect by most psychoanalytical theorists

p. 441
Freud's Followers
  and Critics
Level: Easy
Type: Factual
Ans: D

127. Regarding Freud's theory of psychosexual stages, research:
   A. confirms that the genital stage is most important
   B. has established the existence of the Oedipus complex
   C. is currently considering the importance of the anal stage
   D. indicates that personality continues to develop beyond the first five
      years of life

p. 441
Freud's Followers
  and Critics
Level: Moderate
Type: Conceptual
Ans: D

128. How does the existence of resilient children impact Freud's theory of
   psychosexual stages?
   A. They support the theory since the children often experience denial.
   B. They support the theory since the children often become adults with
      serious psychological problems.
   C. Resilient children support the theory since they may develop fixation
      in the psychosexual stages.
   D. Resilient children question the theory since many develop into healthy
      adults.

p. 441
Freud's Followers
  and Critics
Level: Moderate
Type: Factual
Ans: A

129. Which term refers to learning that is out of our awareness, but
   influences conscious thoughts, feelings, and behaviors?
   A. implicit or nondeclarative memory
   B. defense mechanisms
   C. implicit memory
   D. collective unconscious

p. 441
Freud's Followers
  and Critics
Level: Easy
Type: Applied
Ans: B

130. What would be an example of an implicit memory?
   A. juggling three balls while singing a song
   B. walking
   C. learning a foreign language
   D. giving a speech before a large audience

p. 441
Freud's Followers
  and Critics
Level: Moderate
Type: Factual
Ans: C
PS/SG 19-13

131. Cognitive neuroscientists have developed the concept of _____
   to take the place of Freud's theory of repressed unconscious forces.
   A. conscious thoughts
   B. the collective unconscious
   C. implicit or nondeclarative memory
   D. the phenomenological perspective

p. 442
Humanistic Theories
Level: Easy
Type: Factual
Ans: B

132. Which approach to personality stresses the achievement of human
   potential and personal growth?
   A. social-cognitive
   B. humanistic
   C. psychodynamic
   D. trait

p. 442
Humanistic Theories
Level: Easy
Type: Factual
Ans: C
*www*

133. The capacity for growth, the development of our maximum potential, and the freedom to choose our destiny are all characteristic of:
A. psychoanalytic theories
B. cognitive theories
C. humanistic theories
D. social cognitive theories

p. 442
Humanistic Theories
Level: Easy
Type: Applied
Ans: D

134. If you are doing a computerized literature search on the humanistic theories, which group of words would be most appropriate to use?
A. situation, observation, modeling
B. environment, reinforcement, Big Five
C. unconscious, childhood, anxiety
D. personal growth, potential, self-actualization

p. 442
Humanistic Theories
Level: Moderate
Type: Factual
Ans: C

135. Which statement does not describe the humanistic theory?
A. We have an inherent tendency to develop and reach our true potential.
B. Personality is more than the sum of its individual parts.
C. Personality is influenced by language, observational learning, purposeful behavior, and self-analysis
D. How you perceive the world becomes your reality.

p. 442
Humanistic Theories
Level: Easy
Type: Factual
Ans: B
*PS/SG 19-14*

136. Unlike psychodynamic theories, humanistic theories of personality emphasize:
A. the continual operation of contradictory forces buried deep in our unconscious minds
B. our capacity for personal growth, the development of our potential, and freedom to choose our destiny
C. how difficult it is — even with therapy — to change personality significantly
D. the importance of perceptions and beliefs

p. 442
Humanistic Theories
Level: Easy
Type: Factual
Ans: B

137. The phenomenological perspective proposes that:
A. reality is determined by our unconscious conflicts
B. our perceptions of the world become our reality
C. we base our reality on what we observe in our environment
D. defense mechanisms are helpful in denying reality

p. 442
Humanistic Theories
Level: Moderate
Type: Factual
Ans: A

138. "You are who you are because of your motivation, faith, intelligence, optimism, cheerfulness." This is a good example of:
A. the holistic view
B. the reality principle
C. locus of control
D. self-actualization

p. 442
Humanistic Theories
Level: Moderate
Type: Conceptual
Ans: C

139. Which individual best exemplifies the idea of self-actualization?
A. Mary - she feels as if her talents are going to waste in life
B. Larry - he wants to own his business but is unwilling to take the risk
C. Gary - he fulfilled his dreams of being an educator and now can retire knowing that he put all of his skills and talents to use
D. Terry - he sees himself moving up the ladder in his position at the factory

| | | |
|---|---|---|
| p. 442<br>Humanistic Theories<br>Level: Easy<br>Type: Factual<br>Ans: A<br>*PS/SG 19-17* | 140. | By self-actualization, Maslow meant: |
| | A. | fulfillment of our unique potential |
| | B. | having our deficiency needs satisfied |
| | C. | being loved and loving someone in return |
| | D. | gaining recognition and status in society |
| p. 443<br>Humanistic Theories<br>Level: Easy<br>Type: Factual<br>Ans: B | 141. | Which theorist started his career as a behaviorist and later developed a theory that arranged human needs into a hierarchy of needs? |
| | A. | Freud |
| | B. | Maslow |
| | C. | Bandura |
| | D. | Adler |
| p. 443<br>Humanistic Theories<br>Level: Easy<br>Type: Factual<br>Ans: A | 142. | Maslow's hierarchy of needs suggests that: |
| | A. | biological needs must be satisfied before personal and social needs |
| | B. | regardless of the status of basic needs, the needs for sex and aggression must be fulfilled first |
| | C. | unless self-actualization has occurred, basic needs are meaningless |
| | D. | rewards and punishment are the keys to achieving personal satisfaction and happiness |
| p. 443<br>Humanistic Theories<br>Level: Easy<br>Type: Factual<br>Ans: D | 143. | According to Maslow, which of the following needs must be satisfied first? |
| | A. | need for love |
| | B. | need for self-actualization |
| | C. | need for high self-esteem |
| | D. | need for shelter |
| p. 443<br>Humanistic Theories<br>Level: Moderate<br>Type: Factual<br>Ans: B<br>*www* | 144. | What is the correct order of Maslow's hierarchy of needs? |
| | A. | love and belongingness, esteem, self-actualization, physiological, safety |
| | B. | physiological, safety, love and belongingness, esteem, self-actualization |
| | C. | safety, love and belongingness, physiological esteem, self-actualization |
| | D. | safety, love and belongingness, esteem, self-actualization, physiological |
| p. 443<br>Humanistic Theories<br>Level: Easy<br>Type: Factual<br>Ans: B | 145. | Needs that we try to first fulfill are called _____, while needs at a higher level are termed _____. |
| | A. | fulfillment needs; higher needs |
| | B. | deficiency needs; growth needs |
| | C. | primary needs; secondary needs |
| | D. | elementary needs; secondary needs |
| p. 443<br>Humanistic Theories<br>Level: Easy<br>Type: Factual<br>Ans: B | 146. | The desire for truth, goodness, beauty, and justice are examples of: |
| | A. | deficiency needs |
| | B. | growth needs |
| | C. | actualization needs |
| | D. | regard needs |

p. 443
Humanistic Theories
Level: Easy
Type: Factual
Ans: C

147. Maslow believed that everyone is motivated by:
A. sexual desires
B. aggressive tendencies
C. a self-actualizing tendency
D. personality traits

p. 443
Humanistic Theories
Level: Moderate
Type: Conceptual
Ans: B

148. Which of the following phrases best illustrates self-actualization?
A. "You Deserve A Break Today"
B. "Be All That You Can Be"
C. "Be True to Yourself"
D. "Here Today Gone Tomorrow"

p. 443
Humanistic Theories
Level: Easy
Type: Factual
Ans: A

149. Maslow developed his idea of self-actualization by studying:
A. productive, exceptional people
B. psychologically disturbed patients
C. college students
D. laboratory animals

p. 443
Humanistic Theories
Level: Moderate
Type: Factual
Ans: C

150. Which of the following is not a characteristic of self-actualized persons?
A. perception of reality in an accurate fashion
B. independence
C. deep, loving relationships with many people
D. peak experiences

p. 444
Humanistic Theories
Level: Easy
Type: Factual
Ans: C

151. Which individual is most associated with the self theory?
A. Jung
B. Maslow
C. Rogers
D. Adler

p. 444
Humanistic Theories
Level: Easy
Type: Factual
Ans: D

152. In Carl Rogers' humanistic theory, he emphasizes two assumptions. These assumptions are:
A. need for locus of control and conscious motivation
B. achievement and recognition
C. real self and ideal self
D. self-actualizing tendency and personal need for positive regard

p. 444
Humanistic Theories
Level: Easy
Type: Factual
Ans: B

153. Self-actualization for Rogers refers to one's need to:
A. fulfill our biological needs
B. develop our capacities in ways that are best for one's life
C. maintain control over our lives
D. overcome a sense of inferiority

p. 444
Humanistic Theories
Level: Moderate
Type: Applied
Ans: A

154. At Gwen's 20th high school reunion she visited with some people who made many wrong choices throughout their lives resulting in negative and harmful behaviors. Carl Rogers would say that these people's _____ was dysfunctional.
A. self-actualizing tendency
B. locus of control
C. ego
D. defense mechanism

p. 444
Humanistic Theories
Level: Moderate
Type: Factual
Ans: A

155. According to Carl Rogers, the characteristics you see yourself as having constitute the:
A. self
B. ego
C. id
D. cognitive whole

p. 444
Humanistic Theories
Level: Easy
Type: Factual
Ans: B

156. Self-concept plays an important role in personality because it influences:
A. the id
B. behavior
C. the collective unconscious
D. fixation during the oral stage

p. 444
Humanistic Theories
Level: Moderate
Type: Factual
Ans: C

157. "I see myself as shy and people tend to go out of their way to make me feel comfortable." This person has described her:
A. phenomenological self
B. reveal self
C. real self
D. actual self

p. 444
Humanistic Theories
Level: Moderate
Type: Factual
Ans: B

158. _____ refers to our hopes and wishes as to how we would like to see ourselves.
A. Phenomenological self
B. Ideal self
C. Real self
D. Actual self

p. 444
Humanistic Theories
Level: Moderate
Type: Factual
Ans: B

159. According to Carl Rogers, contradictions between _____ and _____ may result in personality problems.
A. internal locus of control; external locus of control
B. the real self; the ideal self
C. unconscious forces; conscious forces
D. deficiency needs; growth needs

p. 444
Humanistic Theories
Level: Easy
Type: Factual
Ans: C
*PS/SG 19-19*

160. Why are so many people unhappy? Carl Rogers says it is because:
A. happiness is only possible when we become self-actualized
B. happiness is only an illusion
C. we have both a real self and an ideal self, and they are often in conflict
D. we have a positive self and a negative self, and one always dominates

p. 445
Humanistic Theories
Level: Easy
Type: Factual
Ans: D

161. The idea of positive regard refers to:
A. our need to feel good about our accomplishments
B. our subjective belief that we can succeed in doing something
C. influencing other people's lives in healthy and positive ways
D. the love, acceptance and respect that we need from those people who are important to us

p. 445
Humanistic Theories
Level: Easy
Type: Applied
Ans: B

162. "As long as you carry your own, make contributions to this organization, and make your sales quota, you are accepted. If you do not, you will be fired." This statement best illustrates:
A. unconditional positive regard
B. conditional positive regard
C. conditioned response
D. self-efficacy

p. 445
Humanistic Theories
Level: Moderate
Type: Factual
Ans: A

163. Rogers postulated that children would develop a negative self-concept if they:
A. received primarily conditional positive regard
B. ignored the influence of their cognitive unconscious
C. utilized defense mechanisms to deal with anxiety
D. operated under an internal locus of control

p. 445
Humanistic Theories
Level: Moderate
Type: Applied
Ans: C

164. Rudy has a negative self-concept. How would Rogers be most likely to explain Rudy's negative self-concept?
A. Rudy tends to focus on external locus of control.
B. His ego is too powerful .
C. His parents and others around him probably gave him conditional positive regard.
D. He consistently uses defense mechanisms.

p. 445
Humanistic Theories
Level: Easy
Type: Applied
Ans: A

165. Fay knows that, no matter how much trouble she gets in at school, her parents will always accept and love her. Carl Rogers would call this:
A. unconditional positive regard
B. conditional positive regard
C. emotional support
D. parental blindness

p. 445
Humanistic Theories
Level: Easy
Type: Factual
Ans: C

166. Positive regard that is given because the person is valued as a human being is called:
A. a cognition
B. parental blindness
C. unconditional positive regard
D. conditional positive regard

p. 445
Humanistic Theories
Level: Easy
Type: Applied
Ans: D
www

167. Craig's father says, "I'll really love you if you get A's in all your subjects at school." According to Carl Rogers, this statement would be an example of:
A. a cognition
B. parental blindness
C. unconditional positive regard
D. conditional positive regard

p. 446
Humanistic Theories
Level: Easy
Type: Factual
Ans: C
*PS/SG 19-21*

168. The old warning, "Of course Mommy loves you… when you're good!" is an example of Rogers' concept of;
A. self-actualization
B. self-esteem needs
C. conditional positive regard
D. unconditional positive regard

p. 446
Humanistic Theories
Level: Moderate
Type: Conceptual
Ans: A

169. In what way do the humanistic theories of personality differ from almost every other theory?
A. The humanistic theories believe that people are basically good.
B. The humanistic theories believe that people are basically bad.
C. The humanistic theories believe that people are governed by their unconscious mind.
D. People are motivated to get as much pleasure as they possibly can.

p. 446
Humanistic Theories
Level: Moderate
Type: Factual
Ans: A
*PS/SG 19-22*

170. An evaluation of humanistic theories of personality would emphasize their:
A. positive, hopeful philosophy of human nature rather than scientific explanation of personality development
B. rational, scientific assessment of the biological strengths and limitations of our species
C. addition to psychology of new research in personality from genetics and neuroscience
D. demonstration of how human personality is driven by unconscious irrational forces

p. 446
Humanistic Theories
Level: Easy
Type: Factual
Ans: B

171. Roland Gilbert has applied many humanistic ideas to help:
A. delinquent males
B. African-American boys
C. homesick college students
D. shy teenagers

p. 446
Humanistic Theories
Level: Easy
Type: Factual
Ans: C

172. The program developed for at-risk African-American boys emphasizes:
A. getting in touch with id-superego conflicts
B. free association and dream interpretation
C. mentors who provide positive regard
D. psychodynamic techniques

p. 446
Humanistic Theories
Level: Easy
Type: Factual
Ans: A

173. Critics argue that the humanistic theories _____ rather than _____ behavior.
A. describe; explain
B. predict, explain
C study; change
D. correlate; explain

p. 446
Humanistic Theories
Level: Moderate
Type: Factual
Ans: D

174. There are many critics who argue that the humanistic approach is more of a _____ than a _____.
A. scientific explanation of personality development; philosophy of life
B. scientifically proven fact; hypothetical model
C. theory of well-being; theory of abnormality
D. philosophy of life; scientific explanation of personality development

p. 446
Humanistic Theories
Level: Easy
Type: Factual
Ans: B

175. One concern about the humanistic theories of personality presented in the textbook is:
A. there is little evidence to support the notion of positive regard
B. concepts in this perspective are difficult to study or verify
C. personality is not completely formed during the first five years of life
D. that there is too much emphasis on explaining behavior

p. 448
Cultural Diversity:
  High Achievement
Level: Easy
Type: Factual
Ans: D

176. Academic success among Indo-Chinese children is primarily due to:
A. genetic differences
B. low rates of poverty among Indo-Chinese refugees
C. high percentages of Indo-Chinese adults with college degrees
D. cultural and personal values taught by the family

p. 448
Cultural Diversity:
  High Achievement
Level: Easy
Type: Factual
Ans: B

177. Which of the following is not among the primary values held by Indo-Chinese families with high achieving children?
A. mutual respect
B. valuing leisure time
C. cooperation
D. commitment to accomplishment

p. 448
Cultural Diversity:
  High Achievement
Level: Easy
Type: Factual
Ans: A

178. A recent study reports that Indo-Chinese have a higher commitment to accomplishment that American students; Indo-Chinese spend an average of ____ hours a night studying; American children spend an average of ____ hours.
A. 3; 1 1/2
B. 1 1/2; 1/2
C. 5; 2
D. 6; 3

p. 448
Cultural Diversity:
  High Achievement
Level: Easy
Type: Factual
Ans: D
PS/SG 19-23

179. The remarkable academic achievement of children of the Indo-Chinese boat people is best explained by the:
A. political values of anti-communism they shared with their new neighbors
B. restrictive immigration policy that allowed in only well-educated families
C. high value Protestantism places on school achievement
D. personal and cultural values concerning education transmitted by their parents

p. 449
Research Focus:
  Causes of Shyness
Level: Easy
Type: Factual
Ans: C

180. _____ is a feeling of distress that comes from being tense, stressed, or awkward in social situations and from worrying about and fearing being rejected.
A. Fear
B. Anxiety
C. Shyness
D. Phobia

p. 449
Research Focus:
  Causes of Shyness
Level: Easy
Type: Factual
Ans: A

181. Shyness, from the psychodynamic approach, is seen as resulting from:
A. unresolved unconscious feelings of anxiety and fear
B. cognitive factors
C. genetic influences
D. physiological overresponsiveness

p. 449
Research Focus:
  Causes of Shyness
Level: Easy
Type: Factual
Ans: D

182. From the psychodynamic approach, how do people with shyness deal with shyness?
A. experience manifest content
B. shift from internal to external locus of control
C. self-actualize
D. use defense mechanisms

p. 449
Research Focus:
  Causes of Shyness
Level: Easy
Type: Factual
Ans: D

183. Which approach breaks shyness down into three measurable components?
A. the psychodynamic approach
B. the humanistic approach
C. the phenomenological approach
D. the social cognitive approach

p. 449
Research Focus:
  Causes of Shyness
Level: Easy
Type: Factual
Ans: A

184. When studying shyness, social cognitive theorists argue that it can be best understood by:
A. examining the interaction between cognitive, behavioral, and environmental components
B. early childhood experiences
C. the difference between real self and ideal self
D. dream interpretation and cognitive factors

p. 449
Research Focus:
  Causes of Shyness
Level: Easy
Type: Factual
Ans: C

185. According to the social cognitive approach, when the behavior of shy people is studied, it is found that they have:
A. higher rates of nonverbal cues
B. more intense irrational thoughts
C. too few social and communication skills
D. more internal locus of control

p. 450
Application:
Assessment-
  Projective Tests
Level: Easy
Type: Applied
Ans: B

186. Cal is preparing for a blind date with Stephanie. He is nervous and wishes he knew more about her. In fact, _____ would reveal her characteristics, traits, and abilities.
A. neurological testing
B. psychological assessment
C. unconditional positive regard
D. validity and reliability

p. 450
Application:
Assessment-
  Projective Tests
Level: Easy
Type: Factual
Ans: C

187. _____ measure(s) observable and unobservable characteristics. Achievement tests, aptitude tests, and intelligence tests are examples of _____.

A. Ability tests; graphological tests
B. Dream interpretation; personality tests
C. Personality tests; ability tests
D. Self-report tests; projective tests

p. 450
Application:
Assessment-
  Projective Tests
Level: Easy
Type: Applied
Ans: C

188. "I want to find out about your intelligence, what you have learned, and your potential for learning. To do these, I would use _____."

A. neurological tests
B. psychological assessment
C. ability tests
D. personality tests

p. 450
Application:
Assessment-
  Projective Tests
Level: Easy
Type: Factual
Ans: D

189. Tests that provide ambiguous or unstructured stimuli are called:

A. unreliable
B. invalid
C. open-ended
D. projective

p. 450
Application:
Assessment-
  Projective Tests
Level: Easy
Type: Factual
Ans: C
PS/SG 19-24

190. Because they use _____, projective tests often bring out unconscious material.

A. pictures of people
B. simple materials
C. ambiguous stimuli
D. computer analysis

p. 450
Application:
Assessment-
  Projective Tests
Level: Easy
Type: Factual
Ans: A
www

191. The projective tests discussed in the textbook include:

A. Rorschach test and TAT
B. MMPI-2 and structured interview protocols
C. Rorschach test and MMPI-2
D. California Personality Inventory and MMPI-2

p. 450
Application:
Assessment-
  Projective Tests
Level: Easy
Type: Factual
Ans: A

192. Children like to pour ink on one side of a piece of paper, fold the paper, and then figure out what the resulting shape looks like. This activity is most like which of the following personality measures?

A. Rorschach test
B. MMPI-2
C. TAT
D. California Personality Inventory

| | | |
|---|---|---|
| p. 450<br>Application:<br>Assessment-<br>  Projective Tests<br>Level: Easy<br>Type: Conceptual<br>Ans: B | 193. | Rorshach is to TAT as _____ is to _____.<br>A.  Freud; Skinner<br>B.  inkblots; pictures<br>C.  unconscious; conscious<br>D.  neurological; psychological |

| | | |
|---|---|---|
| p. 450<br>Application:<br>Assessment-<br>  Projective Tests<br>Level: Easy<br>Type: Applied<br>Ans: C | 194. | A psychologist wishes to determine the personality of one of her adolescent clients. She also wants to avoid responses that are given just because the client thinks they are what the psychologist wants to hear. If she chooses a test that involves showing the client a series of pictures, it is likely that she is using the:<br>A.  SAT<br>B.  MMPI-2<br>C.  TAT<br>D.  California Personality Inventory |

| | | |
|---|---|---|
| p. 451<br>Application:<br>Assessment-<br>  Projective Tests<br>Level: Easy<br>Type: Factual<br>Ans: B | 195. | Using handwriting analysis to describe an individual's personality :<br>A.  is becoming a more widely-accepted measure<br>B.  lacks validity<br>C.  is a valid approach to personality measurement<br>D.  shows one's strengths and weaknesses |

| | | |
|---|---|---|
| p. 451<br>Application:<br>Assessment-<br>  Projective Tests<br>Level: Easy<br>Type: Factual<br>Ans: C | 196. | Tests of personality must have two characteristics and they are:<br>A.  standardization and validity<br>B.  correlation and standardization<br>C.  reliability and validity<br>D.  standardization and reliability |

| | | |
|---|---|---|
| p. 451<br>Application:<br>Assessment-<br>  Projective Tests<br>Level: Easy<br>Type: Factual<br>Ans: C | 197. | If a test measures what it is supposed to be measuring, then we can say that the test is:<br>A.  reliable<br>B.  consistent<br>C.  valid<br>D.  organic |

| | | |
|---|---|---|
| p. 451<br>Application:<br>Assessment-<br>  Projective Tests<br>Level: Easy<br>Type: Conceptual<br>Ans: D | 198. | The game clock in the basketball game actually measures how much time is left in the game. Therefore, the game clock is a _____ measure.<br>A.  psychometric<br>B.  distributed<br>C.  correlational<br>D.  valid |

p. 451
Application:
Assessment-
  Projective Tests
Level: Moderate
Type: Applied
Ans: A

199. A psychology professor is about to test her student's understanding of the Freudian and Humanistic theories. The test she develops just has questions on it that measure the student's understanding of social cognitive and trait theories. The test lacks:
A. validity
B. reliability
C. practical nature
D. clarity

p. 451
Application:
Assessment-
  Projective Tests
Level: Easy
Type: Factual
Ans: A

200. Handwriting analysis to measure intelligence may have _____, but definitely lacks _____.
A. reliability; validity
B. correlation; heritability
C. validity; heritability
D. reliability; correlation

p. 451
Application:
Assessment-
  Projective Tests
Level: Easy
Type: Conceptual
Ans: C

201. Based on the definition presented in your text, reliability means the same thing as:
A. a correlation
B. standardization
C. consistency
D. validity

p. 451
Application:
Assessment-
  Projective Tests
Level: Easy
Type: Factual
Ans: B
www

202. One advantage of the Rorschach Inkblot test is that:
A. it yields responses that are easy to interpret
B. it prevents the respondent from faking answers
C. responses tend to be reliable
D. the scoring system is free of cultural bias

p. 451
Application:
Assessment-
  Projective Tests
Level: Moderate
Type: Factual
Ans: D

203. The interpretation of a client's response to a projective test reflects:
A. the client's personality
B. the biases of the clinician
C. the unconscious motives of the client
D. maybe both the client's personality and biases of the clinician

p. 451
Application:
Assessment-
  Projective Tests
Level: Easy
Type: Factual
Ans: C
www

204. One of the disadvantages of projective tests is that they:
A. take a long time to administer
B. have to be made up by the psychologist in advance
C. tend to be low in reliability and validity
D. are rarely used by clinical psychologists

True/False

| | | | |
|---|---|---|---|
| T | | 1. | Freud emphasized the influence of unconscious forces on behavior. |
| T | *www* | 2. | In free association, the client is encouraged to talk in a free-flowing way. |
| F | | 3. | A Freudian slip suggests a conscious wish or desire. |
| F | | 4. | The superego follows the reality principle. |
| F | | 5. | Repression means the person is transferring feelings from one person to another person. |
| F | *www* | 6. | Fixation only occurs at the anal stage. |
| T | | 7. | In the phallic stage, the Oedipus complex occurs. |
| T | *www* | 8. | The collective unconscious refers to memory and symbols shared by all cultures. |
| T | *www* | 9. | Research supports how unconscious forces affect us. |
| F | | 10. | Freud's theory acknowledges the importance of genetic factors. |
| T | | 11. | The phenomenological perspective emphasis is on how you perceive the world. |
| F | *www* | 12. | The correct level of Maslow's hierarchy of needs are physiological, self-actualization, safety needs, esteem needs, love and belongingness, and unconscious needs. |
| F | | 13. | Deficiency needs are at the highest levels of Maslow's hierarchy of needs. |
| T | | 14. | In self-actualization, the person reaches fulfillment of potential. |
| T | *www* | 15. | When there is a contradiction between ideal and real self, personality problems can occur. |
| F | *www* | 16. | The ideal self is an important Freudian term. |
| T | | 17. | Positive regard refers to love, sympathy, acceptance, and warmth. |
| T | *www* | 18. | In unconditional positive regard, an individual is accepted no matter what. |
| F | *www* | 19. | The humanistic theory focuses on unconscious conflicts and early childhood experiences. |
| T | | 20. | The humanistic approach is more of a philosophy of life than a scientific theory. |
| F | | 21. | In studying shyness, social cognitive theory focuses on defense mechanisms. |
| F | | 22. | Genetics do not play a role in shyness. |
| T | *www* | 23. | The Rorschach test is an example of a Projective test. |
| T | | 24. | Validity refers to a test measuring what it intends to measure. |
| F | | 25. | Projective tests are valid and reliable measures. |

Short-Answer Essay Questions

1. Discuss the interaction between id, ego, and superego. (*www*)
2. Describe the use of free association, dream interpretation, and analysis of Freudian slips in understanding the unconscious.
3. What are the major criticisms of Freud's theory? (*www*)
4. Describe the levels of Maslow's hierarchy of needs. How might you satisfy each of the levels?
5. What role does the ideal and real self play in Rogers' theory? (*www*)
6. Describe how a parent would apply conditional positive regard and unconditional positive regard in interacting with a child.
7. How is the humanistic perspective helping African-American boys?
8. According to the module, why do Indo-Chinese refugee children do well in school? (*www*)
9. Describe the Rorschach and Thematic Apperception Tests. Which personality perspective would be most likely to use tests and why?
10. Discuss validity and reliability and why they are important characteristics of personality tests. (*www*)

# Module 20 - Social Cognitive and Trait Theories

p. 457
Introduction
Level:  Moderate
Type:  Conceptual
Ans:  B

1. The stories of Nelson Mandela and Beverly Harvard illustrate the idea that:
   A. personality is fixed from birth
   B. personality can help us overcome barriers
   C. luck and fate have as much to do with our lives as persistence
   D. traits are responsible for civil disobedience

p. 457
Introduction
Level:  Moderate
Type:  Factual
Ans:  A

2. According to the textbook, women make good cops because they:
   A. are less authoritarian
   B. are more demanding
   C. are more authoritarian
   D. know what it is like to experience discrimination

p. 457
Introduction
Level:  Easy
Type:  Conceptual
Ans:  A
*PS/SG 20-1*

3. Rod Plotnik tells the stories of leader Nelson Mandela and police chief Beverly Harvard to illustrate the:
   A. beliefs and traits that motivate human personality
   B. powerful personalities that have been produced by the peoples of Africa
   C. key role of prisons and law enforcement in maintaining social stability
   D. unconscious forces that are the foundation of all personality

p. 457
Introduction
Level:  Easy
Type:  Factual
Ans:  C

4. As you are researching your paper on men and women who are law enforcement officers, you find out that:
   A. women are more likely to trigger hostility than men
   B. men are less authoritarian than women
   C. women are better listeners than men
   D. men are better listeners than women

p. 458
Social Cognitive Theory
Level:  Easy
Type:  Factual
Ans:  C
*www*

5. "People are basically good and their personality is shaped by an inborn tendency to reach their greatest potential." What kind of theorist would be most likely to make that statement?
   A. social cognitive
   B. trait
   C. humanistic
   D. analytical

p. 458
Social Cognitive Theory
Level:  Easy
Type:  Applied
Ans:  C

6. As Roger attempts to think about his personality, he remembers what he read once: "Your personality is shaped by the environment, cognitive/personal factors, and behavior." In what source did Roger most likely read that?
   A. *The Handbook of Psychodynamic Theory*
   B. *Maslow's Essays on Being Human*
   C. *The Hitchhiker's Guide to Social Cognitive Theory*
   D. *The Id, Ego, and Superego*

| | | |
|---|---|---|
| p. 458<br>Social Cognitive Theory<br>Level: Easy<br>Type: Factual<br>Ans: A | 7. | "Who you are is shaped by the environment, personal-cognitive factors, and behaviors all interacting and influencing how information is processed and used." What kind of theorist would be <u>most</u> likely to make that statement? |
| | A. | social cognitive |
| | B. | trait |
| | C. | humanistic |
| | D. | analytical |

| | | |
|---|---|---|
| p. 458<br>Social Cognitive Theory<br>Level: Easy<br>Type: Factual<br>Ans: B | 8. | Which name seems out of place with the others based on their theoretical perspective? |
| | A. | Bandura |
| | B. | Erikson |
| | C. | Rotter |
| | D. | Mischel |

| | | |
|---|---|---|
| p. 458<br>Social Cognitive Theory<br>Level: Easy<br>Type: Conceptual<br>Ans: D | 9. | What words are most descriptive of the social cognitive approach? |
| | A. | id, ego, superego |
| | B. | freedom, Electra complex, OCEAN |
| | C. | trait, self-efficacy, unconscious motivation |
| | D. | cognitive-personal factors, observation, locus of control |

| | | |
|---|---|---|
| p. 458<br>Social Cognitive Theory<br>Level: Easy<br>Type: Applied<br>Ans: C | 10. | Ellen's expectation that other people will treat her fairly is an example of what Bandura called: |
| | A. | paradigms |
| | B. | traits |
| | C. | cognitive factors |
| | D. | environmental influences |

| | | |
|---|---|---|
| p. 458<br>Social Cognitive Theory<br>Level: Easy<br>Type: Applied<br>Ans: A | 11. | In social cognitive theory, beliefs, expectations, values, intentions, and social roles are known as: |
| | A. | cognitive factors |
| | B. | dispositional factors |
| | C. | personal factors |
| | D. | traits |

| | | |
|---|---|---|
| p. 458<br>Social Cognitive Theory<br>Level: Easy<br>Type: Applied<br>Ans: D<br>*www* | 12. | Trent always expects to fail. Whenever he tries something new he expects to fail. But most of the time, he actually does very well. He has a hard time trying to remember all of the success he has. The social cognitive theory would suggest that his _____ influence(s) the way he interprets his past accomplishments. |
| | A. | schemas |
| | B. | dispositional factors |
| | C. | intelligence |
| | D. | cognitive factors |

p. 458
Social Cognitive Theory
Level: Easy
Type: Factual
Ans: A

13. Bandura would say that a person's emotional makeup and their biological and genetic influences comprise:
A. personal factors
B. trait factors
C. intelligence
D. cognitive factors

p. 458
Social Cognitive Theory
Level: Easy
Type: Applied
Ans: A

14. In social cognitive theory, your behavior can be influenced by:
A. beliefs and feelings
B. unconscious wishes
C. unresolved desires
D. unconditional positive regard

p. 458
Social Cognitive Theory
Level: Moderate
Type: Factual
Ans: B

15. What are the three interactive factors that play a critical role in shaping our personality according to social cognitive theory?
A. id, ego, and superego
B. cognitive-personal factors, behaviors, and environmental factors
C. unresolved desires, dreams, and self-actualization drives
D. unconditional positive regard, conditional positive regard, and traits

p. 458
Social Cognitive Theory
Level: Moderate
Type: Applied
Ans: A

16. Stephanie expects that other people will treat her unfairly. This belief influences her behavior to the point that she acts in a suspicious and somewhat rude manner. From social cognitive perspective, this contributes to:
A. how people treat her thereby reinforcing her expectations
B. how people treat her thereby weakening her expectations
C. the self-efficacy of other people
D. her internal locus of control

p. 458
Social Cognitive Theory
Level: Easy
Type: Factual
Ans: C

17. In social cognitive theory, the social, political, and cultural influences that impact us are termed:
A. conscious forces
B. cognitive-personal factors
C. environmental factors
D. internal factors

p. 458
Social Cognitive Theory
Level: Easy
Type: Factual
Ans: D

18. In his social cognitive theory, Bandura emphasizes cognitive-personal factors, behavior, and:
A. traits
B. expectations
C. locus of control
D. environmental influences

p. 459
Social Cognitive Theory
Level: Easy
Type: Factual
Ans: B
PS/SG 20-3

19. One of the key cognitive factors in Bandura's social cognitive theory is:
A. need for social approval
B. observational learning
C. self-actualization
D. unconscious conflicts

| | | |
|---|---|---|
| p. 459<br>Social Cognitive Theory<br>Level: Easy<br>Type: Factual<br>Ans: A | 20.<br><br><br>A.<br>B.<br>C.<br>D. | Albert Bandura developed a theory by which personality development is influenced by highly developed language ability, observational learning, purposeful behavior, and self-analysis. His theory is called:<br>social cognitive theory<br>self actualization theory<br>self efficacy theory<br>trait theory |
| p. 459<br>Social Cognitive Theory<br>Level: Easy<br>Type: Factual<br>Ans: D | 21.<br>A.<br>B.<br>C.<br>D. | Locus of control and self-efficacy are examples of:<br>personal factors<br>trait factors<br>unconscious motives<br>cognitive factors |
| p. 459<br>Social Cognitive Theory<br>Level: Easy<br>Type: Factual<br>Ans: B | 22.<br><br>A.<br>B.<br>C.<br>D. | Social cognitive theory was originally known as _____ and changed to reflect the importance of _____ factors.<br>trait theory; social<br>self learning theory; cognitive<br>psychoanalysis; psychological<br>trait theory; cognitive |
| p. 459<br>Social Cognitive Theory<br>Level: Easy<br>Type: Conceptual<br>Ans: B | 23.<br>A.<br>B.<br>C.<br>D. | Bandura is to Skinner as _____ is to _____.<br>voluntary; involuntary<br>cognitive; behavioral<br>classical conditioning; operant conditioning<br>elicited; emitted |
| p. 459<br>Social Cognitive Theory<br>Level: Easy<br>Type: Factual<br>Ans: C | 24.<br><br>A.<br>B.<br><br>C.<br><br>D. | What are the four cognitive processes in Albert Bandura's social cognitive theory?<br>memory, schemas, operant conditioning, and observational learning<br>self-actualization, self-efficacy, locus of control, and classical conditioning<br>language ability, observational learning, purposeful behavior, and self-analysis<br>language ability, gender roles, paradigms, and schemas |
| p. 459<br>Social Cognitive Theory<br>Level: Moderate<br>Type: Applied<br>Ans: B | 25.<br><br><br><br>A.<br>B.<br>C.<br>D. | Luis is about to take an illegal drug. Two friends are standing around him coaxing him claiming he's a coward if he doesn't try the drug to prove himself. The social cognitive theory would point to the role of _____ in this example.<br>observational learning<br>language ability<br>psychodynamics<br>self-analysis |
| p. 459<br>Social Cognitive Theory<br>Level: Easy<br>Type: Factual<br>Ans: A<br>*www* | 26.<br><br>A.<br>B.<br>C.<br>D. | Learning by watching others and performing the modeled behavior is known as _____ learning.<br>observational<br>perceptual<br>operant<br>classical |

p. 459
Social Cognitive Theory
Level: Easy
Type: Applied
Ans: D

27. After watching a basketball game, a group of fifth graders go to the gym to play. Each one of them tries to model what they saw at the game. The cognitive factor most illustrated here is:
A. locus of control
B. sublimation
C. delay of gratification
D. observational learning

p. 459
Social Cognitive Theory
Level: Easy
Type: Applied
Ans: B

28. A visit to the local mall will reveal that many young boys are wearing the football jersey of a famous quarterback. This best illustrates:
A. self-analysis
B. observational learning
C. self-efficacy
D. locus of control

p. 459
Social Cognitive Theory
Level: Easy
Type: Applied
Ans: C

29. A new television show is watched by millions of teenagers. Parents and teachers have noticed that teenagers are imitating the dress and the language of this television show. Bandura would use the factor of _____ to explain this phenomenon.
A. self-analysis
B. self-actualization
C. observational learning
D. locus of control

p. 459
Social Cognitive Theory
Level: Easy
Type: Applied
Ans: D

30. A popular television game show has influenced our society. We imitate what the host says and how he dresses. Imitation best illustrates _____. Is that your final answer?
A. delay of gratification
B. self-actualization
C. locus of control
D. observational learning

p. 459
Social Cognitive Theory
Level: Easy
Type: Factual
Ans: D

31. After reading about Bandura's theory, you realize that you can set goals, plan ahead, and try to anticipate future events. In other words, you are capable of:
A. self-analysis
B. establishing your own locus of control
C. using language
D. purposeful behavior

p. 459
Social Cognitive Theory
Level: Moderate
Type: Applied
Ans: B

32. As part of a class you are interviewing a five-year-old girl. You ask the child to explain how to cook breakfast and how to ride a bike. She doesn't seem to notice that her explanations do not make sense. Since you are familiar with social cognitive theory, you know that this child probably has not yet developed a mature ability of :
A. self-efficacy
B. self-analysis
C. schemes
D. purposeful behavior

p. 459
Social Cognitive Theory
Level: Moderate
Type: Applied
Ans: A

33. You are writing a paper for a class. As you start writing you notice that you keep on evaluating your work. You keep deleting what you've just written and decide to take a different approach in your paper. Your _____ allows you to monitor your writing.
A. self-analysis
B. purposeful behavior
C. locus of control
D. observational learning

p. 459
Social Cognitive Theory
Level: Easy
Type: Factual
Ans: C

34. Our belief about how much control we have over situations or rewards is called:
A. self-efficacy
B. self-analysis
C. locus of control
D. purposeful behavior

p. 459
Social Cognitive Theory
Level: Easy
Type: Applied
Ans: A

35. A father is having a discussion with his 15-year-old daughter. He asks what she plans to do with her life. She replies, "I don't know. Whatever!" Her responses best illustrates a(n) _____ locus of control.
A. external
B. internal
C. primary
D. secondary

p. 459
Social Cognitive Theory
Level: Easy
Type: Applied
Ans: D
*www*

36. "I wear my seatbelt every time I'm in a car. I know that I can take steps to keep myself safe and healthy. I must have a(n) _____ locus of control."
A. secondary
B. primary
C. external
D. internal

p. 459
Social Cognitive Theory
Level: Easy
Type: Factual
Ans: B

37. If you believe that you have control over situations and rewards, you possess:
A. self-efficacy
B. internal locus of control
C. external locus of control
D. self-focused control

p. 459
Social Cognitive Theory
Level: Easy
Type: Applied
Ans: D
*PS/SG 20-4*

38. The only statement below that shows internal locus of control is:
A. often exam questions are so unrelated to course work that studying is useless
B. no matter how hard you try, some people just don't like you
C. it is not always wise to plan too far ahead, because many things just turn out to be a matter of good or bad fortune
D. when I make plans, I am almost certain I can make them work

p. 459
Social Cognitive Theory
Level: Easy
Type: Applied
Ans: D

39. Ann believes that good things happen to her when she works hard. Ann has:
A. self-efficacy
B. self-focused control
C. an external locus of control
D. an internal locus of control

p. 459
Social Cognitive Theory
Level: Moderate
Type: Applied
Ans: C

40. Gwen believes that if she works hard she will get the promotion she has been wanting. Gwen seems to have:
A. an inflated ego
B. a holistic view of life
C. an internal locus of control
D. become fixated at the oral stage of development

p. 459
Social Cognitive Theory
Level: Moderate
Type: Applied
Ans: A
*www*

41. "What's the use? It doesn't matter how hard I prepare for this job interview. Whatever happens is just fate or luck." This thinking reflects:
A. an external locus of control
B. a holistic view of life
C. an internal locus of control
D. becoming fixated at the oral stage of development

p. 459
Social Cognitive Theory
Level: Moderate
Type: Applied
Ans: B

42. Clayton flunked his algebra test and believes his failure was due to trick questions on the exam. Clayton appears to:
A. be using sublimation
B. have an external locus of control
C. be self-actualized
D. have unconditional positive regard

p. 459
Social Cognitive Theory
Level: Easy
Type: Factual
Ans: C

43. Researchers have found correlations between locus of control and psychological functioning. Which of the following is an <u>incorrect</u> summary of the research?
A. People with an internal locus of control are generally higher achievers
B. People with an internal locus of control are generally more likely to take preventive health measures
C. People with an internal locus of control are generally more depressed
D. People with an internal locus of control report less stress

p. 459
Social Cognitive Theory
Level: Easy
Type: Factual
Ans: A

44. Research suggests that people with an internal locus of control are more likely to:
A. report less stress
B. report more depression
C. engage in unhealthy risk-taking behaviors
D. be self-actualized

p. 459
Social Cognitive Theory
Level: Easy
Type: Factual
Ans: C

45. Overall, which type of locus of control appears to be more adaptive and healthy?
A. conscious
B. primary
C. internal
D. external

| | | |
|---|---|---|
| p. 460<br>Social Cognitive Theory<br>Level: Easy<br>Type: Factual<br>Ans: C<br>*www* | 46. | To postpone an immediate reward in favor of completing a task for a future reward is called: |
| | A. | self-efficacy |
| | B. | postponement bias |
| | C. | delay of gratification |
| | D. | self-actualization |

| | | |
|---|---|---|
| p. 460<br>Social Cognitive Theory<br>Level: Moderate<br>Type: Applied<br>Ans: B | 47. | Sarah has just received a job offer for a position that doesn't pay well and has few opportunities for advancement. But jobs are scarce. Does she take the job and forego another more favorable job offer in the future? She decides to say no to the present offer. She is experiencing: |
| | A. | regression |
| | B. | delay of gratification |
| | C. | fixation |
| | D. | an approach approach conflict |

| | | |
|---|---|---|
| p. 460<br>Social Cognitive Theory<br>Level: Easy<br>Type: Factual<br>Ans: C<br>*PS/SG 20-5* | 48. | Children and marshmallows were used in a classic study of: |
| | A. | observational learning |
| | B. | locus of control |
| | C. | delay of gratification |
| | D. | traits |

| | | |
|---|---|---|
| p. 460<br>Social Cognitive Theory<br>Level: Easy<br>Type: Factual<br>Ans: C | 49. | Mischel's concept of delay of gratification is <u>best</u> related to: |
| | A. | fixation |
| | B. | identity |
| | C. | willpower |
| | D. | temperament |

| | | |
|---|---|---|
| p. 460<br>Social Cognitive Theory<br>Level: Easy<br>Type: Applied<br>Ans: D | 50. | Erik has poor delay of gratification. If Erik was given the choice of a least preferred hamburger now or a more preferred lobster later, which would he select? |
| | A. | a hamburger later |
| | B. | a lobster later |
| | C. | a lobster now |
| | D. | a hamburger now |

| | | |
|---|---|---|
| p. 460<br>Social Cognitive Theory<br>Level: Moderate<br>Type: Applied<br>Ans: B | 51. | Denise told her nine-year-old daughter Miranda that she could spend her money now and get an inexpensive toy. On the other hand, Miranda could also save her money and purchase a more expensive and more preferred toy later. Which of the following, according to Bandura, is <u>most</u> likely to influence her decision? |
| | A. | postponement bias |
| | B. | delay of gratification |
| | C. | the Big Five Traits |
| | D. | locus of control |

| | | |
|---|---|---|
| p. 460 | 52. | According to research cited in your textbook, 4-year-old children who |
| Social Cognitive Theory | | can delay gratification tend to: |
| Level: Moderate | A. | strive for higher achievement |
| Type: Factual | B. | get better grades |
| Ans: A | C. | select less preferred rewards |
| | D. | become easily frustrated |

| | | |
|---|---|---|
| p. 460 | 53. | Which of the following is not related to the ability to delay gratification? |
| Social Cognitive Theory | A. | more competence |
| Level: Easy | B. | high intelligence |
| Type: Factual | C. | greater social responsibility |
| Ans: D | D. | lower self-efficacy |

| | | |
|---|---|---|
| p. 460 | 54. | Experiments testing children's ability to delay gratification have found |
| Social Cognitive Theory | | that: |
| Level: Moderate | A. | the desire for immediate gratification is correlated with success in adult |
| Type: Factual | | life |
| Ans: C | B. | a child's ability to delay gratification is determined by the perceived |
| | | strength of that gratification |
| | C. | children who are able to delay gratification develop into adolescents who |
| | | can concentrate better than those who cannot |
| | D. | a child's ability to delay gratification is unrelated to his or her eventual |
| | | personality |

| | | |
|---|---|---|
| p. 460 | 55. | When the 4-year-olds in the delay of gratification experiment were retested |
| Social Cognitive Theory | | 10 years later: |
| Level: Moderate | A. | high delay and low delay children were now about the same |
| Type: Factual | B. | being good at delay was related to many other positive characteristics |
| Ans: B | C. | high delay children had become anxious, worrywart teens |
| PS/SG 20-6 | D. | many had become Scouts, but, curiously, refused to make Samores |

| | | |
|---|---|---|
| p. 460 | 56. | A social cognitive theorist would say that as a college student, you must |
| Social Cognitive Theory | | be able to put off immediate gratification and develop the ability to: |
| Level: Easy | A. | delay gratification |
| Type: Factual | B. | self-actualize without fulfilling deficiency needs |
| Ans: A | C. | tolerate conditional positive regard |
| | D. | resolve any id-superego conflict |

| | | |
|---|---|---|
| p. 460 | 57. | Our personal belief of how capable we are of exercising control over |
| Social Cognitive Theory | | events in our lives is called: |
| Level: Easy | A. | self-actualization |
| Type: Factual | B. | self-esteem |
| Ans: D | C. | self-regard |
| | D. | self-efficacy |

| | | |
|---|---|---|
| p. 460 | 58. | Which of the following does Bandura not include in the keys to |
| Social Cognitive Theory | | determining our sense of self-efficacy? |
| Level: Moderate | A. | successes and failures we have experienced in the past |
| Type: Factual | B. | comparing ourselves to others |
| Ans: D | C. | what others say about our capabilities |
| PS/SG 20-7 | D. | the power of our conscience to make us feel guilty |

p. 460
Social Cognitive Theory
Level: Easy
Type: Conceptual
Ans: D

59. If you think that you can't successfully go on a diet, lose weight, and keep it off, then you have:
A. strong delay of gratification
B. strong self-efficacy
C. Oedipus conflict
D. weak self-efficacy

p. 460
Social Cognitive Theory
Level: Easy
Type: Conceptual
Ans: C

60. Wayne likes to play computer games, and he is especially good at ones that require good eye-hand coordination. He is poor on games that require forethought and critical thinking. His brother Lloyd introduces Wayne to a game that is very similar to the ones he has already excelled at. Based upon your understanding of social-cognitive theory, what is Wayne's self-efficacy and why?
A. weak self-efficacy - he is comparing his performance to Lloyd's
B. strong self-efficacy- he is able to have an external locus of control
C. strong self-efficacy- his success in the past on similar games
D. weak self-efficacy - his body is telling him that he is anxious

p. 460
Social Cognitive Theory
Level: Easy
Type: Factual
Ans: B

61. Which of the following is not used to judge self-efficacy according to Bandura?
A. compare our capabilities with those of others
B. compare our actual experiences to a mythical base rate
C. listen to what other people say about our capabilities
D. use feedback from our bodies

p. 460
Social Cognitive Theory
Level: Moderate
Type: Factual
Ans: B

62. What effect should failure have on self-efficacy?
A. no effect on self-efficacy
B. it depends on the similarity of the past and new tasks
C. weaken self-efficacy
D. strengthen self-efficacy

p. 460
Social Cognitive Theory
Level: Moderate
Type: Conceptual
Ans: A

63. There is a children's story of a little red engine that was confronted with a heavy load. The little red engine kept saying, "I think I can, I think I can" as it attempted to carry the load. Which of the components of social cognitive theory does this story best illustrate?
A. self-efficacy
B. positive regard
C. willpower
D. personal factors

p. 460
Social Cognitive Theory
Level: Moderate
Type: Factual
Ans: A

64. According to the research on self-efficacy, your motivation for doing well on a variety of tasks is influenced by:
A. how strongly you believe in your own capabilities
B. the extent to which you resolved the Oedipus or Electra complex
C. the ability to delay gratification
D. how others treat your capability

<table>
<tr><td>

p. 460
Social Cognitive Theory
Level: Easy
Type: Applied
Ans: D
*www*

</td><td>

65.</td><td>

"I don't think that I'm capable of selecting the right answer to this question." According to Bandura, this best illustrates weak:
A. ideal self
B. transference
C. self-actualization
D. self-efficacy

</td></tr>

<tr><td>

p. 461
Social Cognitive Theory
Level: Easy
Type: Factual
Ans: D

</td><td>66.</td><td>

The case of Christopher Reeve illustrates:
A. the shortcomings of social cognitive theory
B. the person-situation interaction
C. the role that the unconscious mind has on motivation
D. how beliefs influence personality and behavior

</td></tr>

<tr><td>

p. 461
Social Cognitive Theory
Level: Easy
Type: Factual
Ans: B

</td><td>67.</td><td>

An advantage of the social cognitive approach is that:
A. it does consider the importance of unconscious motives
B. it has integrated more influential factors than other theories
C. childhood experiences are examined
D. it is based primarily upon the clinical experiences of Albert Bandura

</td></tr>

<tr><td>

p. 461
Social Cognitive Theory
Level: Easy
Type: Factual
Ans: A

</td><td>68.</td><td>

An accurate evaluation of social-cognitive theory is that social cognitive concepts:
A. are less subject to error and bias
B. cannot be manipulated or experimentally tested
C. form a complete theory of personality
D. include the influence of childhood and emotional factors

</td></tr>

<tr><td>

p. 461
Social Cognitive Theory
Level: Difficult
Type: Conceptual
Ans: C

</td><td>69.</td><td>

Kyle needs to do some research in the Psychology Department's lab to graduate with his degree. Based upon your understanding of personality development, which theory ought to serve as a framework for his laboratory research?
A. humanistic theory
B. Freudian theory
C. social cognitive theory
D. analytical theory

</td></tr>

<tr><td>

p. 461
Social Cognitive Theory
Level: Easy
Type: Factual
Ans: C

</td><td>70.</td><td>

One criticism of social cognitive theory is that:
A. many concepts have not been experimentally based
B. it takes into account interactions among cognitive factors, behavior, and environmental factors
C. too little attention is paid to childhood experiences
D. these concepts have been unsuccessfully used in programs for change

</td></tr>

<tr><td>

p. 461
Social Cognitive Theory
Level: Easy
Type: Factual
Ans: C

</td><td>71.</td><td>

Of the following which is a criticism of social cognitive theory?
A. It describes an interaction among only cognitive-personal factors, behaviors, and environment.
B. It is experimentally based.
C. It pays little attention to genetic factors.
D. Many of the concepts have been manipulated, controlled, and tested.

</td></tr>
</table>

p. 461
Social Cognitive Theory
Level: Easy
Type: Factual
Ans: B

72. Dr. Erkzine says that one of the shortcomings of social cognitive theory is that it is empirically based. What is your reaction to his criticism?
A. You agree and would add that there is more evidence supporting the psychodynamic theory.
B. Being experimentally based is not a weakness of social cognitive theory.
C. He may be right, but that is a mild problem of social cognitive theory.
D. You agree and add another shortcoming in that the theory just focuses on environmental influences.

p. 461
Social Cognitive Theory
Level: Easy
Type: Factual
Ans: C

73. A person's fear of snakes can be successfully treated by observing a fearless model handling a snake. This is based on:
A. psychodynamic theory
B. humanistic theory
C. social cognitive theory
D. the trait approach

p. 462
Trait Theory
Level: Easy
Type: Factual
Ans: C
*PS/SG 20-9*

74. Do women make better cops? Evidence suggests that the answer is:
A. Yes, at least for now, because women have a greater determination to succeed.
B. No, because women in our society tend to have a lower sense of self-efficacy.
C. Yes, because personality traits shared by many women are useful in police work.
D. No, because the performance of male and female officers is about the same.

p. 462
Trait Theory
Level: Easy
Type: Factual
Ans: A

75. A term used to describe female police officers is _____, while male police officers are described as _____.
A. peacekeepers; enforcers
B. negotiators; peacekeepers
C. referees; enforcers
D. enforcers; referees

p. 462
Trait Theory
Level: Easy
Type: Factual
Ans: C

76. Officer Taylor is a 20-year veteran of the police department. If he is typical of male police officers, his traits would include:
A. diplomacy
B. sympathy
C. assertiveness
D. compassion

p. 462
Trait Theory
Level: Moderate
Type: Factual
Ans: D

77. An approach aimed at understanding the structure of personality by measuring, identifying, and analyzing differences in personality is called:
A. social cognitive theory
B. cognitive-behavioral theory
C. psychodynamic theory
D. trait theory

p. 462
Trait Theory
Level: Easy
Type: Factual
Ans: A

78. Using personality characteristics that are relatively stable and enduring to explain behavior is called:
   A. the trait approach
   B. the cognitive-social approach
   C. the psychodynamic approach
   D. the transactional approach

p. 462
Trait Theory
Level: Easy
Type: Factual
Ans: B
*www*

79. A relatively stable and enduring tendency to behave in a particular way is called a(n):
   A. self-concept
   B. trait
   C. internal locus of control
   D. factor

p. 462
Trait Theory
Level: Easy
Type: Applied
Ans: A

80. A personality researcher tells her associates that her goal is to identify the smallest number of enduring tendencies that can describe all the differences between personalities. This researcher appears to subscribe to which theory of personality?
   A. trait
   B. psychodynamic
   C. social cognitive
   D. humanistic

p. 462
Trait Theory
Level: Easy
Type: Applied
Ans: C

81. Just as Professor Howarth is dismissing class, she says, "Tomorrow we will look at relatively stable and enduring tendencies to behave in particular ways." Since you've done the assigned reading already, you know that tomorrow the professor will be presenting the topic of ___ theory.
   A. social cognitive
   B. psychodynamic
   C. trait
   D. humanistic

p. 462
Trait Theory
Level: Easy
Type: Factual
Ans: C

82. Which names are most associated with trait theory of personality?
   A. Richard Lazarus and Simon Binet
   B. Walter Mischel and Julian Rotter
   C. Gordon Allport and Raymond Cattell
   D. Albert Bandura and B. F. Skinner

p. 462
Trait Theory
Level: Easy
Type: Factual
Ans: A

83. In the 1930s, Gordon Allport found _____ traits in the dictionary.
   A. 4,500
   B. 7,500
   C. 10,000
   D. 11,750

p. 462
Trait Theory
Level: Easy
Type: Factual
Ans: D

84. What was the disadvantage to the list of traits developed by Gordon Allport?
   A. traits cannot be measured
   B. some traits were poorly defined
   C. there were too few traits
   D. it was too long

p. 462
Trait Theory
Level: Moderate
Type: Conceptual
Ans: A

85. One major difference between trait theory and social cognitive theory is that trait theory:
A. describes rather than explains behavior
B. deals more directly with the subconscious
C. has had little research attention
D. relies less on words and more on concepts

p. 462
Trait Theory
Level: Moderate
Type: Applied
Ans: B

86. Grant puts considerable effort into changing some of the personality traits of his friend, Bud. If Grant is like most people, his effort is motivated by:
A. the belief that traits are easily modified
B. the belief that traits are the causes of Bud's behaviors
C. the need to have control over others
D. the desire to conduct informal "experiments" in interpersonal psychology

p. 462
Trait Theory
Level: Moderate
Type: Conceptual
Ans: C

87. Which of the following is not an assumption of the trait approach to personality?
A. An individual's personality can be described completely by listing all traits
B. Traits are relatively enduring and stable and influence a person's behavior.
C. Personality is the result of unconscious forces that create conflict within the person.
D. Differences between personalities can be described with the 5-factor model.

p. 462
Trait Theory
Level: Easy
Type: Factual
Ans: B

88. Who was it that constructed a list of traits that was considered too long and therefore impractical to use in research?
A. Albert Bandura
B. Gordon Allport
C. Daryl Bem
D. Raymond Cattell

p. 462
Trait Theory
Level: Easy
Type: Factual
Ans: A

89. The statistical technique that reveals relationships among different items and then puts like-items into groups is called:
A. factor analysis
B. correlation
C. standard deviation
D. linear regression

p. 462
Trait Theory
Level: Easy
Type: Factual
Ans: B

90. Cattell utilized factor analysis to reduce Allport's lengthy list of traits down to:
A. a five-factor model
B. source traits
C. a hierarchy of traits
D. higher-order and lower-order traits

p. 463
Trait Theory
Level: Easy
Type: Factual
Ans: A
*PS/SG 20-12*

91. The result of research in personality is the current belief that human personality is best described by:
A. five supertraits
B. 35 basic traits
C. 4,500 personality traits
D. 18,000 descriptive terms

p. 463
Trait Theory
Level: Easy
Type: Factual
Ans: D

92. In the Big Five, each factor represents:
A. one or two "subtraits"
B. an unconscious construct that cannot be measured
C. a dichotomy
D. a continuum of behavior

p. 463
Trait Theory
Level: Easy
Type: Factual
Ans: C

93. The acronym OCEAN refers to:
A. an objective measure of personality
B. defense mechanisms
C. The Big Five traits
D. the elements of social cognitive theory

p. 463
Trait Theory
Level: Easy
Type: Factual
Ans: B
*www*

94. Which of the following is <u>not</u> one of the five groups of traits in the five-factor model used to describe personality?
A. neuroticism
B. intelligence
C. extroversion
D. agreeableness

p. 463
Trait Theory
Level: Easy
Type: Applied
Ans: A

95. Matt is unfriendly and cold. He doesn't think before he speaks. From the Big Five approach, Matt's personality is described using:
A. the traits of agreeableness and conscientiousness
B. the defense mechanisms of sublimation and projection
C. fixation during anal stage
D. fixation during oral stage

p. 463
Trait Theory
Level: Easy
Type: Applied
Ans: B

96. Jan is quiet, reserved, and thoughtful about her behavior. She dislikes going to parties where she knows few people, and feels uncomfortable with most people. Jan would be considered a(n):
A. neurotic
B. introvert
C. extrovert
D. antagonist

p. 463
Trait Theory
Level: Easy
Type: Applied
Ans: C

97. Jeremy is very outgoing. He enjoys taking risks and being involved in any social activities. He prefers to be with people and dislikes jobs where he has to work alone. Jeremy would be classified as a(n):
A. neurotic
B. introvert
C. extrovert
D. antagonist

p. 463
Trait Theory
Level: Easy
Type: Applied
Ans: A

98. During a meeting Howard presents an idea for a new product. Bobby, who has a tendency to have narrow interests, says, "That new product Howard talks about, it will never work, never, never, never and you can bet on that!" Which of the following traits would be most applicable to Bobby?
   A. openness
   B. conscientiousness
   C. extroversion
   D. neuroticism

p. 463
Trait Theory
Level: Easy
Type: Factual
Ans: C

99. The Big Five traits can be thought of as:
   A. interrelated
   B. out of date since there is little research support for it
   C. supertraits
   D. sharply focused single traits

p. 463
Trait Theory
Level: Easy
Type: Factual
Ans: A

100. A psychologist designs a personality assessment containing the following item: Rate the extent to which you consider yourself to be a patient person using a 10-point scale. This assessment is based on:
   A. trait theory
   B. psychodynamic theory
   C. humanistic theory
   D. cognitive-social learning theory

p. 463
Trait Theory
Level: Easy
Type: Factual
Ans: B

101. In examining cultural differences in the Big Five traits, research has found:
   A. only openness, conscientiousness, and neuroticism to be present in most cultures
   B. support in very different countries and cultures
   C. similarities, but only in individualistic countries
   D. similarities, but only among males of the cultures

p. 464
Trait Theory
Level: Moderate
Type: Factual
Ans: C

102. Walter Mischel, in a discussion of trait theory, commented that:
   A. the five-factor model should be reduced down to a two-factor model
   B. traits accurately predict behavior across situations
   C. individuals do not behave consistently across different situations
   D. traits are not based on inherited factors

p. 464
Trait Theory
Level: Moderate
Type: Applied
Ans: D
*www*

103. Joe is a nice guy. Trait theory would predict:
   A. Joe would be nice in some situations, but not in other situations
   B. his "niceness" would disappear as his fixation is reduced
   C. Joe would be nice only when his ego constructs a defense mechanism
   D. he would be nice across different situations

p. 464
Trait Theory
Level: Moderate
Type: Factual
Ans: A
*PS/SG 20-14*

104. One of the sharpest attacks on the concept of traits was:
A. Mischel's argument that behavior changes in different situations
B. Bandura's theory that we learn by observing others
C. Cattell's discovery that needs are arranged in a hierarchy
D. Allport's list of 18,000 terms that deal with personality differences

p. 464
Trait Theory
Level: Moderate
Type: Conceptual
Ans: D

105. Fran considers herself to be a patient person, as do her close friends and children. If Fran is like many other people tested, she will:
A. be consistently patient in many varied situations
B. be considered patient by others because she considers herself to be patient
C. also be kind
D. show impatience in some situations

p. 464
Trait Theory
Level: Moderate
Type: Factual
Ans: B

106. According to trait theory, you can predict behavior from one situation to another situation provided that:
A. you observe the person several times
B. the two situations are similar
C. the two situations occur in contiguous time
D. the behavior is easily described

p. 464
Trait Theory
Level: Moderate
Type: Conceptual
Ans: D

107. A shipping company is looking for a new manager for its warehouse. Applicants are administered a battery of personality tests. If the company wishes to pick the best person for the job, it should:
A. forget about the personality tests and rely solely on interviews
B. look very carefully at the personality tests and place little emphasis on interviews
C. choose the applicant who scores highest on an intelligence test
D. place the applicants in work situations and watch how they behave

p. 464
Trait Theory
Level: Moderate
Type: Conceptual
Ans: C

108. Vern considers Phil to be a very honest person. In fact, in a psychology class in which the consistency of traits was being discussed, Vern cited his friend as an example of consistency. It may be that Vern is overestimating Phil's consistency because Vern:
A. is not particularly honest himself
B. is externally oriented
C. judges Phil's behavior in the same type of situation each time
D. is not very intelligent

p. 464
Trait Theory
Level: Easy
Type: Factual
Ans: A

109. Walter Mischel noted that to predict behavior, we must take into account:
A. the situation and the trait
B. the self-efficacy of the subject
C. the validity and reliability of the personality test that was used
D. the obviousness of the behavior

p. 464
Trait Theory
Level: Easy
Type: Factual
Ans: D

110. Your behavior is the result of an interaction between your traits and the effects of being in a specific situation. This is called:
A. behavioral biasing
B. situational behavioral interaction
C. trait-environment duo
D. person-situation interaction

p. 464
Trait Theory
Level: Easy
Type: Factual
Ans: D

111. To understand a person's behavior, the person's _____ and the _____ must be considered, according to Walter Mischel.
A. history; situation
B. traits; culture
C. intelligence; culture
D. traits; situation

p. 464
Trait Theory
Level: Easy
Type: Factual
Ans: C

112. From the trait theory perspective, how could you improve the accuracy in predicting behaviors across situations?
A. define the subject's phenomenological experience more exactly
B. decrease the number of judges making the prediction
C. increase the number of observations in many different situations
D. measure the behavior in a few situations

p. 464
Trait Theory
Level: Easy
Type: Applied
Ans: B

113. In a letter of recommendation you are writing for someone, you use _____ as a short cut in describing their personality.
A. cognitive-personal factors
B. traits
C. locus of control
D. self-efficacy

p. 465
Trait Theory
Level: East
Type: Factual
Ans: A

114. At what age would we expect the beginnings of a person's more stable personality traits?
A. age 3
B. age 12
C. age 18
D. age 30

p. 465
Trait Theory
Level: Moderate
Type: Factual
Ans: C

115. Between 20 and 30, people generally become:
A. less cooperative
B. less self-disciplined
C. less emotional
D. more emotional

p. 465
Trait Theory
Level: Moderate
Type: Factual
Ans: B

116. According to McCrae and Costa your personality is most likely to change during what part of the life cycle?
A. between childhood and adolescence
B. before age 30
C. between age 30 and 50
D. after age 30

p. 465
Trait Theory
Level: Easy
Type: Factual
Ans: B
*PS/SG 20-16*

117. When are you most likely to make changes in your personality? Research says:
A. by age five
B. before age 30
C. after age 30
D. when the end is near

p. 465
Trait Theory
Level: Easy
Type: Factual
Ans: A

118. After age 30, there are _____ in personality traits and personality is _____.
A. small changes; stable
B. large changes; instable
C. no changes; instable
D. significant changes; stable

p. 465
Trait Theory
Level: Moderate
Type: Applied
Ans: C

119. As a young adult, Roberta was considered to be sociable and friendly. If we were to meet Roberta in late adulthood, we would:
A. find that those traits had diminished
B. find that those traits had become more prominent
C. be reasonably sure that she would still be sociable and friendly
D. be unable to predict her personality because traits are not stable over long periods of time

p. 465
Trait Theory
Level: Difficult
Type: Factual
Ans: D

120. If there is personality change after the age of 30, it generally is:
A. restricted to openness to new ideas
B. only temporary and tied to the situation
C. adoption of a totally new theme
D. due to stressors and challenges

p. 465
Trait Theory
Level: Difficult
Type: Applied
Ans: B

121. Ross is 35 years old and enjoys collecting stamps. Based on the research described in the textbook, which of the following is most likely to happen to Ross as he ages?
A. He will start tinkering with old cars.
B. He will start collecting beer steins.
C. He will start jogging and lifting weights.
D. He will become less dependent on his wife.

p. 466
Genetic Influences
 on Traits
Level: Easy
Type: Factual
Ans: B

122. The area of behavioral genetics suggest that genetic factors:
A. are fixed
B. set a range for behaviors
C. do not interact with the environment
D. account for more than 75% of the development of personality traits

p. 466
Genetic Influences
  on Traits
Level: Easy
Type: Factual
Ans: D

123. In understanding height and weight, a behavioral geneticist will argue that:
A. identical twins separated at birth will always have the same height and weight
B. genetics will determine two heights and two weights and environmental factors will determine which one actually occurs
C. the influence of genetics on height and weight is fixed
D. genetics set a range for height and weight and environmental influences will interact with that range

p. 466
Genetic Influences
  on Traits
Level: Easy
Type: Factual
Ans: D
*PS/SG 20-17*

124. The new area of psychology called behavioral genetics is providing evidence that:
A. twins are very different from single-birth children
B. twins may appear outwardly similar, but in most respects they are quite different
C. sharing a family environment is the major influence on personality
D. inheritance sets a range of behaviors for many aspects of personality

p. 466
Genetic Influences
  on Traits
Level: Easy
Type: Factual
Ans: C

125. If you are studying how inherited factors influence and interact with psychological factors to shape personality, then you are studying:
A. psychogenetics
B. actualization
C. behavioral genetics
D. OCEAN

p. 466
Genetic Influences
  on Traits
Level: Easy
Type: Factual
Ans: A

126. Who published the first study simultaneously comparing four different groups of twins?
A. Thomas Bouchard
B. Jim Springer
C. Raymond Cattell
D. Julian Rotter

p. 466
Genetic Influences
  on Traits
Level: Easy
Type: Factual
Ans: B

127. Which of the following groups share 100% of their genes?
A. fraternal twins reared together
B. identical twins reared together
C. fraternal twins reared apart
D. brother and sister born 3 years apart

p. 466
Genetic Influences
  on Traits
Level: Easy
Type: Factual
Ans: C
*www*

128. The statistical measure which estimates how much of a behavior is due to genetic factors is called:
A. factor analysis
B. behavioral genetics
C. heritability
D. graphology

p. 466
Genetic Influences
  on Traits
Level:  Moderate
Type:  Factual
Ans:  A

129.  If intelligence has a heritability of .5 to .7, it means that:
A.  50-70% of a person's IQ score is explained by genetic factors
B.  50-70% of IQ scores are explained by genetic factors
C.  5-7% of a person's IQ score is explained by genetic factors
D.  25-47% of a person's IQ score is explained by genetic factors

p. 466
Genetic Influences
  on Traits
Level:  Easy
Type:  Factual
Ans:  D

130.  If genetics plays no role in a behavior, then the heritability would be:
A.  -1
B.  100
C.  1
D.  .0

p. 467
Genetic Influences
  on Traits
Level:  Easy
Type:  Factual
Ans:  C

131.  Which of the following is an accurate evaluation of the genetic influences on traits?
A.  Data for the five-factor model give a complete portrait of personality.
B.  40 to 50% of the development of personality traits is attributable to genetic factors.
C.  Genetic factors establish a range of behaviors.
D.  Traits can be used to effectively predict behaviors across different situations.

p. 467
Genetic Influences
  on Traits
Level:  Easy
Type:  Factual
Ans:  B

132.  The heritability of personality traits range from:
A.  .05-.10
B.  .41-.51
C.  .69-.99
D.  1.56-2.90

p. 467
Genetic Influences
  on Traits
Level:  Easy
Type:  Factual
Ans:  D

133.  Regarding the development of personality, it is currently believed that:
A.  shared environment has a significant effect on the development of personality
B.  individual differences in personality can be attributed primarily to heredity
C.  personality changes most rapidly during adolescence
D.  heredity has some influence on personality, but environment also has a strong influence

p. 467
Genetic Influences
  on Traits
Level:  Easy
Type:  Factual
Ans:  A
PS/SG 20-19

134.  It is now believed that _____ of the development of personality traits is explained by genetics:
A.  about half
B.  about one-fifth
C.  almost all
D.  almost none

p. 467
Genetic Influences
  on Traits
Level: Easy
Type: Factual
Ans: B

135. Researchers argue that the environmental factor which is important in the development of personality traits is:
A. the family environment
B. how a child reacts to the environment
C. heritability
D. extroversion

p. 467
Genetic Influences
  on Traits
Level: Easy
Type: Factual
Ans: A

136. Factors that involve how each individual's genetic factors react and adjust to the environment are called:
A. nonshared environmental factors
B. shared environmental factors
C. nominal environmental factors
D. interactive environmental factors

p. 467
Genetic Influences
  on Traits
Level: Moderate
Type: Factual
Ans: C

137. Two variables that have minimal impact on personality development are:
A. economic status of family and gender of child
B. genetics and non-shared environmental factors
C. parental practices and shared family experiences
D. shared environmental factors and genetics

p. 467
Genetic Influences
  on Traits
Level: Easy
Type: Factual
Ans: D

138. The professor is discussing the various influences on personality. She writes the four factors on the overhead projector. Which one has the least impact on personality?
A. genetics
B. nonshared environmental factors
C. innate predispositions
D. parental practices

p. 467
Genetic Influences
  on Traits
Level: Moderate
Type: Factual
Ans: D

139. Personality appears to be influenced by several factors. Of the following lists, which one correctly orders the factors contributing to personality (from most to least):
A. error, genetic factors, nonshared environmental factors, shared environmental factors
B. genetic factors, shared environmental factors, nonshared environmental factors, error
C. shared environmental factors, genetic factors, nonshared environmental factors, error
D. genetic factors, nonshared environmental factors, error, shared environmental factors

p. 468
Evaluation of Trait
  Theory
Level: Easy
Type: Factual
Ans: B

140. A problem with the five-factor model is that:
A. its comprehensiveness makes it too unmanageable
B. it is too limited and simplistic to give meaningful descriptions of personalities
C. it is based upon unreliable statistical techniques
D. it takes into account genetic influences

p. 468
Evaluation of Trait
 Theory
Level:  Easy
Type:  Factual
Ans:  D

141.    Personality tests based on the five-factor model:
A.    find significant differences between different populations and age groups
B.    allow us to make very accurate predictions across most situations
C.    fail to show the complexity of human personality
D.    lack reliability and validity

p. 468
Evaluation of Trait
 Theory
Level:  Easy
Type:  Factual
Ans:  A

142.    One shortcoming with the trait theory is its insistence that:
A.    behavior is consistent across all situations
B.    personality traits have a strong genetic basis
C.    the Big Five traits are valid
D.    the situation can change behavior

p. 468
Evaluation of Trait
 Theory
Level:  Easy
Type:  Factual
Ans:  C

143.    Traits could be better predictors of future behavior if they were assessed:
A.    through the interview technique
B.    at different times, but in the same situation
C.    in different conditions and situations
D.    using projective techniques

p. 468
Evaluation of Trait
 Theory
Level:  Easy
Type:  Factual
Ans:  D

144.    Environmental factors contribute about _____ to personality traits.
A.    80%
B.    5%
C.    10%
D.    50%

p. 470
Research Focus:
 180 Degree Change
Level:  Easy
Type:  Applied
Ans:  C

145.    "He's changed." "There's something different about him." "I wonder what happened to him?"  These observations refer to someone who experienced a sudden and dramatic shift in personality, beliefs, and values.  This change is called a:
A.    transformation
B.    profound personality alteration
C.    quantum personality change
D.    transference shift

p. 470
Research Focus:
 180 Degree Change
Level:  Easy
Type:  Factual
Ans:  C
*PS/SG 20-21*

146.    Some people experience a very sudden (in a single day) and radical or dramatic shift in personality, beliefs, or values; psychology calls this a:
A.    flash of insight, or "ah ha" experience
B.    born again spiritual experience
C.    quantum personality change
D.    quantitative personality change

p. 470
Research Focus:
 180 Degree Change
Level:  Easy
Type:  Conceptual
Ans:  B

147.    Why are dramatic, sudden changes in personality difficult to believe?
A.    because they are based on psychodynamic techniques
B.    personality traits are stable and typically do not change suddenly
C.    genetics account for 95% of personality and genetics do not change
D.    environment, which influences personality, never changes suddenly

p. 470
Research Focus:
  180 Degree Change
Level: Easy
Type: Factual
Ans: A

148. A significant concern regarding the study of personality is that:
A. the data are only self-report, subject to bias and inaccuracies
B. personality is not subject to dramatic shifts
C. no valid or reliable way to measure personality exists
D. subjects are difficult to recruit

p. 470
Research Focus:
  180 Degree Change
Level: Easy
Type: Applied
Ans: C

149. Ricardo has just experienced a quantum personality change. If his experience is typical, in the past year, Ricardo has:
A. experienced minor fluctuations in personality
B. had an increase in positive life experiences
C. had a high level of emotional distress and negative life experiences
D. successfully met some challenge involving interpersonal relationships

p. 470
Research Focus:
  180 Degree Change
Level: Easy
Type: Factual
Ans: D

150. Of the following statements, which is not true regarding the study on quantum personality change as described in Module 20?
A. structured interviews were used to collect data
B. the study took place in New Mexico
C. 55 subjects participated
D. most subjects had prior histories of antisocial behavior and schizoid personality tendencies

p. 470
Research Focus:
  180 Degree Change
Level: Easy
Type: Factual
Ans: B

151. The results of a study cited in your textbook regarding personality change reveal that:
A. the change in personality was expected
B. change had improved the quality of life
C. the experience lasted only minutes
D. structured interviews yield invalid data

p. 471
Cultural Diversity:
  Suicide Bombers
Level: Easy
Type: Factual
Ans: A

152. Suicide bombers in the Middle East tend to be motivated by:
A. personal and cultural influences
B. peer pressure
C. poorly developed egos
D. unconscious conflict and cultural influences

p. 471
Cultural Diversity:
  Suicide Bombers
Level: Easy
Type: Factual
Ans: C

153. Does there appear to be a specific personality profile in suicide bombers from the Middle East?
A. Yes – they tend to be very individualistic
B. Yes – these individuals tend to be very violent
C. No
D. Yes – suicide bombers tend to be introverted

p. 472
Four Theories of
  Personality
Level: Easy
Type: Factual
Ans: B

154. In reviewing the psychodynamic theory of personality, select the word that does not match the theory.
A. free association
B. trait
C. superego
D. phallic

p. 472
Four Theories of
  Personality
Level: Easy
Type: Factual
Ans: D

155. In reviewing the humanistic theory of personality, select the word that does <u>not</u> match the theory.
A. self-actualization
B. holistic view
C. hierarchy of needs
D. Big Five

p. 473
Four Theories of
  Personality
Level: Easy
Type: Factual
Ans: C

156. In reviewing the social cognitive theory of personality, select the word that does <u>not</u> match the theory.
A. self-efficacy
B. delay of gratification
C. id
D. observational learning

p. 473
Four Theories of
  Personality
Level: Easy
Type: Factual
Ans: A

157. In reviewing the trait theory of personality, select the word that does <u>not</u> match the theory.
A. self
B. Big Five
C. OCEAN
D. factor analysis

p. 474
Application:Assessment -
  Objective Tests
Level: Easy
Type: Factual
Ans: A

158. Personality tests with specific written statements that require clients to respond with a limited range of answers are called:
A. objective tests
B. projective tests
C. factor analyses
D. heritability tests

p. 474
Application:Assessment -
  Objective Tests
Level: Easy
Type: Applied
Ans: C

159. Dr. Donaldson is giving Mark a personality test that consists of ambiguous stimuli. This is an example of a test that is:
A. standardized
B. structured
C. projective
D. objective

p. 474
Application:Assessment -
  Objective Tests
Level: Easy
Type: Factual
Ans: D

160. To find honest and trustworthy employees, a business owner might give:
A. the Thematic Apperception Test
B. behavioral tests
C. projective tests
D. integrity tests

p. 474
Application:Assessment -
  Objective Tests
Level: Easy
Type: Factual
Ans: C

161. A good example of a highly structured objective personality test is the:
A. Thematic Apperception Test (TAT)
B. Rorschach Inkblot Test
C. Minnesota Multiphasic Personality Inventory (MMPI-2)
D. traditional psychological interview

*PS/SG 20-23*

| p. 474<br>Application:Assessment -<br>Objective Tests<br>Level: Easy<br>Type: Factual<br>Ans: C | 162. | One of the best known objective tests for personality is the: |
|---|---|---|
| | A. | Thematic Apperception Test |
| | B. | Rorschach inkblot test |
| | C. | Minnesota Multiphasic Personality Inventory - 2 |
| | D. | Locus of Control Inventory |

| p. 474<br>Application:Assessment -<br>Objective Tests<br>Level: Easy<br>Type: Factual<br>Ans: D<br>*www* | 163. | The Minnesota Multiphasic Personality Inventory contains three scales. Clinical scales, content scales, and: |
|---|---|---|
| | A. | depression scales |
| | B. | mood scales |
| | C. | abnormality scales |
| | D. | validity scales |

| p. 474<br>Application:Assessment -<br>Objective Tests<br>Level: Easy<br>Type: Factual<br>Ans: B | 164. | The purpose of Minnesota Multiphasic Personality Inventory is to: |
|---|---|---|
| | A. | identify locus of control |
| | B. | assess emotional adjustment in people with mental disorders |
| | C. | help students determine their learning style |
| | D. | reveal unresolved unconscious conflicts |

| p. 475<br>Application:Assessment -<br>Objective Tests<br>Level: Easy<br>Type: Factual<br>Ans: C | 165. | Studies investigating the relationship between personality and the signs of the zodiac have found that: |
|---|---|---|
| | A. | there are actually a number of relationships between zodiac sign and personality |
| | B. | there is a relationship between zodiac sign and personality only for people who make a habit of reading horoscopes |
| | C. | no relationship exists between zodiac sign and personality |
| | D. | Aries, Capricorn, and Virgo are the only signs that correlate consistently with personality types |

| p. 475<br>Application:Assessment -<br>Objective Tests<br>Level: Easy<br>Type: Factual<br>Ans: D | 166. | Astrology and horoscopes lack |
|---|---|---|
| | A. | scoring |
| | B. | the Barnum principle |
| | C. | reliability |
| | D. | validity |

| p. 475<br>Application:Assessment -<br>Objective Tests<br>Level: Easy<br>Type: Factual<br>Ans: A<br>*PS/SG 20-24* | 167. | The Barnum principle explains how horoscopes predict your future (but ignore validity): |
|---|---|---|
| | A. | the traits listed are so general that they apply to almost everyone |
| | B. | there is a specific astrological constellation for the date of your birth |
| | C. | astrological signs have been worked out over many millennia |
| | D. | life is a circus — who knows what will happen? |

p. 475
Application:Assessment -
  Objective Tests
Level: Easy
Type: Applied
Ans: B
*www*

168. Juana went to a fortuneteller at the county fair and was amazed at how accurate the fortuneteller was in describing her personality. It is likely that the fortuneteller's accuracy was due to:
A. ESP
B. the Barnum principle
C. inside information
D. projective techniques

p. 475
Application:Assessment -
  Objective Tests
Level: Easy
Type: Applied
Ans: C

169. In his horoscope, Alan reads that he is an interesting person who cares about people. According to the Barnum principle, Alan will:
A. reject the assessment because it is too general
B. reject the assessment unless it refers to traits that Alan values
C. accept the assessment because it is generally true for most people
D. accept the assessment only if he believes it fits his personality

p. 475
Application:Assessment -
  Objective Tests
Level: Easy
Type: Factual
Ans: C

170. A test that produces the same results if administered on different occasions to the same person is considered:
A. probable
B. valid
C. reliable
D. psychologically sound

p. 475
Application:Assessment -
  Objective Tests
Level: Easy
Type: Applied
Ans: B

171. A researcher administers a new personality test to twenty college students. Six months later she readministers the test and finds that her results are not at all consistent with those gathered at the first test administration. The researcher's test has a problem of:
A. validity
B. reliability
C. probability
D. replicative credibility

p. 475
Application:Assessment -
  Objective Tests
Level: Easy
Type: Factual
Ans: D

172. When a test measures what it was constructed to measure, it is considered:
A. reliable
B. psychologically sound
C. constructive
D. valid

p. 475
Application:Assessment -
  Objective Tests
Level: Easy
Type: Applied
Ans: A
*www*

173. A student takes a statistics test that is based on baseball box scores and team standing. Afterward, the student mentions to the instructor that, to do well on the test, a student had to be familiar with baseball, which is not part of the course. The student is criticizing the test's:
A. validity
B. reliability
C. probability
D. psychological worth

p. 475
Application:Assessment -
  Objective Tests
Level: Easy
Type: Factual
Ans: B

174. The main advantage of objective tests is:
A. that most people give honest responses
B. ease of administration and good reliability
C. that they are good predictors of behavior
D. the wide variety of useful tests

p. 475
Application:Assessment -
  Objective Tests
Level: Easy
Type: Factual
Ans: D

175. The reliability of the MMPI-2 ranges from:
A. .01 to .21
B. .34 to .41
C. .43 to .62
D. .68 to .92

p. 475
Application:Assessment -
  Objective Tests
Level: Easy
Type: Factual
Ans: D

176. Which of the following is <u>not</u> among the advantages of objective tests as presented in your textbook?
A. They are easily administered.
B. They are highly structured .
C. They have good reliability.
D. They only measure conscious factors.

p. 475
Application:Assessment -
  Objective Tests
Level: Easy
Type: Applied
Ans: B

177. Professor Freudson, an avid advocate for the Freudian perspective, has criticized objective tests of personality. What is his criticism?
A. They can not predict behaviors in specific situations.
B. They may not measure unconscious personality factors.
C. They are not useful in identifying personality differences.
D. They have low reliability and validity.

p. 475
Application:Assessment -
  Objective Tests
Level: Easy
Type: Applied
Ans: A

178. Slick Lefty, a convicted criminal, is taking an objective test of personality. Slick Lefty wants to give the impression that he is ready for parole. What should the clinician, who is giving the test to Slick Lefty, remember about objective tests?
A. People can figure out how to give socially desirable answers
B. They are not useful in identifying personality differences
C. They have low reliability and validity
D. They are difficult to administer

p. 475
Application:Assessment -
  Objective Tests
Level: Easy
Type: Factual
Ans: A
*www*

179. Which of the following is a disadvantage of objective tests?
A. They cannot predict behaviors in specific situations.
B. They are difficult to administer.
C. They have low reliability and validity.
D. They are not useful in identifying personality differences.

True/False

| F | www | 1. | Social cognitive theory emphasizes unconscious conflicts. |
|---|---|---|---|
| T | | 2. | An important name in social cognitive theory is Bandura. |
| T | www | 3. | Observational learning is an important component of social cognitive theory. |
| F | | 4. | If you believe that you have little control over what happens, then you would have an internal self-efficacy. |
| T | www | 5. | Those with an internal locus of control report having less stress. |
| T | | 6. | Children who can delay gratification tend to be more intelligent. |
| F | | 7. | Previous experiences do not have much effect on a person's self-efficacy. |
| T | www | 8. | Social cognitive theory pays too little attention to genetic factors. |
| T | | 9. | A trait is a relatively stable and enduring tendency to behave in a certain way. |
| T | | 10. | The Big Five refer to traits. |
| F | www | 11. | Little research support has been found in different cultures for OCEAN. |
| F | | 12. | OCEAN does a good job at explaining why people have certain traits. |
| T | | 13. | The trait approach predicts that people are consistent across situations. |
| T | www | 14. | Mischel has found that people act consistently in similar situations. |
| F | | 15. | Personality traits are relatively fixed by age 20. |
| F | | 16. | Identical twins share 50% of their genes. |
| F | www | 17. | The heritability of IQ is about 10%. |
| T | | 18. | The Big Five has been found to be a valid and reliable way to describe personality. |
| F | | 19. | The person-situation interaction supports the trait approach to personality. |
| T | | 20. | Parental practices influences personality less than genetics. |
| F | www | 21. | The quality of life typically decreases following a quantum personality change. |
| F | | 22. | Suicide bombers are more likely to have adjustment problems than non-bombers. |
| F | www | 23. | The MMPI-2 is a projective test. |
| T | | 24. | Objective personality tests tend to have good reliability. |
| F | www | 25. | To say that a psychological test has reliability means that it measures what it claims to measure. |

Short-Answer Essay Questions

1. Present an example to show the interaction between cognitive-personal factors, behaviors, and environmental factors.
2. What is locus of control? Why would it be to your advantage to have an internal locus? (www)
3. Describe the contribution of Gordon Allport to the trait theory.
4. What is OCEAN? How was OCEAN developed? (www)
5. Briefly describe the personality changes that take place across the lifespan.
6. What is heritability? What is the heritability of IQ, mental disorders, and personality? (www)
7. Describe the contributions of genetic factors, nonshared environmental factors, and shared environmental factors on personality. Which one contributes the most to personality?
8. To what extent does the trait approach predict behavior across situations? (www)
9. Contrast objective personality tests with projective tests. (www)
10. Why are reliability and validity desirable characteristics of a personality test?

# Module 21 - Health, Stress, and Coping

Module 21 - Health, Stress, and Coping

p. 481
Introduction
Level: Easy
Type: Factual
Ans: B

1. Compared to other fears, what is unique about the fear of blood or seeing needles?
A. It is much less common that other fears such as snakes and spiders.
B. It is one of the few fears that can cause people to actually faint.
C. The amount of stress that is generated is significantly less than the stress experienced because of other fears.
D. Most people with this fear are males.

p. 481
Introduction
Level: Easy
Type: Conceptual
Ans: A
*PS/SG 21-1*

2. Rod Plotnik uses his problem with having blood drawn in the doctor's office to show that:
A. how we interpret or appraise a situation determines the stress it causes
B. a bad scare in childhood will stay with you for the rest of your life
C. some events, like having blood drawn, are stressful to everyone
D. stress can overcome a person for no apparent reason

p. 481
Introduction
Level: Easy
Type: Factual
Ans: B
*www*

3. When we interpret a situation as threatening but do <u>not</u> feel equipped to handle the situation, we experience:
A. psychosis
B. stress
C. motivation
D. challenge

p. 481
Introduction
Level: Easy
Type: Factual
Ans: C

4. "I don't think I have the resources to handle this situation." This person is experiencing:
A. psychosis
B. anxiety
C. stress
D. challenge

p. 481
Introduction
Level: Easy
Type: Conceptual
Ans: A

5. The example described in your textbook regarding an intense fear of blood that can cause fainting suggests:
A. how the mind and body interact
B. how learning can play a role in phobias
C. that genetics plays a significant part in physiological dysfunction
D. that a phobia is more common among males than females

p. 481
Introduction
Level: Easy
Type: Factual
Ans: A

6. Stress occurs when we:
A. interpret a situation as threatening but do not have the resources to handle it
B. have a secondary appraisal that conflicts with a primary appraisal of a situation
C. realize that our coping resources are socially-based
D. feel our heart beating rapidly and sense our faces turning red

p. 481
Introduction
Level: Easy
Type: Applied
Ans: C

7. "The situation I find myself in is very threatening. In other situations, I do okay, but this particular situation I don't think I can handle." Based upon this statement, this person is most likely experiencing:
   A. burnout
   B. the fight-flight response
   C. stress
   D. a phobia

p. 482
Appraisal
Level: Easy
Type: Factual
Ans: B

8. Most people with a fear of blood report that the fear began:
   A. as teenagers
   B. with a traumatic event
   C. by seeing someone negatively reacting to blood
   D. gradually over time

p. 482
Appraisal
Level: Easy
Type: Factual
Ans: A
*www*

9. The theory of Richard Lazarus emphasizes _____ as the first step in experiencing stress.
   A. appraisal
   B. fear
   C. threat
   D. flight

p. 482
Appraisal
Level: Moderate
Type: Conceptual
Ans: C

10. In regard to Lazarus's theory of stress, "There is nothing neither good nor bad, but thinking makes it so" describes the importance of:
    A. logical thinking
    B. primary metacognition
    C. appraisal
    D. neologistic thinking

p. 482
Appraisal
Level: Easy
Type: Factual
Ans: B

11. Lazarus has concluded that in stressful situations, our anxious feelings arise from:
    A. the nature of the situation
    B. our appraisal of the situation
    C. the level of actual danger associated with the situation
    D. the fight-or-flight response

p. 482
Appraisal
Level: Easy
Type: Factual
Ans: C
*www*

12. Your initial, subjective evaluation of a situation is called:
    A. metacognition
    B. personal evaluation
    C. primary appraisal
    D. hardiness

p. 482
Appraisal
Level: Easy
Type: Applied
Ans: B

13. Heather enters a large classroom and notices that she doesn't know anyone. If Heather turns this situation into a stressful situation, _____ is probably responsible.
    A. secondary appraisal
    B. primary appraisal
    C. the alarm stage
    D. the biofeedback stage

p. 482
Appraisal
Level: Easy
Type: Factual
Ans: D

14. Where do we balance the demands of a potentially stressful situation with our ability to meet those demands?
A. challenge stage
B. perception stage
C. secondary appraisal
D. primary appraisal

p. 482
Appraisal
Level: Easy
Type: Factual
Ans: C

15. The three kinds of primary appraisals, according to Lazarus, are:
A. harm/loss, threat, and challenge
B. hypochondriac, psychosomatic, and physiological
C. irrelevant, positive, and stressful
D. alarm, resistance, and exhaustion

p. 482
Appraisal
Level: Easy
Type: Factual
Ans: D
PS/SG 21-3

16. Which one of the following is *not* a type of primary appraisal?
A. harm/loss
B. threat
C. challenge
D. advantage/resource

p. 482
Appraisal
Level: Moderate
Type: Conceptual
Ans: D

17. A consequence of describing primary appraisal as irrelevant, positive, or stressful is that:
A. stress can be better studied
B. a situation is perceived in similar ways by healthy individuals
C. normal stress reactions are caused by stressful situations
D. different people can appraise the same situation differently

p. 482
Appraisal
Level: Easy
Type: Applied
Ans: D

18. Mia's primary appraisal of a particular situation is that it is irrelevant. What effect will this type of appraisal have on Mia?
A. She will experience much stress since the situation is potentially damaging to her friends and family.
B. Mia will experience a challenge if she remains in the situation.
C. The situation will probably lead to harm/loss.
D. The situation is probably nonstressful.

p. 482
Appraisal
Level: Easy
Type: Applied
Ans: A

19. Cal flunked his final exam. You cannot understand why he just doesn't care about it. It is evident that Cal has made a(n) _____ primary appraisal.
A. irrelevant
B. negative
C. zero-sum
D. inconsequential

p. 482
Appraisal
Level: Easy
Type: Factual
Ans: B

20. _____ primary appraisal means that the situation does <u>not</u> matter to our well being.
A. Inconsequential
B. Irrelevant
C. Positive
D. Negative

p. 482
Appraisal
Level: Moderate
Type: Applied
Ans: A

21. Jenny is going on a job interview for a job that she has already decided she doesn't want. Jenny will probably:
A. make an irrelevant primary appraisal
B. make a stressful primary appraisal
C. operate from the resistance stage
D. operate from the alarm stage

p. 482
Appraisal
Level: Easy
Type: Factual
Ans: D

22. A positive primary appraisal means that the situation will:
A. arouse and prepare the body for action
B. definitely involve danger or threat
C. be dealt with successfully
D. enhance or preserve our well-being

p. 482
Appraisal
Level: Easy
Type: Applied
Ans: C

23. Aaron really wanted to go out with this very attractive woman, but he was turned down. He feels totally rejected and depressed. Aaron is most likely to have experienced:
A. negative appraisal
B. challenge appraisal
C. stressful primary appraisal
D. positive primary appraisal

p. 482
Appraisal
Level: Easy
Type: Factual
Ans: A

24. If you make a stressful primary appraisal of a situation, it means that:
A. your emotional and psychological resources are overtaxed
B. harm or loss has not yet taken place
C. you have the potential for personal growth
D. you have the resources to cope with the situation

p. 482
Appraisal
Level: Easy
Type: Factual
Ans: C

25. According to Lazarus, if a person encounters a situation and makes a stressful primary appraisal, the result will be one of three:
A. techniques: biofeedback, relaxation, or meditation
B. stages: alarm, resistance, or exhaustion
C. reactions: harm/loss, threat, or challenge
D. symptoms: muscle pain, fatigue, or headaches

p. 482
Appraisal
Level: Easy
Type: Factual
Ans: B
*www*

26. If we make a stressful primary appraisal, we then make interpretations of the situation as:
A. irrelevant and positive
B. harm/loss, threat, and challenge
C. dispositional
D. arousing

p. 482
Appraisal
Level: Easy
Type: Factual
Ans: B

27. Appraising a situation as involving harm/loss means that:
A. the situation is potentially dangerous
B. you have already suffered damage or injury
C. you anticipate harm in the near future
D. the situation requires mobilization of resources

p. 482
Appraisal
Level: Easy
Type: Applied
Ans: A

28. Imagine that you have been caught cheating on a test, and you feel your hands trembling. Which appraisal are you most likely to make?
A. a harm/loss appraisal
B. a resistance appraisal
C. a challenge appraisal
D. an alarm appraisal

p. 482
Appraisal
Level: Easy
Type: Factual
Ans: D

29. A stressful appraisal with a threat reaction indicates that:
A. there is a psychosomatic symptom
B. there is a potential for personal growth
C. you have experienced harm/loss
D. you are anticipating harm/loss

p. 482
Appraisal
Level: Easy
Type: Factual
Ans: A

30. According to the discussion on appraisal, one reason why harm/loss appraisals are stressful is that they:
A. elicit negative emotions
B. cause us to avoid stressful situations
C. elicit negative and positive emotions
D. cause physical damage

p. 482
Appraisal
Level: Moderate
Type: Applied
Ans: C

31. Thomas finds himself in a stressful situation. He says to himself, "I'm ok now, but something bad is going to happen soon." Thomas has probably made a _____ appraisal.
A. positive
B. harm/loss
C. threat
D. challenge

p. 482
Appraisal
Level: Moderate
Type: Applied
Ans: C

32. After spending the weekend at home, you find driving back to school very stressful. The roads are very icy and there is snow blowing reducing your visibility. Foremost in your mind is the likelihood of sliding into the ditch. You're probably making a _____ appraisal.
A. positive
B. harm/loss
C. threat
D. challenge

p. 482
Appraisal
Level: Moderate
Type: Applied
Ans: A
www

33. Juan's grades this semester are terrible. He runs the risk of being suspended from school. Juan believes that it is just a matter of time before the suspension occurs. Juan has more than likely made a _____ appraisal.
A. threat
B. challenge
C. positive
D. harm/loss

p. 482
Appraisal
Level: Easy
Type: Applied
Ans: B

34. Which of the following situations would be <u>most</u> likely to elicit a threat appraisal?
A. being offered a better job in a new, exciting city
B. being trapped in a room without light and a fear of the dark
C. being in an auto accident and getting hurt
D. being able to rescue a stranded motorist and feeling proud

p. 482
Appraisal
Level: Easy
Type: Factual
Ans: A

35. Which type of appraisal elicits positive emotions, such as exhilaration?
A. a challenge appraisal
B. a fight appraisal
C. an arousal appraisal
D. a threat appraisal

p. 482
Appraisal
Level: Moderate
Type: Applied
Ans: C
*www*

36. You are taking a course in which the instructor keeps telling you that tests and quizzes are *opportunities* to demonstrate your understanding of the material. The instructor is attempting to elicit what kind of appraisal?
A. irrelevant appraisal
B. harm/loss appraisal
C. challenge appraisal
D. threat appraisal

p. 482
Appraisal
Level: Moderate
Type: Applied
Ans: A

37. Marie serves as a faculty advisor to freshmen at her college. Many of them find the first semester of college overwhelming and stressful. She can best assist them by:
A. helping them see their classes as challenges that require direct action
B. sympathizing with them, because college is stressful for everyone
C. telling them to grow up; they're not in high school any longer
D. threatening them with dismissal if they don't do well in their classes

p. 483
Appraisal
Level: Easy
Type: Factual
Ans: B

38. You are a research subject in an experiment. A computer next to you measures your physiological arousal. You notice that there is a sensor attached to your palm. What must this computer be measuring?
A. palmar index
B. galvanic skin response
C. cephalopalmaric response
D. general adaptation response

p. 483
Appraisal
Level: Moderate
Type: Factual
Ans: C

39. In the power saw study described in the module, which group experienced more arousal and why?
A. those that were told to think of ways that the accidents could have been prevented because they made a challenge appraisal
B. those that were told to think of ways that the accidents could have been prevented because they made a threat appraisal
C. those that were told to put themselves in the place of the accident victims because they made a threat appraisal
D. those that were told to put themselves in the place of the accident victims because they made a challenge appraisal

p. 483
Appraisal
Level: Moderate
Type: Applied
Ans: C

40. Sharon and Claire are watching a movie about an ill-fated love affair. Sharon has just experienced the breakup of a long-term relationship and finds herself identifying with the main character of the movie. Claire has had no serious relationships and watches the movie for its artistic merit. According to Lazarus's view on appraisal:
A. neither Sharon nor Claire should experience stress from the movie
B. both Sharon and Claire will find the movie stressful
C. Sharon will find the movie stressful, but Claire will not
D. Claire will find the movie stressful, but Sharon will not

p. 483
Appraisal
Level: Moderate
Type: Applied
Ans: D

41. Ginger and Mary Ann are enrolled in a driver's education class. One of the requirements of the class is to watch a very graphic video of car accidents and victims. Ginger is having a very hard time watching these videos since she focuses on the agony and pain of the suffering. Mary Ann tries to figure out how the accidents could have been avoided. Besides their reaction to the videos, how else do Ginger and Mary Ann differ?
A. They differ in their experiences with car accidents.
B. Ginger makes a primary appraisal and Mary Ann makes a secondary appraisal.
C. Ginger makes a stressful appraisal and Mary Ann makes an arousal appraisal.
D. Ginger makes a threat appraisal and Mary Ann makes a challenge appraisal.

p. 483
Appraisal
Level: Moderate
Type: Applied
Ans: A

42. Based upon the textbook, which is the single most important variable in determining if a particular situation is stressful for you?
A. how you appraise the situation
B. the length of time you are in the situation
C. the situation itself
D. how other people are reacting to the situation

p. 483
Appraisal
Level: Easy
Type: Factual
Ans: D

43. According to the module, why might two people who are in the same situation have different levels of stress?
A. one is in the alarm stage, the other is in resistance stage
B. one experiences the fight-flight response, the other has an increase in sympathetic activity
C. one engages in primary appraisal, the other does not
D. differences in the kind of primary appraisal

p. 483
Appraisal
Level: Moderate
Type: Factual
Ans: D

44. What effect do harm/loss and threat appraisals have that challenge appraisals do not?
A. an increase in the activity of the parasympathetic division
B. lower physiological arousal
C. a triggering of physiological arousal
D. higher levels of negative emotion

p. 483
Appraisal
Level: Moderate
Type: Applied
Ans: A

45. In a novel you're reading, the three main characters find themselves in a stressful situation. Greg is experiencing a challenge appraisal, Peter a harm/loss appraisal and Bobby is having a threat appraisal. Which one of the characters is most likely to experience the least stress?

A. Greg
B. Peter
C. Bobby
D. there would be no differences

p. 484
Physiological Responses
Level: Easy
Type: Factual
Ans: D

46. A threat appraisal automatically triggers:
A. parasympathetic division activity
B. frustration
C. posttraumatic stress disorder
D. the fight-flight response

p. 484
Physiological Responses
Level: Easy
Type: Factual
Ans: C

47. Stimuli that threaten a person's physical or psychological well-being elicit the bodily reaction called the:
A. stress syndrome
B. emotional upset
C. fight-flight response
D. automaton response

p. 484
Physiological Responses
Level: Easy
Type: Factual
Ans: B

48. At this moment in your body, there are resources being directed toward your muscles and brain in addition to the other changes that prepare your body for action. You are experiencing the:
A. stress syndrome
B. fight-flight response
C. activation stage
D. automaton response

p. 484
Physiological Responses
Level: Easy
Type: Factual
Ans: B

49. The fight-flight response results in:
A. cognitive coping devices
B. increased energy to deal with threatening situations
C. psychosomatic symptoms
D. reduction in corticoids levels

p. 484
Physiological Responses
Level: Easy
Type: Factual
Ans: D

50. One of the first indications that we are experiencing the fight-flight response is:
A. increased worry
B. the realization that our job or school is getting hectic
C. a decrease in productivity
D. when we make a primary appraisal that the situation is threatening

p. 484
Physiological Responses
Level: Easy
Type: Factual
Ans: A

51. The part of the brain that is initially activated when a situation is appraised as threatening is the:
A. hypothalamus
B. cerebellum
C. adrenal medulla
D. occipital lobe

p. 484
Physiological Responses
Level: Easy
Type: Factual
Ans: C

52. What role does the hypothalamus play in the activation of the fight-flight response?
   A.  It releases dopamine into the blood stream.
   B.  It transfers sensory information to the stress centers of the brain.
   C.  It triggers the release of stress-fighting hormone.
   D.  It actives the parasympathetic division.

p. 484
Physiological Responses
Level: Easy
Type: Factual
Ans: A

53. The stress-fighting hormone released from the pituitary gland is called:
   A.  ACTH
   B.  acetylcholine
   C.  dopamine
   D.  mescaline

p. 484
Physiological Responses
Level: Easy
Type: Factual
Ans: B

54. The physiological changes associated with the fight-flight response are caused by the _____ nervous system.
   A.  somatic
   B.  sympathetic
   C.  parasympathetic
   D.  central

p. 484
Physiological Responses
Level: Easy
Type: Factual
Ans: D

55. The sympathetic division:
   A.  calms the body down
   B.  aids in digestion
   C.  secretes a group of hormones called corticoids
   D.  prepares the body to deal with danger

p. 484
Physiological Responses
Level: Easy
Type: Factual
Ans: C

56. Which part of the body calms the body down and returns it to a more relaxed state?
   A.  the endocrine system
   B.  the exhaustion stage
   C.  the parasympathetic division
   D.  the general adaptation syndrome

p. 484
Physiological Responses
Level: Easy
Type: Factual
Ans: A
www

57. Sympathetic is to _____ as parasympathetic is to _____.
   A.  arousal; relaxation
   B.  relaxation; arousal
   C.  intellectual; emotional
   D.  mind; body

p. 484
Physiological Responses
Level: Easy
Type: Factual
Ans: C

58. Brad is about to give his first piano recital. If his fight-flight response is activated, he will experience all of the following except:
   A.  increased heart rate
   B.  increased release of ACTH
   C.  decreased blood pressure
   D.  decreased digestive system activity

| | | |
|---|---|---|
| p. 485 | 59. | The part of the body that releases ACTH in the fight-flight response is the: |
| Physiological Responses | A. | liver |
| Level: Easy | B. | hypothalamus |
| Type: Factual | C. | pituitary |
| Ans: C | D. | adrenal medulla |

| | | |
|---|---|---|
| p. 485 | 60. | What part of the body releases glycogen (blood sugar) to provide a source of energy during stress? |
| Physiological Responses | | |
| Level: Easy | A. | liver |
| Type: Factual | B. | hypothalamus |
| Ans: A | C. | pituitary |
| | D. | adrenal medulla |

| | | |
|---|---|---|
| p. 485 | 61. | The _____ releases epinephrine in the fight-flight response. |
| Physiological Responses | A. | liver |
| Level: Easy | B. | hypothalamus |
| Type: Factual | C. | pituitary |
| Ans: D | D. | adrenal medulla |

| | | |
|---|---|---|
| p. 485 | 62. | During stress our pupils are: |
| Physiological Responses | A. | constricted |
| Level: Easy | B. | dilated |
| Type: Factual | C. | bathed in ACTH |
| Ans: B | D. | less aroused |

| | | |
|---|---|---|
| p. 485 | 63. | A good clue to whether a person is experiencing stress is the |
| Physiological Responses | A. | potential danger of the situation (like operating a chainsaw) |
| Level: Easy | B. | amount of blood at the scene |
| Type: Factual | C. | galvanic skin response |
| Ans: C | D. | "deer caught in the headlights" expression |
| PS/SG 21-4 | | |

| | | |
|---|---|---|
| p. 485 | 64. | When activated by the sympathetic division, the adrenal medulla produce: |
| Physiological Responses | A. | glycogen and dopamine |
| Level: Easy | B. | adrenaline and norepinephrine |
| Type: Factual | C. | ACTH and dopamine |
| Ans: B | D. | glucose and glycogen |

| | | |
|---|---|---|
| p. 485 | 65. | A suspected criminal consents to a lie detector test. When asked where he was on the night of the crime, the suspect says that he was out of town with friends. If this is a lie, it is assumed that the lie detector will pick this up because: |
| Physiological Responses | | |
| Level: Moderate | | |
| Type: Conceptual | | |
| Ans: B | A. | it is capable of doing a computer matching of the details of the man's story with what the police know to be true |
| | B. | guilt causes stress that will cause the hypothalamus to trigger the sympathetic nervous system |
| | C. | we do not maintain eye contact when we lie |
| | D. | we fidget when we lie |

| | | |
|---|---|---|
| p. 485<br>Physiological Responses<br>Level: Easy<br>Type: Factual<br>Ans: C | 66.<br>A.<br>B.<br>C.<br>D. | A woman's response to stress may be described as:<br>"fight and flee"<br>"use and peruse"<br>"tend and befriend"<br>"brief and debrief" |

| | | |
|---|---|---|
| p. 485<br>Physiological Responses<br>Level: Easy<br>Type: Factual<br>Ans: B | 67.<br>A.<br>B.<br>C.<br>D. | An explanation of gender differences in responding to stress is that:<br>women need to gather belongings while men need to fight<br>women need to protect their families while men need to fight<br>women need to share their feelings while men need to protect their family<br>women need to gather belongings while men need to share their feelings |

| | | |
|---|---|---|
| p. 486<br>Physiological Responses<br>Level: Easy<br>Type: Factual<br>Ans: A<br>*www* | 68.<br>A.<br>B.<br>C.<br>D. | Psychosomatic symptoms are:<br>real physical symptoms that are caused by psychological factors<br>imagined physical ailments<br>real physical symptoms that are caused by defense mechanisms<br>symptomatic of Type B personalities |

| | | |
|---|---|---|
| p. 486<br>Physiological Responses<br>Level: Moderate<br>Type: Applied<br>Ans: A | 69.<br><br><br><br><br><br>A.<br>B.<br><br>C.<br>D. | Professor Jensen is reading a student paper on psychosomatic symptoms. One statement in the paper reads, "Psychosomatic symptoms are real and painful and come from the breakdown or damage of body organs but are caused by psychological factors." How should Professor Jensen react to the statement and what should he write in the margins of the student paper?<br>"Good point"<br>"Half right - remember these symptoms are real but usually are not painful."<br>"Not correct - you need to reread your references."<br>"Wrong term - psychosomatic symptoms are not real." |

| | | |
|---|---|---|
| p. 486<br>Physiological Responses<br>Level: Moderate<br>Type: Applied<br>Ans: B | 70.<br><br><br>A.<br>B.<br>C.<br>D. | Kevin is an emergency room nurse who experiences a great deal of stress. He has developed stomach problems that cause him great pain. His doctor has diagnosed an ulcer. In this example, the ulcer may be a:<br>hypochondriac symptom<br>psychosomatic symptom<br>resistance symptom<br>defense mechanism |

| | | |
|---|---|---|
| p. 486<br>Physiological Responses<br>Level: Moderate<br>Type: Applied<br>Ans: B | 71.<br><br><br><br><br>A.<br>B.<br>C.<br>D. | You visit your family doctor complaining of migraine headaches. The doctors says that your headaches are psychosomatic. He further explains that that means that your headaches are just imagined and are not real. So he tells you to go home and stop worrying. Given your knowledge of stress, you correctly conclude:<br>migraine headaches are only psychological<br>your doctor doesn't know what is talking about<br>your doctor is well-trained<br>your doctor's definition of psychosomatic is correct, but he should have given you some medication |

p. 486
Physiological Responses
Level: Easy
Type: Applied
Ans: D

72. As a family practice physician, you estimate that about 70% of the patients you see at the clinic have stress related problems. Is your experience *usual*?
A. yes - about 25% of patients seen in general practice have stress related problems
B. yes - less than 10% of patients seen in general practice have stress related problems
C. no - about 85% to 95% of patients seen in general practice have stress related problems
D. yes - about 50% to 80% of patients seen in general practice have stress related problems

p. 486
Physiological Responses
Level: Easy
Type: Factual
Ans: D

73. One of the most common psychosomatic symptoms is:
A. thinking you are ill when, in fact, you are not
B. fidgeting
C. hyperactivity
D. stomach problems

p. 486
Physiological Responses
Level: Easy
Type: Factual
Ans: D

74. The development of psychosomatic symptoms depends on several factors. Which of the following is not among the factors as presented in the textbook?
A. having a genetic predisposition
B. experiencing prolonged stress
C. experiencing continual activation of the fight-flight response
D. making a challenge appraisal

p. 486
Physiological Responses
Level: Easy
Type: Factual
Ans: A

75. What is the first step in developing psychosomatic symptoms?
A. a genetic predisposition and lifestyle
B. prolonged stress
C. secondary appraisal
D. resistance

p. 487
Physiological Responses
Level: Easy
Type: Factual
Ans: C

76. One of the first researchers to examine the fight-flight response is:
A. Sigmund Freud
B. Albert Bandura
C. Hans Selye
D. Albert Ellis

p. 487
Physiological Responses
Level: Easy
Type: Factual
Ans: D

77. Selye found that continuing stress affects the body:
A. by creating physical symptoms that are only in one's "head" but still are painful
B. by reducing the effectiveness of the immune system
C. by creating imaginary symptoms
D. in the form of physical symptoms

p. 487
Physiological Responses
Level: Easy
Type: Factual
Ans: B

78. The _____ describes the body's reaction to stressful situations as a series of three stages.
A. global adaptation syndrome
B. general adaptation syndrome
C. mind-body connection model
D. locus of control model

p. 487
Physiological Responses
Level: Easy
Type: Factual
Ans: D

79. The _____ describes the body's reaction to stress in three stages.
A. psychoneuroimmunology theory
B. psychodynamic theory
C. mind-body theory
D. general adaptation syndrome

p. 487
Physiological Responses
Level: Easy
Type: Factual
Ans: C

80. The three parts of Selye's general adaptation syndrome are:
A. perception, response, and recovery
B. perception, interpretation, and flight
C. alarm, resistance, and exhaustion
D. adaptation, modification, and adoption

p. 487
Physiological Responses
Level: Easy
Type: Factual
Ans: B
*PS/SG 21-9*

81. Which one of the following is *not* a stage in the general adaptation syndrome?
A. alarm
B. attack
C. resistance
D. exhaustion

p. 487
Physiological Responses
Level: Easy
Type: Factual
Ans: D

82. Hans Selye was one of the first researchers to show that stress can cause:
A. primary appraisal
B. secondary appraisal
C. approach-approach conflict
D. physical symptoms

p. 487
Physiological Responses
Level: Easy
Type: Factual
Ans: B
*www*

83. According to the general adaptation syndrome, our initial reaction to stress with the fight-flight response is called the _____ stage.
A. psychosomatic
B. alarm
C. primary
D. exhaustion

p. 487
Physiological Responses
Level: Easy
Type: Applied
Ans: B

84. Just before her turn to play at a piano recital, Naomi feels her heart rate accelerating and her face flushing. According to Selye, Naomi is in what stage of general adaptation to stress?
A. psychosomatic
B. alarm
C. resistance
D. exhaustion

p. 487
Physiological Responses
Level: Moderate
Type: Applied
Ans: A

85. Brad has been under a lot stress for a considerable amount of time. If Brad is in the resistance stage of the general adaptation syndrome, what should he be experiencing?
A. draining of energy
B. serious psychosomatic symptoms
C. symptoms of hypochondriasis
D. nothing, Brad should feel healthy

p. 487
Physiological Responses
Level: Easy
Type: Factual
Ans: A
*www*

86.   During the _____ stage of the general adaptation syndrome, the body is using large amounts of energy.

   A.   resistance
   B.   alarm
   C.   primary
   D.   exhaustion

p. 487
Physiological Responses
Level: Moderate
Type: Applied
Ans: C

87.   Trent is working on a major presentation for one of his company's clients and is under a lot of stress. He has been working late every night and eating poorly. At first, he experienced a number of physical symptoms such as stomachaches and headaches, but in the last week the symptoms have disappeared. Assuming that the stress is still present, Trent is probably in what phase of general adaptation syndrome?

   A.   psychosomatic
   B.   alarm
   C.   resistance
   D.   exhaustion

p. 487
Physiological Responses
Level: Easy
Type: Applied
Ans: B

88.   Todd has been "stressed-out" for so long, that he has developed an ulcer. Todd must be in the _____ stage of the general adaptation syndrome.

   A.   resistance
   B.   exhaustion
   C.   alarm
   D.   degeneration

p. 487
Physiological Responses
Level: Easy
Type: Factual
Ans: B

89.   In what stage of the general adaptation syndrome is there a breakdown to internal organs and/or weakening of the immune system?

   A.   resistance
   B.   exhaustion
   C.   alarm
   D.   degeneration

p. 487
Physiological Responses
Level: Moderate
Type: Applied
Ans: C

90.   Danielle is a lawyer and has been in a very stressful trial for the past two weeks. What do we know about Danielle's physical health at this time?

   A.   Her heart rate has probably been below normal for almost two weeks.
   B.   Her epinephrine levels have probably been below normal for almost two weeks.
   C.   Her body's energy stores have continued to be depleted for most of the trial.
   D.   She is unlikely to experience physical symptoms of stress in the near future.

p. 487
Physiological Responses
Level: Moderate
Type: Factual
Ans: A

91.   Which of the following is characteristic of the exhaustion stage of the general adaptation syndrome?

   A.   the weakening of the immune system
   B.   the activation of the fight--flight response
   C.   feeling healthy and energetic
   D.   the body returning to normal levels of functioning

p. 487
Physiological Responses
Level: Moderate
Type: Applied
Ans: B

92. Rick is about to be married. He knows he is doing the right thing, but he is very anxious about meeting his fiancée's parents and about his ability to be a good husband. This stress has been continuing for a while. If Rick experiences the third stage of Selye's general adaptation syndrome, what may happen on his honeymoon?
A. Rick may experience a great emotional release.
B. Rick may get physically ill.
C. Rick may take out his pent-up frustrations on his new bride.
D. Rick may realize that all his anxiety was foolish and relax.

p. 487
Physiological Responses
Level: Easy
Type: Factual
Ans: C

93. The idea that our thoughts, beliefs and emotions can cause physiological changes is called:
A. psychosomatic association
B. associationism
C. mind-body connection
D. functionalism

p. 487
Physiological Responses
Level: Easy
Type: Factual
Ans: B
PS/SG 21-10

94. The mind-body connection and mind-body therapy are both based on the idea that:
A. thoughts and emotions come from changes in bodily activity
B. thoughts and emotions can change physiological and immune responses
C. when you have a strong feeling or powerful idea, you must express it through bodily action
D. mind and body are two separate and independent areas of activity

p. 487
Physiological Responses
Level: Easy
Type: Applied
Ans: A

95. Dee says to Maggie, "Don't fret about losing that scholarship. If you worry about it, you could make yourself sick." This best illustrates the:
A. mind-body connection
B. unconscious motivation
C. psychosomatic association
D. psychodynamic thought

p. 487
Physiological Responses
Level: Easy
Type: Factual
Ans: A

96. Techniques such as relaxation, meditation, and biofeedback are often used in _____ to change negative beliefs, thoughts, and emotions to more positive ones.
A. mind-body therapy
B. psychosomatic therapy
C. association therapy
D. psychodynamic therapy

p. 488
Physiological Responses
Level: Easy
Type: Factual
Ans: D

97. The body's defense and surveillance network of cells and chemicals that fight off bacteria and viruses is called the:
A. adrenal system
B. parasympathetic division
C. hypothalamus
D. immune system

p. 488
Physiological Responses
Level: Easy
Type: Conceptual
Ans: C

98. Which of the following would be a good address for a web page on psychoneuroimmunology to illustrate an underlying assumption?
A. www.brain.edu
B. www.biology.edu
C. www.mind-body_connection.edu
D. www.corticoids.edu

p. 488
Physiological Responses
Level: Moderate
Type: Factual
Ans: C
*PS/SG 21-11*

99. Psychoneuroimmunology means the study of:
A. the manner in which physical factors create psychological symptoms
B. how disease can make a person psychotic or neurotic
C. the interaction of physical and psychological factors in health
D. this is a trick question - that is a made-up word

p. 488
Physiological Responses
Level: Easy
Type: Applied
Ans: A

100. Leisal's cognitive reactions to her stress-filled life have resulted in her central nervous system's slowing down her endocrine system. Which area of psychology would be most likely to study Leisal's condition?
A. psychoneuroimmunology
B. graphology
C. appraisal theory
D. psychoanalytic theory

p. 488
Physiological Responses
Level: Moderate
Type: Applied
Ans: D

101. Shirley has many allergies. She sleeps at a friend's house under a bedspread that she believes is filled with goose down. Her eyes and nose run so much that she can't sleep until she takes the bedspread out of the room. In the morning, the friend tells Shirley that the bedspread is filled with a synthetic material that she could not be allergic to. The friend is:
A. obviously lying to Shirley
B. possibly correct, but the pillow must have been down-filled
C. unaware that allergic reactions can flare up without any apparent cause
D. probably telling the truth, since psychological factors can affect Shirley's immune system

p. 488
Physiological Responses
Level: Moderate
Type: Applied
Ans: C

102. Michael is always on edge. He experiences prolonged stress as part of his job. His wife complains that he always perceives his job as a threat to his health. What can we reasonably expect from Michael?
A. eating problems that will lead to a dangerous gain of weight
B. bruxism
C. heightened physiological arousal that strains his immune system
D. depression and possible suicide if he remains in his current job

p. 488
Physiological Responses
Level: Moderate
Type: Factual
Ans: A

103. A man who had been married for 35 years loses his wife to cancer. The grief the man experiences:
A. may reduce his body's defense against disease
B. is a natural reaction that does not affect the man's physical health
C. provides an external release that will help maintain the man's physical health
D. may make the man think that he is ill when, in fact, he is not

| | | |
|---|---|---|
| p. 488<br>Physiological Responses<br>Level: Moderate<br>Type: Applied<br>Ans: B | 104. | Marlene claims that her chronic allergy symptoms are caused by the fact that she is stressed by her on-again off-again engagement to David. Marlene's claim is: |
| | A. | supported by recent research on virus transmission |
| | B. | supported by psychoneuroimmunology |
| | C. | medically incorrect, but would be correct if Marlene had cancer instead of allergy symptoms |
| | D. | physiologically impossible |

| | | |
|---|---|---|
| p. 488<br>Physiological Responses<br>Level: Easy<br>Type: Factual<br>Ans: D | 105. | When we experience the fight-flight response, two hormones are produced. Research in psychoneuroimmunology indicates that these two hormones: |
| | A. | lead to the production of antibodies |
| | B. | make us feel sick |
| | C. | cause dopamine to be released in the brain |
| | D. | suppress the immune system |

| | | |
|---|---|---|
| p. 488<br>Physiological Responses<br>Level: Easy<br>Type: Factual<br>Ans: B | 106. | The two groups of hormones that are activated by the fight-flight response that can suppress the immune system are: |
| | A. | placebos and catecholamines |
| | B. | corticoids and catecholamines |
| | C. | excitatory and inhibitory hormones |
| | D. | GABAs and endorphins |

| | | |
|---|---|---|
| p. 488<br>Physiological Responses<br>Level: Easy<br>Type: Factual<br>Ans: A<br>*PS/SG 21-6* | 107. | The reason why the fight-flight response can harm our health is that: |
| | A. | every time it is triggered our bodies go through an automatic process of arousal |
| | B. | overuse is a kind of "crying wolf" that eventually results in letting our guard down |
| | C. | biologically, humans were designed for quiet, peaceful lives |
| | D. | psychologically, humans do not tolerate challenge very well |

| | | |
|---|---|---|
| p. 488<br>Physiological Responses<br>Level: Easy<br>Type: Factual<br>Ans: D | 108. | Suppression of the immune system can occur when: |
| | A. | experiencing stress |
| | B. | our fight-flight responses are activated |
| | C. | corticoids and catecholamines are produced |
| | D. | all of the above |

| | | |
|---|---|---|
| p. 489<br>Physiological Responses<br>Level: Easy<br>Type: Conceptual<br>Ans: B | 109. | The example of the woman experiencing severe allergic reactions to red roses illustrates that: |
| | A. | operant conditioning can affect the immune system |
| | B. | the immune system can be altered by psychological factors |
| | C. | the immune system functions independently of cognitive factors |
| | D. | the neutral stimulus never reliably predicts the conditioned stimulus |

| | | |
|---|---|---|
| p. 489<br>Physiological Responses<br>Level: Easy<br>Type: Factual<br>Ans: C | 110. | The case of the lady suffering allergic reactions to red roses shows that the functioning of the immune system can be altered through: |
| | A. | behavior |
| | B. | trial and error learning |
| | C. | classical conditioning |
| | D. | operant conditioning |

p. 489
Physiological Responses
Level: Moderate
Type: Factual
Ans: C

111.    Attempts to classically condition the suppression of the immune response in mice have demonstrated that:

A.    conditioning may affect immunity, but this cannot be generalized to responses under stress

B.    the immune system cannot be affected by purely psychological factors

C.    our immune systems can be affected by psychological or cognitive stressors

D.    experimental data derived from mice cannot be generalized to humans

p. 489
Physiological Responses
Level: Easy
Type: Applied
Ans: C

112.    Dr. Clark wishes to condition the immune system of a laboratory rat. Which of the following is incorrect regarding the procedure?

A.    The allergic reaction elicited by the injected substance is the unconditioned response.

B.    The conditioned stimulus is the flashing light.

C.    The conditioned stimulus is the allergy-producing substance.

D.    The conditioned stimulus is the humming fan.

p. 489
Physiological Responses
Level: Moderate
Type: Factual
Ans: A

113.    To condition the immune system of a rat, the CS would be _____ and UCS would be the _____.

A.    flashing light and humming fan; allergic-producing substance

B.    flashing light and humming fan; allergic reaction

C.    allergic-producing substance; allergic reaction

D.    allergic-producing substance; salivation

p. 489
Physiological Responses
Level: Moderate
Type: Factual
Ans: B

114.    In conditioning the immune system of a rat, the UCR would be the _____.

A.    allergic-producing substance

B.    allergic reaction

C.    flashing light

D.    salivation

p. 489
Physiological Responses
Level: Easy
Type: Factual
Ans: D

115.    The section on conditioning the immune system means that:

A.    you can strengthen your immune system by diet and exercise

B.    the immune system is influenced by viruses and bacteria

C.    the immune system functions independently of psychological factors

D.    you can learn to become sick

p. 490
Stressful Experiences
Level: Easy
Type: Factual
Ans: D

116.    _____ are small, irritating, and frustrating events faced in daily life.

A.    Hang-ups

B.    Major life events

C.    Avoiders

D.    Hassles

p. 490
Stressful Experiences
Level: Easy
Type: Factual
Ans: C

117.    Hassles are considered to be situations which:

A.    have an insignificant impact on our lives

B.    result from conditioned emotional responses

C.    are small, irritating, and frustrating events faced in daily life

D.    promote avoidance-avoidance conflict

p. 490
Stressful Experiences
Level: Moderate
Type: Conceptual
Ans: B

118. Which of the following would be a hassle?
A. getting engaged
B. finding a car has double-parked next to you when you have to get to an appointment
C. the death of a spouse
D. being put on academic probation the first semester you are in college

p. 490
Stressful Experiences
Level: Easy
Type: Factual
Ans: D

119. "In an average day, I have to take out the garbage, cook supper, deal with traffic delays, and find a parking space at the college." This person has cited a number of:
A. personal limitations
B. environmental limitations
C. conflicts
D. hassles

p. 490
Stressful Experiences
Level: Easy
Type: Factual
Ans: C

120. The opposite of a hassle is a(n) _____.
A. turn-up
B. provider
C. uplift
D. satisfier

p. 490
Stressful Experiences
Level: Moderate
Type: Conceptual
Ans: A

121. Uplift is to _____ as hassle is to _____.
A. pleasant; unpleasant
B. inconsequential; consequential
C. small; large
D. internal; external

p. 490
Stressful Experiences
Level: Moderate
Type: Factual
Ans: A

122. A potentially disturbing situation that we appraise as having significant impact on our lives is termed a(n):
A. major life event
B. hassle
C. uplift
D. approach-approach conflict

p. 490
Stressful Experiences
Level: Easy
Type: Applied
Ans: A
*www*

123. Getting stuck in traffic is an example of _____, but being hospitalized after being hit by a bus is an example of _____.
A. a hassle; a major life event
B. burnout; hardiness
C. approach-approach conflict; a disease-prone personality
D. internal locus of control; external locus of control

p. 490
Stressful Experiences
Level: Moderate
Type: Applied
Ans: C

124. Michelle has experienced much anxiety, tension, and worrying in the past six months but cannot identify any particularly stressful events in her life during that time. You should suggest that she:
A. see a psychologist, since she is obviously denying some serious conflicts
B. adopt an external locus of control
C. study the day-to-day hassles she experiences
D. develop a Type A personality

p. 490
Stressful Experiences
Level: Easy
Type: Factual
Ans: C

125. Researchers have studied the relationship between the number of life events and subsequent psychosomatic symptoms. They report that:
A. there is little relationship between the two
B. only severe symptoms such as asthma and high blood pressure are related to life events
C. a modest correlation exists
D. a modest correlation exists but only for middle-aged individuals

p. 490
Stressful Experiences
Level: Easy
Type: Factual
Ans: D

126. The scale that measures life events by assigning them a value is called the:
A. Stress Impact Scale
B. Stressful Experiences Scale
C. Personal Stress Scale
D. Social Readjustment Rating Scale

p. 490
Stressful Experiences
Level: Moderate
Type: Applied
Ans: B

127. When Jerry calculated his Social Readjustment Rating Scale, he found it to be quite high. Because of moderate correlation, it may also be that Jerry has:
A. a great deal of satisfaction in life
B. an increased chance that he will contract an illness
C. produced an excess of growth hormones after puberty
D. a high need to achieve

p. 490
Stressful Experiences
Level: Easy
Type: Factual
Ans: D
*PS/SG 21-12*

128. The total score on the Social Readjustment Rating Scale:
A. subtracts positive life events from negative life changes
B. gives a precise cut-off point for becoming ill or staying well
C. reflects how well you cope with stress
D. reflects how many major life events you have experienced in the past year

p. 490
Stressful Experiences
Level: Moderate
Type: Factual
Ans: C

129. One shortcoming of the Social Readjustment Rating Scale is that it:
A. fails to correlate with the development of psychosomatic problems
B. lists only a small number of major life events
C. makes no distinction between appraisal of positive and negative events
D. has not been normed with college students

p. 490
Stressful Experiences
Level: Easy
Type: Factual
Ans: B

130. In examining gender differences in stress, researchers have found that:
A. women tend to have less psychosomatic problems
B. women have more symptoms of depression, anxiety, and psychosomatic problems
C. women are socialized to just "grin and bear" stress
D. no differences

p. 491
Stressful Experiences
Level: Easy
Type: Factual
Ans: A

131. We experience _____ when we try to reach some goal, but our efforts are blocked because of personal, social, or environmental limitations.
A. frustration
B. anxiety
C. burnout
D. avoidance

p. 491
Stressful Experiences
Level: Easy
Type: Applied
Ans: D

132. "Every time I move closer to my goals, something stops me." This person is experiencing _____ as a situational stressor.
A. avoidance
B. anger
C. burnout
D. frustration

p. 491
Stressful Experiences
Level: Easy
Type: Factual
Ans: A

133. You made a number of dumb mistakes on an exam. Your goal of an "A" is blocked and you experience frustration because of:
A. personal limitations
B. social limitations
C. environmental limitations
D. burnout

p. 491
Stressful Experiences
Level: Moderate
Type: Applied
Ans: C

134. "Paper work and more paper work. Regulations and more regulations. I wish the government wouldn't require so much. I don't qualify for a loan so I won't be able to start my own business - thanks to the bureaucrats!" This individual is experiencing _____ because of _____.
A. frustration; personal limitations
B. burnout; social or personal limitations
C. frustration; social or environmental limitations
D. burnout; internal locus of control

p. 491
Stressful Experiences
Level: Moderate
Type: Applied
Ans: A

135. "I work three jobs and I still can't get ahead. I think I'm careful about spending money, but I still have problems making ends meet." This person is frustrated because of:
A. environmental limitations
B. social limitations
C. personal limitations
D. burnout

p. 491
Stressful Experiences
Level: Easy
Type: Factual
Ans: B
*PS/SG 21-13*

136. Having feelings of doing poorly, physically wearing out, or becoming emotionally exhausted because of stress at work is called:
A. frustration
B. burnout
C. conflict
D. stress

p. 491
Stressful Experiences
Level: Easy
Type: Applied
Ans: C
*www*

137. Tina is feeling worn out and exhausted. She is experiencing what kind of situational stressor?
A. frustration
B. cultural stress
C. burnout
D. conflict

p. 491
Stressful Experiences
Level: Moderate
Type: Applied
Ans: A

138. George is an idealist and wants to help people. Larry doesn't really like the people he serves. Phil is a cynic and wants to succeed at all costs. Which one is most likely to burnout?
A. George
B. Phil
C. Larry
D. Phil and Larry are equally likely

p. 491
Stressful Experiences
Level: Easy
Type: Applied
Ans: B

139. "The wind was very strong, and it destroyed everything that I own. I never want to experience another tornado again. It's left me with sleeping problems, a feeling of helplessness and fear." This narrative best describes:
A. burnout
B. posttraumatic stress disorder
C. depression
D. delayed stress reaction disorder

p. 491
Stressful Experiences
Level: Easy
Type: Applied
Ans: B

140. Which of the following is not among the goals to deal with posttraumatic stress disorder as presented in your textbook?
A. provide emotional support
B. relive the experience through journaling
C. bring out the details of the experience
D. build a sense of courage to go on with life

p. 491
Stressful Experiences
Level: Easy
Type: Factual
Ans: D

141. The treatment of posttraumatic stress disorder usually involves:
A. hypnosis
B. antianxiety drugs
C. dream interpretation
D. cognitive-behavior therapy

p. 491
Stressful Experiences
Level: Moderate
Type: Factual
Ans: C

142. Terrifying flashbacks, avoiding similar situations, and experiencing an event that involves actual or threatened death or injury refers to a condition known as:
A. burnout
B. generalized anxiety disorder
C. posttraumatic stress disorder
D. hardiness

p. 492
Stressful Experiences
Level: Easy
Type: Factual
Ans: C

143. When we must choose between two incompatible goals, we experience:
A. motivation
B. hardiness
C. conflict
D. physical illness

p. 492
Stressful Experiences
Level: Easy
Type: Factual
Ans: C

144. Situations involving conflict trigger feelings of stress because:
A. the situation is appraised as challenging
B. only people with an external locus of control experience conflict
C. one choice or goal must be given up
D. they are usually accompanied by many major life changes

| p. 492 | 145. | An approach-approach conflict involves: |
|---|---|---|
| Stressful Experiences | A. | a single situation with both negative and positive aspects |
| Level: Easy | B. | choosing between positive and negative situations |
| Type: Factual | C. | choosing between two positive situations |
| Ans: C | D. | a single situation without any pleasurable consequences |

| p. 492 | 146. | "I just can't decide. Do I want to vacation in the Caribbean or Hawaii? Both are great places." This person is experiencing an: |
|---|---|---|
| Stressful Experiences | | |
| Level: Easy | A. | approach-approach conflict |
| Type: Applied | B. | active-active conflict |
| Ans: A | C. | affect-effect conflict |
| | D. | approach-avoidance conflict |

| p. 492 | 147. | Why might approach-approach conflict be the most stressful kind of conflict? |
|---|---|---|
| Stressful Experiences | | |
| Level: Easy | A. | We are stuck between a rock and a hard place. |
| Type: Conceptual | B. | We must be willing to take the option that is the least pleasant. |
| Ans: D | C. | We must learn how to make decisions that are not always popular. |
| | D. | We must give up a pleasurable consequence no matter what we choose. |

| p. 492 | 148. | Your gruesome, beastly jailer walks in and offers you the choice of being whipped or clubbed as your punishment of the day. Assuming that neither alternative appeals to you, we could assume that you are experiencing: |
|---|---|---|
| Stressful Experiences | | |
| Level: Moderate | | |
| Type: Applied | A. | approach-approach conflict |
| Ans: B | B. | avoidance-avoidance conflict |
| www | C. | approach-avoidance conflict |
| | D. | double conflict |

| p. 492 | 149. | When faced with an avoidance-avoidance conflict, we: |
|---|---|---|
| Stressful Experiences | A. | usually wait until the last minute to make a decision |
| Level: Easy | B. | usually make a decision early in the process |
| Type: Factual | C. | experience a decrease in frustration |
| Ans: A | D. | experience a reduction in stress |

| p. 492 | 150. | Bethany has to do her chores. Her dad lets her decide which one to do, either rake leaves or water the trees. She doesn't like to do either of the chores. Bethany faces a(n): |
|---|---|---|
| Stressful Experiences | | |
| Level: Easy | | |
| Type: Applied | A. | approach-avoidance conflict |
| Ans: B | B. | avoidance-avoidance conflict |
| | C. | double conflict |
| | D. | effect-affect conflict |

| p. 492 | 151. | An approach-avoidance conflict involves: |
|---|---|---|
| Stressful Experiences | A. | two options, neither of which are pleasurable |
| Level: Easy | B. | two options, one positive and one negative |
| Type: Factual | C. | one situation that has both pleasurable and disagreeable aspects |
| Ans: C | D. | one situation that does not cause stress |

| | | |
|---|---|---|
| p. 492<br>Stressful Experiences<br>Level: Easy<br>Type: Applied<br>Ans: B | 152. | A man who is on a diet loves desserts. When offered a dessert, the man will probably experience an _____ conflict. |
| | A. | approach-approach |
| | B. | approach-avoidance |
| | C. | avoidance-avoidance |
| | D. | ambivalent-frustration |

| | | |
|---|---|---|
| p. 492<br>Stressful Experiences<br>Level: Moderate<br>Type: Factual<br>Ans: A | 153. | In the _____ style of dealing with conflict, the person gives in to make the conflict go away, while someone with a(n) _____ style, goes to any lengths to win. |
| | A. | accommodation; domination |
| | B. | domination; active |
| | C. | compromise; integration |
| | D. | integration; domination |

| | | |
|---|---|---|
| p. 492<br>Stressful Experiences<br>Level: Easy<br>Type: Applied<br>Ans: C | 154. | Three friends are having a conflict. Isaac tries to resolve conflicts by finding solutions to please everyone. Jacob avoids the conflict, and Joseph tends to give in to any conflict. Which of these friends has the integration style of dealing with conflict? |
| | A. | Joseph |
| | B. | Jacob |
| | C. | Isaac |
| | D. | Joseph and Jacob |

| | | |
|---|---|---|
| p. 493<br>Stressful Experiences<br>Level: Easy<br>Type: Factual<br>Ans: D | 155. | When an emotional response is classically conditioned to a previously neutral stimulus, the result is a(n): |
| | A. | defense mechanism |
| | B. | internal locus of control |
| | C. | approach-approach conflict |
| | D. | conditioned emotional response |

| | | |
|---|---|---|
| p. 493<br>Stressful Experiences<br>Level: Moderate<br>Type: Factual<br>Ans: B | 156. | Which of the following is *true* regarding conditioned emotional responses? |
| | A. | They are triggered slowly and deliberately. |
| | B. | They are highly resistant to extinction. |
| | C. | They result from observational learning. |
| | D. | They result in the use of sublimation. |

| | | |
|---|---|---|
| p. 493<br>Stressful Experiences<br>Level: Moderate<br>Type: Applied<br>Ans: B | 157. | Josey hated to go to the dentist as a child because he always filled her cavities without giving her any anesthesia. Her dentist had an old radio in his office that always played static-filled classical music. Now, when she hears classical music on a radio that isn't well tuned in, she feels anxious. Josey is experiencing: |
| | A. | vicarious learning |
| | B. | a conditioned emotional response |
| | C. | an unconscious conflict |
| | D. | an avoidance-avoidance conflict |

p. 493
Stressful Experiences
Level: Easy
Type: Factual
Ans: A

158. The acquisition of a behavior through the observation of other people is called:
A. observational learning
B. direct learning
C. classical conditioning
D. operant conditioning

p. 493
Stressful Experiences
Level: Easy
Type: Factual
Ans: B

159. Freud claimed that anxiety stemmed from:
A. things we learn about negative experiences
B. unconscious conflicts that arise between id and superego with the ego in the middle
C. discrepancies between the way the world is and the way we want it to be
D. the subconscious belief that good things cannot last forever but bad things can

p. 493
Stressful Experiences
Level: Easy
Type: Factual
Ans: B
*PS/SG 21-14*

160. According to Freud's explanation, we try to reduce anxiety by employing:
A. problem-focused coping at the ego level
B. defense mechanisms at the unconscious level
C. approach/avoidance choices at the ego level
D. "snap out of it" coping messages at the superego level

p. 493
Stressful Experiences
Level: Easy
Type: Factual
Ans: C

161. According to Freud, how might we try to decrease anxiety?
A. seek out social support
B. develop a sense of hardiness
C. use a defense mechanism
D. engage in primary appraisal

p. 493
Stressful Experiences
Level: Easy
Type: Factual
Ans: D

162. If we use defense mechanisms as our primary means of coping with anxiety, then:
A. we will save ourselves a great deal of undue psychological harm
B. our social relationships will improve
C. we will not have to rely on machines and medication to help us cope
D. we are preventing ourselves from confronting and working on our problems

p. 493
Stressful Experiences
Level: Easy
Type: Factual
Ans: C

163. Active attempts to extinguish anxious feelings can be described as:
A. ineffective
B. conscious coping techniques that are emotion-focused
C. conscious coping techniques that are problem-focused
D. only masking the underlying problem

p. 493
Stressful Experiences
Level: Easy
Type: Factual
Ans: B

164. Defense mechanisms like repression, sublimation, rationalization, and regression can be described as:
A. based on primary appraisal
B. unconscious coping techniques that are emotion-focused
C. conscious coping techniques that are problem-focused
D. based on classical conditioning principles

p. 494
Personality and
  Social Factors
Level: Easy
Type: Factual
Ans: B

165. A person whose control, commitment, and challenge enable him or her to handle stressful situations would be considered to possess the stress-reduction trait of:
A. external locus of control
B. hardiness
C. frustration-aggression
D. approach-avoidance

p. 494
Personality and
  Social Factors
Level: Easy
Type: Applied
Ans: C

166. With only a minute left in today's class, Professor Shepard is previewing tomorrow's lecture on hardiness. She says, "We'll look at the 3Cs of hardiness at our next class meeting." To what "3Cs" is Professor Shepard referring?
A. control, coping, and competence
B. commitment, congruency, and consistency
C. control, commitment, and challenge
D. consistency, control, and competency

p. 494
Personality and
  Social Factors
Level: Moderate
Type: Applied
Ans: A

167. Barb teaches second grade in an inner-city school. Despite the fact that most of her students are already two years behind other children their age, Barb views her job as a challenge. She is constantly looking for new and different methods to interest her students and feels that she has a direct positive effect on their lives. Barb manages her stressful life without experiencing psychosomatic problems because she possesses the trait of:
A. hardiness
B. external locus of control
C. frustration avoidance
D. approach-avoidance

p. 494
Personality and
  Social Factors
Level: Easy
Type: Applied
Ans: D

168. LeRoy is listening to a story about a great American hero. This hero went through incredible odds and endured tremendous stress. Knowing what you do about stress, what personality trait did this hero undoubtedly possess that protected him from the harmful effects of stress?
A. autonomy
B. extroversion
C. locus of control
D. hardiness

p. 494
Personality and
  Social Factors
Level: Easy
Type: Factual
Ans: C

169. A study cited in the textbook reveals that hardy individuals are likely to appraise stressful situations as _____ than those who are less hardy.
A. more challenging and more threatening
B. more difficult and more threatening
C. more challenging and less threatening
D. less challenging and less important

p. 495
Personality and
  Social Factors
Level: Easy
Type: Applied
Ans: A

170. "I know that if I work hard and follow through on my duties, I can control what happens to me." Another person says, "It doesn't matter; whatever I do has no effect." These two individuals differ in regard to their:
A. locus of control
B. affect
C. coping strategies
D. secondary appraisal

| | | |
|---|---|---|
| p. 495<br>Personality and<br>  Social Factors<br>Level: Easy<br>Type: Factual<br>Ans: B | 171. | A person who believes that chance and luck are major factors in our lives is probably: |
| | A. | less stressed than someone who doesn't think this way |
| | B. | exhibiting an external locus of control |
| | C. | exhibiting an internal locus of control |
| | D. | a hardy person |

| | | |
|---|---|---|
| p. 495<br>Personality and<br>  Social Factors<br>Level: Easy<br>Type: Applied<br>Ans: D | 172. | Maria believes that everything good and bad that happens to her is the result of fate, luck, or other people's desires. Maria's belief illustrates the concept of: |
| | A. | hardiness |
| | B. | conflict |
| | C. | internal locus of control |
| | D | external locus of control |

| | | |
|---|---|---|
| p. 495<br>Personality and<br>  Social Factors<br>Level: Moderate<br>Type: Conceptual<br>Ans: C | 173. | Which of the following statements would a person with an external locus of control agree with? |
| | A. | People who can't get others to like them don't understand how to get along with others. |
| | B. | We can have an effect on our external world. |
| | C. | I don't vote in elections because my vote won't change things. |
| | D. | It is of the utmost importance to establish one's power in interpersonal relationships. |

| | | |
|---|---|---|
| p. 495<br>Personality and<br>  Social Factors<br>Level: Easy<br>Type: Applied<br>Ans: C | 174. | Jerry is fond of saying "I am the master of my domain. My future is what I choose it to be." Jerry's statement illustrates the concept of: |
| | A. | hardiness |
| | B. | conflict |
| | C. | internal locus of control |
| | D. | external locus of control |

| | | |
|---|---|---|
| p. 495<br>Personality and<br>  Social Factors<br>Level: Moderate<br>Type: Applied<br>Ans: D | 175. | You only know that Todd typically exhibits an internal locus of control while Terry has an external locus of control. You could reasonably assume that: |
| | A. | Todd generally uses emotion-focused coping and Terry uses problem-focused coping |
| | B. | Todd generally uses threat appraisals and Terry uses challenge appraisals |
| | C. | Both Todd and Terry generally use problem-focused coping, but Terry is more successful |
| | D. | Todd generally uses problem-focused coping and Terry uses emotion-focused coping |

| | | |
|---|---|---|
| p. 495<br>Personality and<br>  Social Factors<br>Level: Easy<br>Type: Factual<br>Ans: A | 176. | Compared to people with an external locus of control, people with an internal locus of control tend to: |
| | A. | develop fewer illness |
| | B. | think the world is a hostile place that one must learn to escape from internally |
| | C. | believe more that fate plays a bigger role in their lives |
| | D. | be Type A people |

p. 495
Personality and
  Social Factors
Level: Easy
Type: Factual
Ans: C

177. Compared to those with an external locus of control, individuals with an internal locus of control are more likely to:
A. use threat appraisals
B. use emotion-focused coping
C. experience more positive emotions
D. experience greater levels of stress

p. 495
Personality and
  Social Factors
Level: Easy
Type: Factual
Ans: B

178. Psychosomatic symptoms, higher levels of stress, and the use of threat appraisals are symptoms associated with:
A. hardiness
B. an external locus of control
C. reaction formation
D. a Type B personality

p. 495
Personality and
  Social Factors
Level: Moderate
Type: Factual
Ans: D

179. Optimists tend to use _____ coping, while pessimists use _____ coping.
A. deductive; reductive
B. reductive; deductive
C. emotion-focused; problem-focused
D. problem-focused; emotion-focused

p. 496
Personality and
  Social Factors
Level: Easy
Type: Factual
Ans: D

180. A chronic and continuing struggle to achieve more and more in less and less time is characteristic of:
A. an internal locus of control
B. an external locus of control
C. Type B behavior
D. Type A behavior

p. 496
Personality and
  Social Factors
Level: Easy
Type: Applied
Ans: D
*www*

181. "Come on! Hurry up and answer this question. You don't have much time!" This is most characteristic of:
A. an internal locus of control
B. an external locus of control
C. Type B behavior
D. Type A behavior

p. 496
Personality and
  Social Factors
Level: Easy
Type: Factual
Ans: D

182. A person who often expresses negative emotions, is aggressively competitive, and is easily frustrated, would be exhibiting:
A. hardiness
B. an external locus of control
C. Type B behavior
D. Type A behavior

p. 496
Personality and
  Social Factors
Level: Easy
Type: Factual
Ans: D

183. The famous "Type A Behavior" research attempted to relate certain personality traits to:
A. hardy personality
B. locus of control
C. increased risk of cancer
D. increased risk of heart attack

*PS/SG 21-16*

p. 496
Personality and
    Social Factors
Level: Easy
Type: Factual
Ans: A

184. What happened to the definition of Type A behavior during the 1980s?
A. impatience and workaholic were dropped
B. impatience and workaholic were added
C. it was confirmed by research studying its relationship to heart disease
D. it was divided into Type A-1 and Type A-2

p. 496
Personality and
    Social Factors
Level: Easy
Type: Factual
Ans: C

185. Some research on the relationship between Type A and heart disease have found that heart disease is related to:
A. a large number of traits most of which are related to negative affect
B. impatience expressed publicly
C. hostility and anger
D. anxiety, frustration, anger, depression, and hardiness

p. 496
Personality and
    Social Factors
Level: Easy
Type: Factual
Ans: A

186. The future of Type A:
A. may lie with studying the protein that causes swelling of arteries
B. is assured since Type A is well established as the primary risk factor for heart disease
C. rests with the longitudinal studies started in the 1960's
D. rests with returning to the definition from the 1970's

p. 496
Personality and
    Social Factors
Level: Moderate
Type: Applied
Ans: C

187. Stephen is an angry person, but he usually suppresses his anger. Based on the research on Type A presented in the module, what would be the best description of Stephen?
A. If you could express his anger, he would be better able to deal with stress.
B. He probably has repressed some unconscious conflict from his childhood
C. He experiences large increases in arousal which can damage the heart
D. Suppression is healthier than showing anger

p. 496
Personality and
    Social Factors
Level: Easy
Type: Factual
Ans: B

188. Why has the definition of Type A behavior changed since the 1970s?
A. Politics have influenced how Type A behavior is defined.
B. Research has led to the changes.
C. The scientists researching this issue have a hard time making decisions.
D. Those subjects with heart disease have very different personalities than those of the 1970s and 1980s.

p. 497
Personality and
    Social Factors
Level: Easy
Type: Conceptual
Ans: C

189. Why did the small town of Roseto, Pennsylvania have an increase in heart attacks, especially among younger men?
A. The town's folk bought a large number of televisions and became couch potatoes.
B. Most of the factories that once supported most families closed down.
C. People had fewer social supports.
D. A large bacon factory moved to town offering free bacon to its employees.

p. 497
Personality and
    Social Factors
Level: Easy
Type: Factual
Ans: B

190. Of the following, which is not a factor in social support, according to the textbook?
A. individuals who can provide social attachments
B. providing feedback to us about what is appropriate coping
C. being able to exchange helpful resources
D. making appraisals that there are supportive relationships and behaviors

p. 497
Personality and
  Social Factors
Level: Easy
Type: Factual
Ans: D

191.   Social support helps us to _____ in order to minimize the effects of stress.
A.  develop hardiness
B.  use sublimation
C.  utilize emotion-focused coping techniques
D.  mobilize our resources

p. 497
Personality and
  Social Factors
Level: Moderate
Type: Applied
Ans: A

192.   Lisa and Jenny are both 14 years old. Lisa's parents are very busy with their careers and, while providing the material necessities, give her little of their time. Jenny's mother has trouble supporting the two of them with her job, but they are very close and spend all their free time together. Regarding the social support offered by the parents of these two girls, it is probable that:
A.  Jenny benefits more from social support
B.  Lisa benefits more from social support because two parents provide a larger social grouping than one
C.  both would have about the same social support from their families
D.  both girls would have to go outside the family for the majority of their social support

p. 497
Personality and
  Social Factors
Level: Moderate
Type: Applied
Ans: B

193.   Jerome has a large circle of acquaintances but no close friends. Mary, his wife, has a few very close friends. Everything else being equal, if Jerome and Mary experience marital difficulties, who would have less trouble dealing with the stressful situation?
A.  Jerome would, because he has many people to tell his trouble to.
B.  Mary would, because the social support of close friends aids in coping with stressful situations.
C.  It is impossible to tell, because friends do not affect one's ability to cope with stress.
D.  They should experience about the same level of stress, because friends of any degree of intimacy provide social support.

p. 497
Personality and
  Social Factors
Level: Easy
Type: Factual
Ans: A

194.   It has been shown that strong social support can:
A.  prevent mild psychiatric symptoms from worsening
B.  not reduce stress but can help someone recover after the symptoms become uncomfortable
C.  increase blood levels of cholesterol
D.  discourage a person from taking on challenges outside the home that may be stressful

p. 497
Personality and
  Social Factors
Level: Moderate
Type: Applied
Ans: C

195.   Annell has an internship at a local psychiatric hospital assisting the staff with the development of programs for the residents. A significant problem with the residents is stress. The staff make several proposals. Based upon the research on stress and mental health, which one would you select?
A.  have more frequent review of their medications and make adjustments as needed
B.  teach residents how to deal with stress with biofeedback
C.  allow residents to develop strong social supports
D.  encourage residents to keep their problems to themselves

| | | |
|---|---|---|
| p. 497<br>Personality and<br>  Social Factors<br>Level: Moderate<br>Type: Factual<br>Ans: C | 196.<br>A.<br>B.<br>C.<br>D. | College students with strong social support systems tend to:<br>learn how to avoid stressful situations<br>handle stress poorly when alone<br>show smaller increases in blood pressure when giving a public speech<br>fail to recognize potentially stressful situations |
| p. 499<br>Kind of Coping<br>Level: Easy<br>Type: Factual<br>Ans: B | 197.<br><br>A.<br>B.<br>C.<br>D. | Deciding what we can do to manage, cope with, or deal with the situation<br>involves making a _____ appraisal.<br>primary<br>secondary<br>threat<br>challenge |
| p. 499<br>Kind of Coping<br>Level: Moderate<br>Type: Conceptual<br>Ans: A | 198.<br><br>A.<br>B.<br>C.<br>D. | Orlando is in a bad situation and has made a threat appraisal. What will he<br>do next?<br>make a secondary appraisal<br>try to increase his sympathetic response<br>decide to escape from the situation<br>make a challenge appraisal |
| p. 499<br>Kind of Coping<br>Level: Moderate<br>Type: Applied<br>Ans: D | 199.<br><br><br>A.<br>B.<br>C.<br>D. | Melanie is going to the dentist. Her decision that the dentist will hurt her is<br>a _____, whereas her deciding to smoke a cigarette before going<br>into the dentist's office is a _____.<br>secondary appraisal; coping appraisal<br>harm/loss appraisal; challenge appraisal<br>challenge appraisal; primary appraisal<br>primary appraisal; secondary appraisal |
| p. 499<br>Kind of Coping<br>Level: Easy<br>Type: Factual<br>Ans: A<br>*PS/SG 21-19* | 200.<br>A.<br>B.<br>C.<br><br>D. | Secondary appraisal means:<br>deciding what we can do to manage, cope, or deal with the situation<br>our subjective evaluation of a situation to decide if we can deal with it<br>the extent to which we appraise a situation as stressful after we have taken<br>time to think about it objectively<br>the extent to which we find a situation stressful the second time we<br>encounter it |
| p. 499<br>Kind of Coping<br>Level: Easy<br>Type: Conceptual<br>Ans: A | 201.<br><br>A.<br>B.<br>C.<br>D. | Problem-focused coping is to _____ as emotion-focused coping is to<br>_____.<br>behavior; feelings<br>feelings; affect<br>primary; secondary<br>passive; active |
| p. 499<br>Kind of Coping<br>Level: Easy<br>Type: Factual<br>Ans: A | 202.<br>A.<br>B.<br>C.<br>D. | Problem-focused coping primarily involves:<br>taking whatever action is needed<br>directing our attention to something else<br>changing how we think about the situation<br>denying that there is a problem |

p. 499
Kind of Coping
Level: Easy
Type: Factual
Ans: A
*PS/SG 21-20*

203. Solving a problem by seeking information, changing your own behavior, or taking whatever action is necessary is called:
A. problem-focused coping
B. emotion-focused coping
C. primary appraisal
D. secondary appraisal

p. 499
Kind of Coping
Level: Moderate
Type: Applied
Ans: D

204. Both Ann and her roommate, Cheryl, like to study in their room. Ann likes complete quiet while Cheryl insists on blaring music. If Ann arrives after Cheryl and asks her to turn the music down, Cheryl will claim that she was there first and can do what she wants. If Ann uses problem-focused coping, she can best handle the situation by:
A. playing her own stereo even louder till Cheryl turns her stereo down
B. screaming at Cheryl that she is selfish
C. refusing to speak to Cheryl until she compromises
D. working out a schedule with Cheryl so that they both can have some study time in the room

p. 499
Kind of Coping
Level: Moderate
Type: Applied
Ans: B

205. Lauren deals with test anxiety by joining a study group. This is an example of:
A. an external locus of control
B. problem-focused coping
C. a defense mechanism
D. reaction formation

p. 499
Kind of Coping
Level: Easy
Type: Factual
Ans: D

206. Emotion-focused coping involves:
A. using the process of extinction
B. changing our own behavior to solve the problem
C. seeking information about what needs to be done
D. dealing with our distress

p. 499
Kind of Coping
Level: Moderate
Type: Conceptual
Ans: C

207. A person who avoids thinking about their problems, or directs their attention to something else is using:
A. problem-focused coping
B. an internal locus of control
C. emotion-focused coping
D. an external locus of control

p. 499
Kind of Coping
Level: Moderate
Type: Factual
Ans: B

208. The major factor which determines which type of coping we use is:
A. our current level of anxiety
B. how much control we have over the situation
C. whether or not the situation is threatening
D. frustration with the situation

p. 499
Kind of Coping
Level: Moderate
Type: Applied
Ans: A

209. The exams in your chemistry class are very difficult and stressful. To pass the course, you must cope. Given that the difficulty level of the exams is beyond your control, what type of coping would be <u>most</u> appropriate?
A. emotion-focused coping
B. problem-focused coping
C. metacognitive coping
D. structural coping

| p. 499 | 210. | Brenda and Krista have both just lost their jobs. Brenda says, "Let's go shopping" and Krista agrees. This best illustrates: |
|---|---|---|
| Kind of Coping | | |
| Level: Moderate | A. | dispositional coping |
| Type: Applied | B. | emotion-focused coping |
| Ans: B | C. | metacognitive coping |
| | D. | problem-focused coping |

| p. 499 | 211. | When is problem-focused coping most appropriate? |
|---|---|---|
| Kind of Coping | A. | when your frustration levels are just starting to peak |
| Level: Moderate | B. | in stressful situations that are familiar to you |
| Type: Factual | C. | when you lack control over the situation |
| Ans: D | D. | when you have control over the situation |

| p. 499 | 212. | You really wanted that job, but didn't get it. It would have been perfect - you could've studied when you weren't busy and the pay was great. You're feeling down. What type of coping might be most beneficial for you? |
|---|---|---|
| Kind of Coping | | |
| Level: Moderate | | |
| Type: Applied | A. | emotion-focused coping |
| Ans: A | B. | problem-focused coping |
| | C. | metacognitive coping |
| | D. | structural coping |

| p. 499 | 213. | Mary and Harry are both experiencing financial crises in their lives. Based upon the discussion of gender differences in coping, what approach are they most likely to take? |
|---|---|---|
| Kind of Coping | | |
| Level: Moderate | | |
| Type: Applied | A. | Mary will tend to use emotion-focused coping; Harry will use problem-focused coping |
| Ans: A | B. | Harry will tend to use emotion-focused coping; Mary will use problem-focused coping |
| | C. | Harry is likely to deal with the distress of the crisis, while Mary will try to take constructive action. |
| | D. | Mary will do primary appraisal and Harry will do secondary appraisal. |

| p. 499 | 214. | All of the following are sex differences in choosing coping strategies except: |
|---|---|---|
| Kind of Coping | A. | women tend to use more coping strategies |
| Level: Moderate | B. | men are more likely to withdraw or avoid problems |
| Type: Factual | C. | men are more likely to engage in emotion-focused coping in dealing with stressors |
| Ans: C | | |
| PS/SG 21-21 | D. | women are more likely to use emotion-focused coping to seek emotional support and advice |

| p. 499 | 215. | "I'm really frustrated with this situation because the conflict between this person and me has gotten worse." What strategy should this person use to cope with this situation? |
|---|---|---|
| Kind of Coping | | |
| Level: Easy | | |
| Type: Applied | A. | emotion-focused coping and metacognitive coping |
| Ans: C | B. | problem-focused coping |
| | C. | emotion-focused and problem-focused coping |
| | D. | structural coping |

p. 500
Research Focus:
  Coping With Trauma
Level: Easy
Type: Factual
Ans: C

216.    Conducting an experiment allows us to identify:
A.      important information about behavior in natural settings
B.      unique or unusual behavior
C.      cause and effect relationships
D.      associations between variables

p. 500
Research Focus:
  Coping With Trauma
Level: Easy
Type: Factual
Ans: B

217.    If you collect a great deal of information regarding the thoughts, feelings, beliefs, and behaviors of an individual person, you are conducting a(n):
A.      survey questionnaire
B.      case study
C.      experiment
D.      standardized test

p. 500
Research Focus:
  Coping With Trauma
Level: Easy
Type: Factual
Ans: D

218.    A disorder that is common among burn victims as they recover is:
A.      generalized anxiety disorder
B.      phobia
C.      survivor guilt
D.      depression

p. 500
Research Focus:
  Coping With Trauma
Level: Easy
Type: Applied
Ans: A

219.    Karen was severely burned in a fire a few years ago. She has attempted to cope with the psychological and physical trauma. According to your textbook, researchers have identified several variables that can increase one's coping with long-term stressful events. What is one of these variables?
A.      self-esteem
B.      self-efficacy
C.      locus of control
D.      financial assistance

p. 500
Research Focus:
  Coping With Trauma
Level: Easy
Type: Applied
Ans: C

220.    In your job as a counselor at a local hospital specializing in treating burn victims, you provide support to the patients. You should help patients use _____ as they cope with the trauma.
A.      sensate-focused coping
B.      problem-focused coping and stress inoculation methods
C.      problem-focused coping and emotion-focused coping
D.      emotion-focused coping

p. 501
Cultural Diversity:
  Tibetan Monks
Tibetan Monks
Level: Easy
Type: Factual
Ans: D

221.    Through the use of meditation, Tibetan monks have learned how to exert control over their:
A.      hypothalamus
B.      pituitary gland
C.      adrenal medulla
D.      autonomic nervous system

p. 501

Cultural Diversity:

  Tibetan Monks

Level: Easy

Type: Factual

Ans: D

222. In a matter of a short time, Tibetan monks can increase the temperature of their fingers as much as:

A. 2 degree

B. 4 degrees

C. 7 degrees

D. 12 degrees

p. 501

Cultural Diversity:

  Tibetan Monks

Level: Easy

Type: Factual

Ans: A

223. Researchers believe that Tibetan monks are capable of raising hand temperatures by:

A. activating their parasympathetic division

B. controlling psychosomatic responses

C. activating their autonomic nervous system

D. focusing the winds in the consciousness into a central channel

p. 502

Application: Stress

  Management Program

Level: Easy

Type: Factual

Ans: C

224. Stress management programs attempt to change what aspects of our lives?

A. physiological responses and emotions

B. perceptions and behaviors

C. thoughts, behaviors, and physiological responses

D. thoughts and emotions

p. 502

Application: Stress

  Management Program

Level: Easy

Type: Factual

Ans: A

225. A successful stress management program should try to:

A. encourage participants to appraise stressful situations as challenges

B. point out that many of the things we worry about are things we can do nothing about anyway

C. get people to reduce the number of challenges in their lives

D. convince people to be less committed

p. 502

Application: Stress

  Management Program

Level: Easy

Type: Factual

Ans: A

226. Research has shown that people who make challenge appraisals tend to:

A. use more problem-focused coping techniques

B. report more overall stress

C. result in feelings of anxiety and fear

D. have an external locus of control

p. 502

Application: Stress

  Management Program

Level: Moderate

Type: Applied

Ans: B

227. A high school teacher is stressed by her work. She feels that her students are deliberately trying to upset her. Which of the following would represent a constructive change in the teacher's appraisal?

A. to stop caring so much about her students

B. to tell herself that that the students' behavior is just normal adolescence and not an attack on her

C. to try to ignore the students' behavior

D. to accept the fact that she is not a particularly good disciplinarian

p. 502

Application: Stress

  Management Program

Level: Moderate

Type: Applied

Ans: D

228. Based upon findings of research, which is the best way to cope with an upcoming exam?

A. using emotion-focused coping

B. "I wish I could have had more study time."

C. "There's not much I can do about my grade, so why worry."

D. "I can demonstrate to my professor that I really do know this material."

p. 502
Application: Stress
  Management Program
Level: Easy
Type: Factual
Ans: C

229.    Why is it important to avoid making negative self-statements?
A.      because they will lead to making challenge appraisals
B.      others will think you are immature
C.      they elicit negative emotions
D.      they tend to cause an internal locus of control

p. 503
Application: Stress
  Management Program
Level: Easy
Type: Factual
Ans: A

230.    An important step in reducing stress is to monitor one's behavior. The
        purpose of this observation is to:
A.      identify stress-reducing and stress-increasing behaviors
B.      learn which situations are stressful
C.      determine how much stress the individual is experiencing
D.      learn emotion-focused coping

p. 503
Application: Stress
  Management Program
Level: Moderate
Type: Applied
Ans: B

231.    Walter is wearing a blood pressure measuring device. He is told the green
        light in front of him will come on when his blood pressure drops, and
        further, that he should try to keep the light on. Walter is being treated with:
A.      mechanized relaxation training
B.      biofeedback training
C.      coping strategy training
D.      self-stimulation training

p. 503
Application: Stress
  Management Program
Level: Easy
Type: Factual
Ans: C

232.    Biofeedback trains people to:
A.      lower the level of epinephrine in their blood stream
B.      use emotion-focused coping
C.      exert more control over their autonomic nervous system
D.      make effective use of defense mechanisms

p. 503
Application: Stress
  Management Program
Level: Easy
Type: Factual
Ans: C
*PS/SG 21-25*

233.    The relaxation technique that involves learning to increase or decrease
        physiological signals from the body is called:
A.      the relaxation response
B.      progressive relaxation
C.      biofeedback
D.      Transcendental Meditation (TM)

p. 503
Application: Stress
  Management Program
Level: Easy
Type: Factual
Ans: B
*www*

234.    Teaching a person how to tense and relax the major muscle groups at will
        to produce relaxation is the procedure known as:
A.      Transcendental Meditation
B.      progressive relaxation
C.      biofeedback
D.      appraisal counseling

p. 503
Application: Stress
  Management Program
Level: Easy
Type: Applied
Ans: A

235.    To cope with stress, Chuck finds a quiet place, closes his eyes, and tries to
        clear his mind by concentrating on a sound. Chuck is using:
A.      Transcendental Meditation
B.      progressive relaxation
C.      biofeedback
D.      appraisal counseling

True/False

| | | | |
|---|---|---|---|
| F | *www* | 1. | Stress is always harmful. |
| T | | 2. | Primary appraisal refers to how we evaluate or interpret a situation. |
| T | | 3. | A threat appraisal triggers negative emotions. |
| T | *www* | 4. | Threat appraisals increase levels of stress. |
| F | | 5. | The pituitary gland signals the hypothalamus to release ACTH. |
| F | *www* | 6. | Psychosomatic symptoms are not really physical, only psychological. |
| T | | 7. | Genetics plays a role in the development of psychosomatic symptoms. |
| F | | 8. | In the resistance stage, the body is saving large amounts of energy. |
| F | *www* | 9. | The idea of mind-body connection is inconsistent with the general adaptation syndrome. |
| T | | 10. | The functioning of the immune system can be affected by stress. |
| T | | 11. | In classically conditioning the immune system, the UCR would be the allergic reaction. |
| F | *www* | 12. | There is a strong correlation between major life events and the development of psychosomatic symptoms. |
| F | | 13. | The most common types of hassles are death of close friend, marriage, and trouble with boss. |
| T | | 14. | Frustration is the experience we have when our movement to a goal is blocked. |
| T | | 15. | An avoidance-avoidance conflict occurs when we must choose between two unpleasant options. |
| F | *www* | 16. | People who used integration to deal with conflict go to any lengths to win. |
| F | | 17. | Hardiness is composed of control, threat appraisal, and confront. |
| T | *www* | 18. | Anger/hostility are the emotions most likely related to heart attacks. |
| T | | 19. | In problem-focused coping, one may seek information to resolve the difficulty. |
| T | *www* | 20. | Females tend to use emotion-focused coping. |
| F | | 21. | Tibetan monks have developed the ability to warm their hands by controlling the sympathetic division. |
| T | *www* | 22. | Stress management programs focus on appraisals, behaviors, and emotional responses. |
| F | | 23. | Students who make challenge appraisals are more likely to use emotion-focused coped. |
| T | *www* | 24. | Problem-focused coping emphasizes the long-term. |
| F | | 25. | Biofeedback is superior to relaxation and meditation for reducing stress. |

Short-Answer Essay Questions

1. What is stress? Present a real-life example of a situation and describe it using the three interpretations of harm/loss, threat, and challenge. (*www*)
2. Discuss what happens to the body during the fight-flight response.
3. Describe the alarm, resistance, and exhaustion stages of the general adaptation syndrome. (*www*)
4. How might hardiness and an internal locus of control help in coping with stress?
5. Describe how our view of Type A has changed since the 1970s. (*www*)
6. Use the example of an upcoming exam to illustrate the difference between emotion-focused coping and problem-focused coping. (*www*)
7. Compare the coping strategies of females and males. Describe how these differences might make relationships between a female and male a challenge.

8.      Discuss how emotional-focused coping and problem-focused coping are both important in helping burn victims cope with stress.

9.      From a western perspective, how do Tibetan monks raise the temperature of their hands?

10.     Describe biofeedback, progressive relaxation, and meditation as techniques to relax. (*www*)

# Module 22 - Assessment and Anxiety Disorders

p. 509
Introduction
Level: Easy
Type: Factual
Ans: B

1. Which of the following characteristics is <u>not</u> true of Jeffrey Dahmer?
A. was young when he committed murders
B. was found to be insane
C. came from a broken home
D. was abused as a child

p. 509
Introduction
Level: Easy
Type: Factual
Ans: C
*PS/SG 22-1*

2. The main issue in the Jeffrey Dahmer trial was whether Dahmer:
A. actually killed 15 young men, or only the one he was arrested for
B. was under the influence of drugs when he killed
C. knew the difference between right and wrong when he killed
D. really intended to kill the five men who said they got away

p. 509
Introduction
Level: Easy
Type: Factual
Ans: A

3. A common characteristic of serial killers is:
A. physical or sexual abuse in childhood
B. being an only child
C. college-educated
D. close relationships with a few friends

p. 509
Introduction
Level: Easy
Type: Factual
Ans: C

4. According to the textbook, the typical serial killer:
A. has stable, intact family backgrounds
B. is middle aged
C. has serious personality deficits
D. was popular in elementary school, but a loner in junior high school

p. 509
Introduction
Level: Easy
Type: Factual
Ans: A

5. One FBI expert suggests that serial killers:
A. are obsessed with control, manipulation and dominance
B. are obsessed with pleasing others
C. lack the capacity to have deep, authentic feelings
D. are perfectionists

p. 509
Introduction
Level: Easy
Type: Factual
Ans: D

6. Jeffrey Dahmer was:
A. found guilty of 15 counts of murder and judged to not know the difference between right and wrong
B. guilty of 15 counts of murder, but the verdict was later overturned on a technicality
C. found guilty of 15 counts of murder and found legally insane
D. found guilty of 15 counts of murder and found legally sane

p. 509
Introduction
Level: Easy
Type: Factual
Ans: B
*www*

7. The legal definition of insanity is:
A. having a diagnosed mental disorder
B. not knowing the difference between right and wrong
C. the inability to remember the crime which was perpetrated
D. having a problem which interferes with the ability to function in society

p. 509
Introduction
Level: Moderate
Type: Applied
Ans: D

8.   Charles has been judged insane. What does that mean?
A.   Charles has paranoid schizophrenia.
B.   Charles has a mental disorder that prevents him from controlling his own behavior.
C.   Charles is crazy.
D.   Charles does not know the difference between right and wrong.

p. 509
Introduction
Level: Easy
Type: Factual
Ans: B
*PS/SG 22-2*

9.   The difference between the terms insanity and mental disorder is that:
A.   insanity is more severe than a mental disorder
B.   insanity is a legal term while mental disorder is a medical term
C.   mental disorders are specific forms of insanity
D.   mental disorders do not qualify for insurance reimbursement

p. 509
Introduction
Level: Moderate
Type: Conceptual
Ans: B

10.   Most people would say that anyone who kills, mutilates, and eats his victims must be insane. Would the law agree?
A.   Maybe - it depends on the prognosis of the mental disorder
B.   No - how the law defines insanity differs from how the general public defines it
C.   Yes - the legal definition of insanity refers to doing acts that are abnormal
D.   Maybe - it depends on what the diagnosis is

p. 509
Introduction
Level: Easy
Type: Factual
Ans: C

11.   A prolonged or recurring problem which interferes with a person's ability to live a satisfying life and function in society is called:
A.   insanity
B.   a neurosis
C.   a mental disorder
D.   a diagnosis

p. 509
Introduction
Level: Easy
Type: Factual
Ans: A

12.   Leo has a recurring problem that interferes with his ability to live a satisfying life. This problem also prevents him from functioning in society. Leo is most likely to:
A.   have a mental disorder
B.   be insane
C.   suffer from a brain malfunction
D.   have a mental condition

p. 509
Introduction
Level: Easy
Type: Factual
Ans: A
*www*

13.   An intense, excessive and irrational fear characterizes:
A.   phobias
B.   panic disorder
C.   mental disorders
D.   insanity

p. 509
Introduction
Level: Easy
Type: Conceptual
Ans: D

14.   What is the most significant similarity between the cases of Jeffery Dahmer and Kate Premo?
A.   The law judged both to be insane.
B.   Both committed acts of cruelty and violence.
C.   Both of them were murderers.
D.   Their cases both involve mental disorders.

| | | |
|---|---|---|
| p. 509<br>Introduction<br>Level: Moderate<br>Type: Applied<br>Ans: C | 15.<br><br>A.<br>B.<br>C.<br>D. | Your friend Juan was attacked and mugged. During the mugging, he said that he was really afraid. Would Juan's fear be considered a phobia?<br>Maybe - it depends on Juan's age at the time of the mugging<br>Yes - fear is an important element in a phobia<br>No - the fear was not irrational<br>No - fear is not a component of a phobia |
| p. 509<br>Introduction<br>Level: Easy<br>Type: Factual<br>Ans: B | 16.<br>A.<br>B.<br>C.<br>D. | The fear that a person experiences in a phobia is:<br>equal to the real danger associated with the object or situation<br>out of all proportion to the danger associated with the object or situation<br>only physiological<br>present even when the person is away from the object or not in the situation |
| p. 510<br>Three Approaches<br>Level: Easy<br>Type: Factual<br>Ans: D | 17.<br>A.<br>B.<br>C.<br>D. | In the Middle Ages, mental disorders were thought to be caused by:<br>failure to self-actualize<br>biological dysfunction<br>unresolved conflicts<br>demon possession |
| p. 510<br>Three Approaches<br>Level: Easy<br>Type: Factual<br>Ans: C | 18.<br><br><br><br>A.<br>B.<br>C.<br>D. | Professor Kaurala is giving a lecture on the causes of abnormal behavior. It's time for class to end and he previews the topic for the next meeting. He says, "We'll consider that mental disorders are unlearned tendencies next time." What cause will he focus on at the next meeting?<br>environmental factors<br>failures to self-actualize<br>genetic factors<br>cognitive factors |
| p. 510<br>Three Approaches<br>Level: Easy<br>Type: Factual<br>Ans: A | 19.<br>A.<br>B.<br>C.<br>D. | A neurological explanation for social phobia is a problem in the:<br>amygdala<br>person's cognitive processes<br>way the person handles stress<br>corpus callosum |
| p. 510<br>Three Approaches<br>Level: Easy<br>Type: Factual<br>Ans: D | 20.<br><br><br>A.<br><br>B.<br><br>C.<br>D. | Joan suffers from social phobia. Maria is very outgoing. If we could look inside each of their amygdalas as they look at pictures of angry faces, what would we notice?<br>Joan's amygdala would have greater activity than Maria's amygdala when looking at female faces.<br>Joan's amygdala would have greater activity than Maria's amygdala when looking at male faces.<br>Maria's amygdala would have greater activity than Joan's amygdala.<br>Joan's amygdala would have greater activity than Maria's amygdala. |
| p. 510<br>Three Approaches<br>Level: Easy<br>Type: Factual<br>Ans: A<br>*www* | 21.<br><br>A.<br>B.<br>C.<br>D. | The role thoughts and beliefs play in mental disorders is highlighted in the _____ approach.<br>cognitive-behavioral<br>psychoanalytic<br>medical<br>humanistic |

p. 510
Three Approaches
Level: Easy
Type: Factual
Ans: B

22. Which of the following approaches would be the most likely to describe an overly anxious person as having learned maladaptive ways of responding to their environment?

A. medical model approach
B. cognitive-behavioral approach
C. psychoanalytic approach
D. statistical frequency approach

p. 510
Three Approaches
Level: Moderate
Type: Factual
Ans: C

23. An individual believing in the importance of thoughts, beliefs, and skill deficits in understanding mental disorders would be likely to utilize _____ in treating mental disorders.

A. psychoanalysis
B. the evaluation of unconscious conflicts
C. cognitive-behavior therapy
D. psychoactive drugs

p. 510
Three Approaches
Level: Easy
Type: Factual
Ans: B

24. The professor says, "I believe that mental disorders are caused by problems such as shyness, helplessness, and lack of social skill." This professor most likely identifies with the _____ approach.

A. biological model
B. cognitive-behavioral
C. psychoanalytic
D. social approach

p. 510
Three Approaches
Level: Easy
Type: Factual
Ans: D
PS/SG 22-4

25. Which one of the following is *not* a way of defining abnormal behavior?

A. statistical frequency approach
B. deviation from social norms approach
C. maladaptive behavior approach
D. slips of the tongue approach

p. 510
Three Approaches
Level: Easy
Type: Factual
Ans: B

26. As you listen to a radio program, the guest says that our faulty beliefs and attitudes have much to do with depression and anxiety. From your psychology class, you know that this person most likely adheres to the _____ approach.

A. biological model
B. cognitive-behavioral
C. psychoanalytic
D. social approach

p. 510
Three Approaches
Level: Easy
Type: Factual
Ans: D

27. "Depression is caused by such things as war, serious accident, or serious illness." A statement like that is most likely to reflect:

A. psychosocial factors
B. cognitive factors
C. behavioral factors
D. environmental factors

p. 511
Three Approaches
Level: Easy
Type: Factual
Ans: D

28. Which of the following is <u>not</u> among the definitions of mental disorders presented in your textbook?
A. maladaptive behavior
B. deviation from social norm
C. statistical frequency
D. latent criteria

p. 511
Three Approaches
Level: Moderate
Type: Applied
Ans: D

29. Sue told Paul that his habit of putting catsup on all his food (including spaghetti and meatballs) was abnormal, as very few people engage in that kind of behavior. Her definition of abnormality depends on which of the following criteria?
A. delinquent behavior
B. maladaptive behavior
C. destructiveness
D. statistical frequency

p. 511
Three Approaches
Level: Moderate
Type: Conceptual
Ans: A
*www*

30. Of the definitions of abnormal behavior, which one best relates to "quantity?"
A. statistical frequency
B. deviation from social norm
C. destructiveness
D. delinquent behavior

p. 511
Three Approaches
Level: Moderate
Type: Applied
Ans: C

31. Which of the following behaviors would be considered abnormal based upon the statistical frequency approach?
A. buying groceries
B. answering the telephone
C. winning a multimillion dollar lottery
D. getting married

p. 511
Three Approaches
Level: Moderate
Type: Factual
Ans: B

32. If a behavior such as stealing a neighbor's possessions is considered normal in one culture and abnormal in another, the normality or abnormality of the behavior is probably being judged according to:
A. statistical frequency
B. social norms
C. maladaptive behavior
D. destructiveness

p. 511
Three Approaches
Level: Moderate
Type: Applied
Ans: C

33. Kristin was dismayed when her son returned from college with his hair dyed purple and his ears pierced in four places. Her first thought was "What will the neighbors think?" Her fear that her neighbors will think her son abnormal is probably based on which criterion of abnormality?
A. maladaptive behavior
B. destructiveness
C. deviation from social norms
D. statistical frequency

p. 511
Three Approaches
Level: Moderate
Type: Applied
Ans: C

34.    As you wait for a bus, you notice a naked man casually walking down the sidewalk. This behavior is not acceptable and therefore is abnormal based upon the _____ definition of abnormal behavior.
A.    maladaptive behavior
B.    destructiveness
C.    deviation from social norms
D.    statistical frequency

p. 511
Three Approaches
Level: Moderate
Type: Conceptual
Ans: A

35.    Which way of defining abnormal behavior is most likely to change as society changes over time?
A.    social norms approach
B.    statistical frequency approach
C.    cognitive-behavioral approach
D.    maladaptive behavior approach

p. 511
Three Approaches
Level: Moderate
Type: Conceptual
Ans: D

36.    Why is defining abnormality based solely on social norms risky?
A.    Most of us, including researchers, do not know what social norms are.
B.    Many behaviors that are desirable then would be considered abnormal.
C.    It is hard to operationally define social norm.
D.    Social norms change over time.

p. 511
Three Approaches
Level: Easy
Type: Factual
Ans: C

37.    The maladaptive behavior approach defines abnormality based on an individual's:
A.    unconscious conflicts
B.    behavior compared to the behaviors of the general population
C.    ability to function as a person or in society
D.    social norms

p. 511
Three Approaches
Level: Moderate
Type: Conceptual
Ans: B

38.    One criterion for the diagnosis of alcoholism is that consumption of alcohol prevents the person from being productive at work. This criterion is based on:
A.    statistical frequency
B.    maladaptive behavior
C.    social norms
D.    destructiveness

p. 511
Three Approaches
Level: Moderate
Type: Factual
Ans: B
*www*

39.    Most mental health professionals agree that the most useful definition of abnormal behavior comes from the _____ approach.
A.    Freudian
B.    maladaptive behavior
C.    statistical frequency
D.    psychoanalytic

p. 511
Three Approaches
Level: Moderate
Type: Factual
Ans: A

40.    Dr. Guspierre, a mental professional finds that the most useful definition of abnormal behavior is statistical frequency. Is she typical of other mental health professionals?
A.    No - most find the maladaptive behavior approach most useful
B.    No - most find the social norm approach most useful
C.    No - most find the psychoanalytic approach most useful
D.    Yes - she is very typical of most mental health professionals

p. 512
Assessing Mental
 Disorders
 Level: Easy
Type: Factual
Ans: A

41. What would a clinician use to evaluate a person's psychological, biological, and social make-up?
A. clinical assessment
B. clinical overview
C. analysis of functioning
D. applied behavioral analysis

p. 512
Assessing Mental
 Disorders
 Level: Easy
Type: Factual
Ans: D
*www*

42. What is the name given to the systematic evaluation of an individual's functioning and symptoms?
A. clinical interview
B. psychosocial assessment
C. diagnostic assessment
D. clinical assessment

p. 512
Assessing Mental
 Disorders
 Level: Easy
Type: Factual
Ans: D

43. "After I was arrested, I was given lots of tests to examine my functioning." This person was given:
A. clinical interview
B. psychosocial assessment
C. diagnostic assessment
D. clinical assessment

p. 512
Assessing Mental
 Disorders
 Level: Moderate
Type: Factual
Ans: B

44. Of the following, which best described what mental health professionals did to determine why Susan Smith killed her children?
A. dream analysis
B. clinical assessment
C. psychosocial assessment
D. psychoanalytic assessment

p. 512
Assessing Mental
 Disorders
 Level: Easy
Type: Factual
Ans: D

45. In order to rule out abnormal behaviors caused by brain tumors or disease, psychologists often utilize:
A. clinical interviews
B. psychological tests
C. the Rorschach inkblot test
D. neurological exams

p. 512
Assessing Mental
 Disorders
 Level: Easy
Type: Applied
Ans: D

46. Reggie's assessment involves measuring his reflexes, motor coordination, brain structures and functions. Most likely, Reggie is taking:
A. clinical interviews
B. psychological tests
C. the MMPI-2
D. neurological exams

p. 512
Assessing Mental
 Disorders
 Level: Easy
Type: Applied
Ans: B

47. The doctor says to her patient, "We need to determine if the memory changes are due to some physical causes or psychological cause." What type of test is most likely to be done on this patient?
A. the MMPI-2
B. neurological exams
C. TAT
D. psychological tests

p. 512
Assessing Mental
  Disorders
Level: Easy
Type: Applied
Ans: B

48.    You've just taken an MRI. What type of test is that?
A.    projective test
B.    neurological test
C.    objective test
D.    psychological test

p. 512
Assessing Mental
  Disorders
Level: Easy
Type: Factual
Ans: C

49.    A common and popular technique used by mental health professionals to evaluate a person's background and emotions is most likely to be:
A.    neurological testing
B.    psychological testing
C.    the clinical interview
D.    the CAT scan

p. 512
Assessing Mental
  Disorders
Level: Easy
Type: Factual
Ans: D
*PS/SG 22-5*

50.    The most commonly used method to assess abnormal behavior is the:
A.    Rorschach inkblot test
B.    neurological examination
C.    personality test
D.    clinical interview

p. 512
Assessing Mental
  Disorders
Level: Moderate
Type: Applied
Ans: A

51.    Sean was experiencing some adjustment problems and went to see a psychologist. This therapist talked to Sean and made him feel comfortable so that he was able to say very personal things and not feel embarrassed. The psychologist learned many important things about Sean in this manner. What assessment technique was the therapist using?
A.    clinical interview
B.    psychological test
C.    neurological test
D.    CAT scan

p. 512
Assessing Mental
  Disorders
Level: Moderate
Type: Conceptual
Ans: D

52.    One of the advantages of the clinical interview is that it:
A.    provides brief and concise details regarding the nature of the client's problems
B.    is usually relaxed and less emotionally draining for the client than written testimonials would be
C.    is the most biased means of assessing abnormality available to psychologists
D.    yields an enormous amount of information about the client's background and current problems

p. 512
Assessing Mental
  Disorders
Level: Easy
Type: Conceptual
Ans: C

53.    Which of the following assessment methods, if administered by two different psychologists, is most likely to result in very different results?
A.    psychological tests
B.    neurological tests
C.    unstructured clinical interviews
D.    personality inventories

p. 512
Assessing Mental
  Disorders
Level: Easy
Type: Factual
Ans: C

54. The Rorschach inkblots and the MMPI are both:
A.   clinical interviews
B.   neurological tests
C.   psychological tests
D.   tests of intelligence

p. 512
Assessing Mental
  Disorders
Level: Easy
Type: Factual
Ans: B

55. Personality tests include which two types of tests?
A.   clinical and social
B.   objective and projective
C.   objective and clinical
D.   self-report and projective

p. 512
Assessing Mental
  Disorders
Level: Easy
Type: Factual
Ans: B
*www*

56. You are taking a personality test in which you must respond with specific answers. This is the _____ type of personality test
A.   subjective
B.   objective
C.   clinical
D.   projective

p. 512
Assessing Mental
  Disorders
Level: Easy
Type: Factual
Ans: D

57. Dr. Steinmetz is giving a personality test to Samuel. The test consists of ambiguous pictures that Samuel makes up a story about. What type of test is he taking?
A.   subjective
B.   objective
C.   clinical
D.   projective

p. 513
Diagnosing Mental
  Disorders
Level: Easy
Type: Factual
Ans: A
*PS/SG 22-6*

58. Rod Plotnik tells the story of Susan Smith in great detail to make the point that:
A.   clinical diagnosis is a complicated yet necessary process
B.   childhood sexual abuse almost always results in adult problems
C.   despite all we know about Susan Smith, we still can't understand why she did it
D.   her friends and neighbors should have seen the tragedy coming

p. 513
Diagnosing Mental
  Disorders
Level: Easy
Type: Factual
Ans: A

59. Susan Smith's past was characterized by:
A.   sexual molestation, depression, and a parental suicide
B.   schizophrenic episodes
C.   a supportive and caring family
D.   poor academic performance

p. 513
Diagnosing Mental
  Disorders
Level: Easy
Type: Factual
Ans: C

60. A psychiatrist who assessed Susan Smith argued that she suffers from:
A.   disorganized schizophrenia
B.   antisocial personality disorder
C.   severe depression
D.   multiple personality disorder

p. 513
Diagnosing Mental
  Disorders
Level: Easy
Type: Conceptual
Ans: B

61. Was Susan Smith legally insane?
A. Yes - she was diagnosed with severe depression
B. No - she was found guilty of murder
C. Yes - she killed her own children
D. Yes - she was found innocent by reason of insanity

p. 513
Diagnosing Mental
  Disorders
Level: Easy
Type: Factual
Ans: D

62. Accurate clinical assessment is important because:
A. the public pays close attention to high profile cases like Susan Smith and Jeffrey Dahmer
B. the reputations of psychology and psychiatry are at stake
C. insurance companies demand it to pay for therapy
D. it has implications for therapy

p. 513
Diagnosing Mental
  Disorders
Level: Easy
Type: Factual
Ans: D

63. Why did others perceive Susan Smith as a good girl?
A. Her crime was committed under the influence of crack and alcohol.
B. She was a good girl until the car accident that caused severe brain damage that led to severe depression.
C. She was a sociopath and a good liar.
D. She hid her symptoms well.

p. 513
Diagnosing Mental
  Disorders
Level: Easy
Type: Factual
Ans: A

64. In clinical diagnosis, the goal is to:
A. match the individual's symptoms to a particular mental disorder
B. determine the cause(s) of a mental disorder
C. evaluate the effectiveness of a particular therapy
D. collect information about the person

p. 513
Diagnosing Mental
  Disorders
Level: Easy
Type: Factual
Ans: B

65. When an individual's specific symptoms are matched to those that define a particular mental disorder, _____ takes place.
A. personality assessment
B. clinical diagnosis
C. psychoanalysis
D. axis construction

p. 513
Diagnosing Mental
  Disorders
Level: Easy
Type: Conceptual
Ans: B

66. What do clinicians have that increases the reliability and validity of clinical diagnosis?
A. Freud's original writings that are available to review
B. *Diagnostic and Statistical Manual of Mental Disorders - IV Test Revision*
C. *The Handbook to Clinical Diagnosis - VI*
D. computer programs that actually make the diagnoses

p. 513
Diagnosing Mental
  Disorders
Level: Easy
Type: Factual
Ans: C

67. In order to have a uniform method of dealing with mental disorders, the American Psychiatric Association developed the:
A. Rorschach inkblot test
B. Psychological Medical Dictionary of Mental Disorders
C. Diagnostic and Statistical Manual of Mental Disorders
D. Freudian Manual of Psychoanalytical Therapy

p. 513

Diagnosing Mental
  Disorders
Level: Easy
Type: Factual
Ans: B
*PS/SG 22-7*

68. The most widely used system of psychological classification is the:
  A.  Freudian Psychoanalytic System (FPS)
  B.  Diagnostic and Statistical Manual of Mental Disorders (DSM-IV-TR)
  C.  Disordered Mind Standards-III (DMS-III)
  D.  Federal Uniform Code of Psychopathology (UCP)

p. 513

Diagnosing Mental
  Disorders
Level: Easy
Type: Factual
Ans: D

69. The number of mental disorders has increased from about _____ in DSM-I to nearly _____ in DSM-IV-TR.
  A.  75; 100
  B.  5; 100
  C.  10; 30
  D.  100; 300

p. 513

Diagnosing Mental
  Disorders
Level: Easy
Type: Factual
Ans: C
*www*

70. DSM-IV-TR is a:
  A.  type of psychotherapy
  B.  drug commonly used to treat depression
  C.  uniform system for assessing symptoms and matching them to mental disorders
  D.  measure of environmental stress

p. 513

Diagnosing Mental
  Disorders
Level: Easy
Type: Factual
Ans: A

71. An advantage of DSM-IV-TR over earlier editions is that it:
  A.  provides specific behavior criteria for diagnoses based on research
  B.  includes definitions of neuroses
  C.  defines proper treatment for each problem
  D.  specifies the underlying causes for the various disorders

p. 513

Diagnosing Mental
  Disorders
Level: Easy
Type: Conceptual
Ans: C

72. DSM-IV-TR is to psychotherapy as:
  A.  free association is to psychoanalysis
  B.  drugs are to depression
  C.  diagnosis is to treatment
  D.  environmental stress is to abnormality

p. 513

Diagnosing Mental
  Disorders
Level: Easy
Type: Factual
Ans: A

73. What Freudian terminology was originally used in DSM?
  A.  psychoses and neuroses
  B.  conscious and unconscious
  C.  mental and psychological
  D.  objective and projective

p. 513

Diagnosing Mental
  Disorders
Level: Easy
Type: Conceptual
Ans: B

74. The DSM has been modified to drop Freudian terminology. What were Freud's concepts in the DSM based upon?
  A.  research findings
  B.  clinical opinion
  C.  scientific experiments
  D.  commonsense reasoning

| | | |
|---|---|---|
| p. 513<br>Diagnosing Mental<br>  Disorders<br>Level: Easy<br>Type: Factual<br>Ans: C | 75. | Which of the following was the first classification system based more on research and evidence than on clinical opinion? |
| | A. | the DSM-II |
| | B. | the DSM-III |
| | C. | the DSM-IV-TR |
| | D. | the DSM-V |

| | | |
|---|---|---|
| p. 514<br>Diagnosing Mental<br>  Disorders<br>Level: Moderate<br>Type: Factual<br>Ans: C | 76. | Mental disorders, according to the DSM-IV-TR, are assessed based on: |
| | A. | neurological functioning |
| | B. | the statistical frequency of abnormal behavior |
| | C. | five separate axes |
| | D. | three types of psychological disorders |

| | | |
|---|---|---|
| p. 514<br>Diagnosing Mental<br>  Disorders<br>Level: Easy<br>Type: Factual<br>Ans: A | 77. | What information is presented on Axis I? |
| | A. | Major Clinical Syndromes |
| | B. | Personality Disorders |
| | C. | Psychosocial and Environmental Problems |
| | D. | Neurological Functioning |

| | | |
|---|---|---|
| p. 514<br>Diagnosing Mental<br>  Disorders<br>Level: Easy<br>Type: Factual<br>Ans: A<br>*www* | 78. | If Phyllis has a mood disorder, the DSM-IV-TR would indicate the diagnosis on: |
| | A. | Axis I |
| | B. | Axis II |
| | C. | Axis III |
| | D. | Section II |

| | | |
|---|---|---|
| p. 514<br>Diagnosing Mental<br>  Disorders<br>Level: Easy<br>Type: Factual<br>Ans: B | 79. | Which of the following is <u>not</u> on "Axis I: Major Clinical Syndromes?" |
| | A. | organic mental disorders |
| | B. | personality disorders |
| | C. | substance-related disorders |
| | D. | mood disorders |

| | | |
|---|---|---|
| p. 514<br>Diagnosing Mental<br>  Disorders<br>Level: Easy<br>Type: Factual<br>Ans: D | 80. | Using the DSM-IV-TR, Susan Smith could be diagnosed on _____ with _____. |
| | A. | Axis I; schizophrenia |
| | B. | Axis II; personality disorder |
| | C. | Axis III; major depressive disorder |
| | D. | Axis I; major depressive disorder |

| | | |
|---|---|---|
| p. 515<br>Diagnosing Mental<br>  Disorders<br>Level: Easy<br>Type: Applied<br>Ans: B | 81. | If Daniel suffers from antisocial personality disorder, on what axis does this diagnosis appear? |
| | A. | Axis I |
| | B. | Axis II |
| | C. | Axis III |
| | D. | Axis IV |

p. 515
Diagnosing Mental
  Disorders
Level: Easy
Type: Applied
Ans: C

82.    A patient suffers from diabetes. On what axis should the clinician make note of this medical condition?

A.    Axis I
B.    Axis II
C.    Axis III
D.    Axis IV

p. 515
Diagnosing Mental
  Disorders
Level: Easy
Type: Applied
Ans: D

83.    As a clinical psychologist, you note that one of your clients has AIDS. Where does this piece of information go on the DSM-IV-TR axes?

A.    Axis II - Major Clinical Syndromes
B.    Axis IV - Psychosocial and Environmental Problems
C.    Axis VI - General Medical Conditions
D.    Axis III - General Medical Conditions

p. 515
Diagnosing Mental
  Disorders
Level: Easy
Type: Applied
Ans: D

84.    You are a clinical psychologist. You are currently interviewing a 52-year-old male who is severely depressed. You learn that this man has recently lost his wife to cancer. Where should the information be placed?

A.    Axis I
B.    Axis II
C.    Axis III
D.    Axis IV

p. 515
Diagnosing Mental
  Disorders
Level: Easy
Type: Factual
Ans: C

85.    Axis IV refers to information about:

A.    personality disorders
B.    medical problems
C.    psychosocial and environmental problems
D.    general functioning

p. 515
Diagnosing Mental
  Disorders
Level: Easy
Type: Factual
Ans: D

86.    On what DSM-IV-TR axis do we place information concerning the person's overall functioning?

A.    Axis III - General Evaluation of Functioning
B.    Axis IV - Psychosocial and Environmental Problems
C.    Axis VI - Global Assessment of Psychosocial Functioning
D.    Axis V - Global Assessment of Functioning

p. 515
Diagnosing Mental
  Disorders
Level: Easy
Type: Factual
Ans: D

87.    We learn that Jeffery Dahmer functioned well enough to hold down a job. On what axis would that information be indicated?

A.    Axis III - General Evaluation of Functioning
B.    Axis IV - Psychosocial and Environmental Problems
C.    Axis VI - Global Assessment of Psychosocial Functioning
D.    Axis V - Global Assessment of Functioning

p. 515
Diagnosing Mental
  Disorders
Level: Moderate
Type: Factual
Ans: B

88.    There are a number of advantages of the DSM-IV-TR. Which of the following is not an advantage of DSM-IV-TR's uniform system?

A.    facilitates communication among mental health professionals
B.    provides labels for patients such as "mentally ill" and "schizo"
C.    facilitates the study of the causes of abnormal behavior
D.    influences the type of treatment program used

p. 516
Diagnosing Mental
  Disorders
Level: Easy
Type: Factual
Ans: C

89. One problem associated with using a uniform system for diagnosing mental
    disorders is that:
A. communication between professionals is hampered
B. diagnosis can interfere with the selection of an appropriate treatment
C. any labels that result may have negative commotations
D. the diagnoses may mean different things to different people

p. 516
Diagnosing Mental
  Disorders
Level: Easy
Type: Factual
Ans: D

90. Labels may have:
A. significant social and political implications
B. negative associations
C. positive associations
D. all of the above

p. 516
Diagnosing Mental
  Disorders
Level: Easy
Type: Factual
Ans: B

91. Which disorder did women protest in the 1980's because it was
    included in earlier editions of the DSM?
A. generalized anxiety disorder
B. self-defeating personality disorder
C. psychogenic amnesia
D. major depressive disorder

p. 516
Diagnosing Mental
  Disorders
Level: Easy
Type: Factual
Ans: D

92. In a wide-scale study of mental disorders among Americans, about ____ of
    the sample reported having had at least one mental disorder during their
    lifetime.
A. 10%
B. 25%
C. 35%
D. 50%

p. 516
Diagnosing Mental
  Disorders
Level: Easy
Type: Factual
Ans: B

93. The wide-scale study of the frequency of mental disorders in the United
    States found that:
A. the most common disorder reported was schizophrenia
B. women report more mood disorders than men
C. women had more disorders than men
D. most people with active disorders were in therapy

p. 516
Diagnosing Mental
  Disorders
Level: Easy
Type: Factual
Ans: B
*PS/SG 22-11*

94. A recent large-scale study showed that _____ of all Americans had at
    least one mental disorder during their lifetime.
A. only 15%
B. almost 50%
C. fully 80%
D. almost 100 %

p. 516
Diagnosing Mental
  Disorders
Level: Easy
Type: Factual
Ans: C

95. What percentage of people with a lifetime mental disorder do not ask for
    nor receive any professional treatment?
A. 25%
B. 40%
C. 60%
D. 75%

p. 516
Diagnosing Mental
  Disorders
Level: Easy
Type: Factual
Ans: A
*www*

96. Data indicate that the most common mental disorder(s) was (were):
   A. substance abuse
   B. psychosexual disorders
   C. mood disorders
   D. personality disorders

p. 516
Diagnosing Mental
  Disorders
Level: Easy
Type: Factual
Ans: D

97. Which of the following mental disorders has a very negative connotation in Japan?
   A. substance abuse
   B. psychosexual disorders
   C. anxiety disorders
   D. depression

p. 516
Diagnosing Mental
  Disorders
Level: Easy
Type: Factual
Ans: C

98. Which of the following disorders is <u>more</u> likely to be found in men than in women?
   A. phobias
   B. depression
   C. substance abuse
   D. schizophrenia

p. 516
Diagnosing Mental
  Disorders
Level: Easy
Type: Factual
Ans: A

99. Which of the following disorders is more likely to be found in women than in men?
   A. depression
   B. drug abuse
   C. antisocial personality
   D. depersonalization disorder

p. 517
Anxiety Disorders
Level: Easy
Type: Factual
Ans: B

100. How common are the anxiety disorders among adults in the United States?
   A. Anxiety disorders are the most common mental disorder.
   B. Anxiety disorders are the second most common mental disorder.
   C. Anxiety disorders are the third most common mental disorder.
   D. Anxiety disorders are the fourth most common mental disorder.

p. 517
Anxiety Disorders
Level: Easy
Type: Factual
Ans: D

101. Which of the following is <u>not</u> considered an anxiety disorder?
   A. panic disorder
   B. phobias
   C. obsessive-compulsive disorder
   D. multiple personality

p. 517
Anxiety Disorders
Level: Moderate
Type: Applied
Ans: C
*www*

102. A patient visits his doctor with complaints of headaches, pounding heart, and muscle tension. With some prodding, the patient begins to talk about his extreme worry about the success of his work, the constant fear that his wife will leave him, and his apprehension about losing other important things in his life. The doctor may feel that this patient's symptoms are due to:
   A. a phobic disorder
   B. hypochondriasis
   C. generalized anxiety disorder
   D. multiple personality

p. 517
Anxiety Disorders
Level: Moderate
Type: Conceptual
Ans: A

103. A songwriter is composing a song describing his brother's experiences with suffering from generalized anxiety disorder. Knowing the symptoms of the disorder, what should be the title of the song?
A. "The Man is Always on Edge"
B. "Fear Comes Out of the Blue"
C. "He Doesn't Go Out in Public"
D. "Losing Control"

p. 517
Anxiety Disorders
Level: Easy
Type: Applied
Ans: D

104. "I can't seem to pinpoint why I am so afraid of things. I can't concentrate on my studies, can't sleep at night, and I have headaches. I've felt like this for more than a year." This person is most likely describing:
A. conversion disorder
B. agoraphobia
C. panic disorder
D. generalized anxiety disorder

p. 517
Anxiety Disorders
Level: Easy
Type: Factual
Ans: A

105. It is estimated that generalized anxiety disorders can be found in about:
A. 5% of the population
B. 10% of the population
C. 20% of the population
D. 25% of the population

p. 517
Anxiety Disorders
Level: Easy
Type: Factual
Ans: B

106. Renee is diagnosed as suffering from generalized anxiety disorder. In addition to psychotherapy, she is treated with drugs. The drugs she receives are likely to be:
A. tranquilizing but not addictive
B. tranquilizing but addictive if taken in high doses
C. stimulating and very addictive
D. capable of causing physical but not psychological addiction

p. 517
Anxiety Disorders
Level: Moderate
Type: Applied
Ans: C

107. During a visit to the local shopping mall, Kim suddenly found her heart pounding, had trouble breathing, felt dizzy, started sweating, and felt as if she were going to die. She ran out of the mall to her car. Kim has experienced a:
A. phobia
B. conversion disorder
C. panic attack
D. somatoform disorder

p. 517
Anxiety Disorders
Level: Easy
Type: Factual
Ans: A
PS/SG 22-13

108. The anxiety disorder that causes the greatest terror and suffering is:
A. panic disorder
B. simple phobia
C. generalized anxiety disorder
D. social phobia

p. 517
Anxiety Disorders
Level: Easy
Type: Applied
Ans: D
*www*

109. In the lunchroom, George is describing an experience he had last week. He said that he suddenly felt short of breath, a pounding heart, dizziness, and a sense of losing control. George has confided in you that he has felt depressed and has been having marital problems. George should seek help since his symptoms sound very much like:
   A. obsessive-compulsive disorder
   B. somatization disorder
   C. generalized anxiety disorder
   D. panic disorder

p. 517
Anxiety Disorders
Level: Easy
Type: Factual
Ans: A

110. A patient is receiving therapy for panic disorder. Which of the following is most likely to be true of this patient?
   A. The patient is female.
   B. The patient is male.
   C. The patient also suffers from generalized anxiety disorder.
   D. The patient is an extrovert.

p. 517
Anxiety Disorders
Level: Easy
Type: Factual
Ans: B

111. After one year following treatment for panic disorder, the percentage of patients symptom-free is:
   A. 5-15%
   B. 30-50%
   C. 60%
   D. 80-90%

p. 517
Anxiety Disorders
Level: Easy
Type: Factual
Ans: B
*PS/SG 22-14*

112. Psychologically, the interesting thing about panic attacks is that:
   A. often people who are fearful in one situation are quite brave in others
   B. realistically, the person suffering the attack is not in danger at all
   C. people suffering these attacks have been shown to crave attention and sympathy
   D. they are brief, relatively mild affairs that the person can laugh about later

p. 517
Anxiety Disorders
Level: Easy
Type: Factual
Ans: D

113. People who suffer from panic disorder are:
   A. usually male
   B. often treated with exposure therapy
   C. classified as having a somatoform disorder
   D. at an increased risk of alcohol and drug abuse

p. 518
Anxiety Disorders
Level: Easy
Type: Factual
Ans: B

114. A phobia is:
   A. a fearful response to a dangerous stimulus
   B. an intense and irrational fear that is out of proportion to the object's actual danger
   C. the feeling that people or organizations are out to get us
   D. mild arousal that results from being in enclosed spaces

p. 518
Anxiety Disorders
Level: Easy
Type: Factual
Ans: A

115. Intense, excessive and irrational fear characterizes:
   A. phobias
   B. panic disorder
   C. mental disorders
   D. insanity

p. 518
Anxiety Disorders
Level: Easy
Type: Factual
Ans: B
*www*

116. The fear that a person experiences in a phobia is:
A. equal to the real danger associated with the object or situation
B. out of all proportion to the danger associated with the object or situation
C. only physiological
D. present even when the person is away from the object or not in the situation

p. 518
Anxiety Disorders
Level: Easy
Type: Factual
Ans: B

117. The intense fear associated with phobias:
A. suggests an unconscious cause
B. makes the individual go to great lengths to avoid the feared object or situation
C. cannot be avoided
D. is proportional to the danger elicited by the object or situation

p. 518
Anxiety Disorders
Level: Easy
Type: Factual
Ans: A

118. With regard to cause, the majority of individuals with phobias:
A. can remember a traumatic event that triggered their phobia
B. cannot remember a traumatic event that triggered their phobia
C. have brothers and sisters with similar irrational fears
D. have an abnormally high level of a protein in their nervous system

p. 518
Anxiety Disorders
Level: Easy
Type: Factual
Ans: D

119. The most common type of phobia is:
A. claustrophobia
B. agoraphobia
C. specific phobia
D. social phobia

p. 518
Anxiety Disorders
Level: Easy
Type: Applied
Ans: C

120. Holly is an excellent pianist, yet she is afraid to play in front of other people because of her fear that people will hate her music and yell at her. Holly is displaying symptoms of:
A. generalized anxiety disorder
B. agoraphobia
C. social phobia
D. a conversion disorder

p. 518
Anxiety Disorders
Level: Easy
Type: Applied
Ans: A

121. Michael has a social phobia. Whenever he finds himself in a social situation:
A. he experiences considerable bodily distress
B. he has a panic attack
C. he doesn't realize that his fear is irrational
D. he understands that his fear is rational

p. 518
Anxiety Disorders
Level: Easy
Type: Factual
Ans: D

122. _____ are also called simple phobias.
A. Target phobias
B. Special phobias
C. Focused phobias
D. Specific phobias

| | | |
|---|---|---|
| p. 518<br>Anxiety Disorders<br>Level: Moderate<br>Type: Conceptual<br>Ans: B | 123. | Vince has the most common type of specific phobia. What situation or which object will Vince most vigorously avoid? |
| | A. | the observation deck of the city's tallest building |
| | B. | an exhibit at the local zoo on bugs and snakes |
| | C. | a swimming pool |
| | D. | a tiny closet |

p. 518
Anxiety Disorders
Level: Easy
Type: Factual
Ans: B

124. Which of the following would not be considered a specific phobia?
A. fear of snakes
B. fear of speaking in front of large groups of people
C. fear of heights
D. fear of enclosed spaces like elevators

p. 518
Anxiety Disorders
Level: Easy
Type: Factual
Ans: A

125. Agoraphobia is a fear of:
A. being in a situation where escape may be difficult or embarrassing
B. snakes
C. heights
D. enclosed spaces

p. 518
Anxiety Disorders
Level: Easy
Type: Factual
Ans: C
www

126. What type of phobia is characterized by anxiety about being in places or situations from which escape might be difficult?
A. obsessive-compulsive phobia
B. social phobia
C. agoraphobia
D. specific phobia

p. 518
Anxiety Disorders
Level: Easy
Type: Factual
Ans: C

127. "I am afraid to have a panic attack in public - it's very embarrassing and I may not be able to get out before the attack starts." The description most reflects:
A. social phobia
B. obsessive-compulsive disorder
C. agoraphobia
D. generalized anxiety disorder

p. 518
Anxiety Disorders
Level: Moderate
Type: Applied
Ans: B

128. Although Linda loves to have her friends come over to her house for social events, she declines any offers to go over to other people's houses. In fact, she declines any offers to go anywhere because she fears being out of her house. Linda probably suffers from:
A. a social phobia
B. agoraphobia
C. a specific phobia
D. generalized anxiety disorder

p. 519
Anxiety Disorders
Level: Easy
Type: Factual
Ans: D
www

129. A mental disorder that involves persistent, recurring thoughts, images, or impulses and senseless behaviors or rituals is called:
A. somatization disorder
B. agoraphobia
C. organic thought disorder
D. obsessive-compulsive disorder

p. 519
Anxiety Disorders
Level: Easy
Type: Factual
Ans: B

130. A person is diagnosed as having obsessive-compulsive disorder. In what DSM-IV-TR category would the disorder be found?
A. Affective Disorder
B. Anxiety Disorder
C. Modern Neurotic Disorder
D. Dissociative Disorder

p. 519
Anxiety Disorders
Level: Easy
Type: Conceptual
Ans: D

131. Obsession is to compulsion as:
A. wanted is to unwanted
B. control is to chaos
C. desire is to need
D. thought is to behavior

p. 519
Anxiety Disorders
Level: Easy
Type: Factual
Ans: C

132. A compulsion is an unwanted, persistent:
A. emotion
B. thought
C. behavior
D. phobia

p. 519
Anxiety Disorders
Level: Moderate
Type: Factual
Ans: A
PS/SG 22-16

133. Remember the case of Shirley, who had to do everything precisely 17 times? The theory is that she was trying to:
A. reduce or avoid anxiety associated with feeling or being dirty
B. obey inner voices which told her God loves cleanliness
C. cleanse her mind of confusing hallucinations
D. please her mother, who used to punish her severely whenever she got her clothes dirty while playing

p. 519
Anxiety Disorders
Level: Easy
Type: Factual
Ans: A

134. The two most common compulsions are:
A. cleaning and checking
B. hoarding and counting
C. putting things in order and washing hands
D. buying and checking

p. 519
Anxiety Disorders
Level: Moderate
Type: Applied
Ans: D

135. Lady Macbeth was burdened with intense guilt after her part in the murder of Duncan. As a result, she washed her hands over and over again, trying to remove the blood she thought she saw on them. Psychologists would call Lady Macbeth's hand-washing:
A. a symbolic release
B. dramatic irony
C. an obsession
D. a compulsion

p. 519
Anxiety Disorders
Level: Easy
Type: Factual
Ans: C

136. As part of a paper on obsessive-compulsive disorder, you are observing a person with this disorder. As you interview her, she says that thoughts of being dirty are too much and she jumps up to wash her hands. You ask her how she feels as she washes her hands. She replies:
A. "washing my hands reduces the anxiety, but only temporarily"
B. "it makes me more nervous"
C. "washing my hands reduces the anxiety"
D. "it keeps my anxiety level pretty much stable"

p. 519
Anxiety Disorders
Level: Moderate
Type: Factual
Ans: A

137. Imagine that you are visiting a clinic specializing in the treatment of obsessive-compulsive behaviors. If it is a modern clinic, it is likely that the treatments are based on the assumption that:
A. the patient's behaviors represent attempts to avoid or reduce anxiety
B. compulsive behaviors will go away on their own
C. if you eliminate the compulsions, the obsessions will disappear on their own
D. these behaviors are much more serious than was once thought and the only successful treatment involves the use of medication

p. 519
Anxiety Disorders
Level: Easy
Type: Factual
Ans: C

138. Phil is being treated for obsessive-compulsive disorder. The treatment involves gradually exposing him to the anxiety-producing situation that Phil is trying to avoid. This treatment is called:
A. anxiety therapy
B. avoidance therapy
C. exposure therapy
D. stimulus therapy

p. 519
Anxiety Disorders
Level: Easy
Type: Factual
Ans: B

139. Current treatment of obsessive-compulsive behavior involves:
A. avoidance of the objects that are believed to cause anxiety for the person
B. confrontation of the anxiety-causing objects through exposure therapy
C. intense psychoanalysis to determine the patient's underlying conflict
D. administration of stimulant drugs

p. 519
Anxiety Disorders
Level: Moderate
Type: Factual
Ans: D

140. Regarding the treatment of obsessive-compulsive disorder, it was discovered that:
A. antidepressant drugs are only effective for compulsions involving checking
B. psychoanalysis is highly effective
C. spontaneous recovery of obsessions occurs within minutes of the therapy session
D. not all people respond to drug treatment

p. 519
Anxiety Disorders
Level: Moderate
Type: Factual
Ans: C

141. For those _____ of OCD suffers who do not respond to drug treatment, an effective remaining option is:
A. 10%; dream analysis
B. 25%; selective serotonin inhibitors
C. 50%; exposure or cognitive-behavioral therapy
D. 50%; psychoanalysis

p. 519
Anxiety Disorders
Level: Easy
Type: Factual
Ans: C

142. The best therapy for OCD appears to be:
A. changes in diet to avoid red dyes
B. exposure therapy
C. clomipramine
D. psychoanalysis

p. 519
Anxiety Disorders
Level: Easy
Type: Factual
Ans: C

143. A new antidepressant drug is often used to treat obsessive-compulsive disorder. What is the drug called?
A. Librium
B. Prozac
C. clomipramine
D. imipramine

p. 520
Somatoform Disorders
Level: Easy
Type: Factual
Ans: C

144. When a group of people share the same fears or delusions and show similar physical symptoms, a diagnosis of _____ can be made.
A. generalized fear disorder
B. conversion disorder
C. mass hysteria
D. somatoform disorder

p. 520
Somatoform Disorders
Level: Easy
Type: Factual
Ans: A
PS/SG 22-20

145. When half of the 500 children gathered to perform in a concert suddenly became ill, the cause was determined to be:
A. mass hysteria
B. mass delusion
C. somatoform disorder
D. somatization disorder

p. 520
Somatoform Disorders
Level: Easy
Type: Factual
Ans: A

146. Behavior attributed to possession by evil spirits or the Devil observed in the Middle Ages is an example of:
A. mass hysteria
B. conversion disorder
C. generalized fear disorder
D. somatoform disorder

p. 520
Somatoform Disorders
Level: Easy
Type: Factual
Ans: C

147. A group of mental disorders that are characterized by real, multiple, and involuntary physical symptoms that have no known physical causes are called:
A. anxiety disorders
B. conversion disorders
C. somatoform disorders
D. dissociative disorders

p. 520
Somatoform Disorders
Level: Easy
Type: Factual
Ans: B
PS/SG 22-18

148. The key feature of somatoform disorder is:
A. pretending to be sick to avoid school or work
B. real physical symptoms but no physical causes
C. imagining physical symptoms that aren't really there
D. psychological problems but no physical symptoms

p. 520
Somatoform Disorders
Level: Easy
Type: Factual
Ans: D

149. In the past, somatization disorder was known as:
A. humor imbalance
B. enclampsia
C. the vapors
D. hysteria

p. 520
Somatoform Disorders
Level: Easy
Type: Factual
Ans: D

150. One explanation for somatoform disorders presented in Module 22 is that:
A. emotional complaints are used instead of physical complaints to express psychological problems
B. the person's pursuit of self-actualization is blocked which leads to the expression of physical problems
C. the ego's use of defense mechanisms creates additional unconscious conflicts
D. bodily complaints are used instead of emotional complaints to express psychological problems

p. 520
Somatoform Disorders
Level: Easy
Type: Applied
Ans: A
*www*

151. Shelly complains of having a number of physical symptoms, 14 to be exact. Her doctor says there's nothing physically wrong. Shelly may be diagnosed with:
   A. somatization disorder
   B. conversion disorder
   C. psychogenic fugue
   D. obsessive-compulsive disorder

p. 520
Somatoform Disorders
Level: Moderate
Type: Applied
Ans: C

152. Lea has somatization disorder. If you were to examine her medical records, you would most likely find:
   A. a history of infections
   B. a family history of depression
   C. a history of extensive use of health services
   D. a history of poor eating habits

p. 520
Somatoform Disorders
Level: Easy
Type: Factual
Ans: C
*PS/SG 22-19*

153. Medical doctors need to know psychology, because some of their patients are likely to be suffering from:
   A. agoraphobia
   B. antisocial personality disorder
   C. somatization disorder
   D. mass hysteria

p. 520
Somatoform Disorders
Level: Easy
Type: Factual
Ans: A

154. Somatization disorder is often associated with:
   A. personality problems
   B. depression
   C. irrational beliefs
   D. a poor educational background

p. 520
Somatoform Disorders
Level: Easy
Type: Factual
Ans: B

155. A person goes to the doctor complaining of paralysis, but no evidence of damage or illness can be found. The person is probably suffering from:
   A. a virus that is unknown to medicine
   B. conversion disorder
   C. an anxiety disorder
   D. holistic disorder

p. 520
Somatoform Disorders
Level: Moderate
Type: Applied
Ans: D

156. Dana has experienced some distress recently. The distress has turned into symptoms that have disrupted her sense of balance. She must have:
   A. hysteria
   B. somatization disorder
   C. hypochondriasis
   D. conversion disorder

p. 520
Somatoform Disorders
Level: Moderate
Type: Applied
Ans: A

157. Divorce, a loss of a job, and other personal problems have plagued Anita in the last several years. Anita has started to have seizures, but her doctor has found no medical reason for the seizures. Which of the following disorders is Anita likely to have?
   A. conversion disorder
   B. somatization disorder
   C. epilepsy
   D. hysteria

p. 522
Cultural Diversity:
  An Asian Disorder
Level: Easy
Type: Factual
Ans: C

158. The fear of offending others in Asian cultures through awkward social or physical behavior is called:
A. agoraphobia
B. a specific phobia
C. taijin kyofusho
D. offensive-compulsive disorder

p. 522
Cultural Diversity:
  An Asian Disorder
Level: Easy
Type: Factual
Ans: A

159. The closest equivalent of taijin kyofusho that is seen in Western cultures is most probably:
A. social phobia
B. bipolar disorder
C. generalized anxiety disorder
D. conversion disorder

p. 522
Cultural Diversity:
  An Asian Disorder
Level: Easy
Type: Factual
Ans: C
*www*

160. The term "taijin kyofusho" literally means:
A. fear of the marketplace
B. desire for interpersonal relations
C. fear of interpersonal relations
D. persistent irresistible thought

p. 522
Cultural Diversity:
  An Asian Disorder
Level: Easy
Type: Factual
Ans: B

161. Which of the following is an example of taijin kyofusho?
A. major depression caused by the death of a spouse
B. a morbid fear of eye-to-eye contact
C. refusing to go out into public places
D. feeling physical pain without a physical cause

p. 522
Cultural Diversity:
  An Asian Disorder
Level: Easy
Type: Conceptual
Ans: A

162. Taijin kyofusho occurs in Asian cultures like Japan because:
A. the culture places much emphasis on the appropriate way to conduct oneself in public
B. of the Japanese love of sushi
C. of the individualistic attitude of most Japanese
D. the culture has a maternal perspective towards others

p. 522
Cultural Diversity:
  An Asian Disorder
Level: Easy
Type: Conceptual
Ans: D

163. The example of taijin kyofusho illustrates:
A. the influence of the popular media in Western cultures
B. the relationship between diet and behavior
C. how biochemistry can influence behavior
D. how symptoms can be influenced by one's culture and social customs

p. 523
Research Focus:
  School Shootings
Level: Easy
Type: Factual
Ans: A

164. A condition where there is a repetitive and persistent pattern of violating established social rules or the rights of others is known as:
A. conduct disorder
B. external locus of control
C. rule conflict syndrome
D. misbehavior disorder

p. 523
Research Focus:
  School Shootings
Level: Easy
Type: Applied
Ans: D

165. For about a year, Barry has had problems getting along with others. He picks fights, steals, lies, and has committed acts of vandalism. Of the following disorders, which one is the <u>most</u> likely diagnosis for Barry?
A. misbehavior disorder
B. external locus of control
C. rule conflict syndrome
D. conduct disorder

p. 523
Research Focus:
  School Shootings
Level: Easy
Type: Factual
Ans: C

166. Questions regarding the motive behind adolescents killing others are primarily answered by:
A. projective tests of personality
B. correlational approach
C. case study approach
D. enthographical approach

p. 523
Research Focus:
  School Shootings
Level: Easy
Type: Factual
Ans: D

167. A number of similarities have been found among adolescent killers. Which of the following is <u>not</u> among the similarities?
A. history of aggression
B. little parental supervision
C. gave warning signs
D. bullied their peers

p. 523
Research Focus:
  School Shootings
Level: Easy
Type: Factual
Ans: A

168. A neurological reason for violent impulses in adolescents is a(n):
A. immature prefrontal cortex
B. wiring defect in the temporal lobe
C. wiring defect in the thalamus
D. underdevelopment hypothalamus

p. 523
Research Focus:
  School Shootings
Level: Easy
Type: Factual
Ans: B
PS/SG 22-23

169. A neurological risk factor for becoming a teenage school shooter is that the:
A. limbic system has not yet learned to control violent behavior
B. prefrontal cortex in the adolescent brain is still immature
C. shooters have a history of aggression and discipline problems at school or home
D. prefrontal cortex is a primitive part of the brain that exhibits emotional and violent impulses

p. 523
Research Focus:
  School Shootings
Level: Easy
Type: Factual
Ans: B

170. It is believed that adolescent killers commit their crime to:
A. gain the attention of their parents
B. get justice against peers or adults
C. get even with former girlfriends
D. become isolated in jail from those people whom they've hurt

p. 524
Application:
  Treating Phobias
Level: Easy
Type: Factual
Ans: C

171. Aviophobia is present in _____ Americans.
A. 5 million
B. 15 million
C. 25 million
D. 45 million

p. 524
Application:
  Treating Phobias
Level: Easy
Type: Factual
Ans: C

172. The phobia of flying is known as:
A. planophobia
B. mecurphobia
C. aviophobia
D. flyophobia

p. 524
Application:
  Treating Phobias
Level: Easy
Type: Factual
Ans: B

173. On a TV show, you hear one person say to another with a phobia, "Don't worry, it's just a stage. You'll outgrow it." Is that factually correct?
A. No. Even with treatment, most phobias return.
B. No. Most phobias do not disappear without some type of treatment.
C. Yes. The majority of phobias disappear with time.
D. Maybe. Some phobias do disappear. Some do not.

p. 524
Application:
  Treating Phobias
Level: Moderate
Type: Factual
Ans: B

174. For the cognitive-behavioral therapist, the two most important aspects of phobia that need to be addressed are:
A. unconscious conflicts and limiting behaviors
B. fearful thoughts and limiting behaviors
C. unconscious conflicts and early childhood experiences
D. fearful thoughts and failure to self-actualize

p. 524
Application:
  Treating Phobias
Level: Easy
Type: Applied
Ans: D

175. A couple of weeks ago, Peter sought help for his phobia. His therapist explained that the therapy would consist of changing negative thoughts into positive thoughts and changing disruptive behavior into adaptive behavior. Peter's therapist must be using:
A. client centered therapy
B. psychoanalysis
C. exposure therapy
D. cognitive-behavioral therapy

p. 524
Application:
  Treating Phobias
Level: Easy
Type: Conceptual
Ans: A

176. A clinic specializing in cognitive-behavioral therapy is considering the use of a slogan for use in an advertisement. Which of the following is the most appropriate slogan given the process of cognitive-behavioral therapy?
A. "Changed Thoughts. Changed Behavior. Changed People"
B. "Better Living Through Dream Interpretation"
C. "Tell Us About Your Childhood Experiences. We'll Listen"
D. "Benzodiazepines R Us"

p. 524
Application:
  Treating Phobias
Level: Easy
Type: Factual
Ans: C

177. What techniques are used in cognitive-behavior therapy that are designed to reduce anxiety?
A. dream interpretation and free association
B. benzodiazepine therapy
C. imagery exercises, breathing, and relaxation
D. transference analysis and dream interpretation

p. 524
Application:
  Treating Phobias
Level: Moderate
Type: Factual
Ans: D
*PS/SG 22-24*

178. Part of the cognitive-behavioral therapy used to help Kate Premo overcome her fear of flying was:
A. gradually exposing Kate to the real anxiety-producing situations until the anxiety decreased
B. placing Kate under hypnosis and implanting the message, "You will not be afraid"
C. simulating actual flying (real airline seats, vibrations, noise) in a virtual reality situation
D. substituting positive, healthy, realistic thoughts for negative, unhealthy, distorted ones

p. 524
Application:
  Treating Phobias
Level: Moderate
Type: Applied
Ans: C

179. Jerry tells Barry about his first meeting with his therapist. Jerry says that the therapist uses exposure therapy. Suddenly Barry says, "That's where you're gradually exposed to the situation or object that causes you to be anxious." Is Barry right?
A. no - exposure therapy involves the gradual use of anti-anxiety drugs
B. no - exposure therapy immediately uses the most anxiety-producing situation or object
C. yes - Barry's summary is correct
D. yes - Barry's summary is correct except objects and not situations are used

p. 524
Application:
  Treating Phobias
Level: Easy
Type: Factual
Ans: A

180. A new therapy of aviophobia where the person is never exposed to a real flight is called:
A. virtual reality therapy
B. exposure therapy
C. in vivo therapy
D. systematic desensitization

p. 524
Application:
  Treating Phobias
Level: Easy
Type: Factual
Ans: B

181. Kate is participating in a fear of flying program. She starts to have feelings of anxiety. What has Kate been taught to do when this happens?
A. try to sleep
B. begin relaxation exercises
C. take a tranquilizer
D. seek out help from other passengers

p. 525
Application:
  Treating Phobias
Level: Easy
Type: Factual
Ans: C

182. There are several components of the cognitive-behavioral and exposure therapies. One of them is to explain. Explain what?
A. explain that culture influences the development of phobias
B. explain that barriers to self-actualization cause phobias
C. explain that the fear in social phobia is learned and therefore can be unlearned
D. explain that childhood conflicts are the cause of social phobia

p. 525
Application:
  Treating Phobias
Level: Easy
Type: Factual
Ans: D

183. Which of the following is not typical of cognitive-behavior programs designed to treat social phobias?
A. explaining that social phobias are learned
B. the person learns new social skills
C. having the person imagine being in the feared situation
D. focusing on how other people cope with the feared situation

p. 525
Application:
  Treating Phobias
Level: Easy
Type: Factual
Ans: C

184. Before real exposure to the feared situation or object, the person with the phobia:
A. is given antidepressant drugs
B. undergoes electroconvulsive therapy
C. imagines the feared situation or object
D. undergoes dream analysis

p. 525
Application:
  Treating Phobias
Level: Easy
Type: Factual
Ans: D

185. In the treatment of social phobia, in vivo exposure means that the patient:
A. is given antidepressant drugs
B. is told to confront the feared situation with no advance preparation
C. watches the therapist model behaviors without the patient having to engage in them
D. is exposed to the feared situation

p. 525
Application:
  Treating Phobias
Level: Easy
Type: Applied
Ans: C

186. Susan's phobia is so intense that she cannot complete her cognitive-behavioral therapy program. She has chosen drug therapy. Which of the following is she most likely to be given?
A. a phenothiazine
B. Tagamet
C. one of the benzodiazepines
D. Thorazine

p. 525
Application:
  Treating Phobias
Level: Easy
Type: Applied
Ans: A

187. Right when Professor Shepard is about to discuss the problems of drug treatment that are presented in your textbook, her overhead projector stops working. What would have been presented on the overhead screen?
A. high relapse rates and side effects
B. high rate of overdose and low success rates
C. symptom substitution and high relapse rates
D. low success rates and side effects

True/False

| | | | |
|---|---|---|---|
| F | | 1. | Jeffery Dahmer was considered insane. |
| T | www | 2. | Insanity is a legal term. |
| F | | 3. | Biological factors refer to cognitive processes. |
| T | www | 4. | If a behavior interferes with a person's ability to function, then it is considered abnormal from the maladaptive approach. |
| F | | 5. | If behavior is infrequent, it could be consider to be abnormal, according to the social norms approach. |
| T | | 6. | To evaluate a person, clinicians perform clinical assessment. |
| F | www | 7. | Clinical interviews are always structured. |
| F | | 8. | DSM-IV-TR provides ideas for the treatment of mental disorders. |
| T | | 9. | Mood disorders would be identified on Axis I. |
| F | www | 10. | Personality disorders are listed on Axis III. |
| F | | 11. | The most common mental disorder is depression. |
| F | www | 12. | In generalized anxiety disorder, the person suffers from unexpected panic attacks. |
| T | | 13. | Women are much more likely than men to suffer from panic disorder. |
| T | www | 14. | A phobia is an irrational fear that is out of proportion to any real danger in the situation or object. |

| T | | 15. | In agoraphobia, the individual has a fear of being someplace where escape may be difficult or embarrassing. |
|---|-----|-----|----------------------------------------------------------------|
| T | www | 16. | An obsession is a persistent recurring thought, impulse, or image. |
| T | | 17. | The somatoform disorders involve bodily symptoms. |
| F | www | 18. | In conversion disorder, the person is faking some physical symptom. |
| F | | 19. | In Japan, taijin kyofusho is similar to somatization disorder. |
| F | www | 20. | Taijin kyofusho illustrates how genetics play a role in mental disorders. |
| T | | 21. | The prefrontal lobe in adolescents is still underdeveloped. |
| F | | 22. | Adolescent school shooters rarely give warning signs of their violent intentions. |
| T | www | 23. | Cognitive-behavioral therapy attempts to change thoughts and beliefs. |
| F | | 24. | Nondrug treatments for social phobia are not effective. |
| T | | 25. | Most people relapse after they stop taking drugs to treat social phobia. |

Short-Answer Essay Questions

1. According to Module 22, what are the causes of abnormal behavior? Why is it important to recognize that abnormal behaviors may be caused by different factors?

2. What tools does a clinician have to collect information on a person with a mental disorder? (*www*)

3. What role does the DSM-IV-TR play? Describe its five axes. (*www*)

4. Why does labeling mental disorders have social and political implications?

5. Describe generalized anxiety disorder by presenting a case that illustrates its characteristics.

6. Discuss the similarities and differences between social phobia, specific phobia, and agoraphobia. Make sure you include a definition of phobia. (*www*)

7. Imagine that a friend of yours suffers from OCD. What treatment approach would you recommended to her and why? (*www*)

8. Present somatization disorder and conversion disorder by creating two cases that describe the characteristics of each disorder.

9. Explain what taijin kyofusho is and why it effectively illustrates why clinicians should consider cultural variables in understanding and treating disorders. (*www*)

10. Describe how social phobia might be treated by combining exposure and cognitive-behavioral therapies.

# Module 23 - Mood Disorder and Schizophrenia

p. 531
Introduction
Level: Moderate
Type: Conceptual
Ans: B

1. The example of Chuck Elliot in the textbook suggests that:
   A. clozapine is effective in treating generalized anxiety disorder
   B. mental disorders can affect anyone regardless of their talents, education, and intelligence
   C. schizophrenia runs in families
   D. psychoactive drugs have undesirable side effects

p. 531
Introduction
Level: Easy
Type: Conceptual
Ans: B
*PS/SG 23-1*

2. Rod Plotnik offers the examples of Chuck Elliot and Michael McCabe to show that:
   A. people who have used illegal drugs are more likely to become mentally ill
   B. mood disorders and schizophrenia can be terrifying, crippling disorders
   C. anyone can become mentally ill at almost any time
   D. brilliant, creative people are more likely to become mentally ill

p. 531
Introduction
Level: Moderate
Type: Factual
Ans: A

3. Why does Chuck Elliot stop taking his medication for his manic episodes?
   A. The medication slows him down.
   B. The medication causes too much energy.
   C. The medication leads to sleeplessness.
   D. The medication gives him headaches.

p. 531
Introduction
Level: Easy
Type: Factual
Ans: C

4. When Michael McCabe was first diagnosed with schizophrenia, he:
   A. attempted suicide
   B. had many personalities
   C. was having auditory hallucinations - he heard voices
   D. was receiving electroconvulsive therapy

p. 531
Introduction
Level: Easy
Type: Factual
Ans: D

5. What has allowed Michael McCabe, who was diagnosed with schizophrenia, to be cared for by his mother Marsha?
   A. He snapped out of schizophrenia.
   B. His mother received special sensitivity training.
   C. He received a prefrontal lobotomy.
   D. He was put on a new antipsychotic drug, clozapine.

p. 531
Introduction
Level: Easy
Type: Conceptual
Ans: C

6. The cases of Chuck Elliot and Michael McCabe presented in the module illustrate:
   A. the role that genetics play in mental disorders
   B. the failure of drug treatment of mental disorders
   C. how mental disorders can be debilitating
   D. how serious mental disorders can heighten one's creativity

p. 532
Mood Disorders
Level: Easy
Type: Factual
Ans: B
*www*

7. A prolonged and disturbed emotional state is known as a(n):
   A. agoraphobia
   B. mood disorder
   C. somatization disorder
   D. conversion disorder

p. 532
Mood Disorders
Level: Easy
Type: Factual
Ans: D

8. Hank suffers from a prolonged and disturbed emotional state. He could be diagnosed as having a(n):
A. maladaptive disorder
B. stress disorder
C. schizophrenic disorder
D. mood disorder

p. 532
Mood Disorders
Level: Easy
Type: Conceptual
Ans: A

9. Normal depression is to abnormal depression as _____ is to _____.
A. paper cut; open heart surgery
B. football; baseball
C. arm; leg
D. home; house

p. 532
Mood Disorders
Level: Easy
Type: Factual
Ans: D

10. The case of singer-songwriter Sheryl Crow illustrates that _____ can affect anyone regardless of fame or talent.
A. OCD
B. alchoholism
C. depression
D. anxiety

p. 532
Mood Disorders
Level: Easy
Type: Factual
Ans: D

11. The most common forms of mood disorders are:
A. bipolar I disorder, schizophrenic disorder, minor depressive disorder
B. seasonal affective disorder, minor depressive disorder, postpartum depression
C. major depressive disorder, minor depressive disorder, bipolar I disorder
D. major depressive disorder, bipolar I disorder, dysthymic disorder

p. 532
Mood Disorders
Level: Easy
Type: Factual
Ans: C
PS/SG 23-2

12. Which of the following is not a mood disorder?
A. major depression
B. bipolar I disorder
C. antisocial personality disorder
D. dysthymic disorder

p. 532
Mood Disorders
Level: Easy
Type: Factual
Ans: A

13. A loss of energy, lack of interest and pleasure in usual activities, negative self-concept, and recurrent thoughts of death and suicide are common symptoms of:
A. major depression
B. schizophrenia disorder
C. somatization disorder
D. conversion disorder

p. 532
Mood Disorders
Level: Moderate
Type: Applied
Ans: B
*www*

14. After being rejected by all the medical schools she applied to, Melanie developed a sad and dejected mood. She had difficulty sleeping, ate much less than normal, no longer took interest in the hobbies and activities that once gave her pleasure, and felt that she was worthless. Melanie would be diagnosed as suffering from:
A. bipolar I disorder
B. depression
C. mania
D. dissociative disorder

p. 532
Mood Disorders
Level: Easy
Type: Factual
Ans: B

15. If you randomly meet 100 people today, how many will have a lifetime episode of major depression?
A. 8
B. 16
C. 32
D. 48

p. 532
Mood Disorders
Level: Easy
Type: Factual
Ans: C

16. What does the research say about the gender difference in major depressive disorder?
A. An equal percentage of males and females have major depressive disorder.
B. A higher percentage of males have major depressive disorder.
C. A higher percentage of females have major depressive disorder.
D. It is impossible to say because gender data on major depressive disorder is not collected.

p. 532
Mood Disorders
Level: Easy
Type: Applied
Ans: C

17. David has been in a bad mood for three weeks. He just stays in bed, doesn't take care of himself, has thoughts of suicide, and feels utterly useless. David's parents can't understand why he just can't snap out of it. David is experiencing:
A. obsessive-compulsive disorder
B. dysthymic disorder
C. major depressive disorder
D. bipolar I disorder

p. 532
Mood Disorders
Level: Easy
Type: Factual
Ans: D
*www*

18. What disorder consists of fluctuations between episodes of depression and mania?
A. histrionic personality disorder
B. major depression
C. dysthymia
D. bipolar I disorder

p. 532
Mood Disorders
Level: Easy
Type: Factual
Ans: B

19. Exaggerated energy, enthusiasm, and elation are characteristic of:
A. dysthymia
B. mania
C. somatoform disorders
D. schizoid personality disorder

| | | |
|---|---|---|
| p. 532<br>Mood Disorders<br>Level: Easy<br>Type: Factual<br>Ans: A<br>*PS/SG 23-3* | 20. | _____ is marked by fluctuations between episodes of depression and mania. |
| | A. | bipolar I disorder |
| | B. | major depressive disorder |
| | C. | dysthymic disorder |
| | D. | minor depressive disorder |

| | | |
|---|---|---|
| p. 532<br>Mood Disorders<br>Level: Moderate<br>Type: Applied<br>Ans: C | 21. | A psychologist is seeing a client who always talks fast, seems to have incredible energy, makes grandiose plans that would be impossible to carry out, and seems to "bounce off the walls." If this person never shows signs of depression, he is likely to be suffering from: |
| | A. | bipolar I disorder |
| | B. | somatoform disorder |
| | C. | mania |
| | D. | hysteria |

| | | |
|---|---|---|
| p. 532<br>Mood Disorders<br>Level: Moderate<br>Type: Conceptual<br>Ans: D | 22. | Of the following, which is the <u>best</u> way to describe bipolar I disorder? |
| | A. | "long plains and high peaks" |
| | B. | "different types of rocks with different shapes and colors, but still rocks" |
| | C. | "long plains followed by low valleys, followed by long plains" |
| | D. | "high peaks and low valleys, high peaks and low valleys" |

| | | |
|---|---|---|
| p. 532<br>Mood Disorders<br>Level: Easy<br>Type: Factual<br>Ans: A | 23. | Bipolar depression differs from major depression in that: |
| | A. | bipolar depression typically involves periods of mania |
| | B. | bipolar depression involves depression caused by two distinct sources |
| | C. | major depression is less common |
| | D. | bipolar depression is often complicated by further emotions such as guilt |

| | | |
|---|---|---|
| p. 532<br>Mood Disorders<br>Level: Moderate<br>Type: Applied<br>Ans: D | 24. | A psychologist is working with a person who has been diagnosed as having major depression. The person rarely talks during their sessions. Then, on one visit, the person begins to talk very rapidly, describing, with great enthusiasm, elaborate plans that are not at all realistic. It would be reasonable for the psychologist to conclude that the: |
| | A. | person is near recovery |
| | B. | depression was less severe than was originally diagnosed |
| | C. | person is actually suffering from schizophrenia |
| | D. | depression is actually bipolar |

| | | |
|---|---|---|
| p. 532<br>Mood Disorders<br>Level: Easy<br>Type: Factual<br>Ans: B | 25. | Dysthymic depression differs from major depression in that dysthymic depression: |
| | A. | has a longer duration |
| | B. | is associated with less serious symptoms |
| | C. | does not involve problems with sleep and appetite |
| | D. | is more intense and has a greater negative effect on normal functioning |

| | | |
|---|---|---|
| p. 532<br>Mood Disorders<br>Level: Easy<br>Type: Factual<br>Ans: C | 26. | A less serious form of major depression is called: |
| | A. | dysfunctional mood disorder |
| | B. | abbreviated mood disorder |
| | C. | dysthymic disorder |
| | D. | bipolar II disorder |

<table>
<tr><td>

p. 532
Mood Disorders
Level: Easy
Type: Factual
Ans: A
*www*

</td><td>

27.

</td><td>

Derek has complained that he is "down in the dumps." Which of the following is Derek <u>most</u> likely to suffer from?

A. dysthymic disorder
B. major depressive disorder
C. bipolar I disorder
D. somatization disorder

</td></tr>
</table>

p. 532
Mood Disorders
Level: Moderate
Type: Applied
Ans: D

28. Most of the time, Lydia is dejected, has difficulty sleeping, and has no energy or interest in her usual activities. However, every now and then, she seems normal for a few days, and then reverses back into her sadness. Lydia probably suffers from:

A. unipolar depression
B. bipolar I disorder
C. conversion disorder
D. dysthymic depression

p. 532
Mood Disorders
Level: Easy
Type: Factual
Ans: B

29. "I've been feeling down for a long time now. I guess that's just the way I am." This comment best illustrates:

A. bipolar I disorder
B. dysthymic disorder
C. major depression
D. seasonal affective disorder

p. 533
Mood Disorders
Level: Moderate
Type: Conceptual
Ans: B

30. A book entitled _____ focuses on the genetic, neurological, and physiological factors related to mood disorders.

A. *Failing to Self-Actualize: The Mood Disorders*
B. *Mood Disorders: The Biological Theories*
C. *Cognitive Theories of Mood Disorders*
D. *Unconscious Conflicts in Mood Disorders*

p. 533
Mood Disorders
Level: Moderate
Type: Factual
Ans: A

31. A psychologist is working with a person who has been diagnosed as having bipolar I disorder. When the psychologist looks at the clinical history of the blood relatives of this person, she would <u>not</u> be surprised to find:

A. there is evidence of similar symptoms being displayed in the person's relatives
B. there is no evidence whatsoever of depressive symptoms in the relatives
C. if there is evidence of depression or mania, it is no more likely to be found in blood relatives than it is in close friends of the family
D. there is evidence of other genetic problems such as Downs syndrome

p. 533
Mood Disorders
Level: Easy
Type: Factual
Ans: C

32. The biological theory of depression has discovered that if one *identical* twin has a mood disorder, then the chance that the other twin does is about:

A. 20%
B. 30%
C. 80%
D. 95%

p. 533
Mood Disorders
Level: Easy
Type: Factual
Ans: A

33. The biological theory of depression has discovered that if one *fraternal* twin has a mood disorder, then the chance that the other twin does is about:
A. 15%
B. 30%
C. 65%
D. 95%

p. 533
Mood Disorders
Level: Easy
Type: Factual
Ans: B

34. The genetics research on depression suggests that:
A. one gene is responsible for producing the risk for mood disorders
B. a combination of genes produces the risk for mood disorders
C. genetics play little if any role in mood disorders
D. environmental factors play little if any role in mood disorders

p. 533
Mood Disorders
Level: Easy
Type: Factual
Ans: D

35. Which of the following statements lends support to the biological theory of depression?
A. the evidence regarding fraternal twins and occurrence of depression
B. Beck's cognitive theory of depression
C. excessive secretion of dopamine during stress
D. the level of the neurotransmitter serotonin is increased by Prozac

p. 533
Mood Disorders
Level: Easy
Type: Factual
Ans: C

36. What group of neurotransmitters has been implicated in mood disorders according to the textbook?
A. lithazines
B. phenothiazines
C. monoamines
D. biamines

p. 533
Mood Disorders
Level: Easy
Type: Factual
Ans: B

37. You are a neuropsychologist studying depression. You are looking at the computerized brain photos of depressed individuals. You conclude that a particular part of the brain of depressed people is about 40% smaller. What is this brain part?
A. hypothalamus
B. prefrontal cortex
C. amygdala
D. cerebellum

p. 533
Mood Disorders
Level: Easy
Type: Factual
Ans: B

38. The area of the brain that appears to play a role in depression is the:
A. Broca's area
B. hippocampus
C. corpus callosum
D. prefrontal cortex

p. 533
Mood Disorders
Level: Easy
Type: Factual
Ans: D

39. A psychologist asks a depressed patient about his personality traits, ability to deal with stress, and his social support. The psychologist is focusing on _____ factors in depression.
A. unconscious
B. psychodynamic
C. psychopathic
D. psychosocial

p. 533
Mood Disorders
Level: Moderate
Type: Factual
Ans: C

40. Why is there interest in the role psychosocial factors play in mood disorders?
A. Most federal research money is targeted for the study of psychosocial causes of mental disorders.
B. Studies have thoroughly concluded that biology only plays a very minor role.
C. Psychosocial factors interact with biological factors to create a predisposition for developing mood disorders.
D. A great majority of bipolar patients do not respond at all to drug treatment.

p. 533
Mood Disorders
Level: Easy
Type: Conceptual
Ans: B

41. Which of the following is best described by sayings like "making a mountain out of a mole hill" and "crying over split milk" in explaining depression?
A. the role of monoamines
B. psychosocial factors
C. immature of the prefrontal cortex
D. socially dependent personality

p. 533
Mood Disorders
Level: Easy
Type: Factual
Ans: A

42. Beck argues that depression results from:
A. negative cognitive states
B. a chemical imbalance in the brain
C. unfulfilled self-actualization
D. unresolved unconscious conflicts regarding inappropriate sexual desires

p. 533
Mood Disorders
Level: Easy
Type: Factual
Ans: A

43. Which of the following statements about stressful life events and mood disorders is the most accurate?
A. A person whose self-esteem is based on how much they are liked is most likely to become depressed when a close relationship fails.
B. Stressful life events play a role in major depression, but not in bipolar disorder.
C. Stressful life events only precede episodes of mania, but not depression.
D. There is no relationship between stressful life events and mood disorders.

p. 533
Mood Disorders
Level: Easy
Type: Factual
Ans: D

44. With regard to mood disorders, personality traits play a significant role in determining:
A. the depth of depression
B. the height of mania
C. frequency of depression
D. one's risk of becoming depressed

p. 533
Mood Disorders
Level: Easy
Type: Factual
Ans: A

45. What kind of personality is more vulnerable to depression when a person loses a close relationship or friendship?
A. socially dependent personality
B. achievement personality
C. borderline personality
D. ego personality

p. 533
Mood Disorders
Level: Easy
Type: Applied
Ans: B

46. Lyle is depressed because he has failed to reach an important goal. Given the research described in the textbook, what type of personality is Lyle likely to have?
A. ego personality
B. achievement personality
C. borderline personality
D. socially dependent personality

p. 534
Mood Disorders
Level: Easy
Type: Factual
Ans: A

47. What effect do antidepressants have on the monoamines?
A. They increase the levels of monoamines.
B. They decrease the levels of monoamines.
C. They change the type of monoamines in the nervous system.
D. They destroy all traces of monoamines.

p. 534
Mood Disorders
Level: Moderate
Type: Factual
Ans: D

48. Antidepressants increase levels of:
A. tricyclics
B. hormones
C. benzodiazepines
D. neurotransmitters

p. 534
Mood Disorders
Level: Easy
Type: Factual
Ans: D
PS/SG 23-6

49. Antidepressant drugs work by:
A. attacking and destroying depressive memory cells that cause depression
B. creating feelings of peace and well being similar to the effects of alcohol
C. preventing neurons from being over stimulated
D. increasing the levels of neurotransmitters involved in regulating emotions and moods

p. 534
Mood Disorders
Level: Easy
Type: Factual
Ans: B

50. The majority of drugs used to treat depression act on:
A. dopamines
B. monoamines
C. benzodiazepines
D. phenothiazines

p. 534
Mood Disorders
Level: Easy
Type: Factual
Ans: C

51. Most of the drugs used to treat depression are:
A. addictive
B. naturally occurring minerals such as lithium
C. selective serotonin reuptake inhibitors
D. tricylics

p. 534
Mood Disorders
Level: Easy
Type: Factual
Ans: A

52. Anders is placed on an antidepressant drug. His psychiatrist says something about the drug being some type of inhibitor. Anders looks up some information about the drug and finds that it is a:
A. selective serotonin reuptake inhibitor
B. general acetylcholine enzyme inhibitor
C. benzodiazepine inhibitor
D. haldol inhibitor

| | | |
|---|---|---|
| p. 534 | 53. | Why is a relatively new antidepressant, called Prozac, such a popular new treatment for depression? |
| Mood Disorders | | |
| Level: Easy | A. | it is more successful in curing depression |
| Type: Factual | B. | it lowers the level of monoamines |
| Ans: D | C. | it prevents episodes of mania |
| | D. | it has fewer side effects |

| | | |
|---|---|---|
| p. 534 | 54. | Antidepressants can take up to _____ before they have the desired effect. |
| Mood Disorders | A. | 3 days |
| Level: Easy | B. | 7 days |
| Type: Factual | C. | 6 weeks |
| Ans: C | D. | 12 weeks |

| | | |
|---|---|---|
| p. 534 | 55. | Of those patients with major depression who continue with Prozac treatment, what percentage reports an improvement? |
| Mood Disorders | | |
| Level: Easy | A. | 25% |
| Type: Factual | B. | 45% |
| Ans: D | C. | 65% |
| | D. | 70% |

| | | |
|---|---|---|
| p. 534 | 56. | Steve has stopped taking the drug prescribed for his depression. What are the odds that he will relapse in the next three months? |
| Mood Disorders | | |
| Level: Easy | A. | 5% |
| Type: Factual | B. | 30% |
| Ans: C | C. | 50% |
| | D. | 80% |

| | | |
|---|---|---|
| p. 534 | 57. | Which of the following is true regarding the use of psychotherapy in treating people with depression? |
| Mood Disorders | | |
| Level: Moderate | A. | interpersonal therapy is more successful than antidepressants |
| Type: Factual | B. | lithium is the most successful treatment |
| Ans: C | C. | in the short-run psychotherapy is as effective as antidepressants with less severe depression |
| | D. | psychotherapy is more successful than lithium |

| | | |
|---|---|---|
| p. 534 | 58. | Pete is moderately depressed. Which of the following treatments would be most beneficial for him? |
| Mood Disorders | | |
| Level: Easy | A. | antidepressant drugs and psychotherapy |
| Type: Applied | B. | antidepressant drugs |
| Ans: A | C. | psychotherapy |
| | D. | psychoanalysis |

| | | |
|---|---|---|
| p. 534 | 59. | Follow-up research on the effectiveness of antidepressants and psychotherapy indicate: |
| Mood Disorders | | |
| Level: Easy | A. | low relapse rates |
| Type: Factual | B. | relapse rates approaching 70% for patients who receive either treatment |
| Ans: B | C. | serious side effects with both forms of treatment |
| | D. | relapse rates of nearly 99% for patients who receive either treatment |

| p. 534 | 60. | One commonly used drug treatment for bipolar depression is: |
|---|---|---|
| Mood Disorders | A. | Valium |
| Level: Easy | B. | tricyclic therapy |
| Type: Factual | C. | MAO |
| Ans: D | D. | lithium |

| p. 534 | 61. | What action does lithium have on the nervous system in the treatment of bipolar I disorder? |
|---|---|---|
| Mood Disorders | | |
| Level: Easy | A. | prevent serotonin reuptake |
| Type: Factual | B. | increase serotonin reuptake |
| Ans: C | C. | prevents neurons from becoming overstimulated |
| | D. | increase the production of serotonin |

| p. 534 | 62. | What percentage of patients with bipolar I disorder receive no help from lithium? |
|---|---|---|
| Mood Disorders | | |
| Level: Easy | A. | 20% |
| Type: Factual | B. | 30-60% |
| Ans: A | C. | 70% |
| | D. | 80% |

| p. 534 | 63. | The most effective treatment for bipolar I disorder is: |
|---|---|---|
| Mood Disorders | A. | exposure therapy |
| Level: Easy | B. | lithium |
| Type: Factual | C. | a combination of lithium and other psychoactive drugs |
| Ans: D | D. | hypnotherapy |

| p. 534 | 64. | Jianwin has stopped taking her lithium. What is the most likely explanation? |
|---|---|---|
| Mood Disorders | | |
| Level: Moderate | A. | She wishes to experience mania again. |
| Type: Factual | B. | The side effects are too much to bear. |
| Ans: A | C. | It is not effective. |
| | D. | The instructions about when and how to take the drug are very confusing. |

| p. 534 | 65. | Dr. Johnson is discussing how he will treat Lori's bipolar I disorder. What is one very important piece of information Dr. Johnson should share with Lori? |
|---|---|---|
| Mood Disorders | | |
| Level: Easy | | |
| Type: Factual | A. | Clozapine has some serious side effects. |
| Ans: B | B. | She will be tempted to stop taking Lithium in order to experience mania. |
| | C. | Lithium may take up to six months before it will provide Lori with relief. |
| | D. | Prozac may take up to six months before it will provide Lori with relief. |

| p. 535 | 66. | The primary disorder that is treated by ECT is: |
|---|---|---|
| Electroconvulsive Therapy | A. | bipolar I disorder |
| Level: Easy | B. | social phobia |
| Type: Factual | C. | substance abuse |
| Ans: D | D. | major depression |

p. 535
Electroconvulsive Therapy
Level: Easy
Type: Factual
Ans: A
*www*

67.  The proper name for the technique known as "shock treatment" is
_____ therapy.
A.  electroconvulsive
B.  tricyclic antidepressant
C.  catecholamine elevation
D.  lithium

p. 535
Electroconvulsive Therapy
Level: Easy
Type: Factual
Ans: C

68.  Bonnie, who is severely depressed, is scheduled to receive ECT. How
many sessions per week can she expect?
A.  one
B.  two
C.  three
D.  six

p. 535
Electroconvulsive Therapy
Level: Easy
Type: Factual
Ans: A

69.  Electroconvulsive therapy may be appropriate in many cases of depression
because:
A.  30% fail to respond to antidepressants
B.  insurance is more likely to cover this form of treatment
C.  many psychiatrists are unwilling to have their patients experience the
serious side effects of antidepressants
D.  depression may be biological in nature

p. 535
Electroconvulsive Therapy
Level: Easy
Type: Conceptual
Ans: B

70.  A psychiatrist is seeing a person who is seriously depressed and has
attempted suicide. The person was on antidepressant medication for
months, with no relief of the depression. It is possible that the psychiatrist
will consider which of the following as the next treatment?
A.  cognitive-behavior therapy
B.  electroconvulsive therapy
C.  tricyclic therapy
D.  interpersonal therapy

p. 535
Electroconvulsive Therapy
Level: Easy
Type: Factual
Ans: D

71.  Electroconvulsive therapy has been effective in _____ of depressed
patients.
A.  10-25%
B.  30-35%
C.  40-50%
D.  60-80%

p. 535
Electroconvulsive Therapy
Level: Easy
Type: Factual
Ans: C

72.  Franklin has been receiving electroconvulsive therapy. What are the
chances that he will need additional ECT treatments?
A.  less than 1%
B.  25%
C.  50%
D.  90%

p. 535
Electroconvulsive Therapy
Level: Easy
Type: Factual
Ans: B

73.  Electroconvulsive therapy is believed to be effective by:
A.  reducing production of serotonin
B.  temporarily reducing blood flow to certain areas of the brain
C.  increasing production of serotonin
D.  preventing reuptake of serotonin

p. 535
Electroconvulsive Therapy
Level: Easy
Type: Factual
Ans: D

74. One side effect of ECT is the:
A. loss of personality
B. loss of emotional responses
C. inability to learn new material
D. impairment of memory

p. 535
Electroconvulsive Therapy
Level: Easy
Type: Factual
Ans: A
*PS/SG 23-8*

75. ECT is a controversial treatment for depression because it:
A. has serious side effects, such as memory loss
B. is based on the use of antidepressant drugs
C. has no effect at all on many patients
D. is prescribed by psychiatrists but not by clinical psychologists

p. 535
Electroconvulsive Therapy
Level: Easy
Type: Factual
Ans: C

76. One study found about _____ of patients given ECT had poor memory three years after treatment.
A. 10%
B. 30%
C. 50%
D. 80%

p. 535
Electroconvulsive Therapy
Level: Easy
Type: Factual
Ans: A

77. What type of endorsement has The National Institute of Mental Health given to the use of ECT as a treatment for severe depression?
A. a cautious endorsement, but ECT should be used only as a last resort
B. a cautious endorsement
C. the Institute has failed to endorse ECT for any purpose
D. an enthusiastic endorsement - ECT should be used as the first treatment for depression

p. 536
Personality Disorders
Level: Easy
Type: Factual
Ans: D
*PS/SG 23-9*

78. Which one of the following is not a personality disorder?
A. paranoid personality disorder
B. histrionic personality disorder
C. obsessive-compulsive personality disorder
D. depressive personality disorder

p. 536
Personality Disorders
Level: Easy
Type: Factual
Ans: C

79. An individual with inflexible and maladaptive traits which cause significantly impaired functioning in one's personal and social life would be diagnosed with a:
A. somatoform disorder
B. schizophrenic disorder
C. personality disorder
D. conversion disorder

p. 536
Personality Disorders
Level: Easy
Type: Factual
Ans: C

80. A person complains that he has few friends. It is discovered that this is because he is cold and aloof in relationships, and takes criticism poorly. If this is diagnosed as being abnormal, the DSM-IV category would probably be _____ disorder.
A. affective
B. schizophrenic
C. personality
D. dissociative

p. 536
Personality Disorders
Level: Easy
Type: Factual
Ans: B

81. What percentage of the adult population in the United States has a personality disorder?
A. 2%
B. 12%
C. 25%
D. 46%

p. 536
Personality Disorders
Level: Easy
Type: Factual
Ans: D

82. If you read descriptive words like "schizoid" and "narcissistic" in a case study, it is likely that you would be looking at the case of someone with a(n) _____ disorder.
A. affective
B. schizophrenic
C. dissociative
D. personality

p. 536
Personality Disorders
Level: Easy
Type: Factual
Ans: A

83. Which of the following is not a characteristic of a personality disorder?
A. being unpopular
B. maladaptiveness
C. inflexibility
D. impaired functioning

p. 536
Personality Disorders
Level: Easy
Type: Factual
Ans: C
www

84. A disorder characterized by maladaptiveness, inflexibility, and impaired function is called:
A. schizophrenic disorder
B. mood disorder
C. personality disorder
D. anxiety disorder

p. 536
Personality Disorders
Level: Easy
Type: Applied
Ans: B

85. "I distrust other people. I think they are up to something bad." Which of the following personality disorders is this person most likely to have?
A. antisocial personality disorder
B. paranoid personality disorder
C. schizotypical personality disorder
D. histrionic personality disorder

p. 536
Personality Disorders
Level: Easy
Type: Applied
Ans: D

86. Jack feels discomfort in developing close relationships and is somewhat odd in his behavior. If Jack has a mental disorder, it would probably be classified as:
A. schizophrenia
B. agoraphobia
C. bipolar I disorder
D. schizotypical personality disorder

p. 536
Personality Disorders
Level: Easy
Type: Factual
Ans: B

87. A dependent personality disorder involves:
A. suspiciousness
B. a pattern of being submissive and clingy
C. guilt and remorse
D. social isolation

p. 536
Personality Disorders
Level: Easy
Type: Factual
Ans: A

88. An individual who is classified as having a histrionic personality disorder will:
A. be excessively emotional and attention seeking
B. be incapable of feeling guilt or remorse
C. have an exaggerated sense of self-importance
D. display socially withdrawn and reckless behaviors

p. 536
Personality Disorders
Level: Easy
Type: Applied
Ans: D

89. If a person has an intense interest in order, achievement, perfectionism, and having control, then that individual might have:
A. schizophrenia
B. dependent personality disorder
C. obsessive-compulsive personality disorder
D. schizotypical personality disorder

p. 536
Personality Disorders
Level: Easy
Type: Applied
Ans: A
www

90. If you visit Laura, you will find a very clean organized house. Everything has its place and if you move an object, Laura will be distressed. She is rigid and tries to control everything. Of the following personality disorders, which one best describes Laura?
A. obsessive-compulsive personality disorder
B. dependent personality disorder
C. histrionic personality disorder
D. schizotypical personality disorder

p. 536
Personality Disorders
Level: Easy
Type: Applied
Ans: C

91. For a project in class, you have decided to create a web site on one of the personality disorders. You have selected paranoid personality disorders and the best name of your site would be:
A. www.obsessive.edu
B. www.emotionality.edu
C. www.suspiciousness.edu
D. www.submissive.edu

p. 536
Personality Disorders
Level: Easy
Type: Applied
Ans: B

92. "She is so clingy. It's like she can't make her own decision. I have to, and she goes along with it. If she has a personality disorder, I bet it would be _____.
A. schizophrenia
B. dependent personality disorder
C. obsessive-compulsive personality disorder
D. schizotypical personality disorder

p. 536
Personality Disorders
Level: Easy
Type: Applied
Ans: A
www

93. On the surface, Chuck is a charming, intelligent, good looking individual. Yet he constantly lies, has no sense of responsibility, is reckless, feels no guilt when his actions harm others, and never learns from his mistakes. If Chuck's behavior is considered abnormal, he would most likely be diagnosed as having a(n):
A. antisocial personality
B. narcissistic personality
C. dissociative disorder
D. schizoid disorder

p. 536
Personality Disorders
Level: Easy
Type: Factual
Ans: C

94. A person with a personality disorder who is sometimes referred to as a sociopath or psychopath can be diagnosed with:
A. paranoid personality disorder
B. schizotypical personality disorder
C. antisocial personality
D. histrionic personality disorder

p. 536
Personality Disorders
Level: Easy
Type: Factual
Ans: C
*PS/SG 23-10*

95. Jeffrey Dahmer represented an extreme case of _____ personality disorder.
A. histrionic
B. paranoid
C. antisocial
D. schizotypical

p. 537
Personality Disorders
Level: Easy
Type: Factual
Ans: C

96. Most individuals diagnosed with antisocial personality disorder are:
A. also diagnosed with dissociative identity disorder
B. female
C. male
D. middle-age

p. 537
Personality Disorders
Level: Easy
Type: Factual
Ans: A

97. Two psychosocial causes have been implicated in antisocial personality disorder. They are:
A. parent-child interaction and physical or sexual abuse in childhood
B. being an only child and lack of adequate interaction with peers
C. parent-child interaction and child-peer interaction
D. low socioeconomic status and overly trustful of others

p. 537
Personality Disorders
Level: Easy
Type: Factual
Ans: B

98. According to researchers, _____ may play an important role in the development of antisocial personality disorder.
A. poor academic performance in elementary school
B. child-parent interaction
C. low socioeconomic status
D. educational opportunity

p. 537
Personality Disorders
Level: Easy
Type: Factual
Ans: D

99. In explaining antisocial personality disorder, children who are difficult may elicit _____ from parents and in turn, make them more _____.
A. compassion; spoiled
B. hostility; spoiled
C. affection; vulnerable
D. hostility; difficult

p. 537
Personality Disorders
Level: Easy
Type: Factual
Ans: C

100. Physical or sexual abuse may play a part in developing an antisocial personality disorder. What percentage of sociopaths report this type of abuse in childhood?
A. 5-10%
B. 19-25%
C. 59-70%
D. 80-93%

p. 537
Personality Disorders
Level: Moderate
Type: Factual
Ans: C

101. The fact that antisocial behavioral patterns appear at such an early age and are so difficult to change lends support to the notion that an antisocial personality may be caused by:
A. behavioral factors
B. environmental factors
C. biological factors
D. cognitive factors

p. 537
Personality Disorders
Level: Moderate
Type: Factual
Ans: D

102. According to research cited in your textbook, what neurological factor may play a role in antisocial personality disorder?
A. enlarged ventricles in the brain
B. abnormally low levels of serotonin
C. abnormally high levels of dopamine
D. smaller than normal prefrontal cortex

p. 537
Personality Disorders
Level: Easy
Type: Factual
Ans: B

103. What part of the brain appears to be related to antisocial personality disorder?
A. amygdala
B. prefrontal cortex
C. pons
D. medulla

p. 537
Personality Disorders
Level: Easy
Type: Applied
Ans: D

104. Kyle is a sociopath. He is not likely to benefit from treatment. This is because:
A. antisocial personality disorder is a permanent disorder
B. treatments for this disorder are only now being developed
C. sociopaths are very gullible and will believe anyone
D. sociopaths tend not to see their behaviors as antisocial

p. 537
Personality Disorders
Level: Easy
Type: Factual
Ans: D

105 Research studying antisocial personality disorder has identified that there may be an abnormality in the sociopath's:
A. information processing system
B. sympathetic division
C. endocrine system
D. serotonin brain system

p. 537
Personality Disorders
Level: Easy
Type: Factual
Ans: B

106. The treatment of psychopaths is:
A. usually quite successful
B. not very promising
C. successful if punishment is used
D. successful if the disorder is diagnosed in childhood

p. 537
Personality Disorders
Level: Easy
Type: Factual
Ans: D

107. Some drugs may be effective in reducing aggressive behaviors in patients with antisocial personality disorder. These drugs:
A. decrease levels of dopamine
B. raise levels of dopamine
C. decrease levels of serotonin
D. raise levels of serotonin

p. 538
Schizophrenia
Level: Easy
Type: Factual
Ans: A
*www*

108. Delusions, hallucinations, disorganized speech, disorganized behavior, and decreased emotional expression characterize:
A. schizophrenia
B. depression
C. somatoform disorders
D. generalized anxiety disorder

p. 538
Schizophrenia
Level: Easy
Type: Factual
Ans: C

109. Schizophrenia is characterized by:
A. a fear of public places
B. alternating periods of mania and depression
C. symptoms that interfere with personal or social functioning
D. feelings of pain which have no physical cause

p. 538
Schizophrenia
Level: Easy
Type: Factual
Ans: D

110. A person reports hearing voices at night that repeat his name. He has a very short attention span and makes up words that have no meaning, so it is difficult to have a conversation with him. How long would these symptoms have to be present before the diagnosis of schizophrenia would be made?
A. 2 weeks
B. 1 month
C. 2 months
D. 6 months

p. 538
Schizophrenia
Level: Easy
Type: Factual
Ans: B

111. What portion of the adult population in the United States does schizophrenia affect?
A. .1%
B. .2 to 2%
C. 5 to 6%
D. 11 to 12%

p. 538
Schizophrenia
Level: Easy
Type: Factual
Ans: A

112. About 30% of all inpatients residing in mental hospitals are diagnosed with:
A. schizophrenia
B. antisocial personality disorder
C. bipolar I disorder
D. conversion disorder

p. 538
Schizophrenia
Level: Easy
Type: Factual
Ans: B
*PS/SG 23-12*

113. The highest percentage of mental hospital inpatients are there because of:
A. major depression
B. schizophrenia
C. antisocial personality disorder
D. dissociative amnesia

p. 538
Schizophrenia
Level: Easy
Type: Factual
Ans: A

114. A psychologist working with schizophrenics is likely to encounter all of the following symptoms except:
A. compulsive focusing on the things happening around them
B. the formation of new words that don't exist in the dictionary
C. strange bodily sensations
D. hearing voices

p. 538
Schizophrenia
Level: Easy
Type: Factual
Ans: C

115. The type of schizophrenia that involves thoughts of being persecuted or thoughts of grandeur is _____ schizophrenia.
A. catatonic
B. disorganized
C. paranoid
D. melancholic

p. 538
Schizophrenia
Level: Easy
Type: Factual
Ans: C

116. A person who believes that strangers are plotting to kidnap him is suffering from what form of schizophrenia?
A. catatonic
B. disorganized
C. paranoid
D. melancholic

p. 538
Schizophrenia
Level: Easy
Type: Factual
Ans: B

117. A man sees someone using a phone booth and believes that the caller is reporting on the man's every move. The man would be diagnosed as having what type of schizophrenia?
A. melancholic
B. paranoid
C. disorganized
D. catatonic

p. 538
Schizophrenia
Level: Easy
Type: Applied
Ans: A

118. Tony truly believes that the FBI and the CIA have implanted listening devices into his eyeglasses. Tony appears to have:
A. paranoid schizophrenia
B. disorganized schizophrenia
C. catatonic schizophrenia
D. conversion schizophrenia

p. 538
Schizophrenia
Level: Easy
Type: Factual
Ans: B

119. Which of the following best describes disorganized schizophrenia?
A. persecution and grandeur
B. bizarre and childish
C. immobility and excitement
D. anxious and obsessed

p. 538
Schizophrenia
Level: Easy
Type: Applied
Ans: D

120. A person complains that her hair is gradually turning into wire and her bones are slowly falling to her feet. While explaining this, she will sometimes laugh hysterically and at other times cry. Which form of schizophrenia would be a likely diagnosis in this case?
A. paranoid
B. catatonic
C. melancholic
D. disorganized

p. 538
Schizophrenia
Level: Easy
Type: Applied
Ans: B

121. Confused speech, bizarre ideas, and childish behavior are all symptoms of:
A. paranoid schizophrenia
B. disorganized schizophrenia
C. affective schizophrenia
D. catatonic schizophrenia

p. 538
Schizophrenia
Level: Easy
Type: Applied
Ans: B

122.    A schizophrenic patient alternates between periods of wild excitement and periods of prolonged immobility. Her diagnosis would be _____ schizophrenia.
A.    paranoid
B.    catatonic
C.    melancholic
D.    disorganized

p. 538
Schizophrenia
Level: Easy
Type: Factual
Ans: C

123.    Type I schizophrenia involves _____ symptoms and has a _____ chance of recovery.
A.    negative; good
B.    negative; poor
C.    positive; good
D.    positive; poor

p. 538
Schizophrenia
Level: Easy
Type: Applied
Ans: D

124.    Janet maintains the same position for hours. However, on rare occasions, she will suddenly become excited and run around the room in circles, only to return to her frozen position. Janet appears to have:
A.    paranoid schizophrenia
B.    disorganized schizophrenia
C.    affective schizophrenia
D.    catatonic schizophrenia

p. 538
Schizophrenia
Level: Easy
Type: Applied
Ans: A

125.    Harold suffers from schizophrenia and has hallucinations and delusions. Harold does not have any intellectual impairment. Harold could be described as having:
A.    Type I schizophrenia
B.    Type II schizophrenia
C.    Type III schizophrenia
D.    unipolar schizophrenia

p. 538
Schizophrenia
Level: Easy
Type: Applied
Ans: B

126.    Jennifer has been diagnosed with schizophrenia. She has experienced negative symptoms. Her psychiatrist believes she has little chance of recovery. Jennifer must have:
A.    Type I schizophrenia
B.    Type II schizophrenia
C.    Type III schizophrenia
D.    unipolar schizophrenia

p. 538
Schizophrenia
Level: Easy
Type: Factual
Ans: B

127.    Type II schizophrenia involves _____ symptoms and has a _____ chance of recovery.
A.    negative; good
B.    negative; poor
C.    positive; good
D.    positive; poor

p. 538
Schizophrenia
Level: Moderate
Type: Applied
Ans: B

128. Steve has been diagnosed as suffering from Type I schizophrenia; Ryan received the diagnosis of Type II schizophrenia. Which of these patients has the better chance of recovery?

A. Both have excellent chances of returning to a normal state within six months.
B. Steve
C. Ryan
D. It is impossible to predict because the course of schizophrenia is so variable

p. 538
Schizophrenia
Level: Moderate
Type: Factual
Ans: C
*PS/SG 23-13*

129. Chances for recovery from schizophrenia are best in patients with:

A. symptoms of dulled emotions, little inclination to speak, and a loss of normal functions
B. Type II schizophrenia (negative symptoms)
C. Type I schizophrenia (positive symptoms)
D. cases of recovery from schizophrenia are so rare as to be statistically insignificant

p. 538
Schizophrenia
Level: Easy
Type: Factual
Ans: D

130. The best predictor of a recovery from schizophrenia is the patient's:

A. gender
B. level of social support
C. age
D. symptoms

p. 538
Schizophrenia
Level: Moderate
Type: Applied
Ans: C
*www*

131. Of the following patients with schizophrenia, who has the best chance of recovery?

A. Chuck - he displays dulled emotions
B. Steven - he has negative symptoms
C. Michael - he suffers from hallucinations and delusions
D. Darin - he experiences intellectual impairment

p. 538
Schizophrenia
Level: Easy
Type: Factual
Ans: D
*PS/SG 23-14*

132. Which of the following are not symptoms of schizophrenia?

A. disorders of thought
B. disorders of attention
C. disorders of perception
D. disorders of moral character

p. 538
Schizophrenia
Level: Easy
Type: Factual
Ans: A

133. Delusions are:

A. irrational beliefs
B. new, made-up words
C. sensory experiences
D. false perceptions

p. 538
Schizophrenia
Level: Easy
Type: Factual
Ans: D

134. In your psychology course, you are watching a video on schizophrenia. One of the patients portrayed in the video is asked a question about her hobbies. She responds with an answer that consists of new words. This is an example of:

A. neuroleptic behavior
B. flat affect
C. hallucinations
D. neologisms

p. 538
Schizophrenia
Level: Easy
Type: Factual
Ans: C

135. Which of the following is an example of a disorder of perception?
A. delusions
B. neologisms
C. hallucinations
D. flat affect

p. 538
Schizophrenia
Level: Easy
Type: Factual
Ans: C

136. A hallucination is:
A. an inability to focus on a single chain of events
B. a belief that an auditory stimulus is a message from God
C. a sensory experience without environmental stimulation
D. composed of incoherent thoughts with no emotional affect

p. 538
Schizophrenia
Level: Easy
Type: Factual
Ans: D

137. When schizophrenics hear voices or feel bugs crawling under their skin, they are experiencing disorders of perception known as:
A. illusions
B. neologisms
C. delusions
D. hallucinations

p. 538
Schizophrenia
Level: Easy
Type: Applied
Ans: D

138. Marilyn, a schizophrenic, breaks into hysterical laughing when told that her home and all her personal belongings were destroyed in a fire. Marilyn is displaying:
A. disorders of thought
B. delusions
C. hallucinations
D. inappropriate emotion

p. 539
Schizophrenia
Level: Moderate
Type: Factual
Ans: C

139. What is so unusual about the Genain quadruplets?
A. They were the first quadruplets born in the United States in a family with parents diagnosed with schizophrenia.
B. They were the first test cases of a new drug for bipolar I disorder.
C. They all developed schizophrenia.
D. They all studied the biological causes of schizophrenia.

p. 539
Schizophrenia
Level: Moderate
Type: Factual
Ans: A
PS/SG 23-15

140. Rod Plotnik tells us about the famous Genain quadruplets to illustrate the fact that:
A. there must be a genetic factor in schizophrenia
B. science is filled with amazing coincidences
C. children can "learn" to be schizophrenic from close contact with family members who are ill
D. schizophrenia strikes in a random, unpredictable fashion

p. 539
Schizophrenia
Level: Easy
Type: Factual
Ans: A

141. Genetic factors for schizophrenia are supported by:
A. studies of twins with schizophrenia
B. brain deficits among schizophrenics
C. the dopamine theory of schizophrenia
D. the diathesis stress theory of schizophrenia

p. 539
Schizophrenia
Level: Moderate
Type: Factual
Ans: B

142. Twin studies of schizophrenia suggest that:
A. the brains of schizophrenics are different from the brains of those with other mental disorders
B. a person may inherit a predisposition for schizophrenia
C. abnormalities in the dopamine system are involved in producing symptoms of schizophrenia
D. the ventricles of schizophrenics are smaller than those of normal people

p. 539
Schizophrenia
Level: Moderate
Type: Factual
Ans: C

143. The strongest research support for the existence of a genetic component to schizophrenia is that:
A. children whose adoptive parents are schizophrenic also tend to be schizophrenic
B. non-identical twins are more likely to share the disorder than identical twins
C. identical twins are more likely to share the disorder than non-identical twins
D. a chromosome abnormality has been found in many diagnosed schizophrenics

p. 539
Schizophrenia
Level: Easy
Type: Factual
Ans: C

144. If one member of a pair of identical twins develops schizophrenia, the other member has about a _____ chance of also developing the disorder.
A. 10-17%
B. 29-33%
C. 48-83%
D. 100%

p. 539
Schizophrenia
Level: Easy
Type: Factual
Ans: A

145. In nontwin siblings, what is the chance that if one has schizophrenia, the other will have it also?
A. 10%
B. 25%
C. 50%
D. 100%

p. 539
Schizophrenia
Level: Easy
Type: Factual
Ans: A

146. One of the strongest predictors of the likelihood that an individual will develop schizophrenia is if:
A. an identical twin has schizophrenia
B. a fraternal twin has schizophrenia
C. a parent has schizophrenia
D. the person already suffers from major depression

p. 539
Schizophrenia
Level: Easy
Type: Factual
Ans: C

147. A _____ refers to an identifiable gene or number of genes or a specific segment of a chromosome that is directly linked to some trait or disease.
A. diathesis marker
B. predisposition
C. genetic marker
D. genetic landmark

p. 539
Schizophrenia
Level: Easy
Type: Factual
Ans: B

148. According to the textbook, when do genetic factors act during prenatal development?
A. 5th to 8th week
B. 9th to 15th week
C. 17th to 19th week
D. 20th to 30th week

p. 539
Schizophrenia
Level: Easy
Type: Factual
Ans: D

149. Recent research on genetic markers suggests that:
A. specific genes have been linked to schizophrenia
B. schizophrenia has no such marker
C. the neurotransmitter dopamine plays little if any role in schizophrenia
D. that a gene that is involved in creating synapses may play a role in schizophrenia

p. 540
Schizophrenia
Level: Easy
Type: Factual
Ans: A

150. In comparison to normal subjects, patients with schizophrenia have (a) relatively larger:
A. ventricles
B. frontal lobe
C. receptors
D. corpus callosum

p. 540
Schizophrenia
Level: Easy
Type: Factual
Ans: C

151. If the _____ is (are) smaller among patients with schizophrenia, then there is an overall reduction in _____.
A. cerebellum; number of motor commands
B. frontal lobe; neural connections
C. ventricles; brain size
D. corpus callosum; messages between the hemispheres

p. 540
Schizophrenia
Level: Easy
Type: Factual
Ans: D

152. Which of the following structures of the brain may be abnormally larger in people suffering from schizophrenia?
A. hypothalamus
B. medulla
C. thalamus
D. ventricles

p. 540
Schizophrenia
Level: Easy
Type: Factual
Ans: D

153. Positron emission tomography (PET) has indicated that schizophrenics have:
A. diathesis stress
B. increased metabolic activity in the frontal lobe
C. smaller ventricles in the brain
D. less activity in the prefrontal cortex

p. 540
Schizophrenia
Level: Moderate
Type: Conceptual
Ans: A

154. What is the best argument that environmental factors play some role in schizophrenia?
A. The risk for developmental schizophrenia in identical twins is less than 100%.
B. The risk for developmental schizophrenia in fraternal twins is less than 100%.
C. Drug treatments are effective in reducing positive symptoms.
D. Schizophrenia appears to run in families.

p. 540
Schizophrenia
Level: Easy
Type: Factual
Ans: B

155. Diathesis refers to a person's:
A. balance of positive to negative symptoms
B. genetic disposition
C. reactions to neuroleptic drugs
D. level of dopamine in the nervous system

p. 540
Schizophrenia
Level: Easy
Type: Factual
Ans: B
*PS/SG 23-17*

156. The diathesis-stress theory of schizophrenia says that some people have a/n:
A. overactive dopamine neurotransmitter system
B. genetic predisposition that interacts with life stressors to cause the disease
C. atypical neuroleptic tendency in their brains
D. overactive diathesis in the prefrontal cortex

p. 540
Schizophrenia
Level: Moderate
Type: Factual
Ans: D

157. Disorganized thinking in schizophrenia may be related to:
A. smaller than normal ventricles
B. over activation of the prefrontal cortex
C. excessive neuron wiring
D. fewer neurons with fewer connections

p. 540
Schizophrenia
Level: Moderate
Type: Factual
Ans: D

158. The current view on the development of schizophrenia is that it is primarily:
A. an inherited disorder
B. due to abnormal levels of neurotransmitters
C. a reaction to the stress of modern life
D. a combination of inherited predispositions that are triggered by environmental stress

p. 540
Schizophrenia
Level: Moderate
Type: Factual
Ans: A

159. The notion that schizophrenics have a genetic predisposition which interacts with life stressors to cause the development of schizophrenia is called the:
A. diathesis stress theory of schizophrenia
B. dopamine theory of schizophrenia
C. concordance theory of schizophrenia
D. cognitive-behavior theory of schizophrenia

p. 541
Schizophrenia
Level: Easy
Type: Factual
Ans: A

160. A patient with schizophrenia displays delusions, hallucinations, and has very distorted speech. These symptoms are examples of:
A. positive symptoms
B. negative symptoms
C. level 1 symptoms
D. level 2 symptoms

p. 541
Schizophrenia
Level: Easy
Type: Factual
Ans: B

161. A patient with schizophrenia shows a loss of normal function such as emotional problems and decreased ability to express thoughts. These symptoms are examples of:
A. positive symptoms
B. negative symptoms
C. level 1 symptoms
D. level 2 symptoms

p. 541
Schizophrenia
Level: Easy
Type: Applied
Ans: C

162. If Dr. Beenken wishes to reduce the positive symptoms in her patients with schizophrenia, she should prescribe:
A. dopamine
B. a benzodiazepine
C. a neuroleptic drug
D. lithium

p. 541
Schizophrenia
Level: Easy
Type: Factual
Ans: D

163. As Laura is preparing for the exam, she keeps in mind that positive symptoms of schizophrenia refer to _____, while negative symptoms refer to _____.
A. environmental causes; biological causes
B. biological causes; environmental causes
C. loss of normal functions; distortion of normal functions
D. distortion of normal functions; loss of normal functions

p. 541
Schizophrenia
Level: Easy
Type: Factual
Ans: D

164. To reduce the level of dopamine activity so that hallucinations and delusions are decreased, psychiatrists may prescribe:
A. lithium
B. benzodiazepines
C. antidepressants
D. typical antipsychotic drugs

p. 541
Schizophrenia
Level: Easy
Type: Factual
Ans: B

165. Typical neuroleptic drugs work by:
A. increasing the level of dopamine
B. decreasing the level of dopamine
C. changing the genetic structure responsible for schizophrenia
D. increasing neural activity throughout the brain

p. 541
Schizophrenia
Level: Easy
Type: Applied
Ans: D

166. During an internship at a mental health clinic, you hear a psychiatrist say, "We need to put Mrs. Smith on a typical neuroleptic drug." You know that this type of drug will:
A. alter the size of her ventricles in the brain
B. reduce serotonin activity in the nervous system
C. increase dopamine activity in the nervous system
D. reduce dopamine activity in the nervous system

p. 541
Schizophrenia
Level: Easy
Type: Factual
Ans: C

167. _____ will reduce positive symptoms, but will have little or no effect on negative symptoms.
A. Benzamides
B. Clozapine
C. Typical neuroleptic drugs
D. Atypical neuroleptic drugs

p. 541
Schizophrenia
Level: Easy
Type: Applied
Ans: D

168. William has been diagnosed with schizophrenia. His doctor wishes to reduce the positive symptoms that William displays. What type of drug should be prescribed for William?
A.   Thorazine (a phenothiazine)
B.   Clozapine
C.   Lithium
D.   an atypical neuroleptic drug

p. 541
Schizophrenia
Level: Easy
Type: Factual
Ans: A

169. The _____ theory of schizophrenia says that the dopamine neurotransmitter system is overactive.
A.   dopamine
B.   bioamine
C.   neuroleptic
D.   biological

p. 541
Schizophrenia
Level: Easy
Type: Factual
Ans: C

170. Kari has been prescribed a typical neuroleptic drug. What part of Kari's brain will be significantly affected by the drug?
A.   corpus callosum
B.   thalamus
C.   basal ganglia
D.   hypothalamus

p. 541
Schizophrenia
Level: Easy
Type: Factual
Ans: B

171. Out of 100 patients with schizophrenia, about how many will not respond to typical neuroleptics?
A.   10
B.   20
C.   30
D.   40

p. 541
Schizophrenia
Level: Easy
Type: Applied
Ans: B

172. If Dr. Price wishes to reduce the serotonin in her patients with schizophrenia, she should prescribe:
A.   dopamine
B.   an atypical neuroleptic drug
C.   a typical neuroleptic drug
D.   lithium

p. 541
Schizophrenia
Level: Easy
Type: Factual
Ans: B

173. The atypical neuroleptic drugs have a significant effect on:
A.   dopamine
B.   serotonin
C.   benzamides
D.   butrophenones

p. 541
Schizophrenia
Level: Easy
Type: Factual
Ans: D

174. _____ will reduce positive symptoms and may slightly improve negative symptoms.
A.   Phenothiazines
B.   Thorazine
C.   Typical neuroleptic drugs
D.   Atypical neuroleptic drugs

p. 541
Schizophrenia
Level: Easy
Type: Factual
Ans: C

175. Atypical neuroleptic drugs are the preferred treatment for schizophrenia since they:
A. increase dopamine activity in the prefrontal cortex
B. are not addictive
C. reduce both positive and negative symptoms
D. do not cause tolerance

p. 541
Schizophrenia
Level: Easy
Type: Factual
Ans: B

176. An example of an atypical neuroleptic is:
A. phenothiazine
B. clozapine
C. haloperodol
D. serotonin

p. 542
Schizophrenia
Level: Easy
Type: Factual
Ans: D

177. Which statement is true of the use of antipsychotic drugs to treat schizophrenia?
A. They do not provide support for the dopamine hypothesis.
B. They bring about a rapid cure for schizophrenics.
C. They make psychotherapy difficult because the patient becomes confused.
D. They may produce serious long-term side effects.

p. 542
Schizophrenia
Level: Easy
Type: Factual
Ans: A
www

178. A woman on a typical neuroleptic for schizophrenia for a long period of time is likely to experience:
A. tardive dyskinesia
B. skin irritation in the sun
C. lower blood pressure
D. grogginess

p. 542
Schizophrenia
Level: Easy
Type: Factual
Ans: C

179. A schizophrenic has taken phenothiazines for a long period of time and has developed tardive dyskinesia. This side effect is manifested by:
A. extreme changes in mood
B. constant agitation
C. uncontrollable movements of the mouth, lips, and limbs
D. hallucinations and delusions

p. 542
Schizophrenia
Level: Moderate
Type: Applied
Ans: C

180. Dixon has been taking a phenothiazine since he was first diagnosed with schizophrenia 10 years ago. What are the chances that he will develop tardive dyskinesia?
A. 5% chance that he will
B. 25% chance that he will
C. 40% chance that he will
D. 65% chance that he will

p. 542
Schizophrenia
Level: Moderate
Type: Applied
Ans: D

181. A patient, who has taken typical neuroleptic drugs for schizophrenia, develops tardive dyskinesia. He is taken off the drug. What are the odds that he will experience the return of tardive dyskinesia?
A. 5% chance that he will
B. 25% chance that he will
C. 50% chance that he will
D. 70% chance that he will

| | | |
|---|---|---|
| p. 542<br>Schizophrenia<br>Level: Moderate<br>Type: Factual<br>Ans: B | 182. | What advantage do the atypical neuroleptic drugs have over the typical neuroleptic drugs? |
| | A. | Only about 25% of patients on atypical neuroleptic drugs develop tardive dyskinesia. |
| | B. | Only about 5% of patients on atypical neuroleptic drugs develop tardive dyskinesia. |
| | C. | Only about 5% of patients on atypical neuroleptic drugs experience a loss of infection-fighting white blood cells. |
| | D. | Only about 5% of patients on atypical neuroleptic drugs develop seizures. |
| p. 542<br>Schizophrenia<br>Level: Moderate<br>Type: Factual<br>Ans: D | 183. | There is good news and bad news about using clozapine to help people with schizophrenia. What is the news? |
| | A. | The good news is that clozapine occurs naturally in some foods; the bad news is that it causes tardive dyskinesia. |
| | B. | The good news is that clozapine can cure schizophrenia; the bad news is that it can cause seizures. |
| | C. | The good news is that the risk for tardive dyskinesia is higher compared to typical neuroleptics; the bad news is that clozapine can cause brain cancer. |
| | D. | The good news is that the risk for tardive dyskinesia is lower than that of typical neuroleptics; the bad news is that clozapine can have the serious side effects. |
| p. 542<br>Schizophrenia<br>Level: Easy<br>Type: Factual<br>Ans: B | 184. | In the long-run, the typical neuroleptics helped about _____ of patients with schizophrenia. |
| | A. | 5-15% |
| | B. | 20-30% |
| | C. | 50-60% |
| | D. | 80-90% |
| p. 542<br>Schizophrenia<br>Level: Moderate<br>Type: Factual<br>Ans: C | 185. | Why should clozapine be allowed to remain available to patients with schizophrenia? |
| | A. | It causes some serious side effects. |
| | B. | There are other less expensive drugs that are much more effective. |
| | C. | A significant portion of those patients receiving it show good improvement. |
| | D. | Up to 90% of patients who receive the drug are cured of schizophrenia. |
| p. 544<br>Dissociative Disorders<br>Level: Easy<br>Type: Factual<br>Ans: B | 186. | A split or breakdown in a person's normally integrated consciousness or identity is indicative of a: |
| | A. | schizophrenic disorder |
| | B. | dissociative disorder |
| | C. | conversion disorder |
| | D. | depressive disorder |
| p. 544<br>Dissociative Disorders<br>Level: Easy<br>Type: Factual<br>Ans: A<br>*PS/SG 23-22* | 187. | The case of "Burt Tate," who turned out to be a missing person named Gene Saunders, illustrates: |
| | A. | dissociative fugue |
| | B. | dissociative amnesia |
| | C. | dissociative identity disorder |
| | D. | multiple personality disorder |

p. 544
Dissociative Disorders
Level: Easy
Type: Applied
Ans: D

188. Norm has been diagnosed with one of the dissociative disorders. Although we don't know the exact diagnosis, we can assume that Norm has experienced:
A. an irrational fear of an object or situation
B. fluctuations between episodes of mania and depression
C. disturbances of thought, attention, motor movements, and perceptions
D. some type of disruption in his consciousness, memory, identity, or perception

p. 544
Dissociative Disorders
Level: Easy
Type: Applied
Ans: B

189. Jared suffered through dissociative amnesia. What does this mean?
A. He has enlarged ventricles.
B. His loss of personal information was due to some stress event.
C. He suddenly left town and adopted a new identify.
D. He forgot some important personal information from drug addiction.

p. 544
Dissociative Disorders
Level: Easy
Type: Factual
Ans: C
*www*

190. The disorder that involves an inability to recall personal information or events is called:
A. dissociative memory
B. dissociative fugue
C. dissociative amnesia
D. obsessive-compulsive disorder

p. 544
Dissociative Disorders
Level: Easy
Type: Factual
Ans: D
*PS/SG 23-23*

191. An underlying cause often reported in dissociative identity disorder is:
A. physical trauma, such as a head injury
B. unstable parents who give their children mixed messages about what they expect
C. a flighty personality along with a tendency to overdramatize every situation
D. severe physical or sexual abuse during childhood

p. 544
Dissociative Disorders
Level: Easy
Type: Applied
Ans: B

192. Following sexual abuse at the age of 15, Lynn forgets her name and identity, and runs away from home assuming a new identify. This is an example of:
A. dissociative amnesia
B. dissociative fugue
C. dissociative identity disorder
D. catatonic schizophrenia

p. 544
Dissociative Disorders
Level: Easy
Type: Factual
Ans: C

193. To make a diagnosis of dissociative amnesia and dissociative fugue:
A. the subject must be committed to a psychiatric hospital
B. the forgotten information must be at least ten years old
C. physicians should rule out physical reasons for the loss of personal information
D. by law, psychologists must administer the Thematic Apperception Test to the subject

p. 544
Dissociative Disorders
Level: Easy
Type: Factual
Ans: B

194. Dissociative fugue occurs when an individual:
A. forgets some of their memories
B. loses all personal memory and assumes a new identity and may be confused about the new, assumed identity
C. loses contact with reality and hallucinates
D. develops more than one personality

p. 544
Dissociative Disorders
Level: Easy
Type: Factual
Ans: B
*PS/SG 23-21*

195. The difference between dissociative amnesia and dissociative fugue is that:
A. in the former you stay in contact with reality; in the latter you become schizophrenic
B. in the former you have memory gaps; in the latter you may wander away and assume a new identity
C. in the former you forget more than in the latter
D. these are really two different terms for the same experience

p. 545
Dissociative Disorders
Level: Easy
Type: Factual
Ans: D

196. Dissociative identity disorder would be placed under what DSM-IV category?
A. Affective Disorders
B. Schizophrenic Disorders
C. Personality Disorders
D. Dissociative Disorders

p. 545
Dissociative Disorders
Level: Easy
Type: Factual
Ans: B

197. Which of the following disorders involves the presence of two or more distinct identities or personality states?
A. depersonalization
B. dissociative identity
C. dissociative fugue
D. multiple trait

p. 545
Dissociative Disorders
Level: Easy
Type: Factual
Ans: A

198. If you were to investigate the case studies of a number of people with dissociative identity disorder, you would probably find that these people:
A. usually demonstrate personalities that are very different from each other
B. usually demonstrate only two personalities
C. are very aware at all times of the various personalities they have
D. often demonstrate personalities that all have a common trait, such as religious fervor

p. 545
Dissociative Disorders
Level: Easy
Type: Factual
Ans: D

199. With regard to the number of world-wide cases of dissociative identity disorder:
A. it has remained relatively stable for the past 100 years
B. the United States has experienced a dramatic decrease compared to other countries
C. Japan is the only industrialized country that has seen an increase in the number of cases
D. an upsurge in the number of reported cases has been seen in the last 25 years

p. 545
Dissociative Disorders
Level: Easy
Type: Factual
Ans: A

200. Before 1970, how many worldwide cases of dissociative identity disorder were reported?
A. 36
B. 109
C. 589
D. 12,562

p. 545
Dissociative Disorders
Level: Easy
Type: Applied
Ans: C
*www*

201.  Which of the following cases is most typical of dissociative identity disorder?
A.  DeeDee - she has a history of generalized anxiety disorder
B.  Ralph - the father of three children
C.  Hope - she has had a number of chronic psychiatric problems before the diagnosis and a history of being abused as a child
D.  Harvey - he was sentenced to life for first-degree murder

p. 545
Dissociative Disorders
Level: Easy
Type: Factual
Ans: B

202.  According to one perspective, people develop dissociative identity disorder:
A.  rapidly in a matter of seconds following trauma
B.  as a way to cope and defend against the trauma of abuse
C.  to create cognitive dissonance
D.  only in childhood

p. 545
Dissociative Disorders
Level: Moderate
Type: Applied
Ans: D

203.  You are conducting research on dissociative identity disorder. You have reviewed many, many cases of the disorder. You note a strong commonality among those women with dissociative identity disorder. What is it?
A.  They come from middle to upper class families.
B.  They were the middle child.
C.  They dropped out of high school.
D.  They were physically or sexually abused during childhood.

p. 545
Dissociative Disorders
Level: Easy
Type: Factual
Ans: A

204.  Treatment of dissociative identity disorder involves:
A.  integration of the various personalities into one unified self
B.  ECT
C.  age regression therapy
D.  atypical neuroleptic drugs

p. 546
Cultural Diversity:
 Interpreting Symptoms
Level: Easy
Type: Factual
Ans: A

205.  Which of the following is false regarding the role of culture in interpreting the symptoms of mental disorders?
A.  Symptoms occur independently of one's own cultural context.
B.  It is rare when culture influences mental disorders.
C.  What might be considered abnormal in one culture could be normal in another culture.
D.  The frequency of mental disorders differ among the countries of the world.

p. 546
Cultural Diversity:
 Interpreting Symptoms
Level: Easy
Type: Factual
Ans: C

206.  A cultural variable that may explain the differences in the percentage of men and percentage of women reporting depression is:
A.  educational opportunities
B.  fear of failure
C.  gender roles
D.  the use of sexist language

p. 546
Cultural Diversity:
 Interpreting Symptoms
Level: Easy
Type: Factual
Ans: B

207.  Which disorder is more common in developed countries than in developing countries?
A.  dissociative fugue
B.  catatonic schizophrenia
C.  depression
D.  dissociative identity disorder

p. 546
Cultural Diversity:
  Interpreting Symptoms
Level: Easy
Type: Factual
Ans: C

208. The stereotypic gender role for women may be related to an increased risk for depression because:
A. the roles stress independence and assertiveness
B. women are more likely to be head of single-parent families
C. the roles reinforce dependence, *not* having control, and being helpless
D. women are taught to be tough, forceful, and to demand loyalty

p. 547
Research Focus:
  Exercise versus Drugs
Level: Easy
Type: Applied
Ans: A
*www*

209. Toni has been in a bad mood for two weeks, has no interest in anything, problems with sleep, and difficulty with concentrating. Toni also doesn't like doing activities that she used to find fun. Toni <u>most</u> likely has:
A. major depression disorder
B. seasonal affective disorder
C. dysthymic disorder
D. cyclothymic disorder

p. 547
Research Focus:
  Exercise versus Drugs
Level: Easy
Type: Factual
Ans: D

210. In the study on the effects of exercise on depression, which of the following was not a level of treatment?
A. 30 minutes of exercise
B. taking an antidepressant
C. meditation
D. combination of exercise and taking an antidepressant

p. 547
Research Focus:
  Exercise versus Drugs
Level: Easy
Type: Factual
Ans: D

211. Based on the study on the effects of exercise, what would be the <u>most</u> effective treatment for depression?
A. reducing carbohydrates from one's diet
B. exercise
C. antidepressant
D. There were no significant differences between the treatments.

p. 547
Research Focus:
  Exercise versus Drugs
Level: Easy
Type: Factual
Ans: A

212. In the study that examined the effectiveness of exercise and drugs on depression, which group experienced the <u>least</u> relapse?
A. exercise
B. antidepressant
C. exercise and antidepressant
D. meditation

p. 548
Application: Dealing with
  Mild Depression
Level: Easy
Type: Factual
Ans: C

213. According to some researchers, the mild depression often experienced by college students is:
A. likely to last for less than a month
B. related more to meeting the expectations of other people than the student's own expectations
C. related more to general distress than major depression
D. likely to be eliminated with time management training

p. 548
Application: Dealing with
  Mild Depression
Level: Easy
Type: Factual
Ans: D

214. One of the factors that increase a college student's vulnerability for developing depression is troubling life events. What is another risk factor?
A. a predisposition to internalize criticism
B. poor social skills
C. unrealistically high expectations for academic performance
D. facing new challenges and threatening situations, events, and feelings

p. 548
Application: Dealing with
  Mild Depression
Level: Easy
Type: Factual
Ans: A

215.  Beck argues that depression results from:
A.  negative thoughts that distort our perceptions and interpretations
B.  a chemical imbalance in the brain
C.  unresolved conflicts between people
D.  unresolved unconscious conflicts regarding inappropriate sexual desires

p. 548
Application: Dealing with
  Mild Depression
Level: Easy
Type: Applied
Ans: C

216.  "Everything I touch I ruin. I am good at nothing. I am an utter failure."
This person has failed to consider the successes in her life and all the good
things that have happened to her. From Aaron Beck's perspective, this
person's thinking best represents:
A.  repression
B.  sublimation
C.  selective attention
D.  neologism

p. 548
Application: Dealing with
  Mild Depression
Level: Easy
Type: Factual
Ans: B
*www*

217.  A therapist tells a mildly depressed individual to work on identifying her
negative, maladaptive thoughts if she wishes to feel better. This
therapist's approach is most associated with:
A.  Freud's psychoanalysis
B.  Beck's cognitive theory of depression
C.  Rogers' client-centered therapy
D.  medical approach

p. 549
Application: Dealing with
  Mild Depression
Level: Easy
Type: Factual
Ans: D

218.  A goal in working with a mildly depressed individual would be to:
A.  learn to prevent unconscious thoughts from entering consciousness
B.  learn how to relax by reducing physical activity
C.  focus on increasing negative thoughts because these are more realistic than
    positive thoughts
D.  break the cycle of being depressed because of poor social skills and others
    not wishing to be around this individual

p. 549
Application: Dealing with
  Mild Depression
Level: Easy
Type: Factual
Ans: C

219.  Depressed people often elicit negative reactions from people. Therefore,
one solution presented in the textbook is to:
A.  ask a psychiatrist for an antidepressant
B.  remind other people that depression can alter one's behavior
C.  replace negative thoughts with positive thoughts of accomplishment so that
    his/her self-esteem increases making him/her more attractive to others
D.  inform those individuals of the depression

p. 549
Application: Dealing with
  Mild Depression
Level: Easy
Type: Factual
Ans: B

220.  All of the following have been suggested as ways of overcoming mild
depression except:
A.  improving social skills
B.  ECT
C.  increasing social support
D.  eliminating negative thoughts

True/False

| F | | 1. | Bipolar disorder involves fluctuations of depression and anxiety. |
|---|-----|-----|---|
| T | | 2. | Dysthymic disorder refers to a mood disorder where the person feels "down in the dumps." |
| T | www | 3. | Monoamines are neurotransmitters involved in mood disorders. |
| T | | 4. | Many patients with bipolar stop taking their medication because they enjoy the mania. |
| F | | 5. | Electroconvulsive therapy is considered the treatment of last resort for schizophrenia. |
| F | | 6. | Personality disorders are very responsive to treatment. |
| T | www | 7. | People with antisocial personality disorder shows no signs of remorse. |
| T | | 8. | Catatonic schizophrenia is characterized by periods of wild excitement and immobility. |
| F | www | 9. | Type I schizophrenia includes having negative symptoms. |
| T | | 10. | Neologism is the formation of new words. |
| T | www | 11. | There is a strong genetic basis to schizophrenia. |
| F | | 12. | The diathesis stress theory illustrates the primary role that genetics play in schizophrenia. |
| T | www | 13. | Schizophrenia is associated with large ventricle size. |
| T | | 14. | A positive symptom of schizophrenia is distorted thinking. |
| F | www | 15. | Typical narcoleptics reduce negative symptoms, but not positive symptoms. |
| F | | 16. | Tardive dyskinesia is a type of schizophrenia. |
| F | | 17. | Atypical narcoleptics cause tardive dyskinesia in most patients with schizophrenia. |
| F | www | 18. | The dissociative disorders involve hallucinations and delusions. |
| T | | 19. | In dissociative fugue, the individual travels away from home. |
| T | www | 20. | A common factor in many cases of dissociative identity disorder is childhood abuse. |
| F | | 21. | The number of cases worldwide of dissociative identity disorder has remained stable over the last 100 years. |
| F | www | 22. | The suicide rate in the U.S. is twice that of China. |
| F | | 23. | Cultural has little influence on mental disorders. |
| T | www | 24. | Mild depression in college students is typically related to facing new and challenging situations. |
| F | | 25. | Beck's treatment of depression is based on the idea that depression is related to serotonin. |

Short-Answer Essay Questions

1.   Discuss the similarities and differences among major depression, Bipolar I, and dysthymic disorders. (www)
2.   Describe the genetic factors and psychosocial factors involved in depression.
3.   What are the most effective treatments for depression and bipolar disorder?  (www)
4.   Why is the treatment of antisocial personality disorder so difficult in the long-term?
5.   Describe the subcategories of schizophrenia by presenting cases that illustrates their characteristics.
6.   Describe the diathesis stress theory of schizophrenia.  Include a brief discussion of the neurological/genetic and environmental causes of the disorder. (www)

7. What are the advantages and disadvantages of using typical and atypical narcoleptics to treat schizophrenia?

8. Contrast dissociative amnesia and dissociative fugue. (www)

9. Explain how gender roles influence the rate of mood disorders among females and males.

10. Describe the approach taken by Beck to treat mild depression. (www)

# Module 24 - Therapies

p. 555
Introduction
Level: Moderate
Type: Factual
Ans: D

1. What case played an important role in the development of psychoanalysis?
   A. Little Albert
   B. Phineas Gage
   C. Sybil
   D. Anna O.

p. 555
Introduction
Level: Easy
Type: Conceptual
Ans: B
*PS/SG 24-1*

2. Rod Plotnik begins the module with the story of Anna O. to make the point that:
   A. Freud had some notable failures as well as famous successes
   B. talking about your problems seems to help
   C. the real credit for inventing psychoanalysis should go to Dr. Breuer
   D. talking won't help unless the client also does something positive

p. 555
Introduction
Level: Easy
Type: Factual
Ans: A

3. The case of Anna O. allowed Freud to:
   A. develop his treatment approach called psychoanalysis
   B. see how incorrect his treatment ideas were
   C. test his new technique called systematic desensitization
   D. conduct experiments on hysteria

p. 555
Introduction
Level: Easy
Type: Factual
Ans: B

4. What happened to Anna's symptoms when she recalled her painful past experiences in therapy?
   A. They disappeared for a time, but reemerged as different symptoms
   B. Her symptoms disappeared
   C. Her hallucinations intensified
   D. She had to be committed to a mental hospital

p. 555
Introduction
Level: Easy
Type: Conceptual
Ans: A

5. Anna O.'s case is important because it reflects Freud's premise that:
   A. emotional problems originate in the unconscious
   B. Americans will pay money to have someone listen to their problems
   C. emotional problems are conditioned
   D. thoughts play no role in psychological problems

p. 555
Introduction
Level: Easy
Type: Factual
Ans: C
*www*

6. Freud believed that Anna's symptoms were caused by:
   A. a conditioned emotional reaction
   B. low self-efficacy
   C. strong, primitive unconscious sexual desires
   D. a hormonal dysfunction

p. 555
Introduction
Level: Moderate
Type: Factual
Ans: A

7. What case played an important role in the development of behavior therapy?
   A. Little Albert
   B. Phineas Gage
   C. Sybil
   D. Anna O.

p. 555
Introduction
Level: Moderate
Type: Factual
Ans: C

8. The case of Little Albert was important in the development of
A. cognitive therapy
B. psychoanalysis
C. behavior therapy
D. client centered therapy

p. 555
Introduction
Level: Easy
Type: Conceptual
Ans: C

9. By what mechanism did Little Albert come to fear a white rat?
A. inferiority complex
B. failure to fulfill deficiency needs
C. conditioning
D. unresolved conflicts

p. 555
Introduction
Level: Easy
Type: Factual
Ans: B

10. Little Albert was conditioned to:
A. sit in a trance-like state
B. fear a rat
C. unlearn his fear of a rat
D. be unresponsive to a rat

p. 555
Introduction
Level: Easy
Type: Conceptual
Ans: D
*PS/SG 24-2*

11. John B. Watson's famous experiment with Little Albert was designed to show that:
A. ethical standards of psychological research are much more stringent today
B. psychological problems affect babies as well as children and adults
C. fear of rats is almost natural and may be inborn
D. emotional problems can be viewed as learned behavior

p. 555
Introduction
Level: Easy
Type: Factual
Ans: D

12. Which psychologist conditioned Little Albert to fear a rat?
A. Aaron Beck
B. Sigmund Freud
C. Carl Rogers
D. John Watson

p. 555
Introduction
Level: Easy
Type: Factual
Ans: A

13. The case of Little Albert demonstrated that:
A. emotional problems may develop through conditioning
B. manifest content is related to latent content
C. serotonin may play a role in fear
D. unconscious conflicts can lead to emotional problems

p. 556
Historical Background
Level: Easy
Type: Factual
Ans: B

14. Out of 50 states, how many do not require the licensing of therapists?
A. 17
B. 22
C. 30
D. 37

p. 556
Historical Background
Level: Easy
Type: Factual
Ans: A
*www*

15. Verbal interaction between therapist and client, a supportive relationship, and analysis of the client's experiences are the three characteristics of:
A. psychotherapy
B. deinstitutionalization
C. meta-analysis
D. transference

| | | |
|---|---|---|
| p. 556<br>Historical Background<br>Level: Moderate<br>Type: Conceptual<br>Ans: C | 16.<br><br><br>A.<br><br>B.<br>C.<br><br>D. | Psychotherapy can be described by three characteristics. Of the statements said by a therapist presented below, which is <u>not</u> among the three characteristics?<br>"Mr. Bear, yesterday you were talking about some of your problems with authority figures. Please continue."<br>"Now, Mrs. Rosenberg, let us talk about your problems."<br>"This therapy consists of forming a personal relationship with your therapists."<br>"Mr. Jones, I would you suggest you set more realistic goals." |
| p. 556<br>Historical Background<br>Level: Moderate<br>Type: Factual<br>Ans: C | 17.<br>A.<br>B.<br>C.<br>D. | During the middle ages, schizophrenics were called:<br>schizophrenics<br>neurotics<br>lunatics<br>idiots |
| p. 556<br>Historical Background<br>Level: Easy<br>Type: Factual<br>Ans: C | 18.<br><br>A.<br>B.<br>C.<br>D. | The typical treatment of individuals with schizophrenics in the 15$^{th}$ to 17$^{th}$ century was:<br>bloodletting<br>exercise and fresh air<br>confinement to asylums or hospitals<br>phenothiazines |
| p. 556<br>Historical Background<br>Level: Moderate<br>Type: Applied<br>Ans: A | 19.<br><br>A.<br>B.<br>C.<br>D. | If you were diagnosed with schizophrenia in the 1600's, you would probably be:<br>put in a straitjacket<br>treated humanely<br>treated at a community mental health center<br>treated with Thorazine |
| p. 556<br>Historical Background<br>Level: Moderate<br>Type: Applied<br>Ans: C | 20.<br><br><br>A.<br>B.<br>C.<br>D. | It is the late 1700s, and you are a colleague of Dr. Benjamin Rush. He invites you into his study to show his therapeutic tool to calm patients down. What does he show you?<br>an antianxiety drug<br>a straitjacket<br>the "tranquilizing chair"<br>an herbal blend |
| p. 556<br>Historical Background<br>Level: Easy<br>Type: Factual<br>Ans: D | 21.<br>A.<br>B.<br>C.<br>D. | Dr. Benjamin Rush tried to cure patients by:<br>teaching them coping skills<br>analyzing their dreams<br>injecting them with neuroleptic drugs<br>drawing large amounts of blood over a period of time from patients |
| p. 556<br>Historical Background<br>Level: Easy<br>Type: Factual<br>Ans: A | 22.<br><br>A.<br>B.<br>C.<br>D. | What did Dorothea Dix do for the treatment of mental patients during the 1800s?<br>She fought for humane treatment.<br>She argued that mental patients could be treated in their homes.<br>She began the process of deinstitutionalization.<br>She developed the country's first community mental health center. |

p. 556
Historical Background
Level: Easy
Type: Factual
Ans: C
*PS/SG 24-3*

23.    In the history of the treatment of mental illness, Dorothea Dix is famous for:
A.    charging admission to watch the crazy antics of the "lunatics"
B.    inventing early treatment techniques like the straitjacket and bleeding
C.    publicizing the terrible living conditions and poor treatment of the mentally ill
D.    emptying the mental hospitals of almost half of their patients

p. 556
Historical Background
Level: Easy
Type: Factual
Ans: D

24.    Dorothea Dix's efforts were important in the development of:
A.    antipsychotic drugs
B.    the tranquilizing chair
C.    institutionalization
D.    moral therapy

p. 556
Historical Background
Level: Easy
Type: Factual
Ans: B
*www*

25.    "Let us take these mental patients and treat them with dignity and give them a relaxed and decent environment." This approach to treatment is known as:
A.    psychoanalysis
B.    moral therapy
C.    cognitive therapy
D.    desensitization

p. 556
Historical Background
Level: Moderate
Type: Applied
Ans: D

26.    Who might have written, "These patients are humans. Thus we must treat them humanly. Let their stay with us be pleasant and relaxing."?
A.    Benjamin Rush
B.    Aaron Beck
C.    Sigmund Freud
D.    Dorothea Dix

p. 556
Historical Background
Level: Easy
Type: Factual
Ans: C

27.    Who is most closely associated with the moral treatment movement?
A.    Sigmund Freud
B.    Aaron Beck
C.    Dorothea Dix
D.    Carl Rogers

p. 556
Historical Background
Level: Moderate
Type: Conceptual
Ans: D

28.    Professor White is writing a book to describe the mental hospitals of the late 1800s. Knowing what you do about that era, what title would you recommend to Professor White for her book?
A.    *Using Behavior Therapy in Mental Hospitals of the Late 1800s*
B.    *Blood Letting as the Preferred Treatment in Mental Hospitals*
C.    *Treatment for Mentally Disturbed Patients in the Late 1800s: Pleasant Settings*
D.    *Snake Pits: "Caring" for the Mentally Ill in the Late 1800s*

p. 556
Historical Background
Level: Easy
Type: Factual
Ans: A

29.    Peaking in the 1950s, psychoanalysis was more effective in treating _____ than _____.
A.    less serious disorders; more serious disorders
B.    males; females
C.    middle-class patients; lower-class patients
D.    psychosis; neurosis

p. 556
Historical Background
Level: Easy
Type: Factual
Ans: C

30. Which of the following is an accurate representation of the life of a mental patient in the early 1900s?
A. Mental patients were sentenced to prison.
B. Hospitals sold tickets so people could come and observe the behavior of mental patients.
C. Mental patients were kept in huge, overcrowded hospitals with little supervision.
D. Hospitals used drug therapy to treat mental patients.

p. 557
Historical Background
Level: Easy
Type: Factual
Ans: B

31. Of the following historical figures, who is most responsible for introducing drugs into the treatment of mental disorders?
A. Sigmund Freud
B. Henri Laborit
C. Benjamin Rush
D. Francine Shapiro

p. 557
Historical Background
Level: Easy
Type: Factual
Ans: C

32. The initial use of chlorpromazine was to:
A. lower blood pressure
B. treat epilepsy
C. calm down a schizophrenic patient before surgery
D. treat the side effects of ECT

p. 557
Historical Background
Level: Easy
Type: Factual
Ans: D

33. The _____ are a group of drugs that reduce the effects of the neurotransmitter dopamine and are used to reduce schizophrenic symptoms.
A. bioamines
B. catacholamines
C. monoamines
D. phenothiazines

p. 557
Historical Background
Level: Easy
Type: Factual
Ans: B
*PS/SG 24-4*

34. The effect of the phenothiazines on schizophrenics is to:
A. increase the effects of the neurotransmitter dopamine
B. reduce symptoms like delusions and hallucinations
C. promote clearer thinking, but at the cost of longer hospital stays
D. promote clearer thinking, but at the cost of emotional agitation

p. 557
Historical Background
Level: Easy
Type: Factual
Ans: B
*www*

35. The phenothiazines are effective in reducing schizophrenic symptoms by:
A. reducing the size of brain ventricles
B. blocking or reducing the effects of dopamine
C. increasing the effects of dopamine
D. blocking or reducing the effects of hormones

p. 557
Historical Background
Level: Easy
Type: Factual
Ans: B

36. The mental health system in the 1950s was marked by:
A. the development of the community mental health center
B. the development and use of antipsychotic drugs
C. an increase in the number of institutionalized mental patients
D. an increase in the severity of symptoms displayed by mental patients

p. 557
Historical Background
Level: Easy
Type: Factual
Ans: A

*PS/SG 24-5*

37. The discovery of antipsychotic drugs led directly to:
A.  deinstitutionalization
B.  the reform movement
C.  reinstitutionalization
D.  the community mental health center

p. 557
Historical Background
Level: Moderate
Type: Factual
Ans: A

38. There was a dramatic decrease in the number of patients in mental hospitals during the 1950's and continuing to the present. This is primarily due to:
A.  deinstitutionalization
B.  admissions to mental hospitals made lenient
C.  the moral treatment movements
D.  psychoanalysis

p. 557
Historical Background
Level: Moderate
Type: Factual
Ans: C

39. In 1950, there were _____ patients in mental hospitals. In 1970, there were _____ patients in mental hospitals.
A.  1,000,000; 555,000
B.  555,000; 750,000
C.  550,000; 150,000
D.  100,000; 5,000

p. 557
Historical Background
Level: Easy
Type: Factual
Ans: C

40. In 2000, there were ____ patients in mental hospitals. Deinstitutionalization has _____ that number over the last 40 years.
A.  1,000,000; reduced
B.  10,000; reduced
C.  80,000; reduced
D.  100,000; increased

p. 557
Historical Background
Level: Easy
Type: Factual
Ans: D

41. The term deinstitutionalization refers to:
A.  moving mental patients from the prisons into mental hospitals
B.  the dramatic increase in the number of mental patients during the 1950s
C.  offering low-cost mental health care to a community
D.  releasing mental patients from mental hospitals and returning them to the community

p. 557
Historical Background
Level: Easy
Type: Factual
Ans: C

42. The goal of deinstitutionalization was to:
A.  improve the training of mental health professionals
B.  test a new form of psychotherapy
C.  get patients back into the community
D.  reduce the amount of money spent on mental patients

p. 557
Historical Background
Level: Easy
Type: Factual
Ans: D

43. Many former mental patients have ended up in the street as America's homeless. Which of the following is probably at least partially responsible?
A.  the failures of psychoanalysis
B.  moral treatment movement
C.  community mental health centers
D.  deinstitutionalization

p. 557
Historical Background
Level: Easy
Type: Factual
Ans: B
*PS/SG 24-6*

44. Deinstitutionalization has led to homelessness, a sad result best explained by a(n):
A. side effect of antipsychotic drugs that makes schizophrenics afraid to be inside
B. lack of funding and adequate supervision of halfway houses
C. reluctance of families to allow the "crazies" to come home again
D. high cost of treatment in community mental health centers

p. 557
Historical Background
Level: Easy
Type: Factual
Ans: C

45. Community mental health centers are:
A. large mental hospitals which house hundreds of patients
B. half-way houses for mental patients
C. places for mental patients who do not need in-patient hospitalization
D. facilities which perform electric shock therapy

p. 557
Historical Background
Level: Easy
Type: Factual
Ans: B

46. Marty requires some professional help, but cannot afford it. He should seek help at:
A. the nearest welfare office
B. his local community mental health center
C. the Department of Social Services
D. the nearest psychiatric hospital

p. 557
Historical Background
Level: Easy
Type: Factual
Ans: C

47. Community mental health centers were introduced to provide:
A. backup services to psychiatric hospitals
B. intense psychoanalytical treatment
C. treatment for the underprivileged and to focus on detection and prevention of psychological problems
D. settings to conduct clinical research

p. 557
Historical Background
Level: Easy
Type: Factual
Ans: A

48. Community mental health centers focus on:
A. early detection and prevention
B. conducting clinical research
C. intense psychoanalysis
D. anxiety disorders

p. 557
Historical Background
Level: Easy
Type: Conceptual
Ans: D

49. Karl is going to visit the local community mental health center. He is most likely to see a:
A. psychiatric nurse
B. psychoanalyst
C. psychiatrist
D. clinical psychologist

p. 558
Questions About
  Psychotherapy
Level: Easy
Type: Factual
Ans: B

50. How many Americans each year need help in dealing with problems, according to the American Psychological Association?
A. 2 million
B. 30 million
C. 50 million
D. 80 million

<table>
<tr><td>

p. 558

Questions About
 Psychotherapy

Level: Easy

Type: Factual

Ans: B

</td><td>

51.   When should a person seek help for some psychological or behavioral problem?

A.   When other people indicate that help should be sought.

B.   When the problem starts to interfere with the person's interactions and activities.

C.   When thoughts of suicide first surface.

D.   When many days of being depressed pass.

</td></tr>
</table>

---

p. 558

Questions About
 Psychotherapy

Level: Easy

Type: Factual

Ans: C

52. What percentage of Americans with psychological problems <u>do not</u> seek help?

A. 10%

B. 20%

C. 40%

D. 50%

---

p. 558

Questions About
 Psychotherapy

Level: Easy

Type: Factual

Ans: A

53. According to the textbook, what is a reason why so many individuals who need help do not seek it?

A. social stigma attached to having a mental disorder

B. difficulty recognizing the point at which people see they need help

C. most people know that no effective treatments exist for mental disorders

D. most disorders are so severe that the person loses touch with reality

---

p. 558

Questions About
 Psychotherapy

Level: Easy

Type: Factual

Ans: D

54. A therapist with an MD is most likely a:

A. neurologist

B. psychoanalyst

C. clinical psychologist

D. psychiatrist

---

p. 558

Questions About
 Psychotherapy

Level: Easy

Type: Factual

Ans: A

55. Which of the following type of therapists is most likely to have a Ph.D.?

A. clinical psychologist

B. psychiatrist

C. psychoanalyst

D. neurologist

---

p. 558

Questions About
 Psychotherapy

Level: Easy

Type: Factual

Ans: B

56. If Dr. Crane views psychological disorders as diseases to be treated with drugs, it is likely that Dr. Crane is:

A. in agreement with current beliefs in psychotherapy

B. a psychiatrist

C. a clinical psychologist

D. a psychoanalyst

<table>
<tr><td>

p. 558
Questions About
  Psychotherapy
Level: Easy
Type: Factual
Ans: C

</td><td>

**57.** The major difference between a clinical and a counseling psychologist is that:
A. clinical psychologists prescribe medication
B. clinical psychologists deal more with problems of living than with mental disorders
C. counseling psychologists place less emphasis on research and experimental method
D. counseling psychologists place more emphasis on the experimental method and research

</td></tr>
<tr><td>

p. 558
Questions About
  Psychotherapy
Level: Easy
Type: Conceptual
Ans: D

</td><td>

**58.** "As a psychologist, I am interested in conducting outcome research studies of various therapies in treating test anxiety." This psychologist is most likely to be a:
A. developmental psychologist
B. counseling psychologist
C. psychiatric psychologist
D. clinical psychologist

</td></tr>
<tr><td>

p. 558
Questions About
  Psychotherapy
Level: Easy
Type: Factual
Ans: D
*www*

</td><td>

**59.** A clinical psychologist has:
A. an MD degree
B. graduated from medical school
C. extensive training in medicine and drugs
D. completed a Ph.D. program

</td></tr>
<tr><td>

p. 558
Questions About
  Psychotherapy
Level: Easy
Type: Applied
Ans: B

</td><td>

**60.** Anita is a junior in college and has been seeing a therapist at the university's health clinic because of feeling homesick. What is the most likely type of professional Anita is seeing?
A. psychiatrist
B. counseling psychologist
C. psychoanalyst
D. clinical social worker

</td></tr>
<tr><td>

p. 558
Questions About
  Psychotherapy
Level: Easy
Type: Factual
Ans: D

</td><td>

**61.** Jenny wants to be a therapist who focuses on people who have problems of living. You would suggest she investigate the career of:
A. psychiatrist
B. psychoanalyst
C. clinical social worker
D. counseling psychologist

</td></tr>
<tr><td>

p. 558
Questions About
  Psychotherapy
Level: Easy
Type: Factual
Ans: A

</td><td>

**62.** If you wanted to choose a therapist who had the most extensive training in basic psychology and the experimental method, you should choose a:
A. clinical psychologist
B. psychiatrist
C. psychoanalyst
D. social worker

</td></tr>
</table>

p. 558
Questions About
 Psychotherapy
Level: Easy
Type: Factual
Ans: C

63.     What was the result of a trial program in which clinical psychologists were
        trained to prescribe drugs?
A.      Clinical psychologists should not be allowed to prescribe drugs since very
        few MD's would be willing to train them.
B.      Clinical psychologists should be allowed to prescribe drugs without any
        additional training.
C.      Clinical psychologists who are properly trained can safely provide drug
        treatment.
D.      Because of their theoretical orientation, clinical psychologists should not be
        allowed to prescribe drugs.

p. 559
Questions About
 Psychotherapy
Level: Easy
Type: Factual
Ans: B

64.     What therapy focuses on the therapist and client talking about the client's
        symptoms and trying to identify the cause of the problem?
A.      cognitive-behavior therapy
B.      insight therapy
C.      medical therapy
D.      the eclectic approach

p. 559
Questions About
 Psychotherapy
Level: Easy
Type: Factual
Ans: C

65.     The popularity of _____ has declined in the last few years.
A.      psychotherapy
B.      antipsychotic drugs
C.      psychoanalysis
D.      the eclectic approach

p. 559
Questions About
 Psychotherapy
Level: Easy
Type: Factual
Ans: A

66.     Which therapy applies the principles of learning to address the client's
        problems?
A.      cognitive-behavior therapy
B.      insight therapy
C.      medical therapy
D.      gestalt approach

p. 559
Questions About
 Psychotherapy
Level: Easy
Type: Factual
Ans: C

67.     Which therapy focuses on the client's thoughts?
A.      behavior therapy
B.      meta therapy
C.      cognitive-behavior therapy
D.      medical therapy

p. 559
Questions About
 Psychotherapy
Level: Easy
Type: Factual
Ans: B
www

68.     In practice, most therapists:
A.      adopt one technique early in their careers and rarely change
B.      use a combination of approaches, rather than a single one
C.      use one approach at a time, but shift between methods according to what is
        currently popular
D.      have an approach of their own that does not resemble any of the classic
        approaches

p. 559
Questions About
  Psychotherapy
Level: Easy
Type: Factual
Ans: C

69. An eclectic approach to psychotherapy involves using techniques that are:
A. unique to a particular therapist
B. determined by the personality of a particular therapist
C. borrowed from a number of different approaches
D. beneficial to a small number of patients only

p. 559
Questions About
  Psychotherapy
Level: Easy
Type: Factual
Ans: C
*PS/SG 24-9*

70. When asked which approach they use in therapy, a majority of psychologists indicated a preference for the _____ approach.
A. psychodynamic
B. behavioral
C. eclectic
D. cognitive

p. 559
Questions About
  Psychotherapy
Level: Easy
Type: Applied
Ans: B

71. Pauline is seeking therapy for her depression. One professional she visits says that he will use a variety of techniques from different therapeutic approaches. Since Pauline has taken an introductory psychology course, she correctly identifies this therapist to take a(n) _____ approach to therapy.
A. client-centered
B. eclectic
C. cognitive
D. behavioral

p. 559
Questions About
  Psychotherapy
Level: Easy
Type: Factual
Ans: D

72. Dr. Dodson uses a variety of insight therapy techniques along with some directive techniques from the cognitive-behavioral approach. Dr. Dodson sounds like he has a(n) _____ approach to therapy.
A. moral movement
B. medical
C. meta-analytical
D. eclectic

p. 559
Questions About
  Psychotherapy
Level: Easy
Type: Factual
Ans: B

73. _____ therapy involves using various psychoactive drugs to treat mental disorders.
A. Moral
B. Medical
C. Meta-analytical
D. Eclectic

p. 559
Questions About
  Psychotherapy
Level: Easy
Type: Factual
Ans: B

74. Your friend believes that psychotherapy is useless and that emotional problems are just as likely to go away without treatment. You disagree because evaluation studies have found that psychotherapy:
A. has an approximate success rate of 50 percent
B. is more effective than no treatment
C. is more effective than drug therapy
D. may be effective because the patient expects it to be effective

p. 559
Questions About
 Psychotherapy
Level: Easy
Type: Factual
Ans: B

75. Of all the patients treated with psychotherapy, approximately what percentage showed <u>no</u> improvement in behavior?
A. 1-5%
B. 10-20%
C. 50-60%
D. 85-95%

p. 559
Questions About
 Psychotherapy
Level: Easy
Type: Factual
Ans: A

76. Meta-analysis is a procedure used to:
A. determine the effectiveness of some treatment across many studies
B. help the patient become aware of and understand the causes of his or her problem
C. identify which mental patients should be deinstitutionalized, and which should not
D. gradually expose a patient to a feared object while simultaneously practicing relaxation

p. 559
Questions About
 Psychotherapy
Level: Moderate
Type: Factual
Ans: A

77. Which of the following statements is <u>true</u> regarding the effectiveness of psychotherapy?
A. There is little significant difference between the different treatment approaches.
B. About 30-50% of clients who receive psychotherapy show great improvement.
C. Some forms of psychotherapy are no more effective than just being placed on a waiting list.
D. The most effective form of psychotherapy is psychoanalysis.

p. 559
Questions About
 Psychotherapy
Level: Easy
Type: Factual
Ans: A
*PS/SG 24-10*

78. How effective is psychotherapy? Studies suggest that psychotherapy is:
A. an effective treatment for many mental disorders
B. no more effective than just waiting
C. no more effective than doing nothing
D. an effective treatment, but only if continued for more than a year

p. 559
Questions About
 Psychotherapy
Level: Easy
Type: Factual
Ans: D

79. When is the greatest amount of improvement likely to occur following psychotherapy?
A. the year following psychotherapy
B. it depends on the disorder and the type of psychotherapy
C. several years following psychotherapy
D. by the end of six months of psychotherapy

p. 560
Insight Therapies
Level: Easy
Type: Factual
Ans: A

80. What therapeutic approach focuses on threatening thoughts and desires that lead to unconscious conflicts that create mental disorders?
A. psychoanalysis
B. client-centered therapy
C. cognitive therapy
D. behavior therapy

p. 560
Insight Therapies
Level: Easy
Type: Factual
Ans: C

81. Psychoanalysis was developed by:
A. John Watson
B. Carl Rogers
C. Sigmund Freud
D. Albert Ellis

p. 560
Insight Therapies
Level: Moderate
Type: Factual
Ans: D

82. Freud believed that one of the essential requirements for improvement was the client's reaching:
A. a new consciousness of the needs of others
B. fulfillment of sexual fantasies
C. self-actualization
D. insight into the causes of the individual's problem

p. 560
Insight Therapies
Level: Easy
Type: Factual
Ans: A
*PS/SG 24-11*

83. The central idea of Freud's psychoanalysis is that each of us has a(n):
A. unconscious part that contains hidden, threatening desires or thoughts
B. conscious mind containing ideas that can be clarified and made more logical
C. history of learned behavior patterns that reveals why we act in certain ways
D. need to grow and develop our full potential as human beings

p. 560
Insight Therapies
Level: Easy
Type: Factual
Ans: C
*www*

84. Psychoanalysis argues that the primary reason for the development of psychological problems is:
A. irrational thoughts and beliefs
B. poor learning history
C. unconscious conflicts
D. lack of unconditional positive regard in the person's life

p. 560
Insight Therapies
Level: Easy
Type: Factual
Ans: C
*PS/SG 24-12*

85. In a typical therapy session, the role of the analyst illustrates all the following assumptions of psychoanalysis *except:*
A. free association
B. interpretation
C. schedules of reinforcement
D. unconscious conflicts

p. 560
Insight Therapies
Level: Moderate
Type: Factual
Ans: D

86. A primary assumption of psychoanalysis is:
A. the client's negative self-statements cause psychological problems
B. a lack of self-actualization leads to mental disorders
C. that therapy must desensitize the client to feared objects
D. unconscious conflicts lead to symptoms

p. 560
Insight Therapies
Level: Easy
Type: Conceptual
Ans: A

87. A psychoanalyst would view a phobia as a symptom of:
A. some unconscious conflict
B. an irrational belief
C. other anxieties in the person's life
D. a poorly learned behavior

p. 560
Insight Therapies
Level: Moderate
Type: Conceptual
Ans: A

88. A person displays an uncontrollable fear of spiders. Freudian analysis would suggest that this fear stems from:
A. an unconscious conflict that manifests itself as a fear of spiders
B. a negative first-hand experience with spiders
C. seeing someone else have a negative experience with spiders
D. an expectation based on the archetypal symbol of spiders as evil

p. 560
Insight Therapies
Level: Easy
Type: Factual
Ans: C

89. From psychoanalysis' perspective, mental disorders are treated:
A. by unlearning conditioned emotional responses
B. as problems of living caused by societal inequities
C. by the patient gaining insight into his or her unconscious conflicts
D. using the principles of learning

p. 560
Insight Therapies
Level: Easy
Type: Factual
Ans: D

90. Freud used techniques which would:
A. modify environmental consequences
B. polarize thinking in order to prevent rational emotive thoughts
C. censor unacceptable material
D. provide clues to unconscious conflicts and repressed thoughts

p. 560
Insight Therapies
Level: Easy
Type: Factual
Ans: A

91. Which of the following is not a technique developed by Freud as a part of psychoanalytic treatment?
A. progressive relaxation
B. free association
C. analysis of slips of the tongue
D. dream interpretation

p. 560
Insight Therapies
Level: Easy
Type: Factual
Ans: C

92. Freud believed that his psychoanalytic techniques would lead to:
A. more rational thoughts
B. an emphasis on observable behavior
C. a reaction from the patient to see the therapist as a substitute parent, lover, or another significant other
D. changes in the serotonin levels

p. 561
Insight Therapies
Level: Moderate
Type: Factual
Ans: C

93. "My cousin has many maladaptive thoughts that probably arise from some unconscious thought or conflicts." According to Freud, this cousin experiences:
A. resistance
B. conditional positive regard
C. neuroses
D. cognitive dissonance

p. 561
Insight Therapies
Level: Easy
Type: Factual
Ans: A
*PS/SG 24-14*

94. Freud used dream interpretation because he thought dreams represent:
A. the purest form of free association
B. sick thinking, which needs to be corrected
C. nonsensical ideas, which the therapist should expose
D. the souls of deceased ancestors attempting to speak to us and help us

p. 561
Insight Therapies
Level: Moderate
Type: Factual
Ans: C

95. A person decides to seek help through psychoanalysis. In the interactions between the person and the therapist, the therapist might use free association, which means, the person is:
A. asked a series of specific questions regarding his or her childhood
B. given a number of specific suggestions regarding ways to improve his or her behavior
C. encouraged to say anything he or she chooses
D. taught ways to avoid harmful thoughts

p. 561
Insight Therapies
Level: Easy
Type: Factual
Ans: B

96. Freud used free association in psychoanalysis because he believed that:
A. the client's constant talking would be relaxing and reduce anxiety
B. the associations would give clues to the unconscious cause of the problem
C. the associations could be used to change negative self-beliefs
D. the associations would ultimately lead to self-denial

p. 561
Insight Therapies
Level: Easy
Type: Factual
Ans: A

97. Which therapy allows the client to say anything that comes to mind?
A. psychoanalysis
B. behavior therapy
C. client-centered therapy
D. medical therapy

p. 561
Insight Therapies
Level: Easy
Type: Factual
Ans: C
*www*

98. What technique did Freud use with Rat Man that was described in the textbook?
A. token economy
B. analysis of transference
C. free association
D. dream interpretation

p. 561
Insight Therapies
Level: Moderate
Type: Applied
Ans: D
*PS/SG 24-15*

99. Transference and resistance are technical terms for what happens in therapy, but perceptive students may also recognize the workings of these processes in their own:
A. thoughts about trying a new school despite their parents' objections
B. attempts to apply knowledge gained in one course to the next higher course
C. desires to find and win over a new sweetheart
D. feelings about their instructors and troubles with some courses

p. 561
Insight Therapies
Level: Easy
Type: Factual
Ans: C

100. Freud believed that _____ represented the purest form of free association.
A. irrational thoughts
B. meta-analysis
C. dreams
D. unconscious conflicts

p. 561
Insight Therapies
Level: Easy
Type: Factual
Ans: D

101. Freud based his psychoanalysis on:
A. correlational studies
B. the experiments of Jung and Rogers
C. a solid foundation of experiments
D. his case studies

p. 561
Insight Therapies
Level: Easy
Type: Factual
Ans: C

102.    One of the most serious criticisms against psychoanalysis was that it was based on:

A.    cross-sectional studies
B.    longitudinal studies
C.    case studies
D.    controlled experiments conducted in Europe, not the United States

p. 562
Insight Therapies
Level: Moderate
Type: Factual
Ans: D

103.    The Rat Man called Freud a "substitute mother."  This best illustrates

A.    empathy
B.    resistance
C.    cognitive dissonance
D.    transference

p. 562
Insight Therapies
Level: Moderate
Type: Factual
Ans: A
*www*

104.    According to psychoanalysts, transference and _____ are two essential problems in improving a patient's mental health.

A.    resistance
B.    polarized thinking
C.    meta-analysis
D.    Freudian slips

p. 562
Insight Therapies
Level: Easy
Type: Factual
Ans: C

105.    The process of projecting onto one's therapist conflict-ridden emotions that one felt toward important people during childhood is called:

A.    free association
B.    resistance
C.    transference
D.    insight

p. 562
Insight Therapies
Level: East
Type: Factual
Ans: D

106.    During his psychoanalysis, Brian reacts to his therapist in the same way he reacted to his mother.  Freud would describe this reaction as:

A.    resistance
B.    conditional positive regard
C.    undesirable
D.    transference

p. 562
Insight Therapies
Level: Easy
Type: Factual
Ans: C
*www*

107.    Many clients have the temporary experience of falling in love with their therapists.  Freud would consider such feelings an example of:

A.    resistance
B.    free association
C.    transference
D.    insight

p. 562
Insight Therapies
Level: Moderate
Type: Factual
Ans: D

108.    Freud believed that one of the main duties of the analyst was to help the patient work through:

A.    meta-analysis
B.    polarized thoughts
C.    irrational interpretations
D.    transference

p. 562
Insight Therapies
Level: Easy
Type: Factual
Ans: B

109. What happens if the feelings involved in transference are not resolved?
A. the patient develops neuroses
B. therapy will be stalled
C. the patient becomes desensitized to therapy
D. irrational interpretations lead to polarized thinking

p. 562
Insight Therapies
Level: Moderate
Type: Applied
Ans: D

110. In working out his transference, Michael becomes defensive because he does not want to admit repressed thoughts and feelings into consciousness. Michael is showing:
A. flooding
B. polarized thinking
C. transference
D. resistance

p. 562
Insight Therapies
Level: Moderate
Type: Conceptual
Ans: A

111. Which of the following is an example of resistance?
A. showing up late for a therapy session
B. revealing unconscious thoughts during free association
C. having a sexually explicit dream
D. explaining irrational beliefs

p. 562
Insight Therapies
Level: Easy
Type: Factual
Ans: C

112. Why was short-term dynamic psychotherapy developed?
A. traditional psychoanalysis does not create enough transference
B. there was a shortage of qualified psychoanalysts
C. traditional psychoanalysis often requires many years of weekly sessions
D. transference was found to be harmful

p. 562
Insight Therapies
Level: Moderate
Type: Factual
Ans: C

113. A person is involved with short-term dynamic psychotherapy. Which of the following is not likely to happen during one of those sessions?
A. breaking down the client's resistance
B. attempting to resolve the client's conflicts
C. the therapist taking a less directive role in identifying the patient's problems
D. working through transference

p. 562
Insight Therapies
Level: Moderate
Type: Factual
Ans: D

114. Short-term dynamic psychotherapy compresses the treatment time of traditional psychoanalysis from:
A. 5 sessions to 2 or 3 sessions
B. 60 sessions to 10 or 20 sessions
C. 100 sessions to 25 or 30 sessions
D. 600 sessions to 25 or 30 sessions

p. 562
Insight Therapies
Level: Easy
Type: Factual
Ans: C

115. Data on the effectiveness of short-term dynamic psychotherapy indicate:
A. claims that the program achieves major psychological changes are greatly exaggerated
B. follow-up visits can, in fact, extend the duration of therapy to that of traditional psychoanalysis
C. effective treatment of disorders like stress disorders and personality disorders
D. much more research must be conducted before the effectiveness of STDP can be properly assessed

p. 563
Insight Therapies
Level: Moderate
Type: Factual
Ans: C

116. Traditional psychoanalysis might *not* be:
A. as unproductive as once believed
B. the most commonly used treatment for much longer
C. fully covered by health insurance plans
D. incorporated into other treatment approaches

p. 563
Insight Therapies
Level: Easy
Type: Factual
Ans: B

117. Which of the following is a reason for the decline of psychoanalysis?
A. There are too few analysts to meet the needs of the number of patients.
B. Drugs are now used to treat problems formerly dealt with in psychoanalysis.
C. Freud's notion of transference is no longer highly regarded.
D. Psychoanalysis is too short-term to generate enough salary for analysts.

p. 563
Insight Therapies
Level: Moderate
Type: Factual
Ans: B

118. Followers of the psychoanalytic approach have:
A. not believed that the client transfers anything to the therapist
B. been very slow to conduct research to test their treatment's effectiveness
C. believed that removal of the symptoms means a cure of the illness
D. allowed the client to express thoughts more frequently and openly

p. 563
Insight Therapies
Level: Moderate
Type: Factual
Ans: B

119. What form of psychoanalysis takes a more directive approach and shortens the total time in therapy?
A. eclectic therapy
B. short-term psychodynamic psychotherapy
C. gestalt therapy
D. client-centered therapy

p. 563
Insight Therapies
Level: Easy
Type: Factual
Ans: D

120. The idea of _____ has been supported by the research, providing evidence of a Freudian concept.
A. id
B. Oedipus complex
C. transference
D. procedural memory

p. 563
Insight Therapies
Level: Easy
Type: Factual
Ans: A

121. Of the following Freudian concepts, which has been tested and found to be valid?
A. defense mechanism
B. id as source of energy
C. role of the Oedipus complex in personality development
D. basic drives limited to sex and aggression

p. 563
Insight Therapies
Level: Easy
Type: Factual
Ans: A
*www*

122. The most popular psychotherapy approach used by psychologists is the _____ approach.
A. eclectic
B. psychodynamic
C. gestalt
D. client-centered

p. 564
Insight Therapies
Level: Moderate
Type: Factual
Ans: A

123. What was Carl Rogers' reaction to Freud's psychoanalytic approach?
A. He disagreed with Freud's belief that psychological problems come from unconscious thoughts.
B. Rogers argued that psychological problems come from unconscious thoughts and not what Freud believed, which was failure to reach one's potential.
C. He disagreed with the argument that Freud made about how the necessity of the therapist is to be more of a helper rather than expert.
D. He argued that Freud focused too much on the role of the conscious mind.

p. 564
Insight Therapies
Level: Moderate
Type: Factual
Ans: B

124. Carl Rogers assumed that:
A. people are essentially apathetic regarding their own lives
B. everyone has the capacity to change
C. a great deal of our behavior is governed by the unconscious
D. removing the symptoms of a client's problem is the same as solving the problem

p. 564
Insight Therapies
Level: Moderate
Type: Applied
Ans: A

125. Chris is in counseling with a therapist who never gives advice or directions to him but who often restates what Chris has said so that he can reflect on his feelings. What type of therapist is Chris seeing?
A. client-centered
B. psychoanalytic
C. cognitive
D. behavioral

p. 564
Insight Therapies
Level: Easy
Type: Factual
Ans: A

126. Which type of therapy makes the assumption that clients have the potential to help themselves, and the therapist's role is to be supportive of the client's efforts?
A. client-centered therapy
B. psychiatry
C. psychoanalysis
D. behavioral therapy

p. 564
Insight Therapies
Level: Easy
Type: Factual
Ans: A
*PS/SG 24-17*

127. The central assumption of Carl Rogers' client-centered therapy is that:
A. each person has the tendency and capacity to develop to his or her full potential
B. psychotherapy must be freely available in community mental health centers
C. we must struggle to overcome our basic human selfishness and hostility
D. therapy should focus on real behavior, not vague thoughts and feelings

p. 564
Insight Therapies
Level: Easy
Type: Factual
Ans: B

128. Which of the following is not one of the three therapist characteristics that Rogers believed would facilitate change in clients?
A. empathy
B. direct
C. positive regard
D. genuineness

p. 564
Insight Therapies
Level: Moderate
Type: Factual
Ans: C
*www*

129. Client-centered therapists emphasize showing their client that they understand what the client is feeling through:
A. systematic desensitization
B. overgeneralization
C. reflection
D. polarized thinking

p. 564
Insight Therapies
Level: Easy
Type: Factual
Ans: B

130. According to Carl Rogers, a therapist should function as a(n):
A. analyzing expert
B. helper or facilitator
C. behavior modifier
D. parent-figure

p. 564
Insight Therapies
Level: Moderate
Type: Factual
Ans: A

131. Positive regard, according to principles of client-centered therapy, is the ability to:
A. communicate caring and respect for a client
B. understand what a client is feeling
C. be nondefensive in interactions with a client
D. modify irrational beliefs and experiences

p. 564
Insight Therapies
Level: Easy
Type: Factual
Ans: D

132. According to Carl Rogers, the therapist's role was to:
A. provide specific programs for behavioral change
B. elevate the client from a laziness that Rogers believed to be inborn
C. help the client discover unconscious motives that are the root of the client's problem
D. demonstrate understanding and positive regard

p. 564
Insight Therapies
Level: Easy
Type: Factual
Ans: A

133. The lasting contribution of client-centered therapy is the importance of:
A. developing a positive working relationship with the client
B. allowing transference to take place
C. directly giving advice to the client
D. free association

p. 564
Insight Therapies
Level: Easy
Type: Factual
Ans: D

134. Therapists from the client-centered approach assume the importance of empathy and reflection in producing change. The research:
A. has supported their assumption
B. has supported the importance of empathy but not reflection
C. has supported the importance of reflection but not empathy
D. has indicated that empathy and reflection may not be as important as previously believed

p. 565
Insight Therapies
Level: Easy
Type: Factual
Ans: D

135. One of the common assumptions of cognitive therapy is that:
A. maladaptive behaviors are learned through one's environment
B. environmental improvement will result in improvement in the client
C. it is important to identify the unconscious conflicts
D. treatment primarily involves changing the client's maladaptive thought patterns

p. 565
Insight Therapies
Level: Easy
Type: Factual
Ans: C

136. What type of therapy involves the identification and changing of maladaptive thought patterns?
A. psychoanalysis
B. behavior therapy
C. cognitive therapy
D. client-centered therapy

p. 565
Insight Therapies
Level: Moderate
Type: Applied
Ans: B

137. Scott has a problem with his parents. His therapist focuses on helping Scott observe and record his thoughts about his parents, and emphasizes how his thoughts affect his feelings. Scott's therapist is practicing:
A. psychodynamic therapy
B. cognitive therapy
C. client-centered therapy
D. behavior therapy

p. 565
Insight Therapies
Level: Easy
Type: Factual
Ans: A

138. Beck developed his cognitive therapy based on his patient's:
A. negative automatic statements
B. unconscious wishes
C. problematic behaviors
D. negative regard

p. 565
Insight Therapies
Level: Easy
Type: Factual
Ans: D
PS/SG 24-18

139. Aaron Beck discovered that depressed people tend to interpret the world through:
A. carefully planned negative statements
B. thoughtless repetitions of what other people believe
C. secretly hostile beliefs
D. automatic negative thoughts

p. 565
Insight Therapies
Level: Easy
Type: Factual
Ans: B

140. Overgeneralization involves:
A. gradually exposing someone to their greatest fear
B. making blanket judgments based on a single incident
C. categorizing information as either "good" or "bad"
D. focusing on one detail so much that you fail to notice others

p. 565
Insight Therapies
Level: Easy
Type: Conceptual
Ans: C

141. Which of the following maladaptive thought patterns is the best example of overgeneralization?
A. "She hates me."
B. "I have many problems."
C. "Every time I try something new I fail."
D. "Sure I got an A in physics, but I barely passed English."

p. 565
Insight Therapies
Level: Easy
Type: Factual
Ans: D

142. Sorting information into the categories of good and bad is characteristic of:
A. empathy
B. flooding
C. overgeneralization
D. polarized thinking

p. 565
Insight Therapies
Level: Easy
Type: Applied
Ans: D
*www*

143. The thought "I could never live anyplace but New York because every other place is boring and awful" is an example of which of Beck's thought patterns?
A. overgeneralization
B. selective attention
C. geographic intelligence
D. polarized thinking

p. 565
Insight Therapies
Level: Easy
Type: Factual
Ans: A

144. When someone focuses on one detail so much that they fail to notice other events, they are said to be engaging in:
A. selective attention
B. flooding
C. empathy
D. polarized thinking

p. 565
Insight Therapies
Level: Moderate
Type: Applied
Ans: B

145. Tina is very upset over her evaluation at work because she has focused on the one minor criticism her boss made and has ignored the highly positive tone of the rest of the report. Which maladaptive thought pattern is Tina exhibiting?
A. overgeneralization
B. selective attention
C. geographic intelligence
D. polarized thinking

p. 565
Insight Therapies
Level: Easy
Type: Factual
Ans: C
*PS/SG 24-19*

146. In his cognitive therapy, Beck attempts to make clients aware of:
A. the importance of education in the contemporary world
B. adaptive thought patterns like open-mindedness, acceptance, love, and will power
C. maladaptive thought patterns like overgeneralization, polarized thinking, and selective attention
D. how much better they could be if they would just "think about it"

p. 565
Insight Therapies
Level: Moderate
Type: Factual
Ans: B

147. Which of the following is true regarding the effectiveness of cognitive therapy?
A. Its benefits tend to be shorter lasting that other forms of therapy.
B. It is effective with a variety of symptoms.
C. Few studies have been conducted to examine cognitive therapy's effectiveness.
D. It is less effective than psychoanalysis.

p. 565
Insight Therapies
Level: Easy
Type: Factual
Ans: D

148. Which of the following mental disorders is <u>most</u> effectively treated by cognitive therapy?
A. borderline personality disorder
B. antisocial personality disorder
C. paranoid schizophrenia
D. depression

| | | |
|---|---|---|
| p. 566 | 149. | Behavior therapy or behavior modification differs from the insight therapies |
| Behavior Therapy | | in that the therapist: |
| Level: Moderate | A. | encourages the client to free-associate |
| Type: Factual | B. | repeats or reflects what the client says |
| Ans: D | C. | discusses the client's tendency to automatically think negative thoughts |
| *PS/SG 24-20* | D. | identifies the specific problem and discusses a program for change |

| | | |
|---|---|---|
| p. 566 | 150. | One advantage of behavior therapy is that it: |
| Behavior Therapy | A. | examines underlying factors |
| Level: Easy | B. | emphasizes the therapist-client relationship |
| Type: Factual | C. | has a strong experimental foundation |
| Ans: C | D. | focuses on cognitive behaviors |

| | | |
|---|---|---|
| p. 566 | 151. | Why could it be said that Joseph Wolpe finished what John Watson had |
| Behavior Therapy | | started? |
| Level: Moderate | A. | Watson discovered the phenothiazines and Wolpe used them to treat |
| Type: Conceptual | | schizophrenia. |
| Ans: C | B. | Watson originated the idea of free association; Wolpe refined it. |
| | C. | Wolpe developed a technique to reduce Little Albert's fear. |
| | D. | Wolpe conducted scientific studies based on Watson's theory of free |
| | | association. |

| | | |
|---|---|---|
| p. 566 | 152. | The principles of classical and operant conditioning are used in _____. |
| Behavior Therapy | A. | client-centered therapy |
| Level: Easy | B. | psychoanalysis |
| Type: Factual | C. | behavior therapy |
| Ans: C | D. | short-term psychodynamic psychotherapy |

| | | |
|---|---|---|
| p. 566 | 153. | Dr. Johnson is a behavior therapist.  The techniques she uses are based  upon |
| Behavior Therapy | | the principles of: |
| Level: Easy | A. | classical and operant conditioning |
| Type: Factual | B. | Freudian psychoanalysis |
| Ans: A | C. | attribution theory |
| | D. | the medical model |

| | | |
|---|---|---|
| p. 566 | 154. | A person with a fear of flying sees a therapist who specializes in behavior |
| Behavior Therapy | | therapy.  Therapy sessions will focus on: |
| Level: Easy | A. | hidden conflicts that are manifested in a fear of flying |
| Type: Conceptual | B. | irrational beliefs about the dangers of flying |
| Ans: D | C. | negative past experiences that caused the fear of flying |
| | D. | changing the specific problem behavior |

| | | |
|---|---|---|
| p. 566 | 155. | Behavior therapists <u>do not</u> focus on: |
| Behavior Therapy | A. | the principles of classical conditioning |
| Level: Moderate | B. | the underlying unconscious conflicts |
| Type: Conceptual | C. | specific problem behavior |
| Ans: B | D. | rewards to change behavior |

p. 566
Behavior Therapy
Level: Moderate
Type: Factual
Ans: D
*www*

156. In behavior therapy, the problem is
A. a lack of self-actualization
B. too much self-actualization
C. the behavior
D. caused by unconscious conflicts

p. 567
Behavior Therapy
Level: Easy
Type: Factual
Ans: D

157. A technique of behavior therapy in which the client is gradually exposed to the feared object while simultaneously practicing relaxation is called:
A. free association
B. transference
C. flooding
D. systematic desensitization

p. 567
Behavior Therapy
Level: Easy
Type: Factual
Ans: C

158. Systematic desensitization involves three steps. Which of the following is not among the three steps?
A. relaxation training
B. stimulus hierarchy construction
C. awareness of negative thoughts
D. exposure

p. 567
Behavior Therapy
Level: Easy
Type: Factual
Ans: A

159. A person is using systematic desensitization to try to overcome his fear of driving on the freeway. The first step in this program would be:
A. relaxation training
B. stimulus hierarchy construction
C. free association
D. building up his self-image

p. 567
Behavior Therapy
Level: Easy
Type: Factual
Ans: C

160. The process of stimulus hierarchy construction involves:
A. identifying the exact responses involved in anxiety-provoking situations
B. listing, in order of priority, the goals that a client wishes to accomplish in therapy
C. listing from least feared to most feared a hierarchy of feared stimuli
D. outlining a session-by-session program for the uncovering of unconscious conflicts

p. 567
Behavior Therapy
Level: Easy
Type: Factual
Ans: D

161. Sylvia is undergoing systematic desensitization. She and her therapist are working on developing a list of feared stimuli. What are they creating?
A. resistance heirarchy
B. transference list
C. exposure list
D. stimulus hierarchy

<table>
<tr><td>p. 567<br>Behavior Therapy<br>Level: Moderate<br>Type: Applied<br>Ans: B</td><td>162.</td><td>Kyle is very afraid of the water. After creating an embarrassing scene at a beach party, he seeks the help of a therapist who uses systematic desensitization. During the sessions, Kyle is asked to go through stimulus hierarchy construction. To do this Kyle would:</td></tr>
</table>

p. 567
Behavior Therapy
Level: Moderate
Type: Applied
Ans: B

162. Kyle is very afraid of the water. After creating an embarrassing scene at a beach party, he seeks the help of a therapist who uses systematic desensitization. During the sessions, Kyle is asked to go through stimulus hierarchy construction. To do this Kyle would:

A. describe in detail his physiological responses when faced with the prospect of going in water

B. identify the first moment when he begins to feel the fear, and then list, in increasing order of severity, other stimuli that would evoke the fear

C. make a list of times when he would most like to be free of his fear

D. list, in order of their relative strength, the rewards that would be available to him if he conquered his fear of the water

p. 567
Behavior Therapy
Level: Moderate
Type: Applied
Ans: D

163. In her systematic desensitization sessions to overcome a fear of snakes, Rene develops a fear hierarchy of stimuli that cause anxiety. The hierarchy, from lowest to highest fear, consisted of seeing the word "snake", seeing a picture of a snake in a magazine, seeing a snake on TV, seeing a snake in the zoo, seeing a live snake in front of her and finally having a snake crawl on her. During the final stages of the systematic desensitization program, the therapist would ask Rene to:

A. make another list of the stimuli that provoke the fear of snakes

B. list the rewards that she would like to attain once the fear is overcome

C. learn relaxation techniques

D. imagine a snake crawling over her body

p. 567
Behavior Therapy
Level: Moderate
Type: Factual
Ans: C

164. In an attempt to cure a person's fear of dogs, a therapist has the person go through systematic desensitization. When the person imagines petting a dog, she becomes quite anxious. In this case, the therapist would:

A. bring in a dog and show that petting it isn't harmful

B. make the person continue to think about petting the dog until the anxiety went away

C. back up in the stimulus hierarchy

D. keep moving right through to the end of the process

p. 567
Behavior Therapy
Level: Moderate
Type: Factual
Ans: C

165. In systematic desensitization, a client who becomes anxious while imagining a step in the stimulus hierarchy, is:

A. instructed to go back to a prior step

B. told to focus on the nature of the anxiety

C. to continue to imagine the step until no longer anxious

D. required to reorder the steps in the stimulus hierarchy

p. 567
Behavior Therapy
Level: Easy
Type: Factual
Ans: D

166. In systematic desensitization, when the client is gradually exposed to the actual situations that are feared, this is called:

A. en passe exposure

B. realistic desensitization

C. in vitro exposure

D. in vivo exposure

p. 568
Behavior Therapy
Level: Easy
Type: Factual
Ans: C

167. Behavior and cognitive therapy grew out of:
A. the psychoanalytic perspective
B. interest in Rogers and Maslow's humanistic theories
C. disillusionment with psychoanalysis
D. research questioning the works of Pavlov and Skinner

p. 568
Behavior Therapy
Level: Easy
Type: Factual
Ans: D

168. _____ focuses on helping clients change their thoughts by learning new skills.
A. Psychoanalysis
B. Short-term psychodynamic psychotherapy
C. Gestalt therapy
D. Cognitive-behavior therapy

p. 568
Behavior Therapy
Level: Easy
Type: Factual
Ans: A

169. What approach to therapy focuses on changing thought patterns by learning new skills?
A. cognitive-behavior therapy
B. short-term psychodynamic psychotherapy
C. psychoanalysis
D. systematic desensitization

p. 568
Behavior Therapy
Level: Easy
Type: Factual
Ans: C

170. Monitoring one's thoughts, setting specific goals, learning to reinforce oneself, and substituting positive for negative thoughts are characteristic of:
A. psychoanalysis
B. short-term psychodynamic psychotherapy
C. cognitive-behavior therapy
D. systematic desensitization

p. 568
Behavior Therapy
Level: Easy
Type: Factual
Ans: D

171. The research on the effectiveness of cognitive-behavior therapy shows that:
A. it is inferior to psychoanalysis
B. any improvements are very short-lived
C. many of the concepts are untestable
D. it is more effective than control procedures

p. 571
Review: Evaluation of
  Approaches
Level: Easy
Type: Factual
Ans: C

172. What does meta-analysis reveal about the effectiveness of psychotherapy in general?
A. Meta-analyses have not been conducted.
B. In the short run, psychotherapy is unnecessary since most problems go away on their own.
C. Psychotherapy was more effective in relieving symptoms than were control procedures.
D. Psychotherapy is inferior to psychoanalysis.

p. 571
Review: Evaluation of
  Approaches
Level: Moderate
Type: Factual
Ans: D

173. According to research, _____ is the most effective form of treatment for most disorders.
A. behavior therapy
B. cognitive-behavior therapy
C. psychodynamic treatment
D. there is very little difference in effectiveness among the treatments

p. 571
Review: Evaluation of
  Approaches
Level: Easy
Type: Factual
Ans: D

174.  Which of the following treatments is probably the <u>least</u> effective for the specific disorders of phobias and depression?
A.  cognitive-behavior therapy
B.  behavior therapy
C.  cognitive therapy
D.  psychodynamic therapy

p. 571
Review: Evaluation of
  Approaches
Level: Easy
Type: Factual
Ans: A

175.  Which of the following types of disorders are best treated with cognitive-behavior therapy?
A.  anxiety and mood disorders
B.  personality disorders
C.  dissociative disorders
D.  schizophrenic disorders

p. 571
Review: Evaluation of
  Approaches
Level: Easy
Type: Factual
Ans: C
www

176.  What explains why different therapies are equally effective?
A.  the education of the therapists is largely the same
B.  the clients' desire to change
C.  common factors
D.  most mental disorders have the same underlying unconscious conflicts

p. 571
Review: Evaluation of
  Approaches
Level: Easy
Type: Conceptual
Ans: B

177.  What is one common factor that appears to be very important?
A.  being nondirective in the therapist's interaction with the client
B.  a warm, trusting, and accepting relationship between client and therapist
C.  successfully identifying the type of unconscious conflict underlying the problem
D.  being reflective

p. 572
Cultural Diversity:
  A Healer
Level: Moderate
Type: Factual
Ans: C

178.  Which of the following is *true* of the Balians of the island of Bali?
A.  They assume that depression has biological causes.
B.  They reject notions of evil spirits and utilize drug therapies.
C.  Their success rates are similar to those of psychotherapies.
D.  Their patients generally do not trust them.

p. 572
Cultural Diversity:
  A Healer
Level: Moderate
Type: Factual
Ans: B

179.  The primary assumption made by the Balians of the cause of problems is:
A.  imbalance of positive and negative energy
B.  evil spirits
C.  too much blood in the head
D.  rotting internal organs

p. 572
Cultural Diversity:
  A Healer
Level: Moderate
Type: Conceptual
Ans: D

180.  Why might Putu, the Bali who complained of depression, get better after receiving the healer's treatment?
A.  blood letting and potent medication
B.  exorcism and blood letting
C.  empathy and positive regard
D.  placebo effect and development of close relationship with healer

p. 573
Research Focus: EMDR
 Level: Easy
Type: Factual
Ans: C

181.   EMDR stands for:
A.     Effective Medical Diagnosis Reporting
B.     Effective Mental Development and Retreatment
C.     Eye Movement Desensitization and Reprocessing
D.     EMotional Disturbance Remedy

p. 573
Research Focus: EMDR
Level: Easy
Type: Factual
Ans: D

182.   The therapist is moving his pen back and forth as the patient is focusing on
       some traumatic event.  This therapy is called:
A.     cognitive-behavior therapy
B.     flooding
C.     systematic desensitization
D.     EMDR

p. 573
Research Focus: EMDR
Level: Easy
Type: Factual
Ans: A

183.   The early support for EMDR's effectiveness came from:
A.     case studies and testimonials
B.     longitudinal studies
C.     experiments
D.     cross-sectional studies

p. 573
Research Focus: EMDR
Level: Easy
Type: Factual
Ans: D

184.   The developer of EMDR claims that the effectiveness of EMDR is that:
A.     it causes thought substitution
B.     it wipes traumatic memories from long-term memory
C.     it teaches a patient's family skills to cope with the disorder
D.     eye movements reprocess traumatic memories and images

p. 573
Research Focus: EMDR
Level: Easy
Type: Factual
Ans: C

185.   What seems to be the most plausible explanation of EMDR's effectiveness?
A.     It causes thought substitution.
B.     It wipes traumatic memories from long-term memory.
C.     It is a form of exposure therapy.
D.     It changes the electrical activity of the brain.

p. 573
Research Focus: EMDR
Level: Easy
Type: Factual
Ans: B

186.   The effectiveness of EMDR in treating traumatic memories is comparable
       to:
A.     psychoanalysis
B.     exposure therapy and cognitive behavioral therapy
C.     client-centered therapy
D.     electroconvulsive therapy

p. 574
Application:
 Cognitive-Behavior
 Techniques
Level: Moderate
Type: Applied
Ans: C
www

187.   "Whenever I am depressed, I keep thinking how worthless I am.  I think
       that I can't do anything right.  And I keep thinking of all my failures.  I just
       keep thinking that way and I don't want to."  These thoughts are:
A.     effectively managed by psychoanalysis
B.     called obsessions
C.     called intrusive thoughts
D.     called negative symptoms

p. 574
Application:
  Cognitive-Behavior
  Techniques
Level: Moderate
Type: Applied
Ans: B

188. David feels that no one likes him and that he is deliberately ignored at work. His therapist asks David to keep track of the number of times in a week that people at work actually say something to him. David discovers that people pay more attention to him than he thought. What cognitive-behavior modification technique did David use?
A. graded task assignments
B. self-monitoring
C. behavioral rehearsal
D. free association

p. 574
Application:
  Cognitive-Behavior
  Techniques
Level: Easy
Type: Factual
Ans: C

189. At the onset of an unwanted thought, the thought stopping procedure suggests:
A. focusing on the unconscious reasons for the unwanted thought
B. doing physical exercise
C. closing one's eyes, silently yelling "Stop!" and counting to ten
D. practicing progressive relaxation

p. 574
Application:
  Cognitive-Behavior
  Techniques
Level: Easy
Type: Factual
Ans: B

190. What can be done to reduce the likelihood that a rebound of undesired thoughts may occur?
A. continue writing down dreams and allow the analyst to interpret them
B. use a combination of thought-stopping and thought substitution
C. use self-monitoring techniques
D. use a combination of flooding and drug treatment

p. 574
Application:
  Cognitive-Behavior
  Techniques
Level: Easy
Type: Applied
Ans: C

191. Ken is very depressed. As he talks to his therapist, it becomes apparent that, no matter how successful he seems to outsiders, he always believes that he is a failure. If the psychologist wants to have Ken think more rational thoughts, he should use:
A. interpersonal therapy
B. tricyclic antidepressants
C. thought substitution
D. lithium

p. 575
Application:
  Cognitive-Behavior
  Techniques
Level: Easy
Type: Factual
Ans: A

192. Making a list of irrational thoughts and a corresponding list of rational thoughts is used in:
A. thought substitution
B. a stimulus hierarchy
C. in vivo desensitization
D. flooding

p. 575
Application:
  Cognitive-Behavior
  Techniques
Level: Easy
Type: Factual
Ans: D

193. After a list of irrational thoughts and a matching list of rational thoughts are created, the next step is to engage in:
A. systematic desensitization
B. free association
C. in vivo desensitization
D. thought substitution

p. 575 | 194. | Which of the following is one of the steps used to treat insomnia?
Application: | A. | Try to make going to sleep at the same time every night a habit.
Cognitive-Behavior | B. | If you cannot sleep, get out of bed and go into a different room.
Techniques | C. | Sleep in when you are very tired.
Level: Easy | D. | Take naps when you feel tired, but only then.
Type: Factual
Ans: B
*www*

p. 575 | 195. | Your roommate's insomnia is interfering with your sleep. Which of the
Application: | | following is <u>not</u> good advice to give your roommate?
Cognitive-Behavior | A. | If you can't sleep, read or watch TV in bed to become more drowsy.
Techniques | B. | Go to bed only when you are sleepy.
Level: Easy | C. | Set the alarm to the same time each morning.
Type: Applied | D. | Do not nap during the day.
Ans: A

True/False

| T | | 1. | Dorothea Dix was an advocate of moral treatment of mental patients. |
|---|---|---|---|
| F | | 2. | The discovery of antidepressants was an important event in the deinstitutionalization of mental patients. |
| T | | 3. | A purpose of community mental health centers is to provide outpatient treatment. |
| T | | 4. | Counseling psychologists tend to focus on problems of living rather than on serious mental disorders. |
| T | *www* | 5. | Most therapists are eclectic meaning that they pick and choose aspects of several therapies. |
| T | | 6. | In free association, the client is asked to say anything that comes to mind. |
| F | *www* | 7. | In resistance, the client forms strong emotions toward the therapist that substitute for someone important in the client's life. |
| F | | 8. | Long-term psychoanalyses is more common than short-term dynamic psychotherapy. |
| T | | 9. | Client-centered therapy argues that problems occur when individuals are not self-actualized. |
| F | *www* | 10. | A client-centered therapist who is nondirective tends to be more effective than one is more directive. |
| T | | 11. | The key factor in client-centered therapy is to develop a good working client-therapist partnership. |
| T | | 12. | According to Rogers, it is important for the therapist to show positive regard. |
| F | *www* | 13. | In overgeneralization, a person sorts information into two categories. |
| F | | 14. | From the behavioral therapy perspective, the problem behavior reflects some unconscious desire. |
| F | *www* | 15. | Systematic desensitization is a client-centered therapy technique. |
| T | | 16. | A stimulus hierarchy is a list of feared stimuli. |
| T | *www* | 17. | A client is actually exposed to their fear stimulus in in vivo exposure. |
| T | | 18. | Behavior therapy is based on classical and operant conditioning. |
| T | *www* | 19. | Cognitive-behavior therapy attempts to modify thoughts and behaviors. |
| T | | 20. | Psychotherapy is more effective for a person than simply being assigned to a waiting list. |
| F | | 21. | Free association is an example of a common factor in different therapies. |

| T | *www* | 22. | It is believed that EMDR is similar to exposure therapy. |
|---|---|---|---|
| F | | 23. | The effectiveness of EMDR is due to the placebo effect. |
| F | *www* | 24. | Irrational beliefs and thoughts are believed to cause emotional and behavioral problems according to psychoanalysts. |
| F | *www* | 25. | Nondrug treatment programs are ineffective in helping individuals with insomnia. |

Short-Answer Essay Questions

1. Illustrate the three basic characteristics of psychotherapy by describing one of the therapies presented in the module.

2. What role did the introduction of phenothiazines have on the deinstitutionalization movement? (*www*)

3. What are the major differences between a psychiatrist, a clinical psychologist, and a counseling psychologist? (*www*)

4. Describe the techniques of free association, dream interpretation, and analysis of slips of the tongue as used in psychoanalysis.

5. How would a psychoanalyst react to transference and resistance in the client?

6. Present an example of overgeneralization, polarized thinking, and selective attention that a depressed college student might experience. (*www*)

7. Describe the use of systematic desensitization in treating a spider phobia.

8. Is psychotherapy effective? What are the variables present in different therapies? (*www*)

9. Describe the current understanding of why EMDR may be an effective treatment for posttraumatic stress disorder.

10. What roles do thought stopping and thought substitution have in cognitive-behavior therapy? (*www*)

# Module 25 - Social Psychology

p. 581
Introduction
Level: Moderate
Type: Applied
Ans: A

1. The example of Lawrence Graham presented in the module illustrates:
A. that physical appearance influences our judgments of other people
B. the influence of motivation on intelligence
C. groupthink in an educational setting
D. how changes in the brain influence social behavior

p. 581
Introduction
Level: Easy
Type: Conceptual
Ans: D
*PS/SG 25-1*

2. Rod Plotnik introduces us to Harvard Law School student Lawrence Graham to make the point that:
A. anyone who has the guts to start at the bottom can work his way up
B. African-American men are overly sensitive to good natured kidding
C. how people behave is more significant than what they believe
D. how we perceive and evaluate others has powerful consequences

p. 581
Introduction
Level: Easy
Type: Applied
Ans: B

3. "Look at them. They've got green hair! I bet they're terrible people, get poor grades, and take drugs." What area of psychology is best suited for studying how people make judgments of others based on physical appearance?
A. forensic psychology
B. social psychology
C. personality psychology
D. counseling psychology

p. 581
Introduction
Level: Easy
Type: Factual
Ans: A
*www*

4. _____ examines how our thoughts, feelings, perceptions, and behaviors are influenced by others.
A. Social psychology
B. Developmental psychology
C. Experimental psychology
D. Cognitive psychology

p. 581
Introduction
Level: Easy
Type: Applied
Ans: C

5. Dr. Hendrickson is interested in how our thoughts, perceptions, and behaviors are influenced by other people. Dr. Hendrickson must be studying:
A. interpersonal psychology
B. clinical psychology
C. social psychology
D. personality psychology

p. 581
Introduction
Level: Easy
Type: Applied
Ans: D

6. Dr. Kaurala published a book on how people perceive, store, and remember information on social interaction. What area of psychology would be Dr. Kaurala's specialty?
A. social influence
B. developmental psychology
C. psychophysics
D. cognitive social psychology

p. 581
Introduction
Level: Easy
Type: Applied
Ans: A

7. Karen is asking Joe about next semester's classes he's registered for. One of the classes is Social Psychology. "What's that?" she asks Joe. Joe's most accurate response is:

A. "The course is on how we are influenced by interactions with others."
B. "It is about how sociologists use psychology."
C. "Social Psych is the study of emotions in social settings"
D. "It's about how people get along with each other."

p. 581
Introduction
Level: Easy
Type: Factual
Ans: C

8. Cognitive social psychology is the study of how people:

A. in a group reinforce the majority's point of view and shift that view to a more extreme direction
B. perform behaviors based solely on group pressure and societal expectations
C. perceive, store, and retrieve information about social interactions and events
D. believe that they must conserve time and effort by taking cognitive shortcuts

p. 581
Introduction
Level: Easy
Type: Factual
Ans: B

9. "I've noticed that when I think about my co-workers, I can only remember those that I really like or really don't like." This is an example of:

A. social schema recall
B. social cognition
C. polarization
D. self-criticizing bias

p. 581
Introduction
Level: Moderate
Type: Conceptual
Ans: A

10. Which of the following topics would be most likely studied by a social psychologist?

A. sexism, attribution, obedience, attitudes
B. systematic desensitization, UCR, dieting, superego
C. unconditional positive regard, hypnotic amnesia
D. formal operations, Korsakoff's syndrome, fight-or-flight response

p. 581
Introduction
Level: Easy
Type: Conceptual
Ans: D

11. What is the best reason why the case of the girls playing touch football introduces the module on social psychology?

A. It illustrates social cognitive theory's concept of self-efficacy.
B. Their behavior illustrates the role of unconscious conflict on behavior.
C. His case illustrates how abnormal behavior can impair judgment.
D. He was able to convince many people to obey him.

p. 582
Perceiving Others
Level: Easy
Type: Factual
Ans: D

12. Will works for a large corporation as an employment interviewer. He visits colleges and universities interviewing job candidates. He says that he can tell if a candidate is the right person by just looking at the person. A social psychologist would call this:

A. prosocial behavior
B. altruism
C. personnel evaluation
D. person perception

p. 582
Perceiving Others
Level: Easy
Type: Factual
Ans: B

13. Forming impressions and making judgments about the traits of others is called:
A. social facilitation
B. person perception
C. social reasoning
D. person polarization

p. 582
Perceiving Others
Level: Easy
Type: Applied
Ans: A

14. Larry has noticed that when he wears jeans and T-shirts he is treated differently when he goes shopping than when he wears a suit and tie. This illustrates how physical appearance can influence:
A. person perception
B. social facilitation
C. deindividuation
D. person polarization

p. 582
Perceiving Others
Level: Moderate
Type: Applied
Ans: D

15. You advise your friend to dress appropriately for a job interview. As a student of social psychology, you recognize the importance of _____ in forming judgments about others.
A. alturism
B. the affective component of an attitude
C. internal attributions
D. physical appearance

p. 582
Perceiving Others
Level: Moderate
Type: Applied
Ans: C

16. Susan is going on a blind date with Michael. When she first meets Michael, she notices that he has long hair, an earring, and wears a leather jacket. She decides that Michael is rebellious, dangerous, and aggressive. She is basing her judgments on which of the following factors?
A. the two-way process
B. seeking information
C. the need to explain
D. social consequences

p. 582
Perceiving Others
Level: Moderate
Type: Applied
Ans: B

17. Laura decides that the stranger sitting next to her in the restaurant is rich. He is well dressed, has a cell phone, and orders lobster to eat. This illustrates which of the following?
A. group polarization
B. need to explain
C. hindsight bias
D. consensus effect

p. 582
Perceiving Others
Level: Easy
Type: Factual
Ans: A

18. The way in which we perceive someone can effect:
A. consequences for the way we would interact with the person
B. causal relevance
C. attribution error
D. cognitive dissonance

p. 582
Perceiving Others
Level: Moderate
Type: Applied
Ans: D

19. At the gym, you run into Jake. Jake is unshaven and is wearing ragged clothes and no-name tennis shoes and he is also very sweaty. He asks you if you want to play some basketball. You think that Jake is a loser and say no. This best illustrates:
A. social cognition
B. situational attribution
C. how groupthink influences individual behavior
D. the influence of person perception on behavior

p. 582
Perceiving Others
Level: Moderate
Type: Applied
Ans: B

20. A man who lives in your town is very wealthy, but does not show it. In fact, he drives an old Chevy pick-up and wears worn clothes. Visitors to town who do not know about his wealth, are often rude and inconsiderate to him. This best illustrates:
A. the central route of persuasion
B. how impressions of others will influence behavior
C. how individual behavior affects diffusion of responsibility
D. the actor-observer effect

p. 582
Perceiving Others
Level: Easy
Type: Factual
Ans: B
*www*

21. Those faces that we might consider the most attractive are those that:
A. are the most symmetrical in shape
B. come closest to the average face found in the general population
C. approximate a round shape
D. approximate a heart shape

p. 582
Perceiving Others
Level: Easy
Type: Factual
Ans: A

22. What have researchers found about attractive faces?
A. Attractive faces come closest to the average face found in the general population.
B. Attractive faces have large eyes and high cheekbones.
C. Attractive faces are those that have a square shape.
D. Attractive faces have dimples, small eyes, low cheekbones, and a small forehead.

p. 582
Perceiving Others
Level: Easy
Type: Conceptual
Ans: B

23. What does the phrase, "What is beautiful is good" mean?
A. physically attractive people are good
B. we stereotypically perceive attractive people as good
C. beauty is only skin deep
D. attractive people have great self-consistency

p. 582
Perceiving Others
Level: Easy
Type: Applied
Ans: C
*PS/SG 25-3*

24. A discouraging finding about physical appearance and first impressions is captured by the phrase:
A. "Good looks are nice, but who cares about looks?"
B. "I want a girl just like the girl who married dear old Dad"
C. "What is beautiful is good"
D. "Do blondes really have more fun?"

| | | |
|---|---|---|
| p. 582 | 25. | Which of the following characteristics is <u>not</u> considered to be true of physically attractive people? |
| Perceiving Others | | |
| Level: Easy | A. | intelligent |
| Type: Factual | B. | interesting |
| Ans: D | C. | kind |
| | D. | introspective |

| | | |
|---|---|---|
| p. 582 | 26. | According to research, an attractive face: |
| Perceiving Others | A. | is mathematically symmetrical |
| Level: Easy | B. | is statistically unusual |
| Type: Factual | C. | implies that the person also possesses desirable personal qualities |
| Ans: C | D. | implies a willingness and openness to be liked |

| | | |
|---|---|---|
| p. 583 | 27. | Professor Varnadore studies how people judge others because they belong to certain groups. In which journal should Professor Varnadore publish her study? |
| Perceiving Others | | |
| Level: Easy | | |
| Type: Conceptual | A. | *American Journal of Attributional Thinking* |
| Ans: D | B. | *Journal of Groupthink* |
| | C. | *Journal of Prosocial Behavior* |
| | D. | *Journal of Stereotypes* |

| | | |
|---|---|---|
| p. 583 | 28. | Based on a study described in the module, who is <u>most</u> likely to receive sophisticated treatment for their chest pain? |
| Perceiving Others | | |
| Level: Easy | A. | women |
| Type: Factual | B. | African-Americans |
| Ans: D | C. | men |
| | D. | white men |

| | | |
|---|---|---|
| p. 583 | 29. | Stereotypes are widely held beliefs that people have certain traits because: |
| Perceiving Others | A. | of their observable behavior |
| Level: Easy | B. | they belong to a particular group |
| Type: Factual | C. | of the fundamental attribution error |
| Ans: B | D. | they hold utilitarian attitudes |

| | | |
|---|---|---|
| p. 583 | 30. | Katy has red hair. When other people see Katy, they assume she has a temper. This illustrates: |
| Perceiving Others | | |
| Level: Easy | A. | impression management |
| Type: Applied | B. | a stereotype |
| Ans: B | C. | conformity |
| | D. | social characteristics |

| | | |
|---|---|---|
| p. 583 | 31. | A person who says that all Scottish people are thrifty and cheap is demonstrating: |
| Perceiving Others | | |
| Level: Easy | A. | discrimination |
| Type: Applied | B. | prejudice |
| Ans: C | C. | stereotyping |
| | D. | segregation |

<table>
<tr><td>

p. 583
Perceiving Others
Level: Easy
Type: Factual
Ans: C

</td><td>

32. How do stereotypes develop according to your textbook?
A. Stereotypes are innate.
B. Stereotypes develop because of an interaction between genetics and the environment.
C. Others reward us for holding certain attitudes and beliefs.
D. There are biological predispositions found in most people that lead to stereotypes.

</td></tr>
<tr><td>

p. 583
Perceiving Others
Level: Easy
Type: Factual
Ans: C

</td><td>

33. A father is talking to his young son. "That's good Kevin, boys know how to play baseball and girls don't." Is this the typical way that stereotypes develop?
A. No, stereotypes are due to genetic factors.
B. No, stereotypes are due to biological dispositions.
C. Yes, same-gender parents mold the attitudes of their children.
D. Yes, other people reward us with approval for holding certain attitudes.

</td></tr>
<tr><td>

p. 583
Perceiving Others
Level: Easy
Type: Factual
Ans: A

</td><td>

34. An unfair, biased, or intolerant attitude toward another group of people is called a(n):
A. prejudice
B. expectation
C. stereotype
D. attribution

</td></tr>
<tr><td>

p. 583
Perceiving Others
Level: Easy
Type: Conceptual
Ans: A

</td><td>

35. Prejudice is to discrimination as:
A. attitude is to behavior
B. underestimation is to overestimation
C. attribution is to schema
D. schema is to stereotype

</td></tr>
<tr><td>

p. 583
Perceiving Others
Level: Easy
Type: Applied
Ans: B
*PS/SG 25-5*

</td><td>

36. When we ask someone, "What do you do?" we are trying to get more information about the person by drawing on our:
A. person schemas
B. role schemas
C. event schemas
D. scripts

</td></tr>
<tr><td>

p. 583
Perceiving Others
Level: Easy
Type: Factual
Ans: C
*www*

</td><td>

37. Specific unfair behavior toward members of a group is known as:
A. prejudice
B. stereotyping
C. discrimination
D. attribution

</td></tr>
<tr><td>

p. 583
Perceiving Others
Level: Easy
Type: Applied
Ans: A

</td><td>

38. "We ought not to vote for a woman for president." This illustrates:
A. discrimination
B. attribution
C. the covariation model
D. groupthink

</td></tr>
</table>

p. 583
Perceiving Others
Level: Easy
Type: Applied
Ans: D
*www*

39. John voted against Linda's promotion because he doesn't think women can do the job. John's behavior is an example of:
A. a stereotype
B. prejudice
C. an event schema
D. discrimination

p. 583
Perceiving Others
Level: Easy
Type: Conceptual
Ans: C

40. Which of the following is an example of discrimination?
A. a woman who thinks that all men are insensitive
B. a teacher who believes that a particular racial group is intellectually superior to all others
C. public washrooms being declared out of bounds to members of a particular ethnic group
D. someone who considers Germans to be orderly

p. 583
Perceiving Others
Level: Moderate
Type: Factual
Ans: D

41. According to the textbook, what is one reason why we frequently use stereotypes?
A. stereotypes are reinforced by the general public
B. stereotypes require deep, reflective thought
C. it requires that we consider attributions and groupthink experiences
D. it saves us time thinking

p. 583
Perceiving Others
Level: Moderate
Type: Factual
Ans: A

42. Stereotypes affect person perception by:
A. activating social information in memory and applying it to a specific person
B. changing the way in which we develop and act upon event schemas
C. causing us to look for factors that go along with the behavior we are trying to explain
D. resulting in cognitive dissonance

p. 583
Perceiving Others
Level: Easy
Type: Factual
Ans: D

43. Stereotypes are described in the textbook as:
A. beliefs validated by fact
B. examples of misplaced attributions
C. the effects of aggression
D. cognitive tools

p. 583
Perceiving Others
Level: Easy
Type: Applied
Ans: C

44. Morton believes that all people from the South are slow and dull-witted. When Morton has a chance to meet with some articulate, intelligent Southerners, his stereotype:
A. is destroyed
B. will be reinforced
C. will dismiss this experience since it doesn't fit with his stereotype
D. will be modified

p. 584
Perceiving Others
Level: Easy
Type: Factual
Ans: A

45. The textbook describes the case of Dr. Fran Conley, a board-certified neurosurgeon. Whenever she would disagree with her male counterparts, they would attribute it to her:
A. menstrual period
B. lack of adequate training in neurology
C. lack of adequate experience
D. nurturing, sensitive nature

p. 584
Perceiving Others
Level: Easy
Type: Factual
Ans: B

46. Schemas are:
A. errors in attribution caused by cognitive dissonance
B. mental categories representing an organized collection of knowledge
C. attitudes resulting in prejudice and discrimination
D. factors that co-vary with the behavior we are trying to explain

p. 584
Perceiving Others
Level: Moderate
Type: Applied
Ans: D

47. State Trooper Kirk has a schema of a drug dealer: a nervous male who drives a nice car at slightly under the speed limit. A disadvantage of this schema is:
A. it slows decision making relating to stopping potential drug dealers
B. there are too many specific details in it leading to confusion
C. "drug dealer" is more appropriate as a self-schema than a person schema
D. drug dealers who do not fit the schema may avoid detection

p. 584
Perceiving Others
Level: Easy
Type: Factual
Ans: C

48. Person schemas that contain general information about people who have membership in groups are called:
A. dispositions
B. attributions
C. stereotypes
D. scripts

p. 584
Perceiving Others
Level: Easy
Type: Applied
Ans: B

49. "I wear glasses even though I don't have to. People say that glasses make me look smart." This idea about intelligence and wearing glasses is an example of:
A. an external attribution
B. a person schema
C. deindividuation
D. counterattitudinal behavior

p. 584
Perceiving Others
Level: Easy
Type: Factual
Ans: D

50. What type of schema describes how we are to perform or act?
A. dispositional schema
B. attributional schema
C. behavioral schema
D. role schema

p. 584
Perceiving Others
Level: Easy
Type: Factual
Ans: C

51. Tim says to his friend Juan, "Your grandfather is pretty fun. I never thought old people could be that much fun." Tim's comment is an illustration of:
A. a dispositional schema
B. an attributional schema
C. a role schema
D. self-serving bias

p. 584
Perceiving Others
Level: Easy
Type: Applied
Ans: B

52. An experienced waiter can tell very quickly if a customer is a potential big tipper and then serve the customer accordingly. To do this, the waiter would probably rely on a(n):
A. self-schema
B. person schema
C. event schema
D. subconscious schema

p. 584
Perceiving Others
Level: Moderate
Type: Applied
Ans: C
*www*

53. A group of friends go out to a Thai restaurant. One of the friends says that he will be in charge of the ordering because, as he puts it, he "knows how this sort of thing is done." If this is, in fact, the case, the person would be making use of a(n):
A. self-schema
B. person schema
C. event schema
D. subconscious schema

p. 584
Perceiving Others
Level: Moderate
Type: Applied
Ans: A

54. Dirk is given a ticket to a college football game. He is happy because he knows that people at college football games scream, drink beer and have a good time. This knowledge is an example of a(n) _____ schema.
A. event
B. person
C. self
D. interpersonal

p. 584
Perceiving Others
Level: Moderate
Type: Applied
Ans: A

55. A foreign exchange student had never been to a dorm party. His friends ask him to watch a movie that portrays typical college partying. His friends are helping him develop a(n) _____ schema.
A. event
B. person
C. self
D. interpersonal

p. 584
Perceiving Others
Level: Moderate
Type: Conceptual
Ans: D

56. Which of the following would be an example of an event schema?
A. not renting an apartment to a lesbian couple
B. knowing that all chess players are smart
C. thinking that dentists cause people to feel pain
D. expecting to wait in line for movie tickets

p. 584
Perceiving Others
Level: Moderate
Type: Applied
Ans: B

57. Danny thinks he is a good athlete. Thus, he has an athletic self-schema. As compared to someone who does not have an athletic self-schema, it is likely that Danny:
A. will pay less attention to other athletic individuals
B. will remember information related to athletics better
C. will have his schema change if he encounters nonathletic information
D. will pay extra attention to information that slightly conflicts with his athletic schema

p. 584
Perceiving Others
Level: Easy
Type: Factual
Ans: B

58. Which of the following statements concerning a schema is not accurate?
A. Information inconsistent with a schema is discounted.
B. Schemas change easily.
C. Information supporting a schema is attended to.
D. Schemas persist.

p. 584
Perceiving Others
Level: Easy
Type: Factual
Ans: C

59. Why are schemas so highly resistant to change?
A. They prevent us from overlooking information.
B. They fail to fill in missing information.
C. We discount information that is inconsistent with them.
D. We forget information that is consistent with them.

p. 584
Perceiving Others
Level: Easy
Type: Factual
Ans: A

60. An advantage of schemas is that they:
A. help us organize complex stimuli
B. force us to focus on all information rather than just parts of it
C. help us see the world as others see it
D. constantly change

p. 584
Perceiving Others
Level: Easy
Type: Factual
Ans: D

61. We are able to select relevant information from a tremendous amount of incoming social information through the use of:
A. stereotypes
B. the cognitive miser model
C. the covariation principle
D. schemas

p. 584
Perceiving Others
Level: Easy
Type: Factual
Ans: A

62. A disadvantage of schemas is that they:
A. restrict what we attend to, store, and recall
B. create disorganization within long-term memory
C. cannot predict how we should behave in social situations
D. are easily changed

p. 584
Perceiving Others
Level: Moderate
Type: Applied
Ans: B

63. A woman's schema about Italians is that they are very emotional and irrational. She travels to Rome and meets many natives. When she returns, it is likely that her memory of the Italians' general behavior will be:
A. consistent with the type of people she met in Rome
B. distorted to be consistent with her schema
C. changed to include more negative judgments
D. unchanged, but she will be more emotional and irrational

p. 585
Attributions
Level: Easy
Type: Factual
Ans: C

64. An attribution is a(n):
A. stereotype
B. belief
C. explanation
D. attitude

p. 585
Attributions
Level: Easy
Type: Conceptual
Ans: A

65. You want to set up a web site for information on the concept of attributions. What would be the most accurate name for the web site?
A. www.explanation.edu
B. www.persuasion.edu
C. www.schema.edu
D. www.stereotype.edu

p. 585
Attributions
Level: Easy
Type: Factual
Ans: A
*www*

66. The explanations given for someone's behavior or beliefs are known as:
A. attributions
B. event schemas
C. person schemas
D. stereotypes

p. 585
Attributions
Level: Moderate
Type: Applied
Ans: B

67. Alfonso sees a news story about a beautiful 22-year-old blond woman who just married an elderly billionaire. Alfonso feels that the woman married the billionaire for his money. Alfonso's explanation is an example of:

A. a fundamental perceptual error
B. an attribution
C. prejudice
D. discrimination

p. 585
Attributions
Level: Easy
Type: Factual
Ans: C
*PS/SG 25-6*

68. In the language of social psychology, _____ means things we point to as the causes of events, other people's behaviors, and our own behaviors.

A. schemas
B. covariations
C. attributions
D. distinctiveness

p. 585
Attributions
Level: Easy
Type: Factual
Ans: A

69. According to psychologists, we generally attribute behavior to:

A. external circumstances or internal characteristics
B. distinctiveness or consistency
C. masculine or feminine schemas
D. the actor or the observer

p. 585
Attributions
Level: Easy
Type: Applied
Ans: C
*www*

70. You see a friend walking towards you. You say "hi." He doesn't even acknowledge you are there. "What a jerk!" You have made a(n) _____ attribution.

A. peripheral
B. central
C. internal
D. external

p. 585
Attributions
Level: Easy
Type: Applied
Ans: A

71. You've asked yourself many times why you do the things you do. Each time you conclude that you are "just that type of person." Therefore, you tend to make _____ attributions about your own behavior.

A. internal
B. external
C. primary
D. central

p. 585
Attributions
Level: Easy
Type: Factual
Ans: D

72. A person's disposition refers to their:

A. peripheral route of persuasion
B. self-serving bias
C. type of schema
D. internal characteristics

p. 585
Attributions
Level: Easy
Type: Factual
Ans: C

73. A person making a situational attribution is explaining a behavior as due to:

A. someone's personality
B. how much ability the person has
C. external factors
D. how hard the person tries

p. 585
Attributions
Level: Easy
Type: Applied
Ans: A

74. Andy believes that he did *not* get a job because the interviewer didn't ask the right questions. Andy is making an attribution based primarily on:
A. the situation
B. disposition
C. schemas
D. cognitive dissonance

p. 585
Attributions
Level: Easy
Type: Applied
Ans: D

75. Mike thinks that Bob did well on the physics test because Bob studied hard and for a long time for it. This is an example of a(n) _____ attribution.
A. internal
B. situational
C. consequential
D. dispositional

p. 585
Attributions
Level: Easy
Type: Factual
Ans: B

76. You are looking for information on the individual who developed the model of covariation. Who was it?
A. Bandura
B. Kelley
C. Asch
D. Milgram

p. 585
Attributions
Level: Easy
Type: Factual
Ans: C

77. Harold Kelley developed the covariation principle in order to:
A. help people overcome responses resulting from obedience
B. categorize and identify the origins of specific attitudes
C. determine whether behavior should be attributed to dispositional or situational factors
D. identify the masculine and feminine components of an individual's self-schema

p. 585
Attributions
Level: Easy
Type: Factual
Ans: A

78. The covariation principle says that in deciding between dispositional and situational explanations, we should look for three factors:
A. consensus, consistency, and distinctiveness
B. person, role, and event schemas
C. behavioral, affective, and cognitive components
D. stereotypes, prejudice, and discrimination

p. 585
Attributions
Level: Easy
Type: Factual
Ans: C

79. In determining whether other people engage in the same behavior in the same situations, we gather information on their:
A. consistency
B. distinctiveness
C. consensus
D. uniqueness

p. 585
Attributions
Level: Easy
Type: Applied
Ans: A

80. Each time Juan is in the student union, he acts very outgoing and will talk to anyone near him. In terms of the model of covariation, Juan shows:
A. consistency
B. distinctiveness
C. consensus
D. uniqueness

p. 585
Attributions
Level: Easy
Type: Factual
Ans: B

81.    How differently a person behaves in one situation compared to other situations is called:
A.    specificity
B.    distinctiveness
C.    consensus
D.    uniqueness

p. 585
Attributions
Level: Easy
Type: Factual
Ans: D

82.    In explaining a friend's behavior, you decide that there is high consistency, low distinctiveness, and low consensus.  You are most likely to make a(n) _____ attribution.
A.    fundamental
B.    situational
C.    external
D.    internal

p. 586
Attributions
Level: Easy
Type: Factual
Ans: A

83.    The term _____ refers to a real but invisible barrier that keeps women and people of color from reaching the top executive positions in business.
A.    "glass ceiling"
B.    "subtle prejudice"
C.    "prejudicial fence"
D.    "promotion cover"

p. 586
Attributions
Level: Easy
Type: Conceptual
Ans: D

84.    "I don't want to use a great deal of energy and time thinking.  So I take the easy way out when it comes to explaining behavior.  From a social psychological perspective, I'm a(n):
A.    internal dispositioner
B.    intellectual miser
C.    cognitive Scrooge
D.    cognitive miser

p. 586
Attributions
Level: Easy
Type: Factual
Ans: A

85.    According to the cognitive miser model, people conserve time and energy in making attributions by:
A.    taking cognitive shortcuts
B.    basing judgments on schemas
C.    forming utilitarian attitudes
D.    using the peripheral route for persuasion

p. 586
Attributions
Level: Easy
Type: Factual
Ans: B

86.    Conserving time and effort through the use of cognitive shortcuts is essential to the:
A.    covariation principle
B.    cognitive miser model
C.    central route for persuasion
D.    foot-in-the-door technique

p. 586
Attributions
Level: Easy
Type: Factual
Ans: B
*www*

87.    The tendency to overestimate the importance of dispositional factors and underestimate the importance of situational ones is known as:
A.    stereotyping
B.    fundamental attribution error
C.    schema-driven processing
D.    prejudice

p. 586
Attributions
Level: Easy
Type: Applied
Ans: D

88. You are walking in a parking lot full of small puddles of water. A car drives through one near you and splashes you with water. You are likely to attribute the driver's behavior to internal dispositions. This is called:
A. stereotyping
B. actor-observer effect
C. covariation
D. the fundamental attribution error

p. 586
Attributions
Level: Easy
Type: Applied
Ans: A
*PS/SG 25-7*

89. "If I look for the causes of your behavior in your disposition and personality traits, and overlook how the situation influenced your behavior, I am guilty of the:
A. fundamental attribution error
B. covariation model factor
C. actor-observer effect
D. self-serving bias

p. 586
Attributions
Level: Moderate
Type: Conceptual
Ans: A

90. Which of the following statements is the best example of fundamental attribution error?
A. "People live in ghettos because they lack the motivation to make anything of themselves."
B. "She was born with a silver spoon in her mouth."
C. "Prison guards are not mean people, they are just victims of a very difficult situation."
D. "There, but for the grace of God, go I."

p. 586
Attributions
Level: Moderate
Type: Applied
Ans: A

91. A car is tailgating Jerry. The car passes him dangerously. Jerry thinks, "What a jerk!" Jerry has ignored the possibility of the situation affecting the other driver. Jerry has committed the:
A. fundamental attribution error
B. primary attribution tendency
C. self-serving bias
D. central attribution error

p. 586
Attributions
Level: Easy
Type: Factual
Ans: B

92. The actor-observer effect suggests that, as actors, we attribute our behaviors to _____, but, as observers, we attribute others' behavior to _____.
A. motivation; conformity
B. the situation; their disposition
C. consensus; consistency
D. self-schema; event schema

p. 586
Attributions
Level: Moderate
Type: Applied
Ans: D

93. While walking down a crowded city street, we hear someone sound his car horn to try to get traffic moving. If we use actor-observer bias to attribute cause to the horn honking, we will:
A. believe that we would never use our own horn in traffic
B. judge the traffic to be very frustrating
C. remind ourselves that there are drivers on the road who deserve to be honked at once in a while
D. consider the horn honker to be impatient

p. 586
Attributions
Level: Moderate
Type: Applied
Ans: D

94. You and your roommate have just received grade reports. Since you and your roommate were in the same class, you are curious about how well he did. Both of you received a "D." You received a "D" because the professor was bad; you believe your roommate got a "D" because he is not too bright. You have just experienced the:
A. primary dispositional effect
B. grading attribution effect
C. fundamental attribution effect
D. actor-observer effect

p. 586
Attributions
Level: Moderate
Type: Applied
Ans: D

95. "When I beat my average bowling score, I attribute it to my skill, but if I score below my average, I blame it on the dent in my bowling ball." This is an example of the:
A. actor-observer effect
B. covariation principle
C. fundamental attribution error
D. self-serving bias

p. 586
Attributions
Level: Moderate
Type: Applied
Ans: B

96. As you share your high school transcript with your children, you notice that you attribute the "A's" to your hard work and discipline. The poor grades are explained by telling your children that the teacher was bad and the tests were unfair. Oops! You realize that you've committed the:
A. covariation principle
B. self-serving bias
C. fundamental attribution error
D. actor-observer effect

p. 586
Attributions
Level: Moderate
Type: Applied
Ans: C
*PS/SG 25-8*

97. "I aced the chem exam because I studied my butt off! The psych exam I flunked? Well, you know he always asks tricky questions." Sounds like the _____ in action, doesn't it?
A. fundamental attribution error
B. actor-observer effect
C. self-serving bias
D. whiner effect

p. 586
Attributions
Level: Easy
Type: Applied
Ans: A

98. Mary thinks she will do well on Dr. Steven's business logistics test. She ends up getting the highest grade in the class. Mary will probably attribute her excellent performance to:
A. ability
B. unstable factors
C. task difficulty
D. luck

p. 586
Attributions
Level: Easy
Type: Applied
Ans: B

99. "As a sales representative for a major company, I often meet my sales quota and make lots of sales because of my hard work and skill. Sometimes, I don't make the quota, but it's because the company doesn't give me a list of potential customers." This person is experiencing:
A. fundamental attribution error
B. self-serving bias
C. actor-observer effect
D. groupthink

p. 587
Research Focus:
  Attributions & Grades
Level: Easy
Type: Factual
Ans: A

100.   In order to convince a freshman that academic problems can be overcome, an instructor must get the freshman to:
A.   attribute problems to temporary factors
B.   attribute problems to innate abilities
C.   believe that a considerable amount of college success is attributable to good fortune
D.   let the instructor assume responsibility for the student's success for a while

p. 587
Research Focus:
  Attributions & Grades
Level: Easy
Type: Factual
Ans: D

101.   To improve students' grades, researchers tried to change their attributions about poor grades from being _____ to _____.
A.   external; internal
B.   internal; dispositional
C.   temporary; permanent
D.   permanent; temporary

p. 587
Research Focus:
  Attributions & Grades
Level: Easy
Type: Factual
Ans: D

102.   Attempts to improve students' grade-point averages by convincing them that their problems were due to temporary factors:
A.   were successful only temporarily
B.   actually caused increased dropout rates among freshman subjects
C.   were successful only for subjects of above average intelligence
D.   were generally very successful

p. 587
Research Focus:
  Attributions & Grades
Level: Easy
Type: Factual
Ans: A

103.   What effect does shifting attributions for poor academic performance to temporary conditions have on college students?
A.   reduced dropout rate
B.   reduced self-serving bias
C.   increased dropout rate
D.   increased self-serving bias

p. 587
Research Focus:
  Attributions & Grades
Level: Easy
Type: Conceptual
Ans: B

104.   Changing the attributions of college freshmen regarding their academic performance demonstrates that:
A.   thought patterns are not as important as innate ability
B.   attributions influence our behaviors
C.   most college students are much more realistic about self-analysis of failure in their first year of college than they are in their fourth year
D.   females attribute cause to failure in much more constructive ways than males do

p. 588
Attitudes
Level: Easy
Type: Factual
Ans: C

105.   Any belief that includes a positive or negative evaluation of some target which predisposes us to act in certain ways toward the target is defined by your text as a(n):
A.   stereotype
B.   schema
C.   attitude
D.   attribution

p. 588
Attitudes
Level: Easy
Type: Factual
Ans: B
*PS/SG 25-10*

106. Which of the following is *not* a component of an attitude?
A. cognitive
B. genetic
C. affective
D. behavioral

p. 588
Attitudes
Level: Easy
Type: Applied
Ans: A

107. Someone speaks up during a Social Problems class and says, "Abortion is murder." Which one of the three components was demonstrated by this student?
A. cognitive
B. affective
C. physiological
D. behavior

p. 588
Attitudes
Level: Easy
Type: Applied
Ans: B

108. "I have strong feelings against black olives." This demonstrates the _____ component of an attitude.
A. cognitive
B. affective
C. physiological
D. behavior

p. 588
Attitudes
Level: Easy
Type: Applied
Ans: D
*www*

109. "I don't eat black olives." This demonstrates the _____ component of an attitude.
A. cognitive
B. affective
C. physiological
D. behavior

p. 588
Attitudes
Level: Easy
Type: Conceptual
Ans: B

110. If you had a negative attitude towards assisted suicide, then the behavioral component would be:
A. your dislike and distrust of those who advocate it
B. voting for politicians who want to make it illegal
C. your belief that assisted suicide is evil
D. your hatred toward assisted suicide

p. 588
Attitudes
Level: Easy
Type: Applied
Ans: D

111. "I donate my time and money to a number of charities for children." This demonstrates which component of an attitude?
A. cognitive
B. affective
C. physiological
D. behavior

p. 588
Attitudes
Level: Easy
Type: Conceptual
Ans: C

112. With regard to attitudes: cognitive component is to _____ as affective component is to _____.
A. beliefs; actions
B. emotions; feelings
C. thoughts; emotions
D. behavior; actions

p. 589
Attitudes
Level: Easy
Type: Factual
Ans: C

113. Attitudes can serve three functions. Which of the following is *not* one of the functions described in the textbook?
A. predispose
B. interpret
C. adjust
D. evaluate

p. 589
Attitudes
Level: Easy
Type: Applied
Ans: A

114. Mr. Stevenson has been a high school teacher for 20 years. He has this attitude about treating students with respect. He doesn't laugh at students nor insult them. Which function of attitudes has guided Mr. Stevenson's behavior?
A. predispose
B. evaluate
C. defend
D. interpret

p. 589
Attitudes
Level: Easy
Type: Factual
Ans: C

115. The predisposing function of an attitude means that an attitude:
A. gives us a way to categorize objects and events
B. influences whether we approach or avoid an object or event
C. guides us to behave in specific ways
D. is targeted toward an object or event

p. 589
Attitudes
Level: Easy
Type: Factual
Ans: B

116. Significant predictors of future behaviors are:
A. instances of group polarization
B. attitudes
C. dispositional attributions
D. situational attributions

p. 589
Attitudes
Level: Easy
Type: Conceptual
Ans: D

117. If your psychology professor wanted to predict your behavior in a future psychology class, she ought to determine your:
A. high school GPA
B. willingness to commit the self-serving bias
C. socioeconomic background
D. attitude toward the current psychology class

p. 589
Attitudes
Level: Easy
Type: Factual
Ans: D

118. Attitudes which serve as convenient guidelines for interpreting and categorizing objects and events and deciding whether to approach or avoid them are said to have a(n) _____ function.
A. expressing
B. defending
C. adjusting
D. interpreting

p. 589
Attitudes
Level: Moderate
Type: Applied
Ans: D

119. Tom, who is a member of the National Rifle Association, voted for a candidate for a local position who holds similar attitudes against gun control. His action angered many of his coworkers and he had to endure much harassment. His ability to stand up under this kind of pressure refers to the _____ function of attitudes.
    A. utilitarian
    B. defensive
    C. adjustive
    D. evaluative

p. 589
Attitudes
Level: Easy
Type: Factual
Ans: C

120. The _____ function of attitudes allows us to stand up for what we believe.
    A. expressive
    B. defensive
    C. evaluative
    D. interpretive

p. 590
Attitudes
Level: Easy
Type: Factual
Ans: B

121. The idea of cognitive dissonance explains how we:
    A. make the fundamental attribution error
    B. deal with inconsistencies
    C. persuade other people to be obedient
    D. develop stereotypes

p. 590
Attitudes
Level: Moderate
Type: Conceptual
Ans: A

122. Which of the following words best describes cognitive dissonance?
    A. clash
    B. harmony
    C. straight
    D. clear

p. 590
Attitudes
Level: Moderate
Type: Factual
Ans: D

123. The state of unpleasant psychological tension that motivates people to reduce our inconsistencies and return to a more consistent state is referred to as:
    A. the self-serving bias
    B. attribution
    C. prejudice
    D. cognitive dissonance

p. 590
Attitudes
Level: Easy
Type: Applied
Ans: D

124. Although Paula loves her work with the American Cancer Society, she smokes cigarettes at home. This is an example of:
    A. the self-serving bias
    B. attribution
    C. prejudice
    D. cognitive dissonance

p. 590
Attitudes
Level: Easy
Type: Applied
Ans: D

125. "I know that I should wear my seat belt in the car, but I don't." This person probably experiences:
    A. external attribution
    B. the self-serving bias
    C. prejudice
    D. cognitive dissonance

p. 590
Attitudes
Level: Moderate
Type: Factual
Ans: A
*PS/SG 25-11*

126. In Leon Festinger's boring task experiment, the subjects who were paid only $1 to tell other students it was interesting (a lie) dealt with their cognitive dissonance by:
A. convincing themselves that it was somewhat interesting after all
B. hoping the students they lied to realized it was just part of the experiment
C. insisting that they should also be paid $20 for telling the lie
D. begging Festinger and his assistants not to reveal their names

p. 590
Attitudes
Level: Easy
Type: Factual
Ans: C

127. When a person takes a public position that is different from their private belief, they are engaging in _____ behavior.
A. persuasive
B. synergic
C. counterattitudinal
D. oppositional

p. 590
Attitudes
Level: Easy
Type: Factual
Ans: C

128. When we start to believe our own lies after engaging in counterattitudinal behavior, it is because of:
A. cognitive dissonance
B. self-schemas
C. self-perception
D. the cognitive miser model

p. 590
Attitudes
Level: Easy
Type: Factual
Ans: A

129. Self-perception theory suggests that we:
A. observe our own behavior and then infer attitudes from the behavior
B. strive to reduce inconsistencies between our attitudes and behavior
C. feel motivated to conserve time and effort by taking cognitive shortcuts
D. attempt to control and regulate the information that we present to others

p. 590
Attitudes
Level: Moderate
Type: Factual
Ans: B

130. "If I said it, it must be true because I've reduced the inconsistency of my beliefs and behavior." This <u>best</u> describes the:
A. arousal-cost-reward model
B. cognitive dissonance theory
C. covariation theory
D. self-perception theory

p. 590
Attitudes
Level: Moderate
Type: Factual
Ans: D

131. "If I said it, it must be true because I've simply explained my own behavior." This *best* describes the:
A. arousal-cost-reward model
B. cognitive dissonance theory
C. covariation theory
D. self-perception theory

p. 590
Attitudes
Level: Easy
Type: Factual
Ans: D

132. Which of the following theories says that attitudes follow behavior?
A. attribution
B. schema
C. self-esteem
D. self-perception

p. 590
Attitudes
Level: Difficult
Type: Conceptual
Ans: A

133. If you were to measure the attitudes towards the wearing of seat belts in a state where wearing them was compulsory and compare those attitudes to those of people living in a state where it was not compulsory, self-perception theory would predict that people in the state with compulsory seat belt legislation tended to:

A. develop a more positive attitude toward the wearing of seat belts
B. develop a more negative attitude toward the wearing of seat belts
C. wear the seat belts only when police officers were visible
D. praise the virtues of seat belts but not wear them

p. 591
Attitudes
Level: Easy
Type: Factual
Ans: D

134. The central route for persuasion presents information with:
A. emotions
B. personal appeals
C. style and image
D. strong arguments, analyses, facts, and logic

p. 591
Attitudes
Level: Easy
Type: Factual
Ans: A

135. If a television commercial selling a new car presents strong arguments, analyses, facts, and logic, we would say that _____ has been used.
A. the central route for persuasion
B. the peripheral route for persuasion
C. cognitive dissonance
D. compliance

p. 591
Attitudes
Level: Easy
Type: Factual
Ans: C

136. You are watching a television commercial for a long distance phone company. In it, two phone companies are being compared for price, service, and quality. This commercial uses the _____ approach:
A. cognitive dissonance
B. the peripheral route
C. the central route
D. compliance

p. 591
Attitudes
Level: Easy
Type: Applied
Ans: C

137. Mr. Johnson is a lawyer for a physician who helps sick people take their own lives. His job is to ensure that the public has a positive attitude toward the assisted suicide. Mr. Johnson uses the central route to foster that kind of attitude. He often released information to the news media. Which of the following types of information might Mr. Johnson release if using the central route?

A. pictures of the suffering patients
B. portray people against assisted suicide as religious fanatics
C. statistics about the cost of long-term health care for these sick patients
D. information about the pain patients are feeling

p. 591
Attitudes
Level: Easy
Type: Applied
Ans: A

138. A candidate for the U. S. Senate wants to use the central route for persuasion during his campaign. This candidate should focus primarily on:
A. presenting clear information about his views
B. making a lot of exciting personal appearances
C. TV commercials with the slogan "for a better tomorrow, vote today for..."
D. getting endorsements from sports figures and other celebrities

| | | |
|---|---|---|
| p. 591<br>Attitudes<br>Level: Easy<br>Type: Factual<br>Ans: C | 139. | The peripheral route for persuasion emphasizes:<br>A. analyses, facts, and logic<br>B. credibility of candidates<br>C. emotional appeal<br>D. devoting sufficient time to understanding the issues |
| p. 591<br>Attitudes<br>Level: Easy<br>Type: Factual<br>Ans: C<br>*PS/SG 25-13* | 140. | Candidate Roberta Reformer, who has an excellent plan for better government, will take the _____ route to persuasion; her opponent Boss Buster, who plans to label Roberta a hysterical feminist, will take the _____ route.<br>A. direct; indirect<br>B. honest; dishonest<br>C. central; peripheral<br>D. logical; emotional |
| p. 591<br>Attitudes<br>Level: Easy<br>Type: Applied<br>Ans: B | 141. | A candidate for the Presidency wants to use the peripheral route for persuasion during her campaign. This candidate should focus primarily on:<br>A. presenting clear information about her views<br>B. making a lot of exciting and enthusiastic personal appearances<br>C. appearing credible and knowledgeable<br>D. being committed to the issues |
| p. 591<br>Attitudes<br>Level: Easy<br>Type: Applied<br>Ans: D | 142. | You and a friend are watching television when a commercial comes on for a fast-food restaurant. The commercial shows happy people talking and laughing at the restaurant, but not much mention is made of the food. You correctly identify the commercial to be an example of the _____ of persuasion.<br>A. covariation model<br>B. attributional route<br>C. central route<br>D. peripheral route |
| p. 591<br>Attitudes<br>Level: Moderate<br>Type: Conceptual<br>Ans: C | 143. | Central routes for persuasion generally work on the _____, whereas peripheral routes for persuasion work primarily on the _____.<br>A. person schema; role schema<br>B. disposition; situation<br>C. cognitive component; affective component<br>D. fundamental attribution error; self-serving bias |
| p. 591<br>Attitudes<br>Level: Easy<br>Type: Factual<br>Ans: A | 144. | Of the routes of persuasion presented in the textbook, which one is <u>most</u> likely to produce more enduring results?<br>A. central route<br>B. peripheral route<br>C. cognitive route<br>D. primary route |

p. 591
Attitudes
Level: Moderate
Type: Factual
Ans: D

145.   Of the following, all have been focused on by the Yale Communication program on persuasion except the characteristics of the:
A.   source
B.   message
C.   audience
D.   outcome

p. 591
Attitudes
Level: Easy
Type: Conceptual
Ans: A

146.   Of the following, which will likely be the least effective in reducing smoking behavior among teenagers?
A.   health threats
B.   a credible source
C.   a familiar source
D.   an attractive source

p. 591
Attitudes
Level: Moderate
Type: Applied
Ans: A

147.   Claire must try to convince the other executives in her company to invest in a major real estate venture. She knows that her colleagues are not initially in favor of the idea. According to what psychologists know about the optimal content for persuasive messages, Claire should:
A.   present both sides of the argument
B.   present one side of the argument
C.   present the facts and let the members of the group make up their own minds
D.   start by suggesting that they not make the investment in the hope that she will get some opposition to that idea

p. 591
Attitudes
Level: Easy
Type: Factual
Ans: C

148.   You are presenting a scientific paper to a group of your professors. Based on Module 25, what approach should you take and why?
A.   the secondary approach since your audience is likely to be much older than you
B.   the peripheral approach since your professors are most concerned with how interesting you can make the presentation
C.   the central approach because the audience is most interested in the facts
D.   the central approach because the audience is most interested in your presentation skills

p. 591
Attitudes
Level: Easy
Type: Factual
Ans: D

149.   If an audience is known to be initially opposed to a persuasive message, which of the following types of communication will be most effective in changing the audience's attitudes?
A.   a one-sided message
B.   a fear-inducing message
C.   a message from a non-credible source
D.   a two-sided message

p. 591
Attitudes
Level: Easy
Type: Factual
Ans: B

150.   A one-sided persuasive message will have the greatest impact on an audience when the audience:
A.   is not concerned about the issue
B.   is already in favor of the issue
C.   is afraid of the issue
D.   is initially opposed to the issue

p. 592
Social & Group
  Influences
Level: Easy
Type: Factual
Ans: D

151. The case of the hazing incident and high school students <u>best</u> illustrates:
A. obedience
B. compliance
C. consistency
D. conformity

p. 592
Social & Group
  Influences
Level: Easy
Type: Factual
Ans: D
*www*

152. "A behavior performed because of group pressure even though that pressure involves no direct requests" is the definition of:
A. obedience
B. compliance
C. consistency
D. conformity

p. 592
Social & Group
  Influences
Level: Easy
Type: Applied
Ans: A

153. At Jack's office a number of men start wearing Hawaiian shirts on Fridays. Soon Jack begins wearing a Hawaiian shirt on Fridays. Jack's behavior is an example of:
A. conformity
B. consistency
C. compliance
D. obedience

p. 592
Social & Group
  Influences
Level: Easy
Type: Applied
Ans: D

154. Have you ever noticed that when people are in the elevator they typically stand facing the door? This <u>best</u> illustrates:
A. compliance
B. consistency
C. obedience
D. conformity

p. 592
Social & Group
  Influences
Level: Easy
Type: Applied
Ans: C

155. You have gone to the local gym to exercise for about a week. You notice that everyone is wearing light colored socks. Tomorrow, you go the store to buy a pair of light colored socks and wear them to the gym. You think you look pretty neat. You have just experienced:
A. primary attribution
B. consensus
C. conformity
D. obedience

p. 592
Social & Group
  Influences
Level: Easy
Type: Factual
Ans: C

156. As a class project, Dr. Thomas asks her class to attempt to replicate the findings of Asch's classic experiment on conformity. What task will students in the class use in their attempted replication?
A. requests for charity
B. the effects of punishment on learning
C. judging the length of lines
D. expressing political opinions

p. 592
Social & Group
  Influences
Level: Easy
Type: Factual
Ans: B

157. In Asch's classic experiment on conformity, _____ percent of the subjects never conformed to the group pressure by giving an incorrect answer on any of the trials.
A. 15
B. 25
C. 35
D. 45

p. 592
Social & Group
  Influences
Level: Easy
Type: Factual
Ans: D

158. In examining cultural factors, conformity decreases when the culture:
A. is paternally oriented
B. has a representative form of government
C. emphasizes collectivism
D. emphasizes individualism

p. 593
Social & Group
  Influences
Level: Easy
Type: Factual
Ans: A

159. If a person gives in to some form of social pressure, but does not change their private beliefs, then the person is demonstrating:
A. compliance
B. obedience
C. the foot-in-the-door technique
D. the self-handicapping strategy

p. 593
Social & Group
  Influences
Level: Easy
Type: Applied
Ans: C

160. You've watched how people behave in an elevator. They all faced towards the front and either look straight ahead or at the floor indicator. Yet, there's no direct request to do so. People in elevators show:
A. group dynamics
B. obedience
C. compliance
D. the self-handicapping strategy

p. 593
Social & Group
  Influences
Level: Easy
Type: Applied
Ans: D

161. Bethany answers the phone and is greeted by a person selling magazines. She says that she's not interested in buying any magazines. But the person persists. She ends up buying several subscriptions that she knows she does not need. Bethany illustrates:
A. the self-handicapping strategy
B. obedience
C. conformity
D. compliance

p. 593
Social & Group
  Influences
Level: Easy
Type: Conceptual
Ans: B

162. Which of the following is an example of compliance?
A. slowing down in a school zone when children are present
B. deciding to work overtime in order to meet a project deadline even though you wish you didn't have to
C. wearing the same clothes as your friends
D. deciding to go on a diet

p. 593
Social & Group
 Influences
Level: Moderate
Type: Conceptual
Ans: B

163. As you visit Rome, the cliché, "When in Rome do as the Romans" is very much in your mind. Even though you change your public behavior, your private beliefs remain unchanged. This is an example of:
A. obedience
B. compliance
C. consistency
D. conformity

p. 593
Social & Group
 Influences
Level: Easy
Type: Factual
Ans: A

164. An increased probability of compliance to a second request if a person complies with a small first request is the definition of:
A. the foot-in-the-door technique
B. the face-in-the-door technique
C. multiple conformity
D. serial obedience

p. 593
Social & Group
 Influences
Level: Moderate
Type: Applied
Ans: A
*PS/SG 25-16*

165. Tell you what… before you quit just do one more of these questions, O.K.? [I'm using the _____ technique on you in my efforts to get you to do all the questions.]
A. foot-in-the-door
b. compliance
C. conformity
D. soft-soaping

p. 593
Social & Group
 Influences
Level: Moderate
Type: Applied
Ans: C

166. Imagine that you have been put in charge of a fundraising campaign for your community organization. You decide to try the foot-in-the-door technique. Which of the following strategies would fit the technique?
A. asking potential donors to contribute a fairly large sum of money and, when they refuse, saying you will settle for a lesser amount
B. asking the same potential donors repeatedly until they give in and contribute
C. asking potential donors for a small contribution and then going back a few weeks later and asking for more
D. offering potential donors a number of benefits and then asking them for a contribution to your cause

p. 593
Social & Group
 Influences
Level: Moderate
Type: Applied
Ans: A

167. At a local health fair, you see a business selling exercise equipment. One of their marketing tools is to give you one-month free rental of any piece of exercise equipment. You realize that this tool is really the:
A. foot-in-the-door technique
B. cognitive dissonance method
C. arousal-cost-reward technique
D. social comparison method

p. 593
Social & Group
 Influences
Level: Easy
Type: Factual
Ans: D

168. When you engage in behavior in response to an order by a powerful person, you are experiencing:
A. conformity
B. constancy
C. compliance
D. obedience

p. 593
Social & Group
  Influences
Level: Easy
Type: Conceptual
Ans: B

169. You are taking this test because your professor told you to do so. Since you are indeed taking this test, you have just experienced:
- A. altruism
- B. obedience
- C. conformity
- D. compliance

p. 593
Social & Group
  Influences
Level: Easy
Type: Applied
Ans: B

170. Captain Janeway orders her crew to stand at attention during a military parade and they do so. The crew's behavior is an example of:
- A. compliance
- B. obedience
- C. conformity
- D. constancy

p. 593
Social & Group
  Influences
Level: Easy
Type: Factual
Ans: C

171. What roles were played in Milgram's study on obedience?
- A. co-workers
- B. artist and critic
- C. teacher and student
- D. patient and doctor

p. 594
Social & Group
  Influences
Level: Easy
Type: Factual
Ans: A

172. When psychiatrists were asked to predict what percentage of the population would deliver the full range of shocks in the Milgram experiment, their prediction was:
- A. less than 1 percent
- B. about 2 percent
- C. between 25 and 30 percent
- D. about 50 percent

p. 594
Social & Group
  Influences
Level: Easy
Type: Factual
Ans: D
*www*

173. In the study of obedience conducted by Stanley Milgram what percentage of "teachers" delivered the maximum 450-volt-shock?
- A. 35 percent
- B. 45 percent
- C. 55 percent
- D. 65 percent

p. 594
Social & Group
  Influences
Level: Easy
Type: Factual
Ans: B
*PS/SG 25-17*

174. In Stanley Milgram's electric shock experiment, most subjects continued to give shocks:
- A. only up to the point they considered dangerous
- B. even beyond the point they believed was dangerous
- C. only if they had been paid a considerable amount to participate in the experiment
- D. only as long as the shocks seemed to be helping the "learner" do better

p. 594
Social & Group
 Influences
Level: Easy
Type: Factual
Ans: A

175. Religious leaders, military officers, doctors, scientists and parents are examples of:
A. authority figures
B. conformity inducers
C. altruistic leaders
D. asocial models

p. 594
Social & Group
 Influences
Level: Moderate
Type: Factual
Ans: C

176. What happened when the authority figure in Milgram's study gave orders over the phone?
A. Subjects were more likely to agree with the group and disagree with the authority figure.
B. "Teachers" were more likely to disobey the authority figure.
C. Subjects were more likely to disobey the authority figure.
D. Subjects were less likely to disobey the authority figure.

p. 594
Social & Group
 Influences
Level: Easy
Type: Factual
Ans: C

177. The results of Milgram's obedience experiments demonstrated:
A. most people will not obey orders to harm others in the lab
B. males but not females will obey orders to shock another person
C. a majority of people will obey orders that they know are unreasonable
D. psychiatrists overestimate the percentage of individuals who will follow orders to harm others in laboratory experiments

p. 594
Social & Group
 Influences
Level: Moderate
Type: Applied
Ans: C

178. A commanding officer gives a soldier an order that he knows the soldier would rather not obey. According to the findings of the Milgram obedience experiments, what should the officer do to increase the likelihood of obedience?
A. accompany the order with a threat
B. leave the soldier alone to obey the order without losing face
C. stay in the presence of the soldier until the order has been obeyed
D. give the order in a friendly way

p. 594
Social & Group
 Influences
Level: Easy
Type: Conceptual
Ans: C

179. During the Vietnam war era, Lt. William Calley was convicted of ordering his men to shoot women and children during the My Lai massacre. This incident most resembles the work of which of the following researchers?
A. Albert Bandura's study of modeling and aggression
B. Solomon Asch's study of conformity
C. Stanley Milgram's study of obedience
D. Leonard Eron's study of TV violence and aggression

p. 594
Social & Group
 Influences
Level: Easy
Type: Factual
Ans: C

180. A concern regarding the Milgram obedience study is that of:
A. mundane realism
B. appropriate control groups
C. ethics
D. adequate testing of the null hypothesis

p. 594
Social & Group
  Influences
Level: Moderate
Type: Factual
Ans: D
*PS/SG 25-18*

181. Milgram's famous experiment could not be conducted today because:
A. people today are too rational and scientific to obey orders they don't agree with
B. the experiment has been so widely written about that everyone is in on the secret
C. few would be fooled by the fake lab, since psychologists are known for deception
D. a new code of ethics screens experiments for potential harm to the subjects

p. 594
Social & Group
  Influences
Level: Easy
Type: Factual
Ans: D

182. A technique whereby experimental subjects are told about the purpose and method of the experiment is called:
A. briefing
B. postexperimental discussion
C. sampling
D. debriefing

p. 595
Social & Group
  Influences
Level: Easy
Type: Applied
Ans: C

183. As part of his job, Joe raises money for the American Cancer Association. Joe's action for the Cancer Association is an example of:
A. altruism
B. reciprocity
C. prosocial behavior
D. diffusion of responsibility

p. 595
Social & Group
  Influences
Level: Easy
Type: Factual
Ans: D

184. In _____, the person who is helping does so without expectation of a reward.
A. diffusion of responsibility
B. reciprocity
C. prosocial behavior
D. altruism

p. 595
Social & Group
  Influences
Level: Easy
Type: Applied
Ans: B

185. A car is rapidly approaching an old lady crossing Hollywood Boulevard. Alan pushes the lady out of the way and is himself hit by the car, but saves her life. This is an example of:
A. empathy
B. altruism
C. diffusion of responsibility
D. reciprocity

p. 595
Social & Group
  Influences
Level: Easy
Type: Factual
Ans: D

186. Helping a victim because of identification with what the victim is going through is an example of which motivation for helping?
A. values
B. reciprocity
C. norms
D. empathy

p. 595
Social & Group
 Influences
Level: Easy
Type: Applied
Ans: B

187. A mugger attacks an old man on a subway car. Bernard gets disgusted when he sees the old man being beat up and he jumps the mugger and begins hitting him. Bernard's motivation for helping appears to be:
A. altruism
B. personal distress
C. reciprocity
D. diffusion of responsibility

p. 595
Social & Group
 Influences
Level: Easy
Type: Factual
Ans: A

188. "Good people help others who are in trouble" represents which motivation for helping others?
A. norms and values
B. empathy
C. norm of reciprocity
D. diffusion of responsibility

p. 595
Social & Group
 Influences
Level: Moderate
Type: Factual
Ans: D

189. The two most prominent models used to explain helping behavior differ in that:
A. one emphasizes the helper whereas the other emphasizes the victim
B. one emphasizes instincts whereas the other emphasizes thought patterns
C. one emphasizes sex whereas the other emphasizes social norms
D. one emphasizes stages whereas the other emphasizes costs and rewards

p. 595
Social & Group
 Influences
Level: Moderate
Type: Factual
Ans: A

190. According to the _____ model, we notice a situation, interpret it as one in which help is needed, assume personal responsibility, choose a form of assistance, and carry out that assistance.
A. decision stage
B. cognitive miser
C. arousal-cost-reward
D. attribution

p. 595
Social & Group
 Influences
Level: Easy
Type: Factual
Ans: C

191. What is the initial stage in the decision stage model of helping?
A. assuming personal responsibility
B. choosing a form of assistance
C. noticing the situation
D. carrying out the assistance

p. 595
Social & Group
 Influences
Level: Easy
Type: Factual
Ans: A

192. Helping others even at one's own risk is called:
A. altruism
B. prosocial behavior
C. diffusion
D. compliance

p. 595
Social & Group
 Influences
Level: Easy
Type: Factual
Ans: A

193. According to the decision-stage model of helping, most people don't help because they don't:
A. assume personal responsibility
B. choose a form of assistance
C. notice the situation
D. carry out the assistance

p. 595
Social & Group
  Influences
Level: Moderate
Type: Applied
Ans: D

194. Keith notices a man violently slapping his girlfriend in a parking lot. This upsets him and makes him want to do something to stop the slapping. According to the arousal-cost-reward model of helping, Keith is experiencing:
A. cost
B. reward
C. activation
D. arousal

p. 595
Social & Group
  Influences
Level: Moderate
Type: Applied
Ans: B

195. Kris sees a child is trapped in a burning building, but is too afraid of fire to offer any assistance. Kris probably based her decision on:
A. the decision stage model
B. the arousal-cost-reward model
C. the frustration-aggression hypothesis
D. cognitive dissonance

p. 596
Social & Group
  Influences
Level: Easy
Type: Factual
Ans: C

196. Group cohesion is determined by:
A. the arousal-cost-reward model
B. the phenomenon called the risky shift
C. how much group members perceive that they share common attributes
D. formal rules used to obtain compliance from members of the group

p. 596
Social & Group
  Influences
Level: Easy
Type: Factual
Ans: A

197. Formal or informal rules about how group members should behave are known as:
A. group norms
B. group perceptions
C. group values
D. group ideals

p. 596
Social & Group
  Influences
Level: Easy
Type: Factual
Ans: A

198. According to Maslow's theory, people become involved with groups in order to:
A. satisfy the need to belong
B. prevent self-handicapping behavior
C. resolve feelings of cognitive dissonance
D. experience group polarization and the risky shift

p. 596
Social & Group
  Influences
Level: Easy
Type: Factual
Ans: C

199. Which theory proposes that we join groups to be able to measure the correctness of our attitudes and beliefs?
A. Maslow's hierarchy of needs
B. attribution theory
C. social comparison theory
D. informational influence theory

p. 596
Social & Group
  Influences
Level: Easy
Type: Applied
Ans: B

200. A teenager is unsure how his new haircut looks. What would Leon Festinger say the teenager should do?
A. determine if his peer group has group cohesion
B. compare his haircut with that of his peers
C. ask his mother
D. use consistency, consensus, and distinctiveness to determine his attribution

| | | |
|---|---|---|
| p. 596<br>Social & Group<br> Influences<br>Level: Easy<br>Type: Factual<br>Ans: C | 201. | Leon Festinger's social comparison theory offers _____ reasons for forming groups.<br>A.  behavioral<br>B.  affective<br>C.  cognitive<br>D.  biological |
| p. 596<br>Social & Group<br> Influences<br>Level: Moderate<br>Type: Applied<br>Ans: D | 202. | Tina needs some help in one of her classes. She decides to join a task-oriented study group. In Group A, the members have specific duties to perform like writing practice questions and writing an outline of each lecture. In Group B, there is more emphasis on developing relationships like making sure everyone shows up to the review sessions. Which group should Tina join?<br>A.  either group<br>B.  neither group<br>C.  Group B<br>D.  Group A |
| p. 596<br>Social & Group<br> Influences<br>Level: Moderate<br>Type: Applied<br>Ans: B | 203. | Lori is being interviewed by a college professor regarding her circle of friends. Lori says that she enjoys her friends because "they give me support and love." To what type of group does Lori belong?<br>A.  facilitative group<br>B.  socially oriented group<br>C.  diffused oriented group<br>D.  task oriented group |
| p. 597<br>Social & Group<br> Influences<br>Level: Moderate<br>Type: Applied<br>Ans: D<br>*www* | 204. | Katy swims faster when there are large crowds at the swim meet than when she practices and no one is around. Her faster times may be due to:<br>A.  social inhibition<br>B.  deindividuation<br>C.  diffusion of responsibility<br>D.  social facilitation |
| p. 597<br>Social & Group<br> Influences<br>Level: Moderate<br>Type: Applied<br>Ans: D | 205. | Jimmy usually beats Ivan in practice tennis matches, but when he plays Ivan again before a packed house during a tournament, Jimmy plays badly and loses. Jimmy's poor performance is likely due to:<br>A.  deindividuation<br>B.  diffusion of responsibility<br>C.  social facilitation<br>D.  social inhibition |
| p. 597<br>Social & Group<br> Influences<br>Level: Moderate<br>Type: Applied<br>Ans: A | 206. | "Whenever I am trying to play a complex piano piece that I've never seen before, my friend usually sits down to listen." Make a likely prediction of the piano player's performance based upon your understanding of social and group influence:<br>A.  the friend will cause social inhibition since the song is new and complex<br>B.  the performance will be better because of social facilitation<br>C.  the performance will be better because of social inhibition<br>D.  the friend will cause deindividuation |

p. 597
Social & Group
  Influences
Level: Moderate
Type: Applied
Ans: C

207.   Tim is a nice, quiet boy, except when he roams the streets as a member of a gang. While with the gang, Tim acts in a violent, vulgar fashion. His antisocial behavior is likely the result of:
A.   social facilitation
B.   social inhibition
C.   deindividuation
D.   infusion

p. 597
Social & Group
  Influences
Level: Easy
Type: Factual
Ans: D

208.   Which of the following is associated with a greater likelihood of taking on an antisocial role?
A.   social facilitation
B.   informational influence
C.   altruism
D.   deindividuation

p. 597
Social & Group
  Influences
Level: Difficult
Type: Conceptual
Ans: A

209.   Your songwriter friend has written a song on deindividuation. Now you have to give it a title. What is the best title?
A.   "Just Another Face in the Crowd"
B.   "Judge Me"
C.   "Nowhere To Go"
D.   "Do What I Say"

p. 597
Social & Group
  Influences
Level: Easy
Type: Factual
Ans: C

210.   What does deindividuation provide an individual in a crowd?
A.   social inhibition
B.   motivation
C.   anonymity
D.   an identity

p. 597
Social & Group
  Influences
Level: Easy
Type: Factual
Ans: B

211.   We use the reactions of other people to judge the seriousness of a situation according to which of the following theories?
A.   implicit personality theories
B.   informational influence theory
C.   diffusion of responsibility theory
D.   cognitive dissonance

p. 597
Social & Group
  Influences
Level: Easy
Type: Applied
Ans: C

212.   "I'm not sure what to do. I'm at the shopping mall and I see someone who looks like he needs help. But, I don't know how serious the situation is." According to the informational influence theory, to determine the seriousness of the situation, we use:
A.   our prior experience
B.   our memories
C.   the reactions of others
D.   the availability heuristic

p. 597
Social & Group
 Influences
Level: Moderate
Type: Applied
Ans: B

213. Burt witnesses a mugging on a crowded bus but does nothing to help the victim. When later asked by the police to explain his inaction, Burt says that he figured someone else would help the victim. Burt has cited which explanation for the bystander effect?
A. arousal-cost-reward
B. diffusion of responsibility
C. group inhibition
D. social contagion

p. 597
Social & Group
 Influences
Level: Moderate
Type: Conceptual
Ans: C

214. Which statement is most related to the diffusion of responsibility theory?
A. "How are these other people reacting?"
B. "It seems whenever I am with others I do a lot better."
C. "Someone else will probably help."
D. "That individual is a legitimate authority figure."

p. 597
Social & Group
 Influences
Level: Moderate
Type: Applied
Ans: C

215. Adam is driving past the scene of an automobile accident. He sees that there are a lot of other people around, so he doesn't feel that he needs to stop. This is an example of the _____ theory.
A. attribution
B. catharsis
C. diffusion of responsibility
D. groupthink

p. 598
Social & Group
 Influences
Level: Moderate
Type: Factual
Ans: B

216. At one time, it was thought that group discussions more often resulted in what was called:
A. diffusion of opinion
B. risky shift
C. deindividuation
D. selective attention

p. 598
Social & Group
 Influences
Level: Moderate
Type: Applied
Ans: D

217. Researchers have discovered that the direction of a group's risky shift is dependent on:
A. the arousal-cost-reward model
B. dispositional and situation attributions
C. the type of person and role schemas maintained by group members
D. how conservative or liberal the group was to begin with

p. 598
Social & Group
 Influences
Level: Moderate
Type: Applied
Ans: B

218. A liberal group is discussing a possible tax increase to fund Medicare. When the group has finished their discussion, their views are even more liberal than they were when the group started. This is an example of:
A. the fundamental attribution error
B. group polarization
C. the diffusion of responsibility
D. social comparison theory

p. 598
Social & Group
  Influences
Level: Moderate
Type: Applied
Ans: D

219. A group of executives meet to decide on cost-cutting options for the company. They eventually decide to fire 15 percent of the employees, a decision more extreme than any of the executives had previously advocated. The decision is an example of:
  A. interaction-oriented leadership
  B. social inhibition
  C. social facilitation
  D. group polarization

p. 598
Social & Group
  Influences
Level: Easy
Type: Factual
Ans: D

220. According to Irving Janis, the mindguard in a group:
  A. keeps discussions open and unbiased
  B. makes sure all group members express their opinions
  C. prevents groupthink from occurring
  D. discourages ideas that threaten group unity

p. 598
Social & Group
  Influences
Level: Easy
Type: Applied
Ans: C

221. As you read about groupthink, you recall a committee you recently served on. There was a person who always discouraged the discussion of ideas that might have caused disunity on the committee. This person may have served in the role of:
  A. presider
  B. unifier
  C. mindguard
  D. cohesive leader

p. 598
Social & Group
  Influences
Level: Easy
Type: Factual
Ans: C
*PS/SG 25-20*

222. Which one of the following decisions was a classic example of groupthink?
  A. atomic bombing of Japan in World War II
  B. assassination of President Kennedy
  C. Bay of Pigs invasion of Cuba
  D. withdrawal of Shannon Faulkner from the Citadel military college

p. 598
Social & Group
  Influences
Level: Easy
Type: Conceptual
Ans: C

223. Ingroup is to outgroup as _____ is to _____.
  A. them; us
  B. difference; similarity
  C. us; them
  D. conservative; liberal

p. 597
Social & Group
  Influences
Level: Difficult
Type: Conceptual
Ans: B

224. Your songwriter friend has written a song on groupthink. Now you have to give it a title. What is the best title?
  A. "Your Presence Makes Me Better"
  B. "We Just Make Bad Decisions"
  C. "What You Say, I Do"
  D. "Just Another Face in the Crowd"

p. 597
Social & Group
 Influences
Level: Moderate
Type: Factual
Ans: A

225. In groupthink, the decision is _____ than _____.
A. less important; reaching agreement
B. more important; having a spirited debate
C. less important; having a spirited debate
D. more important; reaching agreement

p. 598
Social & Group
 Influences
Level: Moderate
Type: Applied
Ans: D

226. As a chairperson of an important committee, you recognize the danger of groupthink. What is one way that your committee can avoid groupthink?
A. provide some time at the beginning of each meeting for small talk
B. allow the members of the group to get to know each other socially
C. during each meeting, emphasize the importance of group unity
D. make sure the group remains task oriented

p. 600
Aggression
Level: Easy
Type: Factual
Ans: C

227. _____ is defined as any act that is intended to do physical or psychological harm according to your textbook.
A. Brutality
B. Violence
C. Aggression
D. Altruism

p. 600
Aggression
Level: Easy
Type: Applied
Ans: A

228. A football player tries to hurt the opposing quarterback so that the quarterback will not be able to continue playing. A psychologist would consider this an example of _____ behavior.
A. aggressive
B. prosocial
C. assertive
D. angry

p. 600
Aggression
Level: Easy
Type: Conceptual
Ans: B

229. Which of the following would a psychologist not consider to be an example of aggression?
A. a boy hitting another boy in the playground
B. a doctor breaking a patient's ribs in an attempt to start the patient's heart
C. a motorist yelling at another in a busy intersection
D. a brother hitting his younger brother

p. 600
Aggression
Level: Easy
Type: Factual
Ans: C

230. In animals there are numerous signals that signal aggressive and submission. According to ethologists, these signals
A. are learned
B. are also found in humans
C. are largely programmed by genetic factors
D. are redundant

p. 600
Aggression
Level: Easy
Type: Conceptual
Ans: D

231. In examining the role of genetics in aggression, genetics accounted for:
A. frustration-aggression hypothesis
B. social learning theory
C. cognitive theory
D. biological theory

p. 600
Aggression
Level: Easy
Type: Factual
Ans: C

232. Twin and adoption studies on aggression show that up to ____ of human aggression is governed by genetic factors.
A. 70%
B. 50%
C. 35%
D. 10%

p. 601
Aggression
Level: Easy
Type: Applied
Ans: C

233. Suzie watches her mother "smack" her little brother Pete to get him to shut up. Later, when Pete begins screaming, Suzie smacks him. According to social cognitive theory, Suzie's behavior illustrates:
A. classical conditioning
B. operant conditioning
C. imitation
D. imprinting

p. 601
Aggression
Level: Easy
Type: Factual
Ans: A

234. Which of the following statements is most reflective of the social cognitive model of aggression?
A. Watching violent television programs contributes to aggression in children.
B. Frustration may result in behaviors other than aggression.
C. Catharsis relieves emotional tension and prevents aggressive behavior.
D. Children learn scripts for aggression through reinforcement.

p. 601
Aggression
Level: Moderate
Type: Factual
Ans: C

235. Which of the following most accurately captures the research regarding the effects on children of viewing violent television programs?
A. There is no relationship between viewing violent TV and later aggression.
B. Boys but not girls become more violent after watching violent TV.
C. Children who watch violent TV may learn that aggression has no negative consequences.
D. There is a correlation between viewing violent TV and later aggression but one does not cause the other.

p. 601
Aggression
Level: Easy
Type: Factual
Ans: B

236. Children who watch 2-3 hours of television daily are _____ times more likely to commit violent and aggressive acts later in life compared to children who watched less television.
A. 2
B. 4
C. 8
D. 10

p. 601
Aggression
Level: Easy
Type: Factual
Ans: C

237. The _____ says that when our pursuit of our goals is blocked we become frustrated and we respond with anger and aggression.
A. diathesis-aggression model
B. peripheral route of aggression
C. frustration-aggression hypothesis
D. negative affect model

p. 601
Aggression
Level: Easy
Type: Factual
Ans: D

238. According to Leonard Berkowitz, a person's reaction to frustration:
A. always involves aggression
B. depends on his or her neurochemical makeup
C. is affected by genetic factors
D. depends on how that person interprets information about the frustrating situation

p. 601
Aggression
Level: Easy
Type: Applied
Ans: B

239. Three-year-old Katy has just had her baby sister tear up an art project that Katy had been working on. Katy is obviously frustrated since she put much time and effort into the picture. But she doesn't hit her sister because "Mom says we can't hit." This would have been predicted by the:
A. diathesis-aggression model
B. modified frustration-aggression hypothesis
C. frustration-aggression hypothesis
D. negative affect model

p. 601
Aggression
Level: Easy
Type: Factual
Ans: C

240. The frustration-aggression hypothesis was modified because of research which indicated that:
A. people always respond to frustration with aggression
B. aggression is genetic
C. cognitive factors can override aggression
D. aggression is an innate, biological phenomenon

p. 602
Aggression
Level: Easy
Type: Factual
Ans: C

241. Most researchers agree that the primary motivation for rape is:
A. sexual urges and libido
B. catharsis
C. aggression, power, and control
D. social inhibition and deindividuation

p. 602
Aggression
Level: Moderate
Type: Factual
Ans: A
PS/SG 25-22

242. Why is rape so common? Researchers point to the fact that:
A. there are other motivations for rape, like aggression, power, and control, that may be more important than sex
B. women are much bolder today, yet still like to be actively pursued, a situation that leaves men confused about what women really want
C. Hollywood movies keep our sexual urges in a state of almost constant arousal
D. unfortunately, rape is as natural as male hormones and female flirtatiousness — but it probably gets reported more often today

p. 602
Aggression
Level: Easy
Type: Factual
Ans: C

243. The majority of rapes are committed by:
A. anger rapists
B. sadistic rapists
C. power rapists
D. rapists out to physically hurt someone

p. 602
Aggression
Level: Moderate
Type: Applied
Ans: D

244. A convicted rapist admits that he often carried a weapon. However, he swears that he carried it with the intention of using it to overcome his victim more easily but not to harm her. It is likely that this person is an example of a(n):
   A. anger rapist
   B. acquaintance rapist
   C. sadistic rapist
   D. power rapist

p. 602
Aggression
Level: Moderate
Type: Applied
Ans: A

245. Reports circulate around Pacific Beach about a rapist who accompanies sexual acts of short duration with abusive language and physical trauma to the victim. Which type of rapist is at large in Pacific Beach?
   A. anger
   B. power
   C. sadistic
   D. acquaintance

p. 602
Aggression
Level: Moderate
Type: Applied
Ans: D
*www*

246. A college coed is found dead near an off ramp of Highway 15. The police determine that she was raped and tortured before being killed. This act apparently was committed by a(n):
   A. acquaintance rapist
   B. anger rapist
   C. power rapist
   D. sadistic rapist

p. 602
Aggression
Level: Moderate
Type: Applied
Ans: A

247. Guy believes that if he goes out on a date with a woman he knows and pays for a nice dinner, she needs to have sex with him. He uses verbal coercion to force his date to have sex. Guy is <u>most</u> likely a(n):
   A. acquaintance rapist
   B. anger rapist
   C. power rapist
   D. sadistic rapist

p. 602
Aggression
Level: Easy
Type: Applied
Ans: A

248. John thinks a woman who accepts a ride from a strange male is responsible if she gets raped. This belief is an example of a:
   A. rape myth
   B. rape stigma
   C. rape schema
   D. rape motif

p. 603
Cultural Diversity:
  National Attitudes
Level: Easy
Type: Factual
Ans: B
*www*

249. In Niger, the beauty ideal for women is:
   A. to be thin
   B. to be heavy
   C. to have very dark skin
   D. to have very light skin

p. 603
Cultural Diversity:
  National Attitudes
Level: Easy
Type: Factual
Ans: C

250.  Younger Nigerian women are starting to reject the traditional view that beautiful women are _____ and to adopt _____ American standards.
A.  heavy; light skinned
B.  dark skinned; light skinned
C.  heavy; trim
D.  light skinned; trim

p. 603
Cultural Diversity:
  National Attitudes
Level: Easy
Type: Factual
Ans: B

1A.  In 1997, how many organ transplants were done in Japan?
A.  0
B.  1,000
C.  10,000
D.  23,000

p. 603
Cultural Diversity:
  National Attitudes
Level: Easy
Type: Factual
Ans: B

2A.  Why are organ transplants not done in Japan?
A.  lack of donors
B.  differing definition of death
C.  doctors lack adequate training
D.  Japanese health insurance does not cover organ transplants

p. 604
Application: Controlling
  Aggression
Level: Easy
Type: Factual
Ans: C

3A.  Which of the following is not among the cognitive-behavioral deficits among children who have aggression problems?
A.  aggressive children do not correctly recall social cues
B.  aggressive children tend to attribute hostile actions to other children
C.  aggressive children tend to use adaptive solutions to problems
D.  aggressive children are reinforced for their aggression

p. 604
Application: Controlling
  Aggression
Level: Moderate
Type: Applied
Ans: B

4A.  Tony, a nine-year-old with a history of aggression problems, is playing in the park. Tommy comes over and says "hi" to Tony. Then Tony responds with insults and jumps on Tommy and hits him repeatedly. This is an example of how aggressive children:
A.  reconstruct their schemas
B.  misinterpret nonharmful social cues
C.  experience catharsis
D.  cope with cognitive dissonance

p. 604
Application: Controlling
  Aggression
Level: Easy
Type: Factual
Ans: B

5A.  One program to curb aggression in children focuses on:
A.  reduction of testosterone
B.  teaching children problem-solving skills
C.  genetic screening and counseling
D.  attitude change and persuasion

p. 604
Application: Controlling
  Aggression
Level: Moderate
Type: Factual
Ans: C

6A.  An aggressive child enrolled in an anger control program would likely learn to do all of the following except:
A.  use self-statements to inhibit impulsive behaviors
B.  generate alternative nonaggressive solutions when frustrated
C.  hit a doll or pillow to release aggressive tension
D.  model other students who have taken steps to control their anger

| p. 605 | 7A. | Freud theorized that engaging in aggressive behavior could get rid of pent-up emotions. This notion is referred to as: |
|---|---|---|
| Application: Controlling Aggression | A. | catharsis |
| Level: Easy | B. | altruism |
| Type: Factual | C. | the risky shift |
| Ans: A | D. | deindividuation |

| p. 605 | 8A. | Which of the following best describes catharsis? |
|---|---|---|
| Application: Controlling Aggression | A. | "cooking up a storm" |
| | B. | "what part of 'no' don't you understand?" |
| Level: Easy | C. | "letting off some steam" |
| Type: Conceptual | D. | "He who is without sin, let him cast the first stone." |
| Ans: C | | |

| p. 605 | 9A. | A good example of how much culture shapes our attitudes is the: |
|---|---|---|
| Application: Controlling Aggression | A. | unlikely prospect that a women will ever be elected President of the United States |
| Level: Easy | B. | rapid improvement in sexual, political, and legal rights for Egyptian women |
| Type: Applied | C. | eagerness of the Japanese to obtain organ transplants from brain dead patients |
| Ans: D | | |
| PS/SG 25-23 | D. | recent change in Nigerian attitudes about female beauty from full to slender |

| p. 605 | 10A. | A group of college students decided to go to a hockey game on Friday night and "blow off some steam." What does the research reveal about catharsis? |
|---|---|---|
| Application: Controlling Aggression | | |
| Level: Easy | A. | catharsis is only effective for moderately aggressive individuals |
| Type: Applied | B. | catharsis works, but only for mildly aggressive individuals |
| Ans: D | C. | observing athletic events is an effective way to reduce aggression |
| www | D. | it may actually increase aggression |

| p. 605 | 11A. | Media portrayals of sexual behavior reinforce the idea that: |
|---|---|---|
| Application: Controlling Aggression | A. | aggressiveness is not normal |
| | B. | sexual aggressiveness causes harm |
| Level: Moderate | C. | sexual aggression is acceptable |
| Type: Factual | D. | no means no |
| Ans: C | | |

| p. 605 | 12A. | When compared to men who are not sexual aggressive, men who are, tend to: |
|---|---|---|
| Application: Controlling Aggression | A. | engage in activities that lead to catharsis |
| | B. | make fundamental attribution errors in explaining a woman's behavior |
| Level: Easy | C. | perceive women as showing sexual interest in nonsexual situations |
| Type: Factual | D. | have lower levels of serotonin |
| Ans: C | | |

| p. 605 | 13A. | All of the following have been shown to be risk factors in date rape except: |
|---|---|---|
| Application: Controlling Aggression | A. | heavy use of alcohol |
| | B. | misinterpretation of sexual interest |
| Level: Easy | C. | thinking that paying for the date entitles the male to sex |
| Type: Factual | D. | the length of time the individuals have known each other |
| Ans: D | | |

Module 25 - Social Psychology
802

True/False

| T |     | 1. | An attractive face is actually related to averaging many faces. |
|---|-----|-----|----------------------------------------------------------------|
| T | www | 2. | A stereotype saves time and energy in terms of thinking about people. |
| F |     | 3. | An example of discrimination would be to think that a woman could not be president. |
| T |     | 4. | Schemas distort what we pay attention to and what we remember. |
| T | www | 5. | Attributions are explanations for behaviors. |
| F |     | 6. | An internal attribution would be an explanation based on the situation. |
| T | www | 7. | The affective component of an attitude refers to emotional feelings. |
| T |     | 8. | Cognitive dissonance is an unpleasant feeling that motivates us to change. |
| F |     | 9. | The peripheral route uses facts, figures, and arguments to persuade. |
| T | www | 10. | Conformity occurs when you change behavior because of group pressure. |
| T |     | 11. | You start with a small request and then a large request in the foot-in-the-door technique. |
| F | www | 12. | According to the Milgram study, most people refused to obey an order to hurt someone. |
| F |     | 13. | Part of the decision-stage model of helping is determining the costs and rewards of helping. |
| T | www | 14. | Social inhibition occurs when the response is new or complex. |
| F |     | 15. | Diffusion of responsibility occurs in social facilitation. |
| T |     | 16. | Group polarization occurs when the groups point of view becomes stronger. |
| F | www | 17. | In groupthink, the groups are most concerned about making good decisions. |
| F |     | 18. | Mindguards increase the odds that groupthink will occur. |
| T | www | 19. | Genetic factors predispose individuals to develop aggressive behaviors. |
| T |     | 20. | Social cognitive theory emphasizes that children model aggression. |
| T | www | 21. | Frustration does not always lead to aggression. |
| T |     | 22. | The most common type of rapist is the power rapist. |
| F |     | 23. | Organ transplants are very common in Japan. |
| F |     | 24. | Aggressive children tend to accurately explain other children's aggressive behaviors. |
| F | www | 25. | Catharsis is effective in reducing anger or aggression. |

Short-Answer Essay Questions

1. Discuss how person perception is influenced by our need to explain someone's physical appearance.
2. Differentiate between stereotypes, prejudice, and discrimination by giving an example of each term. (*www*)
3. What is attribution? What are the common biases or errors we make in attribution? Include a real-life example of each bias. (*www*)
4. Describe the cognitive, affective, and behavioral components of an attitude by using an example from your own experiences. What occurs when these components are not consistent? (*www*)
5. Using the Asch and Milgram studies, describe the power of groups and authority figures. (*www*)
6. Create an ad for a product using the central and peripheral routes of persuasion.
7. Discuss why people help or do not help using the decision-stage model and arousal-cost-reward model.

8.     Why is deindividuation an important factor in rioting? (*www*)
9.     Describe how aggressive children differ from their nonaggressive peers with regard to cognitive-behavioral deficits.
10.    What is catharsis? Is it effective in reducing anger? Why or why not?